FRANKLIN PARK PUBLIC LIBRARY
3 1316 00430 8907

W9-DBN-267

Periodic Table of the Elements

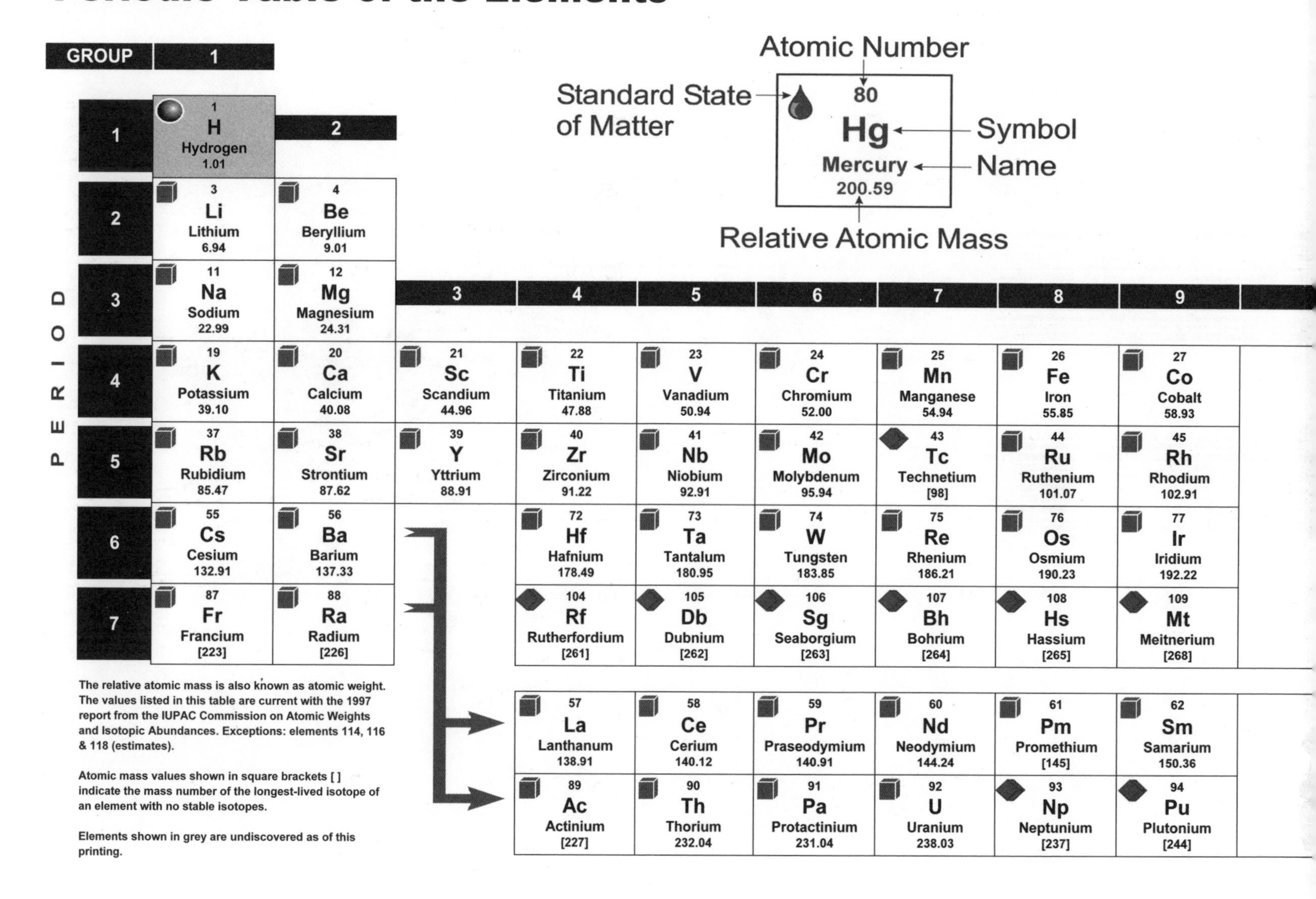
GROUP
1
2
3
4
5
6
7
8
9
PERIOD
Atomic Number
Standard State of Matter
80
Hg
Mercury
200.59
Symbol
Name
Relative Atomic Mass
1 H Hydrogen 1.01
3 Li Lithium 6.94
4 Be Beryllium 9.01
11 Na Sodium 22.99
12 Mg Magnesium 24.31
19 K Potassium 39.10
20 Ca Calcium 40.08
21 Sc Scandium 44.96
22 Ti Titanium 47.88
23 V Vanadium 50.94
24 Cr Chromium 52.00
25 Mn Manganese 54.94
26 Fe Iron 55.85
27 Co Cobalt 58.93
37 Rb Rubidium 85.47
38 Sr Strontium 87.62
39 Y Yttrium 88.91
40 Zr Zirconium 91.22
41 Nb Niobium 92.91
42 Mo Molybdenum 95.94
43 Tc Technetium [98]
44 Ru Ruthenium 101.07
45 Rh Rhodium 102.91
55 Cs Cesium 132.91
56 Ba Barium 137.33
72 Hf Hafnium 178.49
73 Ta Tantalum 180.95
74 W Tungsten 183.85
75 Re Rhenium 186.21
76 Os Osmium 190.23
77 Ir Iridium 192.22
87 Fr Francium [223]
88 Ra Radium [226]
104 Rf Rutherfordium [261]
105 Db Dubnium [262]
106 Sg Seaborgium [263]
107 Bh Bohrium [264]
108 Hs Hassium [265]
109 Mt Meitnerium [268]
57 La Lanthanum 138.91
58 Ce Cerium 140.12
59 Pr Praseodymium 140.91
60 Nd Neodymium 144.24
61 Pm Promethium [145]
62 Sm Samarium 150.36
89 Ac Actinium [227]
90 Th Thorium 232.04
91 Pa Protactinium 231.04
92 U Uranium 238.03
93 Np Neptunium [237]
94 Pu Plutonium [244]
The relative atomic mass is also known as atomic weight. The values listed in this table are current with the 1997 report from the IUPAC Commission on Atomic Weights and Isotopic Abundances. Exceptions: elements 114, 116 & 118 (estimates).
Atomic mass values shown in square brackets [ ] indicate the mass number of the longest-lived isotope of an element with no stable isotopes.
Elements shown in grey are undiscovered as of this printing.

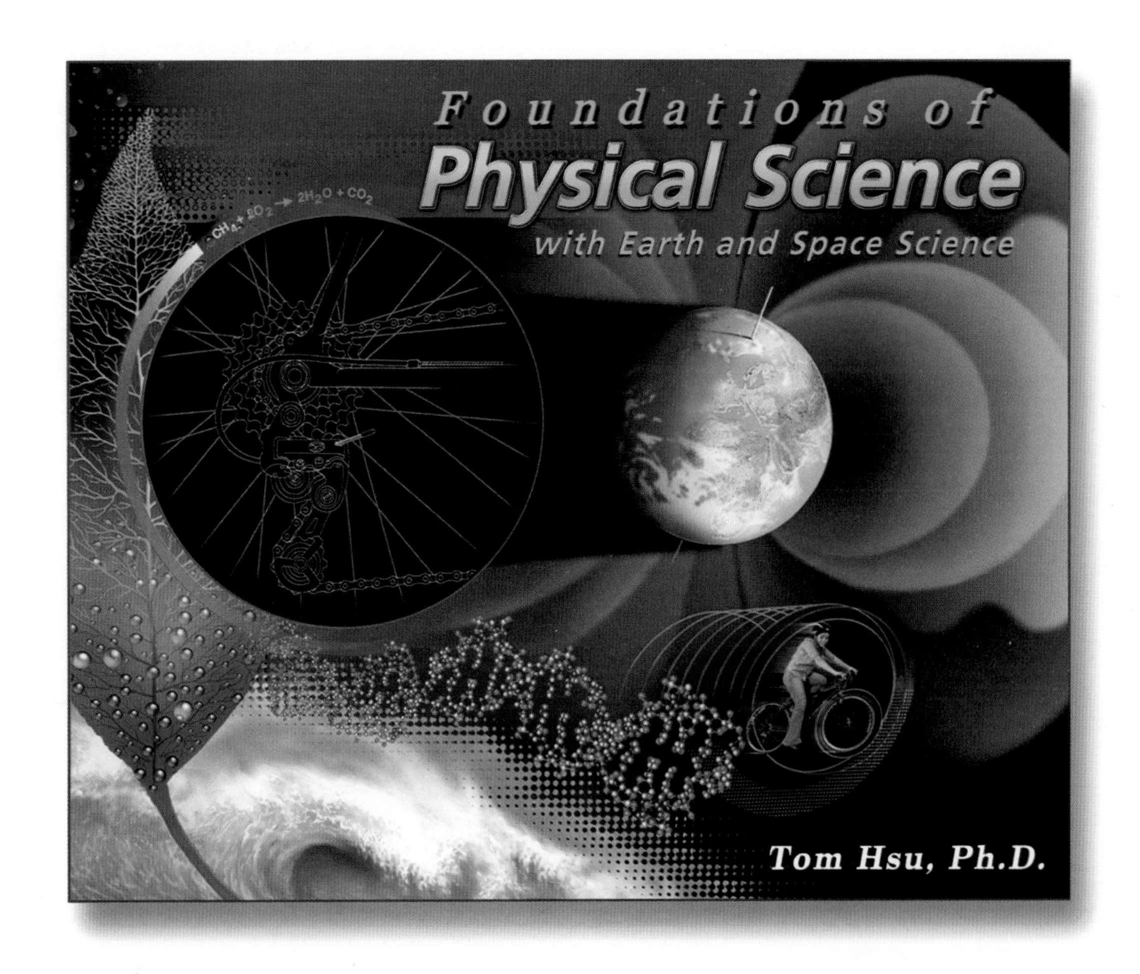

SECOND EDITION
CPO Science
Nashua, NH 03063

About the Author

Dr. Thomas C. Hsu is a nationally recognized innovator in science and math education and the founder of CPO Science (formerly Cambridge Physics Outlet). He holds a Ph.D. in Applied Plasma Physics from the Massachusetts Institute of Technology (MIT), and has taught students from elementary, secondary and college levels across the nation. He was nominated for MIT's Goodwin medal for excellence in teaching and has received numerous awards from various state agencies for his work to improve science education. Tom has personally worked with more than 12,000 K-12 teachers and administrators and is well known as a consultant, workshop leader and developer of curriculum and equipment for inquiry-based learning in science and math. With CPO Science, Tom has published textbooks in physical science, integrated science, and also written fifteen curriculum Investigation guides that accompany CPO Science equipment. Along with the CPO Science team, Tom is always active, developing innovative new tools for teaching and learning science, including an inquiry-based chemistry text.

Foundations of Physical Science with Earth and Space Science, Second Edition

ISBN-10: 1-58892-460-2
ISBN-13: 978-1-58892-460-5
1 2 3 4 5 6 7 8 9 - QWE - 10 09 08 07

CPO Science
80 Northwest Boulevard
Nashua, New Hampshire 03063
(866)588-6951
http://www.cposcience.com

Printed and Bound in the United States of America

CPO Science Development Team

Tom Hsu, Ph.D. – Author

Ph.D., Applied Plasma Physics, Massachusetts Institute of Technology

Nationally recognized innovator in science and math education and the founder of CPO Science (formerly Cambridge Physics Outlet). He has taught students from elementary, secondary and college levels across the nation. He has also worked with more than 12,000, K-12 teachers and administrators and is well known as a consultant, workshop leader and developer of curriculum and equipment for inquiry-based learning in science and math.

Lynda Pennell – Educational Products, Executive Vice President

B.A., English, M.Ed., Administration, Reading Disabilities, Northeastern University; CAGS Media, University of Massachusetts, Boston

Nationally known in high school restructuring and for integrating academic and career education. Served as the director of an urban school with 17 years teaching/administrative experience.

Thomas Narro – Product Design, Senior Vice President

B.S., Mechanical engineering, Rensselaer Polytechnic Institute

Accomplished design and manufacturing engineer; experienced consultant in corporate re engineering and industrial-environmental acoustics.

Scott Eddleman – Project Manager and Principal Writer

B.S., Biology, Southern Illinois University; M.Ed., Harvard University

Taught for 13 years in urban and rural settings; nationally known as trainer of inquiry-based science and mathematics project-based instruction; curriculum development consultant.

Laine Ives – Principal Writer

B.A., English, Gordon College; graduate work, biology, Cornell University, Wheelock College

Experience teaching middle and high school, here and abroad; expertise in developing middle school curriculum and hands-on activities.

Mary Beth Abel Hughes – Principal Writer

B.S., Marine biology, College of Charleston; M.S., Biological sciences, University of Rhode Island

Taught science and math at an innovative high school; expertise in scientific research and inquiry-based teaching methods and curriculum development.

Bruce Holloway – Senior Creative Designer

Pratt Institute, N.Y.; Boston Museum School of Fine Arts

Expertise in product design, advertising, and three-dimensional exhibit design. Commissioned for the New Hampshire Duck Stamp for 1999 and 2003.

Polly Crisman – Graphic Designer and Illustrator

B.F.A., University of New Hampshire

Graphic artist with expertise in advertising and marketing design, freelance illustrating, and caricature art.

Patsy DeCoster – Staff Development and Service Director

B.S., Biology/Secondary education, Grove City College; M.Ed., Tufts University

Curriculum and professional development specialist. Taught science for 12 years. National inquiry-based science presenter.

Erik Benton – Professional Development Specialist

B.F.A., University of Massachusetts

Taught for 8 years in public and private schools, focusing on inquiry and experiential learning environments.

Matt Lombard – Photographing and Marketing

B.S., Salem State College

Oversees all marketing activities for CPO Science. Expertise in equipment photography and catalog design.

Susan Gioia– Education Office Administrator

Oversees all the details necessary to keep the education product team working smoothly.

CPO Science Equipment Development

Greg Krekorian – Production manager
Roger Barous – Manufacturing specialist
Shawn Green – Electronics specialist

Kathryn Gavin – Quality specialist
Agnes Chan – Industrial engineer
David Zucker – Industrial engineer

Dexter Beals – Electrical engineer (Beals Dynamics)
Dr. Jeff Casey – Physicist
Thomas Altman – Light and optics specialist

Technical Consultants

Tracy Morrow – FrameWork consultant, editing
Julie Dalton – Senior Copy Editor
Mary Ann Erickson – Indexing, glossary, editing
James Travers – Graphic designer

David Rosolko – Graphic designer
John Mahomet – Graphic designer
Kelly Story – assessment specialist, editing

Mike Doughty – intern, Endicott College
Jennifer Lockhart – intern, Endicott College

Content Consultants

Dr. Jack Haas – *Professor Emeritus*, Gordon College, Massachusetts

Terri Gipson – *Associate Director of Space Sciences*, St. Louis Science Center, Missouri

Dr. Robert Pockalny – *Associate Marine Research Scientist*, GSO, University of Rhode Island, Rhode Island

Dr. David Guerra – *Chair, Department of Physics*, St. Anselm College, New Hampshire

James Sammons – *Writer/Developer*, Sammons' INK, LTD, Rhode Island

David Bliss – *Teacher*, Mohawk Central High School, New York

Thomas Altman – *Teacher*, Oswego High School, New York

Gary Garber – *Teacher*, Boston University Academy, Massachusetts

Catalina Moreno – *Teacher*, East Boston High School, Massachusetts

John Yonkers – *Retired Adult Educator*, Madison-Oneida Board of Cooperative Education Services, Verona, New York

David Buckley – *Teacher*, Mohawk Central High School, New York

Kent Dristle – *Teacher*, Oswego High School, New York

Reviewers

Bell, Tom
Curriculum Specialist
Cumberland County Schools
North Carolina

Chesick, Elizabeth
Head of Science Department
Baldwin School
Pennsylvania

Curry, Dwight
Assistant Director of Physical Science
St. Louis Science Center
Missouri

Gharooni, Hamid
Program Director, Math & Science
Madison Park Technical-Vocational High School
Massachusetts

Inman, Jamie
Physics Teacher
North Carolina

Lamp, David
Associate Professor
Physics Department
Texas Tech University
Texas

Leeds, Susan
Science teacher, eighth grade
Howard Middle School
Florida

Lowe, Larry
Physics and Electricity Teacher
Masconomet Regional High School
Massachusetts

Madar, Robert
Senior Consultant and Trainer
Impact Consulting
Oregon

Nelson, Genevieve M.
Head of Science Department
Germantown Friends School
Pennsylvania

Ramsay, Willa A.
Science Education Consultant
California

Schafer, Susan
Principal Investigator
College of Engineering
Texas Tech University
Texas

Scott, Janet
Curriculum Specialist
Durham Public Schools
North Carolina

Sewall, Les
Science Education Consultant
Georgia

Tally, Michael
Science Supervisor
Wake County Public Schools
North Carolina

Texas, Leslie A.
Senior Consultant and Trainer
Impact Consulting
Kentucky

Thompson, Gaile B.
Director of Science Collaborative
Region 14 ESC
Texas

Woodring, Kathleen
Physics Teacher
Industrial High School
Texas

Science Through Discovery

The universe is like a safe to which there is a combination, but the combination is locked up in the safe.
Peter de Vries

In many learning situations, you are expected to study prescribed materials and come up with correct answers by yourself. Usually, you read the information and then, in a laboratory, you try out the knowledge you acquired. With the CPO program, you will find that science is an opportunity for you to discover and solve problems—though they sometimes seem like mysteries more than "problems"—while working with others as a team.

Working with your fellow students, you will use very accurate equipment to answer key questions, decide if your findings can be backed up with data and facts, and learn how to prove and justify your end results.

What you learn in school should be connected to what you know about the world around you. These connections will contribute to your success in life, sometimes in obvious ways, and many times in quite surprising ways. In today's workplace and in future educational pursuits, you will need to ask insightful questions, plan and organize your work, look for and analyze information, try out your ideas, and then be able to rethink a problem and try again. You must also be able to work on a team, to come up with a system for organizing information, and to feel comfortable about tackling new problems.

The CPO program provides the opportunity for you to practice answering questions, working with others, and finding your own system for solving problems. In the student text, you will find knowledge and skills needed to answer key questions and explore a variety of science topics. Along with each reading, you will complete an investigation activity so that part of your discovery of science is done with others. Some people may think exactly like you, while others might find different ways of approaching the same problem.

Finally, the ability to communicate effectively is one of the most valued skills in the world today. As a result, analyzing and communicating your findings to others in written, verbal or illustration form will be a major part of the learning process throughout the CPO program.

About the Student Text

There are *Eleven* Major Science Units covered in the CPO student text. Each Unit contains *Chapters* which are divided into multiple *sections*. The chapters and sections are organized so that you will learn basic skills and then build your knowledge to more complex understanding. You will notice that many of the important science concepts are repeated in different ways throughout the sections. Numerous illustrations, charts, graphs, and data tables support your reading and assist you in grasping its content. Also, there are short subheadings on the left margin of each page to help you study the main ideas and find information quickly.

Student Text Main Components

Main text: In addition to reading about science concepts and skills, you will discover brief stories about important scientists, inventions, real world connections, environmental issues, and interesting facts.

Chapter pages: Each chapter starts with two pages that outline what you will learn in the chapter. These pages provide you with a brief summary, the key questions for each Investigation, vocabulary, and learning goals.

Review questions: After each section, there are review questions that evaluate what you have learned and support you and your teacher in choosing what needs to be reviewed and which concepts to discuss further.

Glossary: The glossary is where you will find the meaning of words that are important science concepts and essential vocabulary. You can also find references to important people who are discussed in your reading.

Index: This section helps you find more specific topic information by giving page numbers that refer to the topic. You can use the index while studying to find information.

Reference Tables: A quick reference guide provides you with safety information, problem solving techniques (dimensional analysis), a conversion chart, table of formulas, and a list of physical constants. The inside back cover of the book is a quick reference periodic table and explanation of how to interpret it.

Student Text Pages

Sidenotes (idea headers): In the left margin of each page you will find phrases, short sentences, and questions to guide you in understanding the most important ideas. These sidenotes will also help you skim the text and quickly find information when you are reviewing and studying for tests.

Illustrations: Use the illustrations, graphs, charts, and data tables to help you understand the reading. These reading tools help most students improve their understanding of the key concepts.

Vocabulary words: The vocabulary words are highlighted in blue. You need to understand their meanings to be successful in science and will find the same vocabulary used in many contexts and repeated throughout the text. The definitions can be found in the glossary.

Data tables: These tables will help you understand complex information, organize numerical data, and provide examples of how to collect and present data.

Figure number/captions: As you are reading, notice the references to the word *Figure* followed by a number. These figures are found on the right side of the page in the form of an illustration, picture, or chart. The figure number indicates which figure goes with the text you are reading and gives you another way to understand the information in the reading.

STUDENT TEXT PAGES

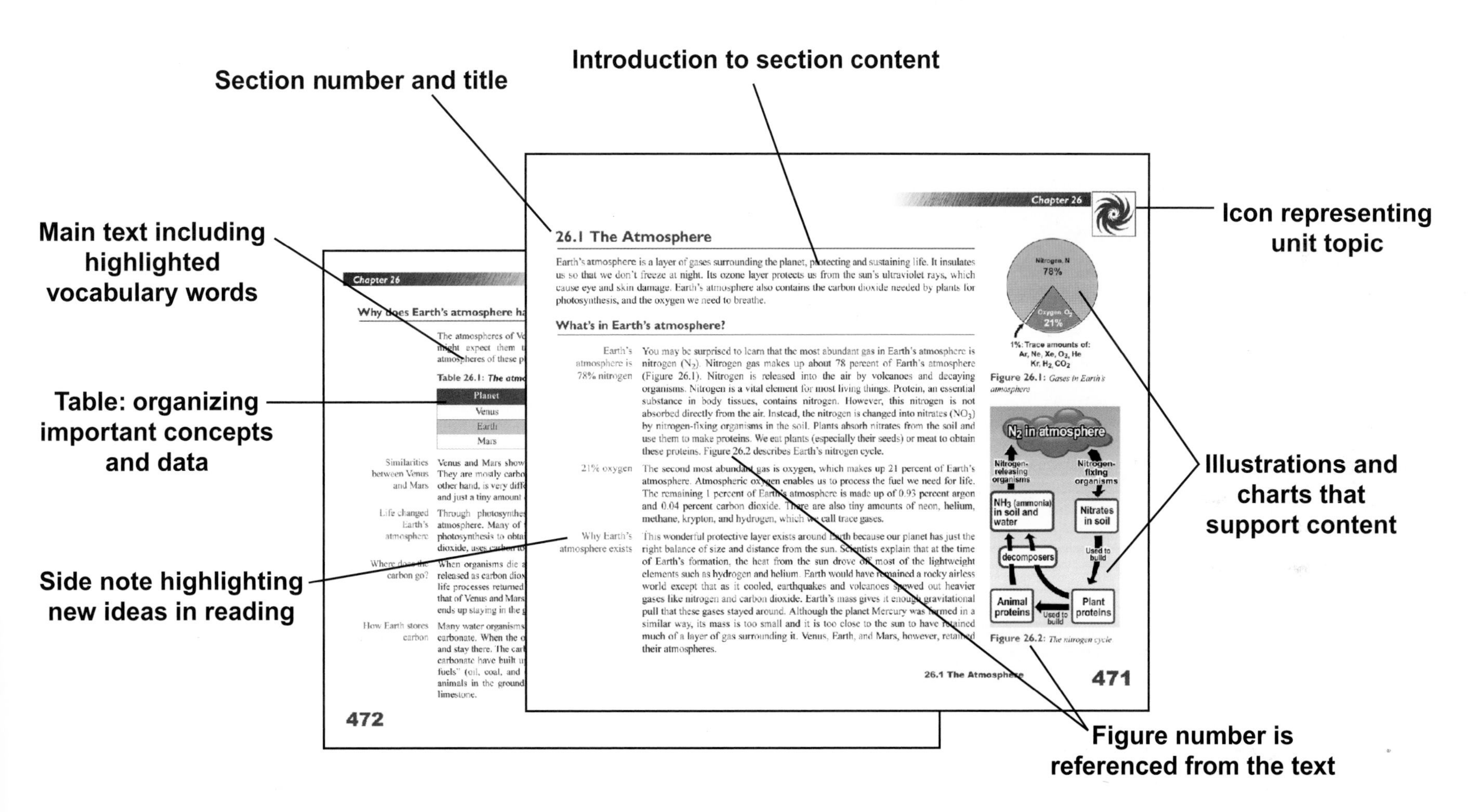

Investigation Text

Hear and you forget;see and you remember; do and you understand.
Confucius

Investigations are hands-on activities that accompany the student text. For each section of the text, you will complete a hands-on activity, answer key questions, and find results. The *Investigation Manual* is a softcover book that contains Investigation activities that accompany each section you are reading. Sometimes you will read the student text before doing an Investigation activity, but usually you will complete the Investigations before you read the section.

The Investigations are the heart of the CPO program. We believe that you will learn and remember more if you have many opportunities to explore science through hands-on activities that use equipment to collect data and solve problems. Most of the Investigations rely on the use of CPO equipment to collect accurate data, explore possibilities and answer the key question. The equipment is easy to set up, and your teacher will help you learn how to use the equipment properly.

Features of the Investigation

Key question: Each Investigation starts with a key question that conveys the focus of the lesson. This question tells you what information you need to collect in order to answer the questions at the end of the Investigation.

Data tables: Data tables help you collect and organize your data in a systematic manner.

Learning objectives (goals): At the top of each investigation are the learning goals. These statements will explain what you will have learned and what you be able to do after completing the Investigation.

Brief introduction: This information helps you understand why the exercise is important to complete and, in most cases, how it connects to other sections of your reading.

Icons and section title: The icon is a reminder of the unit that you are studying. The section title corresponds to the reading in your student text.

Numbered steps: The Investigation sequence numbers point out the sequence of steps you will need to follow to successfully complete the Investigation. These steps highlight specific stages of the scientific method such as: following directions, completing hands-on experiments, collecting and analyzing data and presenting the results. The *Applying your Knowledge* step asks you to reflect on what you have learned and to explain your findings.

Illustrations: The illustrations support your understanding of the Investigation procedures.

Fill-in answer sheets: Your teacher will provide you with answer sheets to fill in the data tables and written responses. At times your teacher may collect this data to compile class results. You can also use the sheets to reinforce your reading in your student text.

INVESTIGATION PAGES

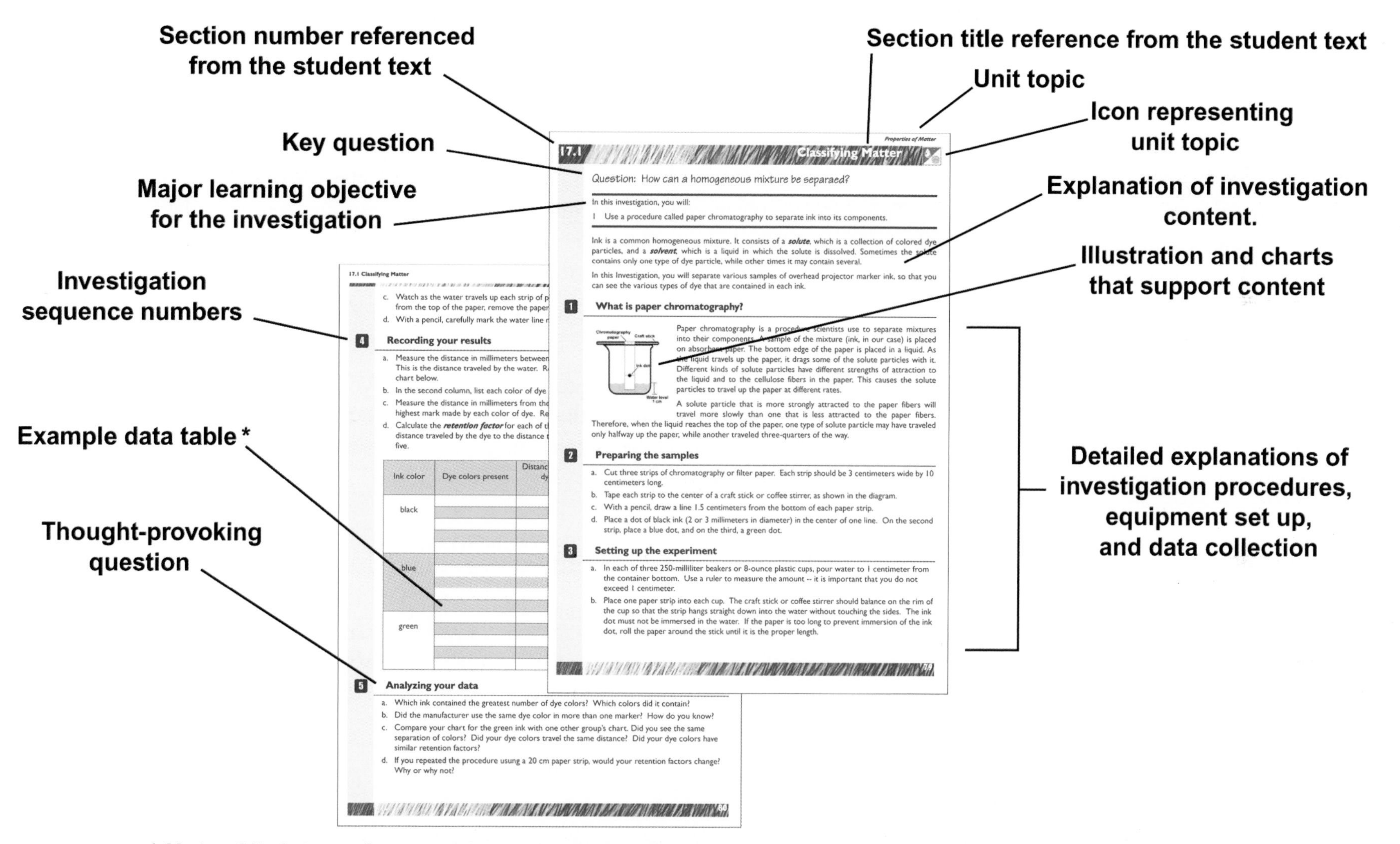

Properties of Matter

17.1 Classifying Matter

Question: How can a homogeneous mixture be separaed?

In this investigation, you will:

1 Use a procedure called paper chromatography to separate ink into its components.

Ink is a common homogeneous mixture. It consists of a ***solute***, which is a collection of colored dye particles, and a ***solvent***, which is a liquid in which the solute is dissolved. Sometimes the solute contains only one type of dye particle, while other times it may contain several.

In this Investigation, you will separate various samples of overhead projector marker ink, so that you can see the various types of dye that are contained in each ink.

1 What is paper chromatography?

Paper chromatography is a procedure scientists use to separate mixtures into their components. A sample of the mixture (ink, in our case) is placed on absorbent paper. The bottom edge of the paper is placed in a liquid. As the liquid travels up the paper, it drags some of the solute particles with it. Different kinds of solute particles have different strengths of attraction to the liquid and to the cellulose fibers in the paper. This causes the solute particles to travel up the paper at different rates.

A solute particle that is more strongly attracted to the paper fibers will travel more slowly than one that is less attracted to the paper fibers. Therefore, when the liquid reaches the top of the paper, one type of solute particle may have traveled only halfway up the paper, while another traveled three-quarters of the way.

2 Preparing the samples

a. Cut three strips of chromatography or filter paper. Each strip should be 3 centimeters wide by 10 centimeters long.
b. Tape each strip to the center of a craft stick or coffee stirrer, as shown in the diagram.
c. With a pencil, draw a line 1.5 centimeters from the bottom of each paper strip.
d. Place a dot of black ink (2 or 3 millimeters in diameter) in the center of one line. On the second strip, place a blue dot, and on the third, a green dot.

3 Setting up the experiment

a. In each of three 250-milliliter beakers or 8-ounce plastic cups, pour water to 1 centimeter from the container bottom. Use a ruler to measure the amount -- it is important that you do not exceed 1 centimeter.
b. Place one paper strip into each cup. The craft stick or coffee stirrer should balance on the rim of the cup so that the strip hangs straight down into the water without touching the sides. The ink dot must not be immersed in the water. If the paper is too long to prevent immersion of the ink dot, roll the paper around the stick until it is the proper length.

17.1 Classifying Matter

c. Watch as the water travels up each strip of p...
from the top of the paper, remove the paper...
d. With a pencil, carefully mark the water line...

4 Recording your results

a. Measure the distance in millimeters between... This is the distance traveled by the water. R... chart below.
b. In the second column, list each color of dye...
c. Measure the distance in millimeters from the... highest mark made by each color of dye. Re...
d. Calculate the ***retention factor*** for each of t... distance traveled by the dye to the distance t... five.

Ink color	Dye colors present	Distance dy...
black		
blue		
green		

5 Analyzing your data

a. Which ink contained the greatest number of dye colors? Which colors did it contain?
b. Did the manufacturer use the same dye color in more than one marker? How do you know?
c. Compare your chart for the green ink with one other group's chart. Did you see the same separation of colors? Did your dye colors travel the same distance? Did your dye colors have similar retention factors?
d. If you repeated the procedure usung a 20 cm paper strip, would your retention factors change? Why or why not?

* Note: All data and answers to questions will be written on a separate fill-in answer sheet.

Student Text Chapter Pages

Each *Unit* has several sections which make up a *Chapter. Chapter pages* outline what you will learn in the Chapter and the Investigations (hands-on activities) that complement the readings. The Chapter pages serve as a map that directs you to the major concepts that will be covered. It is important to refer back to these pages to help you focus your learning on the most important ideas introduced in the chapter.

Features of the Chapter Pages

Introduction: The Chapter page introduction summarizes what you will have learned when you finish all the sections and Investigations. Refer back to this summary after you finish the chapter to check your understanding, and use this summary when studying for exams.

Chapter contents and Investigations: This listing with the chapter numbers outlines the key questions and the content of the Investigations that accompany your student readings. When you read the questions and Investigation descriptions, you will be able to see how the Investigations help you understand the skills and concepts introduced in each chapter.

Learning goals: These goals are the major ideas that you will explore throughout the chapter. You should check your learning by going back to this page to make sure you can explain each of these concepts in writing or to another person.

Vocabulary: The list of vocabulary words at the beginning of the chapter will familiarize you with the words in the chapter. Understanding the science vocabulary will help you learn the concepts in the readings. Thinking and guessing about the meaning of the words before reading and then seeing how close you were to the correct meaning is a good learning tool.

Unit Icons Guide

Unit icons are used to identify what unit topic you are studying. You will see these icons on the Chapter and Investigation corners.

Unit One: Force and Motion	Unit Five: Light and Optics	Unit Nine: Energy in the Earth System
Unit Two: Work and Energy	Unit Six: Properties of Matter	Unit Ten: Earth Science
Unit Three: Electricity and Magnetism	Unit Seven: Changes in Matter	Unit Eleven: Astronomy
Unit Four: Sound and Waves	Unit Eight: Water and the Environment	

CHAPTER PAGES

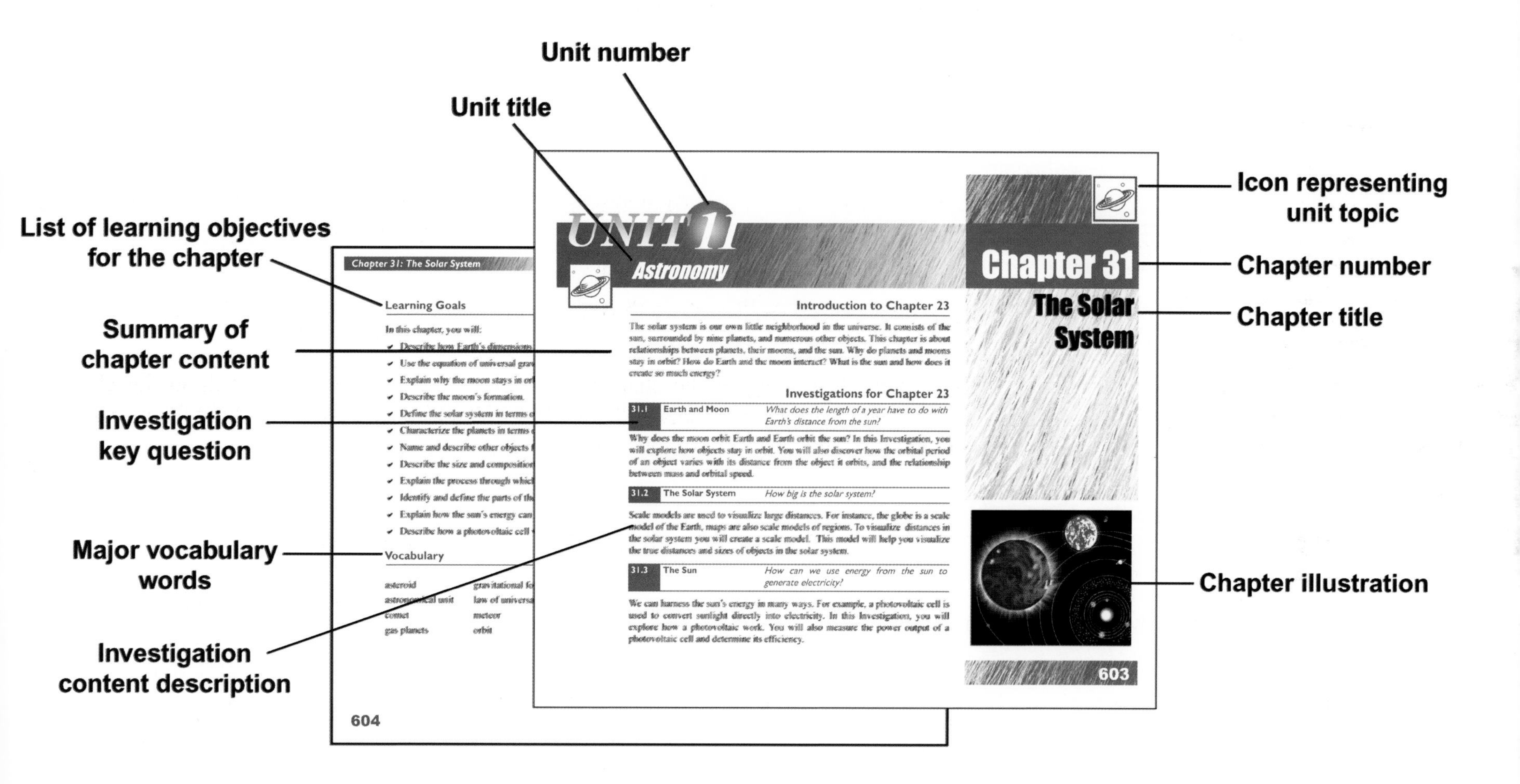

Unit number
Unit title
List of learning objectives for the chapter
Summary of chapter content
Investigation key question
Major vocabulary words
Investigation content description
Icon representing unit topic
Chapter number
Chapter title
Chapter illustration
Chapter 31: The Solar System
Learning Goals
Vocabulary
604
UNIT 11
Astronomy
Introduction to Chapter 23
Investigations for Chapter 23
31.1 Earth and Moon
31.2 The Solar System
31.3 The Sun
Chapter 31
The Solar System
603

Using Icons to Locate Information

The mind is not a vessel to be filled but a fire to be kindled
Plutarch

Icons are small pictures that convey meaning without words. In the CPO program, we use icons to point out things such as safety considerations, real-world connections, and when to find information in the reference pages, complete a writing assignment, or work in a team. The chart below lists the icons that refer to instruction and safety and the meaning of each one:

	Reading: you need to read for understanding.		**Real-world connections:** you are learning how the information is used in the world today.
	Hands-on activity: you will complete a lab or other activity.		**Teamwork:** you will be working in a team to complete the activity.
	Time: tells how much time the activity may take.		**Economics:** you are learning how science impacts the economy.
	Research: you will need to look up facts and information.		**Formula:** you are reading information about a formula or you will need to use an equation to solve a problem.
	Setup: directions for equipment setup are found here.		**Use extreme caution:** follow all instructions carefully to avoid injury to yourself or others.
	History: you are reading historical information.		**Electrical hazard:** follow all instructions carefully while using electrical components to avoid injury to yourself or others.
	Environment: you are reading information about the environment or how to protect our environment.		**Wear safety goggles:** requires you to protect your eyes from injury.
	Writing: you need to reflect and write about what you have learned.		**Wear a lab apron:** requires you to protect your clothing and skin.
	Project: you need to complete an assignment that will take longer than one day.		**Wear gloves:** requires you to protect your hands from injury from heat or chemicals.
	Apply your knowledge: refers to activities or problems that ask you to use your skills in different ways.		**Clean-up:** includes cleaning and putting away reusable equipment and supplies, and disposing of leftover materials.

CONTENTS

Table of Contents

Unit 1: Forces and Motion

Unit 2: Work and Energy

Unit 3: Electricity and Magnetism

Unit 4: Sound and Waves

Unit 5: Light and Optics

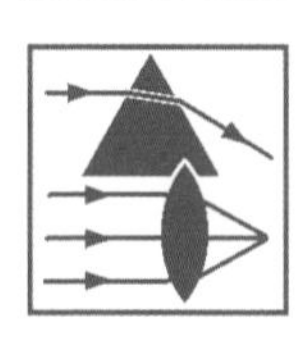

Unit 6: Properties of Matter

Unit 7: Changes in Matter

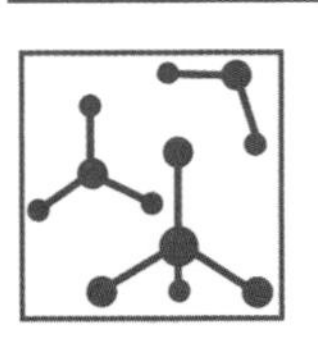

Unit 8: Water and the Environment

CONTENTS

Unit 9: Energy in the Earth System

Unit 10: Earth Science

Unit 11: Astronomy

UNIT 1

Forces and Motion

Chapter 1

Science and Measurement

Introduction to Chapter 1

This chapter is about measurement and how we use measurements and experiments to learn about the world. Two fundamental properties of the universe that we want to measure are time and distance. A third important measurement, speed, tells us how time and distance relate to the motion of objects.

Investigations for Chapter 1

1.1	**Time and Distance**	*How do we measure and describe the world around us?*

In the first Investigation, you will use electronic timers and other measuring tools to explore precision measurement of the fundamental quantities of time and distance.

1.2	**Investigations and Experiments**	*How do we ask questions and get answers from nature?*

Investigating a car rolling down a ramp may seem simple, but it is difficult to understand what is really happening. The key is learning to design careful experiments that test our ideas with observations. In this Investigation, you will examine the motion of a car on a ramp to explore the action of variables in experiments.

1.3	**Speed**	*What is speed and how is it measured?*

The words *fast* and *slow* are not precise enough for many questions in science. We need to know how fast is fast. You will learn to determine the speed of moving objects with great accuracy. This Investigation of speed will be the foundation for answering many questions about motion.

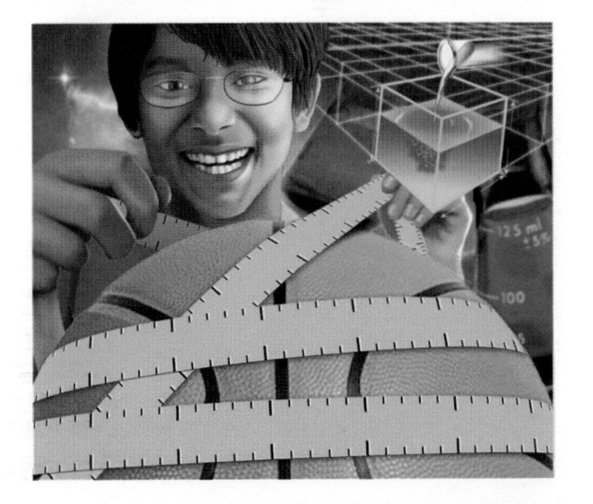

Learning Goals

In this chapter, you will:

- ✔ Accurately measure time using electronic timers and photogates.
- ✔ Use decimals to represent fractions of a second.
- ✔ Develop a research question or hypothesis that can be tested.
- ✔ Identify the variables that affect motion.
- ✔ Develop an experimental technique that achieves consistent results.
- ✔ Draw conclusions from experimental results.
- ✔ Accurately measure distance.
- ✔ Identify metric and English units of distance.
- ✔ Convert between units of distance.
- ✔ Calculate speed in units of inches per second, feet per second, and centimeters per second.

Vocabulary

cause and effect
control variables
controlled experiment
distance
English system
experiment
experimental technique
experimental variable
hypothesis
investigation
length
measurements
metric system
procedure
research question
scientific evidence
scientific method
second
time
trial
variables
velocity

1.1 Time and Distance

In this section, you will learn about two fundamental properties of the universe: time and distance. Learning about how things change with time motivates much of our study of nature. We are born and our bodies change as time passes. The steady forward movement of time creates a present, a past, and a future.

Another important quality of the universe is that it has three dimensions. To observe and learn about objects, their sizes, and their motion in the universe, we need units of length. Common measures for length are inches and meters. Other units of length are used for very small distances like atomic sizes and very large distances like those between cities.

Figure 1.1: *The flow of time is an important part of our experience of life. To understand nature we need to investigate how things change with time.*

Two ways to think about time

What time is it? There are two ways we think about time (Figure 1.2). One meaning for time is to identify a particular moment. If we ask "What time is it?" we usually want to know time relative to the rest of the universe and everyone in it. For example, 3:00 PM, Eastern Time, on April 21 tells the time at a certain place on Earth.

How much time? Another meaning for time is a quantity, or interval of time. The question "How much time?" is asking for an interval of time with a beginning and end. For example, we might measure how much time has passed between the start of a race and when the first runner crosses the finish line.

Figure 1.2: *There are two different ways to understand time.*

How is time measured? For most of physical science we measure and record time in seconds. Some other units of time you may see are hours, minutes, days, and years. Choose the unit most suited to the time you want to measure. Short races are best measured in seconds while the age of a person is best measured in years.

Time comes in mixed units

Many calculations require that time be expressed in seconds. However, seconds are very short. Hours and minutes are more convenient for everyday time measurement. As a result, time intervals are often in mixed units, such as 2 minutes and 15 seconds. If you have a time interval that is in mixed units you will have to convert it to seconds before doing calculations. Table 1.1 gives some useful relationships between units of time.

Table 1.1: *Some units for time*

Time Unit	How Many Seconds	How Many Days
1 second	1	0.0001157
1 minute	60	0.00694
1 hour	3,600	0.0417
1 day	86,400	1
1 year	31,557,600	365.25
1 century	3,155,760,000	36,525

Figure 1.3: *Electronic timers have displays that show mixed units. Colons (:) separate the units.*

Why we have different units for time

How many seconds have there been since you were born? From the table you should see that for every year there are 31,557,600 seconds. To give your age in seconds would be silly. The number would be too big and change too fast. A year is a better unit for describing people's ages.

How do you read a timer?

Most timing equipment (including digital timers) displays time in three units: hours, minutes, and seconds. Colons separate the units into hours, minutes, and seconds. The seconds number may have a decimal that shows fractions of a second. To read a timer you need to recognize and separate out the different units. Figure 1.3 shows a timer display that reads 1 hour, 26 minutes, and 31.25 seconds.

How do you convert to seconds?

To convert a time to seconds you have to first separate out all the different units. For physics problems, the starting units will often be hours, minutes, and seconds. Follow the list below to convert any amount of time to seconds.

1. Separate the total time into the amount of time in each unit.
2. Convert each separate quantity of time to seconds.
3. Add all the seconds.

Example:

Convert the time in Figure 1.3 to seconds.

Solution:

Separate time into each unit.

1 hour

26 minutes

31.25 seconds

Convert each different unit into seconds.

1 hour × 3,600 seconds/hour = 3,600 seconds

26 minutes × 60 seconds/minute = 1,560 seconds

Then add all the seconds.

3,600.00
1,560.00
+ 31.25
5,191.25 seconds

Measuring distance

Distance is measured in units of length

Distance describes how far it is from one point to another. Distance is measured in units of **length**. Like other measurements, distance always has a number and a unit. It is hard to say precisely how far something has moved without units. It would be silly to ask someone to walk 25. They would ask, "Twenty-five what?" There is a big difference between 25 feet and 25 miles! Without units, distance measurements are meaningless.

There are two common systems

There are two common systems of units that are used for measuring distance. You need to understand both systems. The **English system** uses inches, feet, and miles. The **metric system** uses millimeters, centimeters, meters, and kilometers.

Reading the English ruler

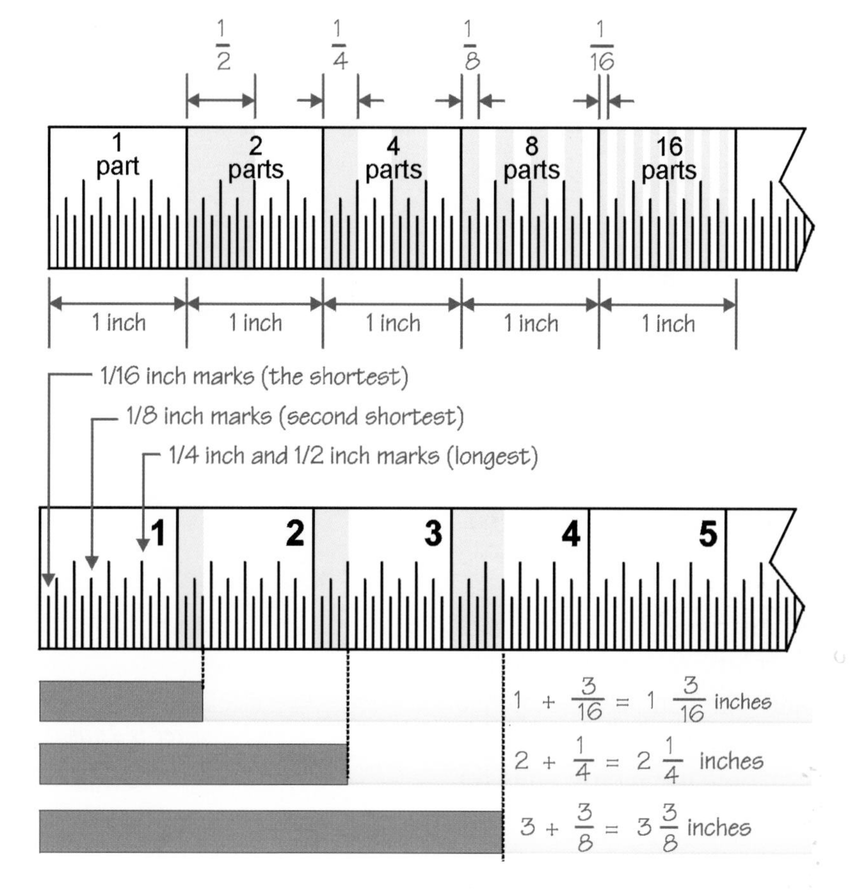

Reading the metric ruler (meter stick)

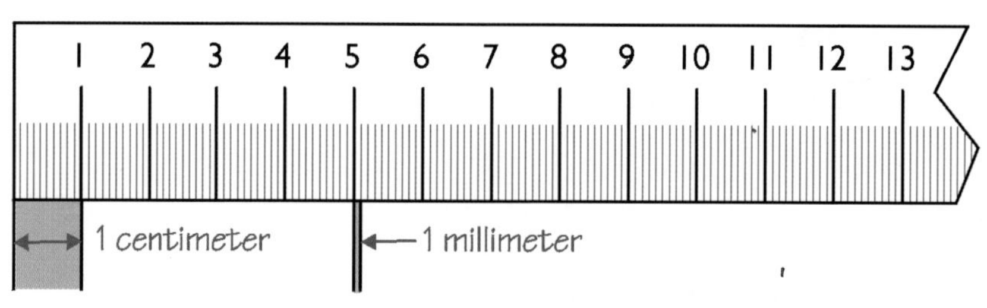

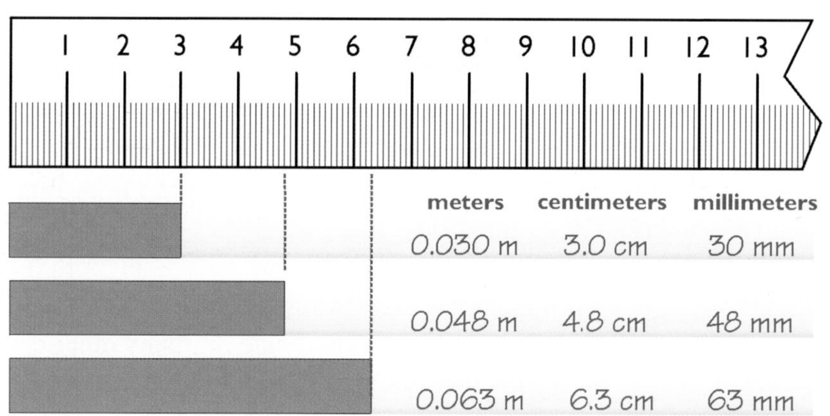

1 2 3 4 5 6 7 8 9 10 11 12 13
meters
centimeters
millimeters
0.030 m
3.0 cm
30 mm
0.048 m
4.8 cm
48 mm
0.063 m
6.3 cm
63 mm

Why are there so many different ways to measure the same thing?

Why units were invented

Units were invented so people could communicate amounts to each other. For example, suppose you want to buy 10 feet of rope. The person selling the rope takes out a ruler that is only 10 inches long (instead of 12 inches) and counts out 10 lengths of the ruler. Do you get your money's worth of rope? Of course not! For communication to be successful, everyone's idea of one foot (or any other unit of measure) must be the same. Figure 1.4 illustrates a hot dog vendor trying to sell a foot-long hot dog that is only 10 inches long. If the girl were to buy a hot dog, would she be getting what the sign says that she is paying for?

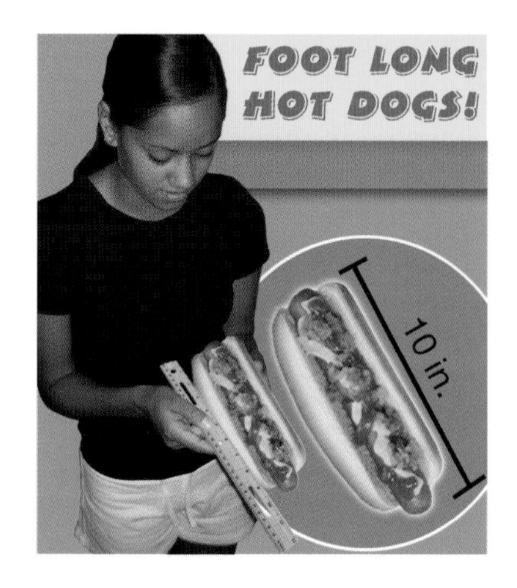

Figure 1.4: *The hot dog vendor and the girl have different ideas about how long a foot is.*

Scientists use metric units

Almost all fields of science use metric units because they are so much easier to work with. In the English system, there are 12 inches in a foot, 3 feet in a yard, and 5,280 feet in a mile. In the metric system, there are 10 millimeters in a centimeter, 100 centimeters in a meter, and 1,000 meters in a kilometer. Factors of 10 are easier to remember than 12, 3, and 5,280. The diagram below will help you get a sense for the metric units of distance.

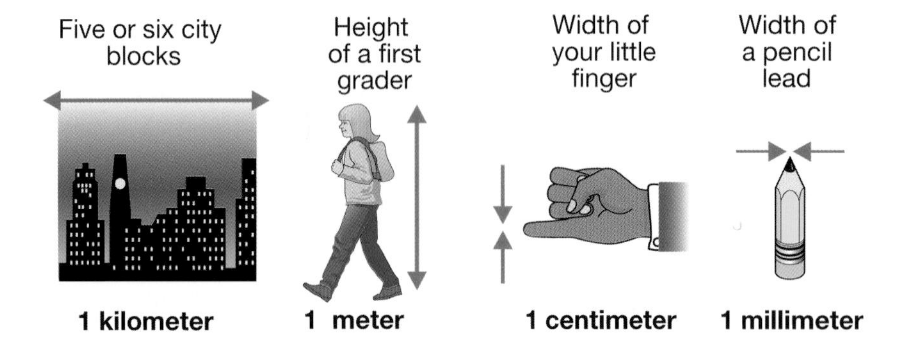

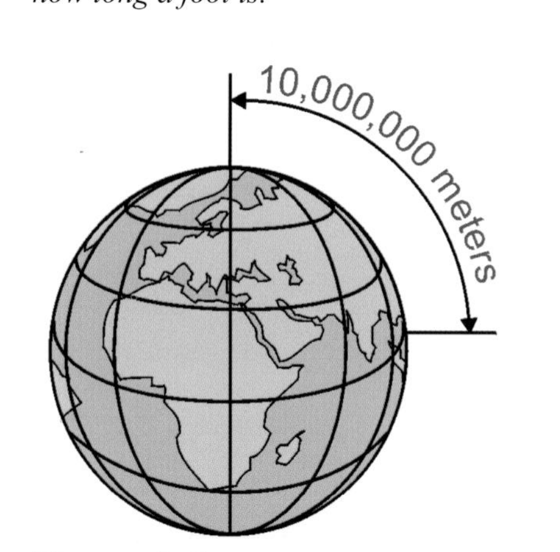

Figure 1.5: *In 1791, a meter was defined as 1/10,000,000 of the distance from a pole of Earth to its equator. Today the meter is defined more accurately using wavelengths of light.*

We use units every day

In your life, and in this book, we use both English and metric units. We measure some quantities, like power and wavelength, in metric units. We measure other quantities, like weight and speed, in both metric and English units. Science measurements are always metric, but you may use units of pounds and miles per hour in your daily experience. In many other countries, people use metric units for everyday measurements.

1.2 Investigations and Experiments

Science is about figuring out cause and effect relationships. If we do something, what happens? If we make a ramp steeper, how much faster will a car roll down? This is an easy question. However, the process we use to answer this question is the same process used to answer more difficult questions, like what keeps the moon in orbit around the Earth?

The rules of nature are often well hidden. We ask questions about nature and then design experiments to find clues. A series of one or more experiments that helps us answer a question is called an **investigation**. In this section you will learn how to design investigations using the scientific method.

Designing experiments

What is an experiment? An **experiment** is any situation we set up to observe what happens. You do experiments every day. You might wear your hair a new way to see if people treat you differently. That is an experiment.

Measurements can be recorded In science, we usually plan our experiments to give us **measurements**, which are observations we can record and think about. You might ask 10 friends if they like your hair the new way or the old way. That would be a way of collecting data from your experiment. From the results of the survey, you might decide to leave your hair the new way, or change it back. We usually do experiments for a reason, because we want to know something.

Experiments start with questions Experiments usually have a question associated with them. The question might be "Will people like my short hair better?" Sometimes you are aware of the question and sometimes you are not. If you push a door to see if it opens, that is an experiment. You often do it without thinking about the question. But the question is still there. "What will happen if I push on this door?"

Answers from nature Experiments are the way we ask questions of nature. You might want to know if salt water freezes at a lower temperature than fresh water. To answer the question you do an experiment. Place containers of salt water and fresh water in a freezer. Observe the water samples, and when ice forms measure and record the temperature of the sample. You can now compare the freezing points. Nature answers our questions about how things work through the results of experiments.

Ernest Just

Ernest Just was born in South Carolina in 1883. His father died when Ernest was four. His mother, a teacher, instilled in him a love of learning.

Ernest earned a scholarship to attend a boarding school in New Hampshire. The only African-American student at the school, Ernest excelled in his classes and graduated as the class valedictorian. Just went on to earn a degree in zoology from Dartmouth college and his Ph.D. in embryology from the University of Chicago.

Just taught at Howard University in Washington DC and spent summers researching marine mammal reproductive systems at the Woods Hole Oceanographic Institute on Cape Cod. He published over 50 papers detailing this work.

Just was the first American invited to join a prestigious research team at the Kaiser Wilhelm Institute in Berlin. This led to invitations to Naples, Sicily, and Paris. Just's work was greatly admired across Europe's scientific community.

The process of science

How did people learn science?

Have you ever wondered why people know so much about the world? Nobody told Sir Isaac Newton about how force and motion worked. There was no physics course he could take to learn it. Newton did his own experiments and figured it out. Once he knew, he told others, who told others, and now this course will tell *you*. But, we understand force and motion today because people did the original experiments to figure it out.

Scientists learn new information

Learning new information about the world—and the universe—is the most important thing scientists do. It is also important to *you*. Every day you have to figure out how to solve problems, like how to get your car to start in the cold. Science is a way of collecting information that can help you solve problems.

Experiments provide clues

Suppose your car will not start. You probably check obvious things first. Looking at your gas gauge is a simple experiment to test if there is any gas in your tank. Another experiment is to check the battery by trying the lights. If you are a mechanic, every experiment provides a clue. You keep doing experiments until you have enough clues to figure out what's wrong with the car.

Why doesn't the car start?

- Is there any gas?
- Is the battery dead?
- Are the wires loose?

Scientific evidence

Every experiment you do provides you with evidence. If you are a good mechanic you might try each experiment a couple of times to be sure of your evidence. For example, you might test the lights two or three times to see if the battery is really dead or maybe you just did not turn the switch all the way the first time. **Scientific evidence** is any observation that can be repeated with the same result.

Earth is round?

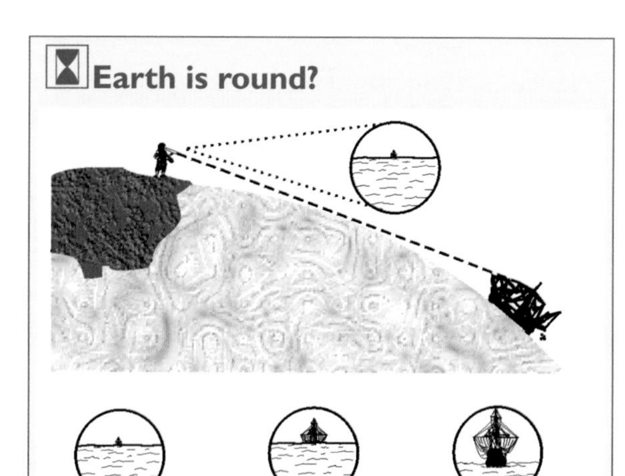

A ship 10 miles away seen with a telescope. *A ship 5 miles away seen with a telescope.* *A ship 1 mile away seen with a telescope.*

A good example of science is how people figured out that Earth is round. If you look out your window, you don't see a round Earth. Earth looks flat. People figured out it was round by thinking scientifically about what they saw and experienced.

People saw that the tops of ships appeared first as the ships approached shore. This could be explained if Earth was round.

Over a period of time people collected all kinds of evidence that suggested Earth was round. The evidence did not make sense if Earth was flat. When there was enough evidence, people were convinced and understood that Earth really is round.

The scientific method

The scientific method

The process you use to figure out what is wrong with your car is an example of the **scientific method**. As you try to fix your car, you ask yourself questions (Is there any gas? Is the battery dead?) and formulate ideas (or hypotheses) about what is wrong. By testing your ideas, you are experimenting and collecting data. You may be able to use this data to fix the car. Even if you conclude that the car can't be fixed, you have learned information to use the next time you are faced with a similar problem. Table 1.2 shows the steps of the scientific method.

Steps in the scientific method

Table 1.2: *Steps in the scientific method*

Step		Example
1	Ask a question.	Why doesn't the car start?
2	Formulate a hypothesis.	Maybe the battery is dead.
3	Design and conduct an experiment.	Turn the lights on to test the battery.
4	Collect and analyze data.	The lights go on.
5	Make a tentative conclusion.	Battery is OK.
6	Test conclusion, or if necessary, refine the question, and go through each step again.	Are the ignition wires loose or wet?

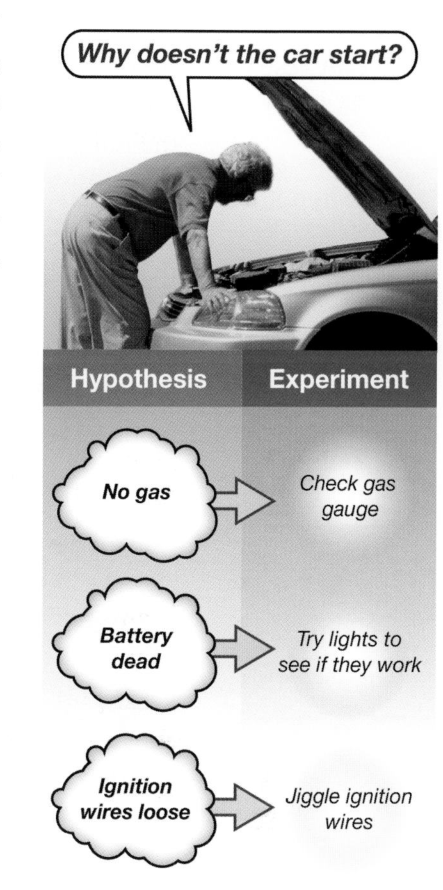

Figure 1.6: *Science is a process of collecting information through observation and experiment. The information is used to solve problems and test ideas about how things work.*

The research question and hypothesis

A research question

Suppose you are interested in how the angle of a hill affects the speed of a car rolling down. Your research question could be, "How is the speed of the car down the ramp affected by changing the steepness of the hill?"

The hypothesis

It is often useful to start with a guess (or hunch) about how something will happen. For example, you might start with a guess that making the ramp steeper will make the car roll faster. Your guesses or intuitions can take the form of a hypothesis, a prediction that can be tested by experiment. A good hypothesis might be: "Steeper hills result in cars with faster speeds." The hypothesis represents the tentative answer to the question "How is the speed of the car down the ramp affected by the angle of the hill?"

Hypothesis:
Cars go faster on steeper hills.

A hypothesis is an educated guess about what will happen.

Making a good hypothesis or research question

Forming a good hypothesis or research question depends on already knowing a little about how things might happen. You need to do a little experimenting before trying to form a hypothesis. For this reason, the word "hypothesis" is also defined as "an educated guess." Your experience with how objects roll down a smooth surface will help you make a hypothesis for a car and ramp experiment. However, don't worry if you cannot think of a hypothesis before you start your experiment. A good hypothesis can only be formed when you know a little about what is going to happen. The more experience you have, the better your hypothesis will be. It may be helpful to keep in mind that good hypotheses and research questions are those that you can test with an experiment.

Happy accidents

Not all discoveries in science are made using the scientific method! In fact, many important new discoveries and inventions happen by trial and error, a lucky experiment, or by accident.

The discovery of a way to waterproof fabric is a good example. Scientists tried to stretch Teflon®, a special kind of plastic into thin films. The plastic kept breaking. One day, in frustration, one scientist just ripped a piece very fast. It stretched without breaking! The resulting thin plastic film was waterproof but let water vapor through.

Stretched Teflon® film eventually became a breathable waterproof fabric called GoreTex®, used for outdoor clothing.

Designing experiments

Start with a good question

Will a car roll faster down a steeper hill?

This is a good research question because we can test it with an experiment. We could set up ramps at different angles and measure the speeds of cars as they roll down the ramp. Once you have a good question, you can design an experiment to help you find the answer.

Suppose you find that a car on a steep ramp rolls faster than a car on a ramp at a lower angle. Can you say that your experiment proves steeper ramps make cars go faster?

Identify all the factors when designing experiments

Maybe, and maybe not. Before you can design a good experiment, you must identify all the factors that affect how fast the car moves down the ramp. Maybe you pushed the car on one ramp. Maybe one car was heavier than another. Your observation of higher speed *because* the angle was steeper *could* be correct. Or, the speed could be higher for another reason, like a push at the start.

Variables

Factors that affect the results of an experiment are called **variables**. You can think about variables in terms of **cause and effect**. The weight of the car is one variable that may have an effect on the speed of the car. Some other variables are the angle of the ramp and how far down the ramp you measure the speed.

Change one thing at a time

When you can identify more than one variable that could affect the results of your experiment, it is best to change *only one variable at a time*. For example, if you change both the weight of the car and the angle of the ramp, you won't know which of the two variables caused your speed to change. If you want to test the effect of changing the angle, keep ALL the other variables the same.

Control variables and experimental variables

The variable that you change is called the **experimental variable**. The variables that you keep the same are called **control variables**. When you change one variable and control all of the others, we call it a **controlled experiment**. Controlled experiments are the preferred way to get reliable scientific evidence. If you observe that something happens (like the car goes faster), you know *why* it happened (because the ramp was steeper). There is no confusion over which variable caused the change.

Seven variables that affect speed

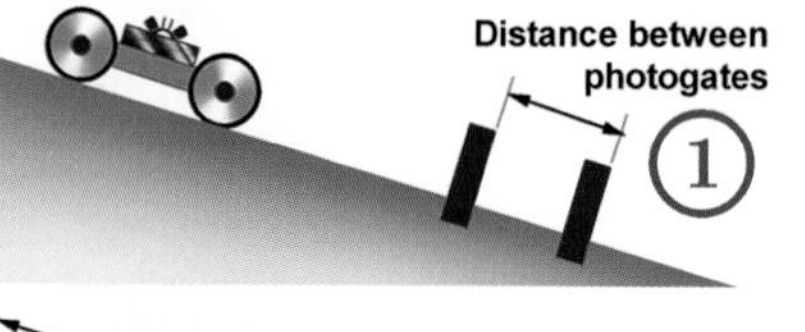

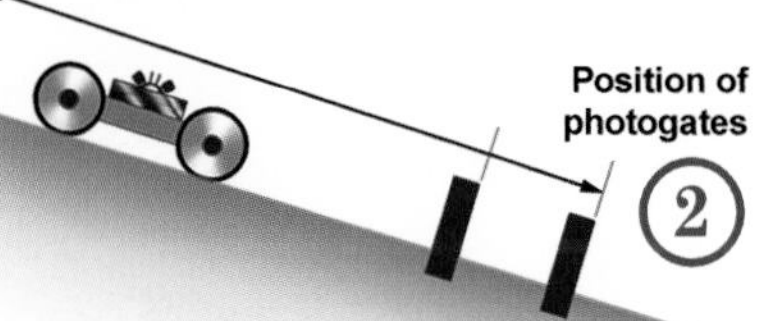

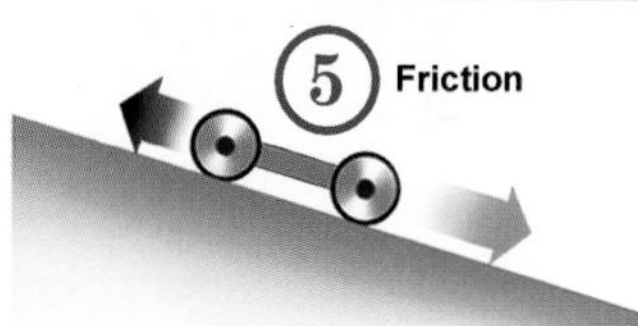

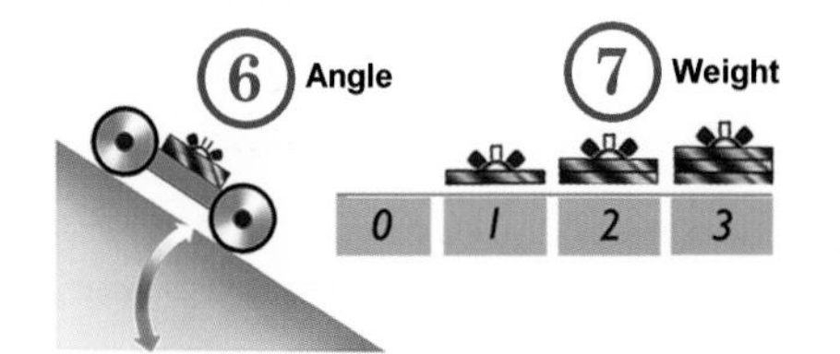

Figure 1.7: *Variables that affect a car rolling down a ramp.*

Experimental techniques

Experiments often have several trials

Many experiments are done over and over with only one variable changed. For example, you might roll a car down a ramp 10 times, each with a different angle. Each time you run the experiment is called a trial. To be sure of your results, each trial must be as close to identical as possible to all the others. The only exception should be the one variable you are testing.

Experimental technique

Your experimental technique is how you actually do the experiment. For example, you might release the car using one finger on top. If this is your technique, you want to do it the same way every time. By developing a good technique, you make sure your results accurately show the effects of changing your experimental variable. If your technique is sloppy, you may not be able to tell if any results are due to technique or changing your variable.

Procedures

The procedure is a collection of all the techniques you use to do an experiment. Your procedure for testing the ramp angle might have several steps (Figure 1.8). Good scientists keep careful track of their procedures so they can come back another time and repeat their experiments. Writing the procedures down in a lab notebook is a good way to keep track (Figure 1.9).

Scientific results must always be repeatable

It is important that your experiments produce measurements that are reliable and accurate. What good would a new discovery or invention be if nobody believed you? Having good techniques and procedures is the best way to be sure of your results.

Scientific discoveries and inventions must always be able to be tested by someone other than you. If other people can follow your procedure and get the same results, then most scientists would accept your results as being true. Writing good procedures is the best way to ensure that others can repeat and verify your experiments.

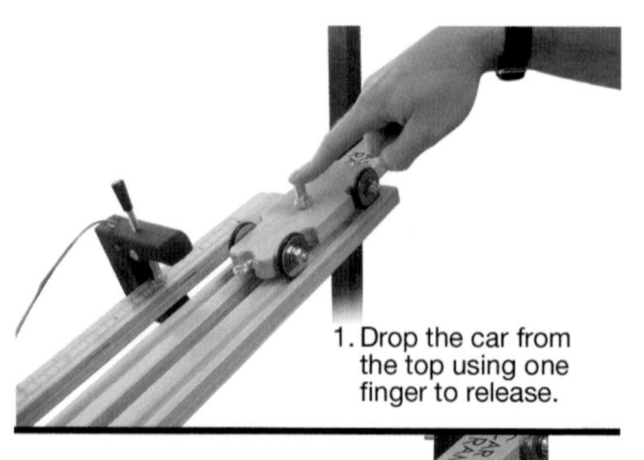

1. Drop the car from the top using one finger to release.

2. Use photogates to measure speed every 10 centimeters.

Figure 1.8: *A procedure is a collection of all the techniques that someone else would need to repeat your experiments in order to confirm your results.*

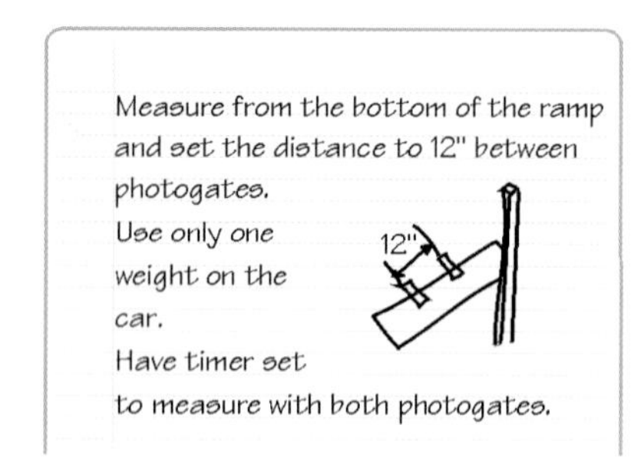

Measure from the bottom of the ramp and set the distance to 12" between photogates.
Use only one weight on the car.
Have timer set to measure with both photogates.
12"

Figure 1.9: *A notebook keeps your observations and procedures from getting lost or being forgotten.*

1.3 Speed

Just saying that something is fast is often not enough description for a scientist. You can easily walk faster than a turtle, yet you would not say walking was fast compared with the speed of driving a car. In this section, you will learn how to be very precise about speed.

What do we mean by speed?

- Exactly how fast are you walking?
- How many meters do you walk for each second?
- Do you always walk the same number of meters every second?

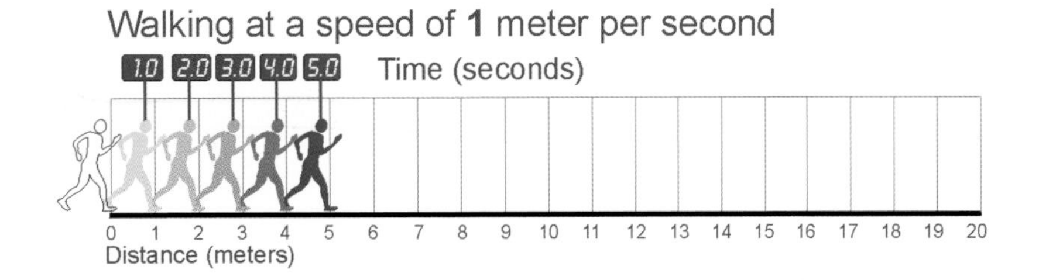

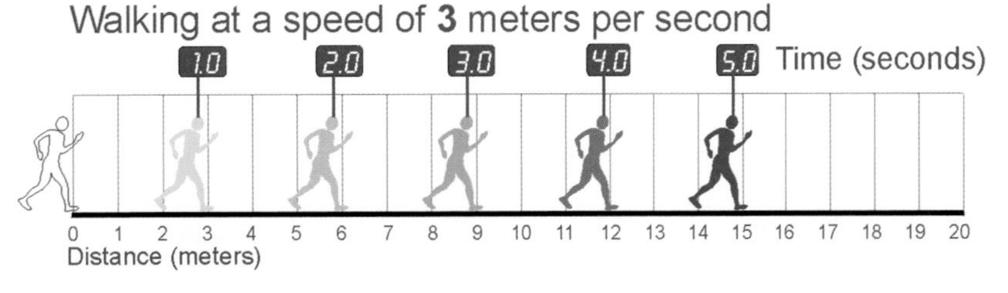

What is speed? Describing movement from place to place naturally leads you to think about **speed**. The speed of an object is a measure of how quickly the object gets from one place to another. Speed is a characteristic of all objects. Even objects that are standing still have a speed of zero.

Fast trains

Fast trains are being used for transportation in several countries. In Japan, where cities are crowded, people have to travel from far away to reach their jobs. Japan's 500 Series train is the world's fastest, operating at a speed of 300 km/h (186 mph).

In France, the TGV goes almost as fast. In the United States, Amtrak runs high-speed trains from Boston to Washington, DC. Fast trains are also being considered in California and the Midwest.

Fast trains offer benefits like performance and friendliness to the environment. As airports become more crowded, the use of fast trains for long-distance travel will probably increase.

Calculating speed

Calculating speed

There are several ways to look at the concept of speed. In the simplest interpretation, speed is the distance traveled divided by the time taken. For example, if you drive 90 miles in 1.5 hours (Figure 1.10), then your speed is 90 miles divided by 1.5 hours, equal to 60 miles per hour. To determine a speed, you need to know two things:

- The distance traveled
- The time taken

Speed is calculated by taking the distance traveled divided by the time taken.

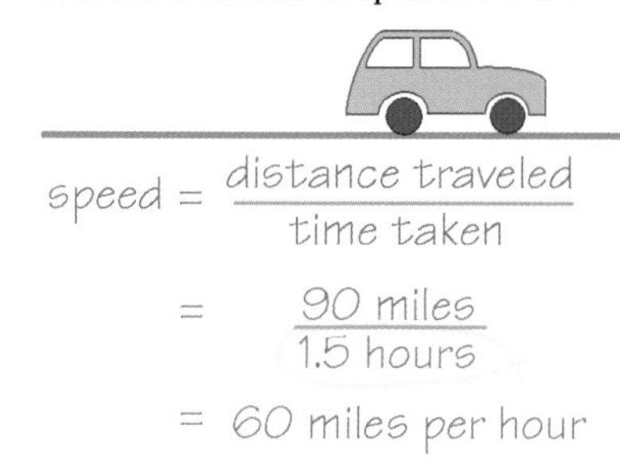

Problem:
A car goes 90 miles in one hour and 30 minutes. What is the speed of the car?
speed = distance traveled / time taken
= 90 miles / 1.5 hours
= 60 miles per hour

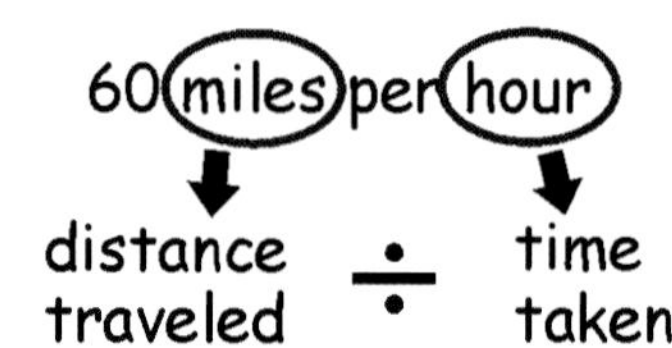

Figure 1.10: *If you drive 90 miles in 1.5 hours, your speed is 60 miles per hour. This is calculated by dividing the distance traveled (90 miles) by the time taken (1.5 hours).*

Units for speed

Since speed is a ratio of distance over time, the units for speed are a ratio of distance units over time units. If distance is in miles and time in hours, then speed is expressed in miles per hour (miles/hours). We will often measure distance in centimeters or meters, and time in seconds. The speeds we calculate would then be in units of centimeters/second or meters/second. Table 1.3 shows many different units commonly used for speed.

What does "per" mean?

The word "per" means "for every" or "for each." The speed of 60 miles per hour is really a shorthand for saying 60 miles *for each* hour. When used with units, the "per" also means "divided by." The quantity before the word per is divided by the quantity after it. For example, if you want speed in meters per second, you have to divide meters by seconds.

Table 1.3: ***Some Common Units for Speed***

Distance	Time	Speed	Abbreviation
meters	seconds	meters per second	m/sec
kilometers	hours	kilometers per hour	km/h
centimeters	seconds	centimeters per second	cm/sec
miles	hours	miles per hour	mph
inches	seconds	inches per second	in/sec, ips
feet	minutes	feet per minute	ft/min, fpm

Relationships between distance, speed, and time

How far did you go if you drove for 2 hours at 60 mph?

Mixing up distance, time, and speed

This seems like a fair question. We know speed is the distance traveled divided by the time taken. Now we are given the time and the speed. We are asked to find the distance. How do you take the new information and figure out an answer?

Let the letter v stand for "speed," the letter d stand for "distance traveled," and the letter t stand for "time taken." If we remember that the letters stand for those words, we can now write our definition of speed much faster.

Speed

$$v = \frac{d}{t}$$

Speed (m/sec) → v; Distance traveled (meters) → d; Time taken (seconds) → t

Using formulas

Also remember that the words or letters stand for the values that the variables really have. For example, the letter t will be replaced by the actual time when we plug in numbers for the letters. You can think about each letter as a box that will eventually hold a number. Maybe you don't know what the number is yet. Once we get everything arranged according to the rules we can fill the boxes with the numbers that belong in each one. The last box left will be our answer. The letters (or variables) are the labels that tell us which numbers belong in which boxes.

Three forms of the speed formula

There are three ways to arrange the three variables that relate distance, time and speed. You should be able to work out how to get any of the three variables if you know the other two.

Equation	Gives you...	If you know...
v = d/t	speed	time and distance
d = vt	distance	speed and time
t = d/v	time	distance and speed

Why *v* is used to represent speed in an equation.

When we represent speed in a formula, we use the letter *v*. If this seems confusing, remember that *v* stands for velocity.

For this chapter, it isn't important, but there is a technical difference between *speed* and *velocity*. Speed is a single measurement that tells how fast you are going, like 60 miles per hour.

Velocity really means you know both your speed, and also what direction you are going. If you told someone you were going 60 mph straight south, you told them your velocity. If you just told them you were going 60 mph, you told them your speed.

How to solve science problems

An example — An airplane is flying at a constant speed of 150 meters per second. After one hour, how far has the plane traveled?

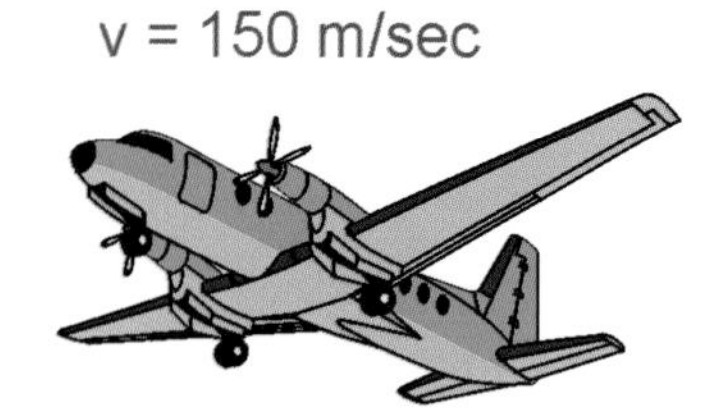

Solution — There is a five-step process that works for almost all science problems.

Step 1 — Identify what you are asked.

The problem asks for the distance.

Step 2 — Write down what you are given.

You are given time and speed.

Step 3 — Write down any relationships you know that involve any of the information you are asked, or given.

$v = d/t$, 1 hour = 3,600 seconds.

Step 4 — Pick which relationship to start with and try to arrange it to get the variable you want on the left-hand side of an equals sign.

$d = vt$

Step 5 — Plug in the numbers and get the answer.

$$d = vt = (150 \text{ m/sec}) \times (3{,}600 \text{ sec})$$
$$= 540{,}000 \text{ meters}$$
$$= 540 \text{ kilometers}$$

For this example, you may have figured out the answer in your head. Other problems may not be obvious. It is worth going through the whole process (all five steps) with an easy problem so you know how to approach a harder problem.

Solving science problems

There is a step-by-step approach that can solve almost any science problem. It may not always be the fastest way, but it will always get you started and on the path to the correct answer.

Step 1

Read the problem carefully and figure out what it is asking for.

Step 2

Read the problem again and write down all the information you are given, such as speed and distance.

Step 3

Write down all the relationships or formulas that apply to either the answer or the information you are given.

Step 4

Choose, combine, or rearrange the relationships until you get the variable you want (the answer) by itself on one side of an equals sign.

Step 5

Plug in the numbers and calculate the answer.

Chapter 1 Review

Vocabulary review

Match the following terms with the correct definition. There is one extra definition in the list that will not match any of the terms.

Set One

1. time
2. second
3. distance
4. length
5. English system

a. How far it is from one point to another
b. A system of measuring that uses length units of inches, feet, and miles
c. A type of distance measurement
d. A measurement that describes the interval between two events; the past, present, and future
e. A system of measuring time based on the Babylonian number system
f. A common unit used in measuring time

Set Two

1. metric system
2. investigation
3. experiment
4. measurement
5. scientific evidence

a. A series of experiments connected to a basic question
b. An observation that can be recorded and thought about
c. An observation that can be repeated with the same result
d. An observation that is reported in a newspaper
e. A situation that is set up in order to observe what happens
f. A system of measuring that uses length units of millimeters, centimeters, meters, and kilometers

Set Three

1. scientific method
2. research question
3. hypothesis
4. variables
5. cause and effect

a. An educated guess about what will happen
b. When one variable affects another
c. A process used to solve a problem or test an idea about how things work
d. A process used to build a device
e. Factors that affect the result of an experiment
f. A question that can be answered by an experiment or series of experiments

Set Four

1. experimental variable
2. control variable
3. controlled experiment
4. trial
5. experimental technique

a. A variable that is kept the same in an experiment
b. How an experiment is done
c. The running of an experiment
d. A variable that is not important in an experiment
e. An experiment in which one variable changes and all other variables are kept the same
f. A variable that is changed in an experiment

Concept review

1. Units of time include seconds, minutes, hours, days, and years. Why are there so many units for time?
2. To make sense, a measurement must always have a _______ and a _______.
3. How are an investigation and an experiment related to each other?
4. Experiments usually have a question associated with them. True or false?
5. List the steps of the scientific method.
6. When doing an experiment, you must change only one________ at a time.
7. A hypothesis is a random guess. True or false?
8. Scientific discoveries and inventions must always be verified by more than one person. True or false?
9. What is the definition of speed?
10. How are speed and velocity different? Use each in a sentence.
11. Write the speed equation that you would use in each of the following scenarios:
    a. You know distance and speed.
    b. You know time and distance.
    c. You know speed and time.
12. What is the speed of an object that is standing still?
13. Describe, in your own words, how you determine the speed of an object.

Problems

1. Which one of the following times is equal to 75 seconds?
    a. 3 minutes (3:00)
    b. 1 minute, 15 seconds (1:15)
    c. 1 minute, 25 seconds (1:25)
2. How many seconds are in half an hour? Show your work.
3. Match the measurement in the first column to the corresponding equal measurement in the second column:

a) 1 centimeter	1) 12 inches
b) 1 foot	2) 1 meter
c) 5, 280 feet	3) 10 millimeters
d) 1000 millimeters	4) 1 mile

4. A student is 5 feet, 2 inches tall. What is her height in meters?
5. A model car is 30 cm in length. How many inches long is it?

6. What is the correct order of the following lengths from shortest to longest? Show your work.

 a. 16 inches
 b. 26.6 centimeters
 c. 1.1 feet
 d. 0.4 meters

7. You would like to find out whether a sports drink or plain water is better for an athlete. You have several friends on the field hockey team and the soccer team. You conduct an experiment at practice one day. You give the field hockey players the plain water and the soccer players the sports drink.

 Did you run a controlled experiment? Why or why not?

8. You have heard that plants grow better in response to music. You have permission to do an experiment to find out if this is true. You have 20 small plants and two rooms that face the same direction. Each room has a window that gets the same amount of light. Describe the experiment you would do to see if music affects plants. Write down your question, your hypothesis, and the procedure you would follow in your experiment.

9. Three groups of students are doing car and ramp experiments. Each group does three identical releases of the car and measures the following times from photogate A to photogate B.

Group 1	Group 2	Group 3
0.2315 seconds	0.2442 seconds	0.2315 seconds
0.2442 seconds	0.2437 seconds	0.2202 seconds
0.3007 seconds	0.2443 seconds	0.2255 seconds

 Which group did the best experiment and why do you think so? Be sure that you include the term *variable* in your answer.

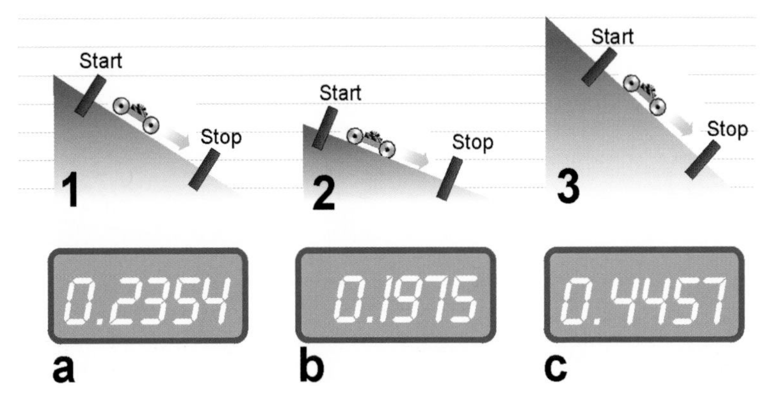

10. Match the timer with the corresponding ramp in the diagram above. You may assume that only the angle of the ramp is different, and all of the other variables are the same.

 a. Timer A corresponds to ramp # ________.
 b. Timer B corresponds to ramp # ________.
 c. Timer C corresponds to ramp # ________.

11. An armadillo is a peculiar animal that is common in the southwestern United States. You are a wildlife biologist and you observe an armadillo that moves 5 feet in 1 minute.

 a. Calculate the speed of the armadillo in feet/minute.
 b. Calculate the speed of the armadillo in inches/second.
 c. Calculate the speed of the armadillo in centimeters/second.

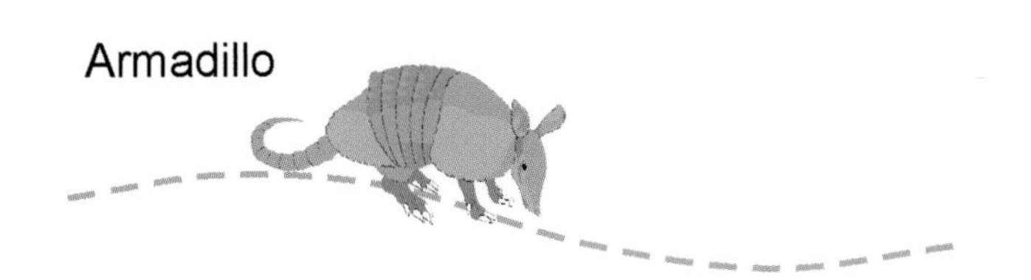

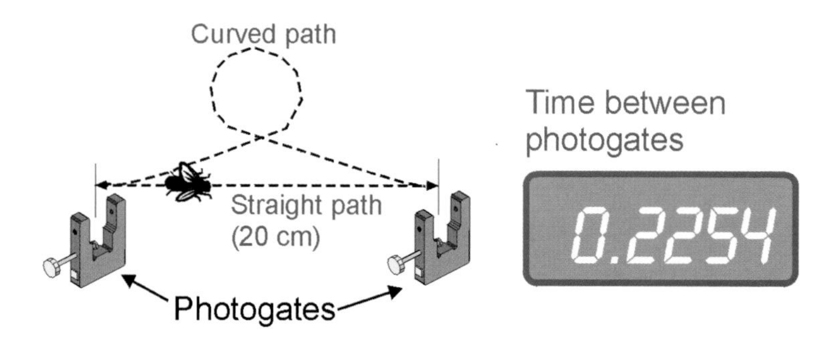

12. A bumblebee flies through two photogates that are spaced exactly 20 centimeters apart. The timer shows the measurement made for the time between gates in seconds.

    a. Calculate the speed of the bumblebee assuming it flies a straight line between the two light beams. Show your work.

    b. If the bumblebee flies a curved path in the same amount of time, will its actual speed be different? Explain your reasoning.

35 cm
Time between
photogates
0.2061
Photogate A
Photogate B

13. A car was timed as it passed through two photogates. The distance between the photogates is 35 centimeters. Calculate the speed of the car as it passed through the two photogates. The timer displays time in seconds.

14. A group of students is doing a speed experiment, and they measure the speed of a car rolling down a ramp five times at the exact same location on the ramp. Review their data below:

    66.7 cm/sec; 70.5 cm/sec; 64.9 cm/sec; 67.8 cm/sec; 69.1 cm/sec

    What factors could explain the variability in their data?

Applying your knowledge

1. Many old number systems were based on 12's because of the following way of counting with the hands:

    - By using the thumb on one hand, a person can easily count to twelve on the four fingers by touching the tip and then the first two joints of each finger.
    - By using the same method on the other hand, the same person could keep track of how many times he or she reached 12 on the first hand.

    Try out this method and calculate how high it is possible to count using this method.

2. Research the number system and units of an ancient civilization and write a short report on what you learned.

3. Read an article in a science magazine and try to identify how scientists have used the scientific method in their work.

4. Research the speeds of many kinds of animals and make a table showing slowest to fastest.

5. Prepare a short report on important speeds in your favorite sport.

Chapter 2

Mathematical Models

Introduction to Chapter 2

This chapter is about graphing data from your experiments with the car and ramp. You will learn that graphs are mathematical models used for making predictions and solving equations.

Investigations for Chapter 2

2.1	Using a Scientific Model to Predict Speed	*How can you predict the speed of the car at any point on the ramp?*

In this Investigation you will create a graphical model that you can use to predict the speed of the car at any point on the ramp. You will do this by determining the speed of the car at six points along the ramp and then graphing the speed of the car against the distance traveled.

2.2	Position and Time	*How do you model the motion of the car?*

In this Investigation you will make a distance vs. time graph from the data you collect with the car and ramp. You are going to model the motion of one trip of the car down the ramp. To get enough data to model motion, you will collect data at 10 or more points along the ramp. Your teacher will assign your group's ramp angle.

2.3	Acceleration	*How is the speed of the car changing?*

Since acceleration depends on the angle of the hill, a car and ramp make a good tool to discover the behavior of *uniform acceleration*, or when speed changes at a constant rate. Shallow (nearly level) angles will give very little acceleration, and the increasing speed is easy to observe. Steep (nearly vertical) angles resemble *free fall* or motion that is entirely under the influence of gravity.

Learning Goals

In this chapter, you will:

- ✔ Construct a speed vs. distance graph.
- ✔ Use a graph to make a prediction that can be quantitatively tested.
- ✔ Calculate the percent error between a measurement and a prediction.
- ✔ Create and analyze a distance vs. time graph.
- ✔ Determine the slope of a line.
- ✔ Distinguish between linear and nonlinear graphs.
- ✔ Distinguish between speed and acceleration.
- ✔ Calculate acceleration from a formula.
- ✔ Calculate acceleration from the slope of a speed vs. time graph.

Vocabulary

accelerate
acceleration
average speed
conceptual model
deceleration
dependent variable
free fall
graphical model
gravity
independent variable
instantaneous speed
physical model
scientific model

2.1 Using a Scientific Model to Predict Speed

In this section, you will learn how to make a model that will accurately predict the speed of a car. Making models is an important part of science and engineering. For a given situation, models tell us how all the variables, like speed, distance, and time, fit together. If we have a model, we can predict what will happen because we know how changes in one variable affect the others.

Why make models?

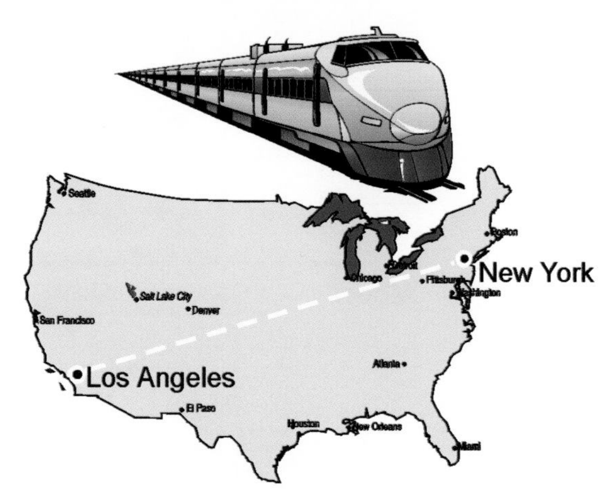

Suppose it is your job to design a train to go from New York to Los Angeles in the shortest possible time. Your train would have to go up and down hills and across flat plains carrying 1,000 people.

How powerful a motor do you need?
How powerful do the brakes need to be?
How much fuel do you need to carry?

There are many things you have to know. You want the answers to the questions *before* you build the train. How do you get answers to a complicated problem such as how to design a high-speed train?

The way we answer complicated questions is to break them down into smaller questions. Each smaller question can be answered with simple experiments or research. One question might be how fast a train will roll down a hill of a given angle. You might do an experiment with a miniature train to get some data on downhill speeds that would help you design the brakes for the train. Other questions might be answered with research, in order to learn how other people solved similar problems.

You can often use the results of an experiment to produce a model that tells how each of the variables in the experiment are related. One model you might make is a graph showing how fuel efficiency depends on the size of the engine. If you know the engine size needed to climb the steepest hill, the model tells you how much fuel you have to carry on the train. Once you have models for each part of the train, you can evaluate different choices for your design.

Big complex question

How can I design a high-speed train that can cross the United States?

Smaller questions

How powerful does the train's motor need to be to go up hills?

How good do the train's brakes need to be to go down hills?

How much fuel should the train carry?

Experiment and research

Design experiments, collect data, do research, and create models for each question. Then figure out how all the systems of the train work together.

Figure 2.1: *We solve complex questions by breaking them down into smaller problems. Each small problem is solved and the results are used to solve the larger question.*

Scientific models

What do experiments tell us?

An experiment tells us about the relationship between variables. If we roll a car downhill to learn about its motion, we will need to measure its speed at several distances from the top. Speed and distance are the variables.

We will be looking for a way to connect these variables. We need to know exactly how much speed is gained by the car for every centimeter it rolls down the ramp. We collect experimental data to figure out the relationship between the variables.

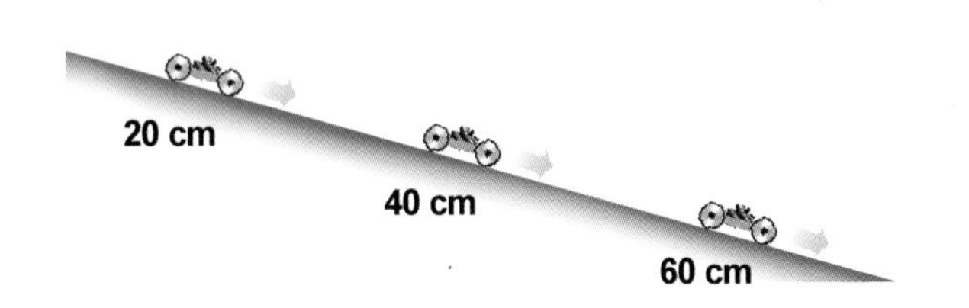

Distance	Speed
20 cm	140 cm/sec
40 cm	198 cm/sec
60 cm	242 cm/sec

What is a scientific model?

We then take the results and make a scientific model that shows how each variable relates to another. For example, how does the distance traveled relate to the speed? The data above shows that for every 20 centimeters traveled, the speed increased by 40 cm/sec. If we graph this data, we can use it to make predictions about the speed of the car at other places along the ramp. A similar process could be used in the train design. A graphical model could answer the question "If the hill is longer by a kilometer, how much faster will the train go if the brakes fail?"

Solving the big question

Once we have models for the smaller relationships, we can put them together to solve the bigger question of how to design the train. Experiments and research have given us enough information to create and test models that tell us how each part will work. Once we know how each part of the train will work, we can design a train where all the parts work together.

Accurate measurements

Instruments like an electronic timer allow you to make *very* accurate measurements of speed. The more accurate your measurements, the better your model will be. By using very accurate data to make the graphical model, you can be sure that your predictions will be accurate also.

Variables

Experiment

Distance (cm)	Speed (cm/sec)
10	100
20	140
30	171
40	198
50	221
60	242
80	280
90	297

Model

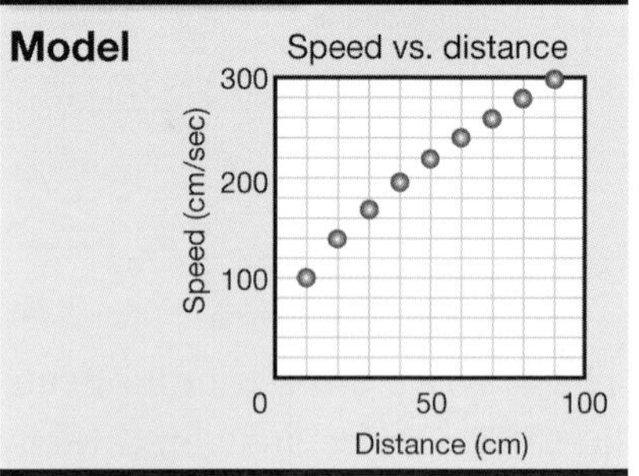

Prediction

At 55 centimeters, the speed of the car will be 231 cm/sec.

Figure 2.2: *A model is something we make that identifies the relationships between the variables. The model can answer questions like "If I change the distance down the ramp, how much will the speed change?"*

We all make mental models

Our models of nature can take many forms. For example, suppose you want to kick a soccer ball into the goal. In your mind, you know how the ball moves on the grass of the field or through the air because of your previous experience. This mental image is a kind of model you use to make adjustments in how you kick the ball toward the goal.

Figure 2.3: *Mental models help us imagine how something will happen.*

Physical models

Some models are physical. **Physical models** are models that we can look at, touch, feel, and take measurements from. Engineers often construct scale models of bridges and evaluate them for strength and design. The word *scale* means that lengths on the model are proportional to lengths on the real object. For example, a scale of 1 inch = 10 feet (120:1) means that every inch on the model represents 10 feet in real life. It is much easier to do experiments on scale models than it is to build full-size bridges! If properly constructed, models tell the engineers about the behavior of the real bridge, and help them avoid dangerous mistakes.

Early civilizations believed the Earth was covered by a dome on which the sun, stars and planets moved.

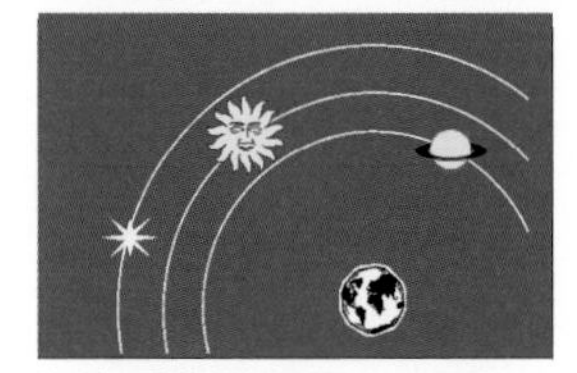

In the Middle Ages people thought the sun, stars, and planets circled the Earth which sat in the center.

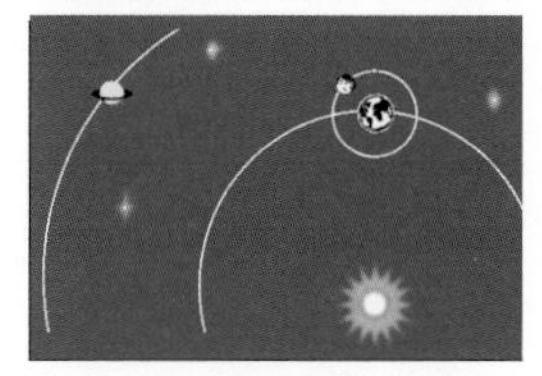

Today we know the Earth and planets orbit around the sun and the stars are very far away.

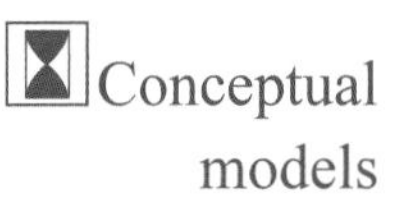

Conceptual models

Much of our scientific understanding of nature is expressed in the form of **conceptual models**. These types of models are *descriptive*, that is, we use them to describe how something works. For example, in 1543, Nicholaus Copernicus, the great astronomer, described a conceptual model of the heavens in which the Earth revolves in an orbit around the sun. Copernicus's conceptual model was a major revolution in our understanding of astronomy, since most people of his time believed in Ptolemy's model in which the sun moved around the Earth. Other astronomers added to Copernicus' model. Galileo invented the telescope in 1609, and Johannes Kepler used the telescope to work out detailed orbits for other planets. In 1687, Isaac Newton's law of universal gravitation finally provided a model that explained why planets move in orbits. Our models improve as our understanding grows.

Figure 2.4: *Some models are physical, like this model of a bridge. Models can tell engineers and architects a lot about how a project will be built.*

Making a graphical model

Graphical models

While conceptual models are very useful, often they are only the first step toward making a model that can make predictions. The next step is often a graph. A graph shows how two variables are related with a picture that is easy to understand. A **graphical model** uses a graph to show a relationship between the variable on the x-axis and the variable on the y-axis. Because a graph uses numbers it is also known as a mathematical model.

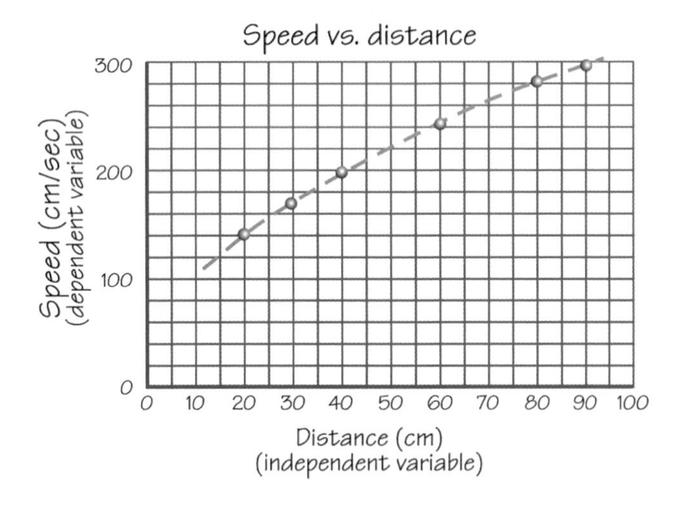

Distance (cm)	Speed (cm/sec)
20	140
30	171
40	198
60	242
80	280
90	297

The dependent variable

The graph shows how the speed of a rolling car changes as it rolls downhill. We expect the speed to change. Speed is the **dependent variable** because we think the speed *depends* on how far down the ramp the car gets.

The independent variable

The distance is the **independent variable**. We say it is *independent* because we are free to make the distance anything we want by choosing where on the ramp to measure.

Choosing x and y

People have decided to always put the independent variable on the horizontal (x) axis. You should too, since this is how people will read any graph you make. The dependent variable goes on the vertical (y) axis.

How to Make a Graph

1. Decide what to put on x and y.

Each box = 1 (0, 5, 10, 15) · Each box = 10 (0, 50, 100, 150) · Each box = 20 (0, 100, 200, 300)

Letting each box = 20 fits the biggest data point (297 cm/sec)

2. Make a scale for each axis by counting boxes to fit your largest value. Count by multiples of 1, 2, 5, or 10 to make it easier to plot points. Make the graph big, try to use as much of the graph paper as you can.
3. Plot your points by finding the x value, and drawing a line up until you get to the right y value. Put a dot for each point.
4. Draw a smooth curve that shows the pattern of the points. Don't simply connect the dots.
5. Make a title for your graph.

Reading a graph

Why are graphs useful? One purpose of making a graph is to organize your data into a model you can use to make predictions. Pictures are much easier to understand than tables of data (Figure 2.5). By making a graph, you are making a picture that shows the exact relationship between your variables.

Making predictions from a graph Suppose you want to find out what the speed of the car would be 50 centimeters from the start. You did not measure the speed there. Yet the graph can give you an answer.

1. To predict the speed, start by finding 50 centimeters on the x-axis.
2. Draw a line vertically upward from 50 centimeters until it hits the curve you drew from your data.
3. Draw a line horizontally over until it reaches the y-axis.
4. Use the scale on the y-axis to read the predicted speed.
5. For this example, the model graph predicts the speed to be 220 cm/sec.

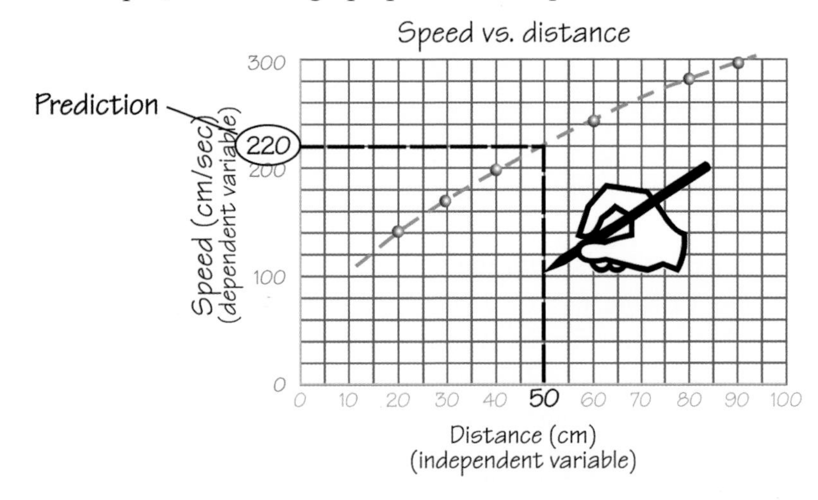

Checking the accuracy of a model If the graph is created from accurate data, the prediction will also be accurate. You could check by doing another experiment and measuring the speed of the car at 50 centimeters. You should find it to be very close to the prediction from your graph.

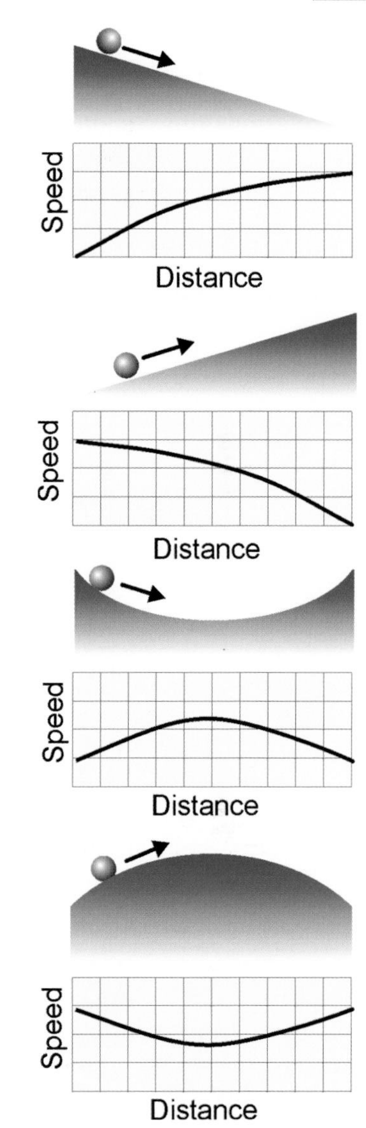

Figure 2.5: *Some different shapes for ramps and their corresponding speed vs. distance graphs.*

Cause and effect relationships

Cause and effect relationships

In many experiments we are looking for a cause and effect relationship. How does changing one variable effect another? Graphs are a good way to see whether there is a connection between two variables or not. You cannot always tell from looking at tables of data. With a graph, the connection is clear.

Patterns indicate relationships

When there is a relationship between the variables the graph shows a clear pattern. The speed and distance variables show a strong relationship. When there is no relationship the graph looks like a collection of dots. No pattern appears. The number of musical groups a student listed in one minute and the last two digits of his or her phone number are an example of two variables that are not related.

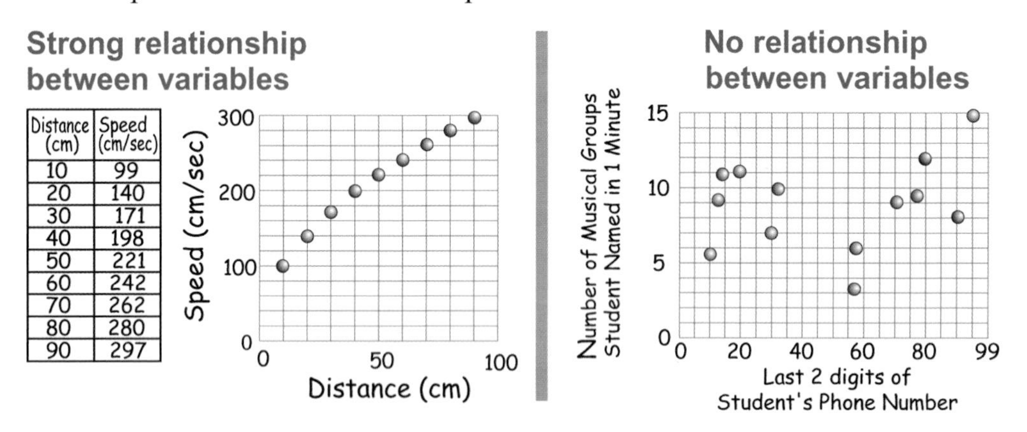

Distance (cm)	Speed (cm/sec)
10	99
20	140
30	171
40	198
50	221
60	242
70	262
80	280
90	297

Strong and weak relationships

You can tell how strong the relationship is from the pattern. If the relationship is strong, a small change in one variable makes a big change in another. If the relationship is weak, even a big change in one variable has little effect on the other. In weak relationships, the points may follow a pattern but there is not much change in one variable compared to big changes in the other (Figure 2.6)

Inverse relationships

Some relationships are inverse. When one variable increases, the other decreases. If you graph how much money you spend against how much you have left, you see an inverse relationship. The more you spend, the less you have. Graphs of inverse relationships always slope down to the right (Figure 2.7).

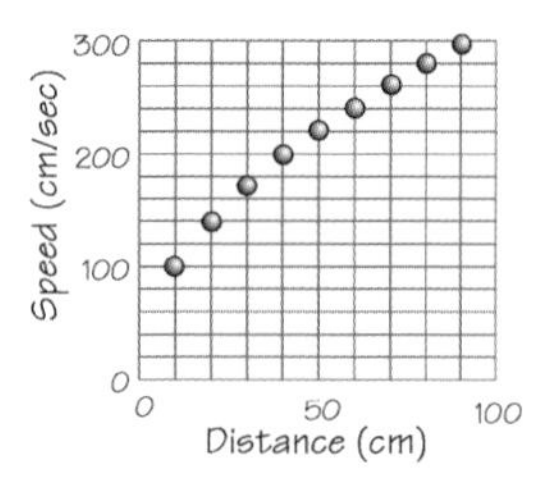

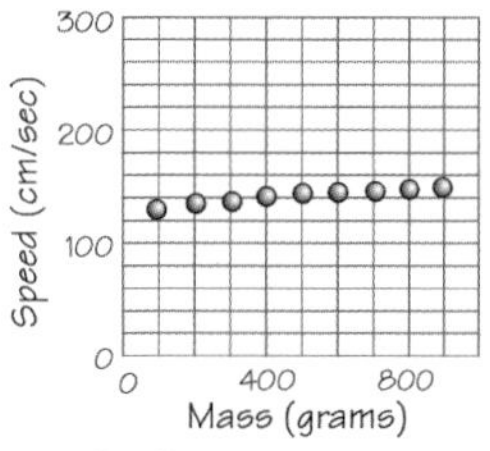

Figure 2.6: *In a strong relationship (top), a big change in distance creates a big change in speed. In a weak relationship (bottom), a big change in mass makes almost no change in speed.*

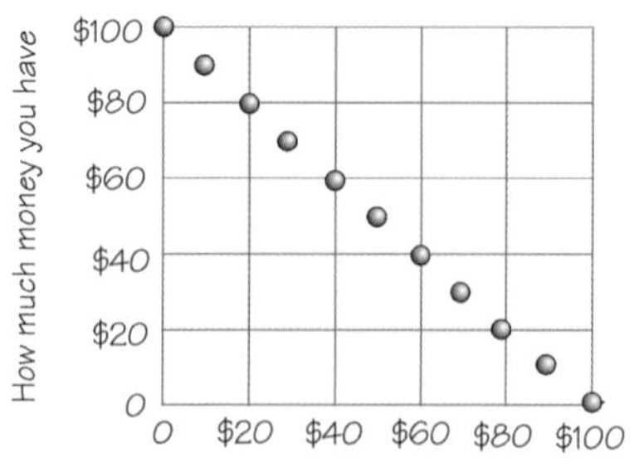

Figure 2.7: *A typical graph for an inverse relationship.*

2.2 Position and Time

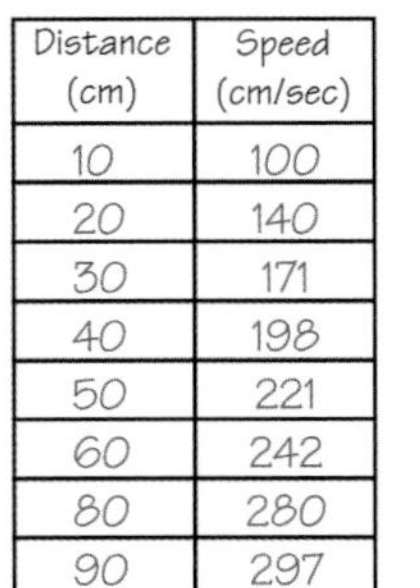

Distance (cm)	Speed (cm/sec)
10	100
20	140
30	171
40	198
50	221
60	242
80	280
90	297

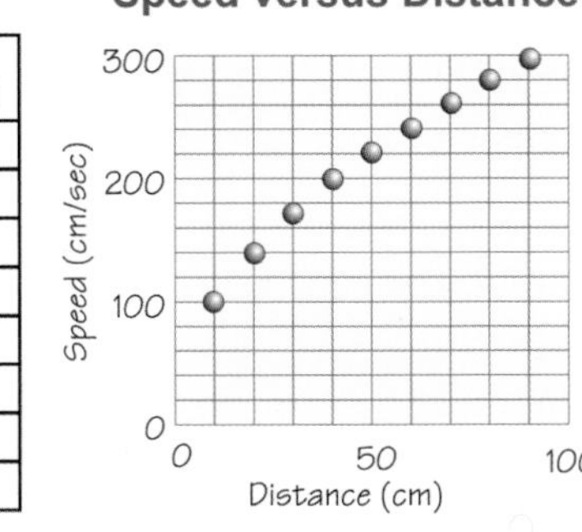

Distance (cm)	Time (sec)
2	0.1
10	0.2
22	0.3
39	0.4
61	0.5
88	0.6
120	0.7
157	0.8

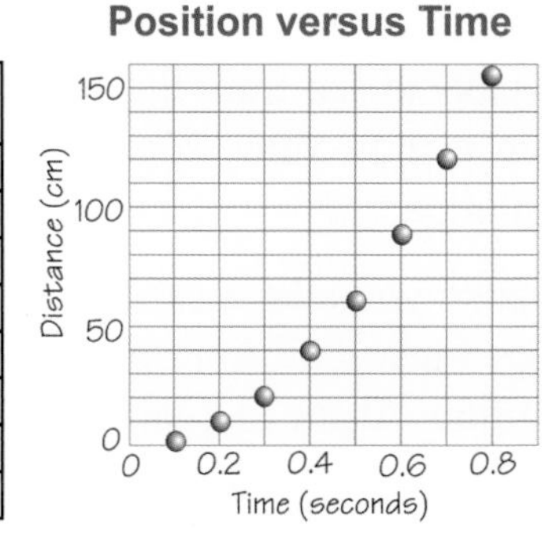

Graphical models like the speed vs. distance graph are good for organizing data so you can make predictions. In this section, you will learn how to model motion with another graph: position vs. time. The position vs. time graph offers a new way to find the speed of a moving object. The position vs. time graph will also be our example as we explore different ways to use and interpret graphs. The techniques you learn in this section will help you understand acceleration, the next important idea in motion.

Time	Position
1:00	0 (start)
2:00	3 km
3:00	6 km
4:00	7 km
5:00	5 km
6:00	3 km
7:00	1 km

Figure 2.8: *You leave at 1:00 and walk away from school in a straight line until 4:00. Then you turn around and walk back. At 7:00, you are still 1 kilometer away from school.*

Position

Position In physics, the word position means where something is compared with where it started, including direction. As things move their position changes. If you walked in a straight line away from your school, your position would keep getting larger (Figure 2.8). If you stopped walking, your position would stop changing.

Distance Distance is an interval of length without regard to direction. You can walk a distance of 10 miles in a circle and end up exactly where you started. If you walk a curved path, the distance you walk could be much greater than the distance between where you started and where you end up (Figure 2.9).

Position and distance Position and distance are different. If you are 7 kilometers north of school, that is a statement of your position. If you walk back towards your school, your position decreases. If you get back to where you started, your position is zero even though the distance you walked is 14 kilometers (7 km away plus 7 km back)!

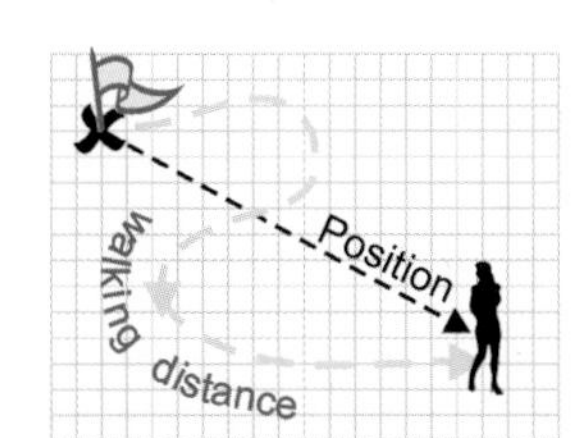

Figure 2.9: *If there are turns, the position might be different from the distance you travel.*

The position vs. time graph

What does the graph tell you?

The position vs. time graph shows where things are at different times. If things have moved, it is easy to see from the graph. You might think giving the speed is enough description of how things have moved. But speed does not always give you enough information.

A car trip with a rest

For example, suppose you take a car trip that includes 1.5 hours of driving and a half-hour rest stop, for a total time of 2 hours. You drive a total distance of 90 miles in a straight line. At the end you call your friends to tell them it took you 2 hours and they calculate your speed to be 45 mph (90 miles divided by 2 hours).

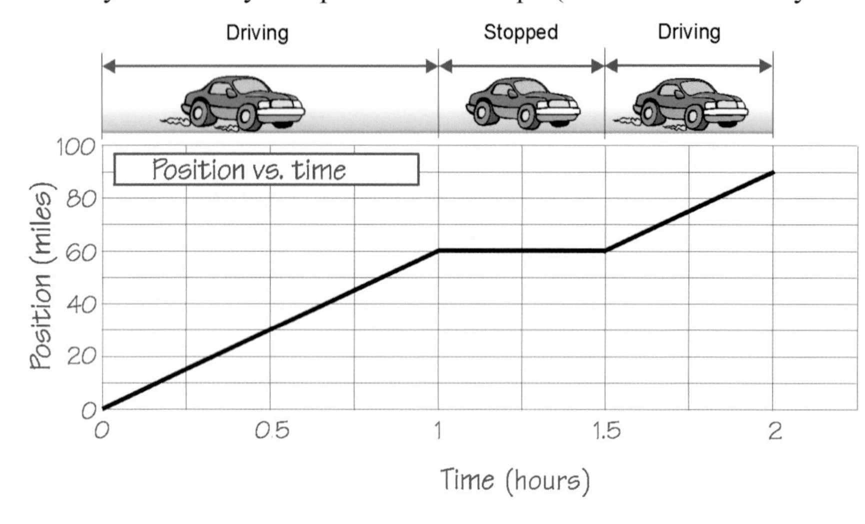

Actually, you drove a lot faster than 45 mph to make up for the half-hour rest stop. You really covered the 90 miles in 1.5 hours, at a speed of 60 mph. You stopped (with zero speed) for a half hour.

The graph is a better picture of the trip

The position vs. time graph shows your trip much more accurately than saying you covered 90 miles in 2 hours. For the first hour, your position gradually increases from zero (start) until you are 60 miles away. Your position stays the same between 1 hour and 1.5 hours because you stopped. Then you get going again and cover the last 30 miles in a half hour. The position vs. time graph shows a complete history of your trip including your stop.

Moving away from start

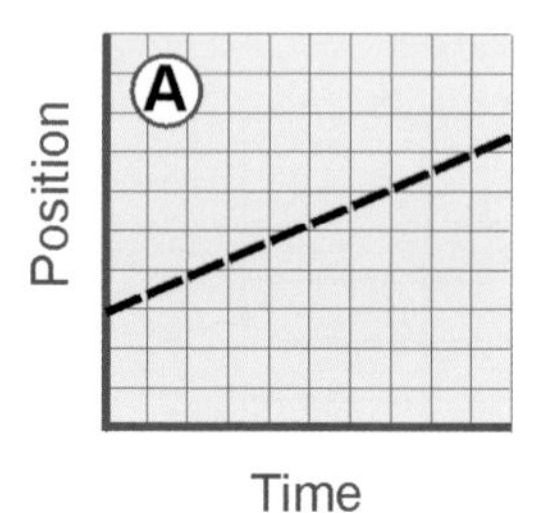

Moving back toward start

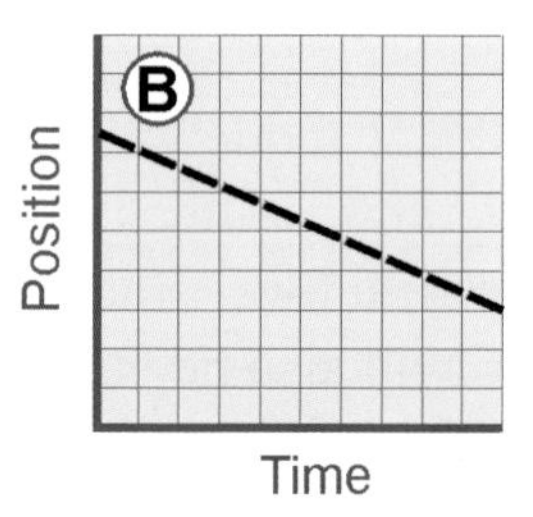

Stopped (zero speed)

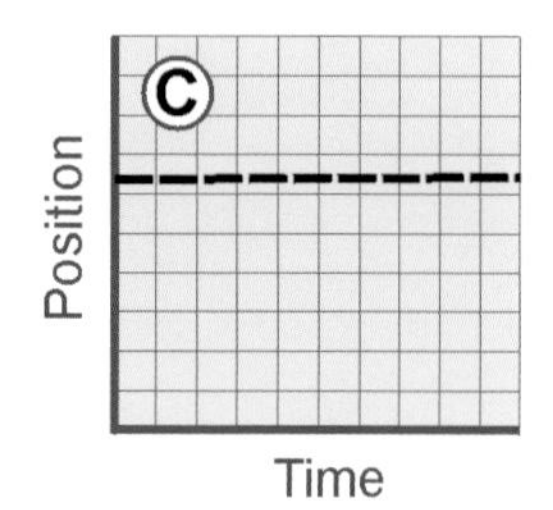

Figure 2.10: *Examples of graphs showing different speeds.*
Graph A shows movement away from start.
Graph B shows movement back toward start.
Graph C shows no motion. The object is stopped with zero speed.

Determining speed from the slope of a graph

Look at the distance vs. time

Let's take a closer look at the first hour of your driving trip (Figure 2.11). You drove at a constant speed of 60 mph. The position vs. time graph shows the position of your car on the highway as it changes with time. The line on the graph represents the motion of the car. If the graph is a complete description of the motion, you should be able to figure out the speed of the car from the graph.

The definition of slope

The definition of slope is the ratio of "rise" (vertical change) to the "run" (horizontal change) of a line. The rise is determined by finding the height of the triangle shown. The run is determined by finding the length along the base of the triangle. For this graph, the x-values represent time and the y-values represent position.

Speed is the slope of the position vs. time graph

Speed is the distance traveled divided by the time taken. The distance is really the difference in position between where you finished and where you started. This is equal to the rise (vertical distance) on the graph. The run on the graph is the time taken for the trip. The slope is rise over run, which is the distance traveled over the time taken, which is the speed.

Speed is the slope of the position vs. time graph.

The slope of a graph

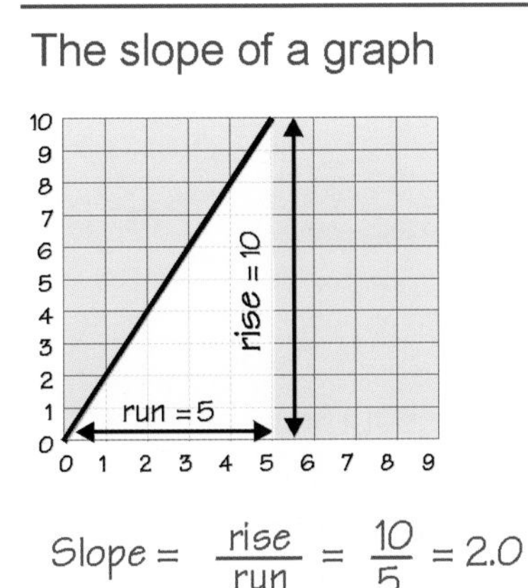

Speed from the slope of the position vs. time graph

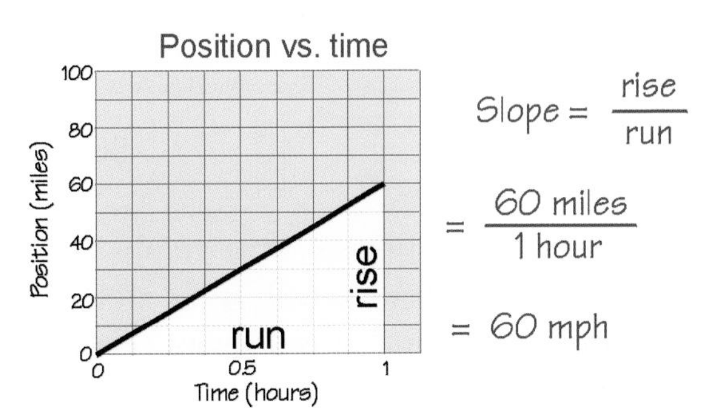

Driving at constant 60 mph in a straight line

Position vs. time

Figure 2.11: *The first hour of the driving trip. The car has a constant speed of 60 mph.*

Instantaneous and average speed

Speed does not usually stay constant

Does your speed stay exactly the same during a real trip? The answer is, of course not. Your speed is almost always changing. You slow down for stop lights, and speed up to pass people. For the next example, consider taking a bicycle trip. You may remain on flat ground for a moment, but eventually you come to a hill. As you climb the hill, you slow down. As you go down the hill, you speed up.

Average speed

There are two ways you should think about speed. If it takes you 2 hours to ride 50 kilometers, your average speed is 25 kilometers per hour (25 km/h). To calculate average speed, you simply take the total distance traveled divided by the total time taken.

Instantaneous speed

At some points along the way, you may go slower, or faster than average. The instantaneous speed is the speed you have at a specific point in your journey. You might go uphill at 10 km/h and downhill at 60 km/h, with an average speed of 25 km/h even though your speed may have been 25 km/h only momentarily during the trip!

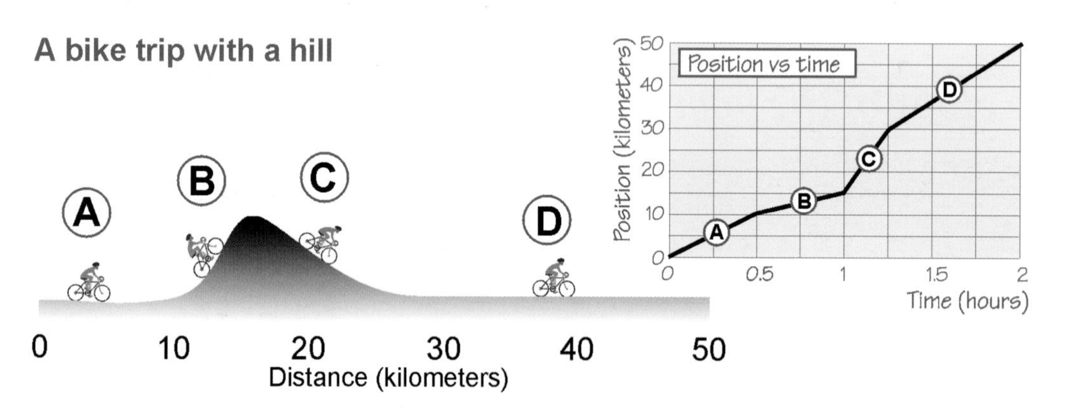

The position vs. time graph

The real story is told by the position vs. time graph. The graph captures both the instantaneous speed and the average speed. If the slope of the graph is steep (**C**), you have lots of position changing in little time (Figure 2.12) indicating a high speed. If the slope is shallow (**B**), relatively little position changes over a long time, giving a slow speed. If the graph is level the slope is zero, so the speed is also zero, indicating you have stopped and are not moving.

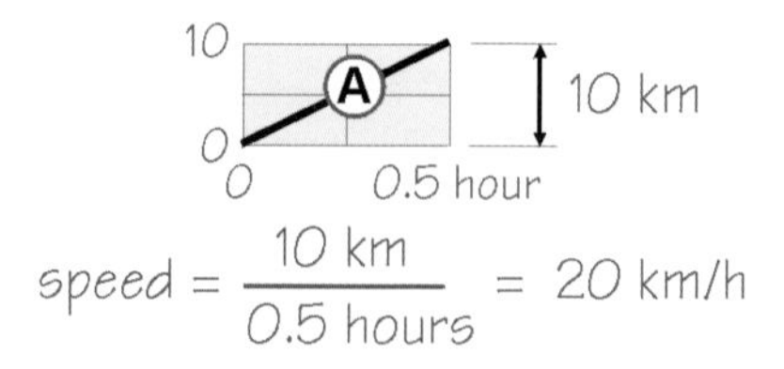

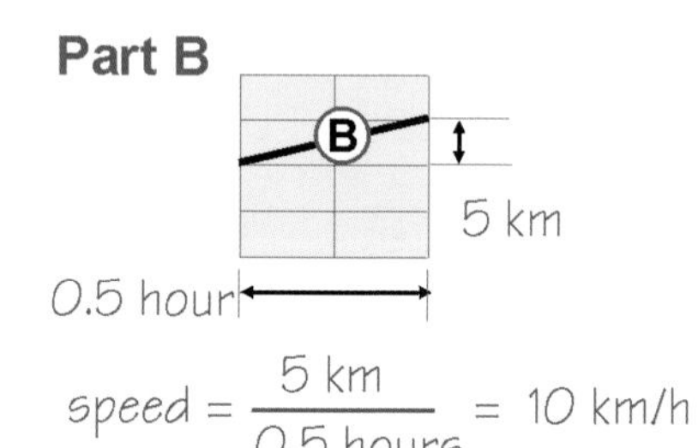

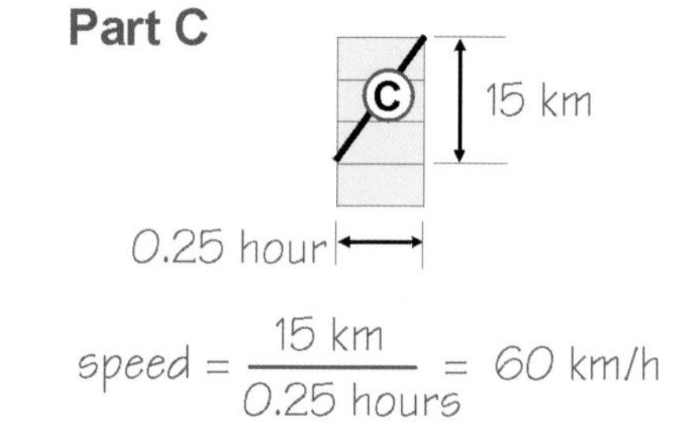

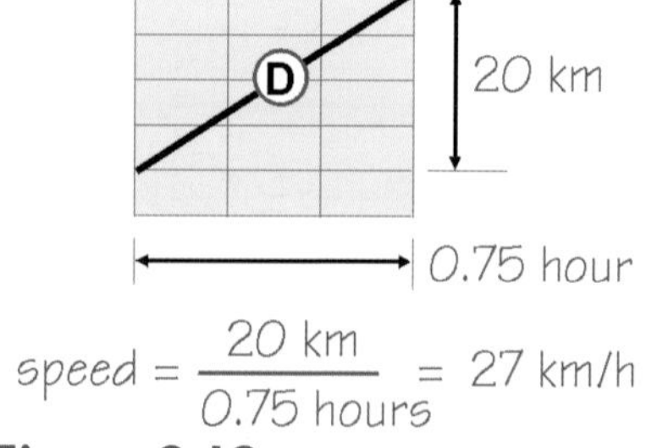

Figure 2.12: *Calculating the speed of each part of the trip.*

2.3 Acceleration

The speed of things is always changing. Your car speeds up and slows down. If you slow down gradually, it feels very different from slamming on the brakes and stopping fast. In this section we will learn how to measure and discuss changes in speed. Specifically, we will investigate objects rolling downhill. You already know that an object rolling downhill speeds up. The rate at which its speed changes is called acceleration.

Acceleration

You accelerate coasting downhill

What happens if you coast your bicycle down a long hill without pedaling? You accelerate, that is your speed increases steadily. If your bike has a speedometer you find that your speed increases by the same amount every second!

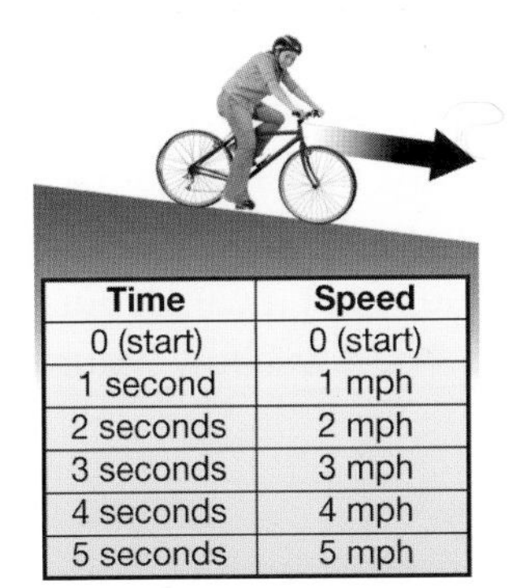

Time	Speed
0 (start)	0 (start)
1 second	1 mph
2 seconds	2 mph
3 seconds	3 mph
4 seconds	4 mph
5 seconds	5 mph

Time	Speed
0 (start)	0 (start)
1 second	2 mph
2 seconds	4 mph
3 seconds	6 mph
4 seconds	8 mph
5 seconds	10 mph

Steeper hills

On a steeper hill, your findings are similar. Your speed increases every second, but by a bigger amount. On the first hill your speed increased by 1 mph every second. On the steeper hill you find your speed increases by 2 mph every second.

Acceleration is the amount that your speed increases, compared to how long it takes. Increasing speed by 1 mph every second means you accelerated at 1 mph per second. Every second your speed increased by 1 mile per hour. It is common to describe acceleration in units of speed (changed) per second.

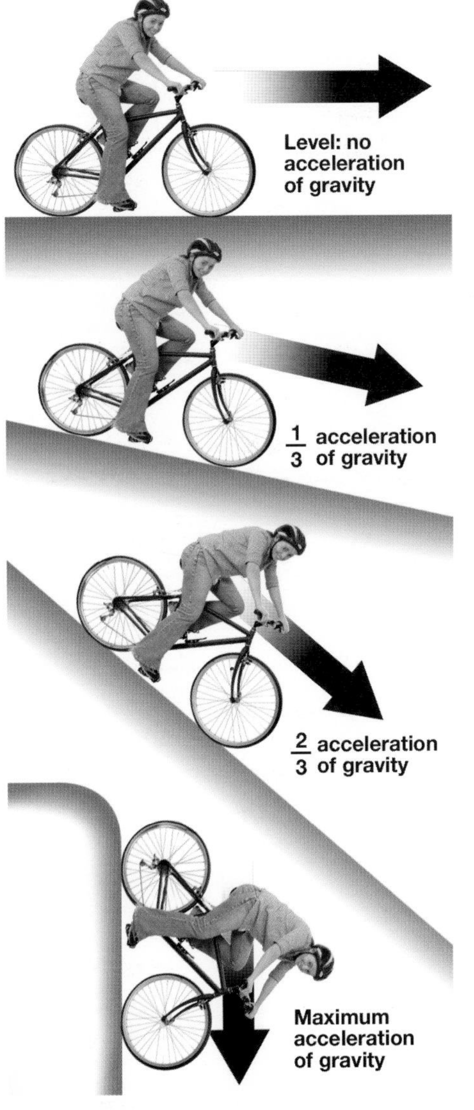

Figure 2.13: *How much of the acceleration of gravity you experience depends on the angle of the hill.*

Acceleration when speed is in miles per hour

Acceleration Acceleration is the rate of change in the speed of an object. Rate of change means the ratio of the amount of change divided by how much time it took to change.

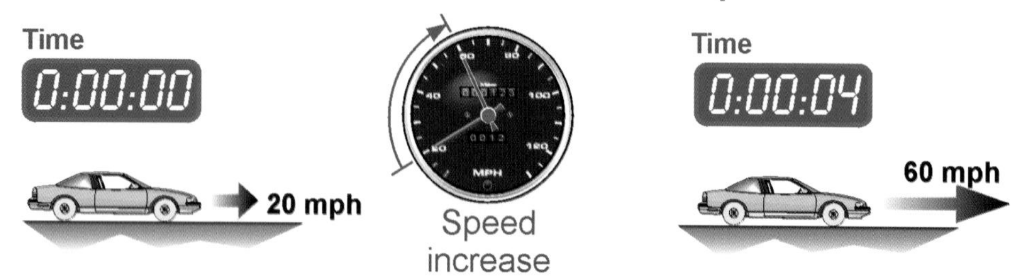

An example of acceleration Suppose you are driving and your speed goes from 20 mph to 60 mph in four seconds. The amount of change is 60 mph minus 20 mph, or 40 miles per hour. The time it takes to change is 4 seconds. The acceleration is 40 mph divided by 4 seconds, or 10 mph/sec. Your car accelerated 10 mph per second. That means your speed increased by 10 miles per hour each second. Table 2.1 shows how your speed changed during the four seconds of acceleration.

Table 2.1: ***Your speed while accelerating***

Time	Speed
0 (start)	20 mph
1 second	30 mph
2 seconds	40 mph
3 seconds	50 mph
4 seconds	60 mph

Thinking about acceleration

Aristotle
365 B.C.

Newton
1686

People have been thinking about acceleration for a long time. In the fourth century BC two Greek scientists, Aristotle and Strato, described free fall as acceleration. In the 1580s European scientists Simon Stevinus and Galileo determined that all objects fall equally fast, if other forces do not act on them.

About 100 years later, Isaac Newton figured out the three laws of motion. Newton's attempts to fully describe acceleration inspired him and others to develop a whole new kind of math, called *calculus*. We will not be learning about calculus in this course, but we will follow some of Newton's experiments with acceleration.

Acceleration in metric units

The units of acceleration The units of acceleration can be confusing. Almost all of the calculations of acceleration you will do will be in metric units. If we measure speed in cm/sec, then the change in speed is expressed in cm/sec as well. For example, 2 cm/sec is the difference between a speed of 3 cm/sec and a speed of 1 cm/sec.

Calculating acceleration Acceleration is the change in speed divided by the change in time. The units for acceleration are units of speed over units of time. If speed is in cm/sec and time in seconds, then the units for acceleration are cm/sec/sec, or *centimeters per second per second*. What this means is that the acceleration is the amount that the speed changes in each second. An acceleration of 50 cm/sec/sec means that the speed increases by 50 cm/sec *every second*. If the acceleration persists for three seconds then the speed increases by a total of 150 cm/sec (3 seconds × 50 cm/sec/sec).

What do units of *seconds squared* mean? While it may seem confusing, an acceleration in cm/sec/sec is written cm/sec^2 (centimeters per second squared). Likewise, an acceleration of m/sec/sec is written m/sec^2 (meters per second squared). If you use the rules for simplifying fractions on the units of cm/sec/sec, the denominator ends up having units of seconds times seconds, or sec^2. Saying *seconds squared* is just a math-shorthand way of talking. The units of square seconds do not have physical meaning in the same way that square inches mean surface area. It is better to think about acceleration in units of speed change per second (that is, centimeters per second *per second*).

$$\text{Acceleration} = \frac{\text{Change in speed}}{\text{Change in time}}$$

How we get units of cm/sec^2

plug in values / clear the compound fractions / final units

$$= \frac{50\frac{\text{cm}}{\text{sec}}}{\text{sec}} = \frac{50\frac{\text{cm}}{\text{sec}} \times \frac{\text{sec}}{}}{\text{sec} \times \text{sec}} = \frac{50\frac{\text{cm}}{\cancel{\text{sec}}} \times \frac{\cancel{\text{sec}}}{}}{\text{sec}^2} = 50\frac{\text{cm}}{\text{sec}^2}$$

Acceleration in m/sec^2 Many physics problems will use acceleration in m/sec^2. If you encounter an acceleration of 10 m/sec^2, this number means the speed is increasing by 10 m/sec every second.

Example

A car rolls down a ramp and you measure times and distances as shown. Calculate the acceleration in cm/sec^2.

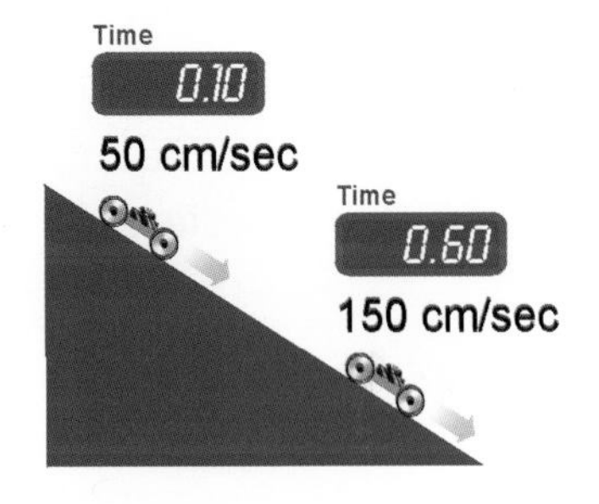

Change in speed

$$\begin{array}{r} 150 \text{ cm/sec} \\ -\ 50 \text{ cm/sec} \\ \hline = 100 \text{ cm/sec} \end{array}$$

Change in time

$$\begin{array}{r} 0.60 \text{ sec} \\ -\ 0.10 \text{ sec} \\ \hline = 0.50 \text{ sec} \end{array}$$

$$\text{Acceleration} = \frac{\text{Change in speed}}{\text{Change in time}} = \frac{100 \text{ cm/sec}}{0.50 \text{ sec}} = 200 \text{ cm/sec}^2$$

Figure 2.14: *An example of calculating acceleration for a car on a ramp.*

Different examples of acceleration

Any change in speed means acceleration

Acceleration means changes in speed or velocity. *Any* change in speed means there is acceleration. If you put on the brakes and slow down, your speed changes. In the example of slowing down, the acceleration is in the negative direction. We also use the term deceleration to describe this situation. *Acceleration occurs whenever the speed changes, whether the speed increases or decreases.*

Zero acceleration

An object has zero acceleration if it is traveling at constant speed in one direction. You might think of zero acceleration as "cruise control." If the speed of your car stays the same at 60 miles per hour, your acceleration is zero.

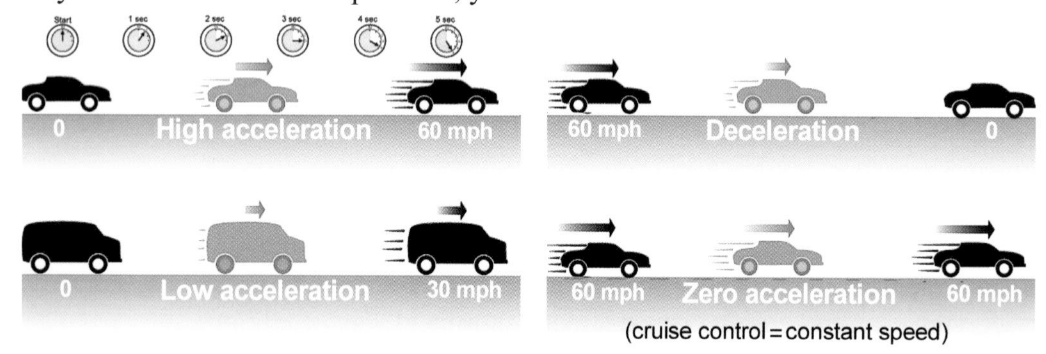

Acceleration when turning

If you change direction, some acceleration happens. When you turn a sharp corner in a car you feel pulled to one side. The pull you feel comes from the acceleration due to turning. To explain this, you need to remember velocity encompasses speed *and direction*. Any time you change either speed or direction, you are accelerating.

Steep hills and acceleration

You have probably noticed that the steeper the hill, the faster you accelerate. You may already know this effect has to do with gravity. Gravity pulls everything down toward the center of Earth. The steeper the hill, the greater the amount of gravity pulling you forward, and the greater your acceleration.

Free fall

If you drop something straight down it accelerates in free fall. The speed of a free falling object in a vacuum increases by 9.8 meters per second for every second it falls (Figure 2.15). This special acceleration is called the acceleration of gravity because it is the acceleration of objects under the influence of Earth's gravity. The acceleration of gravity would be different on the moon or on other planets.

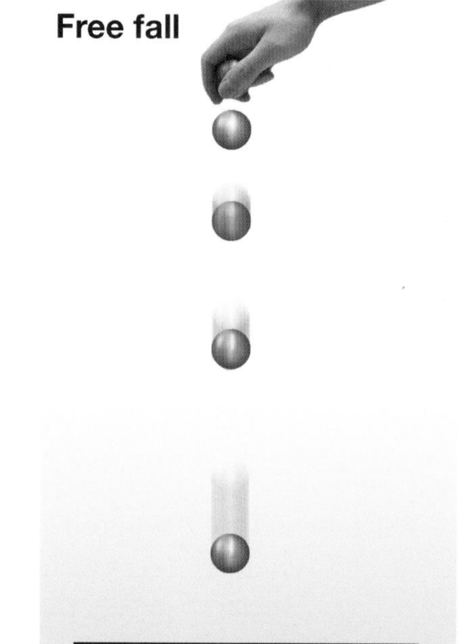

Time	Speed
0 (start)	0
1 second	9.8 m/sec
2 seconds	19.6 m/sec
3 seconds	29.4 m/sec
4 seconds	39.2 m/sec

The speed of free falling objects increases by 9.8 m/sec every second they fall.

This is how we know the acceleration of gravity is 9.8 m/sec^2 at Earth's surface.

Figure 2.15: *In free fall, the speed of objects increases by 9.8 m/sec each second. Free fall is most accurately measured in a vacuum, since air friction changes the rate of fall of different objects in different ways.*

Acceleration and the speed vs. time graph

The speed vs. time graph

Another motion graph we need to understand is the graph of speed vs. time. This is the most important graph for understanding acceleration because it shows how the speed changes with time.

The graph below shows an example from an experiment with a car rolling down a ramp. The time is the time between when the car was first released and when its speed was measured after having moved farther down the ramp. You can see that the speed of the car increases the longer it rolls down.

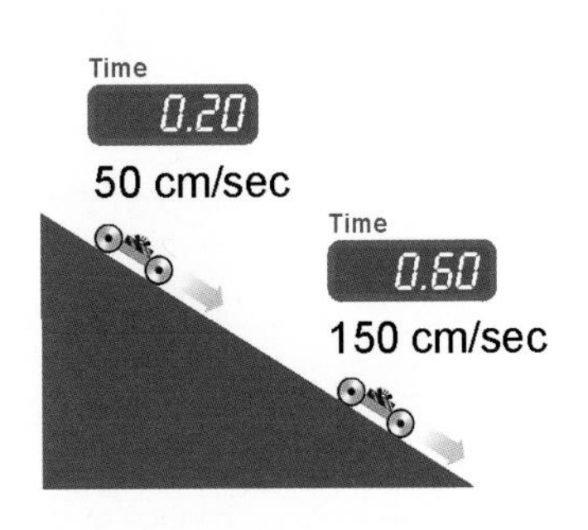

Time (sec)	Speed (cm/sec)
0.1	25
0.2	50
0.3	75
0.4	100
0.5	125
0.6	150
0.7	175
0.8	200

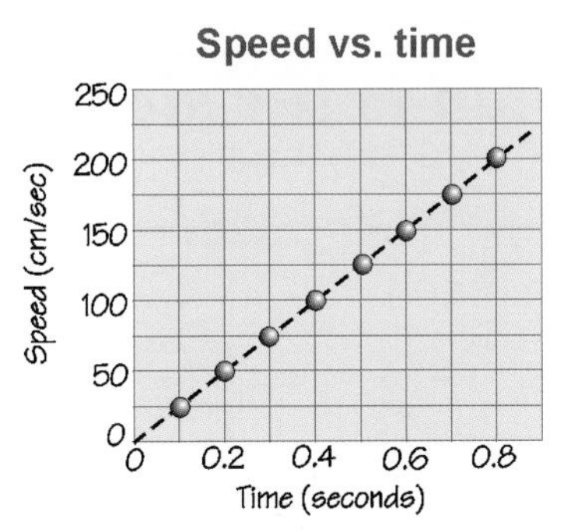

The graph shows a straight line

The graph shows a straight line. This means that the speed of the car increases by the same amount every second. The graph (and data) also shows that the speed of the car increases by 25 cm/sec every one-tenth (0.1) of a second.

Acceleration

You should be thinking of acceleration. This graph shows an acceleration of 250 cm/sec/sec or 250 cm/sec^2. This is calculated by dividing the change in speed (25 cm/sec) by the change in time (0.1 seconds).

Seeing acceleration on a graph

If you see a slope on a speed vs. time graph, you are seeing acceleration. Figure 2.16 shows some examples of graphs with and without acceleration. *Any time* the graph of speed vs. time is not perfectly horizontal, it shows acceleration. If the graph slopes down, it means the speed is decreasing. If the graph slopes up, the speed is increasing.

Positive acceleration
(speeding up)

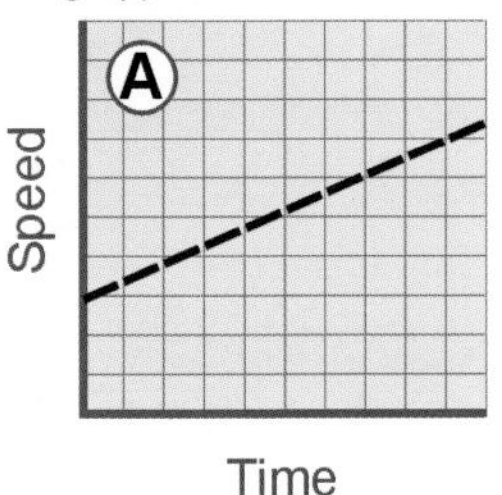

Negative acceleration
(slowing down)

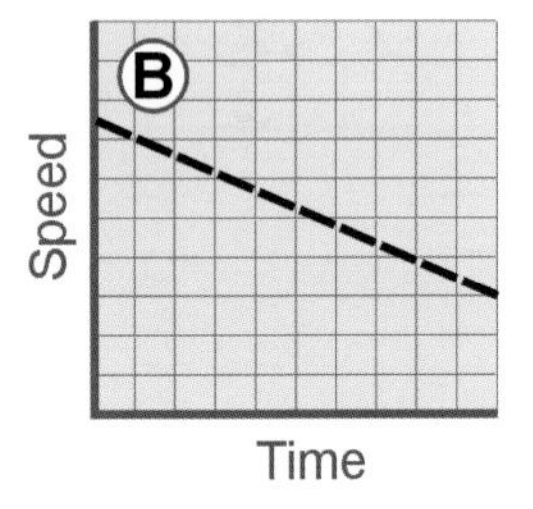

No acceleration
(constant speed)

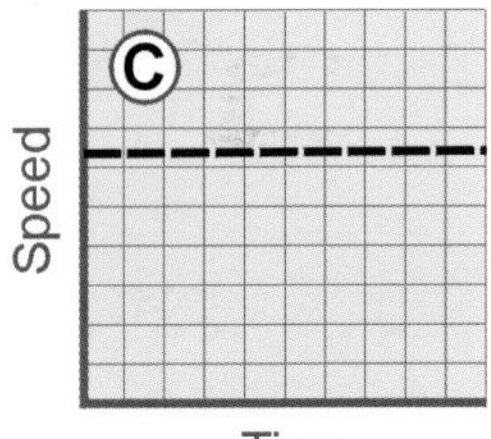

Figure 2.16: *Examples of graphs with different amounts of acceleration.*
Graph **A** *shows positive acceleration, or speeding up.*
Graph **B** *shows negative acceleration, or slowing down.*
Graph **C** *shows zero acceleration.*

Calculating acceleration from the speed vs. time graph

Slope From the last section, you know that the slope of a graph is equal to the ratio of *rise* to *run*. On the speed vs. time graph, the rise and run have special meanings, as they did for the distance vs. time graph. The *rise* is the amount the speed changes. The *run* is the amount the time changes.

Acceleration and slope Remember, acceleration is the change in speed over the change in time. This is *exactly the same* as the rise over run for the speed vs. time graph. The slope of the speed vs. time graph is the acceleration.

Acceleration is the slope of a speed vs. time graph.

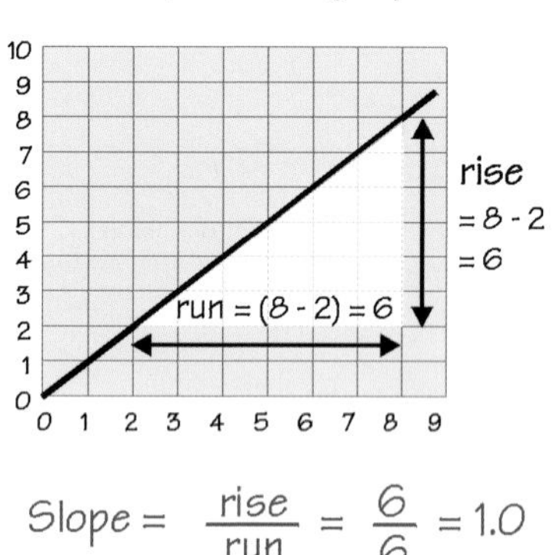

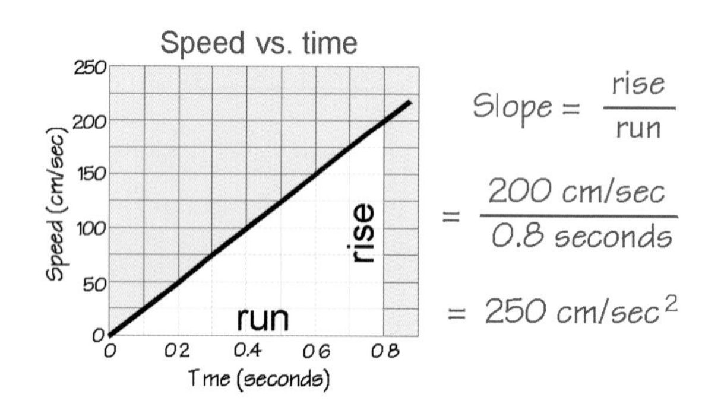

Make a triangle to get the slope To determine the slope of the speed vs. time graph, take the rise or change in speed and divide by the run or change in time. It is helpful to draw the triangle shown above to help figure out the rise and run. The rise is the height of the triangle. The run is the length of the base of the triangle.

Complex speed vs. time graphs Slope helps you identify acceleration in complicated speed vs. time graphs. A flat line on the graph means speed is constant and acceleration is zero (Figure 2.17).

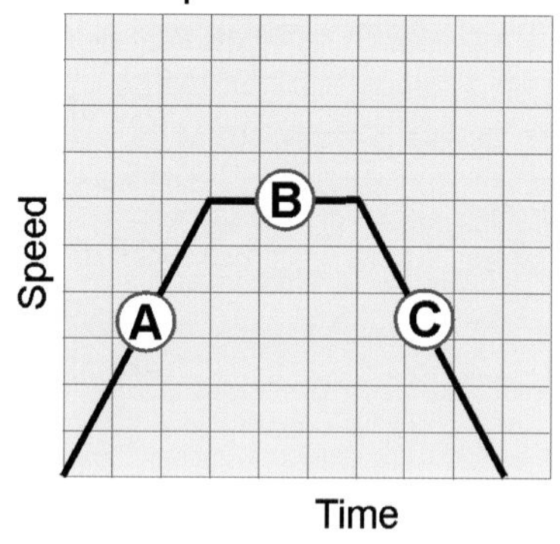

(A) Positive acceleration

(B) Zero acceleration

(C) Negative acceleration

Figure 2.17: *How to recognize acceleration on speed vs. time graphs.*

A. Positive slope means positive acceleration (speeding up).
B. No slope (level) means zero acceleration (constant speed).
C. Negative slope means negative acceleration (slowing down).

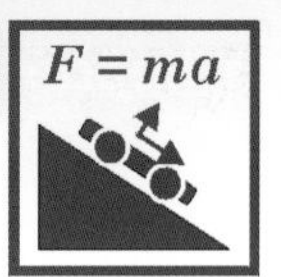

Chapter 2 Review

Vocabulary review

Match the following terms with the correct definition. There is one extra definition in the list that will not match any of the terms.

Set One

1. scientific model
2. conceptual model
3. graphical model
4. dependent variable
5. independent variable

a. A way to show how something works that is descriptive in nature
b. A variable that changes in response to another variable
c. A variable that doesn't change during an experiment
d. A variable that we set in an experiment
e. A way to show how variables are connected
f. A graph that shows how variables are connected

Set Two

1. position
2. slope
3. average speed
4. instantaneous speed
5. acceleration

a. Total distance traveled divided by total time elapsed
b. The amount of time elapsed during an experiment
c. How speed changes over time
d. A measurement of a line on a graph, equal to vertical change divided by horizontal change
e. Where something is compared with where it started
f. Speed at one moment in time

Set Three

1. deceleration
2. gravity
3. free fall

a. A measurement of a line on a graph, equal to horizontal change divided by vertical change
b. A force that tends to pull things toward the center of the earth
c. A decrease in speed over time
d. An object that is moving freely towards the center of the Earth exhibits this type of motion

Concept review

1. One of the early conceptual models of the solar system showed the other planets and the sun orbiting around the Earth. Copernicus developed a new model of the solar system that shows the Earth and other planets orbiting around the sun. Draw a picture of these two models of the solar system.

2. The following terms and phrases refer to the two axes of a graph. Divide the terms and phrases according to which group they belong in.

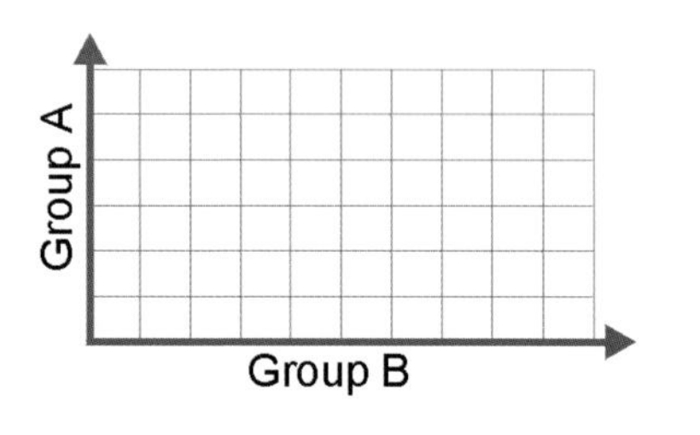

Words to sort
horizontal
vertical
X-axis
Y-axis
dependent variable
independent variable

Group A	Group B

3. Which of the following types of scientific models is frequently used to make numerical predictions that you can test with measurements? You may choose more than one.

   a. a graph

   b. an equation

   c. a conceptual model

   d. a physical model

4. You take a walk from your house to your friend's house around the block. If you graph your position during your walk, the longest distance on the graph is 15 meters. But you actually walked 20 meters. Explain why your position (distance from start) and the actual distance you walked were different.

5. You know the average speed of a trip, and you have a position versus time graph of the trip. Which gives you more information about the trip? Explain your answer.

6. The slope of a position vs. time graph is equal to ____________.

7. What is the difference between *average speed* and *instantaneous speed*? Use a real-life example to help you explain.

8. Is it possible for an object to simultaneously have a speed of zero but an acceleration that is not zero? Answer with an example.

9. What is the acceleration of a car that is going at a steady speed of 60 mph?

10. Does a car accelerate when it goes around a corner at a steady speed? Explain your answer.

11. Does the speedometer of a car give you the average speed or the instantaneous speed of the car? Explain your answer.

12. The slope of a speed vs. time graph is equal to ____________.

Problems

1. Engineers propose to build a bridge that is 30 meters in length. They build a model of the bridge that is 3 meters in length. What is the scale of the model? Express your answer in the form 1:x, where x is the corresponding number of meters on the bridge, when compared with 1 meter on the model.

2. You do an experiment where you measure the height of plants and calculate their growth rate. The growth rate is the amount each plant gets taller per day. You collect the following data on height and growth rate:

Week	Height of plant (cm)	Average daily growth rate (mm/day)
start	2.2	
1	7.9	8.1
2	11.8	5.6
3	15.2	4.9
4	17.7	3.6
5	19.9	3.1
6	21.2	1.9
7	22.1	1.3
8	22.3	0.3

   a. Graph the above data with height on the x-axis and growth rate on the y-axis.

   b. Does the data show (you may choose more than one):

   1) a strong relationship between variables
   2) a weak relationship between variables
   3) an inverse relationship between variables
   4) a direct relationship between variables

3. A woman goes to a store three blocks away from her home. She walks in a straight line and at a steady pace. Draw a position vs. time graph of her walk. Regard home as start.

4. A woman leaves a store and goes to her home three blocks away. She walks in a straight line and at a steady pace. Draw a position vs. time graph of her walk.

5. A car rolling down a ramp starts with a speed of 50 cm/sec. The car keeps rolling and 0.5 seconds later the speed is 150 cm/sec. Calculate the acceleration of the car in cm/sec^2.

6. Think about the relationship between the amount of gas you have in your car and how far you can travel. Make a graphical model of this relationship. Which is the dependent variable (the effect)? Which is the independent variable (the cause)?

7. The data table below contains information from an experiment where a car was rolling down a ramp. You suspect some of the numbers are incorrect. Which numbers are suspect? Make a graph that demonstrates how you found the bad data.

Distance (cm)	Speed (cm/sec)
10	110
20	154
30	205
40	218
50	243
60	266
80	275
90	327

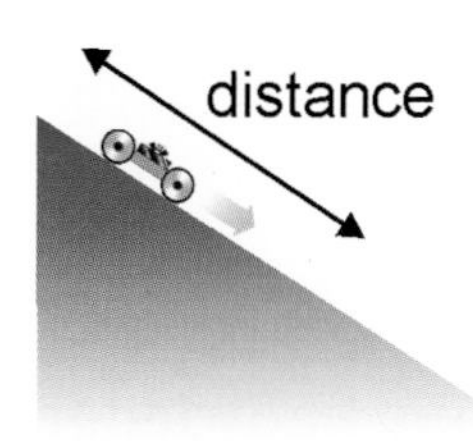

8. Use the graph below to predict the speed of the car at the following distances: 20 cm, 35 cm, 60 cm, 80 cm

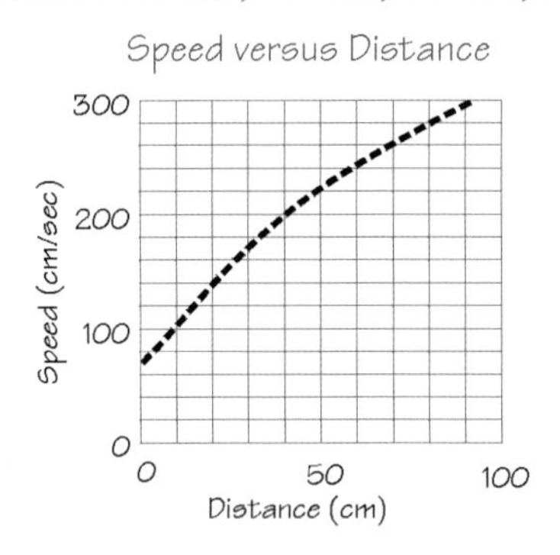

9. Arrange the four points on the distance vs. time graph in order from slowest to fastest.

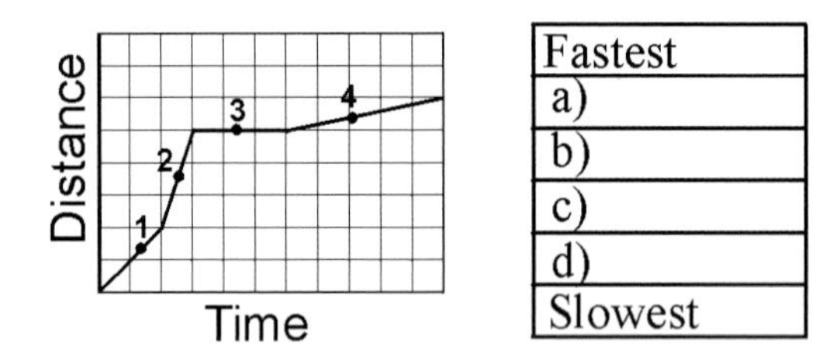

Fastest
a)
b)
c)
d)
Slowest

10. A bicyclist, traveling at 30 miles per hour, rides a total of 48 miles. How much time did it take?

11. A turtle is moving in a straight line at a steady speed of 15 cm/sec for 3 hours. How far did the turtle travel?

12. Match each of the three distance vs. time graphs with the corresponding speed vs. time graph. All three distance vs. time graphs contain only straight-line segments.

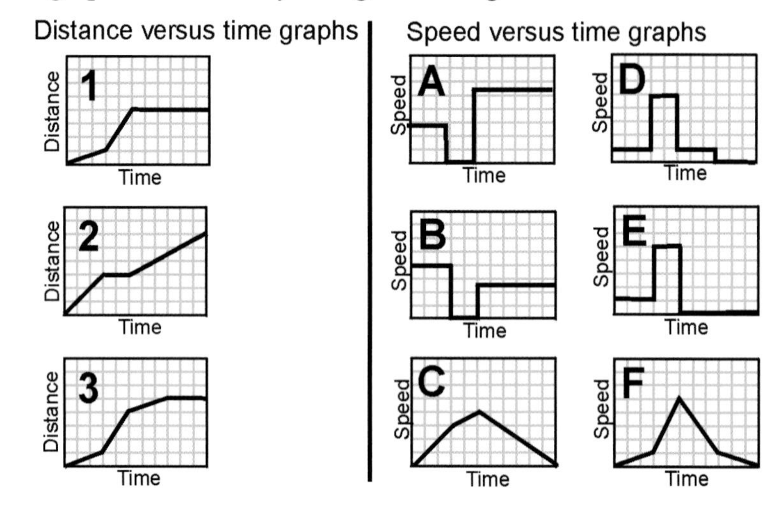

13. Calculate speed from the position vs. time graph on the left. Show all of your work.

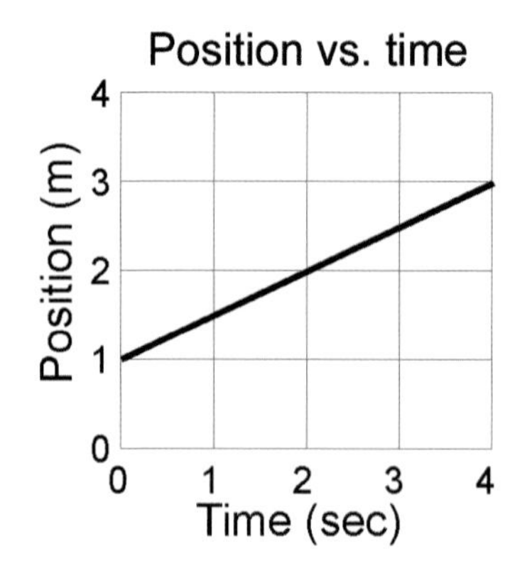

Applying your knowledge

1. Research the following: What is the fastest acceleration in a human in a sprint race? What is the fastest acceleration of a race horse? Which animal is capable of the fastest acceleration?

2. How fast do your fingernails grow? Devise an experiment to determine the answer. How would you represent your measurement? What units would you use to represent the speed?

Chapter 3

Forces and Motion

Introduction to Chapter 3

Things in the universe are always moving, but what gets them going? In this chapter you will follow Sir Isaac Newton's brilliant discoveries of the link between force and motion. Newton's three laws of motion have become a foundation of scientific thought.

Investigations for Chapter 3

3.1	**Force, Mass, and Acceleration**	*What is the relationship between force, mass and acceleration?*

In this Investigation you will devise ways to measure force and acceleration. By graphing force, mass, and acceleration, you will deduce Newton's second law of motion.

3.2	**Weight, Gravity, and Friction**	*How does increasing the mass of the car affect its acceleration?*

Do heavier objects fall faster? And if so, why? In this Investigation you will measure the Earth's gravity and learn why perpetual motion machines are impossible.

3.3	**Equilibrium, Action, and Reaction**	*What is Newton's third law of motion?*

For every action there is an equal and opposite reaction. What does this famous statement really mean? In this Investigation you will explore how Newton's third law of motion explains the interaction and motion of everyday objects.

Learning Goals

In this chapter, you will:

- ✔ Explain the meaning of force.
- ✔ Show how force is required to change the motion of an object.
- ✔ Use a graph to identify relationships between variables.
- ✔ Explain and discuss Newton's second law and the relationship between force, mass, and acceleration.
- ✔ Describe how changing the mass of the car affects its acceleration.
- ✔ Draw conclusions from experimental data.
- ✔ Demonstrate qualitatively how friction can affect motion.
- ✔ Explain Newton's third law of motion.
- ✔ Identify action-reaction pairs of forces.
- ✔ Recognize how Newton's third law of motion explains the physics behind many common activities and useful objects.

Vocabulary

air friction	inertia	newton	rolling friction
equilibrium	law of conservation of momentum	Newton's first law of motion	sliding friction
force	mass	Newton's second law of motion	viscous friction
friction	momentum	Newton's third law of motion	weight
gravity	net force	pounds	

3.1 Force, Mass, and Acceleration

Sir Isaac Newton discovered one of the most important relationships in physics: the link between the force on an object, its mass, and its acceleration. In this section, you will learn about force and mass, and then apply all that you have learned to complete an important Investigation on acceleration. Through your experiments and data analysis, you will follow the path taken by one of history's most innovative thinkers.

Introduction: Sir Isaac Newton's laws of motion

Sir Isaac Newton

Sir Isaac Newton (1642-1727), an English physicist and mathematician, is one of the most brilliant scientists in history. Before the age of 30, he formulated the basic laws of mechanics, discovered the universal law of gravitation, and invented calculus! His discoveries helped to explain many unanswered questions, such as how do the planets move? What causes the tides? Why doesn't the moon fall to the Earth like other objects?

Table 3.1: *Newton's Laws of Motion*

The Three Laws	What Each One Says	In Other Words...
Newton's first law of motion	An object at rest will remain at rest unless acted on by an unbalanced force. An object in motion will continue with constant speed and direction, unless acted on by an unbalanced force.	Unless you apply force, things tend to keep on doing what they were doing in the first place.
Newton's second law of motion	The acceleration of an object is directly proportional to the force acting on it and inversely proportional to its mass.	Force causes an object to accelerate, while the object's mass resists acceleration.
Newton's third law of motion	Whenever one object exerts a force on another, the second object exerts an equal and opposite force on the first.	For every action, there is an equal and opposite reaction. If you push on the wall, you feel the wall pushing back on your hand.

Newton's *Principia*

Published in England in 1687, Newton's *Principia* is possibly the most important single book in the history of science. The *Principia* contains the three laws of motion and the universal law of gravitation.

Force

If your teacher asked you to move a cart containing a large, heavy box, would you: (a) push it; (b) pull it; or (c) yell at it until it moved (Figure 3.1)?

Of course, the correct answer is either (a) push it or (b) pull it!

Figure 3.1: *Which action will move the cart, yelling at it or applying force to it?*

You need force to change motion

Every object continues in a state of rest, or of motion, unless force is applied to change things. This is a fancy way of saying that things tend to keep doing what they are already doing. There is no way the cart with the heavy box is going to move unless a force is applied. Of course, the force applied has to be strong enough to actually make the cart move.

Once the cart is set into motion, it will remain in motion, unless another force is applied to stop it. You need force to start things moving and also to make any change in their motion once they are going.

What is force?

A **force** is what we call a *push or a pull*, or *any action that has the ability to change motion*. This definition does not, however, mean that forces always change motion! If you push down on a table, it probably will not move. However, if the legs were to break, the table *could* move.

Force is an action that has the ability to change motion.

Unit	Equivalents
1 newton	0.228 pounds
1 pound	4.448 newtons

Figure 3.2: *Units of force.*

Pounds and newtons

There are two units of force that are commonly used: **pounds** and **newtons** (Figure 3.2). Scientists prefer to use newtons. The newton is a smaller unit than the pound. There are 4.448 newtons in one pound. A person weighing 100 pounds would weigh 444.8 newtons.

The origin of the pound

The origin of the pound is similar to the origin of many standard units of length. Merchants needed a standard by which to trade goods without dispute. Weight is an obvious measure of quantity so the pound was standardized as a measure of weight. The oldest known standard weight was the *mina* used between 2400 and 2300 BC. One *mina* was a little more than one modern pound.

Example:

A person stands on a scale and measures a weight of 100 pounds. How much does the person weigh in newtons?

Solution:

(1) Multiply by conversion factors

$$100 \text{ lbs} = 100 \text{ lbs} \times \left(\frac{4.448 \text{ N}}{1 \text{ lb}}\right)$$

(2) Cancel units

$$= \frac{444.8 \cancel{\text{lb}} \times \text{N}}{1 \cancel{\text{lb}}}$$

(3) Answer $= 444.8$ lb

The difference between force and mass

The origin of the newton The metric unit of force, the newton, relates force and motion. One newton equals 1 kilogram multiplied by 1 meter per second squared. This means that a force of one newton causes a 1-kilogram mass to have an acceleration of 1 m/sec^2. In talking about force, "newton" is easier to say than "1 kilogram · m/sec^2."

Use the correct units in formulas Force and mass have different units. Force units are pounds or newtons. Mass units are grams or kilograms. To get the right answer when using formulas that include force or mass, you need to use the correct units.

Defining force and mass Force is a push or pulling action that can change motion. Mass is the amount of "stuff" or matter in an object. Mass is a basic property of objects. Mass resists the action of forces by making objects harder to accelerate.

Weight is different from mass The weight of a person can be described in pounds or newtons. On Earth, a child *weighs* 30 pounds or about 134 newtons. In other words, the force acting on the child, due to the influence of Earth's gravity, is 134 kg·m/sec^2.

Your mass is the same everywhere in the universe, but your weight is different A child that weighs 30 pounds on Earth has a *mass* of about 14 kilograms because on Earth 2.2 pounds equals 1 kilogram. Because mass is an amount of matter, mass is independent of the force of gravity. Therefore, the mass of a person is the same everywhere in the universe. However, the *weight* of a person on Earth is different from what it would be on the moon or another planet because the force of gravity is different at these other places.

Units of force and mass can describe a quantity Mass and weight are commonly used to describe the quantity of something. For example, a kilogram of bananas weighs 2.2 pounds. You can describe the quantity of bananas as having a mass of 1 kilogram, or a weight of 2.2 pounds. Using two different kinds of measurement to describe the same quantity of bananas does *not* mean pounds and kilograms are the same thing.

Different units can describe the same quantity We often use different units to describe a quantity. For bananas, you can use a unit of mass (kilograms) or a unit of force (pounds). Likewise, buying one gallon of milk is the same as buying 8.4 pounds of milk. Pounds and gallons both describe the same quantity but one unit is a measure of volume (gallons) and one is a measure of force (pounds).

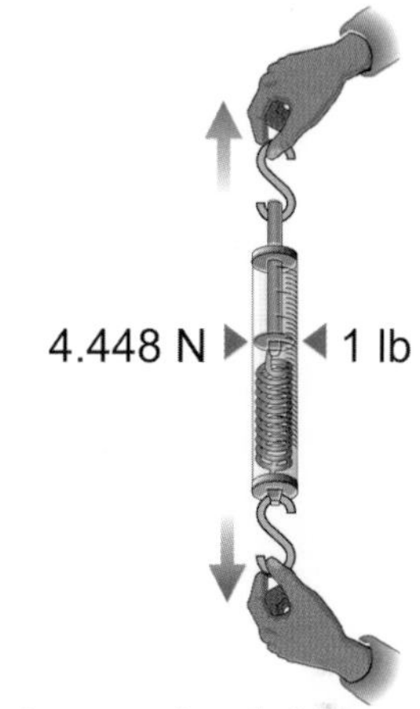

1 pound = 4.448 newtons

Figure 3.3: *A spring scale is a tool for measuring force. A force of 1 pound is the same as a force of 4.448 newtons.*

Newton

A newton is the metric unit of force.

A force of 1 newton

on a mass of 1 kilogram ...

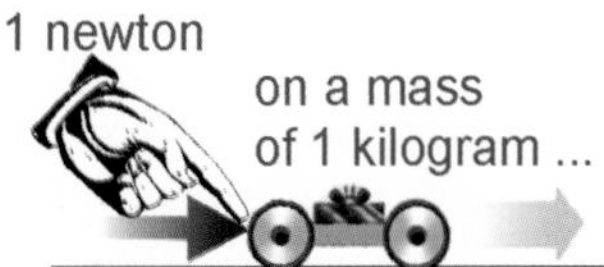

creates an acceleration of 1 m/sec^2.

A force of one newton acting on a mass of 1 kilogram produces an acceleration of 1 m/sec^2.

Mass and inertia

Newton's first law

Newton's first law is also called the *law of inertia*. Inertia is defined as the property of an object to resist changing its state of motion. An object with a lot of inertia takes a lot of force to start or stop. Big trucks have more inertia than small cars, and bicycles have even less inertia (Figure 3.4).

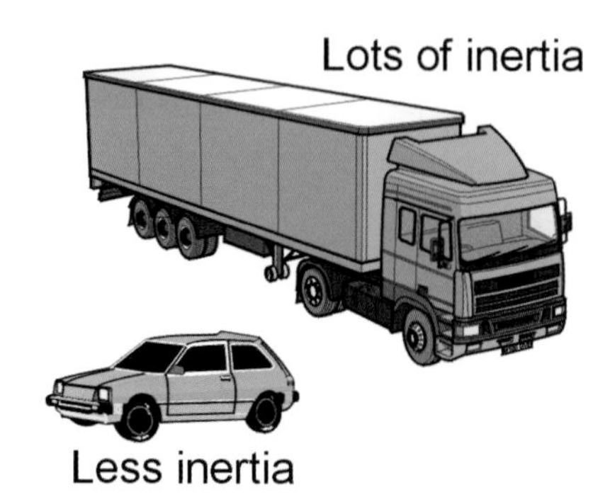

Figure 3.4: *A large truck has more inertia than a small car. As a consequence it is much harder to push a truck than to push a car.*

Discussion question:

What part of a bicycle or car is designed to overcome the law of inertia?

Inertia is a property of mass

The amount of inertia an object has depends on its mass. Mass is a measure of the inertia of an object. Mass is what we usually think of when we use words like "heavy" or "light." A heavy object has a large mass while an object described as "light as a feather" has a small mass. We can also define mass as the amount of matter an object has.

The kilogram

Mass is measured in kilograms. The kilogram is one of the primary units of the metric system, like the meter and second. For reference, 1 kilogram has a weight of about 2.2 pounds on the Earth's surface. That means gravity pulls on a mass of 1 kilogram with a force of 2.2 pounds.

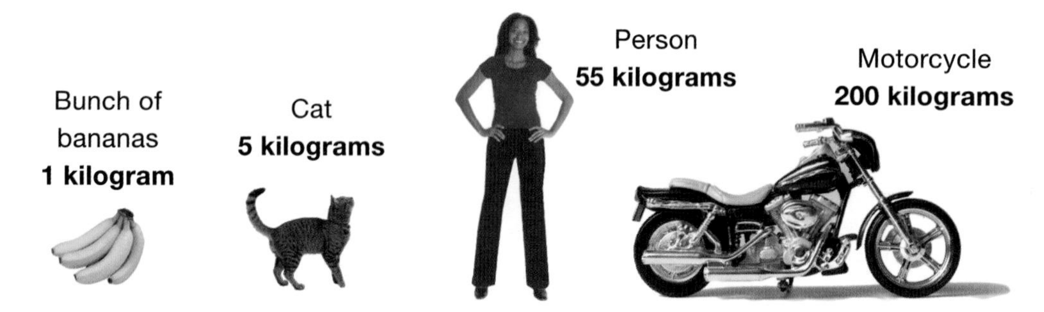

You feel inertia by moving things

Which is harder to push: a ball that has a mass of 1 kilogram, or a ball that has a mass of 100 kilograms (Figure 3.5)? Once you get each ball moving, which is easier to stop? Of course, the 100 kilogram ball is harder to start and harder to stop once it gets moving. This is a direct example of the law of inertia in action.

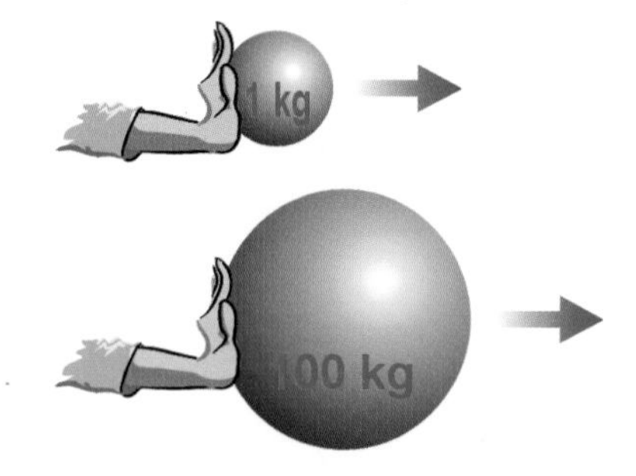

Figure 3.5: *The 100 kilogram ball has much more inertia, which makes it much harder to push.*

Mass is a constant property of an object

The mass of an object does not change, no matter where the object is, what planet it is on, or how it is moving. The only exception to this rule is when things go extremely fast, close to the speed of light. For the normal world, however, mass is an unchanging property of an object. The only way to change the mass is to physically change the object, like adding weights or breaking off a piece.

Newton's second law of motion

Newton's second law

Newton's second law relates the applied force on an object, the mass of the object, and acceleration.

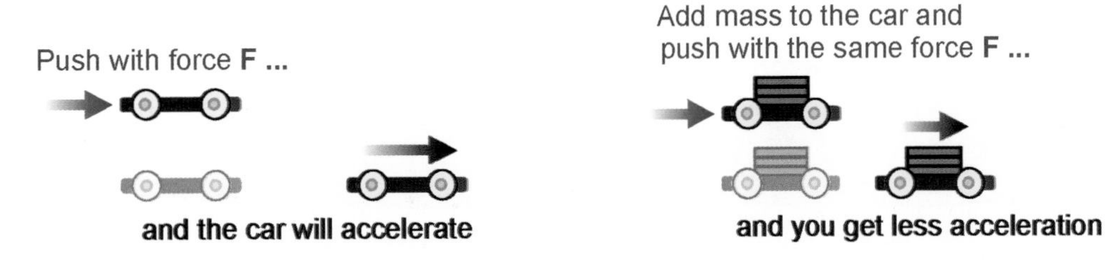

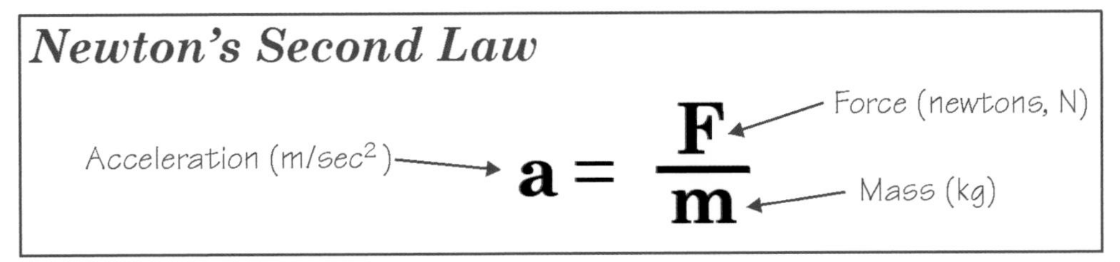

Push with force F ...
and the car will accelerate
Add mass to the car and push with the same force F ...

Newton's Second Law
Acceleration (m/sec2)
a = F/m
Force (newtons, N)
Mass (kg)

What the second law tells us

Newton's second law is one of the most famous equations in physics. It says that:

- Force causes acceleration.
- Mass resists acceleration.
- The acceleration you get is equal to the ratio of force over mass.

The second law is common sense when you think about it. If you make something very heavy (more mass), it takes proportionally more force to cause acceleration. It does not matter whether the acceleration is a speeding up or a slowing down.

Force is related to acceleration

There are many examples that demonstrate why force should be linked to acceleration. Force isn't necessary to keep an object in motion at constant speed. An ice-skater will coast for a long time without any outside force. However, the ice-skater does need force to speed up, slow down, turn or stop. Recall that changes in speed or direction all involve acceleration. *Force* causes *acceleration*; this is how we create changes in motion.

Example:

A car rolls down a ramp and you measure a force of 2 newtons pulling the car down. The car has a mass of 500 grams (0.5 kg).

Calculate the acceleration of the car.

m = 0.5 kg (500g)

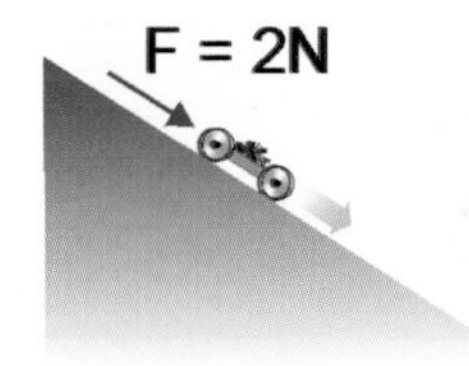

Solution:

(1) What are you asked for?

The acceleration

(2) What do you know?

Mass and force

(3) What relationships apply?

$a = F/m$

(4) Solve for what you need.

$a = F/m$

(5) Plug in numbers. Remember that $1\ N = 1\ kg \cdot m/sec^2$.

$a = (2\ N) / (0.5\ kg)$

$= (2\ kg \cdot m/sec^2) / (0.5\ kg)$

(6) Cancel units. In this case, kilogram cancels. The car's acceleration is:

$= 4\ m/sec^2$

Using the second law of motion

Writing the second law The formula for the second law of motion uses *F*, *m*, and *a* to represent force, mass, and acceleration. The way you write the formula depends on what you want to know. Three ways to write the law are summarized in Table 3.1.

Table 3.1: *The three forms of Newton's second law*

Form of Newton's second law	if you want to know...	and you know....
a = F/m	the acceleration (**a**)	the mass (**m**) and the force (**F**)
F = ma	the force (**F**)	the mass (**m**) and the acceleration (**a**)
m = F/a	the mass (**m**)	the force (**F**) and the acceleration (**a**)

Units for the second law One newton is the amount of force that causes an acceleration of 1 meter/sec^2 for a body of 1-kilogram mass. To use Newton's second law in calculations, you must be sure to have units of meters/sec^2 for acceleration, newtons for force, and kilograms for mass. In these calculations, remember that *m* stands for *mass* in the formula. In the units for acceleration, *m* stands for *meters*.

Applications of the second law Newton's second law is frequently used by scientists and engineers to solve technical problems. For example, for an airplane to take off from a runway, it has to reach a minimum speed to be able to fly. If you know the mass of the plane, Newton's second law can be used to calculate how much force the engines must supply to accelerate the plane to take off speed.

Applying the second law to cars Cars offer another example. If a car engine can produce so much force, the second law is used to calculate how much acceleration the car can achieve. To increase the acceleration, car designers can do two things: reduce the mass by making the car lighter, or increase the force by using a bigger engine. Both options are based directly on the Newton's second law.

Example:

An airplane with a mass of 5,000 kilograms needs to accelerate at 5 m/sec^2 to take off before it reaches the end of the runway. How much force is needed from the engine?

Solution

(1) What are you asked for?

The force

(2) What do you know?

Mass and acceleration

(3) What relationships apply?

a = F/m

(4) Solve for what you need.

F = ma

(5) Plug in numbers. Remember that 1 N = 1 kg·m/sec^2.

$F = (5{,}000\ \text{kg}) \times (5\ \text{m/sec}^2)$

$= 25{,}000\ \text{kg·m/sec}^2$

(6) Convert the units to newtons. The force needed is:

= 25,000 N

Balanced and unbalanced forces

Net force The motion of an object depends on the *total* of all forces acting on the object. We call the total of all forces the **net force**. To figure out the net force, we usually have to make some forces positive and some negative so they can cancel out. Choose a direction to be positive, and be consistent about treating forces in the opposite direction as negative (Figure 3.6).

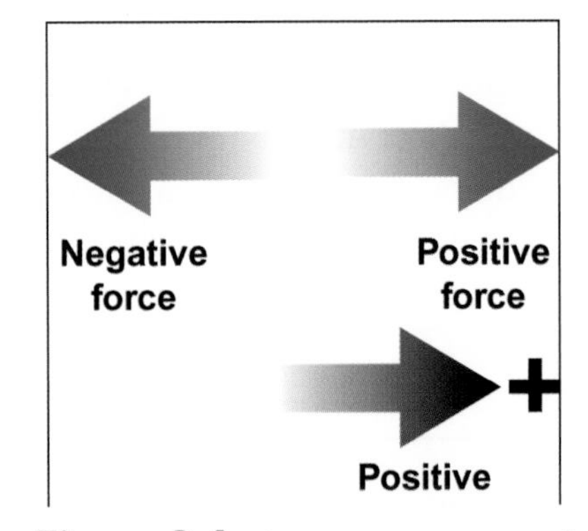

Figure 3.6: *Assigning positive and negative values to forces in opposite directions.*

What is equilibrium? When forces on an object are balanced, the net force is zero, and we say that the object is in **equilibrium**. In equilibrium there is no change in motion. An object at rest stays at rest, and an object already moving keeps moving at the same speed.

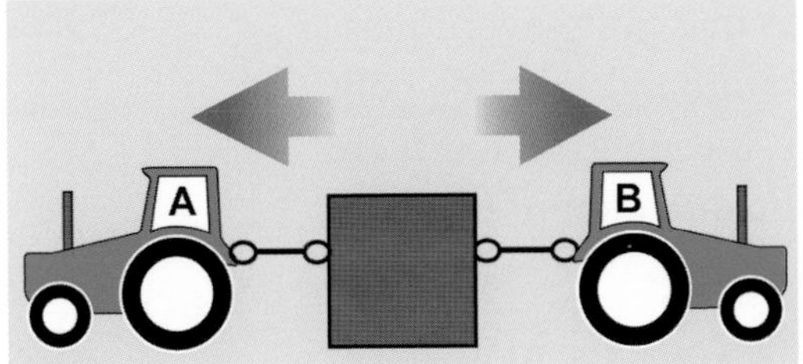

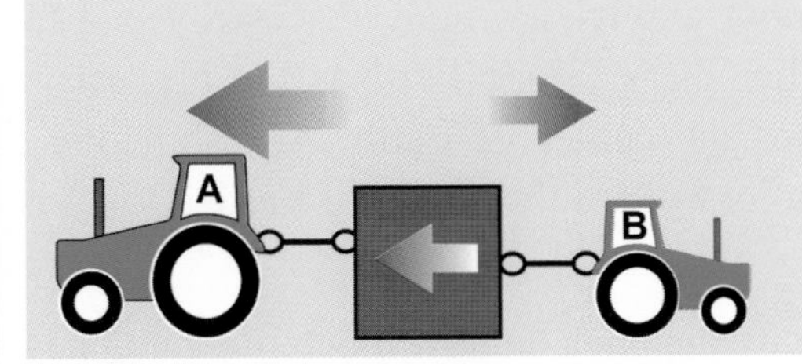

An example of equilibrium and nonequilibrium The diagram above illustrates the difference between balanced and unbalanced forces. Imagine a giant box being pulled on both sides by tractors. If the tractors are equal, the forces are equal, the box is in equilibrium and does not move. If tractor A is 10 times stronger than tractor B, the forces are *not* in equilibrium. The net force points toward tractor A, so the box accelerates toward tractor A.

The second law refers to net force The force that appears in the second law is really the net force acting on an object. Acceleration is caused by a net force that is *not* zero. For motion to change, the forces acting on the object have to be unbalanced. In other words, a force acting on one side of the object has to be greater than the force acting on the other side of the object.

Solving force problems We often use equilibrium and the second law to prove the existence of forces. If we see that an object is at rest, we know its acceleration is zero. That means the net force must also be zero. If we know one force (like weight), we know there is another force in the opposite direction to make the net force zero (Figure 3.7).

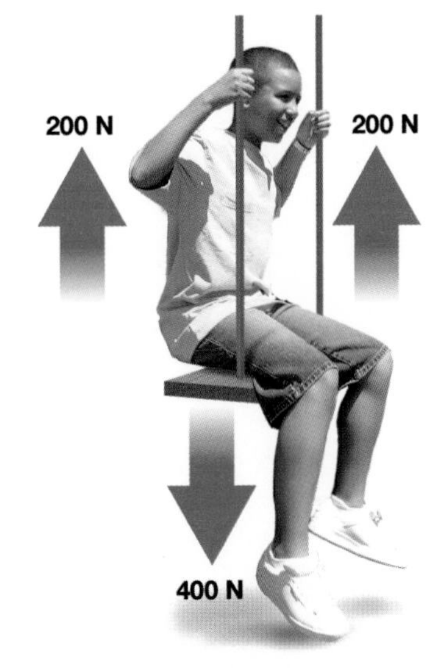

Figure 3.7: *This swing is not moving so the net force must be zero. If the weight of the person is 400 N, then each rope must pull upwards with a force of 200 N to make the net force zero.*

3.2 Weight, Gravity, and Friction

Suppose you and a friend are riding your bicycles in San Francisco. You both reach the top of a hill and stop to take in the view. You decide to coast to the bottom of the hill without pedaling. If you both push off at the same time, and with the same amount of force, will you both reach the bottom of the hill at the same time? Who will accelerate the fastest? In this section, you will learn about weight and friction. These two forces determine who gets down the hill first.

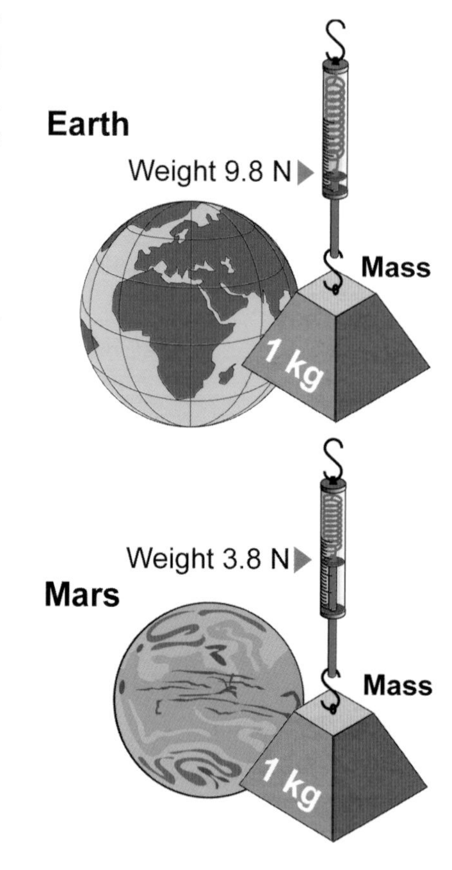

Figure 3.8: *Weight is a force that comes from gravity pulling on mass. The weight depends on how strong gravity is. Earth is bigger than Mars and has stronger gravity. A kilogram weighs 9.8 newtons on Earth but only 3.8 newtons on Mars.*

Gravity

What is gravity

What is the force that causes an object like a car to accelerate down a ramp?

You probably know gravity is involved. Gravity is a force that pulls every mass toward every other mass. Since Earth is the biggest mass around, gravity pulls everything toward the center of Earth. Ask someone the meaning of the word *down* and they point toward the center of Earth. Down is the direction of the force of gravity.

Gravity depends on mass

The force of gravity depends on how much mass you have. If you have more mass, gravity pulls on you with more force. That is why we can use force to measure mass. When you use a digital balance to measure the mass of a sample, you are really measuring the force of gravity acting on your sample. If you are on the surface of Earth, every kilogram of mass creates a gravitational force of 9.8 newtons. You may recognize this number—9.8 newtons is the same as 9.8 m/sec^2, the acceleration of gravity. We will talk more about the relation between newtons and the acceleration of gravity on the next page.

Mars' gravity is weaker than Earth's

If you were on Mars, your force/mass balance would have to be adjusted. The planet is much smaller than Earth and therefore Mars's gravity is weaker. Every kilogram of mass on Mars results in a gravity force of only 3.8 newtons (Figure 3.8). The larger the planet you are on, the greater the force of gravity. On Jupiter, the largest planet, gravity has a force 2.6 times stronger than on the surface of Earth. If you weighed 110 pounds on Earth, you would weigh 286 pound on Jupiter!

Mass and weight

What is weight? Weight is what we call the force created by gravity on objects. The weight of an object depends on its mass. Your mass is constant throughout the universe, but your weight changes depending on what planet you happen to be on. For example, because the gravitational force on Mars is less than that on Earth, you *weigh* less on Mars than on Earth, but your *mass* is the same at both locations!

How to calculate weight If you know the mass of an object, you can calculate its weight using Newton's second law. When you drop something on Earth, gravity causes it to accelerate at 9.8 m/sec^2. Because there is acceleration, you know there must be a force. You also know the force is exactly equal to mass times acceleration. The force we call weight is equal to an object's mass times the acceleration of gravity (9.8 m/sec^2).

Weight in formulas Since weight is a force, we use the letter F to represent it. To remind us that we are talking about the weight force, we add a little w next to the F. The w is called a **subscript**, and we would say "F sub w" if we wanted to tell someone what we were writing. The F and w always stay together since they are really one symbol for the weight force.

Weight

$$F_w = mg$$

Weight force (N) → F_w; mass (kg) → m; Acceleration of gravity (9.8 m/sec^2) → g

DON'T use kilograms for weight Because we live and work on the surface of Earth, we tend to use weight and mass interchangeably. Heavy objects have lots of mass and light objects have little mass. Boxes and people are "weighed" in both kilograms and pounds. This is OK for everyday use, but you must remember the difference when doing physics. Physics is about the true nature of how the universe works and mass is truly a fundamental property of an object. Force often depends on outside influences, like gravity. You cannot interchange force and mass in a formula; doing so would be like substituting a fork for a spoon when you are trying to eat soup. In physics, force and mass are different quantities with different units.

Example:

A legend has it that, around 1587, Galileo dropped two balls from the Leaning Tower of Pisa to see which would fall faster.

a) Calculate the weight of each ball.

b) Calculate the acceleration of each ball's fall.

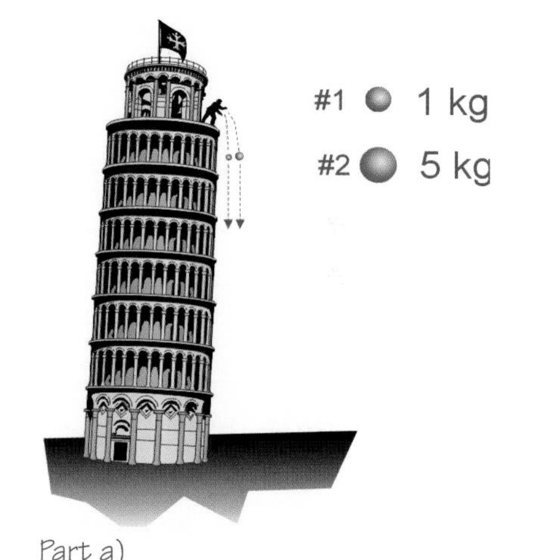

Part a)

#1 $F_w = mg$
$= (1 \text{ kg}) \times (9.8 \text{ m/sec}^2)$
$= 9.8 \text{ N}$

#2 $F_w = (5 \text{ kg}) \times (9.8 \text{ m/sec}^2)$
$= 49 \text{ N}$

Part b)

#1 $a = F/m$
$= (9.8 \text{ N})/1 \text{ kg}$
$= 9.8 \text{ m/sec}^2$

#2 $a = (49 \text{ N})/5 \text{ kg}$
$= 9.8 \text{ m/sec}^2$

The acceleration of both balls is the same!

Newton's law of universal gravitation

Why does the moon orbit Earth?

Mars and Earth are two massive objects that orbit the sun. Similarly, Earth's moon is a massive object that orbits around Earth. The same gravity that gives you weight is what holds Earth and its moon together. If you could simply drop the moon, it would fall to Earth just like an apple falls down from a tree. That does not happen because the moon is moving quite fast in a direction perpendicular to Earth's attractive gravity. The force of gravity bends the path of the moon toward the center of Earth, resulting in a nearly circular orbit.

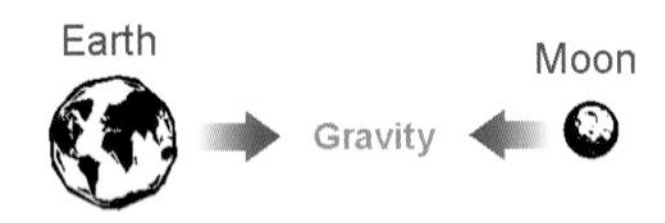

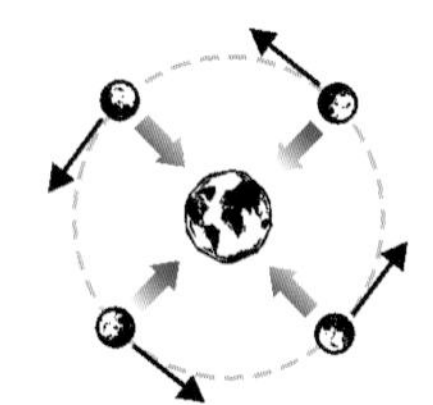

The velocity of the Moon is perpendicular to its distance from the Earth. Because gravity pulls toward the center of the Earth, the Moon's path is bent into a (nearly) circular orbit.

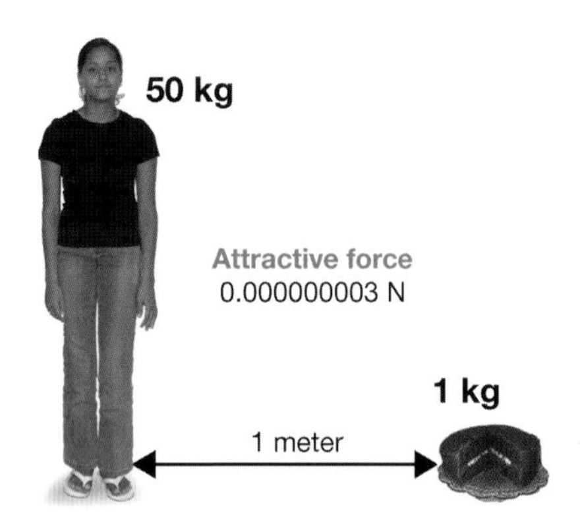

Figure 3.9: *The attractive force from gravity between objects of ordinary mass is incredibly small.*

What is the law of universal gravitation?

Gravity is a force of attraction that exists between any two objects that have mass. This idea is known as the **law of universal gravitation**. The force of attraction increases when the mass of the objects increases. The force of gravity also increases when the objects get closer together. Given this information, does this mean that we feel forces of attraction between ourselves and other objects?

The force of attraction between two objects is directly related to the masses of the objects and inversely related to the square of the distance between them.

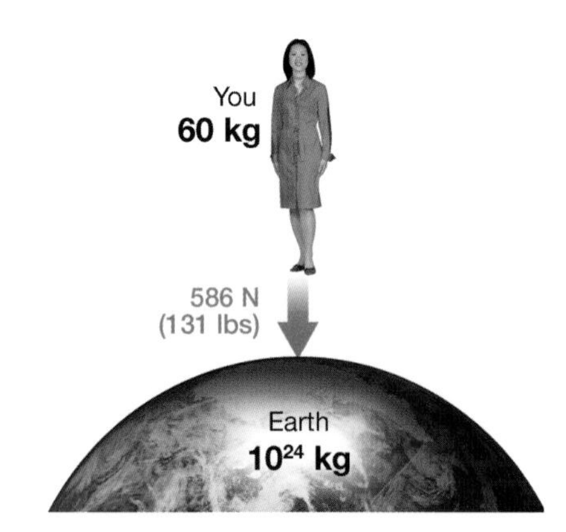

Figure 3.10: *You feel weight because the mass of Earth is large enough to create significant gravity forces.*

It takes a lot of mass to create gravity you can feel

You may feel attracted to a chocolate cake, but gravity has nothing to do with it! The force of gravity between ordinary masses is so weak that you can't really feel it (Figure 3.9). We notice the effects of gravity because the mass of one particular object (Earth) is huge, and relatively close to us. For gravity to create noticeable forces between two objects, the mass of at least one of them must be very large, like a planet or a star (Figure 3.10).

Calculating the gravitational force between objects

Calculating the force of gravity

You can calculate the gravity force between two objects using the equation for universal gravitation. The attractive force between two objects is equal to 'G' times the product of their masses divided by the square of the distance between them. 'G' is the gravitational constant, and is the same everywhere in the universe. This one equation describes gravity for small things, like people and chocolate cakes. It also works for huge things like galaxies, stars, and planets.

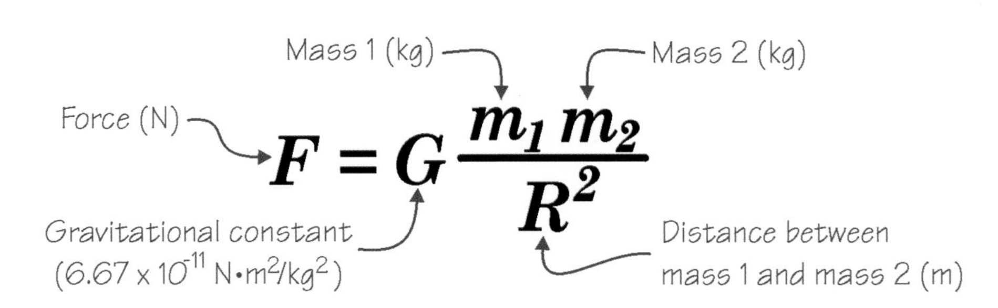

Example:

The mass of Jupiter's third largest moon, Io, is 8.9×10^{22} kg. The radius of Io is 1,815 kilometers. Use the equation of universal gravitation to calculate your weight if you were on the surface of Io and had a mass of 50 kilograms.

1) Use the formula for the universal law of gravitation.

$$F = G \times \frac{m_1 \times m_2}{d^2}$$

2) Plug in values.

$F = 6.7 \times 10^{-11}\ \text{N}\cdot\text{m}^2/\text{sec}^2$; $m_1 = 50$ kg; $m_2 = 8.9 \times 10^{22}$ kg; $R = 1{,}815{,}000$ m

$= [(6.7 \times 10^{-11}\ \text{N}\cdot\text{m}^2/\text{sec}^2) \times (50\ \text{kg}) \times (8.9 \times 10^{22}\ \text{kg})] \div (1{,}815{,}000\ \text{m})^2$

$= 91$ N or 20 lbs (4.448 N = 1 lb)

Your weight on Io is about 20 pounds! On Earth your weight would be 110 pounds. With such a small weight, you could jump 13 meters (43 feet) high on Io.

Newton and gravity

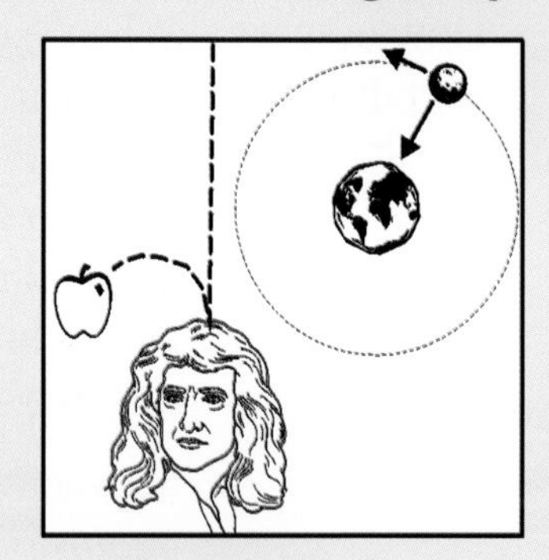

Many people associate the discovery of the law of gravitation with a falling apple. As the story goes, Newton observed an apple fall from a tree and was inspired to wonder if the moon experienced a similar force that affected its motion around Earth. Newton deduced that the force responsible for accelerating a falling apple is the same force involved in keeping the moon in orbit. As Newton developed his theories about motion, he concluded that gravity is a force that behaves the same throughout the universe—it's universal!

Friction

How is space travel different from Earth travel?

When Newton was developing the law of universal gravitation, he realized that with enough speed, an object would orbit forever as long as nothing slowed it down. For an object like a space shuttle, orbiting around Earth can be nearly effortless because there is no air resistance in space. Air resistance "resists" forward movement of cars and other objects on Earth. Air resistance is a kind of force kind called **friction**.

What is friction?

Friction is a term that is used to describe forces that result from relative motion between objects (like the wheel and axle of a car). *Frictional forces always work against the motion that produces them.* For example, when a model car rolls down a ramp frictional forces resist the motion. Friction is a force that holds the car back. Axles and ball bearings are inventions that help reduce friction.

What causes friction?

Friction comes from two surfaces moving against each other. Surfaces of objects that appear smooth and shiny actually have microscopic hills and valleys. As the surfaces slide across each other the hills and valleys interfere causing friction.

Friction and wear

Objects that continuously rub against each other cause **wear**. Wear refers to how moving parts can erode each other. In old cars, the parts are often so worn down due to friction that they are too loose and no longer fit correctly.

Kinds of friction

We use the word *friction* to describe any force that is caused by motion and that acts to slow motion down. Some examples of friction include:

- **Air Friction**: The air moving around moving objects creates an opposing force. This is why many cars have rounded, *aerodynamic* shapes. A rounded design reduces air friction, allowing cars to go faster and get better gas mileage.
- **Sliding Friction**: When two surfaces rub against each other, we get sliding friction. Sliding friction is caused by irregularities in the surfaces.
- **Viscous Friction**: Objects that move in water or other fluids create this type of friction. Oil changes sliding friction to viscous friction and helps reduce wear.
- **Rolling Friction**: This type of friction is caused by one object rolling over another, like a wheel rolling over the road. Ball bearings in wheels are designed to reduce the effect of rolling friction.

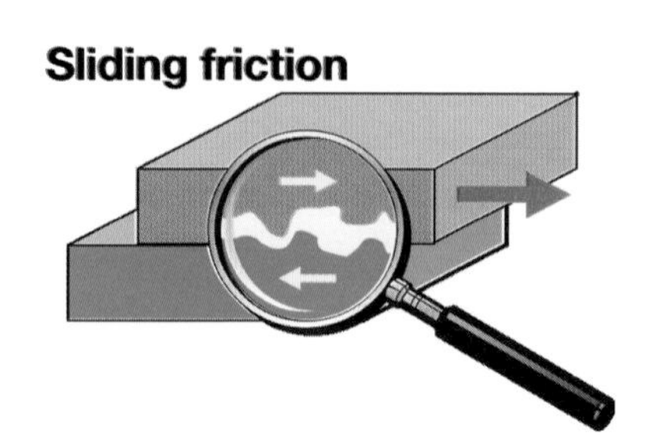

Figure 3.11: *Sliding friction is caused by microscopic hills and valleys on the surface of materials.*

Figure 3.12: *The wheels of the car have ball bearings to reduce sliding friction. Even ball bearings have rolling friction and may also have viscous friction from oil.*

Friction and motion

How does friction affect acceleration? Friction is a force that always opposes motion. That means the force of friction is opposite whatever force is causing motion. For a car rolling downhill, gravity supplies a force pulling down the hill. Friction opposes motion, so it pushes the car up the hill while gravity is pulling the car down the hill.

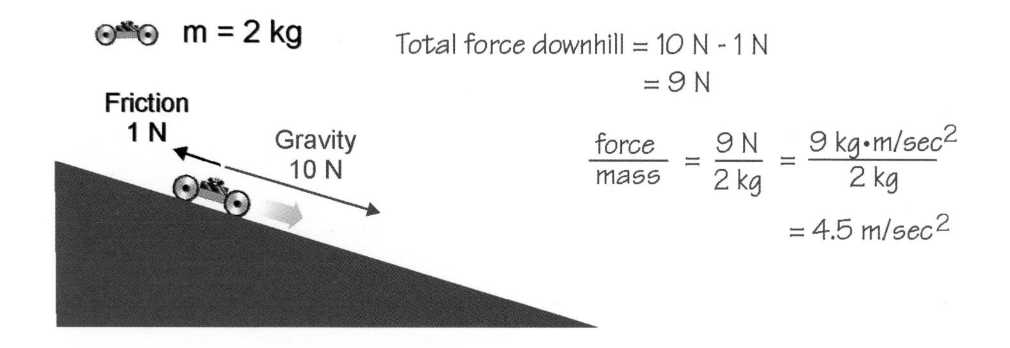

The net force The F that appears in Newton's second law stands for the total force acting on the car. This includes gravity and friction. To find out the total force we need to subtract the friction force from gravity. What is left is often called the net force. When talking about forces, the word *net* means total.

Friction reduces acceleration The acceleration we observe will always be less than it would have been if there were no friction. This is because the friction force partly cancels some of the gravity force pulling the car down.

All machines have friction All true machines have friction. That means there are always forces that tend to oppose motion. Unless you continually supply force, eventually, friction slows everything to a stop. Bicycles have very low friction, but even the best bicycle slows down if you coast on a level road.

Perpetual Motion

Throughout history, many people have claimed to have invented a machine that will run forever with no outside force. We call them perpetual motion machines and none have ever worked.

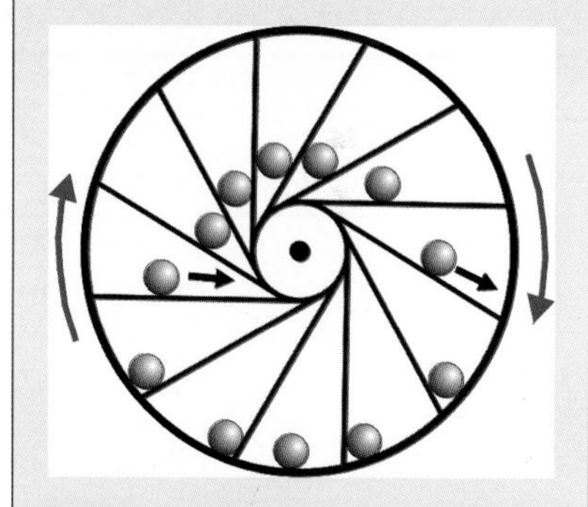

Perpetual motion machines never work because there is always some friction. Friction always opposes motion so sooner or later everything slows down.

If someone shows you a device that seems to go without stopping, be suspicious. There is no escape from friction. Somewhere, you will always find a hidden plug or battery supplying force.

3.3 Equilibrium, Action, and Reaction

In this section, you will come to understand the truth behind the phrase "For every action there is an equal and opposite reaction." This statement is known as Newton's third law of motion and it explains the interaction and motion of objects. You will learn that forces are always at work when the motion of an object changes. However, this is not to say that objects at rest experience no forces. What keeps your book perfectly still on a table as you are trying to read it (Figure 3.13)? Why would your book fall to the ground if you lifted the table at one end? "Force" is a good answer to both of these questions.

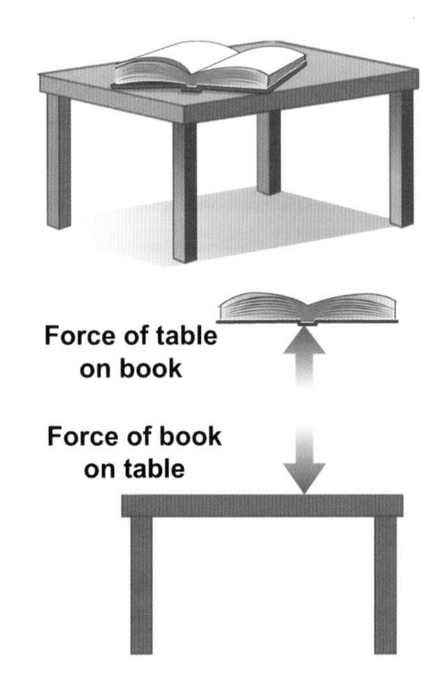

Figure 3.13: *Even when things are not moving there are forces acting. Gravity pulls the book down with a force. The table pushes back up with an equal and opposite force. The book stays still because the two forces are balanced*

Newton on a skateboard

An imaginary skateboard contest

Imagine a skateboard contest in which each person has to move his or her skateboard without their bodies touching the ground. Neither their feet nor their hands may touch the ground. How would you win this contest? How would you move your skateboard? Here are some possible strategies.

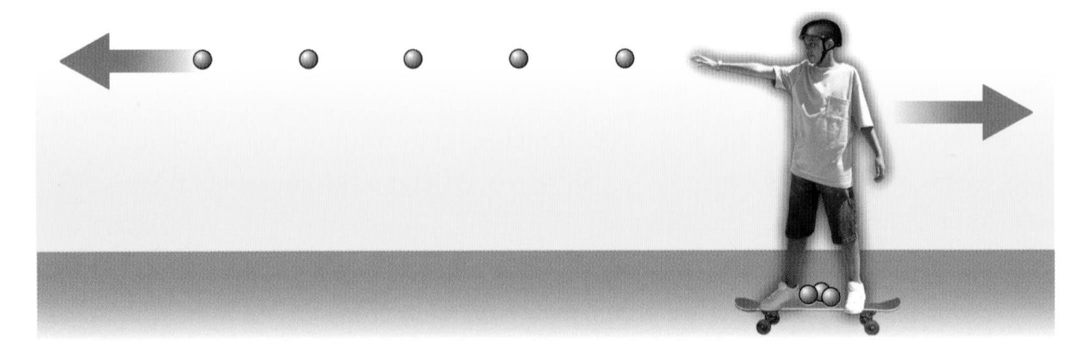

- Wave your arms back and forth.
- Walk from one end of the skateboard to the other.
- Start the contest at the top of an inclined plane.
- Stuff tennis balls in your pockets and throw them away from you.

Which strategies would work? Can you think of any others? Newton's third law of motion explains why you use your feet in the first place to get a skateboard moving. This law also explains why you can move a skateboard even if you don't use your hands or feet.

Newton's third law of motion

Review the first and second laws

The first and second laws apply to single objects. For example, the first law states that an object will remain at rest or in motion at constant velocity unless acted upon by an external force. The second law states that the acceleration of an object is directly proportional to force and inversely proportional to the mass.

The third law operates with pairs of objects

In contrast to the first two laws, the third law of motion deals with pairs of objects. This is because *all forces come in pairs*. **Newton's third law states that for every action force there has to be a reaction force that is equal in magnitude (in size) and opposite in direction to the action force.**

The third law applied to a skateboard

The action/reaction forces act on separate objects, *not* the same object. For example, the action-reaction pair required to move your skateboard includes your foot and the ground. Your foot pushing against the ground is the action force. The ground pushing back on you is the reaction force. The reaction force makes you move because it acts on *you* (Figure 3.14). If you were on slippery ice, you could push just as hard, but without a reaction force you would not move.

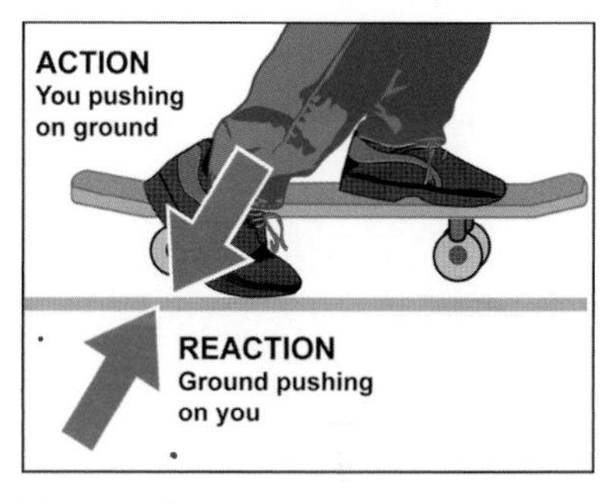

Figure 3.14: *All forces come in pairs. When you push on the ground (action), the reaction of the ground pushing back on your foot is what makes you move.*

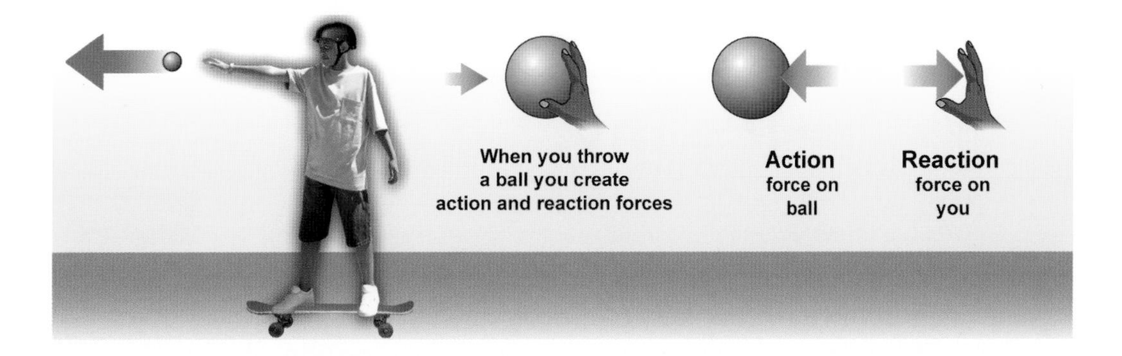

Stopping action and reaction confusion

It is easy to get confused thinking about action and reaction forces. Why don't they always cancel each other out? The reason is that the action and reaction forces act on different objects. When you throw a ball you apply the action force to the ball, creating acceleration of the ball. The reaction is the ball pushing back against your hand. The forces don't cancel because they act on different objects.

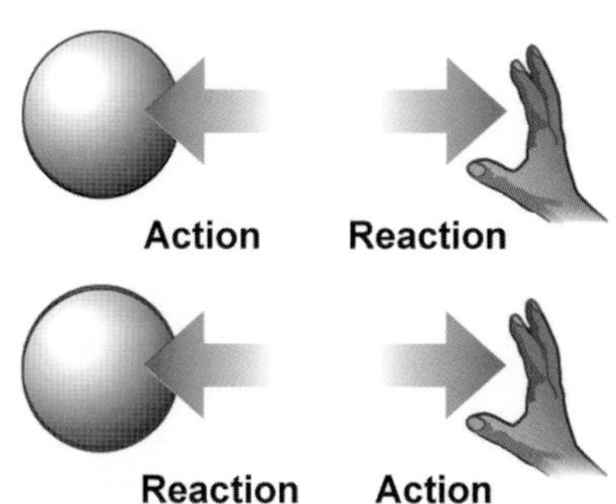

Figure 3.15: *It doesn't matter which force you call the action and which the reaction. The action and reaction forces are interchangeable.*

Momentum

The motion of objects When two objects exchange forces in an action-reaction pair, their motions are also affected as a pair. If you throw a ball from your skateboard you must apply a force to the ball. The third law says the ball exerts an equal and opposite force on you. Your force makes the ball accelerate in one direction and the reaction makes you accelerate in the opposite direction.

What happens if you throw faster or heavier balls? Because of the third law, the speed at which you and the ball move away from each other are related in a special way. If you throw the ball away very fast, your backward acceleration is higher than when you throw the ball away slowly. If you throw a heavier ball away fast, your backward acceleration is greater than if you throw a lighter ball (Figure 3.16). The backward acceleration from the reaction force is called recoil.

Momentum is mass times velocity Momentum is the mass of an object multiplied by its speed or velocity. If you increase the mass or the speed of an object, you increase its momentum. The units for momentum are kilograms-meters per second or kg-m/sec.

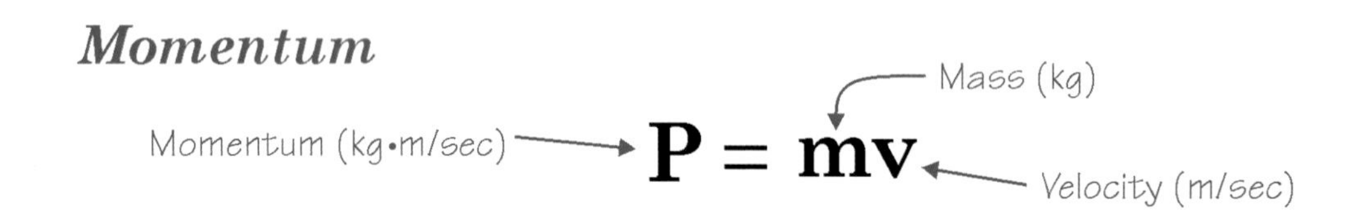

The law of conservation of momentum Because of the third law, the momentum of you and the ball are connected. If the ball takes away momentum to the left, you must take away an equal amount of momentum to the right. This rule is an example of the law of conservation of momentum. The law of conservation of momentum says that as long as interacting objects are not influenced by outside forces (like friction), the total amount of momentum cannot change.

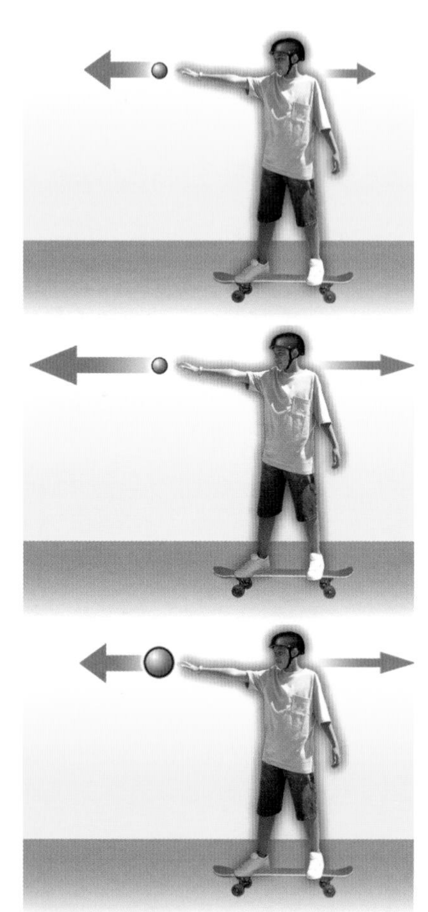

Figure 3.16: *The speed and mass of the ball you throw affect your backward acceleration (recoil).*

Using positive and negative

When talking about momentum we usually need to use positive and negative to tell the direction of motion (Figure 3.17). That means momentum can also be positive (moving to the right) or negative (moving to the left).

Before you throw the ball, your speed (and the ball's) is zero. Since momentum is mass times speed, the total momentum is also zero. The law of conservation of momentum says that *after* you throw the ball, the total momentum *still* has to be zero.

An example of the conservation of momentum

If the ball has a mass of 1 kilogram and you throw it at a speed of -20 m/sec to the left, the ball takes away -20 kg·m/sec of momentum. To make the total momentum zero, *you* must take away +20 kg·m/sec of momentum. If your mass is 40 kg and you ignore friction, then your speed is +0.5 m/sec to the right (Figure 3.18).

Rockets and jet planes

Rockets and jet planes use the law of conservation of momentum to move. A jet engine pushes exhaust air at very high speed out of the back of the engine. The momentum lost by the air going backward must be compensated by the momentum gained by the jet moving forward. A rocket can accelerate in space without touching anything because it throws mass at high speed out the end of the engine. The forward momentum of a rocket is exactly equal to the momentum of the escaping mass ejected from the end of the engine.

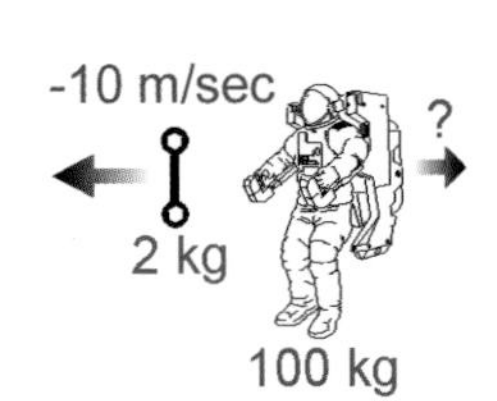

Example: An astronaut in space throws a 2-kilogram wrench away from him at a speed of -10 m/sec. If the astronaut's mass is 100 kilograms, at what speed does the astronaut move backward after throwing the wrench?

Solution: (1) You are asked for the speed. Since the astronaut is in space, we can ignore friction.

(2) You are given the mass and speed of the wrench and the mass of the astronaut.

(3) This is enough to apply the law of conservation of momentum.

$m_1 v_1 + m_2 v_2 = 0$

(4) Plug in numbers.

$[2 \text{ kg} \times (-10 \text{ m/sec})] + [(100 \text{ kg}) \times v_2] = 0$

$v_2 = +20 / 100 = +0.2 \text{ m/sec}$

The astronaut moves backward at a speed of +0.2 m/sec.

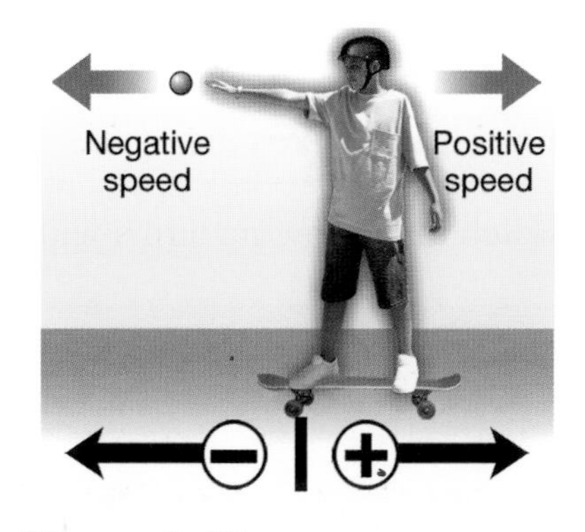

Figure 3.17: *The direction is important when using the law of conservation of momentum. We use positive and negative numbers to represent opposite directions.*

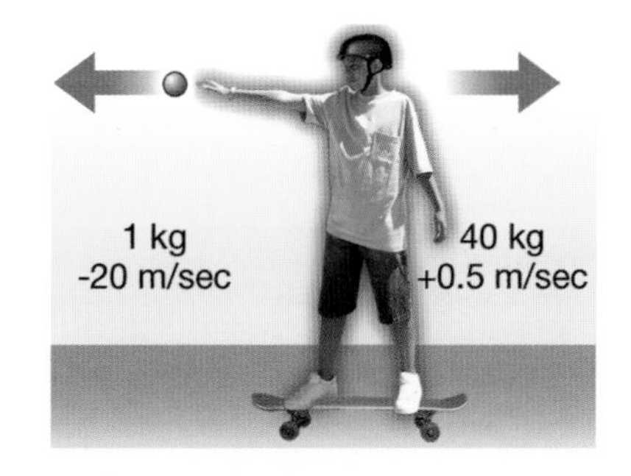

Figure 3.18: *The result of the skateboarder throwing a 1-kg ball at a speed of -20 m/sec is that he and the skateboard with a total mass of 40 kg move backward at a speed of +0.5 m/sec if you ignore friction. If you account for friction, would the calculation for speed of the skateboarder on the skateboard end up being less or more than 0.5 m/sec?*

Chapter 3 Review

Vocabulary review

Match the following terms with the correct definition. There is one extra definition in the list that will not match any of the terms.

Set One

1. force	a. The metric unit of force
2. pound	b. Objects at rest stay at rest, and objects in motion stay in motion, unless acted on by a force
3. newton	c. The English unit of force
4. Newton's first law of motion	d. An object that is in a state of motion
5. inertia	e. An action that has the ability to change motion
	f. The property of a body to resist changing its state of motion

Set Two

1. mass	a. When an object has a net force of zero acting on it
2. kilogram	b. A measurement of the amount of matter
3. Newton's second law of motion	c. The total forces acting on an object
4. net force	d. Force causes an object to accelerate, while the object's mass resists acceleration
5. equilibrium	e. When an object has a net force acting on it
	f. The metric unit of mass

Set Three

1. gravity	a. Forces that result from chemical reactions
2. weight	b. Pulls every mass toward every other mass
3. friction	c. For every action, there is an equal and opposite reaction
4. wear	d. Force that results from the relative motion between objects
5. Newton's third law of motion	e. The grinding away of moving parts that are in contact with each other
	f. The force created by gravity

Set Four

1. viscous friction	a. Friction caused by the movement of two surfaces against each other
2. sliding friction	b. Friction caused by one object rolling over another
3. rolling friction	c. Friction caused by the movement of air around moving objects
4. air friction	d. Friction caused by the movement of an object through a liquid
5. momentum	e. The mass of an object multiplied by its acceleration
	f. The mass of an object multiplied by its velocity

Concept review

1. Define the term *force*, and give some examples of forces.
2. Give an example of Newton's first law in everyday life.
3. Which has more inertia, a 1-kilogram ball or a 10-kilogram ball?
4. An object with more inertia is both harder to __________ and to __________.
5. Give an example of Newton's second law in everyday life.
6. Explain how the unit of 1 newton is defined.
7. Any object with mass exerts a force on any other object with mass. This force is called __________.
8. On the surface of the Earth, the force of gravity acting on one kilogram is:
   a. 9.8 pounds
   b. 3.8 newtons
   c. 9.8 newtons
   d. varies according to your mass
9. What is the difference between the *mass* of an object and the *weight* of an object?
10. According to the law of universal gravitation, what two factors are important in determining the force of gravity between two objects?
11. Name a unit for measuring:
    a. force
    b. mass
    c. weight
12. The net force acting on a car rolling down a ramp is the addition of three forces. One of the forces is the ramp pushing up to support the car. Name the other two forces acting on the car.
    a. Name the two forces on the car.
    b. Which of these two forces helps the motion of the car?
    c. Which of these two forces opposes the motion of the car?
13. Give an example of Newton's third law acting in everyday life.
14. Fill in the blanks in the following statements:
    a. Forces always occur in __________.
    b. Each force in an action-reaction pair of forces is equal in __________.
    c. Each force in an action-reaction pair of forces is opposite in __________.
15. The momentum of an object depends on what two factors?
16. Give an example of the law of conservation of momentum from everyday life.

Problems

1. A company uses a ramp to slide boxes of parts to a shipping area. Each box has a mass of 10 kilograms. When sliding down the ramp, the boxes accelerate at a rate of 0.1 m/sec^2. What is the force acting on each box? For this problem, ignore the effects of friction acting on each box.
2. You have an object that has a mass of 4 kilograms.
   a. What is its weight in newtons?
   b. What is its weight in pounds?
3. You drop an object from a second-floor window.
   a. Describe the speed of the object after 1 second.
   b. Describe the speed of the object after 2 seconds.
4. A heavy block of lead is placed on a table. The block of lead has a weight, or a force, of 500 newtons. Explain why it doesn't fall through the table.
5. From the text you learned that a 110-pound person would weigh 20 pounds (89 N) on Jupiter's moon Io. The mass of Jupiter is 1.9 x 10^{27} kg and its diameter is 142, 984 km. Would this same person weigh more on Io or on Jupiter? Explain your answer. What would this person weigh on Jupiter?
6. In the supermarket you return a cart to the cart area. You stand still and push the cart towards the other carts. You've just learned that the cart pushes back on you too, according to Newton's third law.
   a. Explain why the cart moves and you do not.
   Hint: Consider the cart and yourself separately. Also consider all the forces acting on you and on the cart.
   b. Is the cart in equilibrium once you let go of the handle? Explain.
7. What is the momentum of a 0.5-kilogram object traveling at

Applying your knowledge

1. You learned in this chapter that an object in motion will stay in motion unless acted on by a force. However, in everyday life, friction always slows things down. Research ways that people reduce friction in machines, such as by using ball bearings.
2. Joints like knees and elbows are designed to move freely. Find out how friction is reduced in a joint.
3. Research the effects of weightlessness on people and what astronauts do to counter those effects.
4. When an ice skater is on ice, a small amount of melting occurs under the blades of the skates. How does this help the skater glide? Your answer should discuss two different types of friction.
5. A situation involving conservation of momentum: A fish swims forward and pushes a mass of water backward with its tail.
   a. Identify $\boldsymbol{m}_1$ and $\boldsymbol{v}_1$, and $\boldsymbol{m}_2$ and $\boldsymbol{v}_2$ for this situation.
   b. How might the fish's tail and body size affect how fast it swims?

UNIT 2

Work and Energy

Chapter 4

Machines and Mechanical Systems

Introduction to Chapter 4

Engineering is the process of applying science to solve problems. Technology is the word we use to describe machines and inventions that result from engineering efforts. The development of the technology that created computers, cars, and the space shuttle began with the invention of simple machines. In this chapter, you will discover the principles upon which simple machines operate. You will study several simple machines closely and learn how machines can multiply and alter forces.

Investigations for Chapter 4

4.1	Forces in Machines	*How do simple machines work?*

Machines can make us much stronger than we normally are. In this Investigation, you will design and build several block and tackle machines from ropes and pulleys. Your machines will produce up to six times as much force as you apply. As part of the Investigation you will identify the input and output forces, and measure the mechanical advantage.

4.2	The Lever	*How does a lever work?*

Archimedes said "Give me a lever and fulcrum and I shall move the Earth." While the lever you study in this Investigation will not be strong enough to move a planet, you will learn how to design and build levers than can multiply force. You will also find the rule which predicts how much mechanical advantage a lever will have.

4.3	Gears and Design	*How do gears work?*

Many machines require that rotating motion be transmitted from one place to another. In this Investigation, you will learn how gears work and then use this knowledge to design and build a gear machine that solves a specific problem.

Learning Goals

In this chapter, you will:

- ✔ Describe and explain a simple machine.
- ✔ Apply the concepts of input force and output force to any machine.
- ✔ Determine the mechanical advantage of a machine.
- ✔ Construct and analyze a block and tackle machine.
- ✔ Describe the difference between science and engineering.
- ✔ Understand and apply the engineering cycle to the development of an invention or product.
- ✔ Describe the purpose and construction of a prototype.
- ✔ Design and analyze a lever.
- ✔ Calculate the mechanical advantage of a lever.
- ✔ Recognize the three classes of levers.
- ✔ Build machines with gears and deduce the rule for how pairs of gears turn.
- ✔ Design and build a gear machine that solves a specific problem.

Vocabulary

engineering	gear	lever	output arm
engineering cycle	input	machine	output force
engineers	input arm	mechanical advantage	output gear
force	input force	mechanical systems	prototype
fulcrum	input gear	output	simple machine

4.1 Forces in Machines

How do you move something that is too heavy to carry? How do humans move mountains? How were the Great Pyramids built? The answer to these questions has to do with the use of simple machines. In this section, you will learn how simple machines manipulate forces to accomplish many tasks.

Mechanical systems and machines

The world without machines Ten thousand years ago, people lived in a much different world. Their interactions were limited by what they could pick up and carry, how fast they could run, and what they could eat (or what could eat them!). It would be quite a problem for someone to bring a woolly mammoth back home without today's cars and trucks.

What technology allows us to do Today's technology allows us to do incredible things. Moving huge steel beams, digging tunnels that connect two islands, or building 1,000-foot skyscrapers are examples. What makes these accomplishments possible? Have we developed super powers since the days of our ancestors?

What is a machine? In a way we *have* developed super powers. Our powers came from our clever invention of **machines** and **mechanical systems**. A machine is a device with moving parts that work together to accomplish a task. A bicycle is a good example. All the parts of a bicycle work together to transform forces from your muscles into speed and motion. In fact, a bicycle is one of the most efficient machines ever invented (Figure 4.1).

The concepts of input and output Machines are designed to do something useful. You can think of a machine as having an **input** and an **output**. The *input* includes everything you do to make the machine work, like pushing on the pedals. The *output* is what the machine does for you, like going fast (Figure 4.2).

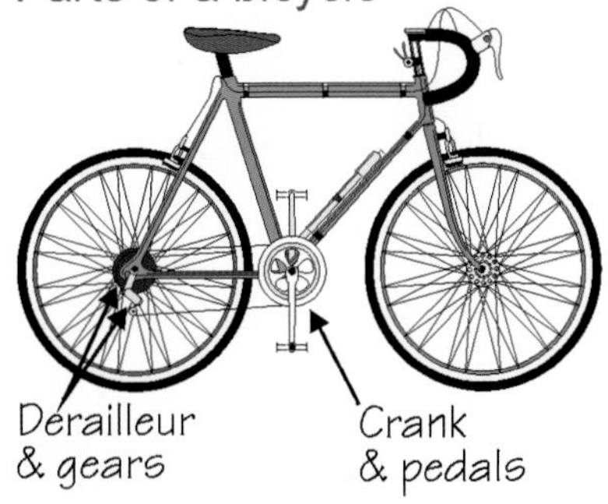

Figure 4.1: *A bicycle is a good example of a machine. A bicycle efficiently converts forces from your muscles into motion.*

Figure 4.2: *Applying the ideas of input and output to a bicycle.*

Simple machines

The beginning of technology

The development of the technology that created computers, cars, and the space shuttle begins with the invention of simple machines. A simple machine is an unpowered mechanical device, such as a lever. A lever allows you to move a rock that weighs 10 times as much as you do (or more). Some other important simple machines are the wheel and axle, the block and tackle, the gear, and the ramp.

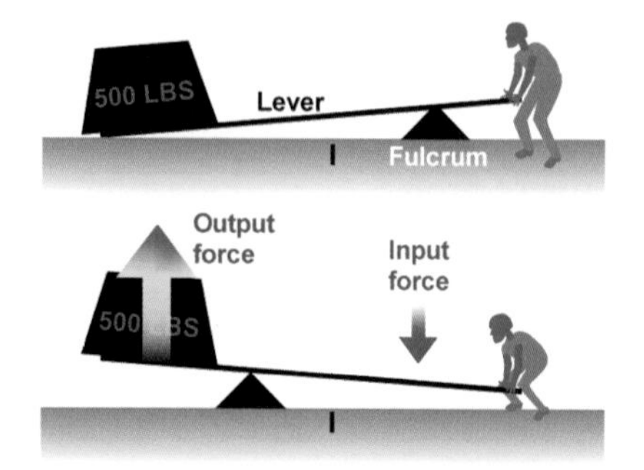

Figure 4.3: *With a properly designed lever, a person can move many times his own weight.*

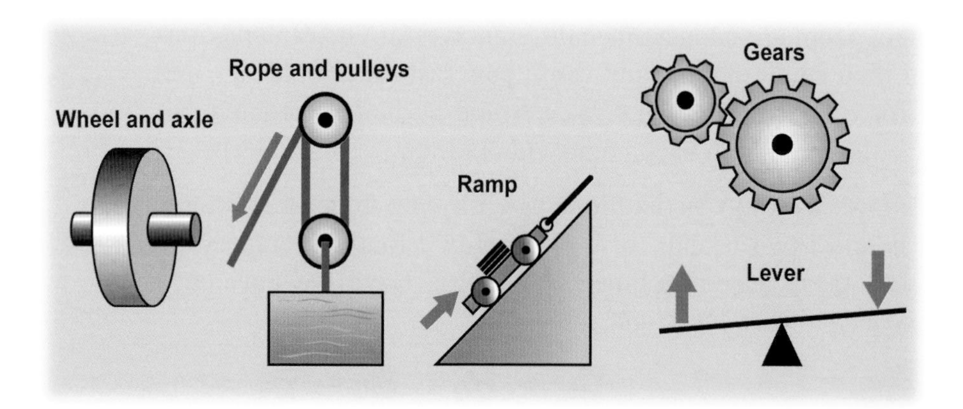

Input force and output force

Simple machines work by manipulating forces. It is useful to think in terms of an *input force* and an *output force*. With a lever the input force is what you apply. The output force is what the lever applies to what you are trying to move. Figure 4.3 shows an example of using a lever to move a heavy load.

The block and tackle

The block and tackle is another simple machine that uses ropes and pulleys to multiply forces. The input force is what you apply to the rope. The output force is what gets applied to the load you are trying to lift. One person could easily lift an elephant with a properly designed block and tackle! (Figure 4.4)

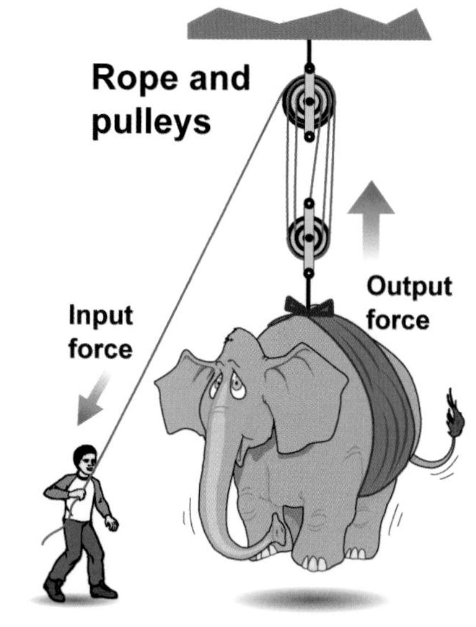

Figure 4.4: *A block and tackle machine made with ropes and pulleys allows one person to lift tremendous loads.*

Machines within machines

Most of the machines we use today are made up of combinations of different types of simple machines. For example, the bicycle uses wheels and axles, levers (the pedals and a kickstand), and gears. If you take apart a VCR, a clock, or a car engine you will also find simple machines adapted to fit almost everywhere.

Mechanical advantage

Definition of force

Simple machines work by changing force and motion. Remember that a **force** is an action that has the ability to change motion, like a push or a pull. Forces do not always result in a change in motion. For example, pushing on a solid wall does not make it move (at least not much). But, if the wall is not well built, pushing *could* make it move. Many things can create force: wind, muscles, springs, motion, gravity, and more. The action of a force is the same, regardless of its source.

Units of force

Recall from the last unit that there are two units we use to measure force: the newton and the pound. The newton is a smaller unit than the pound. A quantity of 4.448 newtons is equal to 1 pound. A person weighing 100 pounds would weigh 444.8 newtons.

Simple machines and force

As discussed, simple machines are best understood through the concepts of input and output forces. The input force is the force applied to the machine. The output force is the force the machine applies to accomplish a task.

Mechanical advantage

Mechanical advantage is the ratio of output force to input force. If the mechanical advantage is bigger than one, the output force is bigger than the input force (Figure 4.5). A mechanical advantage smaller than one means the output force is smaller than the input force.

Mechanical Advantage

$$MA = \frac{F_o}{F_i}$$

Mechanical advantage → MA; F_o = Output force (N); F_i = Input force (N)

Mechanical engineers

People who design machines are called *mechanical engineers*. Many of the machines they design involve the multiplication of forces to lift heavy loads; that is, the machines must have a greater output force than input force in order to accomplish the job.

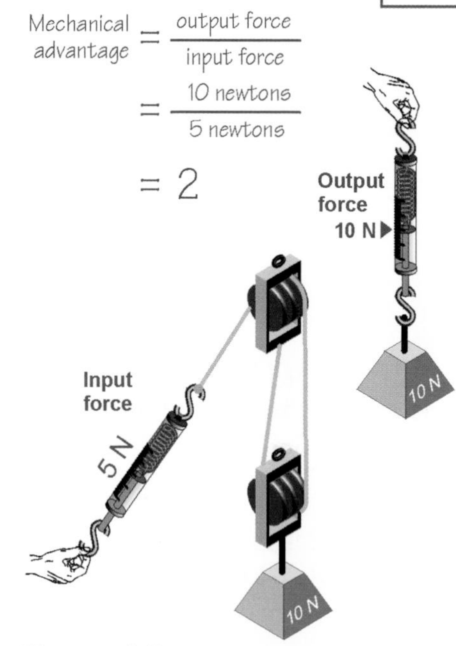

Figure 4.5: *A block and tackle with a mechanical advantage of two. The output force is twice as strong as the input force.*

The human body

Your arms operate at a mechanical advantage of less than one. This means that the input force exceeds the output force. The advantage of your arms working this way is that they have a range of motion. Small movements in tiny muscle fibers near your elbow lead to throwing a ball or turning a page!

How a block and tackle works

The forces in ropes and strings

Ropes and strings carry tension forces along their length. A tension force is a pulling force that always acts along the direction of the rope. Ropes or strings do *not* carry pushing forces. This would be obvious if you ever tried to push something with a rope. We will be using the term rope, but the strings used in your lab investigations behave just like ropes used in larger machines.

Every part of a rope has the same tension

If friction is very small, then the force in a rope is the same everywhere. This means that if you were to cut the rope and insert a force scale, the scale would measure the same tension force at any point.

The forces in a block and tackle

The diagram in (Figure 4.6) shows three different configurations of block and tackle. Notice that the number of ropes attached directly to the load is different in each case. Think about pulling with an input force. This force appears everywhere in the rope. That means in case A the load feels two upward forces equal to your pull. In case B the load feels three times your pulling force, and in case C the load feels four times your pull.

Mechanical advantage

If there are four ropes directly supporting the load, each newton of force you apply produces 4 newtons of output force. Configuration C has a mechanical advantage of 4. The output force is four times bigger than the input force.

Multiplying force with the block and tackle

Because the mechanical advantage is 4, the input force for machine C is 1/4 the output force. If you need an output force of 20 N, you only need an input force of 5 N! The block and tackle is an extremely useful machine because it multiplies force so effectively.

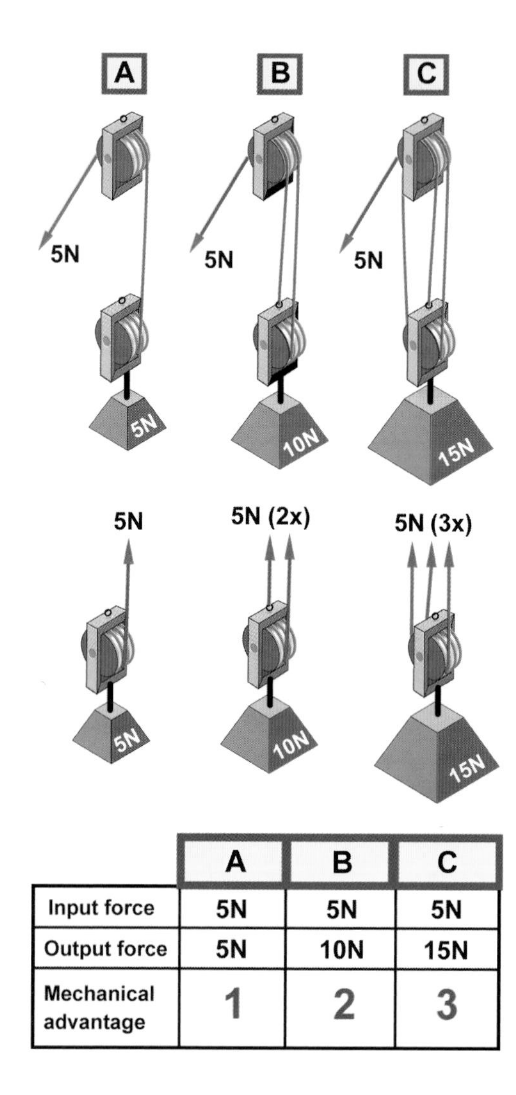

	A	B	C
Input force	5N	5N	5N
Output force	5N	10N	15N
Mechanical advantage	1	2	3

Figure 4.6: *How the block and tackle creates mechanical advantage using forces in ropes.*

4.2 The Lever

The lever is another example of a simple machine. In this section, you will learn about the relationships between force and motion that explain how a lever works. You will also learn that certain parts of the human body are levers. After reading this section and doing the Investigation, you should be able to design a lever to move almost anything!

What is a lever?

Examples of levers A lever can be made by balancing a board on a log (Figure 4.7). Pushing down on one end of the board lifts a load on the other end of the board. The downward force you apply is the input force. The upward force the board exerts on the load is the output force. Other examples of levers include: pliers, a wheelbarrow, and the human biceps and forearm.

Your muscles and skeleton use levers You may have heard the human body described as a machine. In fact, it is: Your bones and muscles work as levers to perform everything from chewing to throwing a ball (Figure 4.8).

Parts of the lever All levers includes a stiff structure (the **lever**) that rotates around a fixed point called the **fulcrum**. The side of the lever where the input force is applied is called the **input arm**. The **output arm** is the end of the lever that moves the rock or lifts the heavy weight. Levers are useful because you can arrange the fulcrum and the input and output arms to adapt to the task you need to perform. The ability of a lever to perform a task depends on its mechanical advantage. The formula for the mechanical advantage of a lever is below.

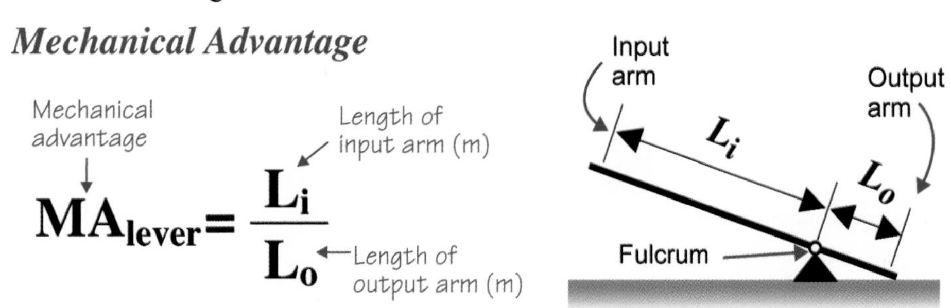

$$MA_{lever} = \frac{L_i}{L_o}$$

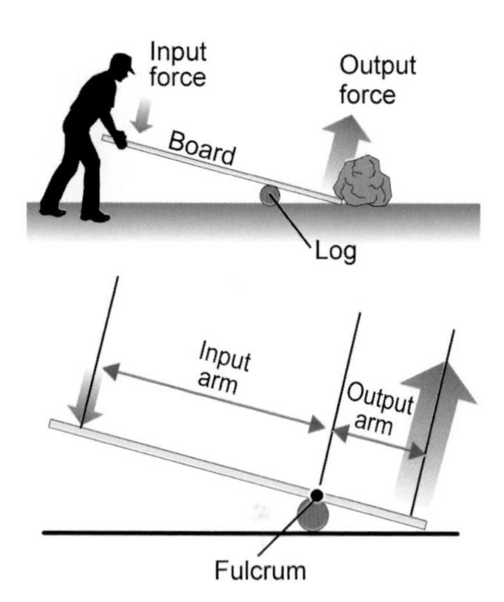

Figure 4.7: *A board and log make a lever.*

Figure 4.8: *Many parts of the human body are levers. Your jaw, feet, arms, and head all work as levers.*

The mechanical advantage of a lever

Input and output arms

The *mechanical advantage* of a lever is the ratio of the lengths of the input arm and the output arm. For example, if the input arm is 5 meters and the output arm is 1 meter, then the mechanical advantage is 5. The output force will be five times as large as the input force.

Input and output forces

The input force that is applied to a lever and the output force are related to the lengths of the input and output arms. When the input and output arms are the same length (because the fulcrum is in the middle of the lever), the input and output forces are the same. The input and output forces are different if the fulcrum is not in the center of the lever. The side of the lever with the longer arm has the smaller force. For example, if the input arm is 10 times longer than the output arm, the output force is 10 times greater than the input force.

The output force can be *less* than the input force

For some levers, the output arm is longer than the input arm and the output force is *less* than the required input force. Levers designed this way achieve a wide range of motion on the output side as in a broom (Figure 4.9).

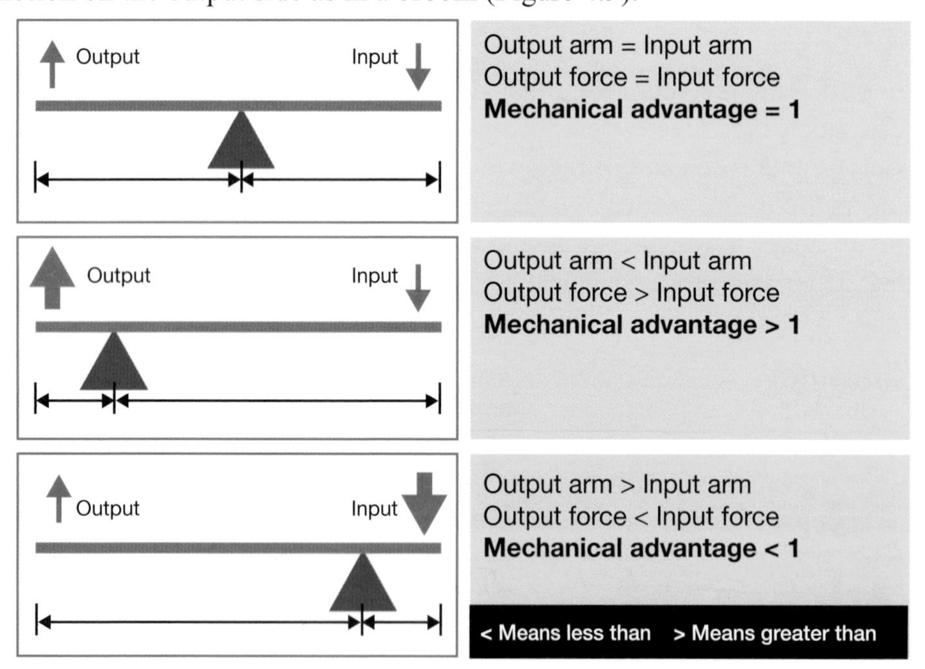

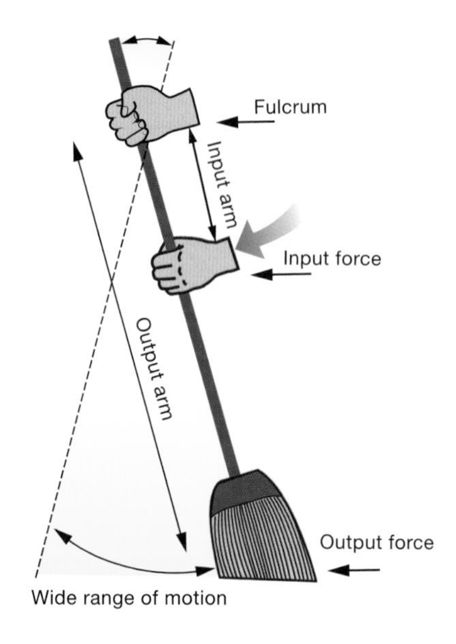

Figure 4.9: *Since the length of the output arm of the broom is less than the length of the input arm, the input force is greater than the output force. This lever works well because the output force is only needed to move dust.*

The three classes of levers

The three types of levers There are three types of levers, as shown in Figure 4.10. They are classified by the locations of the input and output forces relative to the fulcrum. All three types are used in many machines.

First-class levers First-class levers always have the fulcrum between the input force and the output force. If the input arm of this lever is larger than the output arm, then it is possible to produce a large output force relative to the input force. In this case, a first-class lever multiplies force. Sometimes, however, the input arm of a first-class lever is shorter than the output arm and the output force is less than the input force. The advantage of a lever designed this way is that work done by the lever can be done faster—a small amount of motion of the input arm translates into a huge motion made by the output arm. The mechanical advantage of a first-class lever can be greater than one or less than one. Examples of first-class levers include pliers and see-saws.

Second-class levers Second-class levers always have the output force between the fulcrum and the input force. Therefore, the input arm will always be longer than the output arm in second-class levers. What does this mean in terms of mechanical advantage? It means that mechanical advantage will always be greater than one. Second-class levers always multiply force. Wheelbarrows are second-class levers.

Third-class levers Third-class levers always have the input force between the fulcrum and the output force. This means that the output arm is always longer than the input arm and mechanical advantage is less than one. If mechanical advantage is less than one, then you can never multiply force by using a third-class lever. However, third-class levers do result in a wide range of motion that is important in moving your arms and sweeping large areas when you use a broom.

The human body is a simple machine On the next page, you will learn that parts of your body work as levers. In particular you arms and jaw work as levers. Before reading the next page, think about how your body works. Can you think of a body part that works as a first-class lever? Which parts of you body work as second-class or third-class levers?

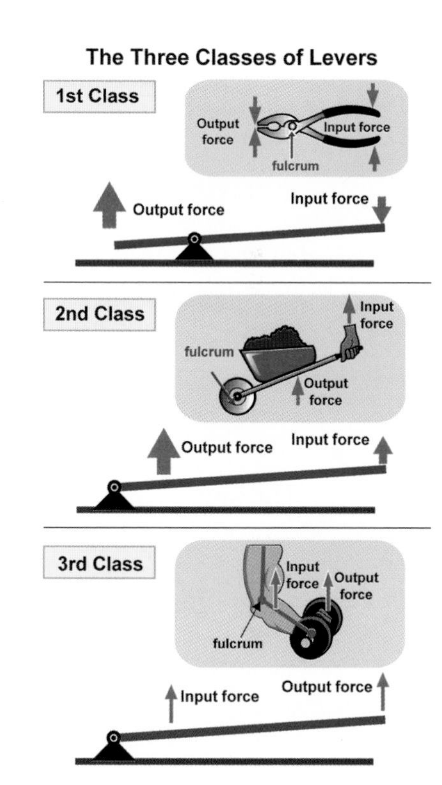

Figure 4.10: *Examples of three kinds of levers.*

Levers in the human body

What do levers do? A lever is a stiff structure that rotates around a fixed point. In the human body, all bones act as levers and each joint can serve as a fulcrum. For an applied force, levers can change the direction of force, the distance or speed of the motion, or change the strength of the force. A see-saw illustrates that a downward force on one end results in an upward force on the other end. A broom is efficient at sweeping a room because a small range of motion provided by the arms results in large sweeps on a floor. If the input arm is longer than the output arm, applied force can be multiplied For example, an input force of one newton can lift a five-newton object if the lever has a mechanical advantage of 5.

The neck Stop reading for a moment. Relax your neck so that your head drops slowly forward. The head is a heavy object—about 4.5 kilograms. Your head drops forward when you relax your neck because your head and neck work like a first-class lever (Figure 4.11). The fulcrum is at the top of the neck. The muscles in the neck provide an input force that allows you to raise your head. When you relax these muscles, gravity causes your head to fall forward.

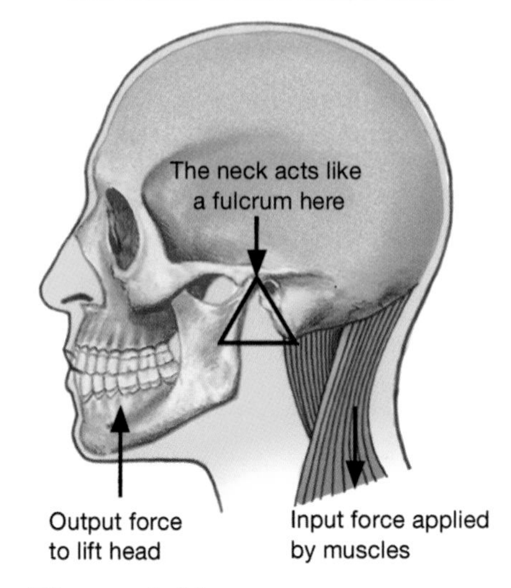

Figure 4.11: *The neck is an example of a first-class lever.*

The jaw Think about how your jaw works when you bite into an apple. When biting, your jaw works as a third-class lever. The input force (applied by your jaw muscles) occurs between the fulcrum (the joint where your jaw bone connects to your skull) and the output force which is applied to the apple.

The arms Your forearms work as third-class levers (see Figure 4.10 on the previous page). As you have learned from the reading, third-class levers require more input force than output force. However, the gain in third-class levers is range of motion. The range of motion of your arms is very important in that it makes it possible to reach, pick up objects, and lift them. Often, we are doing tasks that don't require a lot of output force. For example, when you turn a page of this book, you need range of motion to move the page, but you don't need a lot of force!

Feet When you stand on your toes, the feet act as second-class levers (Figure 4.12). Your toes are the fulcrum. The input force is provided by your calf muscles. The output force is the weight of your foot being lifted.

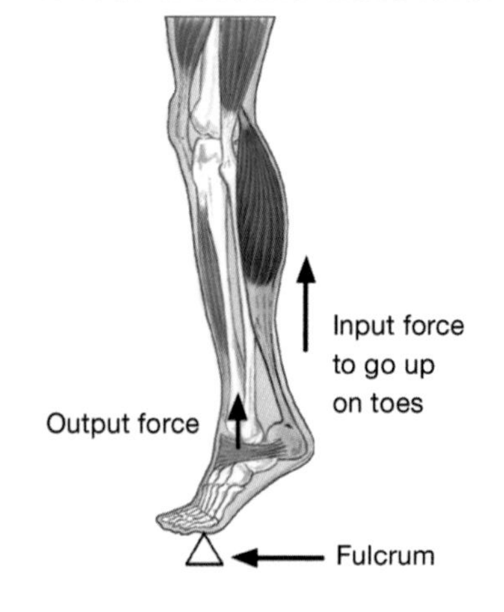

Figure 4.12: *The foot is an example of a second-class lever.*

4.3 Gears and Design

In this section, you will learn how people design complex machines to solve real problems. You may have practiced designing machines with gears in your Investigation. The process of learning how gears work and then using that information to solve a problem is common to the invention of almost every kind of machine, from the wheel and axle to the space shuttle. This process is called the engineering cycle, which is how ideas for inventions become something real you can actually use.

Science and engineering

Inventions solve problems

You are surrounded by inventions, from the toothbrush you use to clean your teeth to the computer you use to do your school projects (and play games). Where did the inventions come from? Most of them came from a practical application of science knowledge.

What is technology?

The application of science to solve problems is called **engineering** or technology. From the invention of the plow to the microcomputer, all technologies arise from someone's perception of a need for things to be done better. Although technology is widely different in the details, there are some general principles that apply to all forms of technological design or innovation. People who design technology to solve problems are called **engineers**.

Science	Engineering	Technology
Physics	Mechanical engineer	Automobile
Chemistry	Chemical engineer	Plastics
Biology	Electrical engineer	Telephone
Astronomy	Aerospace engineer	Airplane
Earth Science	Civil engineer	Suspension bridge
	Nuclear engineer	MRI scanner

Science and technology

Scientists study the world to learn the basic principles behind how things work. Engineers use scientific knowledge to create or improve inventions that solve problems.

Narciso Monturiol

Narciso Monturiol a Spanish lawyer and inventor, was born in 1819. While visiting a seaside village, Monturial observed the dangerous work of coral harvesters. He wondered if he could design and build a submarine to transport them safely to and from the reefs.

In 1859, Monturiol's seven-meter submarine, the *Ictineo*, was launched. It had a spherical inner hull built to withstand water pressure and an elliptical-shaped outer hull for ease of movement. Between the two hulls were tanks that stored and released water to control the sub's depth. Oxygen tanks were also stored in this space. The submarine was powered by four men turning the propeller by hand. Next, Monturiol built a larger, 14-meter steam-powered submarine that could stay under water for up to seven hours.

Monturiol didn't receive much credit for this work in his lifetime, but he is now recognized as an important contributor to submarine development.

A sample engineering problem

Suppose you are given a box of toothpicks and some glue, and are assigned to build a bridge that will hold a brick without breaking. After doing research, you come up with an idea for how to make the bridge. Your idea is to make the bridge from four structures connected together. Your structure is a truss because you have seen bridges that use trusses. Your idea is called a *conceptual design.*

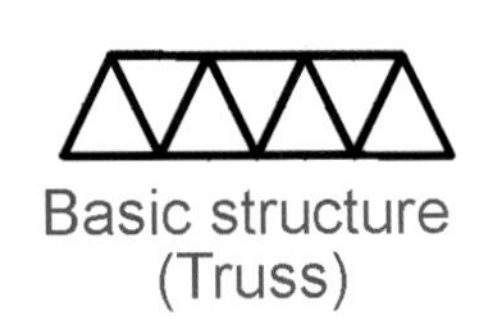

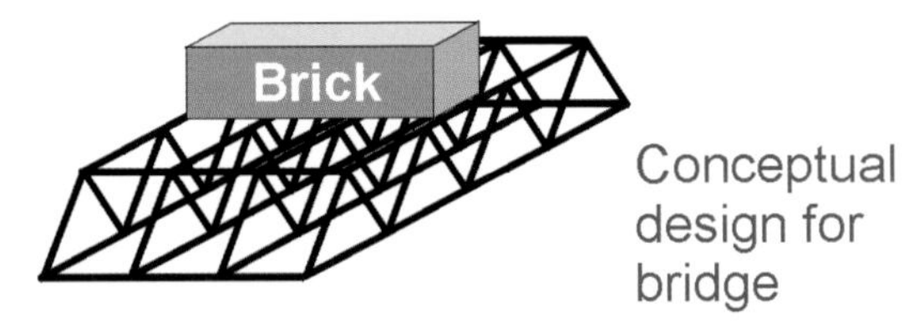

The importance of a prototype

You need to test your idea to see if it works. If you could figure out how much force it takes to break *one* structure, you would know if four structures will hold the brick. Your next step is to build a prototype and test it. Your prototype should be close enough to the real bridge that what you learn from testing can be applied to the final bridge. For example, if your final bridge is to be made with round toothpicks, your prototype also has to be made with round toothpicks.

Testing the prototype

You test the prototype truss by applying more and more force until it breaks. You learn that your truss breaks at a force of 5 newtons. The brick weighs 25 newtons. Four trusses are not going to be enough. You have two choices now. You can make each truss stronger, by using thread to tie the joints. Or, you could use more trusses in your bridge (Figure 4.13). The *evaluation* of test results is a necessary part of any successful design. Testing identifies potential problems in the design in time to correct them. Adding more trusses should make the bridge strong enough to withstand additional newtons before breaking, which gives an extra margin of safety.

Changing the design and testing again

If you decide to build a stronger structure, you will need to make another prototype and test it again. Good engineers often build many prototypes and keep testing them until they are successful under a wide range of conditions. The process of design, prototype, test, and evaluate is the engineering cycle (Figure 4.14). The best inventions go through the cycle many times, being improved each cycle until all the problems are worked out.

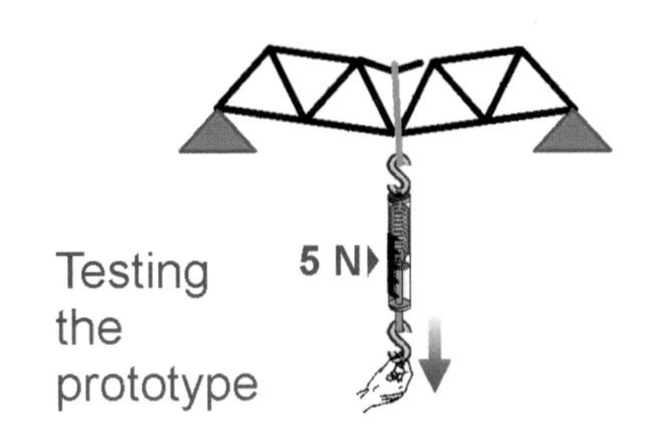

Figure 4.13: *Testing the prototype tells you if it is strong enough. Testing often leads to a revised design, for example, using more trusses.*

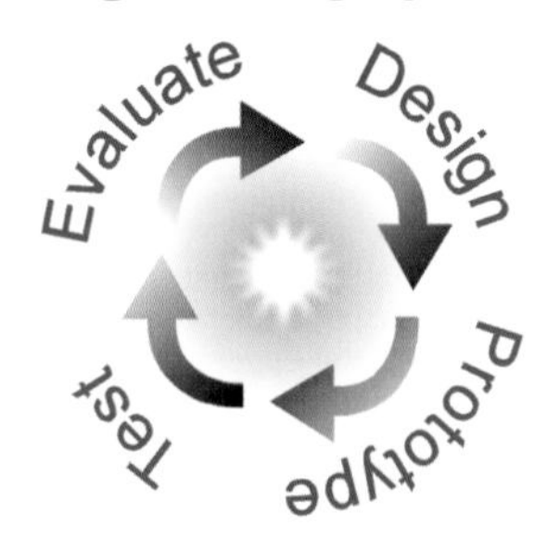

Figure 4.14: *The engineering design cycle is how we get an invention from concept to reality.*

Gears and rotating machines

Why are gears used? Many machines require that rotating motion be transmitted from one place to another. The transmission of rotating motion is often done with shafts and gears (Figure 4.15). When one or more shafts are connected with gears, the shafts may turn at different speeds and in different directions.

Gears change force and speed Some machinery, such as small drills, require small forces at high speed. Other machinery, such as mill wheels, require large forces at low speed. Since they act like rotating levers, gears also allow the forces carried by different shafts to be changed with the speed.

The relationship between gears and wheels Gears are better than wheels because they have teeth and don't slip as they turn together. Two gears with their teeth engaged act like two touching wheels with the same diameters as the *pitch diameters* of the gears (Figure 4.16). You can transmit much more force (without slipping) between two gears than you could with smooth wheels. Gears find application in a wide range of machines, including everything from pocket watches to turbocharged engines.

How gears work The rule for how gears turn depends on the number of teeth in the gears. Because the teeth don't slip, moving 36 teeth on one gear means that 36 teeth have to move on any connected gear. If one gear has 36 teeth it turns once to move 36 teeth. If the connected gear has only 12 teeth, it has to turn 3 times to move 36 teeth ($3 \times 12 = 36$).

What is the gear ratio? Like all machines, gears have input and output. The *input gear* is the one you turn, or apply forces to. The *output gear* is the one that is connected to the output of the machine. The *gear ratio* is the ratio of output turns to input turns. Smaller gears turn faster, so the gear ratio is the inverse of the ratio of teeth in two gears.

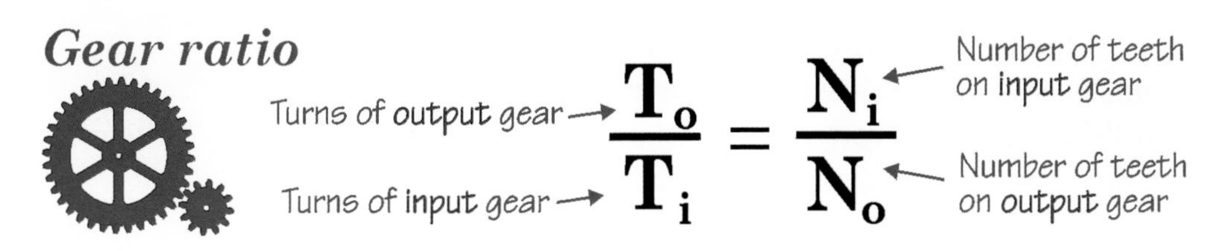

$$\frac{T_o}{T_i} = \frac{N_i}{N_o}$$

4 turns of rotating motion (small gear)
Gear
Shaft
2 turns of rotating motion (large gear)

Figure 4.15: *Gears are used to change the speeds of rotating shafts. By using gears of different sizes, the shafts can be made to turn at different rates.*

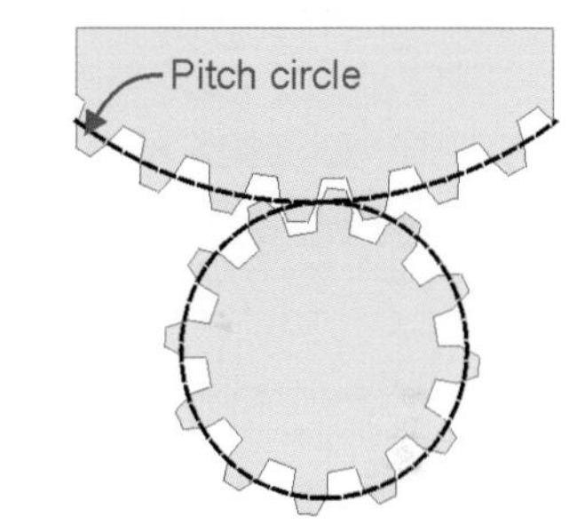

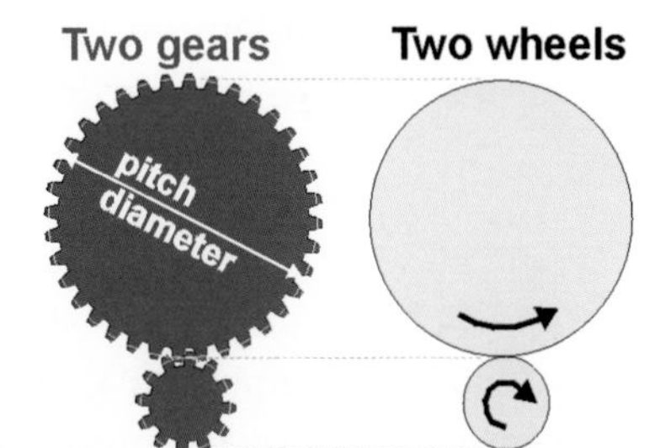

Figure 4.16: *Gears act like touching wheels, but with teeth to keep them from slipping as they turn together.*

Designing machines

How machines are designed

Machines are designed to do specific things, such as carry passengers or move earth around. To design a machine you need to know how each part works, and how the parts work together to create a machine that does what you want it to. You need the right parts and the right design to fit the job the machine has to accomplish. A machine designed to do one task may not be able to do another task effectively. A bus is a good machine for moving passengers, but a poor machine for moving earth around. A bulldozer is good for moving earth but poor for carrying passengers.

Simple and complex machines

Simple machines can be combined to solve more complex problems. You can use two pairs of gears with ratios of 2 to 1 to make a machine with a ratio of 4 to 1. Figure 4.17 shows an example of a how you could make a ratio of 4 to 1 with 12-tooth and 24-tooth gears.

How to combine simple machines into complex machines

To design complex machines from simpler machines, you need to know how each simple machine relates to the whole. For gears you need to know how the ratios from each pair of gears combine to make an overall ratio for the whole machine. For the example in Figure 4.17, the two ratios of 2:1 multiply together to make the final ratio of 4:1. When combining two gear machines, the total ratio for the machine is found by multiplying together the ratios of turns for each pair of gears. This works because the two gears that are stacked on the middle axle are connected so they turn together.

Design involves trade-offs

Combining gears to get higher speeds also affects the amount of force the machine creates. If you design a gear machine for higher output speed, you will get less output force. Design often involves trading off improvements in one area for costs in another area.

Even the best designs are always being improved

It is *very* rare that an invention works perfectly the first time. In fact, machines go through a long history of building, testing, analyzing, redesigning, building, and testing again. Most practical machines such as the automobile are never truly completed. There are always improvements that can be added as technology gets better (Figure 4.18). The first cars had to be cranked by hand to start! Today's cars start with the touch of a key.

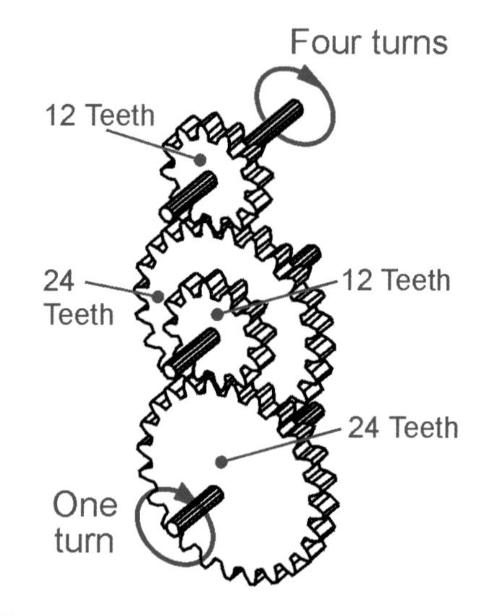

Figure 4.17: *A machine that uses two pairs of gears to make a larger ratio of turns.*

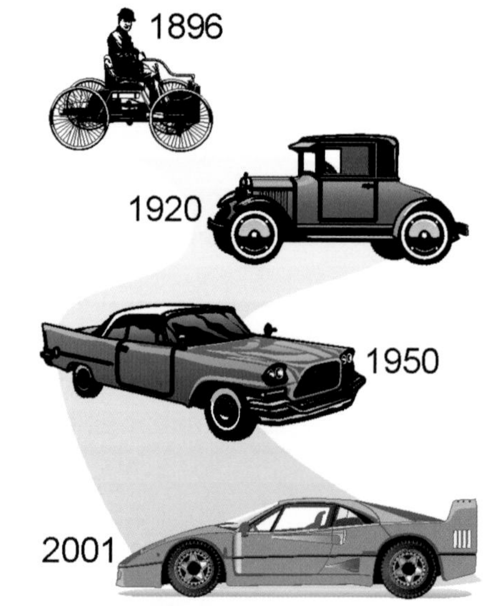

Figure 4.18: *Many inventions are continually being redesigned and improved.*

Chapter 4 Review

Vocabulary review

Match the following terms with the correct definition. There is one extra definition in the list that will not match any of the terms.

Set One

1. input force	a. The force applied by a machine to accomplish a task after an input force has been applied
2. machine	b. A device that multiplies force
3. mechanical system	c. An unpowered mechanical device, such as a lever, that has an input and output force
4. output force	d. The force applied to a machine
5. simple machine	e. A measurement used to describe changes in events, motion, or position
	f. An object with interrelated parts that work together to accomplish a task

Set Two

1. fulcrum	a. The force applied to a machine to produce a useful output force
2. input arm	b. The pivot point of a lever
3. lever	c. The distance from the fulcrum to the point of output force
4. output arm	d. The distance from the fulcrum to the point of input force
	e. A simple machine that pivots around a fulcrum

Set Three

1. engineering cycle	a. A working model of a design
2. engineering	b. A scientific field devoted to imagining what machines will be used in the future
3. prototype	c. Output force divided by input force
4. mechanical advantage	d. A wheel with teeth that is used to change direction and/or speed of rotating motion
5. gear	e. The process used by engineers to develop new technology
	f. The application of science to solve problems

Concept review

1. Why is a car a good example of a mechanical system? Write a short paragraph to explain your answer.
2. What does the phrase *multiply forces* mean? Include the terms machine, input force, and output force in your answer.
3. Compare and contrast the scientific method and the engineering cycle.
4. You are an inventor who wants to devise a new style of toothbrush. Describe what you would do at each phase of the engineering cycle to invent this new toothbrush.
5. Describe a problem that would have to be solved by an engineer. Try to think of example problems you see in your school, home, city, or state.
6. Describe an example of a new technology that you have seen recently advertised or sold in stores.
7. How would you set up a lever so that it has a mechanical advantage greater than 1? Include the terms input arm, output arm, and fulcrum in your answer.
8. Draw diagrams that show a seesaw at equilibrium and at nonequilibrium. Include captions that describe each of your diagrams. Be sure to discuss forces and motion in your captions.
9. Why are levers considered to be simple machines?
10. Which configuration is the best lever for lifting the rock?

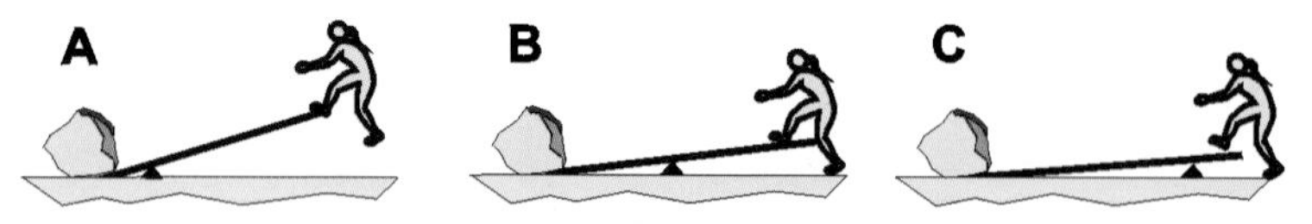

11. The lever in the picture will:
    a. stay balanced.
    b. rotate clockwise.
    c. rotate counterclockwise.

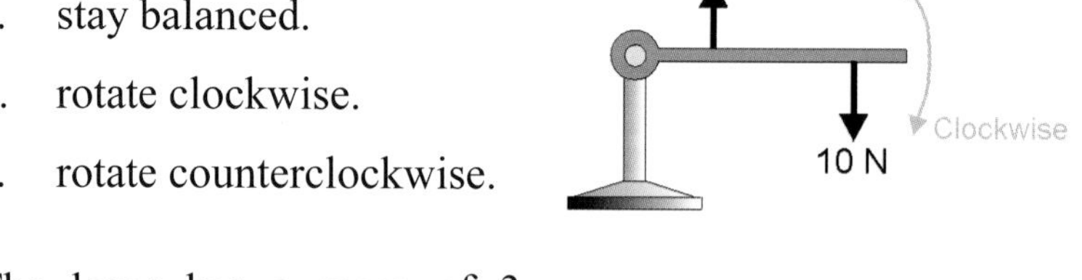

12. The lever has a mass of 3 kilograms at 30 centimeters on the left, and a mass of 2 kilograms at 30 centimeters on the right. What mass should be hung at 10 centimeters (on the right) for the lever to be in balance?

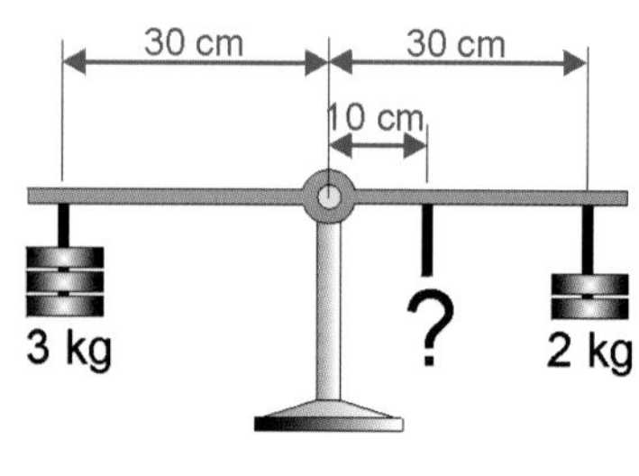

    a. 1 kg
    b. 2 kg
    c. 2.5 kg
    d. 3 kg
    e. 10 kg

13. How are force and distance related to how a lever works?
14. Would you rather use a machine that has a mechanical advantage of 1 or a machine that has a mechanical advantage of more than 1? Explain your reasoning in your answer.
15. You have a kit of gears, which contains many gears with 12, 24, and 36 teeth. Can you make a clock mechanism with a 12:1 gear ratio? Why or why not?

Problems

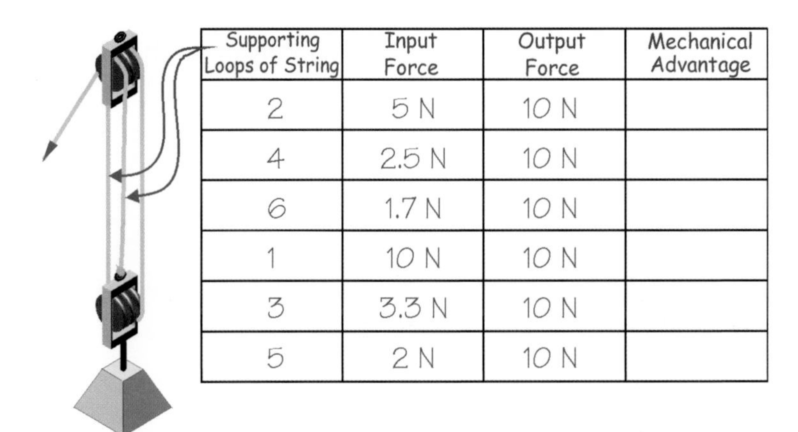

Supporting Loops of String	Input Force	Output Force	Mechanical Advantage
2	5 N	10 N	
4	2.5 N	10 N	
6	1.7 N	10 N	
1	10 N	10 N	
3	3.3 N	10 N	
5	2 N	10 N	

1. Above is a data table with sample data for lifting (input) force vs. the number of supporting strings in a block and tackle machine. Use the data to answer the following questions.
   a. Describe the relationship between the lifting (input) force and the number of supporting strings in the pulley.
   b. Make a graph that shows the relationship between lifting (input) force and number of supporting strings. Which variable is dependent and which is independent?
   c. Calculate the mechanical advantage for each number of supporting strings.
2. If you were going to use a pulley to lift a box that weighs 100 newtons, how much force would you need to use if the pulley had:
   a. 1 supporting string?
   b. 2 supporting strings?
   c. 5 supporting strings?
   d. 10 supporting strings?
3. Use the input and output forces listed in the table below to calculate the mechanical advantage.

Input Force	Output Force	Mechanical Advantage
10 newtons	100 newtons	
30 N	30 N	
500 N	1,350 N	
625 N	200 N	

4. One of the examples in the table in problem 3 has a very low mechanical advantage. Identify this example and explain why you might or might not want to use this machine to lift something that weighs 200 newtons.
5. Does mechanical advantage have units? Explain your answer.
6. If you lift a 200-newton box with a block and tackle machine and you apply 20 newtons to lift this box, what would be the mechanical advantage of the machine?
7. If a lever has an input arm that is 15 feet long and an output arm that is 25 feet long, does the lever have mechanical advantage? Why or why not?
8. Betsy wants to use her own weight to lift a 350-pound box. She weighs 120 pounds. Suggest input and output arm lengths that would allow Betsy to lift the box with a lever. Draw a lever and label the input and output arms with the lengths and forces.

Applying your knowledge

1. Why is a ramp a simple machine? Describe how a ramp works to multiply forces using your knowledge of simple machines.

2. You need a wheelbarrow to transport some soil for your garden. The one you have gives you a mechanical advantage of 3.5. If you use 65 newtons of force to lift the wheelbarrow so that you can roll it, how much soil can you carry with this wheelbarrow? Give the weight of the soil in newtons and be sure to show your work.

3. The block and tackle machine on a sailboat can help a sailor raise her mainsail. Without a machine, she needs 500 newtons of force to raise the sail. If the block and tackle gives her a mechanical advantage of 5, how much input force must be applied to raise the sail? Be sure to show your work.

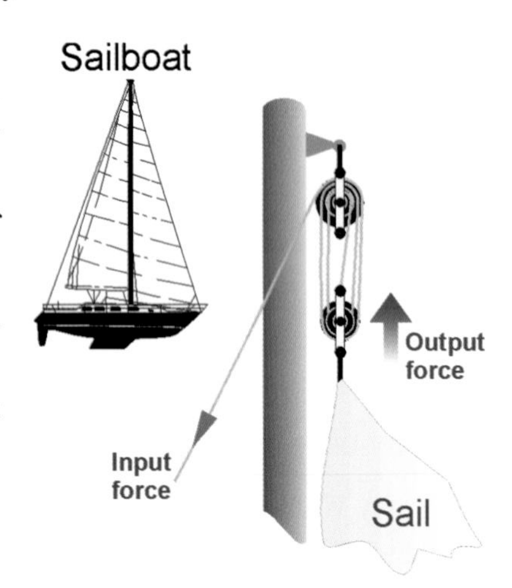

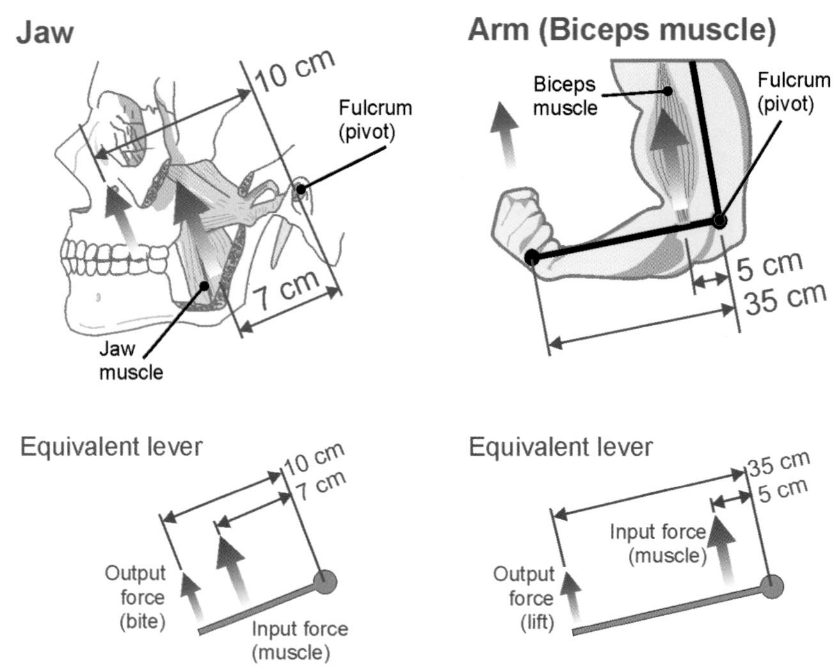

Your jaw works as a lever when you bite an apple. Your arm also works as a lever, as do many of the bones in your body. Using the diagrams above, answer the following questions by analyzing the changes in force and distance.

4. Using the distances shown, calculate and compare the mechanical advantage of the jaw and arm. Which is larger?

5. Suppose the jaw and biceps muscles produce equal input forces of 800N (178 lbs.). Calculate and compare the output forces in biting (jaw) and lifting (arm). Which is larger?

6. Suppose you need an output force of 500N (112 lbs). Calculate and compare the input forces of the jaw and biceps muscles required to produce 500 N of output force. Explain how your calculation relates to the relative size of the two muscles.

UNIT 2
Work and Energy

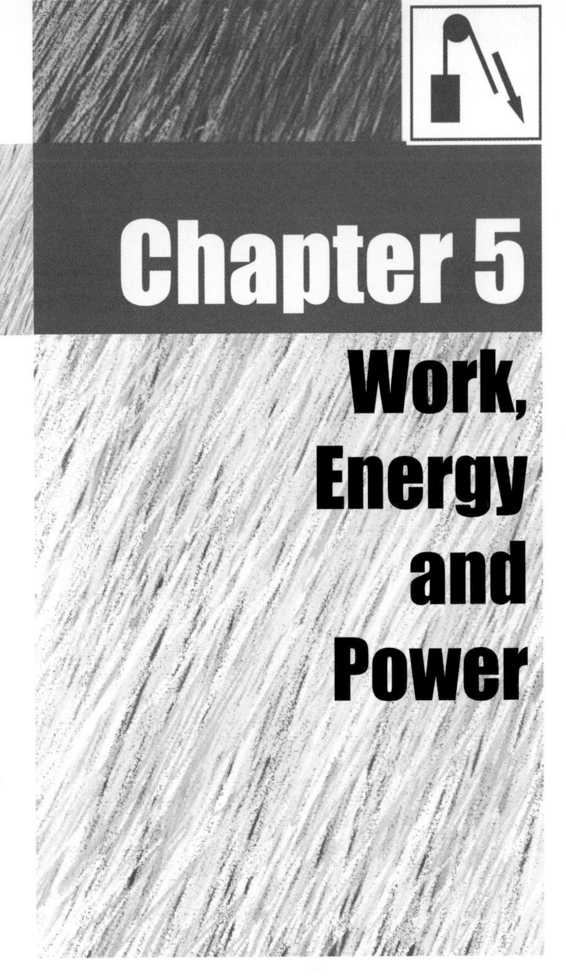

Introduction to Chapter 5

This chapter introduces the concept of work. Understanding the scientific meaning of work leads to an understanding of energy. Once we understand energy, we can look at both natural and human-made systems from the perspective of the flow and transformation of energy from one form to another.

Investigations for Chapter 5

5.1	**Work**	*What happens when you multiply forces in a machine?*

Nature gives nothing away for free. In this Investigation you will discover what you pay for making clever machines that multiply force. You will come to an interesting conclusion about work and energy that is true for all machines.

5.2	**Energy Conservation**	*What is energy and how does it behave?*

What happens to the speed of a marble as it rolls up and down hills? By making measurements of height and speed, you will investigate one of the most important laws in physics: the law of conservation of energy. By applying the concepts of potential and kinetic energy, you will develop a theory for how objects move.

5.3	**Energy Transformations**	*Where did the energy go?*

Our world runs on energy. Working with a group of students, you will analyze and identify the energy transformations that occur in real-life situations. By charting the flow of energy you will come to understand some of the interactions between humans and their environment. This Investigation requires you not only to apply what you have learned so far, but also to use your creativity and imagination.

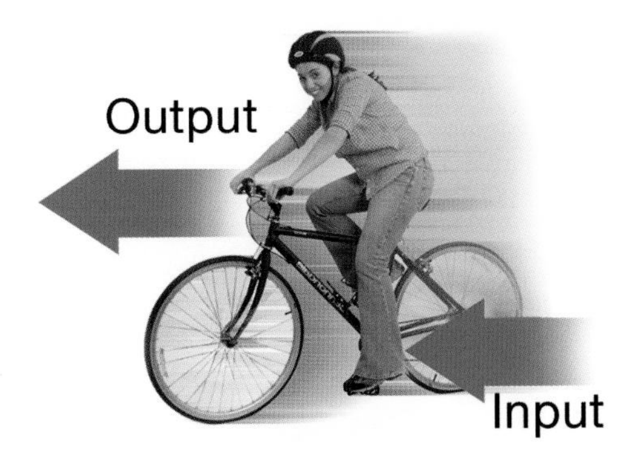

Learning Goals

In this chapter, you will:

- ✔ Calculate the amount of work done by a simple machine.
- ✔ Use units of joules to measure the amount of work done.
- ✔ Analyze the effects of changing force or distance in a simple machine.
- ✔ Calculate the efficiency of a machine.
- ✔ Calculate power in machines.
- ✔ Discuss perpetual motion machines.

Vocabulary

chemical energy
efficiency
electrical energy
energy
energy transformations
heat
horsepower
joule
kinetic energy
law of conservation of energy
nuclear energy
potential energy
power
radiant energy
radiation
solar power
watt
work

5.1 Work

When you arranged the string on the ropes and pulleys to pull with less force, you had to pull more string to raise the weight. When you built a lever with a large advantage, you had to move the input arm down a great distance while the output arm moved only a little. These details are clues to one of the most powerful laws of physics. In this chapter, you will learn about work and energy and about a fundamental rule that applies to all machines.

is the amount of work done by pushing with a force of 1 newton for a distance of 1 meter.

What is work?

The word work means many different things

The word *work* is used in many different ways.

- You *work* on science problems.
- You go to *work*.
- Your toaster doesn't *work*.
- Taking out the trash is too much *work*.

What *work* means in physics

In science, work has a very specific meaning. If you push a box with a force of one newton for a distance of one meter, you have done exactly one joule of work (Figure 5.1). In physics, work is force times distance. When you see the word *work* in a physics problem, it means force times distance.

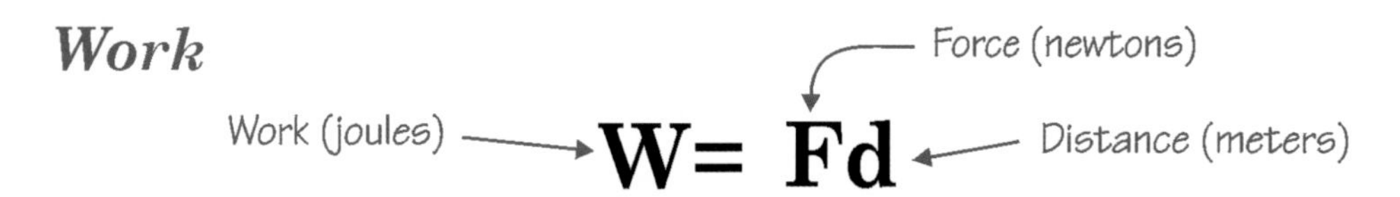

To be exact, work is force times the distance moved in the direction of the force. A force at an angle (Figure 5.2) is not as effective at doing work. Only the part of the force in the direction of the motion does work in the physics sense.

Machines do work in the physics sense

When we apply force to machines we are doing work. For example, when a block and tackle machine lifts a heavy weight, force is applied. As a result of the force, the weight moves a distance. Work has been done by the machine because force was exerted over some distance.

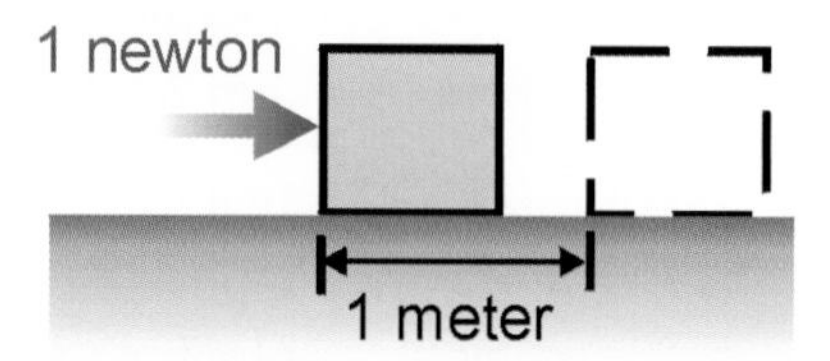

Figure 5.1: *One joule of work. One joule = 1 newton-meter.*

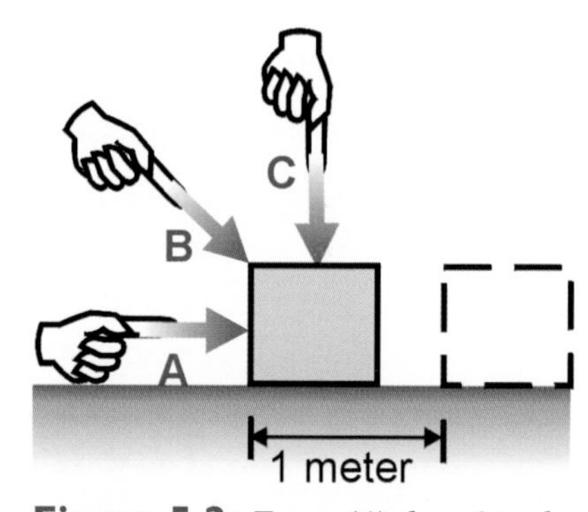

Figure 5.2: *Force (A) does 1 joule of work if it moves the box one meter. Only part of force (B) does work on the box since it is at an angle. None of force (C) does work on the box because it does not help move the box to the right at all.*

Work done by a machine

Work is done *by* forces *on* objects

In physics, work is done *by* forces. When thinking about work you should always be clear about which force is doing the work. Work is done *on* objects. If you push a block one meter with a force of one newton, you have done one joule of work *on the block*. We need to keep careful track of where the work goes because later we will see that it may be possible to get the work back.

Units of work

The unit of measurement for work is the joule. One joule is equal to one newton of force times one meter of distance. Joules are a combination unit made of force (newtons) and distance (meters).

Input work and output work

Just as we did for forces, we want to analyze machines in terms of work input and work output (Figure 5.3). As an example, consider using the block and tackle machine to lift a load weighing 10 newtons. Suppose you lift the load a distance of 1/2 meter. Your machine has done five joules of work on the load (Figure 5.4) so the work output is five joules.

What about the work input? You pulled on the string with a force of only five newtons because your machine gave you an advantage of two. But you had to pull the string twice as far as you lifted the block. The weight moved up 1/2 meter, but you pulled one whole meter of string. The work input is the force you apply times the distance you pulled the string. This is five newtons times one meter, or five joules. The work input is the same as the work output!

The work output of a simple machine can never exceed the work input.

The example illustrates a rule that is true *for all machines*. You can *never* get more work out of a machine than you put into it. Nature does not give something for nothing. When you design a machine that multiplies force, you pay by having to apply the force over a greater distance.

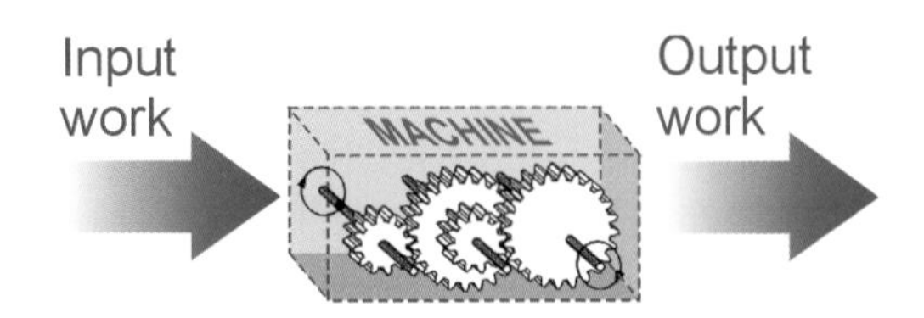

Figure 5.3: *You can think about any machine in terms of the work input and the work output.*

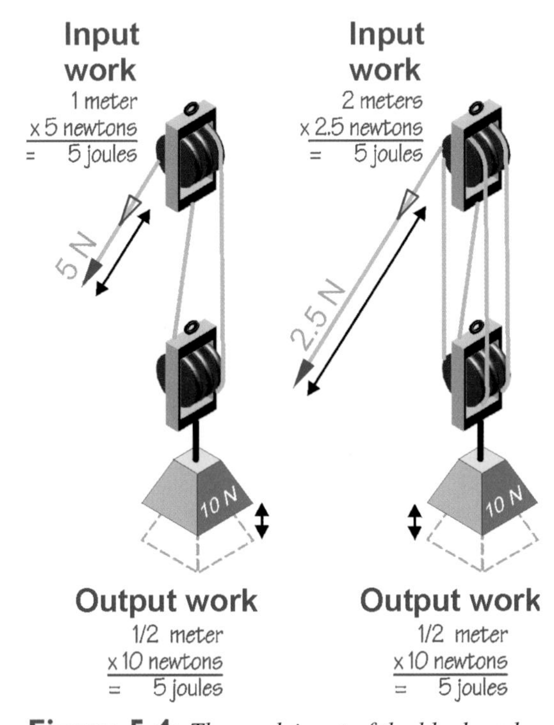

Figure 5.4: *The work input of the block and tackle is the same as the work output. You get mechanical advantage by trading force for distance.*

Efficiency

What is an efficient machine? In a very efficient machine, all (or most) of the work input becomes work output. In the block and tackle machine on the previous page, all five joules of input work were transformed to five joules of output work. This machine is 100 percent efficient, because all input work became output work and none was lost.

How friction affects real machines In real machines, the work output is always less than the work input. Other forces, like friction, use up some of the input work before it reaches the output of the machine. For example, a wheel turning on an axle can get very hot. When the wheel gets hot, it means some of the input work is being converted to heat. The work output is reduced by the work that is converted to heat.

The definition of efficiency Efficiency is the ratio of work output to work input and it is usually expressed as a percent. A machine that is 75 percent efficient produces three joules of output work for every four joules of input work. One joule out of every four (25 percent) is lost to friction. Efficiency is calculated by dividing the work output by the work input, and multiplying by 100 to get a percent.

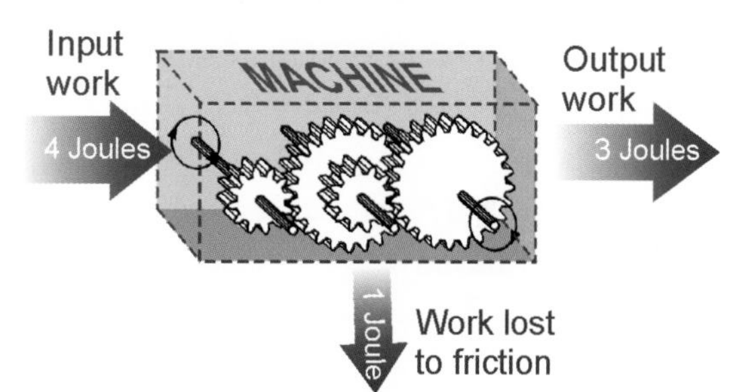

The ideal machine Even though friction always lowers efficiency, engineers strive to design machines to be ideal—as close to 100 percent as possible. Is the human body an ideal machine? Unfortunately, at under 8 percent efficiency, the human body is not an ideal machine!

A most efficient machine

The bicycle is the most efficient machine ever invented for turning the work of human muscles into motion. Its efficiency is more than 95 percent.

The need for simple, efficient machines for traveling inspired many inventions that led to today's bicycle. In the mid-1800s, a very shaky ride could be achieved with the "bone shaker," which had a huge front wheel. The big wheel allowed the rider to travel farther with one push of the pedals, but it was not always safe!

James Starley (1830-1881) of the Coventry Sewing Machine Company in Britain is credited with building the first modern two-wheel bicycle in 1885. The derailleur, which is the heart of a modern multispeed bike, was invented by the Italian bicycle racer Tullio Campagnolo in 1933.

The bicycle also figured into another important invention: the airplane. Wilbur and Orville Wright were bicycle mechanics and inventors. They used their expertise in racing and building lightweight bicycles to create the first successful powered airplane in 1903.

Power

How fast the work is done

It makes a difference how fast you do work. Suppose you drag a box with a force of 100 newtons for 10 meters, and it takes you 10 seconds. You have done 1,000 joules of work. Suppose your friend drags a similar box but takes 60 seconds. You both do the same amount of work because the force and distance are the same. But something is different. You did the work in 10 seconds and your friend took six times longer.

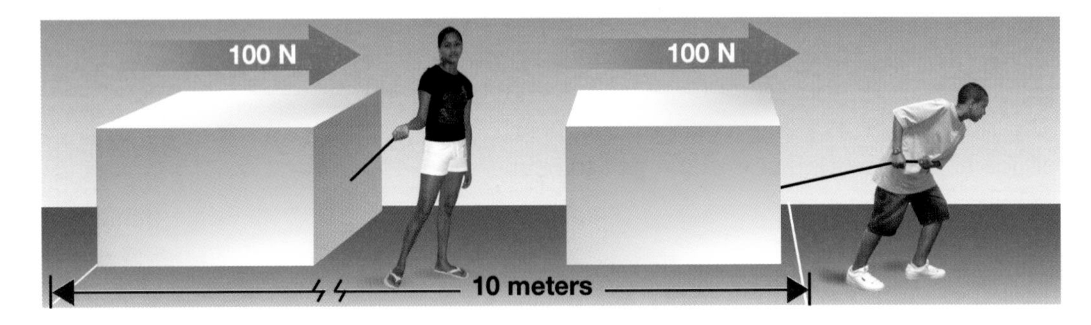

What is power?

The rate at which work is done is called **power**. You and your friend did the same amount of work, but you used six times more power because you did the work six times faster. You can determine the power of a machine by dividing the amount of work done by the time it takes in seconds. A more powerful machine does the same amount of work in less time than a less powerful machine.

Power

$$P = \frac{W}{t}$$

Power (watts); Work (joules); Time (seconds)

The units of power

The unit of power is called the **watt**, named after James Watt (1736-1819), the Scottish engineer and inventor of the steam engine. One watt is equal to one joule of work done in one second. Another unit of power commonly used is the **horsepower**. One horsepower is equal to 746 watts. As you might have guessed, one horsepower was originally the average power output of a horse.

Example:

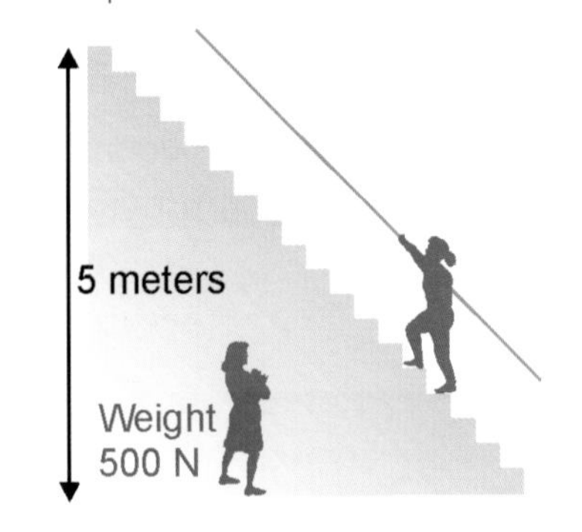

You can lift your own weight (500 newtons) up a staircase that is 5 meters high in 30 seconds.

a) How much power do you use?

b) How does your power compare with a 100-watt light bulb?

Solution:

(1) You are asked for power.

(2) You know force, distance, and time.

(3) Relationships that apply:
$W = Fd \quad P = W/t$

(4) Solve for power.
$P = Fd/t$

(5) Plug in numbers. Remember:
1 joule = 1 N·m
1 watt = 1 N·m/sec

$P = (500\ N) \times (5\ m) / 30\ sec$

Answers:

(a) 2500 N-m/30 sec = 83 watts

(b) This is less power than a 100-watt light bulb. Most human activities use less power than a light bulb.

Efficiency in natural systems

The meaning of efficiency Energy drives all the processes in nature, from winds in the atmosphere to nuclear reactions occurring in the cores of stars. In the environment, efficiency is interpreted as the fraction of incoming energy that goes into a process. For example, Earth receives energy from the sun. Earth absorbs this sunlight energy with an average efficiency of 78 percent. The energy that is not absorbed is reflected back into space.

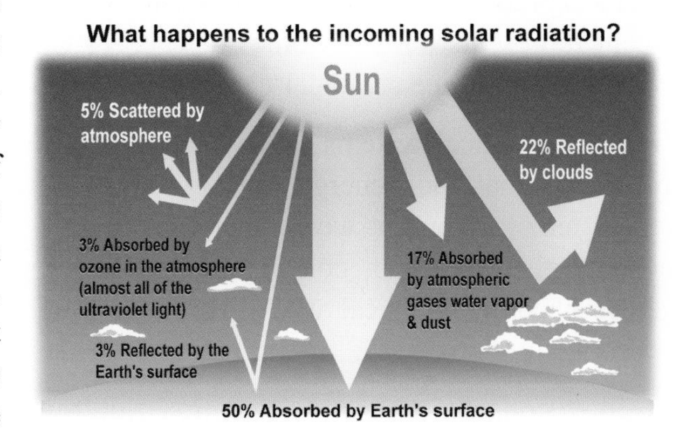

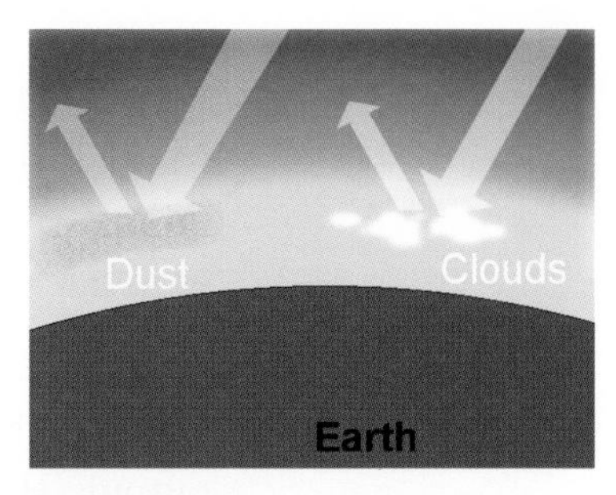

Figure 5.5: *Dust and clouds reflect light back into space, decreasing the efficiency with which Earth absorbs energy from the sun.*

The importance of solar efficiency Earth's efficiency at absorbing solar energy is critical to living things. If the efficiency decreased by a few percent, Earth's surface would become too cold for life. Some scientists believe that many volcanic eruptions or nuclear war could decrease the absorption efficiency by spreading dust in the atmosphere. Dust reflects solar energy (Figure 5.5). On the other hand, if the efficiency increased by a few percent, it would get too hot to sustain life. Too much carbon dioxide in the atmosphere increases absorption efficiency (Figure 5.6). Scientists are concerned that the average annual temperature of Earth has already warmed 1°C degree since the 1880s as a result of carbon dioxide released by human technology.

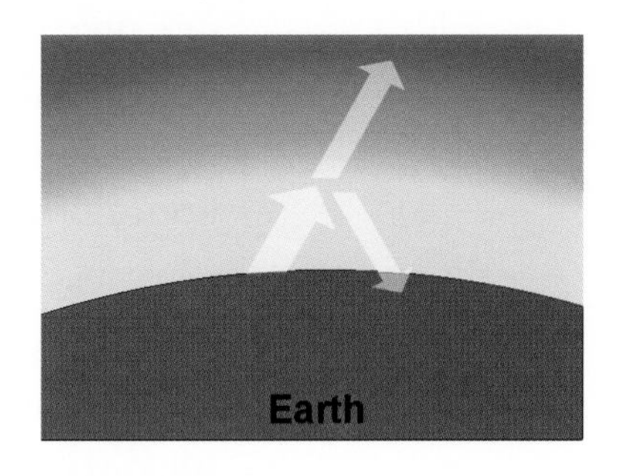

Figure 5.6: *Carbon dioxide and other greenhouse gases in the atmosphere absorb some energy that otherwise would have been radiated back into space. This increases the efficiency with which Earth absorbs energy from the sun.*

Efficiencies always add up to 100% In any system, all of the energy goes somewhere. Another way to say this is that energy is conserved. You will learn more about energy conservation in the next chapter. For example, rivers flow downhill. Most of the potential energy lost by water moving downhill becomes kinetic energy in motion of the water. Erosion takes some of the energy and slowly changes the land by wearing away rocks and dirt. Friction takes some of the energy and heats up the water. If you could add up the efficiencies for every single process in which water is involved, that total would be 100 percent.

Energy conservation and efficiency in biological systems

Calories in food

People and animals eat to obtain energy. Food energy is measured in kilocalories (or Calories—with a capital C—on food labels). A kilocalorie equals 4,187 joules. A pint of ice cream represents 800,000 joules of energy! One joule is the work equivalent to lifting the pint of ice cream 21 centimeters (Figure 5.7).

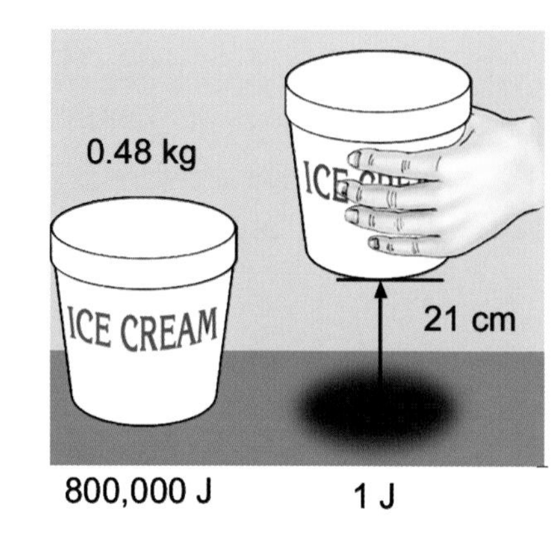

Figure 5.7: *Food contains a huge amount of energy compared with typical work output.*

Efficiency is low for living things

Human beings and all biological systems follow the *law of conservation of energy.* Briefly, this law means that food energy (energy input) always equals energy output. However, in terms of output work, energy efficiency of living things is very low. Almost all the energy in consumed food becomes heat and waste products; very little becomes physical work. This work includes the energy is takes to read this book and think!

Estimating the efficiency of a human

To estimate efficiency, consider a person climbing a 1,000-meter high mountain. For a person with a mass of 70 kilograms, the increase in potential energy is 686,000 joules. The potential energy comes from work done by muscles. A human body doing strenuous exercise uses about 660 kilocalories per hour. It takes about three hours to climb the mountain, during which time the body uses 1,980 kilocalories (8,300,000 J). The energy efficiency is about 8 percent (Figure 5.8).

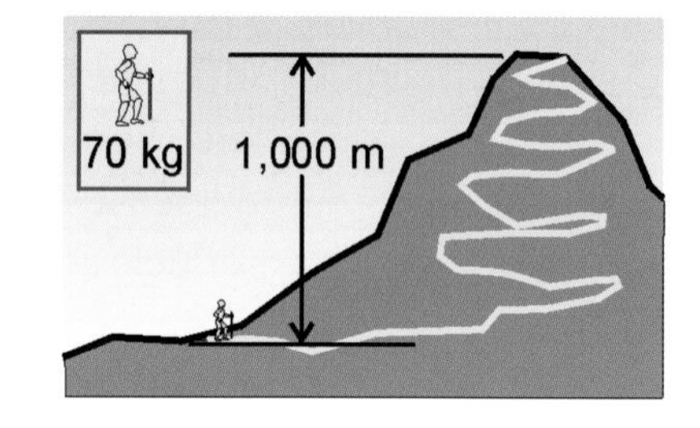

$$E_p = mgh$$
$$= (70 \text{ kg})(9.8 \text{ N/kg})(1{,}000 \text{ m})$$
$$= 686{,}000 \text{ J}$$

Figure 5.8: *A 70-kilogram hiker gains 686,000 joules of potential energy climbing a 1,000-meter mountain.*

Baseline metabolic rate

However, the overall energy efficiency for a person is lower than 8 percent. An average person uses 55-75 kilocalories per hour when sitting still. The rate at which your body uses energy while at rest is called your baseline metabolic rate (or BMR). During a 24-hour period, a person with a BMR of 65 kcal/hr uses 1,536 kilocalories, or 6,430,000 joules. Even if you did the equivalent work of climbing a 1,000- meter mountain every day, your average efficiency is only 4.6 percent.

Efficiency of plants

Photosynthesis in plants takes input energy from sunlight and creates sugar, a form of chemical energy. The output of a plant is the energy stored in sugar, which can be eaten by animals. The efficiency of photosynthesis under optimal conditions is about 26 percent, meaning 26 percent of solar energy absorbed by a leaf becomes stored chemical energy. However, under normal growing conditions plants absorb sunlight poorly and are much less efficient—usually less than 1 percent.

5.2 Energy Conservation

In this unit you will learn about energy. *Energy* is one of the fundamental building blocks of our universe. Energy appears in different forms, such as motion and heat. Energy can travel in different ways, such as light, sound, or electricity. The workings of the universe (including all of our technology) can be viewed from the perspective of energy flowing from one place to another and changing back and forth from one form to another.

What is energy?

The definition of energy

Energy is the ability to do work. That means anything with energy can produce a force that is capable of acting over a distance. The force can be any force, and it can come from many different sources, such as your hand, the wind, or a spring.

Energy is the ability to do work. Any object that has energy has the ability to create force.

- A moving ball has energy because it can create forces on whatever tries to stop it or slow it down.
- A sled at the top of a hill has energy because it can go down the hill and produce forces as it goes.
- The moving wind has energy because it can create forces on any object in its path.
- Electricity has energy because it can turn a motor to make forces.
- Gasoline has energy because it can be burned in an engine to make force to move a car.
- You have energy because you can create forces.

Units of energy

Energy is measured in joules, the same units as work. That is because energy is really stored work. Any object with energy has the ability to use its energy to do work, which means creating a force that acts over a distance.

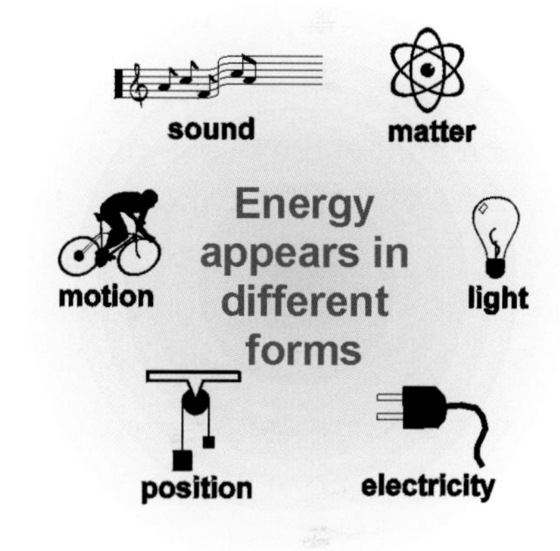

Figure 5.9: *Energy appears in many different forms.*

Potential energy

What is potential energy? The first type of energy we will explore is called potential energy. Potential energy comes from the position of an object relative to Earth. Consider a marble that is lifted off the table (Figure 5.10). Since Earth's gravity pulls the marble down, we must apply a force to lift it up. Applying a force over a distance requires doing work, which gets stored as the potential energy of the marble. Potential energy of this kind comes from the presence of gravity.

Where does potential energy come from? How much energy does the marble have? The answer comes from our analysis of machines from the last section. It takes work to lift the marble up. Energy is stored work, so the amount of energy must be the same as the amount of work done to lift the marble up.

How to calculate potential energy We can find an exact equation for the potential energy. The force required to lift the marble is the weight of the marble. From Newton's second law we know that the weight (the force) is equal to mass of the marble (m, in kilograms) times the acceleration of gravity (g, equal to 9.8 m/sec^2). We also know that work is equal to force times distance. Since force is the weight of the marble (mg) and the distance is how far we lift the marble (h), the work done equals weight times height.

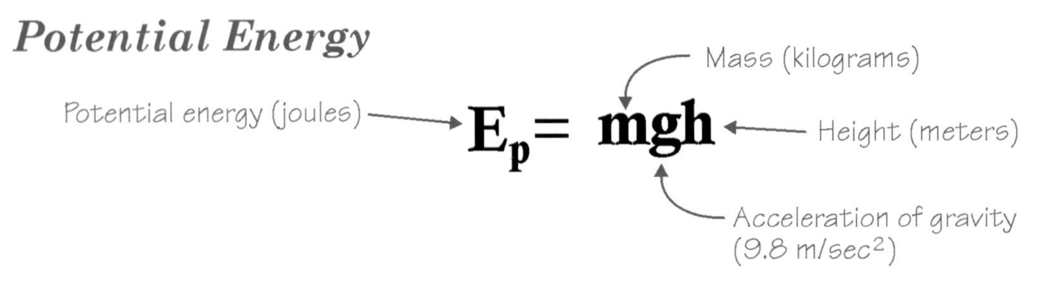

Why is it called potential energy? Objects that have potential energy don't use their energy until they move. That's why it is called *potential* energy. Potential means that something is capable of becoming active. Any object that can move to a lower place has the potential to do work on the way down, such as a ball rolling down a hill.

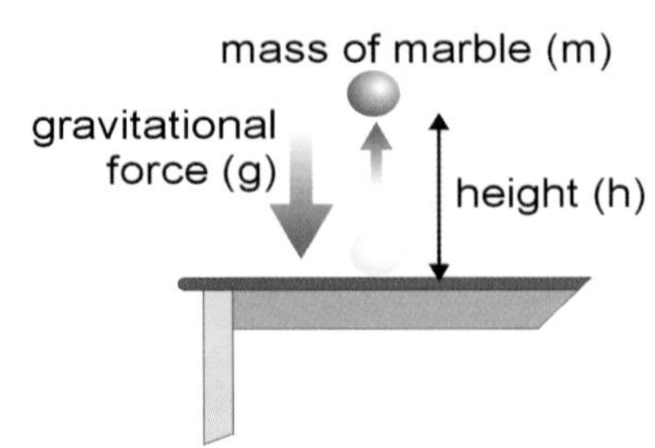

Figure 5.10: *The potential energy of a marble is equal to its mass times gravity (9.8 m/sec^2) times the height of the marble above the surface.*

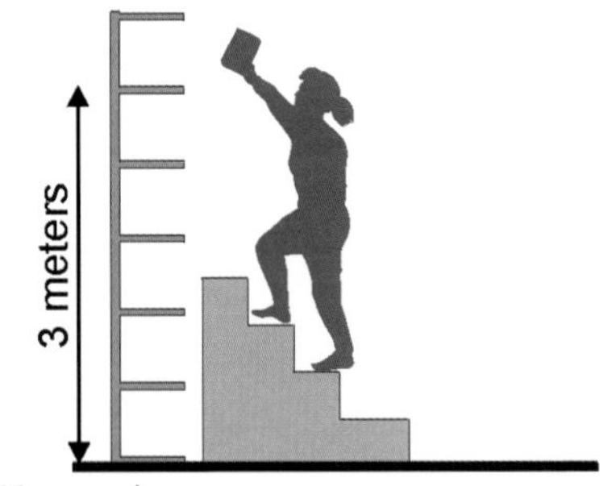

Example:

You need to put a 1-kilogram mass that is on the floor, away on a shelf that is 3 meters high. How much energy does this require?

Solution:

(1) You are asked for the potential energy.

(2) You know the mass and height.

(3) The equation for potential energy is $E_p = mgh$.

(4) The equation is already in the right form.

(5) Plug in numbers. Remember: 1 N = 1 kg·m/sec^2, and 1 joule = 1 N·m.
$E_p = (1 \text{ kg}) \times (9.8 \text{ m/sec}^2) \times (3 \text{ m})$
= 29.4 joules

Kinetic energy

Kinetic energy is energy of motion

Objects also store energy in motion. A moving mass can certainly exert forces, as you would quickly observe if someone ran into you in the hall. Energy of motion is called kinetic energy.

Kinetic energy increases with speed

We need to know how much kinetic energy a moving object has. Consider a shopping cart moving with a speed v. To make the cart move faster you need to apply a force to it (Figure 5.11). Applying a force means you do some work, which is stored as energy. The higher the speed of the cart, the more energy it has because you have to do work to increase the speed.

Kinetic energy increases with mass

If you give the cart more mass, you have to push it with more force to reach the same speed. Again, more force means more work. Increasing the mass increases the amount of work you have to do to get the cart moving, so it also increases the energy. Kinetic energy depends on two things: mass and speed.

The formula for kinetic energy

To get an equation for kinetic energy, we would look at work, just like we did for potential energy. The energy is equal to the amount of work you have to do to get a mass (m) from rest up to speed (v). The amount of work you need can be calculated from the formula for kinetic energy.

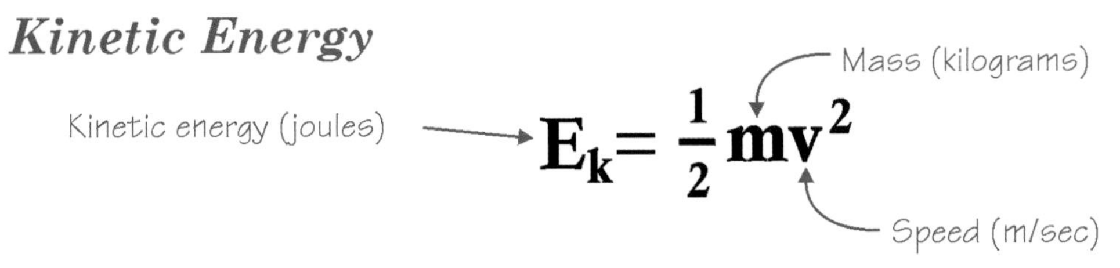

Kinetic energy increases as the square of the speed

The kinetic energy increases as the square of the speed. This means if you go twice as fast, your energy increases by four times ($2^2 = 4$). If your speed is three times higher, your energy is nine times bigger ($3^2 = 9$). More energy means more force is needed to stop, which is why driving fast is so dangerous. Going 60 mph, a car has four times as much kinetic energy as it does at 30 mph. At a speed of 90 mph you have *nine times* as much energy as you did at 30 mph.

A cart at rest has no kinetic energy.
Applying force can give the cart speed, and therefore kinetic energy.
Applying more force increases the speed and the kinetic energy.
Increasing the mass also increases the kinetic energy because it takes even more force.

Figure 5.11: *Kinetic energy depends on two things: mass and speed. The amount of kinetic energy the cart has is equal to the amount of work you do to get the cart moving.*

Conservation of energy

The law of conservation of energy

Nature never creates or destroys energy; energy only gets converted from one form to another. This concept is called the law of conservation of energy. The rule we found for the input and output work of a machine was an example of the law of conservation of energy.

Energy can never be created or destroyed, just transformed from one form into another

An example of energy transformation

What happens if you throw a ball straight up in the air? The ball leaves your hand with kinetic energy from the speed you give it when you let go. As the ball goes higher, it gains potential energy. The potential energy gained can only come from the kinetic energy the ball had at the start, so the ball slows down as it gets higher.

Eventually, all the kinetic energy has been converted to potential energy. At this point the ball has reached as high as it will go and its upward speed has been reduced to zero.

The ball falls back down again and gets faster and faster as it gets closer to the ground. The gain in speed comes from the potential energy being converted back to kinetic energy. If there were no friction the ball would return to your hand with exactly the same speed it started with—except in the opposite direction (Figure 5.12)!

The total energy never exceeds the starting energy

At any moment in its flight, the ball has exactly the same energy it had at the start. The energy is divided between potential and kinetic, but the total is unchanged. In fact, we can calculate exactly how high the ball will go if we know the mass and speed we have at the beginning.

Friction can divert some energy

The law of conservation of energy still holds true, even when there is friction. Some of the energy is converted to heat or wearing away of material. The energy converted to heat or wear is no longer available to be potential energy or kinetic energy, but it was not destroyed.

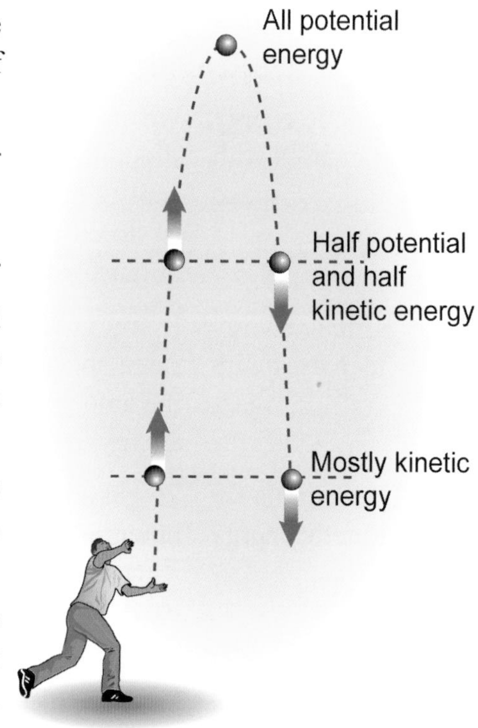

Figure 5.12: *When you throw a ball in the air, its energy transforms from kinetic to potential and back to kinetic.*

5.3 Energy Transformations

In the last section, you investigated how energy is changed from one form to another. You discovered that kinetic and potential energy change back and forth with the total amount of energy staying constant. In this section, you will apply what you learned to a wide variety of real-life situations involving other kinds of **energy transformations**.

Figure 5.13: *Anything you do involves transforming energy from one kind to another. Exercise transforms chemical energy from food into kinetic and potential energy.*

Following an energy transformation

The different kinds of energy

Kinetic energy and potential energy are only two of the forms energy can take. Sometimes these two forms are called mechanical energy because they involve moving things. There are many other kinds of energy, including *radiant energy, electrical energy, chemical energy* and *nuclear energy*. Just as you saw with kinetic and potential, any of these forms of energy can be transformed into each other and back again. Every day of your life, you experience multiple energy transformations (Figure 5.13) whether you know it or not!

An example of energy transformation

For example, suppose you are skating and come up to a steep hill. You know skating up the hill requires energy. From your mass and the height of the hill you can calculate how much more potential energy you will have on the top (Figure 5.14). You need at least this much energy, plus some additional energy to overcome friction.

Chemical energy to potential energy

The energy you use to climb the hill comes from food. The **chemical potential energy** stored in the food you ate is converted into simple sugars. These sugars are burned as your muscles work against external forces to climb the hill—in this case, the external force is gravity. In climbing the hill you convert some chemical energy to potential energy.

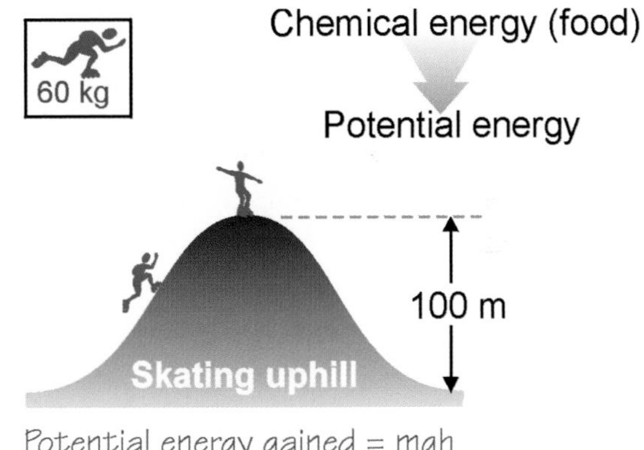

Potential energy gained = mgh

$= (60 \text{ kg}) \times (9.8 \text{ m/sec}^2) \times (100 \text{ m})$

$= 58{,}800$ joules

Figure 5.14: *At the top of the hill you have gained 58,800 joules of potential energy. This energy originally started as chemical energy in food.*

Where does "spent" energy go?

Upon reaching the top of the hill, you will probably feel like you "spent" a lot of energy. Where did the energy you spent climbing the steep hill go? Some of the energy you spent is now stored as potential energy because your position is higher than when you began. Some of the energy was also converted by your body into heat, chemical changes in muscles, and the evaporation of sweat from your skin. Can you think of any other places the energy might have gone?

How does potential energy get used?

Once you get over the top of the hill and start to coast down the other side, your speed increases. An increase in speed implies an increase in kinetic energy. Where does all this kinetic energy come from? The answer is that it comes from the potential energy that increased while you were climbing up the hill. Energy was saved and used to "purchase" greater speed as you descend down the other side of the hill.

Kinetic energy is used up in the brakes

If you are not careful, stored up potential energy can generate too much speed! Assuming you want to make it down the hill with no injuries, some of the kinetic energy must change into some other form. Brakes on your skates slow you down and use up the extra kinetic energy. Brakes convert kinetic energy into heat and the wearing away of the brake pads.

As you slow to a stop at the bottom of the hill, you should notice that your brakes are very hot, and some of the rubber is worn away. This means that some of the energy from the food you ate for lunch ended up heating your brake pads and wearing them away!

The flow of energy

During the trip up and down the hill, energy flowed through many forms. Starting with chemical energy, some energy appeared in the form of potential energy, kinetic energy, heat, air friction, sound, evaporation, and more. During all these transformations no energy was lost because energy can never be created or destroyed. All the energy you started with went somewhere.

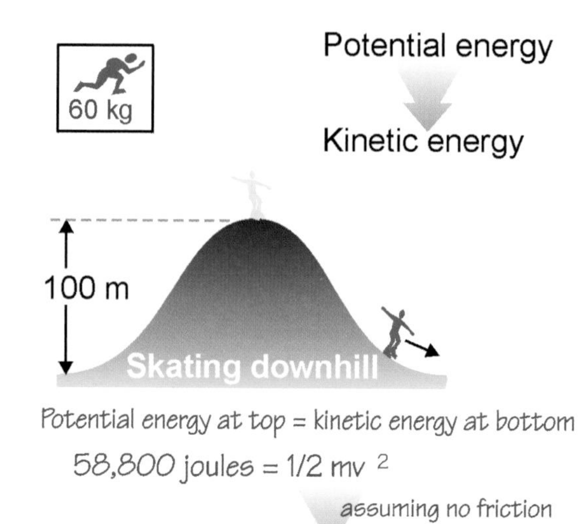

Figure 5.15: *On the way down, your potential energy is converted to kinetic energy and you pick up speed. In real life not all the potential energy would become kinetic energy. Air friction would use some and you would use your brakes*

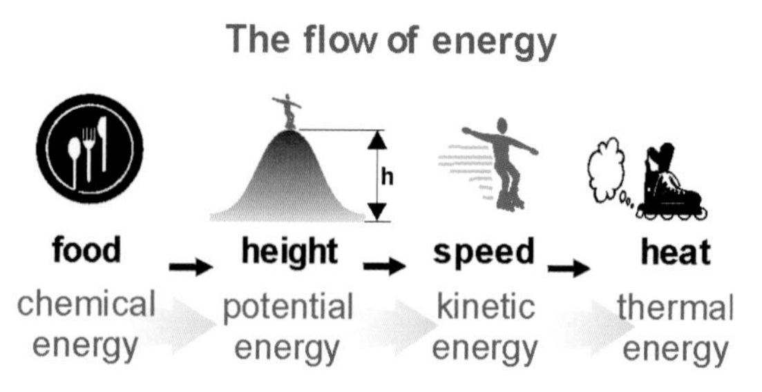

Figure 5.16: *A few of the forms the energy goes through during the skating trip.*

Other forms of energy

Energy: nature's money One way to understand energy is to think of it as nature's money. It is spent and saved in a number of different ways any time you want to do something. You can use energy to buy speed, height, temperature, mass, and other things. But you have to have some energy to start with, and what you spend diminishes what you have left.

Mechanical energy Mechanical energy is the energy possessed by an object due to its *motion* or its stored energy of *position*. Mechanical energy can be either kinetic (energy of motion) or potential (energy of position). An object that possesses mechanical energy is able to do work. Mechanical energy is the form involved in the operation of the simple machines you have studied in this unit.

Radiant energy Radiant (meaning light) energy is also known as electromagnetic energy. Light is made up of waves called electromagnetic waves (Unit 5). There are many different types of electromagnetic waves, including the light we see, ultraviolet light, X rays, infrared radiation (also known as heat – that's how you feel the heat from a fire), radio waves, microwaves, and radar.

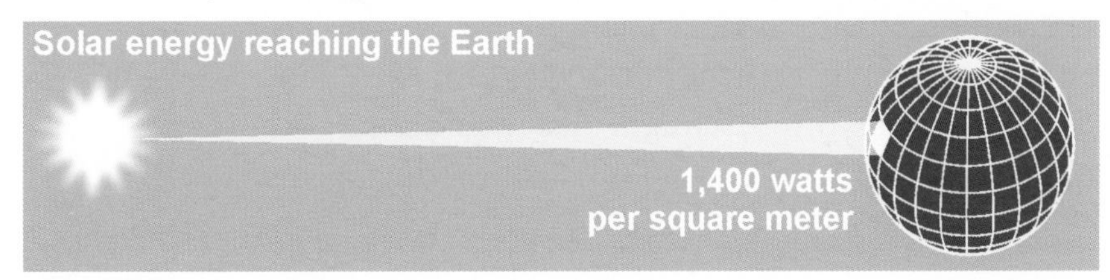

Energy from the sun Radiant heat from the sun is what keeps the Earth warm. The sun's energy falls on the Earth at a rate of about 1,400 watts for each square meter of surface area. Not all of this energy reaches the Earth's surface though; even on a clear day, about one-fourth of the energy is absorbed by the Earth's atmosphere. When we use the radiant energy from the sun, it is called solar power.

Example:

A water-powered turbine makes electricity from the energy of falling water. The diagram shows a turbine where 100 kg of water falls every second from a height of 20 meters.

(a) 100 kg of water 20 meters high has how much potential energy?

(b) How much power in watts could you get out of the turbine if it was perfectly efficient?

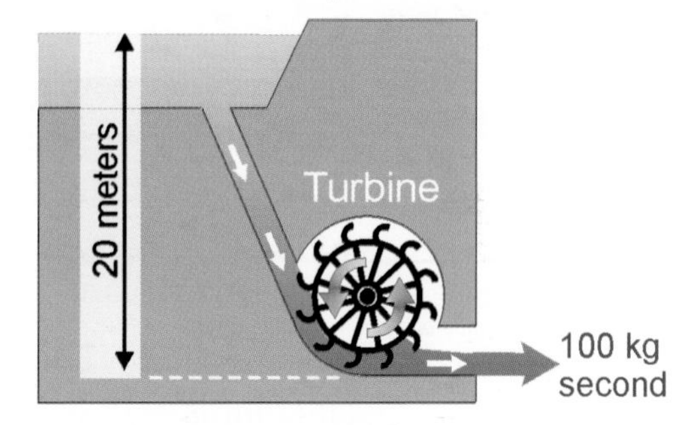

Solution: Part a

(1) You are asked for potential energy.

(2) You are given mass (100 kg) and height (20 m).

(3) The relationship you need is $E_p = mgh$.

(4) Plug in numbers:

$$E_p = (100 \text{ kg}) \times (9.8 \text{ m/sec}^2) \times (20 \text{ m})$$
$$= 19{,}600 \text{ joules}$$

Solution: Part b

(1) You are asked for power.

(2) You know energy (19,600 J) and time (1 sec).

(3) The relationship you need is $P = W/t$.

(4) Plug in numbers:

$$P = 19{,}600 \text{ J} / 1 \text{ sec}$$
$$= 19{,}600 \text{ watts}$$

This is enough energy for nearly 200 light bulbs if each bulb uses 100 watts.

Electrical energy

Electrical energy is something we take for granted whenever we plug an appliance into an outlet. The electrical energy we use in our daily lives is actually derived from other sources of energy. For example, in a natural gas power plant the energy starts as chemical energy in the gas. The gas is burned, releasing heat energy. The heat energy is used to make high-pressure steam. The steam turns a turbine which transforms the heat energy to mechanical energy. Finally, the turbine turns an electric generator, producing electrical energy.

Chemical energy

Chemical energy is the type of energy stored in molecules. Chemical reactions can either absorb or release chemical energy. One example of chemical energy is a battery. The chemical energy stored in batteries changes to electrical energy when you connect wires and a light bulb. Your body also uses chemical energy when it converts food into energy so that you can walk or run or think. All the fossil fuels we depend on (coal, oil, gas) are useful because they contain chemical energy we can easily release.

Nuclear energy

Nuclear energy comes from splitting an atom, or fusing two atoms together. When an atom is split or fused, a huge amount of energy is released. Nuclear energy is used to generate or make electricity in power plants. A new kind of environmentally safe nuclear power (fusion) is the focus of a worldwide research program. If we could extract the fusion energy from a single teaspoon of water, it would be the equivalent of 55 barrels of oil. Nuclear energy is really the basic source for all other energy forms because it is how the sun and stars make energy. The chemical energy in fossil fuels comes from sunlight that was absorbed by plants millions of years ago. Nuclear energy is also used in medicine to treat cancer and other diseases.

Thermal energy

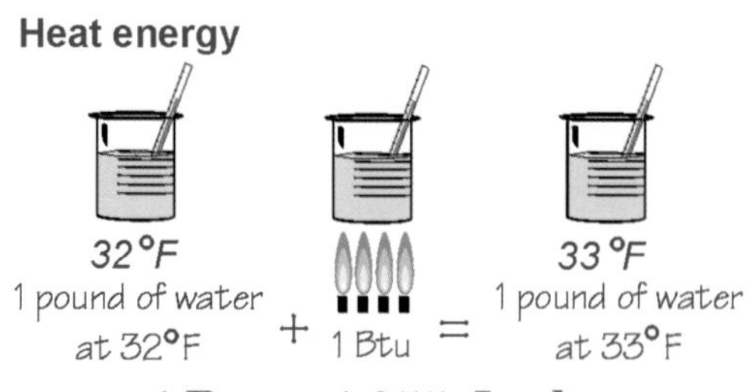

Heat is a form of thermal energy. When you design a heating system for a house, you need to specify how much heat energy you need. Heating contractors measure heat using the British thermal unit (Btu). One Btu is the same amount of energy as 1,055 joules.

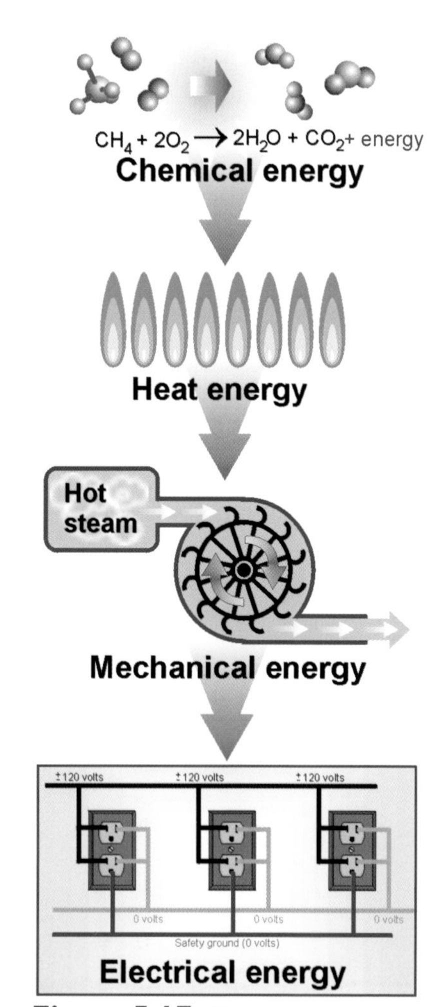

Figure 5.17: *Power plants convert chemical energy, mechanical energy, and heat into electrical energy.*

Energy and running

Humans have high endurance

You know that you cannot run as fast a dog or many other animals, like the cheetah. Human beings get tired and have to rest after running fast. However, although humans are not the best sprinters on the planet, they are the best runners in terms of endurance. Scientists are learning that the human body is ideal for running long distances.

Heat production

Machines, including the human body, are not 100% efficient because some of the energy input is always lost as heat. Car engines and computers all produce heat that can cause damage unless it is removed. This is why cars have radiators and computers have fans.

Humans keep cool

The human body works a little like a radiator by directing blood toward the skin surface. Blood flowing near the surface can lose some heat to the relatively cooler air. A more effective way of removing heat is sweating. As sweat leaves the body, it evaporates from the skin and carries away heat. This one mechanism—sweating—makes is possible for human beings to run for long periods of time. Humans can continuously cool down while performing strenuous exercise like running. Animals with fur, like cheetahs, quickly get overheated and need to rest (see sidebar at right). Scientists believe that sweating has allowed mankind to be successful at hunting large game throughout human history.

Energy conservation and the Achilles' tendon

The Achilles' tendon is a good example of energy conversion between kinetic and potential energy (Figure 5.18). When the heel is down, the Achilles' tendon stretches like a rubber band and potential energy is stored. Let's say 100 units of energy are stored. As the foot moves through the running stride, the tendon shortens and pulls up the heel using about 90 units of this stored energy. In effect, the energy transformation by the Achilles tendon and the associated muscles in the foot is 90 percent. Only 10 percent of the stored energy is lost as heat!

Human energy efficiency

The high energy efficiency of the Achilles tendon helps make humans about 20 to 25 percent efficient while running. The energy efficiency of top cyclists is about 25 percent. The efficiency of rowers is about 15 percent and swimmers are 3 to 9 percent. Twenty-five percent efficiency means that for every 100 units of energy eaten, 25 are used for moving forward and 75 are "lost" as heat and friction.

Speed versus endurance

The top speed of a cheetah is 30 m/sec and the top speed of a human being is 10 m/sec. A human cannot outrun a cheetah over a short distance. However, a human being could win a long distance race. Because the furry body of a cheetah does not effectively release heat, it gets overheated quickly and is exhausted after a high-speed sprint. Humans, on the other hand, constantly release heat from the skin surface by sweating and have greater endurance as a result.

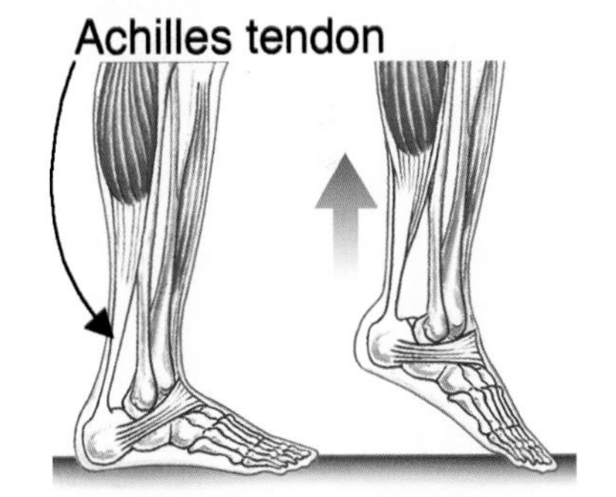

Figure 5.18: *The Achilles tendon illustrates energy conversion.*

Energy and swimming

Running versus swimming

The higher energy efficiency of humans while running (20 to 25 percent) versus swimming (about 3 to 9 percent) indicates that human beings are better adapted for running than for swimming. This is illustrated by the fact that we do not have relatively large hands and feet. Having paddle-like hands would be useful for swimming efficiently, but the extra mass in our hands would throw off our balance for running. Having most of our mass located in our torso keeps us balanced.

Ways to improve swimming efficiency

In spite of being inefficient swimmers, people still like to swim and improve their ability to swim. Efficiency in swimming can be improved by reducing any splashing that occurs while swimming. Swimming quietly without splashing means that more energy is devoted to moving forward and not lost to produce waves. Swimmers also improve their efficiency by working on the amount of distance they cover with one stroke. For example, the most elite swimmers can swim 50 meters in about 25 strokes, whereas an average swimmer uses about 75 strokes to cover 50 meters.

Fins make swimming more efficient

The relative smallness of the hands and feet makes it harder for humans to be efficient and fast swimmers. In order to improve swimming efficiency while scuba diving, divers wear large fins on their feet (Figure 5.19). These fins help divers push a greater mass of water than is possible with bare feet. Pushing more water means that a scuba diver can travel a farther distance with less energy expended.

Conservation of momentum and swimming

Moving water away from you so that you can swim forward is an example of Newton's third law of motion (action and reaction). You can also think about swimming in terms of the law of conservation of momentum. For example, you and your mass must equal the mass of the water moving backward and the speed at which the water moves backward. It is actually more energy efficient to move a large amount of water slowly than a small amount of water fast. This is because you want to reduce the amount of energy you give to the water. The formula for kinetic energy is $1/2\ mv^2$. Since the value for velocity (v) is squared, you lose more energy to the water if you try to move it very fast. If you move a large mass (m) of water slowly, you lose less energy to the water (Figure 5.20).

Figure 5.19: *Scuba divers improve their energy efficiency while swimming by using big fins to move more water. Having higher energy efficiency while swimming, means the diver has more energy for other activities like exploring!*

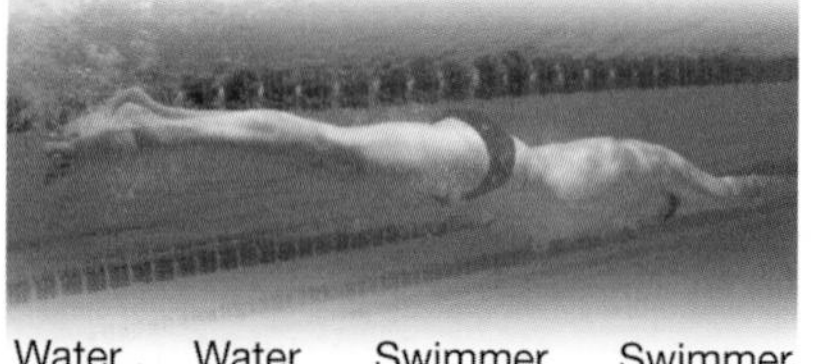

Momentum of water backward = Momentum of swimmer forward
Water mass × Water velocity = Swimmer mass × Swimmer velocity

Figure 5.20: *According to the law of conservation of momentum, the forward momentum of the swimmer equals the backward momentum of water pushed by the swimmer. Swimming efficiency can be increased if the amount of energy lost to the water is decreased. The way to do this is to move more water (more mass) slowly.*

Chapter 5 Review

Vocabulary review

Match the following terms with the correct definition. There is one extra definition in the list that will not match any of the terms.

Set One	
1. energy	a. The ability to do work
2. joule	b. The combined units of force and distance used to quantify work
3. law of conservation of energy	c. One newton-meter is equal to one of these
4. newton-meter	d. Energy is never created or destroyed
5. work	e. The amount of work that can be done by an object is equal to the energy available in the object
	f. Force times distance

Set Two	
1. efficiency	a. Force times distance
2. perpetual motion machine	b. The amount of work performed over time
3. power	c. One joule of work performed in 1 second
4. watt	d. An imaginary machine that can be 100 percent efficient
	e. The ratio of work output to work input

Concept review

1. Why is it correct to say that energy is *conserved* in a machine?
2. In your own words, explain the relationship between work and energy.
3. You want to prove the law of conservation of energy to a friend. For your demonstration you show that you can use a block and pulley machine to lift 100 newtons with only 20 newtons of input force. What would you say to your friend to explain how this is possible?
4. You have a machine that tells you exactly how much work in joules is put into a machine and how much work was produced. The readings that you just received from the machine state that the input work was 345 joules and the output work was 330 joules. The law of conservation of energy states that input should equal output. How can you explain the "lost" 15 joules?
5. The following diagram shows a cart rolling along a hilly road. Ignore the effect of friction. Arrange the five locations in order of increasing potential and kinetic energy.

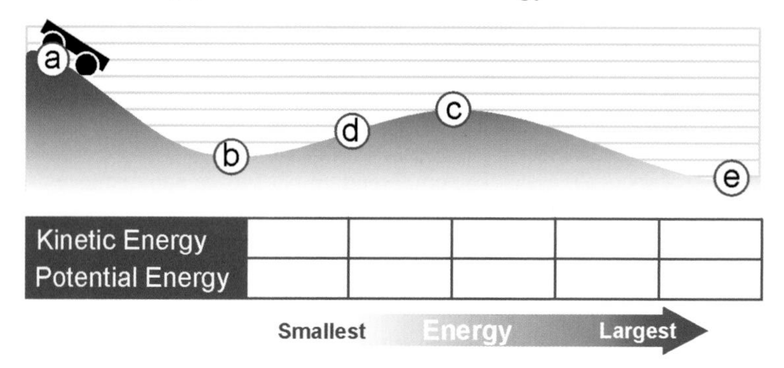

Kinetic Energy					
Potential Energy					

Problems

1. Calculate work using the following values for force and distance. Give your answers in joules.
   a. 12 newtons lifted 5 meters
   b. 3 newtons pushed 3 meters
   c. 400 newtons dragged 10 meters
   d. 7.5 newtons lifted 18.4 meters
2. How many joules of work are done if you carry a box that weighs 28 newtons up a ladder for a distance of 2 meters?
3. For each statement, write W if work is being done and NW if no work is being accomplished.
   a. I carried my books upstairs to my bedroom.
   b. The wind blew the lawn chair across the yard.
   c. The wall in my classroom won't budge no matter how much I push on it.
   d. I blew some dust off my paper.
   e. I stood very still and balanced a book on my head.

4. Which requires more work, lifting a 15-newton load a distance of 3 meters with a block and tackle, or lifting a 7-newton load a distance of 10 meters with the same block and tackle machine? Be sure to show your work and explain your answer clearly.

5. A block and tackle machine performed 30 joules of work on a 15-newton block. How high did the machine lift the block?

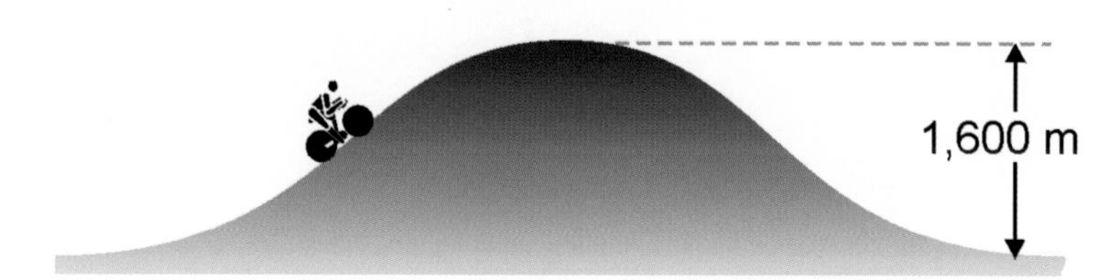

6. At the end of the ride up a steep hill, Ken was at an elevation of 1,600 meters above where he started. He figured out that he and his bicycle had accomplished 1,000,000 joules of work. If Ken has a mass of 54 kg, what is the mass of his bicycle?
(Note: $g = 9.8\ m/sec^2$.)

7. If a block and tackle machine has a mechanical advantage of 2, you can use 20 newtons of force to lift a 40-newton load. If you lift the block 1 meter, what length of rope do you have to pull?

8. A machine has a work output of 45 joules. In order to accomplish the work, 48 joules of work was put into the machine. What is the efficiency of this machine? Be sure to give your answer as a percentage.

9. One machine can perform 280 joules of work in 40 seconds. Another machine can produce 420 joules of work in 2 minutes. Which machine is more powerful? Justify your answer by calculating the amount of power in watts each machine produces.

10. You attach a motor to a block and tackle machine. After using it, you find that you want a more powerful motor. You purchase one that has twice the power of the old motor.

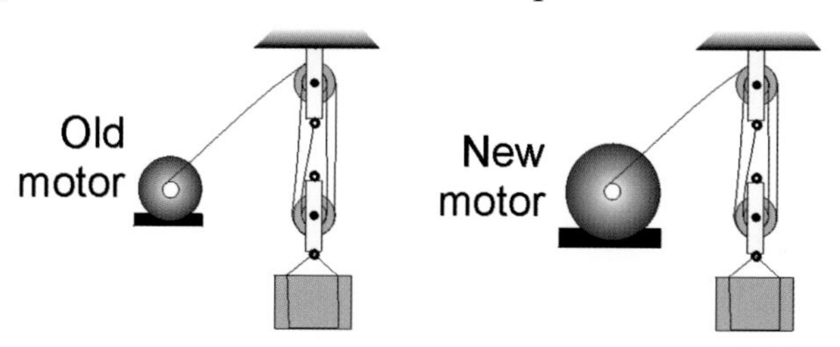

   a. How much bigger a load can the new motor lift in the same amount of time?

   b. If the new motor lifts the same load as the old motor, how much faster can it go?

11. A motor pushes a car with a force of 35 newtons for a distance of 350 meters in 6 seconds.

   a. How much work has the motor accomplished?

   b. How powerful is the motor in watts?

12. How much power is required to do 55 joules of work in 55 seconds?

13. The manufacturer of a machine said that it is 86 percent efficient. If you use 70 joules to run the machine (input work), how much output work will it produce?

14. A machine is 72 percent efficient. If it produces 150 joules of work output, how much work was put into the machine?

Applying your knowledge

1. A car is about 15 percent efficient at converting energy from gas to energy of motion. The average car today gets 25 miles for each gallon of gas.
   a. What would the gas mileage be if the car could be made 100 percent efficient?
   b. Name three things that contribute to lost energy and prevent a car from ever being 100 percent efficient.
2. Why, according to the laws of physics, is it impossible to build a perpetual motion machine?
3. Research question: Investigate light bulb wattage and describe what watts mean in terms of power and work.
4. Imagine we had to go back to using horses for power. One horse makes 746 watts (1 hp). How many horses would it take to light up all the light bulbs in your school?
   a. First, estimate how many light bulbs are in your school.
   b. Estimate the power of each light bulb, or get it from the bulb itself where it is written on the top.
   c. Calculate the total power used by all the bulbs.
   d. Calculate how many horses it would take to make this much power.
5. Make a chart that shows the flow of energy in the situation described below. In your chart, use some of the key concepts you learned, including potential energy and kinetic energy.

Martha wakes up at 5:30 am and eats a bowl of corn flakes. It's a nice day, so she decides to ride her bicycle to work, which is uphill from her house. It is still dark outside. Martha's bike has a small electric generator that runs from the front wheel. She flips on the generator so that her headlight comes on when she starts to pedal. She then rides her bike to work. Draw a diagram that shows the energy transformations that occur in this situation.

UNIT 3

Electricity and Magnetism

Chapter 6

Electricity and Electric Circuits

Introduction to Chapter 6

Electricity is everywhere around us. We use electricity to turn on lights, cool our homes, and run our TVs, radios, and portable phones. There is electricity in lightning and in our bodies. Even though electricity is everywhere, we can't easily see what it is or how it works. In this chapter, you will learn the basic ideas of electricity. You will learn about electric circuits and electric charge, the property of matter responsible for electricity.

Investigations for Chapter 6

6.1	**What Is a Circuit?**	*What is an electric circuit?*

Can you make a bulb light? In this Investigation, you will build and analyze a circuit with a bulb, battery, wires, and switch. You will also learn to draw and understand diagrams of electric circuits using standard electrical symbols.

6.2	**Charge**	*What is moving through a circuit?*

In this Investigation, you will create two kinds of static electricity and see what happens when the two charges come together. During the Investigation, you will also demonstrate that there only two kinds of charge.

Learning Goals

In this chapter, you will:

- ✔ Build simple circuits.
- ✔ Trace circuit paths.
- ✔ Interpret the electric symbols for battery, bulb, wire, and switch.
- ✔ Draw a circuit diagram of a real circuit.
- ✔ Explain why electrical symbols and circuit diagrams are useful.
- ✔ Explain how a switch works.
- ✔ Identify open and closed circuits.
- ✔ Charge pieces of tape and observe their interactions with an electroscope.
- ✔ Identify electric charge as the property of matter responsible for electricity.
- ✔ List the two forms of electric charge.
- ✔ Describe the forces electric charges exert on each other.
- ✔ Describe how lightning forms.

Vocabulary

circuit diagram
closed circuit
coulomb
electric charge
electric circuits
electrical symbols
electrically charged
electrically neutral
electroscope
natural world
negative charge
open circuit
positive charge
static electricity
versorium

6.1 What Is a Circuit?

There are lots of electrical devices and wires around us. What is inside those light bulbs, stereos, toasters, and other electrical devices? All these devices contain electric circuits. In this section, you will figure out how to build circuits with a bulb, batteries, wires, and a switch, and learn how to draw circuit diagrams using electrical symbols.

Electricity

Why learn about electricity? We use electricity every day. Our homes, stores, and workplaces all use many electrical appliances and devices such as electric ovens, TVs, stereos, toasters, motors that turn fans, air conditioners, heaters, light bulbs, etc. In fact, the use of electricity has become so routine that many of us don't stop to think about what happens when we switch on a light or turn on a motor. If we do stop to look, we find that most of what is "happening" is not visible. What exactly is electricity? How does it work?

What is electricity? *Electricity* usually means the flow of something called *electric current* in wires, motors, light bulbs, and other devices. Think about making a water wheel turn. Water flows over the wheel and as it falls, it gives up energy and the wheel turns. We build ponds, canals, and pipes to carry water from one place to another where we want to use it.

Electric current Electric current is like water, except it flows through solid metal so we can't usually see it. Just like water, electric current can carry energy over great distances. Look around you and you can probably see wires carrying electric current into houses and buildings.

Electricity can be powerful and dangerous Electric current can be very powerful. An electric saw can cut wood 30 times faster that a hand saw (Figure 6.2). An electric motor the size of a basketball can do as much work as five big horses or 15 strong men. Electric current can also be dangerous. Touching a live electric wire can give you a very serious injury. The safe use and understanding of electricity is what this unit is about.

Figure 6.1: *A water wheel uses a current of water to turn a wheel and do useful work.*

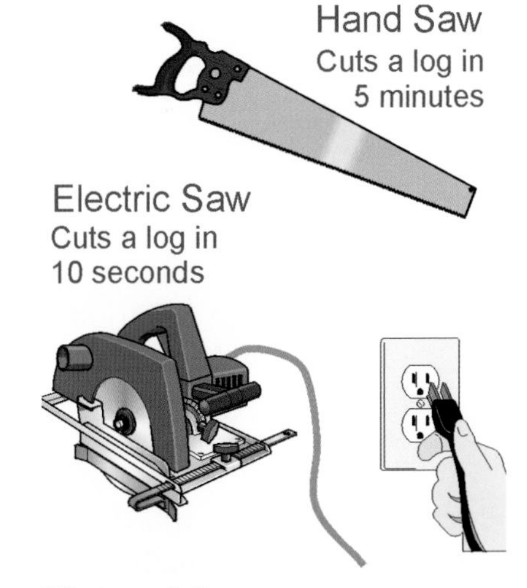

Figure 6.2: *Electricity uses an electric current to power light bulbs and electric motors.*

Electric circuits

What is an electric circuit?

To start to understand electricity, let's look inside a simple electrical appliance, like an electric blender. Inside are lots of wires and other electrical parts. The wires, switches, and motors are connected in electric circuits. An electric circuit is something that provides a path through which electricity travels.

Electric blender

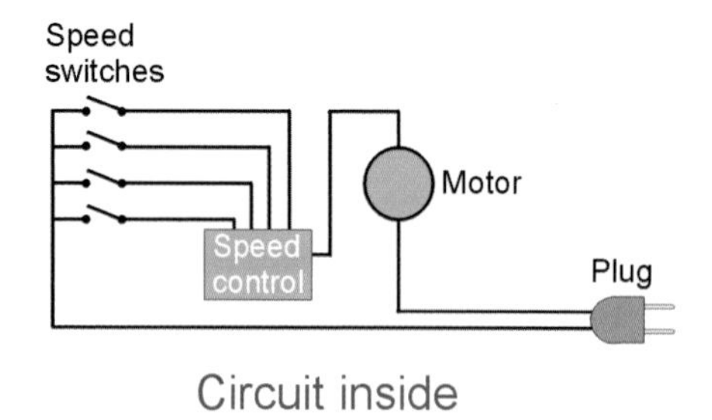

Circuit inside

Circuits also exist in the natural world

Circuits are not confined to appliances, wires, and devices built by people. People's first experience with electricity was in the natural world. Some examples of circuits are:

- The wiring that lights your house is an electric circuit.
- The nerves in your body create electric circuits.
- Lightning, clouds, and the planet Earth form an electric circuit.
- The car battery, ignition switch, and starter form an electric circuit.

Electric circuits are like water pipes

Electric circuits are similar to pipes and hoses for water (Figure 6.3). You can think of wires as pipes for electricity. The big difference is that you can't get the electricity to leave the wire. If you cut a water pipe, the water comes out. If you cut a wire, the electricity immediately stops flowing. Electric current cannot flow except in complete circuits.

Switches turn circuits on and off

Because a complete path through wire is need for electricity to work, a switch works by breaking or completing the circuit path. When a switch is on, the circuit path is complete. When a switch is off, the circuit path is broken (Figure 6.4).

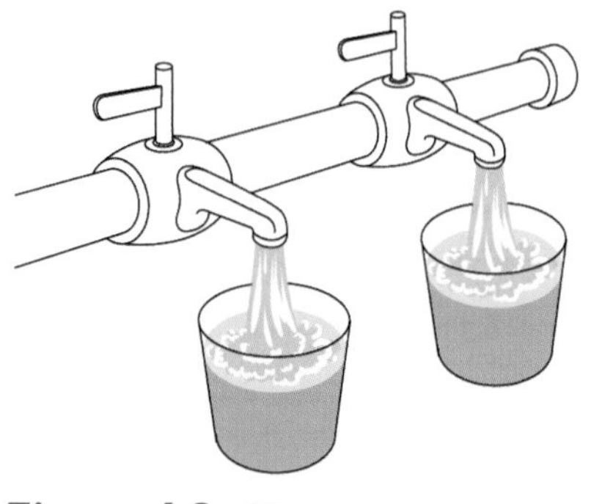

Figure 6.3: *We use pipes to carry the flow of water where we need it.*

Electric current only flows in closed circuits.

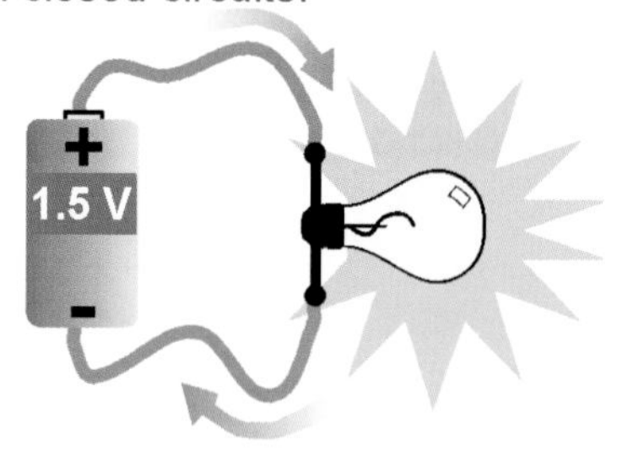

Electric current does not flow in open circuits.

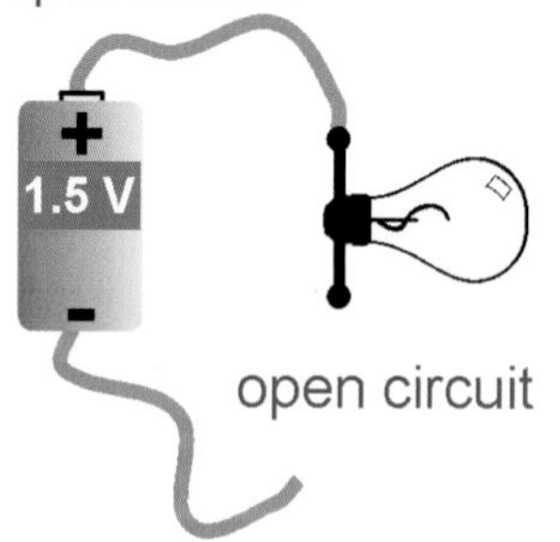

Figure 6.4: *We use electric circuits with wires to carry the flow of electricity where we need it.*

Circuit diagrams and electrical symbols

Circuit diagrams

Circuits are made up of wires and electrical parts, such as *batteries*, *light bulbs*, *motors*, or *switches*. When people build and design circuits to accomplish a task, they use a special kind of drawing called a circuit diagram. In a circuit diagram we use symbols to represent parts of the circuit. These electrical symbols are quicker to draw and can be read by anyone familiar with electricity.

A circuit diagram uses electrical symbols

A circuit diagram is a shorthand method of describing a real circuit. By using a diagram with standard symbols you don't have to draw a battery and bulb realistically every time you need to write down a circuit you have made. Figure 6.5 shows some common things you find in a circuit and their electrical symbols.

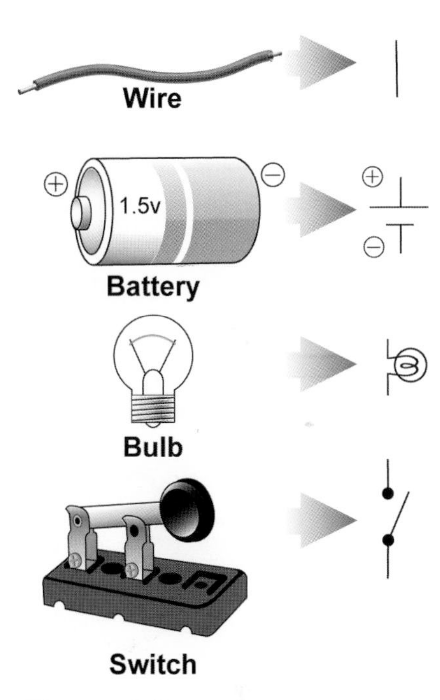

Figure 6.5: *Commonly used electric parts and their symbols*

The graphic below shows a photograph of a simple circuit and a circuit diagram. The circuit diagram represents the simple circuit. See if you can match the symbols in the circuit diagram with each part of the simple circuit.

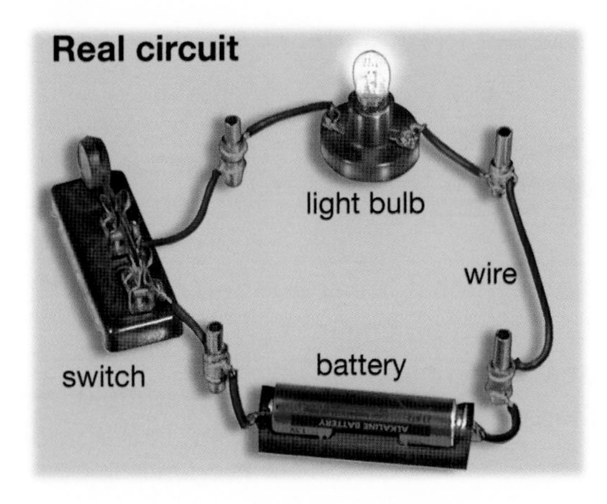

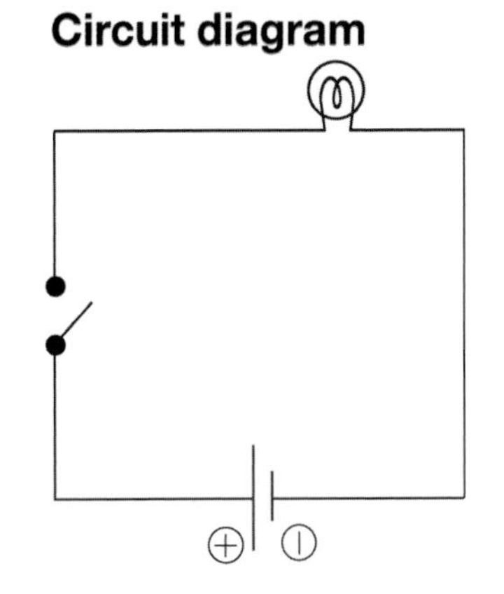

Resistors and what they represent

In many circuit diagrams any electrical device is shown as a *resistor*. A resistor is an electrical component that uses energy. In a few sections, you will see that when analyzing how a circuit works, we often treat things like light bulbs as if they were resistors.

Open and closed circuits

Circuits are controlled by switches

You have just learned that we use switches to turn electricity on and off. Turning the switch off creates a break in the wire. The break stops the flow of current because electricity travels through the metal wire but can't normally travel through air.

Open and closed circuits

A circuit with a switch turned to the off position or a circuit with any break in it is called an open circuit. Electricity can't travel through an open circuit. When the switch is turned to the on position, there are no longer any breaks anywhere in the wire and the light goes on. This is called a closed circuit. Electricity can travel easily through a closed circuit.

Open circuit - No current flows

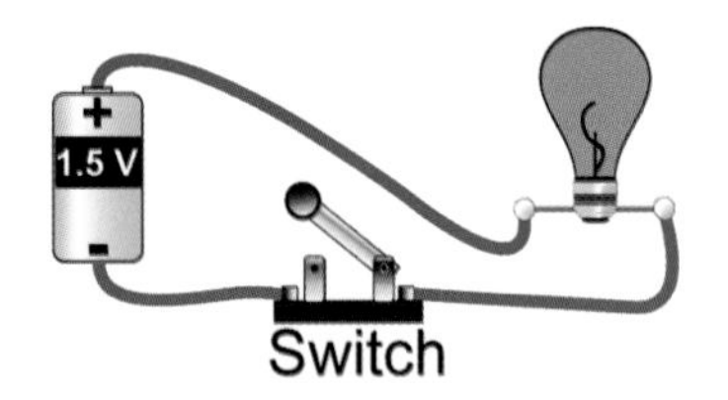

Closed circuit - Current flows

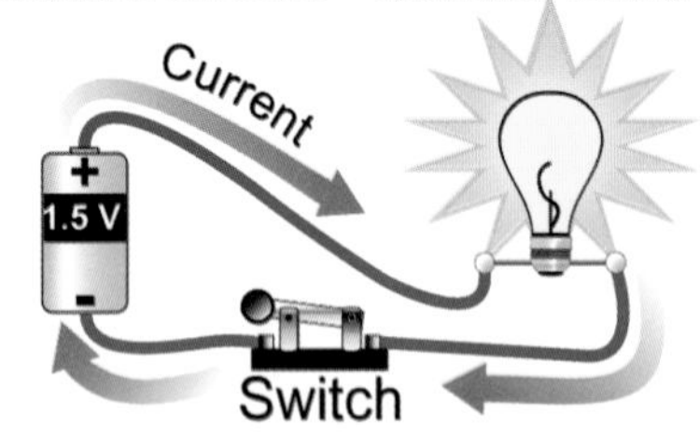

Trace circuits to test them

A common problem found in circuits is that an unintentional break occurs. When building circuits it is a good idea to trace your finger around the wires to tell if the circuit is open or closed. If there are any breaks, the circuit is open. If there is a complete loop then the circuit is closed.

Short circuits

A *short circuit* is not the same as either open or closed circuits. A short circuit is usually an accidental extra path for current to flow. Short circuits are covered in more detail in a later section when we talk about *parallel* and *series* circuits.

Spinal cord injuries

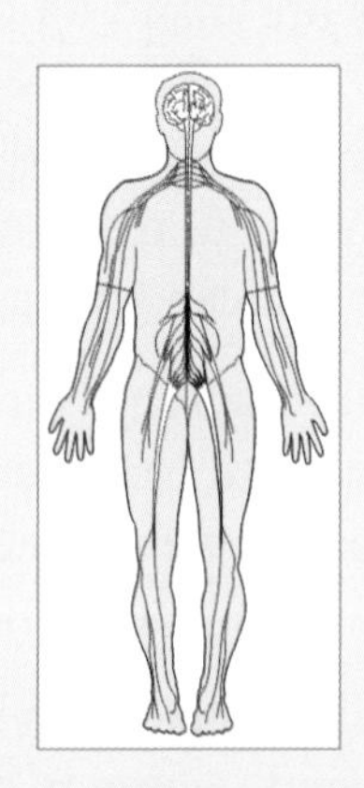

Our nervous system is a network of electric circuits including the brain, spinal cord, and many nerves. Motor nerves branch out from the spinal cord and send electrical messages to muscles, telling them to contract so that you can move. If a motor nerve is injured, an open circuit is created. The message from the brain can no longer reach the muscle, so the muscle no longer works.

Although a surgeon can sew the two ends of a broken nerve back together, scar tissue forms that blocks the circuit. If a person injures a small nerve (a motor nerve in the thumb, for example), they may regain movement after a period of time as other nerves create alternate paths for the signal. However, injury to a large bundle of nerves, like the spinal cord, is irreparable. That is why spinal cord injuries can cause paralysis.

6.2 Charge

You have built circuits and made light bulbs glow. Now we will find out exactly what is moving through those wires. In this section, you will learn about electric charge and build a simple electroscope to observe the electrical forces exerted by electric charges on each other.

Electricity

Use of electricity is relatively new

The understanding and use of electricity is relatively recent history. Michael Faraday discovered the principles of the electric motor in 1830. The electric light was invented by Thomas Edison in 1879. Two lifetimes later we now see light bulbs and motors everywhere.

Faraday and Edison were only two of the many people who observed, investigated, and thought about electricity. Today's technology results from an accumulation of knowledge about electricity over a long period of time.

First experiments in electricity

To understand electricity, people first studied events like lightning and the sparks that can occur when certain materials are rubbed together. We observe the same effect when we rub our feet on a carpet and then feel a shock or see a spark when we touch a metal doorknob. *Something* in ordinary materials "electrifies" our body. What is it?

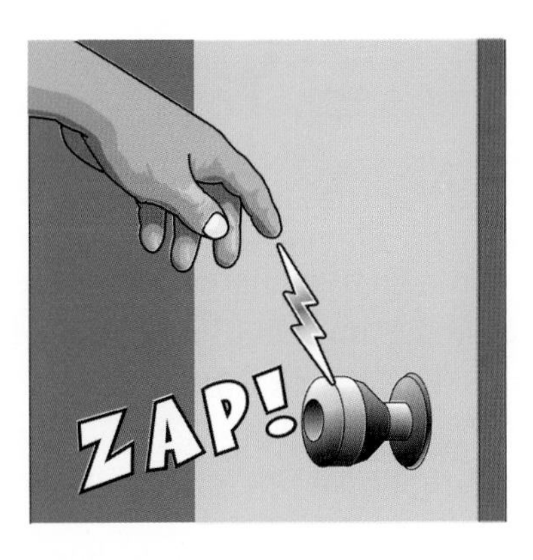

Electric charge

The source of the shock and the sparks is *electric charge*. **Electric charge**, like mass, is a fundamental property of matter. An important difference between mass and charge is that charge comes in two kinds, called **positive charge** and **negative charge**.

History of the terms positive and negative charge

The terms *positive* and *negative* to describe the opposite kinds of charge were first used by Benjamin Franklin (1706-1790). He and other scientists were seeking to describe their new observations about electricity. In 1733, French scientist Charles DuFay had published a book describing how like charges repel and unlike charges attract. He theorized that two fluids caused electricity: vitreous (positive) fluid and resinous (negative) fluid.

Later that century, Franklin invented his own theory that argued that electricity is a result of the presence of a single fluid in different amounts. Franklin claimed that when there was too much fluid in an object, it would exhibit positive charge behavior, and if there were not enough, the object would exhibit negative charge behavior. Although scientists no longer believe that electricity is caused by different kinds of fluids, the words positive and negative are still used to describe the two types of charge.

Electric charge

Static electricity

When we acquire a static charge from walking across a carpet, our bodies gain a tiny amount of excess negative charge. In general, if materials or objects carry excess positive or negative charge we say they are electrically charged. When charge builds up on an object or material it is sometimes referred to as static electricity.

The explanation of static cling

What happens when there is a buildup of excess charge? We observe that clothes fresh out of a dryer stick together. This is because all the tumbling and rubbing makes some clothes positive and others negative. Do you notice what happens when you brush your hair on a dry day? Each hair gets the same kind of charge and they repel each other, making your hair appear fuller.

Like charges repel, unlike charges attract

These scenarios show us how charges affect each other. A positive and a negative charge will pull each other closer. Two positive charges will push each other away. The same is true of two negative charges. The rule for the force between two charges is: Unlike charges attract each other and like charges repel each other.

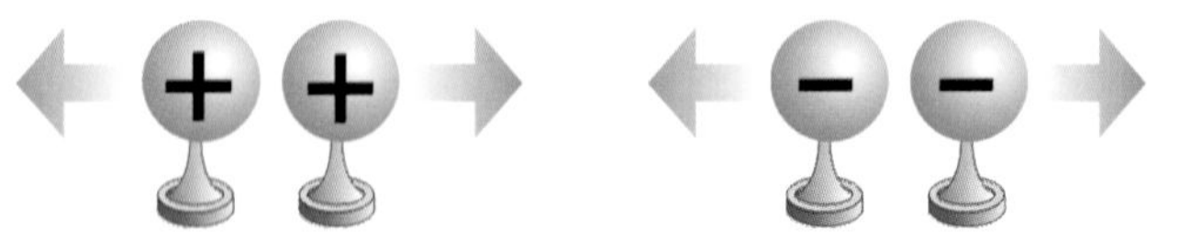

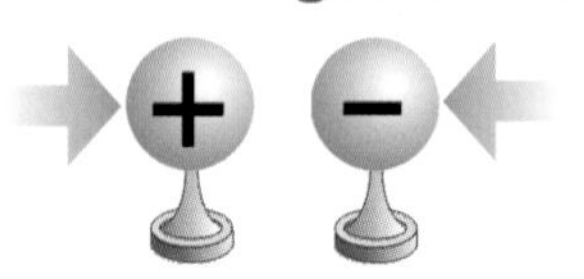

Electrical forces

These forces between positive and negative charges are called electrical forces or electrostatic forces. If you increase the amount of one kind of charge on an object, it exerts a greater electrical force. This kind of force is very strong! Suppose you could separate the positive and negative charges in a bowling ball. The force between the separated charges would be 10 times the weight of the entire Earth!

Most matter is neutral

It is very difficult to separate the positive and negative charges in a bowling ball or in anything else. Most matter has the exact same amount of positive and negative charges. Total charge is zero, since the positives cancel the negatives. An object with zero charge is electrically neutral. The electrical events we observe are the result of the separation of relatively small amounts of charge.

This object is neutral

positive charge +8
negative charge -8
total 0

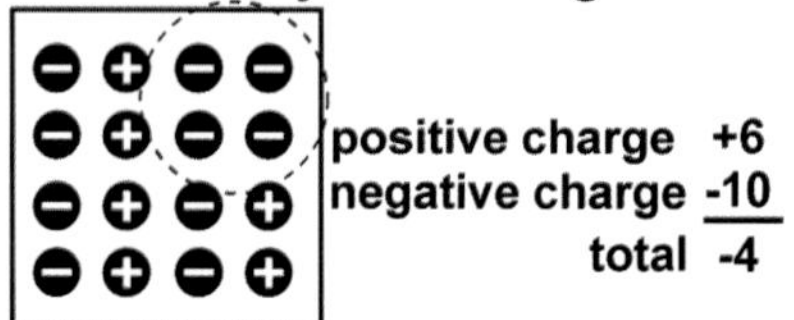

Figure 6.6: *Most matter is neutral, with equal amounts of positive and negative charge. If an object gains or loses one kind of charge, it is said to be charged.*

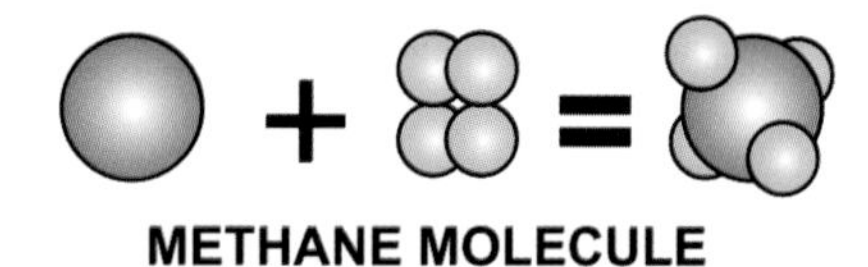

Figure 6.7: *You will study chemical reactions like the one shown above later in this book. Electrical forces are the cause of many properties of matter and all reactions.*

The coulomb and the atom

Electric charge is measured in coulombs

The unit of electric charge is the **coulomb** (C). The name is chosen in honor of Charles-Augustin de Coulomb (1736-1806), a French physicist who succeeded in making the first accurate measurements of the forces between charges in 1783.

The charge of protons and electrons

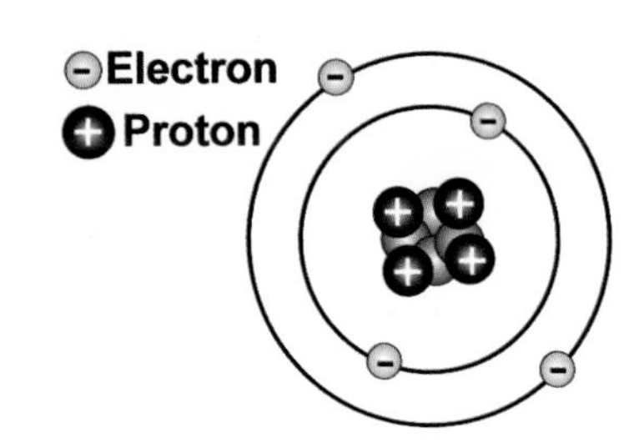

Since Coulomb's time, people have discovered that different parts of the atom carry electric charge. The protons in the nucleus are positive and the electrons in the outer part of the atom are negative.

Electrical forces in atoms

Electrons in atoms stay close to the protons because they are attracted to each other. If you could put 1 coulomb of positive charge a meter away from the same amount of negative charge, the electrical force between them would be 9,000,000,000 (9 billion) newtons!

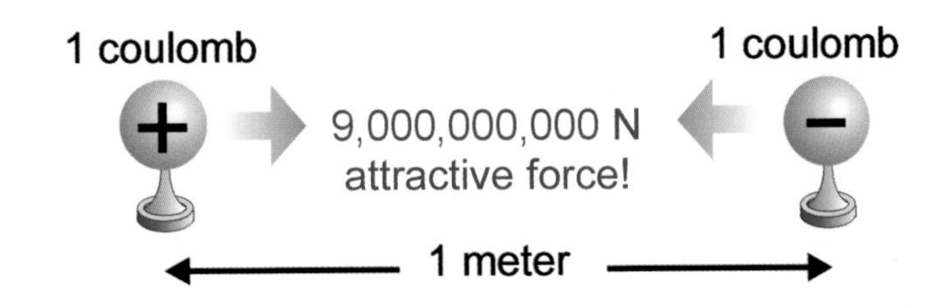

Lightning and charged particles

Lightning is caused by a giant buildup of static charge. Before a lightning strike, particles in a cloud collide and charges are transferred from one particle to another. Positive charges tend to build up on smaller particles and negative charges on bigger ones.

The forces of gravity and wind cause the particles to separate. Positively charged particles accumulate near the top of the cloud and negatively charged particles fall toward the bottom. Scientists from the National Aeronautics and Space Administration (NASA) have measured enormous buildups of negative charge in storm clouds. These negatively charged cloud particles repulse negative charges in the ground, causing the ground to become positively charged. This positive charge is why people who have been struck by lightning sometimes say they first felt their hair stand on end.

The negative charges in the cloud are attracted to the positively charged ground. When enough charges have been separated by the storm, the cloud, air, and ground act like a giant circuit. All the accumulated negative charges flow from the cloud to the ground, heating the air along the path (to as much as 20,000°C!) so that it glows like a bright streak of light.

The electroscope

Detecting charge with an electroscope

We can detect charged objects by using an electroscope. The electroscope has two very light leaves that hang down. The leaves attract or repel each other depending on the charge nearby. By watching the leaves you can tell what kinds of electric charges are near, and roughly how strong they are. A more complex electroscope can measure the exact amount of charge present on an object. Figure 6.8 shows how the electroscope works.

The history of the electroscope

In sixteenth-century England, Queen Elizabeth I had a physician named William Gilbert who was very interested in magnetism because he thought that it might help his patients. Gilbert discovered that rubbing semiprecious stones would cause them to attract light objects. Like others of his time, Gilbert thought that static attraction was caused by magnetism. In his experiments, he found that some stones attracted better than others.

The versorium

To measure just how well these objects worked, he invented the first electrical instrument, the versorium. Like a compass needle, the thin, balanced pointer would swing to show a very small attraction. The versorium was the earliest version of today's electroscope.

Electrics and non-electrics

Objects like paper and straw that were attracted to the versorium Gilbert called electrics. Those that were not attracted, he called non-electrics. From these two words, Gilbert gets credit for making up the word ***electricity***.

The electroscope

Neutral

Metal rod and ball

Insulator

Leaves

Separating charges

Leaves

The negative rod repels free electrons into the leaves so they repel each other. The ball is positive because it lost electrons.

Charging by contact

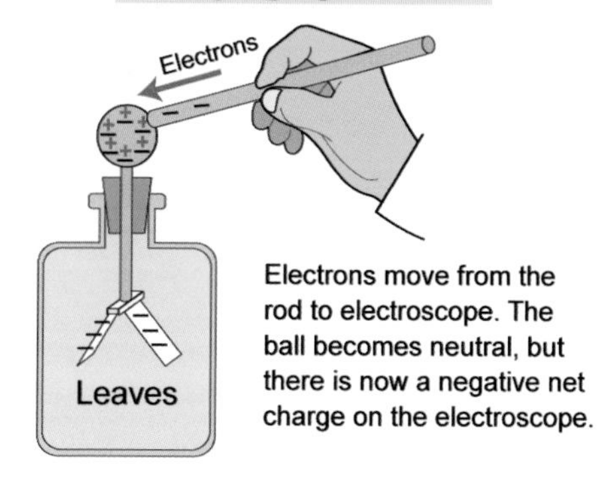

Electrons
Leaves
Electrons move from the rod to electroscope. The ball becomes neutral, but there is now a negative net charge on the electroscope.

Figure 6.8: *How the electroscope works.*

Chapter 6 Review

Vocabulary Review

Match the following terms with the correct definition. There is one extra definition in the list that will not match any of the terms.

Set One	
1. electrical circuits	a. A shorthand method of drawing an electrical part
2. open circuit	b. A device that turns a circuit on and off by causing a break in a circuit
3. closed circuit	c. A circuit with no breaks in it
4. circuit diagram	d. Structures that provide paths through which electricity travels
5. electrical symbol	e. A shorthand method of drawing the physical arrangement of a circuit
	f. A circuit with one or more breaks in it

Set Two	
1. electric charge	a. A unit used in measuring the amount of charge
2. static electricity	b. The pushes and pulls that electric charges exert on each other
3. electrical force	c. Property of matter responsible for electrical events; it has two forms, positive and negative
4. electroscope	d. An instrument that can detect, and sometimes measure the amount of, electric charges
5. coulomb	e. An object that has equal amounts of positive and negative charges
	f. A buildup of charge on an object or material

Concept review

1. How are electrical circuits and systems of carrying water (such as the pipes that bring water to your house) alike? List at least two ways
2. List three examples of circuits from the reading.
3. Describe how a switch turns a circuit on and off.
4. Why do people use electrical symbols and circuit diagrams to describe a circuit?
5. What happens to the electrical connection of a nerve in the human body if the nerve is cut? Does the nerve ever fully heal?
6. List the kinds of electric charge and where they are found in an atom.
7. Objects can be charged or neutral. Explain what these two terms mean.
8. State the rules of attraction and repulsion between electric charges.
9. If you brush your hair for a long time, your hair may look fuller. Explain what is happening in terms of electric charges.
10. Use your own words to describe how lightning forms.
11. What is the name of the earliest electroscope?

Problems

1. Circle each diagram that shows a closed circuit that will light the bulb.

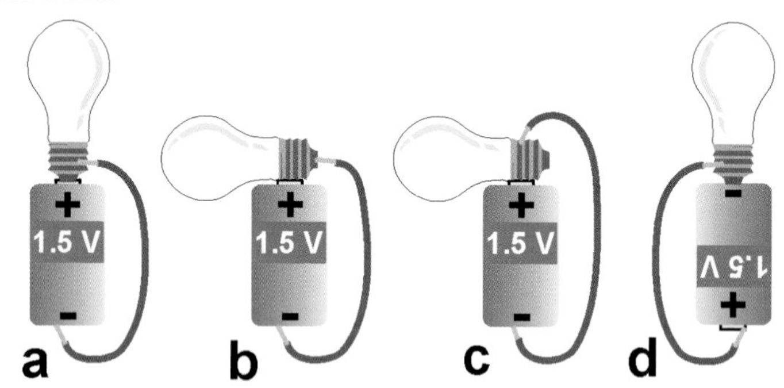

2. If any of the diagrams are not closed circuits, explain what you would do to close the circuit. You may, if you wish, draw your own picture to support your answer.
3. Build a circuit that has a battery, three wires, a bulb, and a switch. Draw a circuit diagram of this circuit.
4. In the electric charge Investigation, you used pieces of Scotch tape. If you simply took two pieces of tape off the roll and put them on the electroscope, you would see no interaction. If you put two pieces of tape together and then tear them apart quickly the two pieces of tape now attract each other. Explain what happened to the two pieces of tape that caused the attraction to occur.
5. A lightning rod is a safety device that is meant to be hit by lightning. Charges tend to concentrate on the pointed end of the lightning rod. Explain why the lightning rod would draw the lightning to itself.
6. In general, excess negative charge can move within a material, or be transferred from material to material. If you rub a balloon on your hair on a dry day, negative charge is transferred from your hair to the balloon. You bring the balloon close to a wall. The excess negative charge on the balloon repels the negative charges in the wall and the charges move to another part of the wall. The surface of the wall near the balloon is now positively charged. Will the balloon stick to the wall? Why or why not?

Applying your knowledge

1. Write a paragraph describing on what a typical day at home or school would be like if we had no electricity.
2. Examine the labels or instructions that come with home appliances and see if you can find examples of circuit diagrams. What parts of the diagrams do you recognize?
3. Research Benjamin Franklin's experiments in electricity. Draw and label a picture showing one of his experiments.
4. Static cling causes clothes to stick together when they come out of the dryer. What kinds of material seem to stick together?

UNIT 3

Electricity and Magnetism

Chapter 7

Measuring Electricity

Introduction to Chapter 7

Have you ever thought about how electricity is measured? If you look at the back of many appliances you will see electrical units that are most likely unfamiliar to you, such as volts and amperes. Like all units, electrical units are measurements of useful quantities. In this chapter you will learn about voltage, the energy of charges, current, the rate of travel of charges, and resistance, the ability of objects to carry charges.

Investigations for Chapter 7

7.1	**Voltage**	*Why do charges move through a circuit?*

In this Investigation, you will learn how to use an electrical meter to measure voltage, and you will observe how a change in voltage affects a light bulb.

7.2	**Current**	*How do charges move through a circuit?*

In this Investigation, you will learn how to use an electrical meter to measure current, and you will observe how a change in current affects a light bulb.

7.3	**Resistance**	*How well does current travel through different materials and objects?*

In this Investigation, you will learn how to use an electrical meter to measure resistance, and you will observe how differences in materials and size affect current.

Learning Goals

In this chapter, you will:

- ✔ Measure volts with an electrical meter.
- ✔ Describe the role of a battery in a circuit.
- ✔ Describe the transfer of energy in a circuit.
- ✔ Explain the relationship between voltage and energy in a circuit.
- ✔ Describe current as a flow of electric charge.
- ✔ Measure amperes with an electrical meter.
- ✔ Classify materials as conductors, semiconductors, or insulators.
- ✔ Differentiate between electrical conductivity and resistance.
- ✔ Explain why metals are good electrical conductors.
- ✔ Measure ohms with an electrical meter.

Vocabulary

alternating current
ampere
battery
current
direct current
electrical conductivity
electrical conductor
electrical insulator
ohm
resistance
semiconductor
volt
voltage

7.1 Voltage

Atoms are in everything and are made up of equal amounts of positive and negative charges. How is this useful in an electric circuit? In this section, you will learn that a battery adds energy to charge and makes it flow through circuits to do work for us.

Voltage

What does a battery do? A **battery** uses chemical energy to move charges. If you connect a circuit with a battery the charges flow out of the battery carrying energy. They can give up their energy to electrical devices, like a light bulb. When a bulb is lit, the energy is taken from the charges which return to the battery to get more energy. A battery is an energy source for charges that flow in circuits.

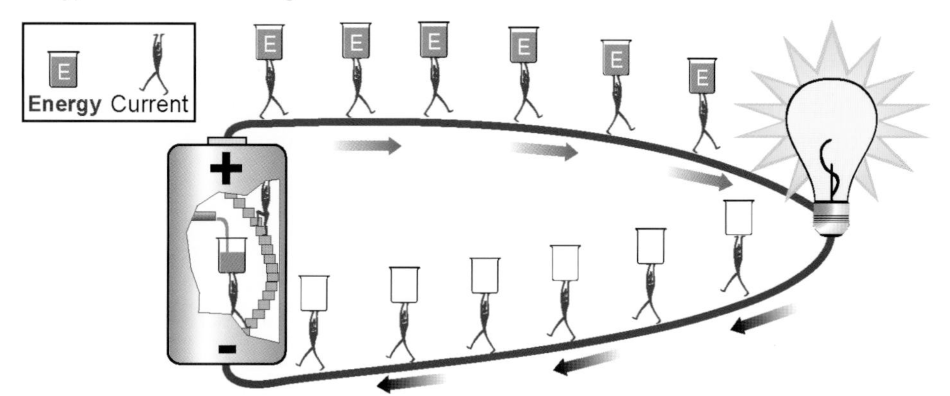

Volts measure the energy level in a circuit We measure the energy level of any place in a circuit in **volts**. Charges gain and lose energy by changing their voltage. If a charge goes up from 1 volt to 3 volts, it *gains* 2 joules of energy. If the charge goes down from 3 volts to 1 volt, it *loses* 2 joules of energy.

Batteries add energy A fully charged battery adds energy proportional to its voltage. The positive end of a 1.5 volt battery is 1.5 volts higher in energy than the negative end. That means every charge that leaves the positive end has 1.5 joules more energy than it had going in. This energy is what lights the light bulb. When the battery is dead, there is almost no energy to give to charges flowing through.

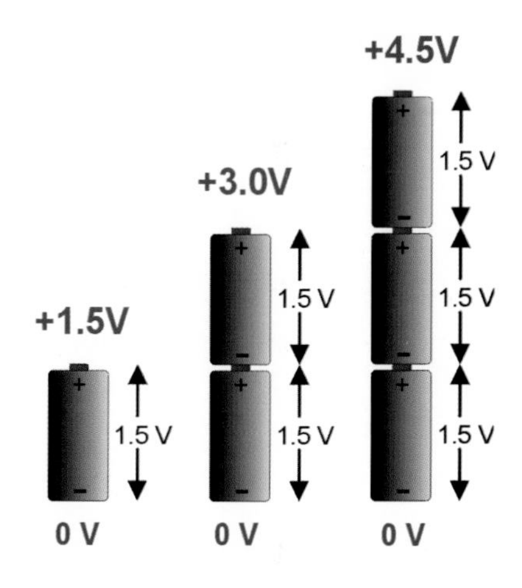

Figure 7.1: *The positive end of a 1.5 volt battery is 1.5 volts higher than the negative end. If you connect batteries positive-to-negative, each battery adds 1.5 volts to the total. Three batteries make 4.5 volts. Each charge coming out of the positive end of the 3-battery stack has 4.5 volts of energy.*

Voltage is related to potential energy

Voltage is related to *potential energy*, just like height is related to pressure in water flow. Imagine you have two tanks of water. One is higher than the other (Figure 7.2). The water in the higher tank has more energy than water in the lower tank. The water flows downhill, from high energy to low energy. A greater difference in height means that the water has more potential energy.

Differences in electrical energy are measured in volts. If there is a difference in volts, current will flow from the higher voltage to the lower voltage, just like water flows from higher energy to lower energy.

A battery is like a water tower

A water tower and pump make a good analogy for a battery. The pump lifts water up to the tower by giving it energy. The water can flow out and give the energy back. In a battery, chemical reactions provide energy to pump charges from low voltage to high voltage. The charges can then flow back to low voltage and give their energy back to turn motors and light bulbs.

Wires are like water pipes

The water tower is connected by a pipe to a faucet in a house that is lower than the tower. If you open the faucet, the difference in energy makes the water flow. In a circuit, the wires act like pipes to carry the charges from high voltage to low voltage. If you connect the switch, the current will flow.

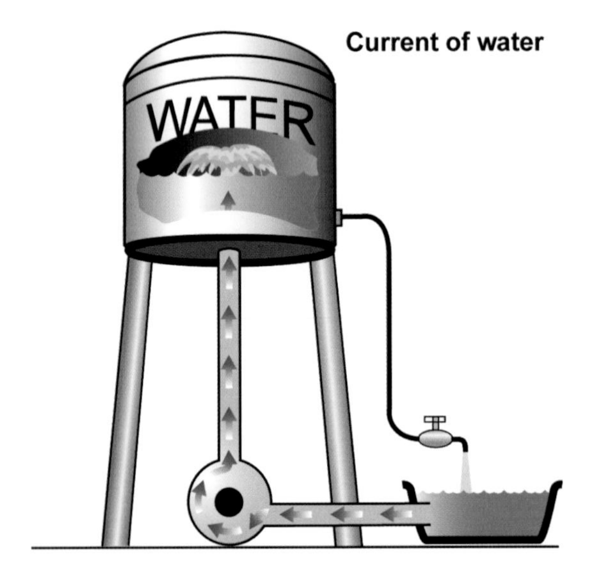

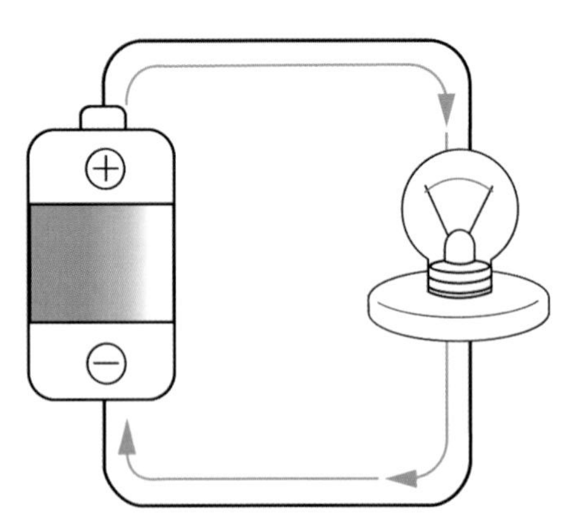

Water flows from high energy (height) to lower energy.

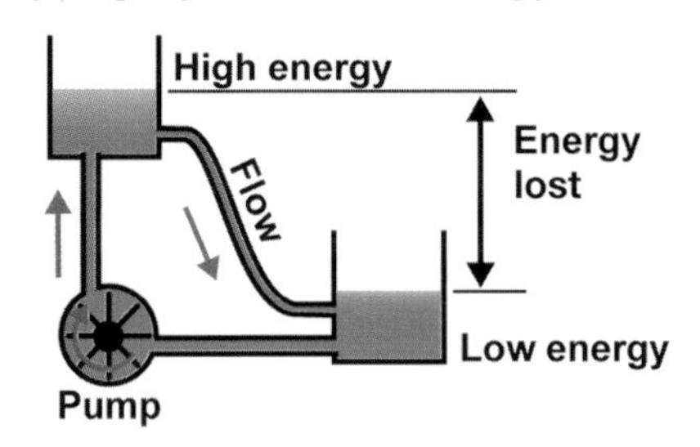

Electric charge flows from high energy (voltage) to lower energy.

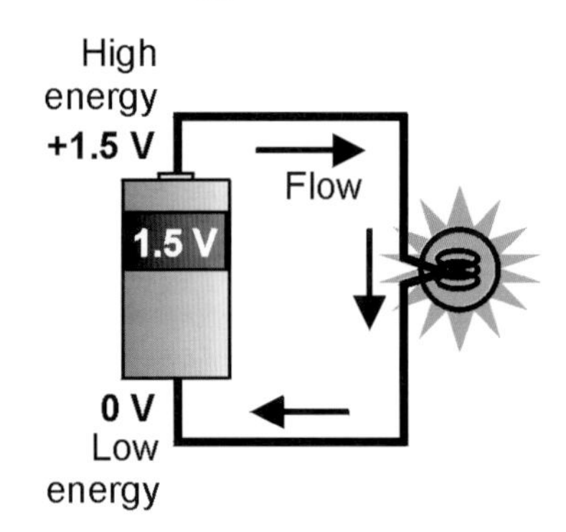

Figure 7.2: *Water flows from high energy to low energy. The energy difference is related to the difference in height. Electric charge also flows from high energy to low energy, but the energy difference is related to the difference in volts.*

Measuring voltage

Connecting a meter to measure volts

Volts measure the energy difference between two places in a circuit. To measure volts you have to connect a meter to two places. The meter measures the voltage difference between the two. If you connect a meter to the two ends of a battery you should read at least 1.5 volts from the negative end to the positive end. A fresh battery might even give you more than 1.5 volts.

Measuring the voltage of a battery

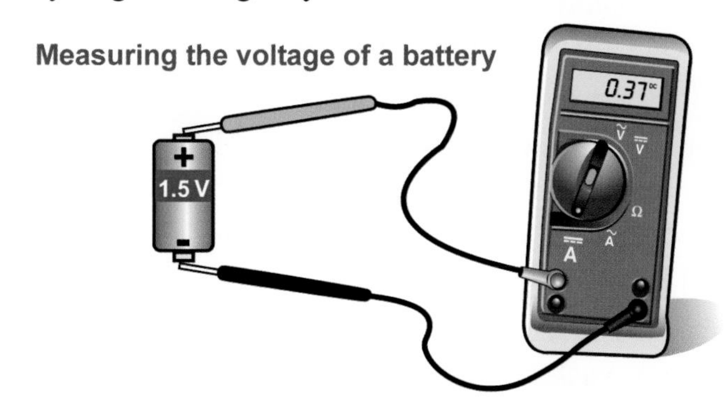

Choosing a voltage reference

Since voltage is measured from one point to another, we usually assign the negative terminal of a battery to be zero volts (0 V). This makes the voltage of every other place in the circuit relative to the negative end of the battery.

All points on a wire are the same voltage

Every point in a circuit connected to the same wire is at the same voltage. Charges move easily through copper so they do not lose much energy. That is why we make electrical wires out of copper. Since the charges all have the same energy, the voltage is the same everywhere along the wire.

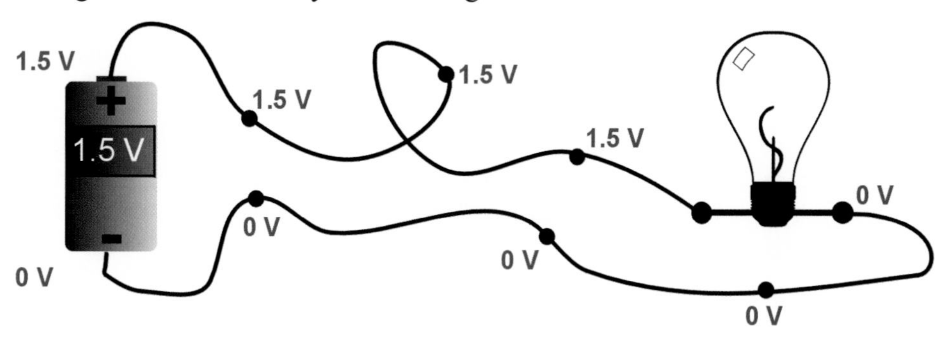

The volt

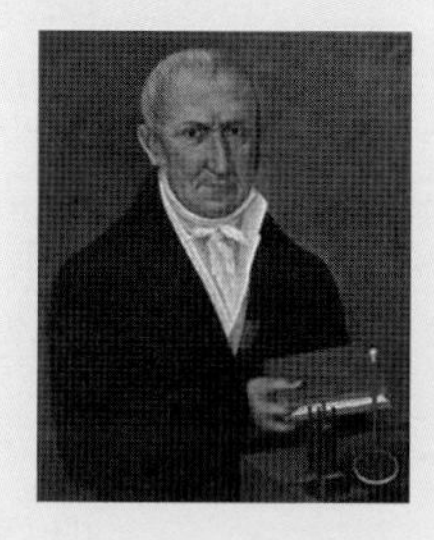

Voltage is measured in volts (V). The volt is named for the Italian physicist Alessandro Volta (1745-1827), who invented the first battery in 1800. Volta's batteries used pans of different chemicals connected by metal strips. Today's batteries are very similar except the chemicals are contained in convenient, safe packages of useful sizes.

One volt is equal to 1 joule of energy for each coulomb of charge.

Voltage drops when energy is used

Voltage is reduced when energy is used

If we connect anything that uses energy, like a light bulb, we reduce the voltage. This should make sense since voltage is a measure of energy. Anything that uses energy (motors, bulbs, resistors) lowers the voltage since it takes energy away from any moving charges in the circuit.

Two examples of circuits

Suppose you connect two circuits as shown in Figure 7.3. Both circuits have 1.5 volts as the highest voltage and zero volts as the lowest voltage. One circuit has a single light bulb and the other circuit has two bulbs.

The single-bulb circuit is much brighter. This is because all the energy is used up in one bulb. The voltage goes from 1.5 V to 0 V across the bulb.

In the two-bulb circuit, the voltage drops from 1.5 volts to 0 across *two* bulbs. The voltage starts at 1.5 volts. After the first light bulb the voltage is reduced to 0.75 volts because the first bulb used half the energy. The second light bulb reduces the voltage another 0.75 volts, to get down to zero. Each bulb only "sees" a voltage difference of 0.75 volts so each of the two bulbs gets less energy, and is dimmer.

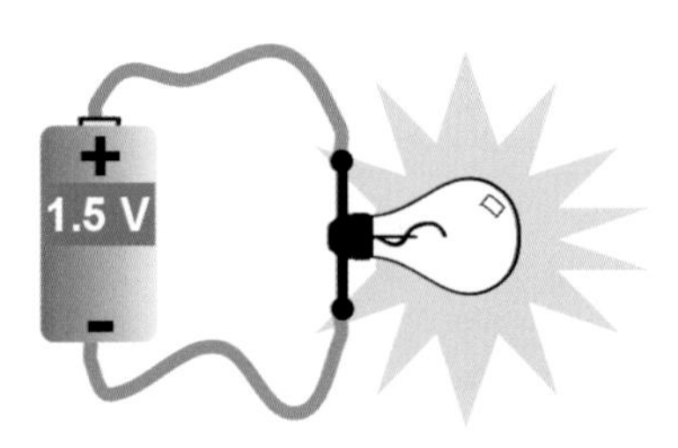

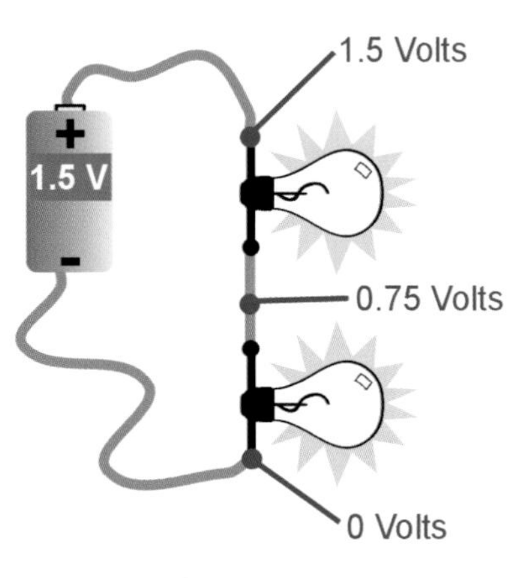

Figure 7.3: *Every time you connect something that uses energy, like a light bulb, some of the voltage is reduced. One bulb is bright because it gets all the energy. Two bulbs are dimmer because each one gets only half the energy. The voltage is lower between the two bulbs because the first bulb uses up half the energy.*

Batteries, energy, and voltage

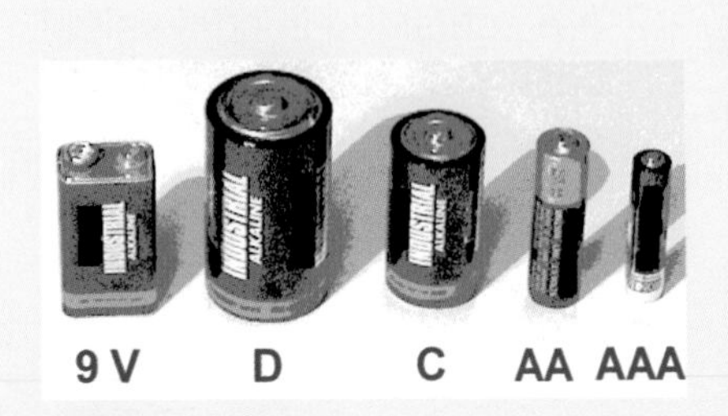

What is the difference between AA, AAA, C, and D batteries? If you measure the voltage of each, you will see that it is the same. The main difference between them is that the AAA battery is small, and does not store as much energy. AAA batteries will not last as long as D batteries. Think of two identical cars, one with an extra-big gas tank and one with a regular gas tank. Both cars go the same speed, but the one with the big gas tank will keep going longer.

If you need charge that has more energy, you must increase the voltage. Radio batteries have 9 volts and car batteries have 12 volts. In a 12-volt battery each charge that flows carries 12 joules of energy.

Some kinds of batteries can be recharged. Batteries made with nickel and cadmium (NiCad) are used in cell phones and power tools because they can be recharged many times.

7.2 Current

In the last section, you learned that charges move from places of high voltage in a circuit to places of lower voltage. Electrical current is how we describe the flow of charges. Current is what flows through wires and does work, like making light or turning a motor.

Current

Current is flow of charge

Current is the flow of electric charges. You can think of electrical current much as you would think of a current of water. If a faucet is on, you can measure the rate of water flow by finding out how much water comes out in one minute. You might find that the current (or flow) is 10 gallons per minute. In a circuit, you can measure the current, but it is measured in amperes. One ampere is a flow of one coulomb per second. A current of 10 amperes means that 10 coulombs of charge flow through the wire every second.

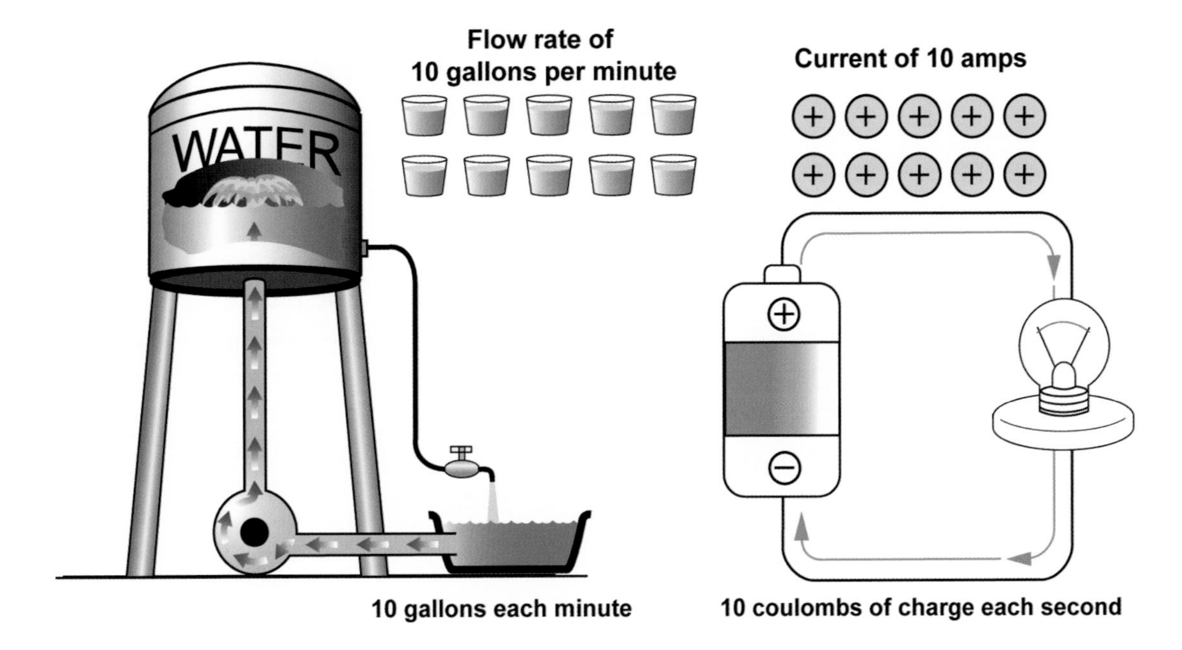

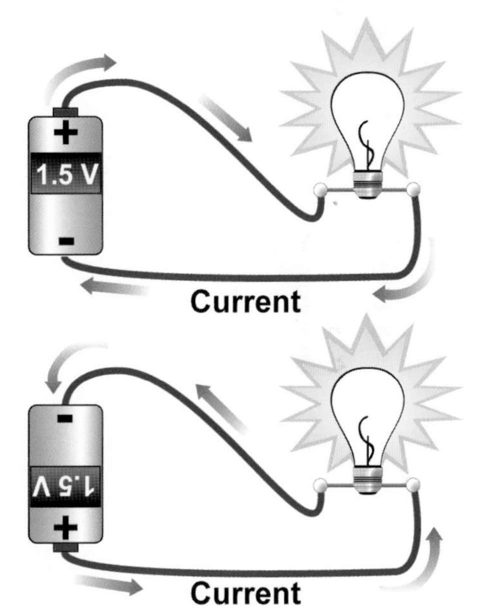

Figure 7.4: *Current flows from plus to minus, or from high voltage to low voltage.*

Where does electrical current come from?

Charges are very small

When you look at a wire, you can't see current. The particles that carry charge are electrons. Electrons are parts of atoms, and they are so small that they can flow in the spaces between atoms. That is why we can't see any movement in a wire.

The charges are already in the wire

Batteries do not provide most of the charges that flow in a circuit. Current occurs because electrons in the battery repel electrons in the wire, which repel other electrons in the wire, and so on. This is why a light goes on as soon as you connect your circuit together. Since the wire is made of copper atoms, there are plenty of electrons. When there is no voltage, electrons in the wire do not flow in a current.

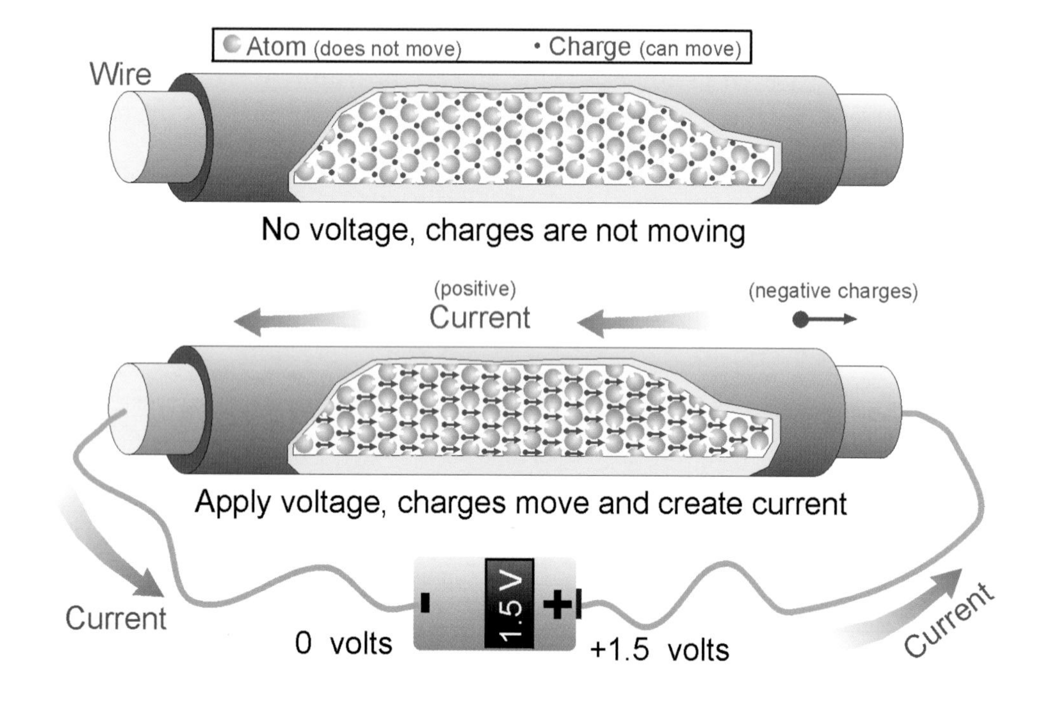

Things to remember:

A voltage difference supplies energy to make charges flow.

Current carries energy and does work.

What really flows?

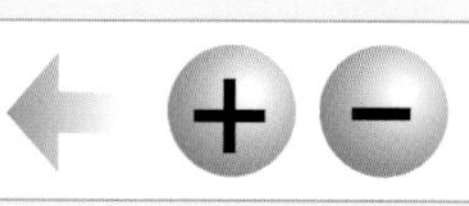

Either positive charges or negative charges can move to make an electric current. The type of charge depends upon the materials that make up the circuit. For example, in the human body, current is the movement of both positive and negative charges in nerves.

Electric current was first thought to be positive charge moving from plus to minus.

In reality, most charge flow in circuits is the movement of *negative* charge from minus to plus.

In practical electricity, we still say current flows from plus to minus or from high voltage to low voltage. The fact that it is actually negative charge moving does not matter when working with most electric circuits.

Measuring current

The ampere or amp

Current is measured in units called amperes (A), or amps for short. The unit is named in honor of Andre-Marie Ampere (1775-1836), a French physicist who studied electromagnetism.

Definition of 1 amp

One amp is a flow of 1 coulomb of charge per second. A 100-watt light bulb uses a little more than 1 amp of current. A single D battery can supply a few amps of current for about a half hour before being completely drained.

Measuring current

To measure current you have to make it flow through the meter. The moving charges can't be counted unless they pass through the meter. That means you must connect the meter into your circuit so the current is forced to flow through it.

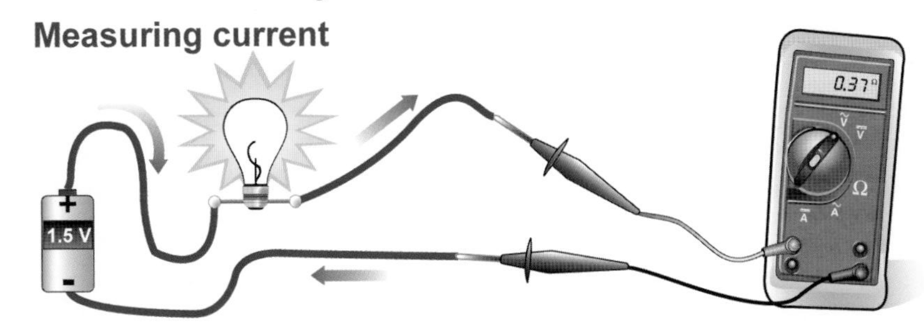

Setting up the meter

Most meters have settings for both voltage and current. You will need to set your meter to measure current. Meters can also measure alternating current (AC) and direct current (DC). We will discuss AC and DC in a later section. For circuits with light bulbs and batteries you want to use the DC settings.

Be careful measuring current

The last important thing about measuring current is that the meter itself can be damaged by too much current. Your meter may contain a *circuit breaker* or *fuse*. Circuit breakers and fuses are two kinds of devices that protect circuits from too much current. If your meter does not work the circuit breaker or fuse may have acted. A circuit breaker can be reset but a fuse must be replaced.

Circuit breakers

Electrical circuits in your house have a *circuit breaker* that stops too much current from flowing. Many wires in your house can carry 15 or 20 amps of current. Wires can get dangerously hot if they carry more current than they are designed for.

One of the things that can overload a circuit is using too many electrical appliances at once, such as an air conditioner and an iron on the same circuit. If many appliances try to draw too much current, the circuit breaker trips and breaks the circuit before the wires get hot enough to cause a fire.

A circuit breaker uses temperature-sensitive metal that expands with heat. When the current gets too high, the expanded metal bends and breaks the circuit. You have to unplug some appliances and reset the circuit breaker.

Electricity in your house

Circuits in your house You use electric current in your house every day. When you plug in an electrical appliance, you connect it to a circuit created by wires in the walls. The wires eventually connect to power lines outside your house that bring the current from a power station.

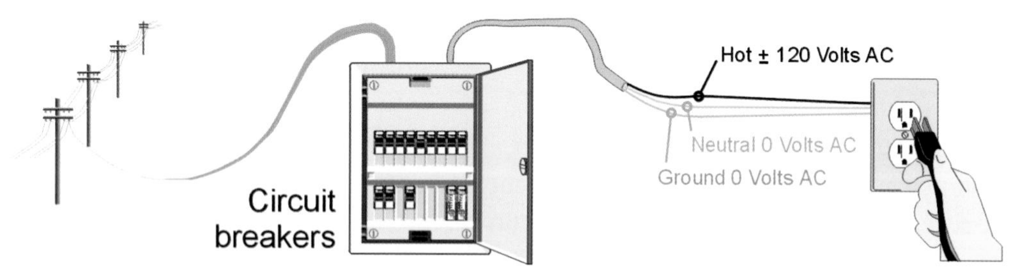

AC current The electricity in your house uses **alternating current**, also called **AC** current. This means the direction of the current goes back and forth. In the electrical system used in the United States, the current reverses direction 60 times per second. Each wall socket has three wires feeding it. The hot wire carries 120 volts AC. The neutral wire stays at zero volts. When you plug something in, current flows in and out of the hot wire, through your appliance (doing work) and back through the neutral wire. The ground wire is for safety and is connected to the ground near your house. If there is a short circuit in your appliance, the current flows through the ground wire rather than through you!

DC current The current from a battery does not alternate. A battery only makes current that flows in one direction. This is called **direct current**, or **DC**. Most of the experiments you will do in the lab use DC current.

Household electricity is AC For large amounts of electricity, we use AC current because it is easier to transmit and generate. All the power lines you see overhead carry AC current. Other countries also use AC current. However, in Europe, the current reverses itself 50 times per second rather than 60, and wall sockets are at a different voltage. When traveling in Europe, you need special adapters to use electrical appliances you bring from home.

What is a ground fault circuit interrupter?

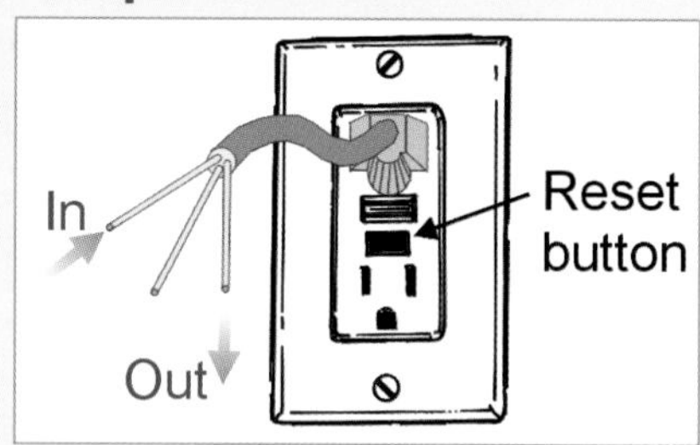

Circuits in wet or damp locations are wired with a ground fault circuit interrupter (GFCI). You may have seen this device, with its red button, in a bathroom, or near the kitchen sink.

Plugs usually have two or three wires. Electricity goes in one wire of a plug and out another wire. The same current should go in and out. If there is a difference, then some of the electricity could be going through YOU instead of back through the plug. Current flowing through the human body is dangerous.

The GFCI senses differences and breaks the circuit if the current coming out of the plug is different from the current going back in. The GFCI disconnects the circuit in 0.03 seconds if it detects a leak as small as a few thousandths of an amp. A GFCI protects you from being electrocuted.

7.3 Resistance

Parts of electrical devices are made up of metals but often have plastic coverings. Why are these materials chosen? How well does current move through these materials? In this section, you will learn about the ability of materials and objects to carry electrical current.

Conductors and insulators

What is a conductor? Charge flows very easily through some kinds of materials, like copper. We call a material like copper an **electrical conductor** because it can *conduct*, or carry, electrical current. Most metals are good conductors.

What is an insulator? Other materials, like glass or plastic, do not allow charge to flow. We call these materials **electrical insulators** because they insulate (or block) the flow of current.

What is a semiconductor? The third category of materials are not as easy-flowing as conductors, but not quite insulators either. These materials are named **semiconductors** because they are between conductors and insulators in their ability to carry current. Computer chips, LED's and some kinds of lasers are made from semiconductors.

Electrical current is usually carried by moving electrons, atoms stay fixed in place.

In an *insulator*, the electrons are tightly bound to atoms and cannot move.

In a *conductor,* the electrons come free and can move to create electrical current. Since electrons are negative, they move in the opposite direction as the (positive) current.

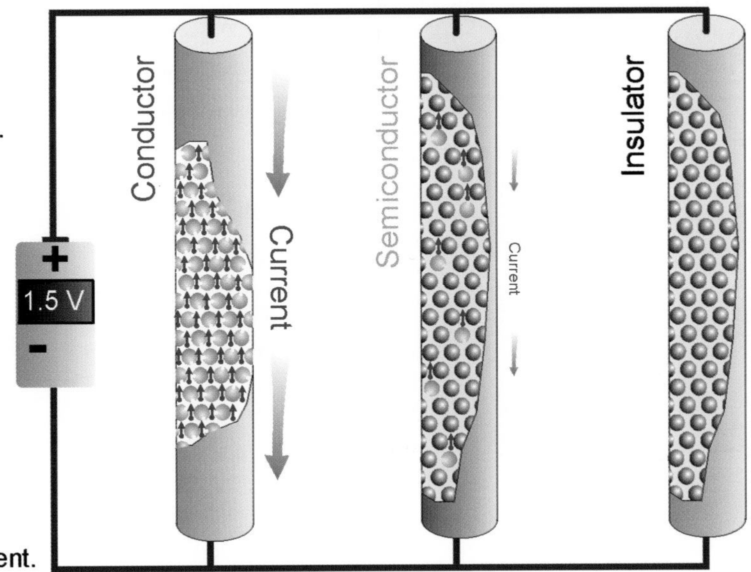

Why are some materials conductors and some insulators?

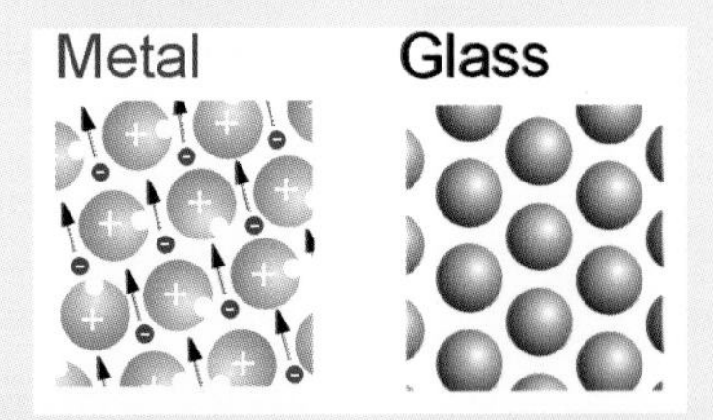

Metals are good conductors. To understand why, we have to understand how metal atoms behave. When many metal atoms are together, like in a wire, they each lose one or more electrons. These "free" electrons can move around in a sea of atoms. Metals are good conductors because there are lots of "free" electrons to carry charge.

Glass is a good insulator. Glass does not have free electrons. When atoms of glass are together they keep their electrons tightly bound. Since no electrons can move free of their atoms, glass is a good insulator.

Conductivity

What makes a material a conductor or insulator?

Materials are not pure conductors or insulators. A little charge flows through all materials if you connect them to a battery. The difference is in how much current flows. If you do the experiments you find that the amount of current varies from very small to very large. The property of a material to allow charge to flow is called its electrical conductivity. Materials with high conductivity (like metals) allow charge to flow easily and are conductors. Materials with low conductivity block charge from flowing and are insulators.

Electrical conductivity	Category	Material
High	**conductors**	silver
		copper
		gold
		aluminum
		tungsten
		iron
	semiconductors	carbon
		silicon
		germanium
	insulators	air
		rubber
		paper
		Teflon
		plastics (varies by type)
		glass
Low		mica

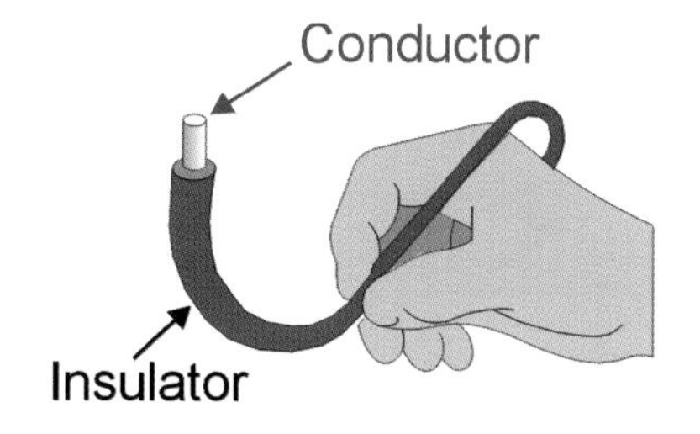

Figure 7.5: *A wire uses both conductors and insulators. The conductor carries the current through the center. The insulator keeps the current from reaching you when you touch the wire.*

Resistance

Current and resistance The **resistance** of an object measures how easily charges flow through. High resistance means it is difficult for current to flow. Low resistance means it is easy for current to flow.

Resistance of water flow Emptying a jar of water through a narrow opening is a good example of resistance. If the opening of the jar is large, there is low resistance. Lots of water flows out quickly. If the opening of the jar is small, there is a lot of resistance. Water does not flow out as fast.

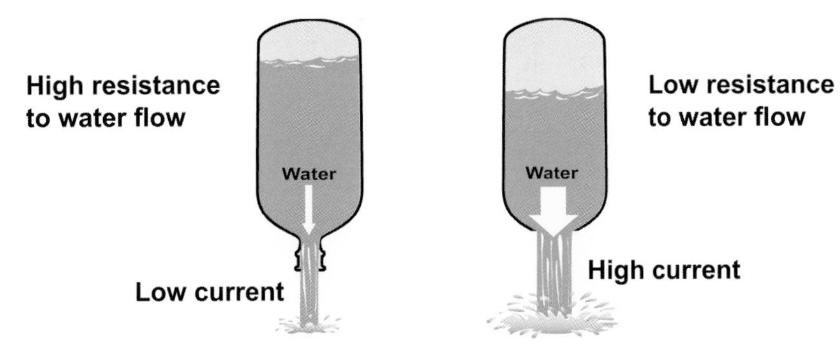

Electrical resistance Electrical resistance restricts the flow of current. If the resistance is high, not much current flows. If the resistance is low, a lot of current flows.

Devices that use electrical energy have resistance. For example, light bulbs have resistance. If you string more light bulbs together the resistance adds up and the current goes down.

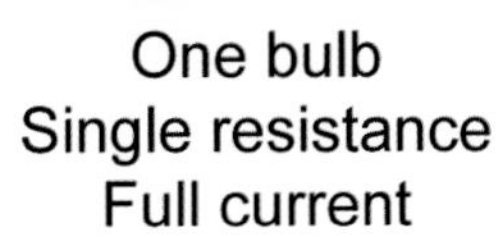

One bulb
Single resistance
Full current

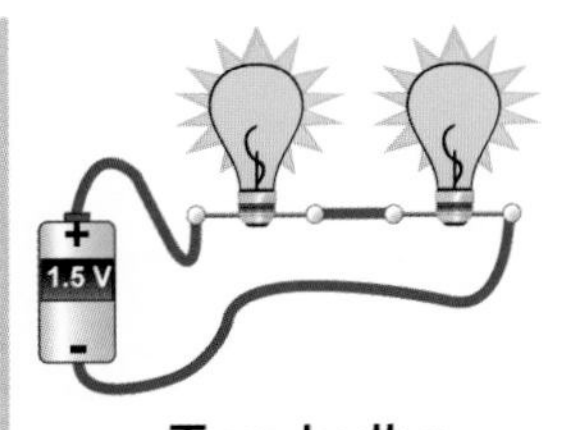

Two bulbs
Twice the resistance
Half the current

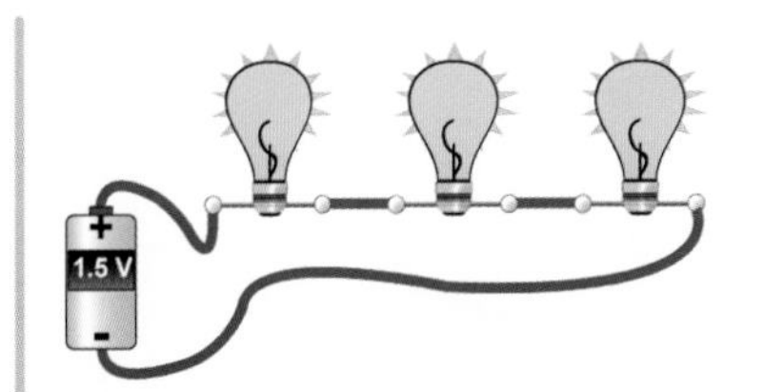

Three bulbs
Three times the resistance
One-third the current

Breakdown voltage

You previously learned that lightning is caused by electric charge. In a thunderstorm, positive and negative charges become separated. The voltage difference becomes huge, reaching 10,000 volts per centimeter.

Air, usually a good insulator, breaks down under these conditions. The high voltage created by the storm rips the electrons away from atoms of air. The air conducts, and we see lightning.

The lowest voltage at which an insulator turns into a conductor is called its breakdown voltage. The breakdown of air occurs when 8,000 volts or more is applied across a centimeter of air.

The ohm

Units of resistance

Electrical resistance is measured in units called ohms. This unit is abbreviated with the Greek letter omega (Ω). When you see Ω in a sentence, think or read "ohms." The ohm is named for the German physicist Georg S. Ohm (1787-1854). Ohm spent many years studying how circuits work.

How much current flows in a circuit?

We can now answer the question of how much current flows in a circuit. If the voltage goes up, the current goes up too. If the resistance goes up, the current goes *down*. Voltage and resistance determine how much current flows in a circuit. If a circuit has a resistance of 1 ohm (1 Ω), then a current of 1 amp flows when a voltage of 1 volt is applied.

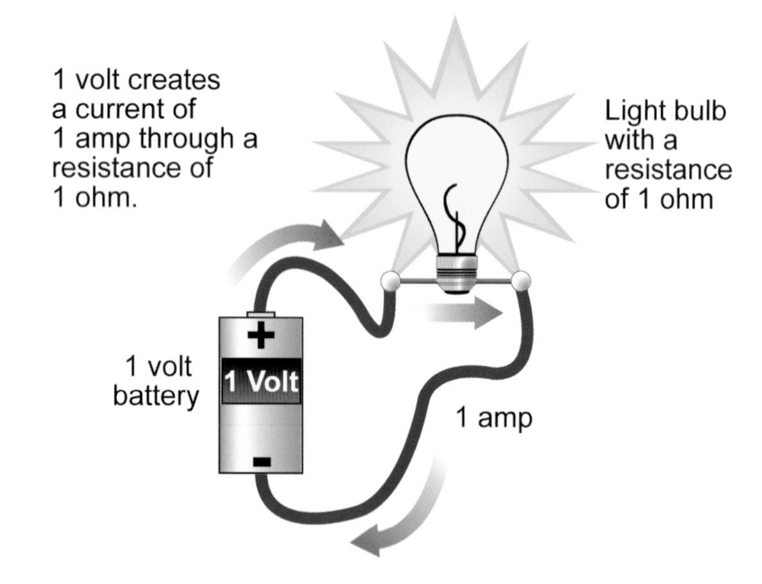

How a photocopier works

A photocopier has a plate coated with a thin layer of a special material (like selenium, arsenic, or tellurium) that acts as an insulator in the dark but as a conductor when exposed to light.

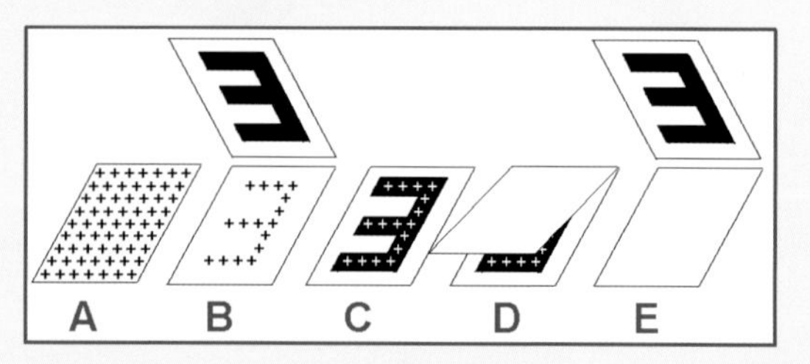

(**A**) The plate starts with a positive charge. Light creates an image on the plate (**B**). The white areas of the image become conductive and let the charge flow away. The dark areas stay insulating and keep their positive charge.

Next, a negatively charged powdered ink (called toner) is brushed over the plate. Because opposite charges attract, the toner sticks to the positively charged areas of the plate (**C**).

A piece of paper is given a positive charge, and held on the plate (**D**). The paper attracts the ink and now has a perfect image made of powder (**E**). To prevent the image from rubbing off, the paper is heated, which melts the toner onto the paper.

Why does a bulb light?

What's in a light bulb? Electricity would not be so useful if it flowed equally through every material. Let's look at some of the materials in a light bulb. A light bulb contains a copper wire and a thin tungsten filament in a glass bulb filled with argon gas (Figure 7.6). Why are these materials chosen?

Copper wire We use copper wire to conduct current to a light bulb filament because copper is a good conductor.

Tungsten filament We use a thin tungsten filament for several reasons. Just as a narrow pipe resists water flow more than a wide pipe, the very thin filament resists the flow of current. Because of the high resistance of the tungsten filament, the current going through it generates a lot of heat. The filament continues to heat up until it reaches 2,500°C (4,500°F). The filament glows white as it heats up, creating the light that we see.

Most substances would melt under these circumstances. Tungsten is chosen because it does not melt until it reaches an even higher temperature. Tungsten also doesn't corrode easily.

Argon gas We use argon inside the bulb because it is an inert gas. An inert gas will not interact with the hot tungsten. If the hot tungsten filament were in air, it would interact with the oxygen in air and burn up quickly like a match. The argon protects the tungsten so that it can heat up many, many times before breaking down.

Other kinds of light bulbs Much of the electrical power going into a light bulb becomes heat, and not light. Fluorescent bulbs are more efficient because they convert more of the electrical energy to light than does a regular (incandescent) bulb. Researchers are trying to make lights from many new materials that are even more efficient. In the laboratory, tiny light emitting diodes (LED's) have been made that produce more light from less electricity than any other type of light source.

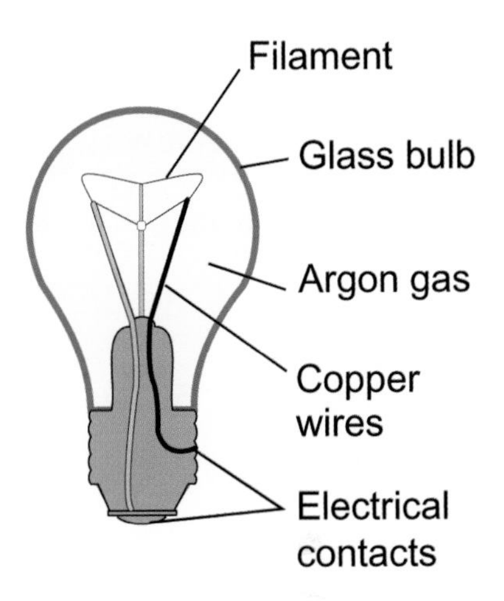

Figure 7.6: *Some parts of a light bulb. There are two electrical contacts in the base of the light bulb. Both of these must come in contact with an electrical circuit for the light bulb to work.*

Chapter 7 Review

Vocabulary Review

Match the following terms with the correct definition. There is one extra definition in the list that will not match any of the terms.

Set One

1. battery
2. voltage
3. volt
4. current
5. ampere

a. Flow rate of electric charges
b. The representation of circuit current as the flow of positive charges
c. The commonly used unit of measurement for current, equal to coulombs/second
d. A device that uses energy of chemical reactions to separate positive and negative charges
e. The amount of potential energy per unit of charge
f. The commonly used unit of measurement for voltage, equal to joules/coulomb

Set Two

1. amp
2. alternating current
3. direct current
4. conductor
5. insulator

a. Current that moves in only one direction through a wire
b. A material that conducts current easily
c. A material that conducts current poorly
d. The abbreviation often used for ampere
e. Current that reverses direction through a wire
f. The representation of circuit current as the flow of negative charges

Set Three

1. semiconductor
2. electrical conductivity
3. resistance
4. ohm

a. A material that conducts current when exposed to light
b. The ability of an object to resist current
c. The ability of a material to conduct current
d. The commonly used unit of measurement for resistance
e. A material that conducts current at a medium rate

Concept review

1. Explain in two or three sentences how a battery creates potential energy.
2. Explain how a water pump and battery are similar in terms of creating potential energy.
3. Explain the difference between a AA alkaline battery and a D alkaline battery. Discuss both voltage and life span.
4. The measurement of current in a circuit is similar to the measurement of the flow of water out of a faucet. Explain why this is so.
5. A circuit breaker is a safety device that shuts down a circuit when the current is too high. Describe how a circuit breaker works.
6. The electrical system in the United States runs on __________ current.
7. A battery circuit runs on ___________ current.
8. A ground fault circuit interrupter is usually wired into circuits that are in wet or damp locations. What is the main purpose of this device?
9. Explain why a circuit contains a copper wire with a plastic cover over the wire.
10. List one example of each of the following.
    a. electrical conductor
    b. electrical insulator
    c. semiconductor
11. A light bulb uses a very thin tungsten filament to provide light.
    a. Why is the filament thinner than the copper wire used in circuit wiring?
    b. Why is tungsten a good material for the filament?

Problems

1. When two batteries are connected together correctly, their voltage adds together. If a circuit has two AA alkaline batteries (connected correctly!), how many joules of energy does each coulomb of charge have at the battery terminals?
2. When you use a meter to measure battery voltage, you place one probe on one battery terminal and one probe on the other battery terminal. Why do you measure voltage in this way?
3. When measuring the voltage of a D alkaline battery, which is usually at 1.5 volts, you accidentally reverse the probes. The probe that is set at zero volts is placed at the positive terminal and the other probe is placed at the negative terminal. What will the meter read now?
4. A toaster oven uses a current of 650 coulombs each minute. What is the current in amps?

5. You build a circuit with one battery and a bulb. You remove the wire from the positive terminal of the battery, insert the meter in the circuit, and measure the current. The meter reads 0.5 amps. You remove the meter and rebuild your circuit. Now you remove the wire from the negative terminal of the battery, insert the meter, and measure the current at this new point in the circuit. What will the meter read now?
6. When you measure current of a circuit with an electrical meter you keep the circuit on and insert the meter at one point in the circuit. Explain why.
7. List these materials in order from least to greatest resistance: light bulbs, clip leads, air, and pencil lead.
8. You have two pieces of wire of the same size, one made of copper and the other made of iron. Which wire is the better conductor?
9. An electrical meter measures resistance of an object by applying a voltage through the material and then measuring how much current the object will carry. Do you measure resistance of an object when it is in a working circuit, or do you turn the circuit off first? Explain your answer.

Applying your knowledge

1. With an adult, inspect all cords and plugs in your home. Make sure that the insulation cover on them is in good condition, without breaks or cracks. With help, replace any damaged cords or plugs.
2. Brain and nerve cells communicate by the movement of charged chemicals, which is a type of current. Some diseases, like epilepsy, occur because of currents that occur when they shouldn't. Research electrical currents in the brain and problems that occur when the system doesn't work correctly.
3. Create a table that lists how the nerves in your body are alike and different from electrical wires used in your home. Come up with two statements that show how they are alike and two statements that show they are different.
4. The "electricity" generated by the beating heart is monitored by an electrocardiograph (an ECG or EKG). The results called an electrocardiogram are used to diagnose heart problems. Write a brief paragraph describing how an electrocardiograph works.
5. With an adult, find out the location of the circuit breakers for your home. If the circuit breakers aren't labeled, determine which outlets are connected to which fuse or circuit breaker, and then label them.

UNIT 3

Electricity and Magnetism

Chapter 8

Electrical Relationships

Introduction to Chapter 8

You have learned that mathematical models are used to describe the exact relationships between physical quantities. What relationships exist among voltage, current and resistance? How can we use these relationships to analyze circuits? What are practical applications of these relationships?

Investigations for Chapter 8

8.1	**Ohm's Law**	*How are voltage, current, and resistance related?*

In this Investigation, you will use a step-by-step method to determine the mathematical relationship between voltage, current, and resistance in a circuit.

8.2	**Work, Energy, and Power**	*How much does it cost to use the electrical appliances in your home?*

You previously studied power in a mechanical system. What does power mean in an electric circuit? How much power do everyday appliances need? In this Investigation, you will learn how to read power ratings on electrical appliances and use this information to estimate electrical costs in your home.

Learning Goals

In this chapter, you will:

- ✔ Measure how current changes when voltage is increased.
- ✔ Measure how current changes when resistance is increased.
- ✔ Describe how voltage, current, and resistance are related.
- ✔ Use Ohm's law to solve circuit problems.
- ✔ Explain why resistors are used in a circuit.
- ✔ Define power as the rate at which energy flows.
- ✔ Describe relationships between work, energy, and power.
- ✔ Calculate power use in a circuit.
- ✔ Rank the amount of power used by various household appliances.
- ✔ Estimate the cost per month of using a common household appliance.
- ✔ Use dimensional analysis to find out what we buy from electric utility companies.
- ✔ Explain how to choose a safe extension cord.

Vocabulary

horsepower	kilowatt-hour	potentiometer	resistor
kilowatt	Ohm's law	power	watt

8.1 Ohm's Law

You know about three important electrical quantities: voltage, current, and resistance. Of the three, current is the one that carries energy through a circuit. How does the current depend on the voltage and resistance? In this section you will learn the fundamental relationship for circuits known as Ohm's law.

One volt causes a current of 1 amp to flow through a resistance of 1 ohm.

What is Ohm's law?

The relationship between amps, volts, and ohms If you have been working with circuits, you probably have an idea of how voltage, current, and resistance are related. You know that if you increase the voltage, the current goes up. You know that if you increase the resistance by adding a second light bulb, the current goes down.

Ohm's law German physicist Georg S. Ohm (1787-1854) experimented with circuits to find the exact mathematical relationship present in most circuits. The relationship that he discovered is called Ohm's law.

Ohm's law

$$I = \frac{V}{R}$$

Current (amps) → I

Voltage (vo ts) → V

Resistance (ohms, Ω) → R

Equation	Gives you...	If you know...
I = V/R	current (I)	voltage and resistance
V = IR	voltage (V)	current and resistance
R = V/I	resistance (R)	voltage and current

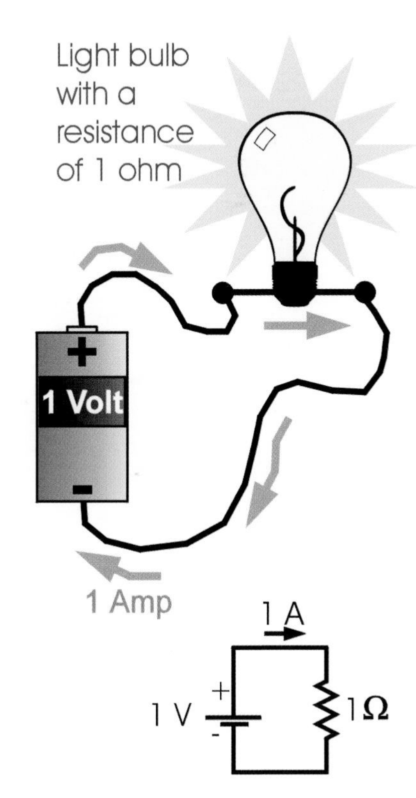

Figure 8.1: *Ohm's law in a circuit.*

Using Ohm's law to analyze circuits

Ohm's law can be used to predict any of the three variables given the other two. Sometimes you want to know the current in the circuit. Sometimes you want to know voltage or resistance. Use the problem-solving steps to help set up and work through problems.

Example: A light bulb with a resistance of 2 ohms is connected to a 1.5 volt battery as shown. Calculate the current that will flow.

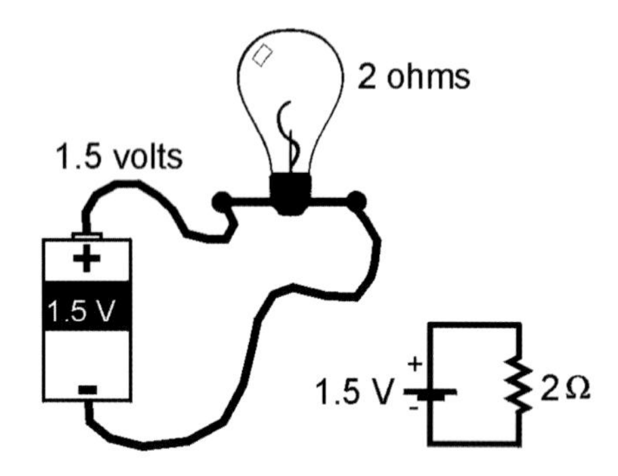

Solution:

(1) We are asked for the current, I.

(2) We know V and R.

(3) Use the formula $I = V \div R$.

(4) Plug in numbers.
$I = 1.5\ V \div 2\ \Omega = 0.75\ A$

Answer: 0.75 amps will flow in the circuit.

Example: A light bulb requires 3 amps to produce light. The resistance of the bulb is 1.5 ohms. How many batteries do you need if each battery is 1.5 volts?

(1) We are asked for the number of batteries, which means we need to know the voltage since each battery is 1.5 volts.

(2) We know current and resistance.

(3) Use the formula $V = IR$.

(4) Plug in numbers.
$V = 3\ A \times 1.5\ \Omega = 4.5\ V$

Answer: Each battery can produce 1.5 volts so we need three batteries to get the required 4.5 volts.

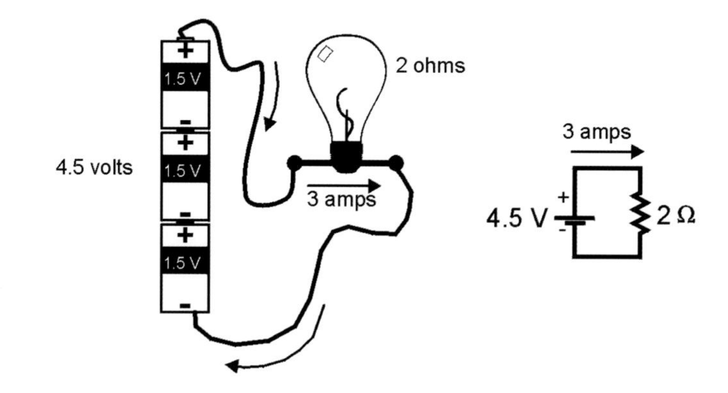

Graphing and Ohm's law

Devices and Ohm's law Ohm's law tells us how much current flows for different amounts of voltage. If a device has the same resistance under different conditions we say that it obeys Ohm's law. We can predict current flow at different voltages. Not all electrical devices obey Ohm's law! If resistance changes, a device does *not* obey Ohm's law. For example, a light bulb's resistance increases when voltage and current increase.

The current vs. voltage graph A current vs. voltage graph shows us if resistance changes. Often, these graphs have both positive and negative values of current and voltage. These positive and negative values are just a way to refer to the direction of current in a wire. You can apply voltage two ways across a wire (Figure 8.2). How you apply voltage determines current direction. One direction is positive and the other negative.

I vs. V for a diode A simple resistor obeys Ohm's law—its current vs. voltage graph is a straight line. Resistance is the same at all values of voltage and current. For a *diode*, the graph is not a straight line. A diode only allows charge to flow in one direction! This is why current is zero when voltage is negative. Diodes do not obey Ohm's law. Diodes, like computer chips, are made from semiconductors.

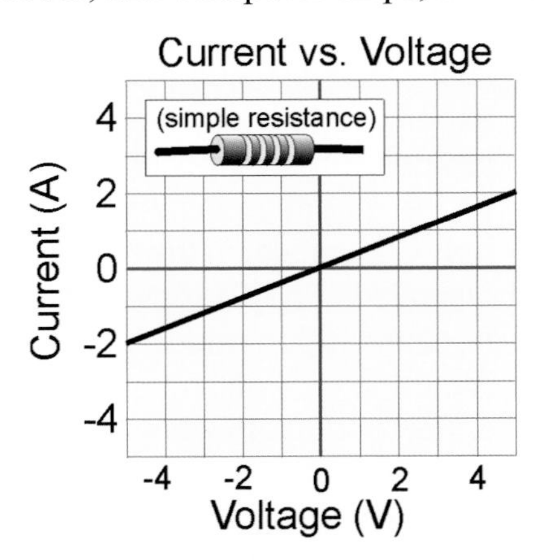

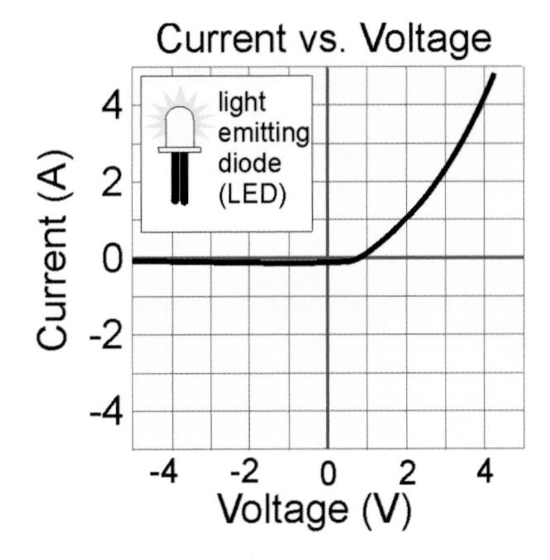

Finding resistance from a graph You can find resistance from a current vs. voltage graph. If the graph is a straight line (obeying Ohm's law), pick a point on the line. Read voltage and current (Figure 8.3) from the graph. Calculate resistance using the R = V/I form of Ohm's law.

Positive and negative

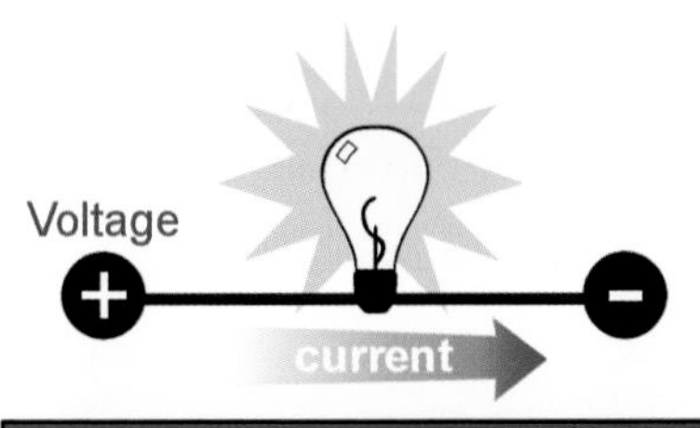

You choose that ...

Current is positive when it flows from left to right.

Voltage is positive when + is on the left and - on the right.

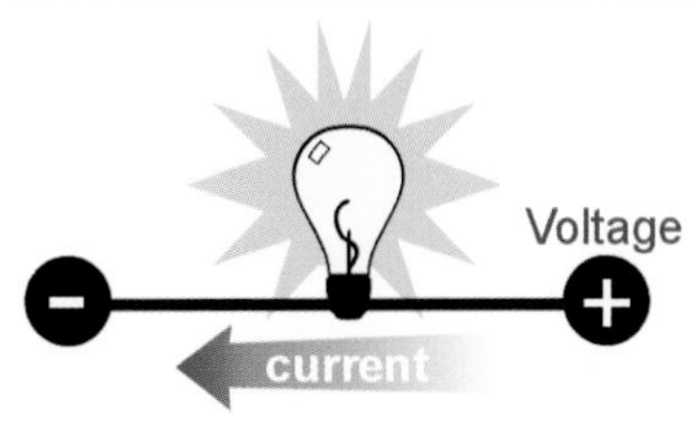

That means IF current goes the other way you call it NEGATIVE current.

Figure 8.2: *How to interpret positive and negative voltage. You have to choose which direction to call positive. After you choose, the other direction is negative!*

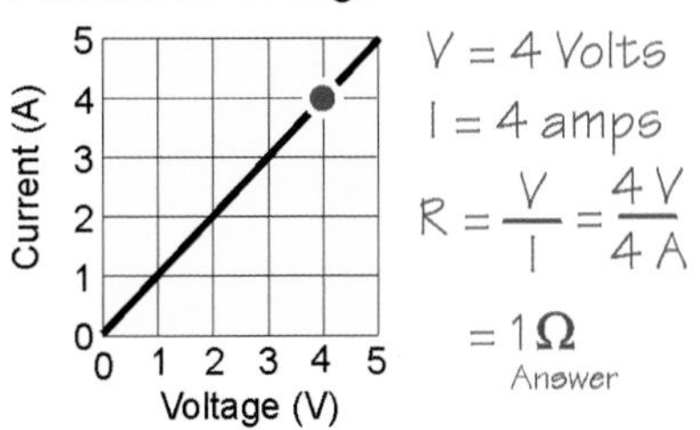

Figure 8.3: *Using a graph of current vs. voltage to determine resistance.*

Temperature and Ohm's law

The cause of resistance

Resistance happens because the charges bounce into and around atoms as they weave their way through a material. If the voltage goes up, the charges move a little faster between atoms and we get more current. Think about a highway. On a stretch of road there may be the same number of cars whether they are going 30 or 60 miles per hour. But, at 60 mph, twice as many cars flow past you per minute compared with 30 mph. Materials obey Ohm's law because the speed of moving charges increases proportionally with voltage.

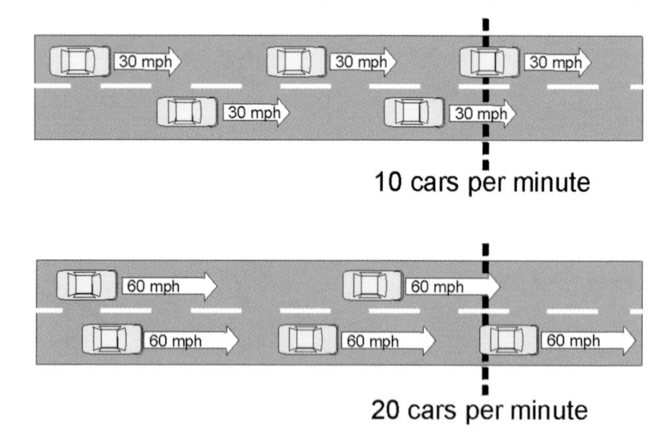

Resistance of metals increases with temperature

Even if a material obeys Ohm's law, its resistance can change when it is cooler or warmer. Atoms gain energy when they are heated up. With extra energy, the atoms move around more. They collide more often with moving charges that make up the current. The extra collisions mean that hot metal has more resistance than cold metal.

Superconductivity

The LDX experiment at MIT uses a superconducting coil to explore fusion energy.

What happens to the resistance of a material as its temperature is lowered? This question intrigued Dutch physicist Heike Kamerlingh Onnes (1853-1926). In 1911, he discovered that when mercury is cooled to 269 degrees below zero (-269°C), its resistance suddenly drops to zero. He called this property "superconductivity." A *superconductor* allows current to flow without losing *any* energy as heat or light.

Until the 1960s, superconductivity remained of little practical value because it was very hard and expensive to cool wires down to such extremely low temperatures. A few practical uses were invented, such as the magnetic resonance imaging machines found in many hospitals. In the 1980s, scientists made another big discovery. They discovered special ceramic materials that become superconductors at higher temperatures. Although they still must be cooled to -70°C, the new superconductors work at temperatures 200 degrees warmer than mercury. Engineers are working with these "high temperature" superconductors to see if they can be used to make more efficient motors, generators, power cables, and magnetically levitated trains.

Resistors

What is a resistor?

Using Ohm's law, if the voltage is prescribed, then the only way we can change the current is by changing the resistance. Components called **resistors** are used to control current in many circuits. Resistors are made from materials that keep the same resistance over a wide range of temperatures and currents.

Fixed and variable resistors

There are many kinds of resistors. The two basic kinds are fixed and variable. A fixed resistor always has the same value. An application of fixed resistors is a three-way light switch. Each setting connects the circuit to a different resistor. The three values of resistance determine three levels of current. The three levels of current control the brightness of the bulb.

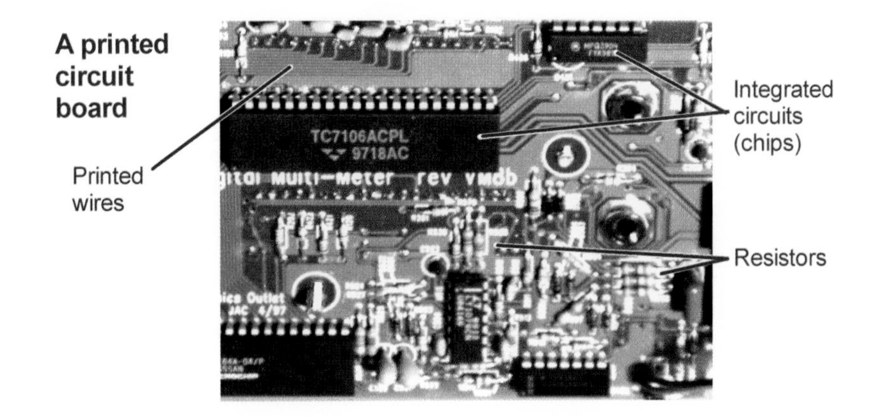

If you look inside a stereo or telephone you will find a circuit board. The circuit board has wires printed on it and is covered with little parts. The little parts are called **electronic components** and are soldered to the circuit board. Many of the components are resistors, which look like small skinny cylinders with colored stripes on them. Because they are so tiny, it is impossible to write how much resistance each one has. The colored stripes are a code that tells you the resistance.

Example:

Figure out the value of this resistor.

(1) The first two stripes are a number. Red (2) and green (5) make 25.

(2) The third stripe is the multiplier. Orange is 1,000.

(3) The fourth stripe is the accuracy tolerance. Silver is +/- 10%.

The example resistor is 25,000 ohms.

Resistor Color Codes

Color	Digit	Multiplier
Black	0	1
Brown	1	10
Red	2	100
Orange	3	1,000
Yellow	4	10,000
Green	5	100,000
Blue	6	1,000,000
Violet	7	10,000,000
Gray	8	not a multiplier
White	9	not a multiplier

Electrical controls

What are controls? Every time you turn a knob or push a switch you are using an electrical control. We use controls for lights, motors, air conditioners, and almost every electrical device you can think of. Many controls use variable resistors.

Making a dimmer switch An application of variable resistors is a dimmer switch. As you turn the dimmer switch from low to high, it changes the resistance, which also changes the current. Current is increased as the resistance goes down, and the bulb glows brighter in response.

The potentiometer A potentiometer is a variable resistor. Inside the potentiometer is a circular resistor and a little sliding contact called a wiper. As shown in the diagram below, the wiper moves when you turn the knob and is connected to a wire (B). You choose the resistance by turning the knob.

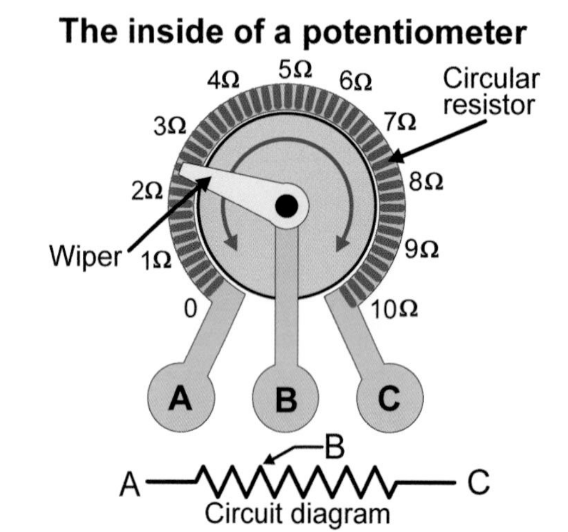

How the potentiometer works Potentiometers (or *pots* for short) have three wires. The resistance between A and C always stays the same. As you turn the knob the resistance between A and B changes. The resistance between B and C also changes. With the wiper rotated like the diagram above, the resistance between A and B is 2 ohms. The resistance between B and C is 8 ohms (10 minus 2).

You can choose how to connect a potentiometer into your circuit to change the resistance from zero to the maximum value of the potentiometer. For the potentiometer in the diagram the resistance can vary between zero and 10 ohms.

Lewis Latimer

Photo courtesy of Queens Library

Lewis Latimer was born in Chelsea, Massachusetts in 1848, six years after his parents escaped from slavery in Virginia.

As a child, Lewis loved to read and draw. When he was sixteen, Lewis joined the U.S. Navy, fighting for the Union in the Civil War. Afterward, He worked in a law office in Boston that specialized in helping people patent their inventions. There he taught himself how to use draftsmen's tools to make scale drawings of machines.

Latimer met Alexander Graham Bell at that office. Working late, Latimer made blueprints and helped Bell file the papers for his telephone patent—just hours before a rival.

A new job as a mechanical draftsman for the U.S. Electric Lighting company helped Latimer learn about incandescent lighting. Four years later, Thomas Edison hired Latimer as an electrical engineer and patent advisor. Latimer was later invited to join the prestigious research team known as Edison's pioneers. Latimer improved incandescent bulb design by replacing a paper filament with a carbon one. He also wrote the first engineer's handbook on electric lighting.

8.2 Work, Energy, and Power

If you look carefully at a stereo, hair dryer, or other household appliance, you find that most devices list a "power rating" that tells how many watts the appliance uses. In this section you will learn what these power ratings mean, and how to figure out the electricity costs of using various appliances.

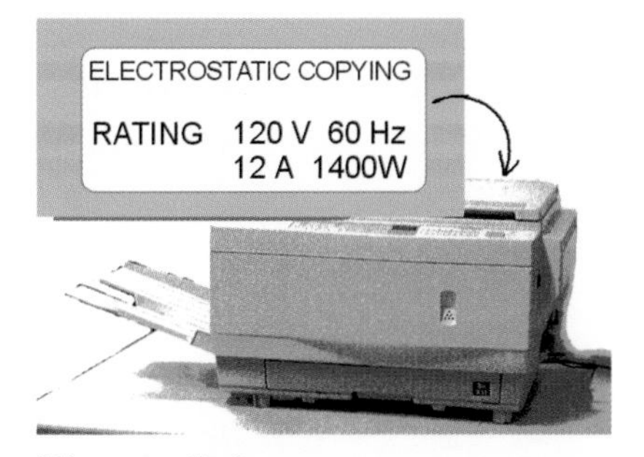

Figure 8.4: *The back of an electrical device often tells you how many watts it uses.*

Electric power

The three electrical quantities

We have now learned three important electrical quantities:

Amps	Current is what flows in a circuit. Current is measured in amps.
Volts	Voltage measures the potential energy difference between two places in a circuit. Voltage differences make current flow.
Ohms	Resistance measures the ability to resist the flow of current.

Paying for electricity

Electric bills sent out by utility companies don't charge by the volt, the amp, or the ohm. You may have noticed that electrical appliances in your home usually include another unit – the *watt*. Most appliances have a label that lists the number of watts or kilowatts. You may have purchased 60-watt light bulbs, or a 900-watt hair dryer, or a 1500-watt toaster oven. Electric companies charge for the energy you use, which depends on how many watts each appliance consumes in a given month.

A watt is a unit of power

The **watt** (W) is a unit of **power**. Power, in the scientific sense, has a precise meaning. Power is the rate at which energy is flowing. Energy is measured in joules. Power is measured in joules per second. One joule per second is equal to one watt. A 100-watt light bulb uses 100 joules of energy *every second*.

Where does the electrical power go?

Electrical power can be easily transformed into many different forms. An electric motor takes electrical power and makes mechanical power. A light bulb turns electrical power into light and a toaster oven turns the power into heat. The same unit (watts) applies to all forms of energy flow, including light, motion, electrical, thermal, or many others.

Figure 8.5: *One watt is an energy flow of one joule per second. A 100-watt light bulb uses 100 joules every second. A person running uses about 300 watts, or 300 joules every second.*

How can we measure power in a circuit?

Power in a circuit

Power in a circuit can be measured using the tools we already have. Remember that one watt equals an energy flow of one joule per second.

Amps	One amp is a flow of one coulomb of charge per second
Volts	One volt is an energy of one joule per coulomb of charge

If these two quantities are multiplied together, you will find that the units of coulombs cancel out, leaving the equation we want for power.

Voltage x Current = Power

$$\frac{\text{Joules}}{\cancel{\text{Coulomb}}} \times \frac{\cancel{\text{Coulomb}}}{\text{Second}} = \frac{\text{Joules}}{\text{Second}}$$

Power = voltage × current

Watts equal joules/second, so we can calculate electrical power in a circuit by multiplying voltage times current.

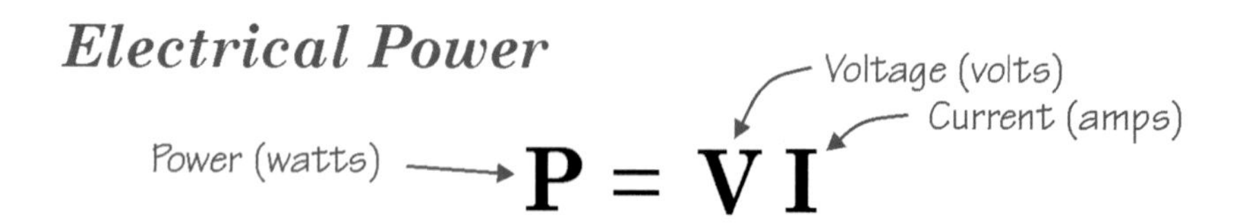

Watts and kilowatts

A larger unit of power is sometimes needed. The 1500-watt toaster oven may instead be labeled "1.5 kW." A kilowatt (kW) is equal to 1000 watts or 1000 joules per second.

Horsepower

The other common unit of power often seen on electric motors is the horsepower. One horsepower is 746 watts. Electric motors you find around the house range in size from 1/25th of a horsepower (30 watts) for a small electric fan to 2 horsepower (1492 watts) for an electric saw.

Electric cars

Many people believe that all cars will eventually be electric because electric cars give off little or no pollution. Electric cars are challenging to build because of the power you need. A gas engine for a car makes 100 horsepower, or about 75,000 watts.

Suppose you want to use 12-volt batteries, like the ones used to *start* cars today. To make 75 kilowatts of power at 12 volts, you need a current of 6,250 amps! By comparison, most people's homes use less than 100 amps.

The solution is to use more efficient motors and higher voltages. Research into electric cars is being done all over the world.

You buy electricity by the kilowatt-hour

Kilowatt-hours What do we buy from the electric utility company? Let's look at a utility bill. Utility companies charge customers for a unit called the kilowatt-hour (abbreviated kWh). One kilowatt-hour means that a kilowatt of power has been used for one hour.

You pay for kilowatt-hours Electric companies charge for kilowatt-hours over a set period of time, often a month. Your home is connected to a meter that counts up total number of kilowatt-hours used and a person comes to read the meter once a month.

Estimating your electric bill If you know the cost per kilowatt-hour that your utility company charges, you can estimate the cost of running an appliance for a period of time.

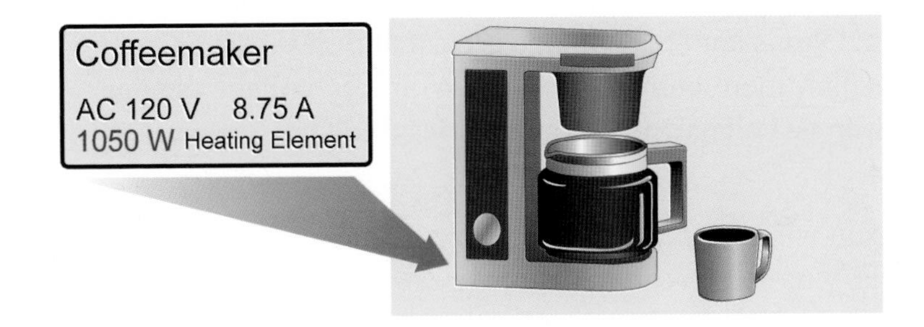

Example: Your electric company charges 14 cents per kilowatt-hour. Your coffeemaker has a power rating of 1,050 watts. The coffeemaker is on for about 1 hour each day. What does this cost you each month in electricity?

Solution: Find the number of kilowatts of power that the coffeemaker uses.
$1{,}050 \text{ W} \times 1 \text{ kW}/1{,}000 \text{ W} = 1.05 \text{ kW}$

Find the kilowatt-hours used by the coffeemaker each day.
$1.05 \text{ kW} \times 1 \text{ hr/day} = 1.05 \text{ kWh per day}$

Find the kilowatt-hours of electricity used by the coffeemaker each month. Assume there are 30 days in a month.
$1.05 \text{ kWh/day} \times 30 \text{ days/month} = 31.5 \text{ kWh per month}$

Find the cost of using the coffeemaker for one month.
$31.5 \text{ kWh/month} \times \$0.14/\text{kWh} = \$4.41 \text{ per month}$

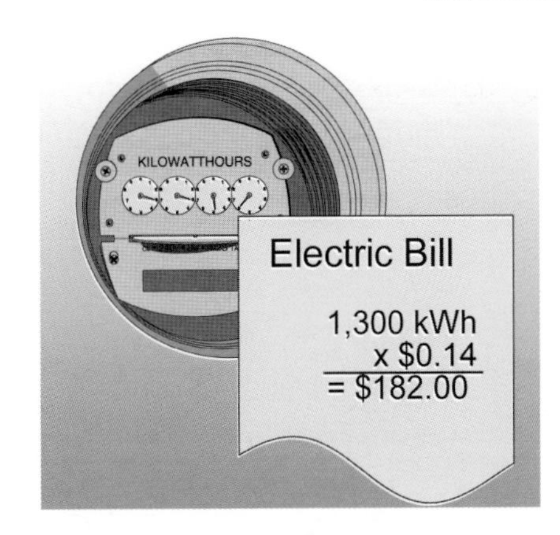

Figure 8.6: *Every month most people pay an electric bill that charges for the kilowatt-hours of energy used.*

Typical power ratings

Appliance	Power (watts)
Electric stove	5,000
Electric heater	1,500
Hair dryer	1,200
Iron	800
Washing machine	750
Light	100
Small fan	50
Clock radio	10

Electricity, power, and heat

How do you get more power?

How do you get more power when you need it? From the power formula we can see that increasing voltage or current will increase power. The disadvantage of raising voltage is that the electricity in your standard outlets is at 120 volts, and it is hard to change. Some appliances use 240 volts, but they have special plugs because 240 volts is more dangerous than 120 volts.

Higher power usually means more current

The more usual way to get higher power is to use more current. However, when current flows through a wire, part of the energy is transformed into heat. More current means more heat. If too much power goes into heat, the wire could melt or start a fire.

Reducing heat in electrical wires

Fortunately, there is a way to let more current flow through a wire without making more heat. Remember (from Ohm's law) that voltage is current times resistance. If we make the resistance smaller, more current can flow with less voltage change along the wire. Since power is voltage times current, less voltage means less power is lost as heat.

Different size wires have different resistance

Lower resistance is the reason wires come in different sizes. Thick wire has lower resistance and can safely carry more current than thin wire (Figure 8.7). Often we use extension cords to plug in electric tools or appliances. Extension cords come with many thicknesses, or *gauges*, of wire. Typical kinds of extension cords you can buy have 18 gauge wire, 16 gauge wire, 14 gauge wire, and 12 gauge wire (Figure 8.8). The bigger the gauge, the higher the resistance. To carry a lot of current, you want low resistance, so you need lower gauge (fatter) wires.

Length and resistance

The length of a wire also affects its resistance. The longer a wire is, the more resistance it has. Think about moving around your school and how you can get through a short, crowded hallway quickly. But, it takes a long time to get down a long, crowded hallway.

Check your extension cords for safety

If you look at an extension cord, it will tell you how many amps of current it can safely carry. The length and wire thickness are both important. *Always* check to see if the extension cord can carry *at least* as much current as the device you plug in will require. Many fires have been caused by using the wrong extension cord!

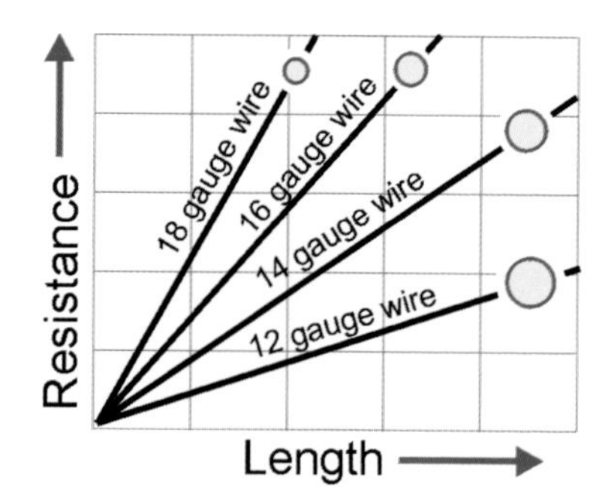

Figure 8.7: *The resistance of a wire depends on the length and size. Longer length means greater resistance. Bigger diameter means lower resistance.*

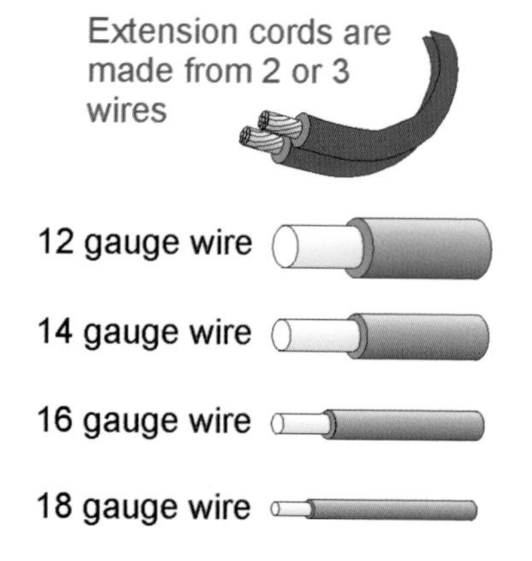

Wire Gauge	Current (amps)
12	20
14	15
16	10
18	7

Figure 8.8: *The safe amount of current for different gauges of wire.*

Chapter 8 Review

Vocabulary review

Match the following terms with the correct definition. There is one extra definition in the list that will not match any of the terms.

Set One	
1. Ohm's law	a. A semiconductor component that allows current to flow in one direction only
2. diode	b. A shorthand method of describing the resistance of a resistor
3. superconductor	c. A component used to control current in circuits because it has a relatively constant resistance
4. resistor	d. A part soldered onto a circuit board
5. electronic component	e. An equation relating voltage, current and resistance in a circuit
	f. A material that has zero resistance at low temperatures

Set Two	
1. potentiometer	a. A unit equal to 100 watts
2. watt	b. The use of a kilowatt of power for one hour
3. power	c. The unit commonly used to measure power, equal to joules/second
4. kilowatt	d. A unit equal to 1000 watts
5. kilowatt-hour	e. The rate at which work is being performed
	f. A variable resistor

Concept review

1. Explain what will happen to the value of current in a circuit if the voltage is increased.
2. Explain what will happen to the value of current in a circuit if the resistance is increased.
3. High resistance leads to an increase in heat. A person repaired a broken light in a house and replaced the copper wire with a thin piece of aluminum. Explain why this replacement is a fire hazard.
4. Explain why the amps rating on an extension cord should be the same as, or larger than, the current drawn by the device plugged into the extension cord.
5. What is the scientific definition of power?
6. What type of work is done by an electric fan? (In other words, electrical energy is changed into what other form(s) when the fan is running?)
7. What is the metric unit used to measure power?
8. List three appliances and their power ratings.

9. Express the metric unit of power in fundamental units.

10. Power companies charge us for kilowatt-hours. What type of quantity is being measured by a kilowatt-hour?

Problems

1. A hair dryer draws a current of 10 amps. If it is plugged into a 120-volt circuit, what is the resistance of the hair dryer?
2. A child's toy robot draws a current of 2.0 amps. The robot's circuit has a total resistance of 4.5 ohms. What is the total voltage of the battery or batteries required by the toy?
3. A flashlight bulb has a resistance of approximately 6 ohms. It works in a flashlight with two AA alkaline batteries. About how much current does the bulb draw?
4. Household circuits in the United States commonly run on 120 volts of electricity. Frequently, circuit breakers are installed that open a circuit if it is drawing more than 15 amps of current. What is the minimum amount of resistance that must be present in the circuit to prevent the circuit breaker from activating?
5. A 2,500-watt room air conditioner could also be called a ________ kilowatt appliance.
6. If you bake potatoes in a 900-watt microwave oven for 15 minutes, how many kilowatt-hours of electrical energy have you consumed?
7. If a toaster oven draws 6 amps of current when plugged into a 120-volt outlet, what is the power rating of the appliance?
8. A student uses three appliances in her dormitory room: a 1,200-watt iron, which she uses 3.5 hours per month; a lamp with a 100-watt bulb which she uses 125 hours per month; and a 700-watt coffee maker, which she uses 15 hours per month
   a. How many kilowatt-hours of electrical energy are consumed in one month by each of these appliances?
   b. If the local utility company charges 15 cents per kilowatt-hour of electrical energy consumed, how much does it cost per month to operate each appliance?
9. Calculate the current through each of the following bulbs if they are connected to a 120-volt circuit in your house.
   a. 40 W   b. 60 W   c. 100 W   d. 150 W

Applying your knowledge

1. Using power ratings, analyze how much your family spends to run every appliance in your home. Enact a plan to reduce electricity use and see if your family saves money.
2. With an adult, check the safety of appliances that are plugged into extension cords, in your home or school. Make sure that the current ratings of the extension cord meet or exceed the current ratings of the appliance.
3. Find out what programs are available through your local utility company to reduce electricity use (discounted low-wattage bulbs, home energy checks, etc.). Prepare a pamphlet on the programs.
4. Research superconductivity. Find out what it is and what applications it may have.

UNIT 3 Electricity and Magnetism

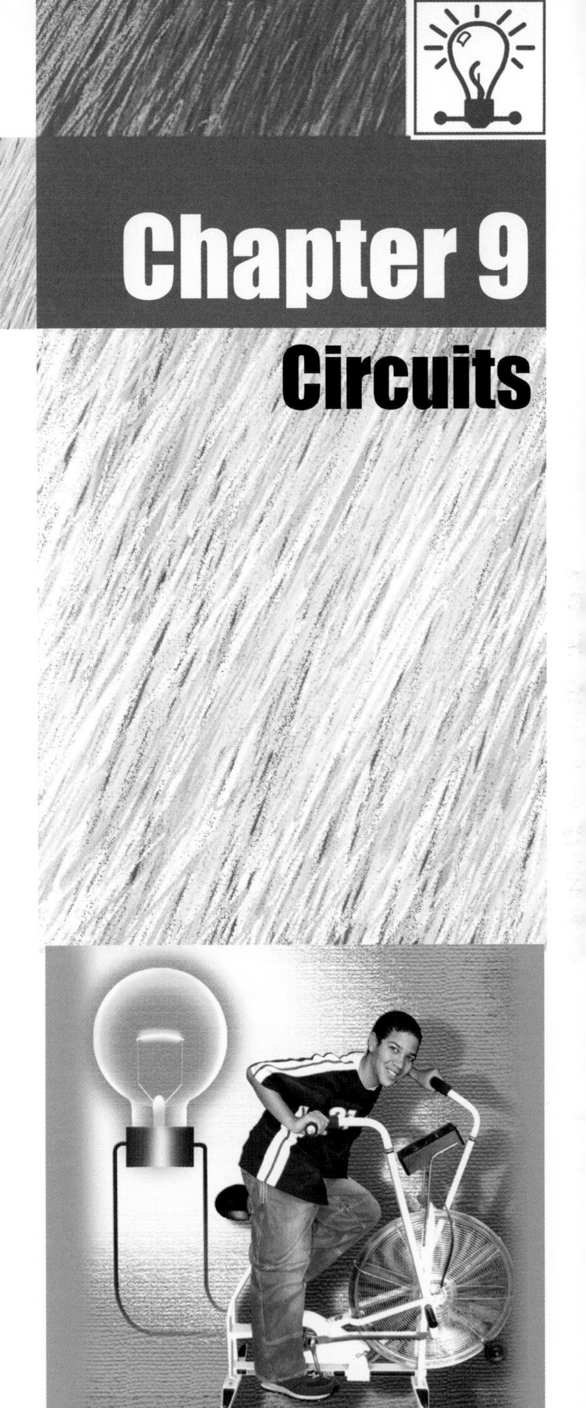

Chapter 9 Circuits

Introduction to Chapter 9

In our homes, you can have many electrical devices on at any one time. How is this possible? What do circuits in our homes look like? In this chapter, you will learn about the two kinds of circuits, called *series circuits* and *parallel circuits*. In series circuits, all the current flows through one path. In parallel circuits, current can flow through two or more paths.

Investigations for Chapter 9

9.1	More Electric Circuits	*What kinds of electric circuits can you build?*

In this Investigation, you will compare how two kinds of circuits work by building and observing series and parallel circuits. You will explore an application of these circuits by wiring two switches in series and in parallel.

9.2	Series Circuits	*How do you use Ohm's law in series circuits?*

In this Investigation, you will find out how to add resistance in a series circuit. You will also build a light bulb circuit with a dimmer switch and use this circuit to graph the resistance of a light bulb at different levels of current.

9.3	Parallel Circuits	*How do parallel circuits work?*

In this Investigation, you will analyze how a parallel circuit works by measuring voltage and current in different parts of the circuit. You will use your understanding of parallel circuits to design a battery voltage tester circuit.

Learning Goals

In this chapter, you will:

- ✔ Identify a series circuit.
- ✔ Identify a parallel circuit.
- ✔ Describe how our houses are wired.
- ✔ Build series and parallel circuits.
- ✔ Calculate total resistance in series circuits.
- ✔ Build circuits with fixed and variable resistors.
- ✔ Analyze series circuits using Ohm's law.
- ✔ Use Kirchhoff's voltage law to find the voltage drop across a circuit component.
- ✔ Compare current in series and parallel circuits.
- ✔ Compare voltage in series and parallel circuits.
- ✔ Use Kirchhoff's current law to find an unknown current in a parallel circuit.
- ✔ Identify a short circuit.
- ✔ Explain why a short circuit is dangerous.

Vocabulary

Kirchhoff's current law	parallel circuit	short circuit
Kirchhoff's voltage law	series circuit	

9.1 More Electric Circuits

We use electric circuits for thousands of different things from cars to computers. In this section you will learn about two basic ways to put circuits together. These two types of circuits are called *series* and *parallel*. Series circuits have only one path; the flow of charge has only one place to go. Parallel circuits have branching points and multiple paths for current to flow.

Series circuits

Two bulbs in a series circuit

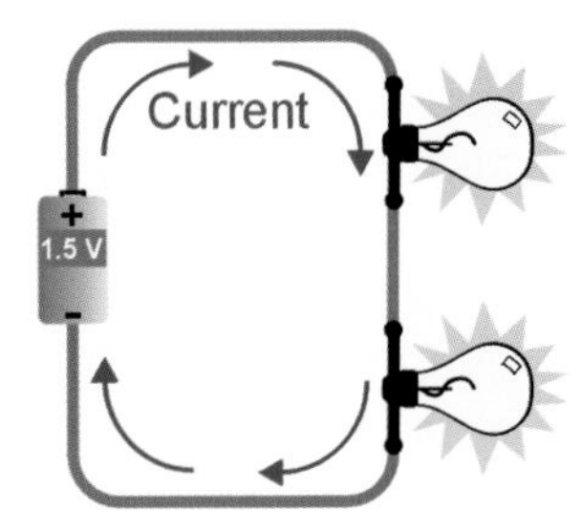

Two bulbs in a parallel circuit

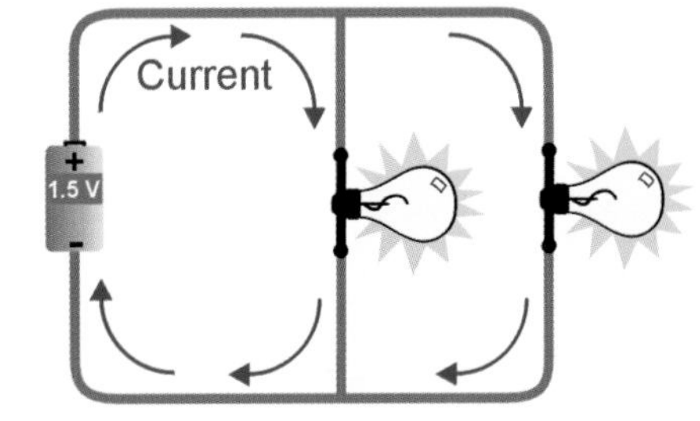

What is a series circuit? In a **series circuit** the current can only take one path. All the current flows through every part of the circuit. All the circuits you have studied so far have been series circuits. For example, if you have a battery, a light bulb, and one switch, everything is connected in series because there is only one path through the circuit.

What is a parallel circuit? In a **parallel circuit** the current can take more than one path. Parallel circuits have at least one branch where the current can split up.

Combinations It is possible to create circuits with both series and parallel wiring. You need at least three light bulbs. Can you think of a way to wire three bulbs using both series and parallel connections?

Holiday lights

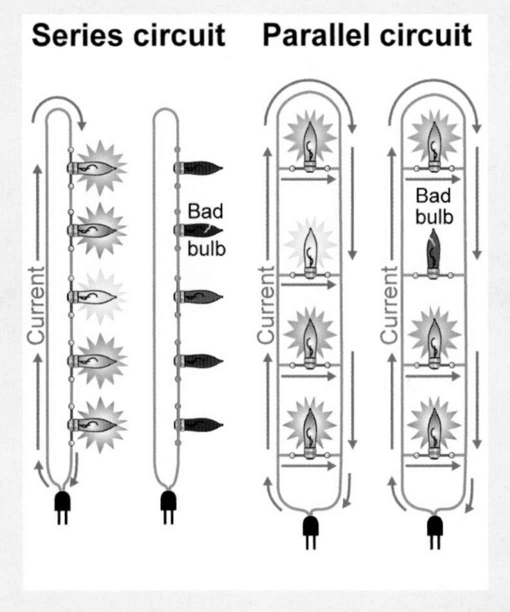

Many people use strings of lights to decorate their houses, especially at holiday time. Inexpensive versions of lights are wired in series, while better ones are wired in parallel.

In the series circuit, if one bulb goes bad the whole circuit is broken and no bulbs light. It is very difficult to find the bad bulb to replace it because all the lights are out.

In the parallel circuit, each bulb has its own path for current, independent of the others. If one bulb fails, the others will still light. The bad bulb is easy to spot and replace.

Household wiring

Parallel circuits for homes and buildings

The electrical circuits in homes and buildings are parallel circuits. There are two great advantages of parallel circuits that make them a better choice than series circuits.

1. Each outlet has its own current path. This means one outlet can have something connected and turned on (with current flowing), while another outlet has nothing connected or something turned off (no current flowing).
2. Every outlet sees the same voltage because one side of each outlet is connected to the same wire.

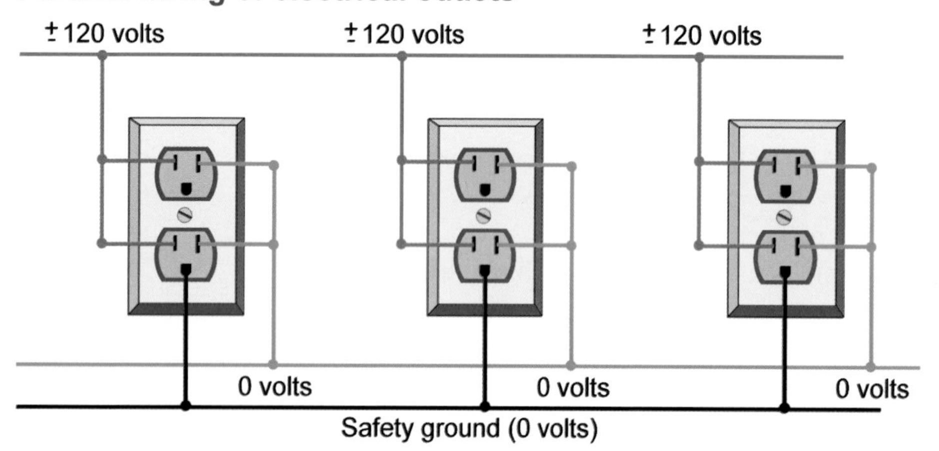

Why series circuits would not work

Parallel circuits mean that a light in your home can be on at the same time that the TV is off. If our homes were wired in series, turning off *anything* electrical in the house would break the whole circuit. This is not practical; we would have to keep everything on all the time just to keep the refrigerator running! Also, in a series circuit, everything you plugged in would use some energy and would lower the voltage available to the next outlet.

What happens if you plug in too many things?

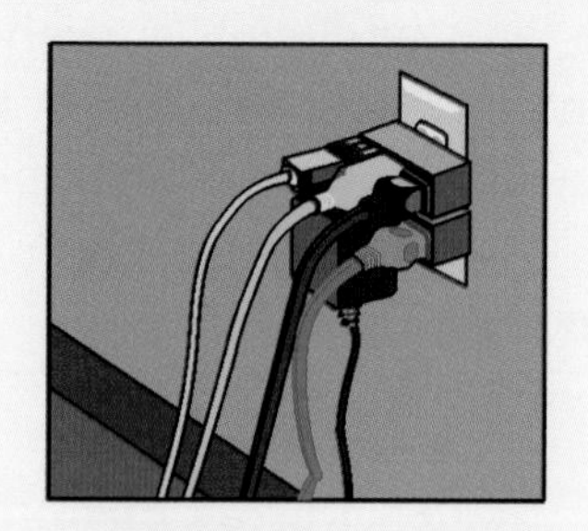

In a parallel circuit, each connection uses as much current as it needs. If you plug in a coffeemaker that uses 10 amps and a toaster oven that uses 10 amps, a total of 20 amps needs to come through the wire.

If you plug too many appliances into the same outlet, you will eventually use more current than the wires can carry without overheating. Your circuit breaker will click open and stop the current. You should unplug things to reduce the current in the circuit before resetting the circuit breaker.

9.2 Series Circuits

Ohm's law is a powerful tool for analyzing circuits. You have studied Ohm's law in a series circuit with one resistor. In this section you will learn how to analyze more complex series circuits with more than one resistance.

Current and voltage in a series circuit

In a series circuit, current is the same at all points

In a series circuit, all current flows through a single path. What goes into one end of the wire must come out the other end of the wire. The value of current is the same at all points in the circuit. The amount of current is determined by the voltage and resistance in the circuit, using Ohm's law.

Voltage is reduced by each resistance

The law of conservation of energy helps us to understand what happens to energy in a series circuit. Consider a circuit with three bulbs. Using two batteries, every charge starts at 3 volts. As each charge moves through the circuit, some energy is transformed into light by each bulb. That means that after every bulb, the energy must be lower. We see the lower energy as a drop in voltage from 3 volts, to 2 volts, to 1 volt and finally down to zero volts after the last bulb.

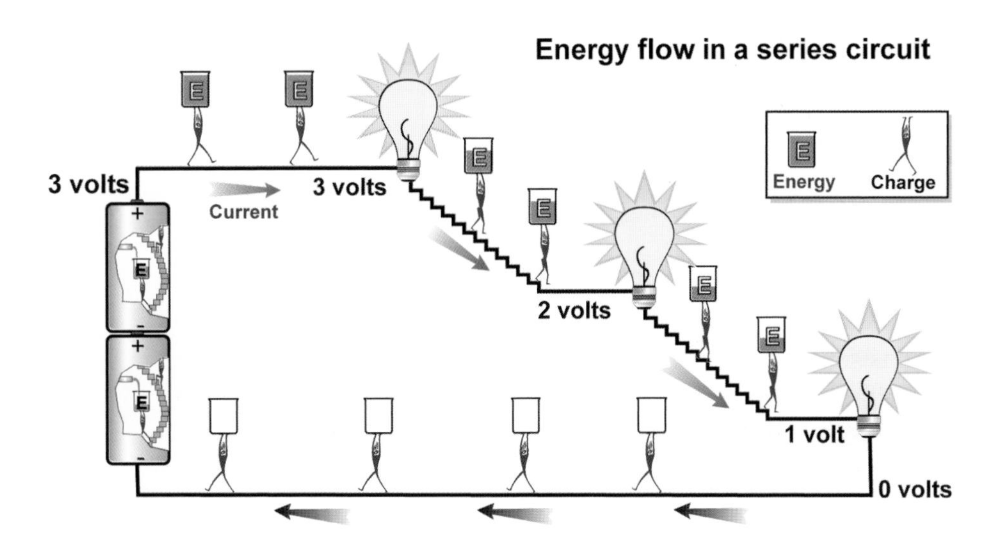

Using power tools

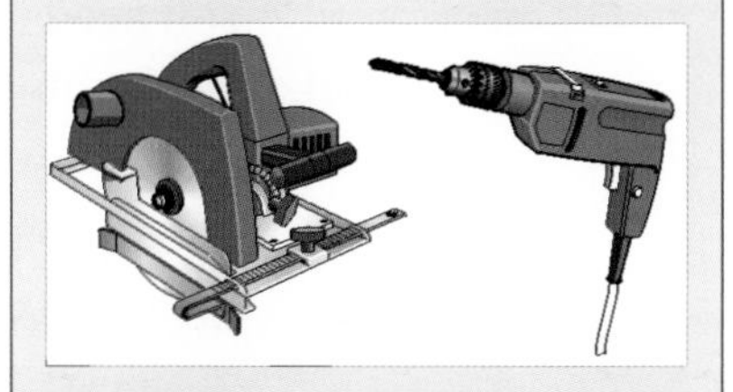

If you know people who work with power tools, you may have noticed that they use a heavy extension cord when the regular cord can't reach. One reason to use a heavy cord is that it can safely carry the amps used by power tools.

There is a second reason as well. If a thin extension cord is used, the motor in a power tool can overheat and burn out. This happens because the voltage available for the motor is lower than it should be.

The motor gets lower voltage when energy is lost along the cord. This energy loss is called a voltage drop, and is related to resistance. Heavy extension cords have lower resistance and use less energy than thin cords of the same length.

How to find the current in a series circuit

Start with resistance and voltage

You need to know how much resistance the circuit has to find the current. In many cases you know the voltage, such as from a battery. If you know the resistance, Ohm's law can be used to find the current.

Each resistance in a series circuit adds to the total. You can think of it like adding pinches to a hose (Figure 9.1). Each pinch adds some resistance. The total resistance is the sum of the resistances from each pinch.

Two ways to find the current

How would you find the exact amount of total resistance in a series circuit? You could use several methods:

- You could measure total voltage and current through the circuit, and use Ohm's law to calculate the total resistance of the circuit (R = V/I).
- You could add together the resistance of each component in the circuit.

Add up resistances to get the total

If you know the resistance of each component, you can simply add them up to get the total for the circuit. Once you know the total resistance, use Ohm's law to calculate the current.

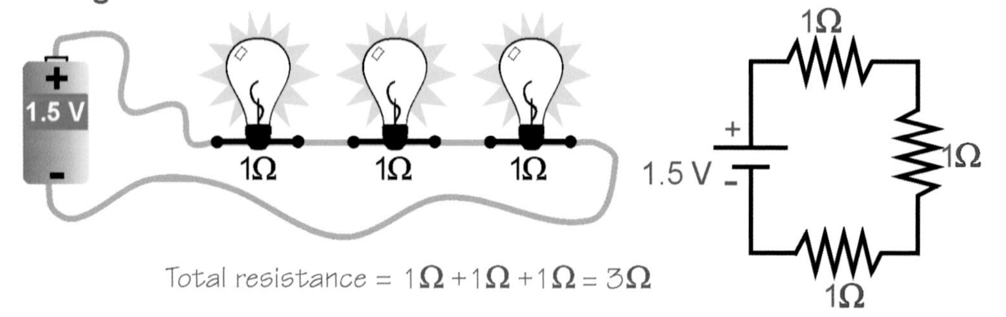

Ignore resistance of wires and batteries

Every part in a circuit has some resistance, even the wires and batteries. However, light bulbs, resistors, motors and heaters usually have much greater resistance than wires and batteries. Therefore, when adding resistances up, we can almost always leave out the resistance of wires and batteries.

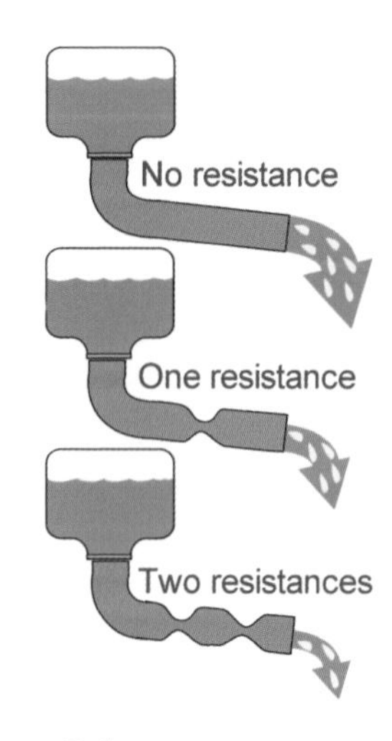

Figure 9.1: *Each time a hose is pinched, the flow of water slows more.*

Example:

How much current is in a circuit with a 1.5 volt battery and three 1 ohm resistances (bulbs) in series?

Solution

Add the resistance of each component:

1 ohm + 1 ohm + 1 ohm = 3 ohms

Use Ohm's law to calculate the current from the voltage and the total resistance.

I = V/R = 1.5 volts ÷ 3 ohms = 0.5 amps

Answer: 0.5 amps

Voltage in a series circuit

Each resistance drops the voltage You have learned that energy is not created or destroyed. This rule is known as the law of conservation of energy. However, energy is constantly being transformed from one form to another. As current flows along a series circuit, each resistance uses up some of the energy. As a result, the voltage gets lower after each resistance.

The voltage drop We often say each separate resistor creates a *voltage drop*. If you know the current and resistance, Ohm's law can be used to calculate the voltage drop across each resistor. For example, in the three-bulb series circuit, the voltage drop across each bulb is 0.5 volts (Figure 9.2).

Each resistance drops the voltage

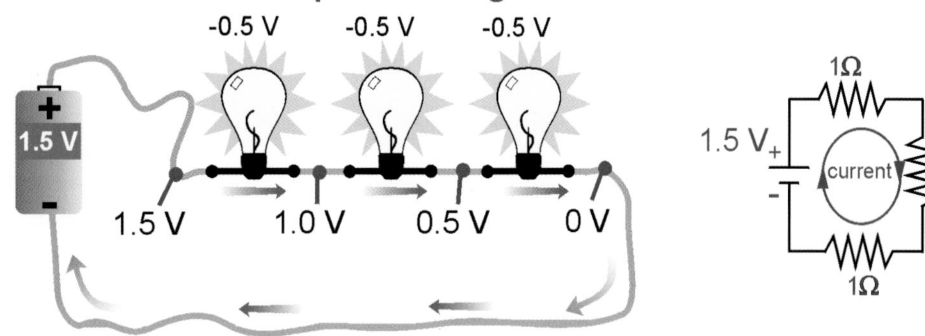

Voltage drop across a resistor (bulb)

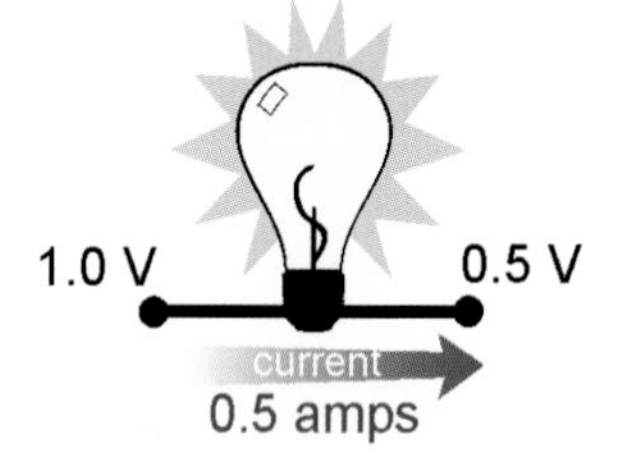

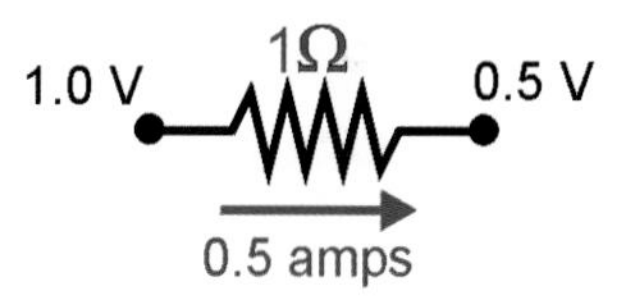

Calculating the voltage drop

Ohm's law

$V = IR$

$= (0.5 \text{ amps}) \times (1 \text{ ohm})$

$= 0.5 \text{ volts}$

Figure 9.2: *When current flows through any resistance the voltage drops because some of the energy is used up. The amount of the voltage drop is given by Ohm's law.*

Kirchhoff's law Over the entire circuit, the energy taken out must equal the energy supplied by the battery. This means the total of all the voltage drops must add up to the total voltage supplied by the battery (energy in). This rule is known as Kirchhoff's voltage law, after German physicist Gustav Robert Kirchhoff (1824-87):

Kirchhoff's voltage law

Around any closed circuit, all the voltage changes must add up to zero.

Batteries raise voltage, resistances lower voltage.
For the example circuit above, the total of all voltage changes is:

$$\text{Voltage changes} = \underset{\text{Battery}}{+1.5\text{ V}} - \underset{\text{Bulb}}{0.5\text{ V}} - \underset{\text{Bulb}}{0.5\text{ V}} - \underset{\text{Bulb}}{0.5\text{ V}} = 0$$

9.3 Parallel Circuits

In the last section, you learned how to analyze series circuits. In this section, you will take a closer look at parallel circuits. You previously learned that parallel circuits are used for almost all electrical wiring in houses and buildings.

Current in a parallel circuit

Separate paths are parallel branches

A parallel circuit has at least one point where the circuit divides, creating more than one path for current to flow. Each path in the circuit is sometimes called a *branch*. The current through a branch is also called the *branch current*.

Kirchhoff's current law

When analyzing a parallel circuit, remember that the current always has to go somewhere. If current flows into a branching point in a circuit, the same total current must flow out again. This rule is known as Kirchhoff's current law.

Example, three bulbs in parallel

For example, suppose you have three light bulbs connected in parallel, and each has a current of 1 amp. The battery must supply 3 amps since each bulb draws 1 amp and there are 3 bulbs. At the first branch, 3 amps flow in, 1 amp flows down to the first bulb, and 2 amps flow on to the remaining 2 bulbs.

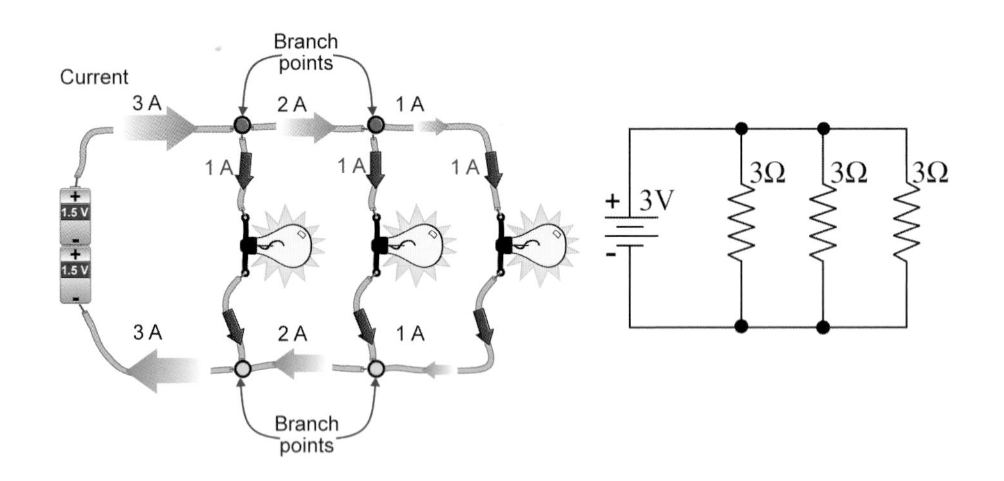

Why aren't birds electrocuted?

If high-voltage wires are so dangerous, how do birds sit on them without being instantly electrocuted? First, the bird's body has a higher resistance than the electrical wire. The current tends to stay in the wire because the wire is an easier path.

The most important reason, however, is that the bird has both feet on the same wire. That means the voltage is the same on both feet and no current flows through the bird.

If a bird had one foot on the wire and the other foot touching the electric pole, then there would be a voltage difference. A lot of electricity would pass through the bird.

Voltage and resistance in a parallel circuit

Each branch sees the same voltage In a parallel circuit the voltage is the same across each branch because all the branch points are on the same wire. One way to think of a parallel circuit is to imagine several series circuits connected to the same battery. Each branch has a path back to the battery without any other resistance in the way.

Branches don't always have the same current The amount of current in each branch in a parallel circuit depends on how much resistance is in the branch. When you plug a desk lamp and a power saw into an outlet, they each use very different amounts of current (Figure 9.3).

Lower resistance means more current flows You can calculate current through the lamp and saw with Ohm's law (Figure 9.4). The 100-watt bulb has a resistance of 145 ohms. Since the outlet has 120 volts across it, the bulb draws about 0.8 amps. A power saw has a much lower resistance, 12 ohms. Consequently, the power saw draws a much higher current of 10 amps when connected to the 120-volt outlet.

Desk lamp
0.8 amps

Power saw
10 amps

Figure 9.3: *Different appliances use different amounts of currrent.*

Example: Calculating currents in a parallel circuit

For the circuit and its diagram shown below, a student was able to calculate the currents from the information given about the circuit. Can you duplicate her work?

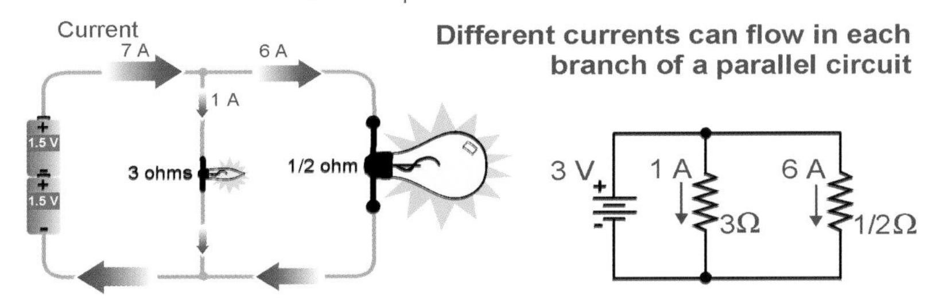

Step 1: Calculate current through each part of the circuit.

Step 2: You are given total voltage and the resistance of each bulb.

Step 3: Useful equations are: Ohm's law, $V = IR$, and Kirchhoff's current law, $I_t = I_1 + I_2$

Step 4: Branch 1 current: $I_1 = V/R_1$ Branch 2 current: $I_2 = V/R_2$ Total current: $I_t = I_1 + I_2$

Step 5: $I_1 = 3\ V / 3\ \Omega = 1$ $I_2 = 3\ V / 0.5\ \Omega = 6\ A$ $I_t = 1\ A + 6\ A = 7\ A$

Light bulb
145 ohms

Power saw
12 ohms

$$I = \frac{V}{R} = \frac{120\ V}{145\ \Omega} = 0.83 \text{ amps}$$

$$I = \frac{V}{R} = \frac{120\ V}{12\ \Omega} = 10 \text{ amps}$$

Figure 9.4: *Calculating the current from the resistance and voltage. Household electric circuits are wired in parallel at 120 volts.*

Open circuits and short circuits

What is a short circuit? A short circuit is a circuit path with zero or very low resistance. You can create a short circuit by connecting a wire directly between two ends of a battery. Often, short circuits are accidentally caused by connecting a wire between two other wires at different voltages. This creates a parallel path with very low resistance. In a parallel circuit, the branch with the lowest resistance draws the most current (Figure 9.5).

Why short circuits are dangerous Short circuits are dangerous because they can cause huge amounts of current. For example, suppose you connect a length of wire across a circuit creating a second current path as shown below. The resistance of the wire could be as low as 0.001 ohms. That means the current through your wire could be as high as 1,500 amps! This much current would melt the wire in an instant and probably burn you as well. Short circuits should always be a concern when working around electricity. Fuses or circuit breakers are protection from the high current of a short circuit.

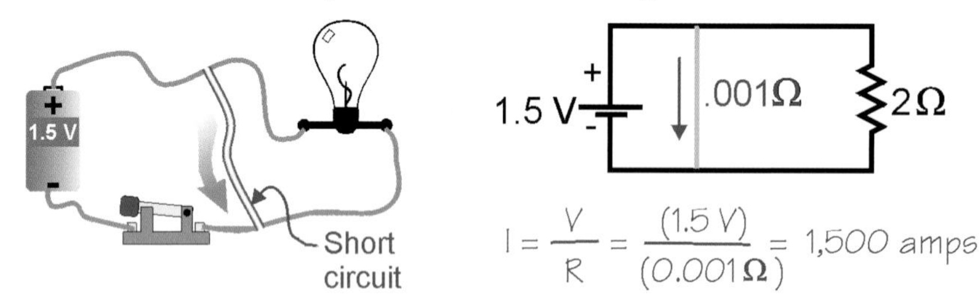

Open and closed circuits Open and closed circuits are not the same as short circuits. An open circuit means the current path has been broken, possibly by a switch (Figure 9.5). Current cannot flow in an open circuit. A closed circuit is a circuit that is complete and allows current to flow.

Protecting against short circuits Every electrical outlet in your house or apartment is connected to a circuit breaker that allows a maximum of 15 or 20 amps to flow. If something electrical breaks and causes a short circuit, the breaker will open before the current has time to cause a fire. If a circuit breaker always trips when you plug in an appliance, that appliance probably has a short circuit.

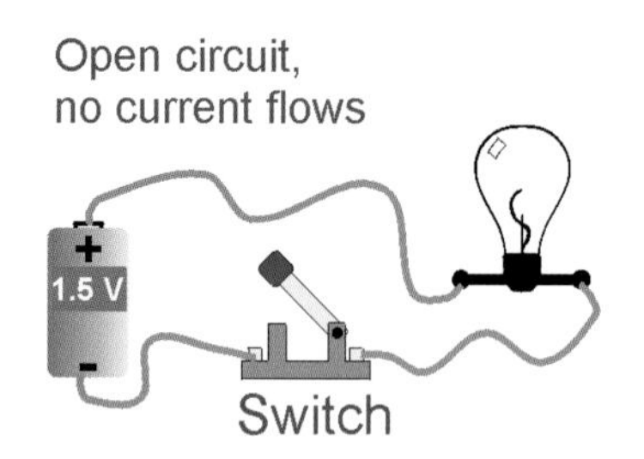

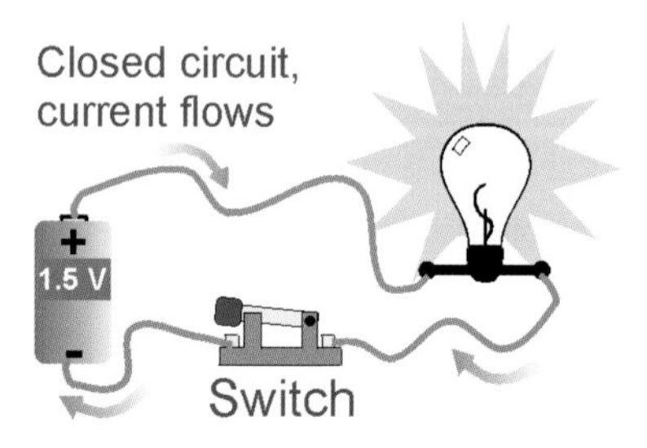

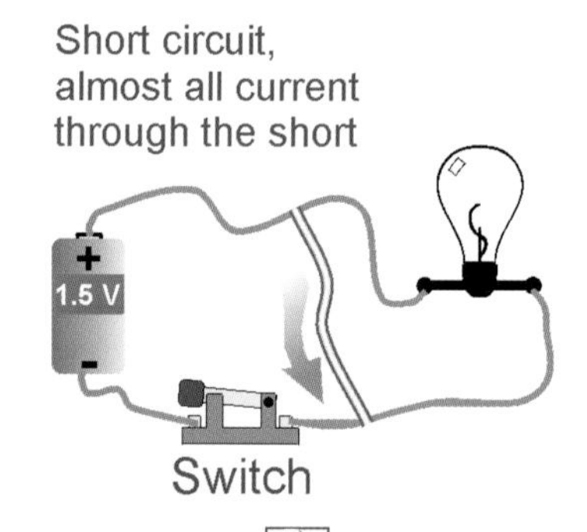

Figure 9.5: *A short circuit is a very low resistance path that can draw huge amounts of current. An open circuit is a break in the circuit that shuts off the flow of current. Switches are used to open and close circuits.*

Chapter 9 Review

Vocabulary review

Match the following terms with the correct definition. There is one extra definition in the list that will not match any of the terms.

Set One	
1. series circuit	a. In a circuit, all the voltage drops must add up to the total voltage supplied by the battery
2. parallel circuit	b. A circuit that has only one path for the flow of charge
3. Kirchhoff's voltage law	c. A circuit that has more than one path for the flow of charge
4. Kirchhoff's current law	d. Two switches wired in parallel
5. short circuit	e. A circuit path with very low resistance
	f. If current flows into a branch in the circuit, the same amount of current must flow out again

Concept review

1. Explain the advantage of using a parallel circuit if you have more than one device in the circuit.
2. Imagine that an electrician wired the kitchen in your house so that all the outlets were connected in a single series circuit. Describe what you would have to do to keep the refrigerator running constantly.
3. If you have a light, and one switch that controls it, the light and the switch are wired in ________.
4. Is the current at every point in a series circuit the same?
5. What happens to the total resistance of a series circuit as you add more resistance? Does total resistance of the circuit decrease, increase, or stay the same?
6. Explain why Kirchhoff's voltage law is an application of the law of conservation of energy.
7. Describe what happens to the potential energy of charges in a circuit as they move through a bulb.
8. What happens to the total current of a parallel circuit as you add more branches with current through them? Does total current of the circuit decrease, increase, or stay the same?

9. The voltage across each branch of a parallel circuit is equal to the ________.
10. If a parallel circuit has two branches with equal resistance, what is the total resistance of the circuit?
11. For each diagram below, label the circuit *series*, *parallel*, or *short circuit*. The arrows indicate the flow of current.

   a.

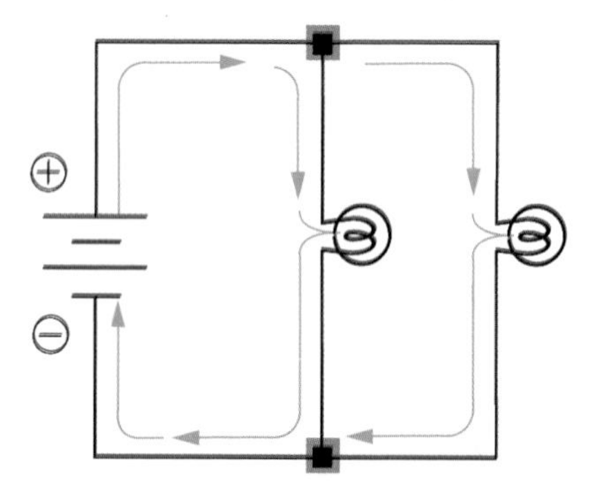

   b.

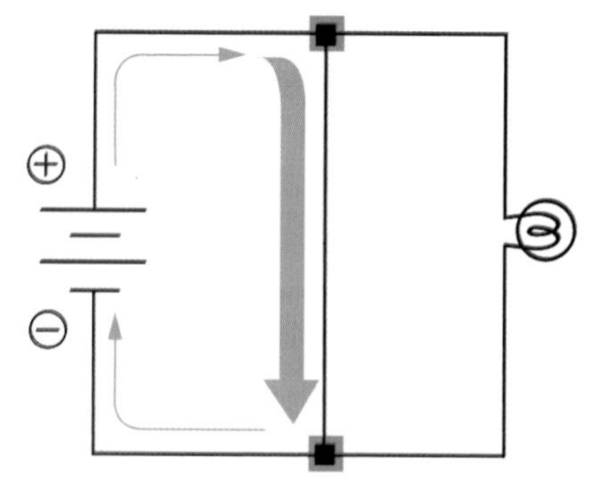

   c.

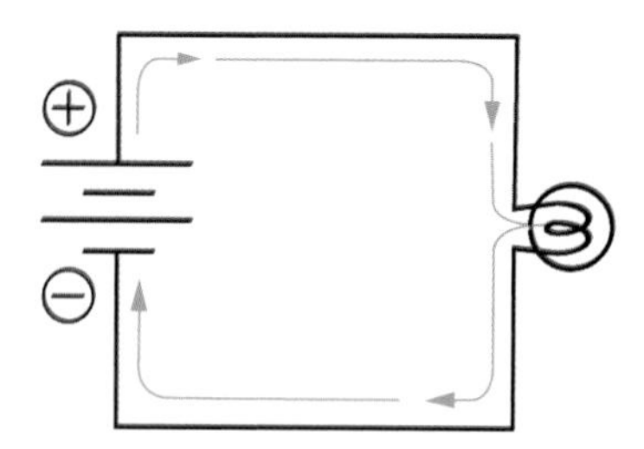

Problems

1. Answer the following:
   a. A circuit with three 1.5-volt batteries has two matching light bulbs. What is the voltage drop across each light bulb?
   b. Explain how you figured out your answer.
2. A student builds a circuit using three 1-ohm resistors in series. The current in the circuit is 1.5 amps. Use Ohm's law to determine the voltage of the circuit. (Hint: Draw the circuit described in the question.)
3. A student sets up a series circuit with four 1.5-volt batteries, a 5-ohm resistor, and two 1-ohm resistors. (Hint: Draw the circuit described in the question.)
   a. What is the total resistance in her circuit?
   b. Use Ohm's law to determine the value of current for the circuit.
4. A lab group was given a kit containing four 1.5-volt batteries, eight wires, and a resistor set containing three 1-ohm resistors and two 5-ohm resistors. They use all the batteries to build a series circuit. They use a meter to find that the current is 0.857 amps. What resistors did they use and what was the total resistance in the circuit?

5. A lab group was asked to create two circuits with two 1.5-volt batteries. They are given three 1-ohm resistors and two 5-ohm resistors.
   a. The first circuit should have the highest possible current without creating a short circuit. Which resistor(s) should they use and what will the current in the circuit be?
   b. The second circuit should have a current of exactly 1 amp. Which resistor(s) should they use?

6. A circuit breaker in your house is set for 15 amps. You have plugged in a coffeemaker that uses 10 amps. You want to plug in four more things. Which of the four items will cause the circuit breaker to trip because the current is too high?
   a. A light that uses 1 amp.
   b. A can opener that uses 2 amps.
   c. A mixer that uses 6 amps.
   d. An electric knife that uses 1.5 amps.

7. Which of the following statements are **true** about the circuit drawn?

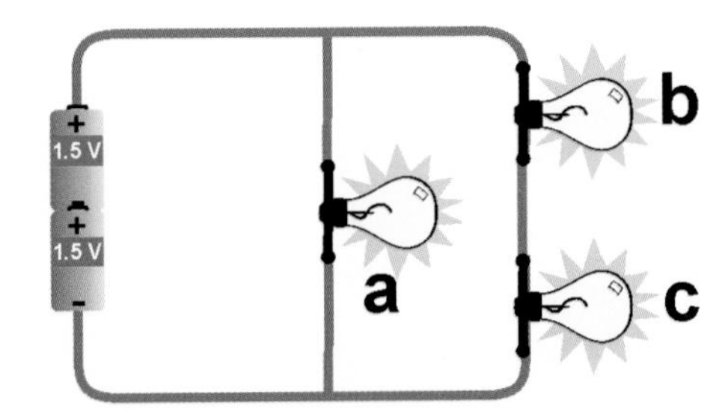

   a. Bulb **a** is brighter than bulb **b** or bulb **c**.
   b. Bulb **a** is dimmer than bulb **b** or bulb **c**.
   c. Bulb **b** is the same brightness as bulb **c**.
   d. Bulb **c** is brighter than bulb **b**.

8. Shown below is a parallel circuit with three branches. Branch 1 contains a 1-ohm resistor, branch 2 contains a 2-ohm resistor, and branch 3 contains a 3-ohm resistor. The circuit is powered by one 9-volt battery.

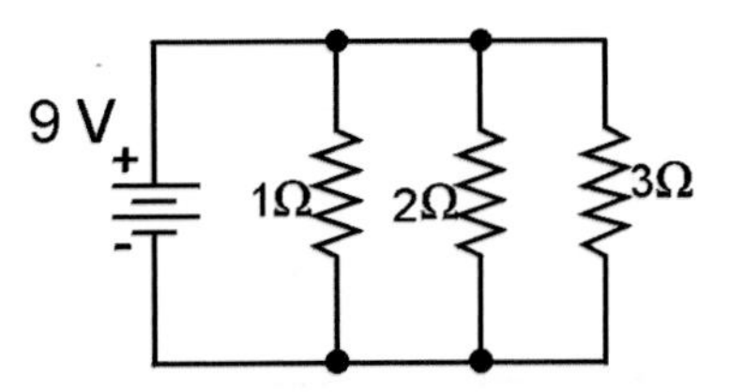

   a. Use Ohm's law to calculate the current in each branch of the circuit.
   b. Use Kirchhoff's current law to calculate the total current in the circuit.
   c. It is possible to replace all three resistors with a single resistor and have the total current in the circuit be the same. Use Ohm's law to calculate what the value of the single resistor should be to keep the total current the same.
   d. If someone were to add a fourth branch (containing a 4-ohm resistor) to the circuit, would the total current of the circuit decrease, increase, or stay the same?

9. Two 1.5-volt batteries are used to connect the circuit below.

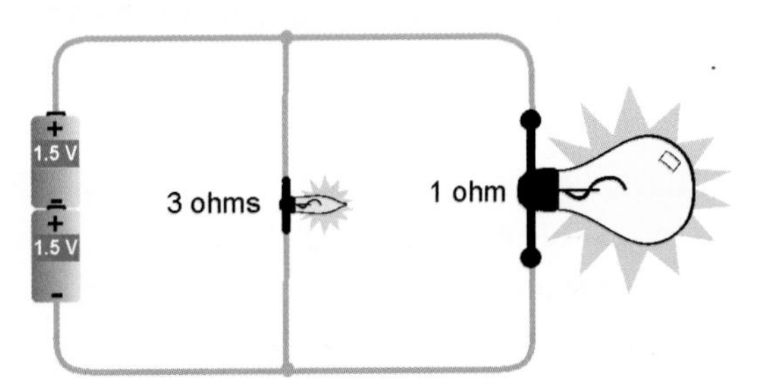

   a. What is the total current in the circuit?
   b. Which bulb uses more current?

10. If one bulb is removed from the circuit below, the other bulbs will:

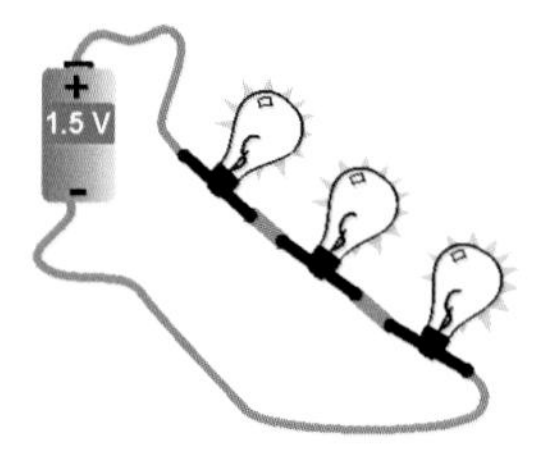

a. get brighter.

b. go out.

c. get dimmer.

d. stay at the same brightness.

11. The resistance of each of the three bulbs in the circuit below is:

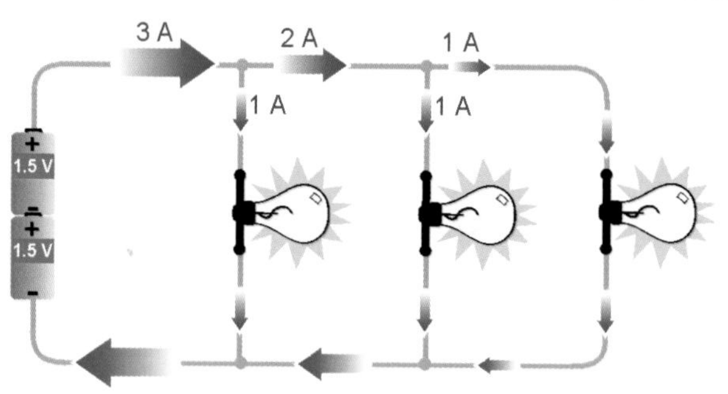

a. 1 ohm.

b. 2 ohms.

c. 6 ohms.

d. 3 ohms.

Applying your knowledge

1. In an automobile, the warning bell turns on if you open the door while the key is in the ignition. The bell also turns on if you open the door while the headlights are on. A single circuit with three switches and a bell can be built to ring in both cases. One switch is attached to the door, one switch is attached to the ignition, and one switch is attached to the headlights. Figure out what circuit would make the bell ring at the right times and build or draw your circuit.
2. A burglar alarm system has switches in each door and window. If the door or window is opened, the switch opens a circuit. Draw a circuit that uses one battery and one light bulb to check five doors and windows. The bulb should go out if any of the five doors or windows is opened.

UNIT 3

Electricity and Magnetism

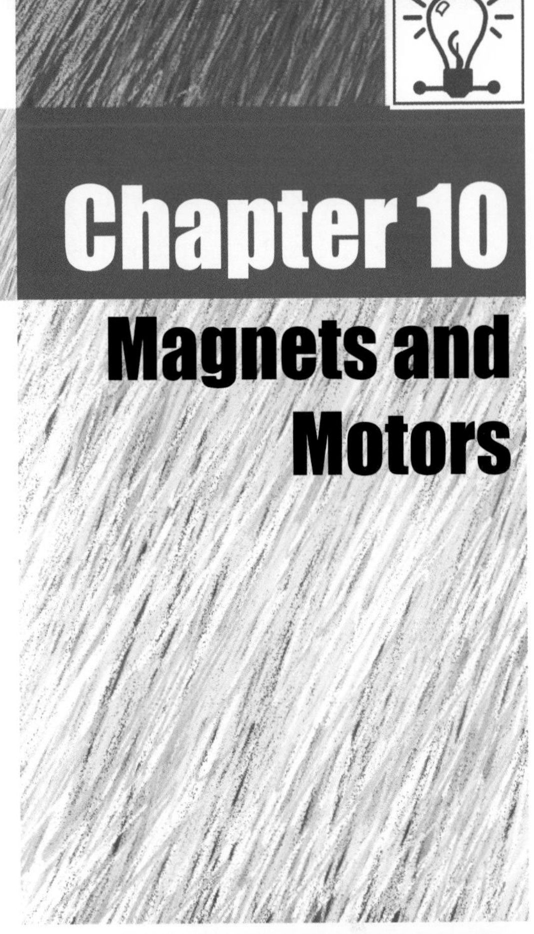

Chapter 10

Magnets and Motors

Introduction to Chapter 10

Electricity and magnetism are related to each other. As you will learn in this chapter, the interactions between electricity and magnetism are the core of many important technologies, from the generation of electricity to recording data on computer disks.

Investigations for Chapter 10

10.1	**Permanent Magnets**	*What effects do magnets have?*

Like charges, magnets exert forces on each other. Every magnet has two distinct ends, called the north pole and the south pole. In this Investigation, you will explore how magnets affect each other, and discover which materials are attracted to magnets.

10.2	**Electromagnets**	*Can electric current create a magnet?*

In this Investigation, you will build an electromagnet and measure the electromagnet's strength as the current is varied.

10.3	**Electric Motors and Generators**	*How does an electric motor or generator work?*

In this Investigation, you will design and build different electric motors and evaluate them for speed and electric power. You will also build and test several designs of an electric generator.

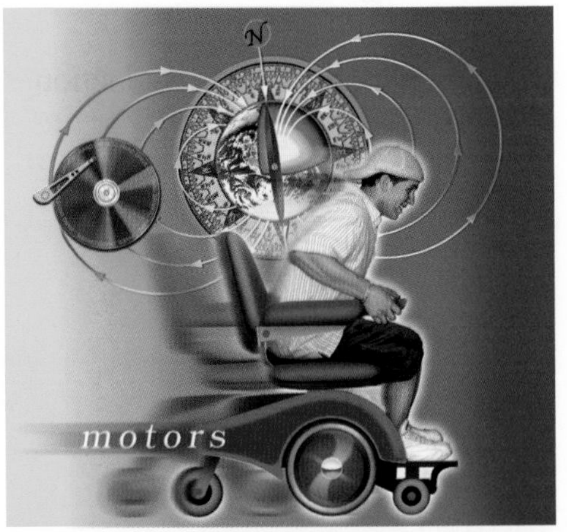

Learning Goals

In this chapter, you will:

- ✔ Describe the properties of a permanent magnet.
- ✔ Describe the forces that magnets exert on other.
- ✔ Explain why materials like iron and steel are attracted to magnets.
- ✔ Explain why a compass points north.
- ✔ Build an electromagnet.
- ✔ Analyze how electric current affects the strength of the magnetic field in an electromagnet.
- ✔ List three ways that the strength of an electromagnet can be increased.
- ✔ Compare permanent magnets and electromagnets.
- ✔ List several applications of electromagnets.
- ✔ Explain electromagnetic induction.
- ✔ Describe how electric motors and generators work.

Vocabulary

electromagnet
electromagnetic induction
generator
magnetic field
magnetic field intensity
magnetic force
magnetic north pole
magnetic south pole
permanent magnet

10.1 Permanent Magnets

What effects do magnets have, both on each other and on other materials? What is magnetic force? What is a magnetic field? In this section you will learn about magnets, magnetic forces, and the magnetic field.

What is a magnet?

A magnet is a material that is magnetic

Magnetism has fascinated people since the earliest times. Up until the Renaissance, many people thought magnetism was a form of life-force since it could make rocks move. We know that magnets stick to refrigerators and pick up paper clips or pins. They are also part of electric motors, computer disc drives, burglar alarm systems, and many other common devices.

What does magnetic mean?

Magnetic means the ability to make forces on magnets or other magnetic materials. Some materials are actively magnetic, and we call them magnets. Other materials are attracted to nearby magnets but do not show magnetism otherwise. Iron and steel are in the second category because they are attracted by magnets but are not themselves magnetic.

Permanent magnets

A **permanent magnet** is a material that keeps its magnetic properties, even when it is not close to other magnets. Bar magnets, refrigerator magnets, and horseshoe magnets are good examples of permanent magnets.

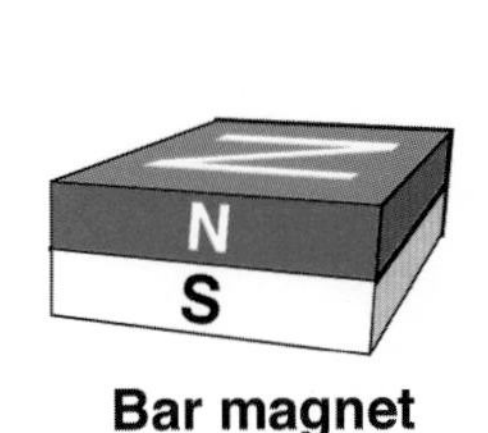

Bar magnet

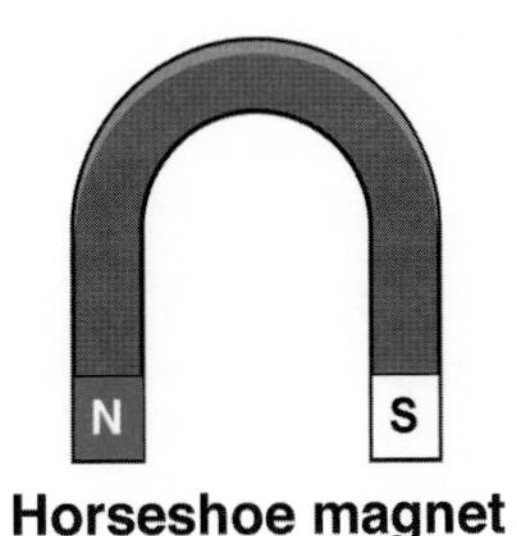

Horseshoe magnet

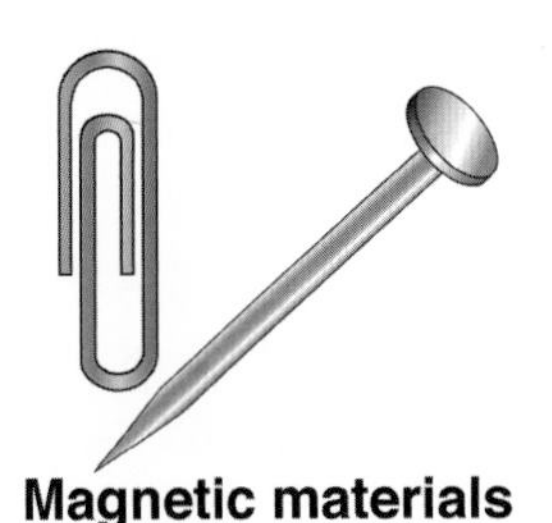

Magnetic materials

How a computer disc works

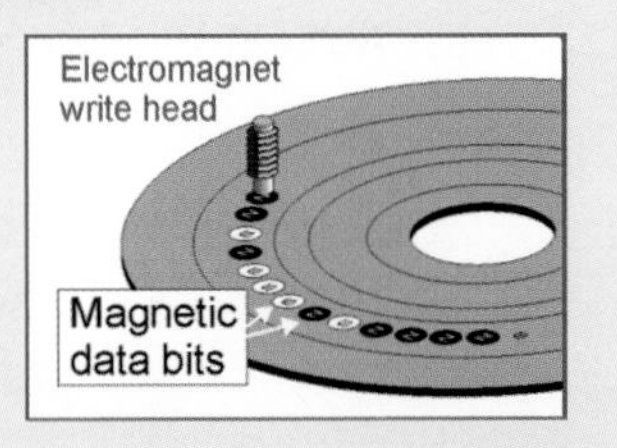

Computer discs are coated with a material that can become magnetized by tiny electromagnets. By pulsing on and off, an *electromagnet* writes data by creating tiny north and south poles in the surface of the disc.

When reading data, a second electromagnet senses the north and south poles from the spinning disc. When a north pole changes to a south pole, these changes are converted to binary numbers used in programs and data.

A strong magnet can change the north and south poles on a disc surface. This removes the data just like an eraser removes pencil marks.

Properties of magnets

Magnets have common properties

All magnets have the following common properties:

- Magnets always have two opposite "poles," called north and south.
- If divided, each part of a magnet has both north and south poles; we never see an unpaired north or south pole.
- When near each other, magnets exert magnetic forces on each other.
- The forces between magnets depend on the alignment of the poles; two unlike poles will attract each other and two like poles will repel each other.

Why magnets attract a paperclip

The fact that magnets exert forces on each other explains why a permanent bar magnet is able to pick up a paperclip. When near the magnet, the paperclip becomes a temporary magnet. The two magnets are then attracted to each other. This magnetic force is so strong it easily overcomes the gravitational force that would otherwise cause the paperclip to fall down.

North pole on this face

N

S

South pole on this face

Figure 10.1: *The north and south poles of a small rectangular magnet.*

Exceptional scientists: Michael Faraday

Michael Faraday was born in London in 1791. After basic schooling, Faraday worked as a bookbinder and became very good at it. In fact, some of the books he bound are still in existence today!

Faraday often read the books he bound. From these books, he became interested in science and began to repeat the experiments that he read about. He was particularly interested in electricity and chemistry. At age 21, he decided to pursue further education in science.

At the age of 30, Faraday made his first electrical discovery. He then went on to became one of the great scientists of his time. He invented early motors using *electromagnets* (you will study these in the next section) and made many other discoveries in physics and chemistry.

Faraday loved to show children demonstrations of the exciting experiments of his day. He gave his demonstrations during an annual Christmas lecture at the Royal Institution where he worked. This tradition is still carried on today, and is televised. If you ever go to London you can still see Faraday's laboratory at the Royal Institution's museum.

The three interactions between two magnets

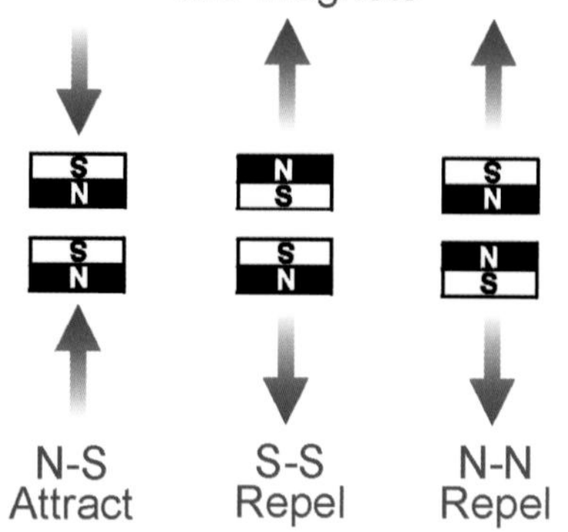

Figure 10.2: *Depending on their position, two magnets can either attract each other or repel each other.*

Discovering and using magnetism

Natural materials are magnetic

As early as 500 B.C. people discovered that some naturally occurring materials have magnetic properties. These materials include *lodestone* and *magnetite.* Ptolemy Philadelphos (367-283 B.C.) plated the entire surface of a temple in Egypt with magnetite, a magnetic mineral capable of attracting iron. He was hoping to suspend a statue of himself in midair!

Lodestone

In about 500 B.C., the Greeks discovered that a stone called lodestone had special properties. They observed that one end of a suspended piece of lodestone pointed north and the other end pointed south, helping sailors and travelers to find their way. This discovery was the first important application of magnetism, the *compass*.

The Chinese "south pointer"

The invention of the compass is also recorded in China, in 220 B.C. Writings from the Zheng dynasty tell stories of how people would use a "south pointer" when they went out to search for jade, so that they wouldn't lose their way home. The pointer was made of lodestone. It looked like a large spoon with a short, skinny handle. When balanced on a plate, the "handle" was aligned with magnetic south.

The first iron needle compass

By 1088 A.D., iron refining had developed to the point where the Chinese were making a small needle-like compass. Shen Kua recorded that a needle-shaped magnet was placed on a reed floating in a bowl of water. Chinese inventors also suspended a long, thin magnet in the air, realizing in both cases that the magnet ends were aligned with geographic north and south. Explorers from the Sung dynasty sailed their trading ships all the way to Saudi Arabia using compasses among their navigational tools. About 100 years later a similar design appeared in Europe and soon spread to the rest of the region.

The compass allows explorers to sail away from land

By 1200, explorers from Italy were using a compass to guide ocean voyages beyond the sight of land. The Chinese also continued exploring with compasses, and by the 1400s, they were traveling to the eastern coast of Africa. The compass, and the voyages that it made possible, led to many interactions among cultures.

1820 A.D.	Principle of electromagnetism discovered
1200 A.D.	Italian explorers use compass to sail open ocean
1183 A.D.	Modern compass appears
1088 A.D.	Iron compass needle made in China
220 B.C.	South pointing lodestone compass made in China
500 B.C.	Lodestone discovered in Greece

Figure 10.3: *Timeline of the discovery of lodestone and the development of the modern compass.*

How does a compass work?

The north pole of a magnet points north

A compass needle is a magnet that is free to spin until it lines up in the north-south direction. The origin of the terms "north pole" and "south pole" of a magnet come from the direction that a magnetized compass needle points. The end of the magnet that pointed north was called the north pole of the magnet and the end that pointed south was called the south pole.

Remember that two unlike poles of a magnet attract each other. So the north pole of the compass needle must point north because it is attracted by the south pole of another magnet. Where is this other magnet?

Figure 10.4: *A Chinese compass dating from 220 B.C., made of lodestone. The "handle" of the spoon points south.*

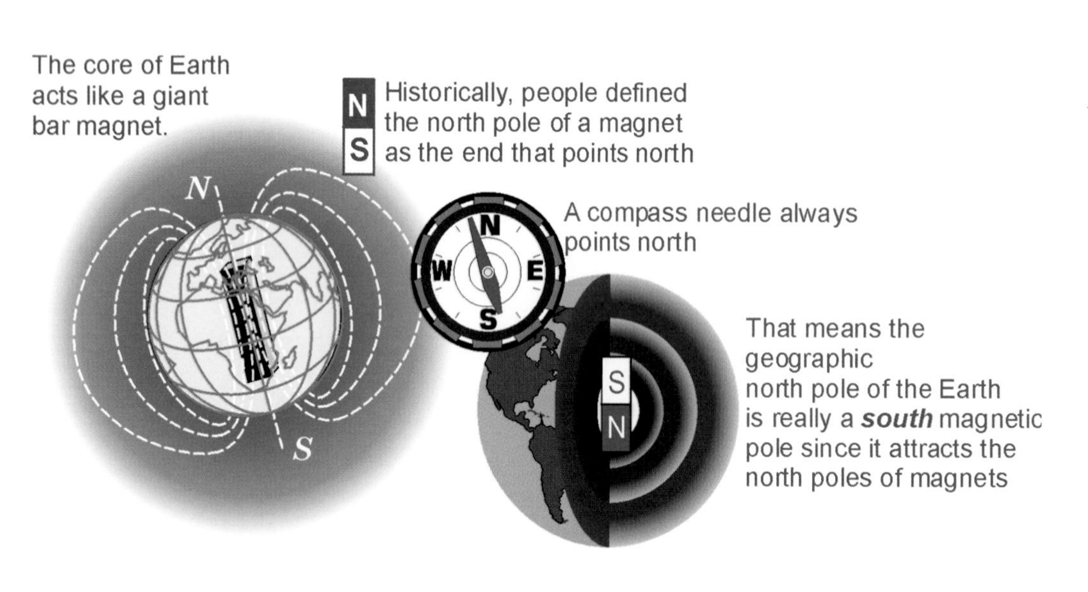

The core of Earth acts like a giant bar magnet.
N
S
Historically, people defined the north pole of a magnet as the end that points north
N
S
A compass needle always points north
N
W
E
S
That means the geographic north pole of the Earth is really a ***south*** magnetic pole since it attracts the north poles of magnets
S
N

The center of the Earth is a large magnet

It turns out that the core of our planet acts like a large magnet made of molten iron ores. This giant magnet is roughly aligned in the north-south direction. When the compass needle's north pole swings towards the *geographic north pole*, it is actually attracted by the *magnetic south pole* of Earth. The Earth's magnetic south pole is within a few degrees of geographic north!

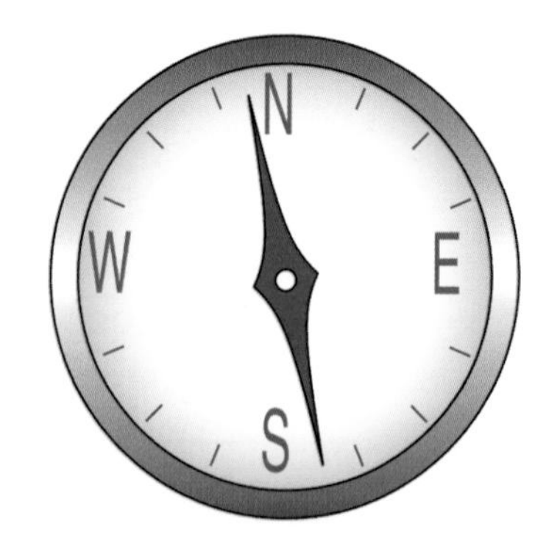

Figure 10.5: *A modern compass.*

The magnetic field

Why the magnetic field is a useful concept People investigating magnetism needed a way to describe the forces between two magnets. They knew that the force depended on the direction and orientation of the two magnets and also on the distance between them. The model of a magnetic field was developed to describe how a magnet exerts magnetic force.

Imagine testing one magnet with another Imagine you have a small test magnet (Figure 10.6) that you are moving around another magnet (the source magnet). The north pole of your test magnet feels a force everywhere in the space around the source magnet. To keep track of the force, imagine drawing an arrow in the direction your test magnet is pulled as you move it around.

What is a field? The arrows that you draw show you the magnetic field. If you connect all the arrows from north to south, you get lines called *magnetic field lines*. In physics, the word "field" means that there is a quantity (such as force) that is associated with every point in space. There can be many other kinds of fields. For example, the "odor field" near a sewer would be strongest nearest the sewer and get weaker farther away!

The magnetic field How do you interpret a drawing of a magnetic field? The number of field lines in a certain area indicates the relative strength of the source magnet in that area. The arrows on the field lines show where the north pole of a test magnet will point. Figure 10.7 shows the magnetic field lines around a small rectangular magnet.

Magnets interact through their fields It is useful to think about the interactions between two magnets in two steps.

- First, every magnet creates an energy field, called the magnetic field, in the space around it.
- Second, the field (not the magnet directly) exerts forces on any other magnet that is within its range.

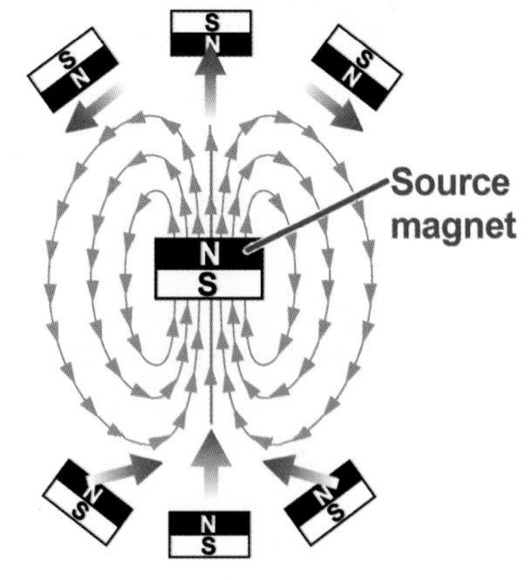

Figure 10.6: *The magnetic field is defined in terms of the force exerted on the north pole of another magnet.*

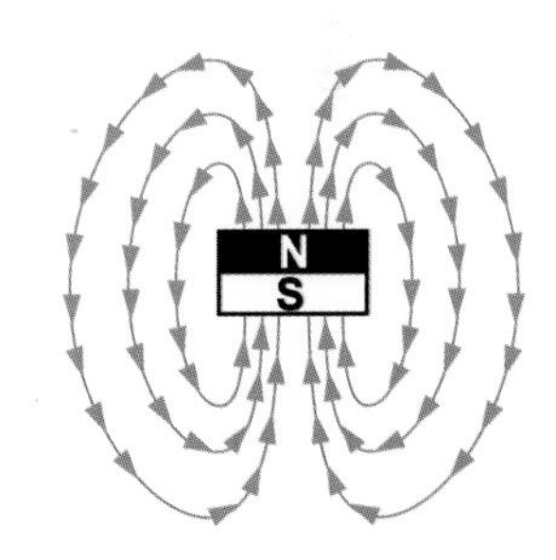

Figure 10.7: *Magnetic field lines around a magnet.*

10.2 Electromagnets

In the last section you learned about permanent magnets and magnetism. There is another type of magnet, one that is created by electric current. This type of magnet is called an electromagnet. What is an electromagnet? Why do magnets and electromagnets act the same way? In this section, you learn about electromagnets and how they helped scientists explain all magnetism.

What is an electromagnet?

Searching for a connection For a long time, people thought about electricity and magnetism as different and unrelated effects. Starting about the 18th century, scientists suspected that the two were related. As scientists began to understand electricity better, they searched for relationships between electricity and magnetism.

The principle of an electromagnet In 1819, Hans Christian Øersted, the Danish physicist and chemist (1777-1851), noticed that a current in a wire caused a compass needle to deflect. He had discovered that moving electric charges create a magnetic field! A dedicated teacher, he made this discovery while teaching his students at the University of Copenhagen. He suspected there might be an effect and did the experiment for the very first time in front of his class. With his discovery, Øersted was the first to identify the principle of an electromagnet.

How to make an electromagnet **Electromagnets** are magnets that are created when there is electric current flowing in a wire. The simplest electromagnet uses a coil of wire, often wrapped around some iron (Figure 10.8). Because iron is magnetic, it concentrates the magnetic field created by the current in the coil.

The north and south poles of an electromagnet The north and south poles of an electromagnet are located at each end of the coil (Figure 10.8). Which end is the north pole depends on the direction of the electric current. When your fingers curl in the direction of current, your thumb points toward the magnet's north pole. This method of finding the magnetic poles is called the *right hand rule* (Figure 10.9). You can switch north and south by reversing the direction of the current. This is a great advantage over permanent magnets. You can't easily change the poles of a permanent magnet.

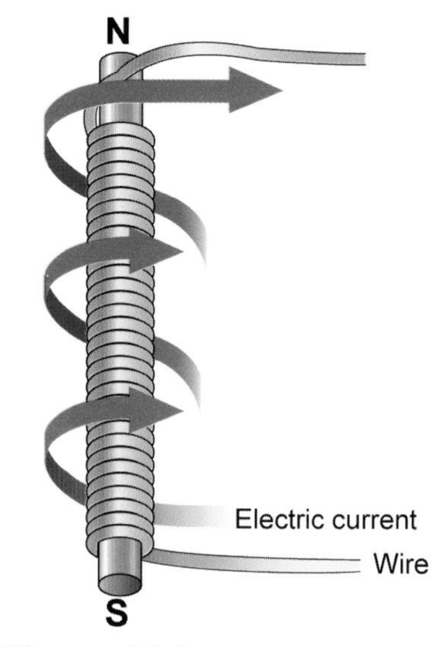

Figure 10.8: *The simplest electromagnet. In the picture, the arrows indicate the direction of current.*

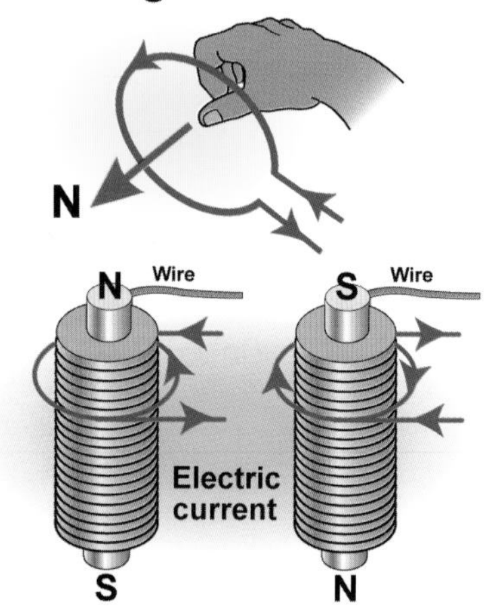

Figure 10.9: *The right hand rule: When your fingers curl in the direction of current, your thumb points toward the magnet's north pole.*

Applications of electromagnets

Current controls an electromagnet

By changing the amount of current, you can easily change the strength of an electromagnet or even turn its magnetism on and off. Electromagnets can also be much stronger than permanent magnets because the electric current can be large. For these reasons, electromagnets are used in many applications.

Magnetically levitated trains

Magnetically levitated (abbreviated to maglev) train technology uses electromagnetic force to lift a train a few inches above its track (Figure 10.10). By "floating" the train on a powerful magnetic field, the friction between wheels and rails is eliminated. Maglev trains achieve high speeds using less power than a normal train. In 1999, in Japan, a prototype five-car maglev train carrying 15 passengers reached a world-record speed of 552 kilometers (343 miles) per hour. Maglev trains are now being developed and tested in Germany, Japan, and the United States.

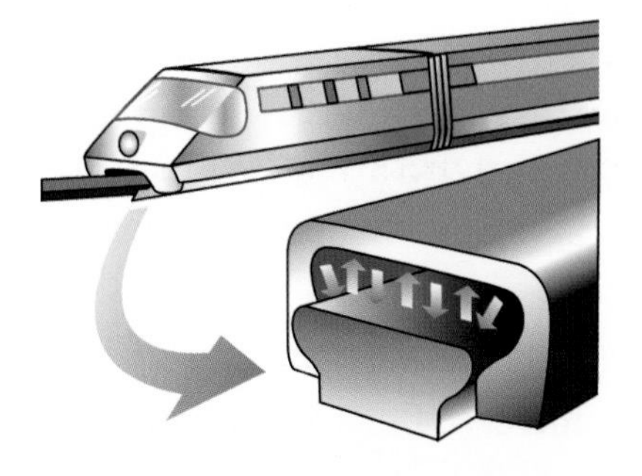

Figure 10.10: *A maglev train track has electromagnets in it that both lift the train and pull it forward.*

How does a toaster work?

The sliding switch on a toaster does several things: First, it turns the heating circuit on. Secondly, it activates an electromagnet that then attracts a spring-loaded metal tray to the bottom of the toaster. When a timing device signals that the bread has been toasting long enough, current to the electromagnet is cut off. This releases the spring-loaded tray that then pushes up on the bread so that it pops out of the toaster.

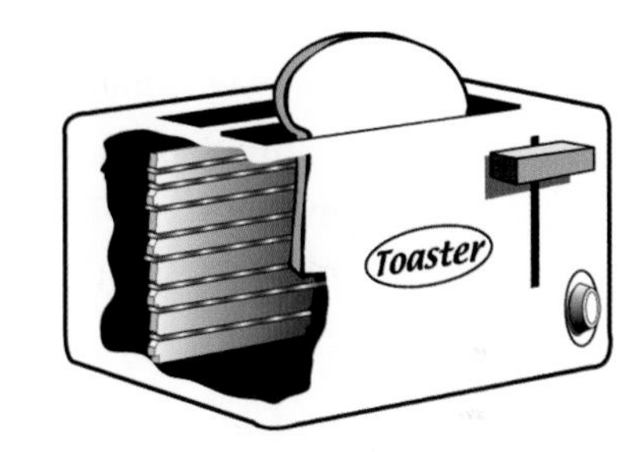

Figure 10.11: *A toaster tray is pulled down by an electromagnet while bread is toasting. When the toast is done, current is cut off and the tray pops up. The cutaway shows the heating element -- nichrome wires wrapped around a sheet of mica.*

How does an electric doorbell work?

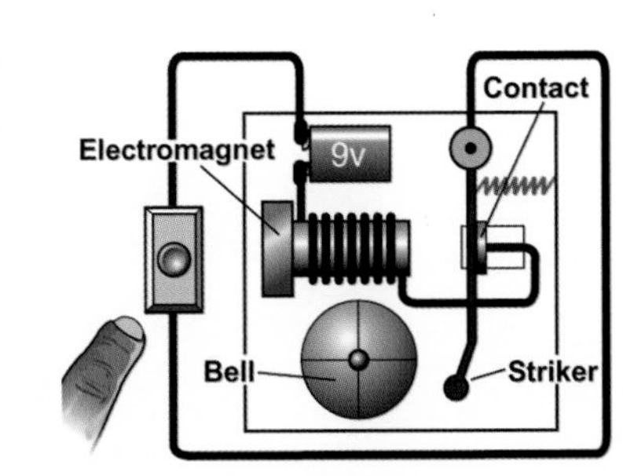

A doorbell contains an electromagnet. When the button of the bell is pushed, it sends current through the electromagnet. The electromagnet attracts a piece of metal called the striker. The striker moves towards the electromagnet but hits a bell that is in the way. The movement of the striker away from the contact also breaks the circuit after it hits the bell. A spring pulls the striker back and reconnects the circuit. If your finger is still on the button, the cycle starts over again and the bell keeps ringing.

Building an electromagnet

Make an electromagnet from wire and a nail

You can easily build an electromagnet from wire and a piece of iron, such as a nail. Wrap the wire in many turns around the nail and connect a battery as shown in Figure 10.12. When current flows in the wire, the nail becomes a magnet. Use the right hand rule to figure out which end of the nail is the north pole and which is the south pole. To reverse north and south, reverse the connection to the battery, making the current flow the opposite way.

Increase the strength of an electromagnet

You might expect that more current would make an electromagnet stronger. You would be right, but there are two ways to increase the current.

1 You can apply more voltage by adding a second battery.

2 You can add more turns of wire around the nail.

Why adding turns works

The second method works because the magnetism in your electromagnet comes from the *total* amount of current flowing *around* the nail. If there is 1 amp of current in the wire, each loop of wire adds 1 amp to the total amount that flows around the nail. Ten loops of 1 amp each make 10 total amps flowing around. By adding more turns, you use the same current over and over to get stronger magnetism.

More turns also means more resistance

Of course, nothing comes for free. By adding more turns you also increase the resistance of your coil. Increasing the resistance makes the current a little lower and generates more heat. A good electromagnet is a balance between too much resistance and having enough turns to get a strong enough magnet.

Factors affecting the force

The magnetic force exerted by a simple electromagnet depends on three factors:

- The amount of electric current in the wire
- The amount of iron or steel in the electromagnet's core
- The number of turns in the coil

In more sophisticated electromagnets, the shape, size, material in the core and winding pattern of the coil also have an effect on the strength of the magnetic field produced.

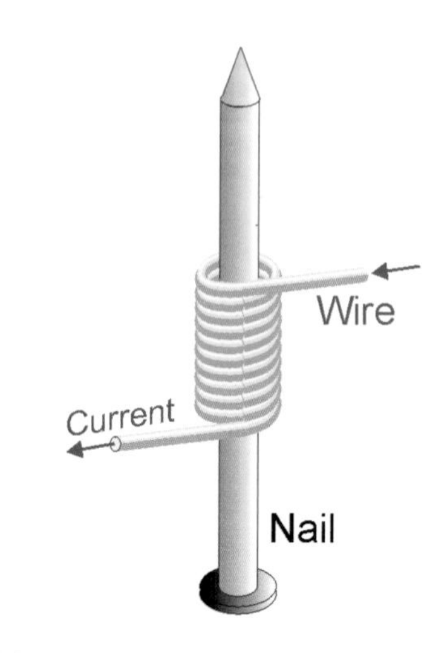

Figure 10.12: *Making an electromagnet from a nail and wire.*

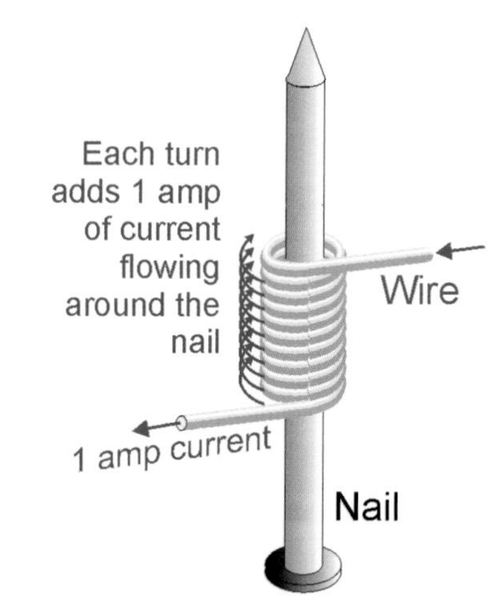

Figure 10.13: *Adding turns of wire increases the total current flowing around the electromagnet. The total current in all the turns is what determines the strength of the electromagnet.*

The relationship between permanent magnets and electromagnets

Electric currents cause all magnetism

Why do permanent magnets and electromagnets act the same way? The discovery of electromagnets helped scientists to determine why magnetism exists. Electric current through loops of wire creates an electromagnet. Atomic-scale electric currents create a permanent magnet.

Electrons move, creating small loops of current

Remember, atoms contain two types of charged particles, protons (positive) and electrons (negative). The charged electrons in atoms behave like small loops of current. These small loops of current mean that atoms themselves act like tiny electromagnets with north and south poles!

We don't usually see the magnetism from atoms for two reasons.

1. Atoms are very tiny and the magnetism from a single atom is far too small to detect without very sensitive instruments.
2. The alignment of the atomic north and south poles changes from one atom to the next. On average the atomic magnets cancel each other out (Figure 10.14).

How permanent magnets work

If all the atomic magnets are lined up in a similar direction, the magnetism of each atom adds to that of its neighbors and we observe magnetic properties on a large scale. This is what makes a permanent magnet. On average, permanent magnets have the magnetic fields of individual atoms aligned in a similar direction.

Why iron always attracts magnets and never repels them

In magnetic materials (like iron) the atoms are free to rotate and align their individual north and south poles. If you bring the north pole of a magnet near iron, the south poles of all the iron atoms are attracted. Because they are free to move, the iron near your magnet becomes a south pole and it attracts your magnet.

If you bring a south pole near iron, the opposite happens. The iron atoms nearest your magnet align themselves to make a north pole, which also attracts your magnet. This is why magnetic materials like iron always attract your magnet, and never repel, regardless of whether your test magnet approaches with its north or south pole.

Non-magnetic materials

The atoms in non-magnetic materials, like plastic, are not free to move and change their magnetic orientation. That is why most objects are not affected by magnets.

Nonmagnetic material

Permanent magnet

south pole

north pole

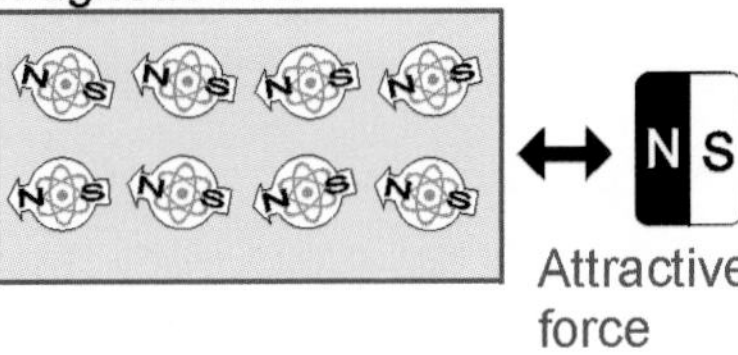

Figure 10.14: *Atoms act like tiny magnets. Permanent magnets have their atoms partially aligned, creating the magnetic forces we observe.*

The magnetic properties of iron occur because iron atoms can easily adjust their orientation in response to an outside magnetic field.

10.3 Electric Motors and Generators

Permanent magnets and electromagnets work together to make electric motors and generators. In this section you will learn about how a real electric motor works. The secret is in the ability of an electromagnet to reverse form north to south. By changing the direction of electric current, the electromagnet changes from attract to repel, and spins the motor! Electric motors convert electrical energy into mechanical energy.

Using magnets to spin a disk

Imagine a spinning disk with magnets

Imagine you have a disk that can spin. Around the edge of the disk are magnets. You have cleverly arranged the magnets so they alternate north and south. Figure 10.15 shows a picture of your rotating disk.

How to make the disk spin

To make your disk spin, you bring a magnet near the edge. The magnet attracts one of the magnets in the disk and repels the next one. These forces make the disk spin a little way (Figure 10.15)

Reversing the magnet is the key

To keep the disk spinning, you need to reverse the magnet in your fingers as soon as each magnet comes by. This way you first attract a magnet, then reverse your magnet to repel it away again. You make the disk spin by using your magnet to alternately attract and repel the magnets on the disk.

Knowing when to reverse the magnet

The disk is called the *rotor* because it can rotate. The key to making the rotor spin smoothly is to reverse your magnet when the disk is at the right place. You want the reversal to happen just as a magnet passes by. If you reverse too early, you will repel the magnet in the rotor backwards before it reaches your magnet. If you reverse too late, you attract the magnet backwards after it has passed. For it to work best, you need to change your magnet from north to south just as the magnet on the rotor passes by.

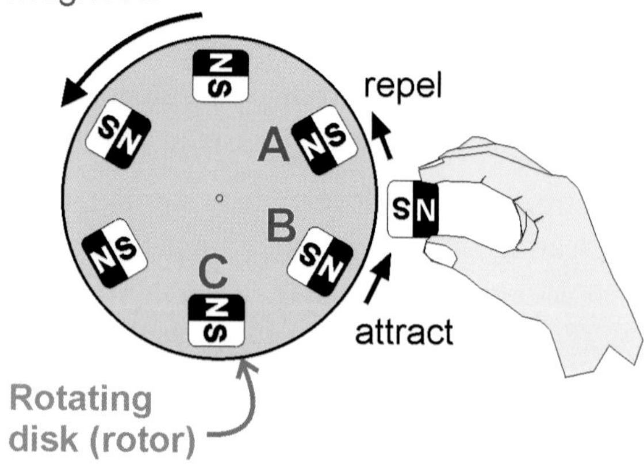
First you repel magnet A and attract magnet B
repel
attract
A
B
C
Rotating disk (rotor)

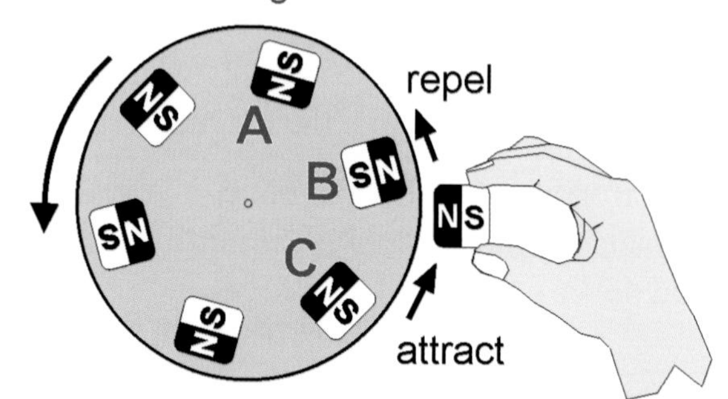
Reverse your magnet to repel magnet B and attract magnet C.
repel
attract
A
B
C

Figure 10.15: *Using a single magnet to spin a disk of magnets. Reversing the magnet in your fingers attracts and repels the magnets in the rotor, making it spin.*

Using electricity to reverse the magnet

How electromagnets are used in electric motors

The spinning disk of magnets is like the rotor of a real electric motor. In a real electric motor, the magnet you reversed with your fingers becomes an electromagnet. The switch from north to south is done by reversing the electric current in a coil. The sketch below shows how the electromagnets switch to make the rotor keep turning.

First the electromagnet repels magnet A and attracts magnet B

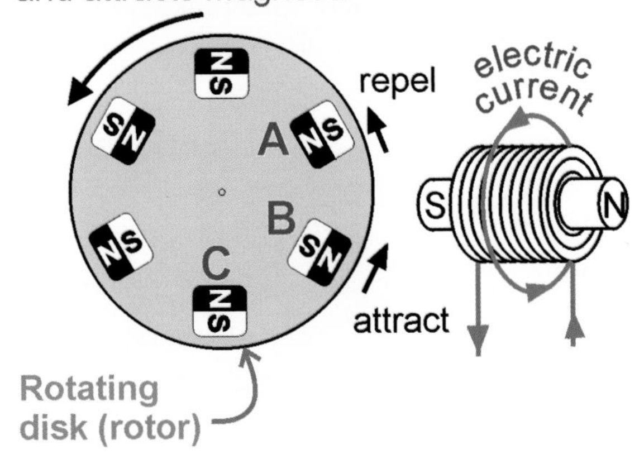

Then the electromagnet switches so it repels magnet B and attracts magnet C.

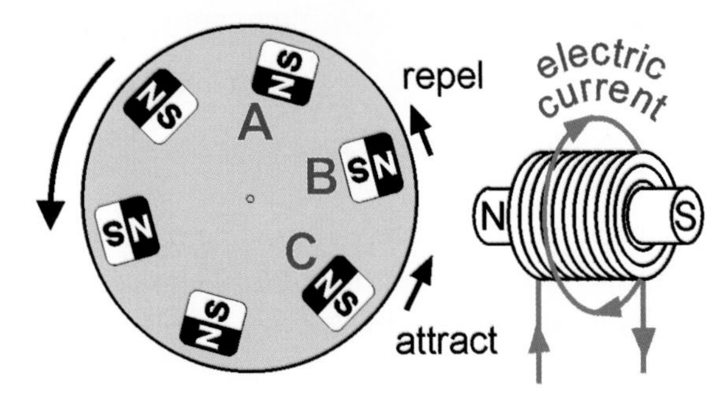

Figure 10.16: *There are electric motors all around you, even where you don't see them. The heating system in your house or school uses electric motors to move hot air or water to heat rooms.*

The commutator is a kind of switch

Just as with the finger magnet, the electromagnet must switch from north to south as each rotor magnet passes by to keep the rotor turning. The switch that makes this happen is called a *commutator*. As the rotor spins, the commutator switches the direction of current in the electromagnet. This makes the electromagnet change from north to south, and back again. The electromagnet attracts and repels the magnets in the rotor, and the motor turns.

The three things you need to make a motor

All types of electric motors must have three things to work. The three things are:

1. A rotating element (rotor) with magnets.
2. A stationary magnet that surrounds the rotor.
3. A commutator that switches the electromagnets from north to south at the right place to keep the rotor spinning.

How a battery-powered electric motor works

Inside a small electric motor

If you take apart an electric motor that runs from batteries, it doesn't look like the motor you built in the lab. But the same three mechanisms are still there. The difference is in the arrangement of the electromagnets and permanent magnets. The picture below shows a small battery-powered electric motor and what it looks like inside with one end of the motor case removed. The permanent magnets are on the outside, and they stay fixed in place.

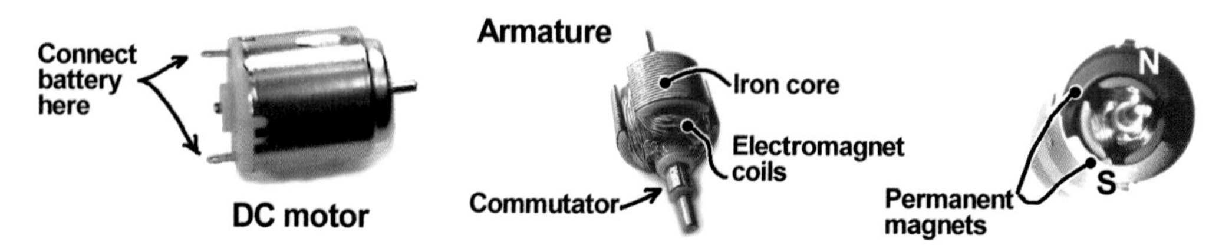

Electromagnets and the armature

The electromagnets are in the rotor, and they turn. The rotating part of the motor, including the electromagnets, is called the *armature*. The armature in the picture has three electromagnets, corresponding to the three coils (A, B, and C) in the sketch below.

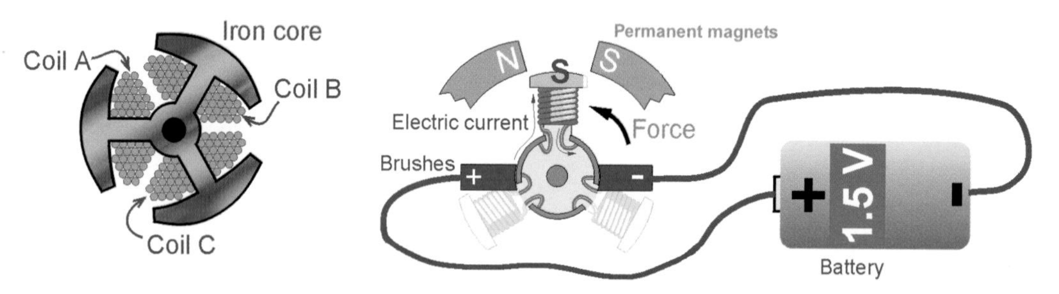

How the switching happens

The wires from each of the three coils are attached to three metal plates (commutator) at the end of the armature. As the rotor spins, the three plates come into contact with the positive and negative *brushes*. Electric current flows through the brushes into the coils. As the motor turns, the plates rotate past the brushes, switching the electromagnets from north to south by reversing the positive and negative connections to the coils. The turning electromagnets are attracted and repelled by the permanent magnets and the motor turns.

AC and DC motors

Almost all the electric motors you find around your house use AC electricity. Remember, AC means alternating current, so the current switches back and forth as it comes out of the wall socket. This makes it easier to build motors.

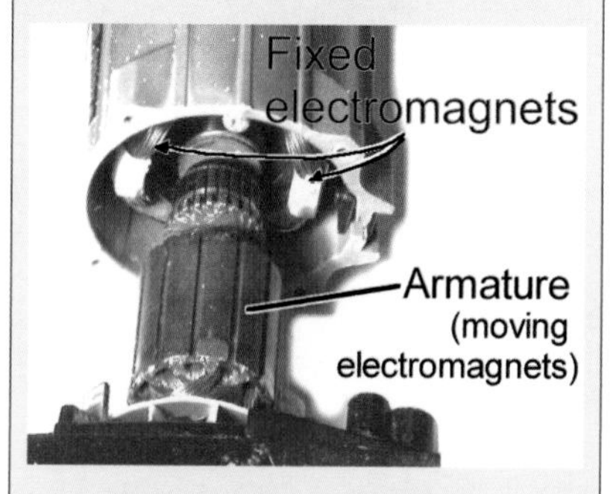

Most AC motors use electromagnets for the rotating magnets on the armature, and also for the stationary magnets around the outside. The attract-repel switching happens in both sets of electromagnets.

Electromagnetic force and electromagnetic induction

Electromagnetic force Both electrical force and magnetic force exist between electric charges. Scientists now believe both forces are two aspects of one force, the **electromagnetic force**. Many laws in physics display an elegant kind of symmetry. This symmetry is seen in the interactions between magnetism and electricity. A current through a wire creates a magnet. The reverse is also true: If you move a magnet through a coil of wire, then electric current is created. This process is called **electromagnetic induction** (Figure 10.17) because a moving magnet *induces* electric current to flow.

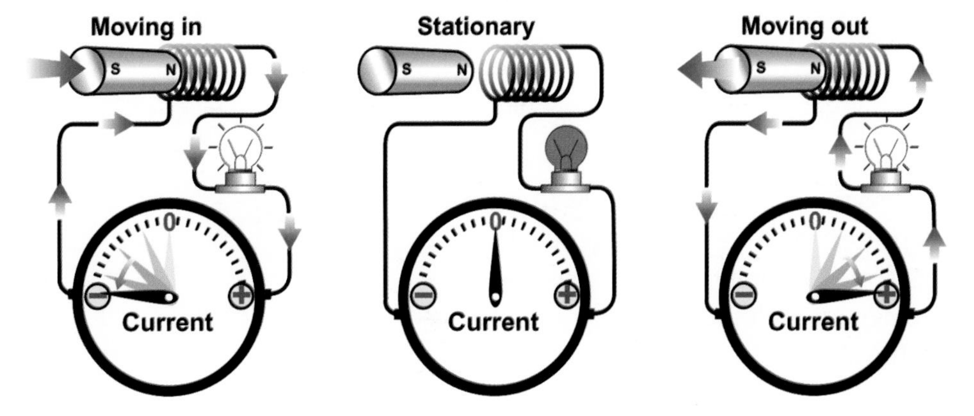

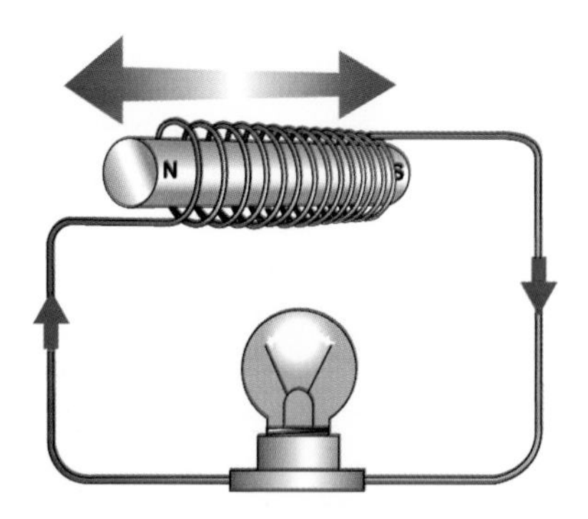

Figure 10.17: *Electromagnetic induction: Moving a magnet in loops of wire generates current in the wire.*

Moving magnets make current flow When a magnet moves into a coil of wire, it induces electric current to flow in the coil (diagram above). The current stops if the magnet stops moving. If you pull the magnet back out again, the current flows in the opposite direction. A changing magnetic field is what makes the electricity flow. If the magnetic field does not change, no electricity flows. As you might expect, the faster we make the magnetic field change, the greater the amount of electric current we generate.

Induction and energy transformations Electromagnetic induction enables us to transform mechanical energy (moving magnets) into electrical energy. Any machine that causes magnets to move past wire coils generates electric currents. These machines include giant electric power plants and computer disk drives. Tiny sensors on the disk drive read data on a magnetic disk by looking at the pulses of current that are generated as a high-speed disk spins past the coil of wire in the drive's sensor head (Figure 10.18).

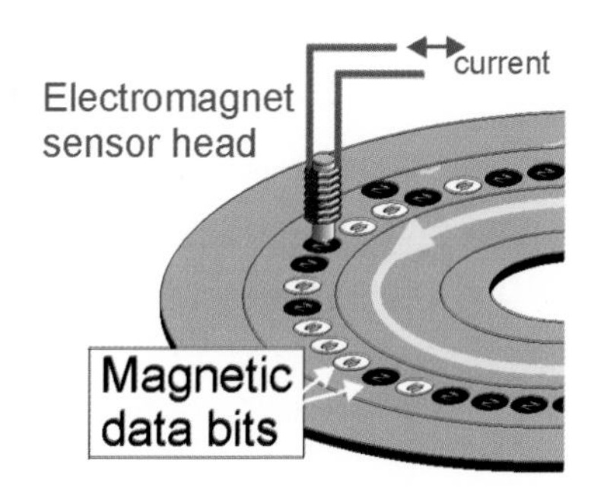

Figure 10.18: *A computer hard drive uses induction to read data from the magnetic writing on a spinning disk.*

Generating electricity

What is a generator? Power plants use electromagnetic induction to create electricity. A generator is a combination of mechanical and electrical systems that converts kinetic energy into electrical energy (Figure 10.19).

Batteries are not powerful enough Although batteries can convert energy from chemical reactions into electrical energy, batteries are not practical for creating large amounts of electric current. Power plants, which supply current to homes and businesses, use generators.

How a generator works As an example of how the electricity is made, consider a disk with magnets in it (Figure 10.20). As the disk rotates, first a north pole and then a south pole passes the coil. When the north pole is approaching, the current flows one way. When the north pole passes and a south pole approaches, the current flows the other way. As long as the disk is spinning, there is a changing magnetic field near the coil and electric current is induced to flow.

Generators make alternating current Because the magnetic field alternates from north to south as the disk spins, generators produce *alternating current* (AC). Alternating current is used in the electrical system in your home and school.

Energy is conserved The electrical energy created from a generator isn't free. You have to do work to turn the disk and make the electric current flow. Power plants contain a rotating machine called a *turbine*. The turbine is kept turning by a flow of air heated by gas, oil, coal, or nuclear energy. One kind of energy is transformed into another and energy is conserved. The energy stored in the gas, oil, coal, or nuclear fuel is transformed into the movement of the turning turbine, which is then transformed into electrical energy.

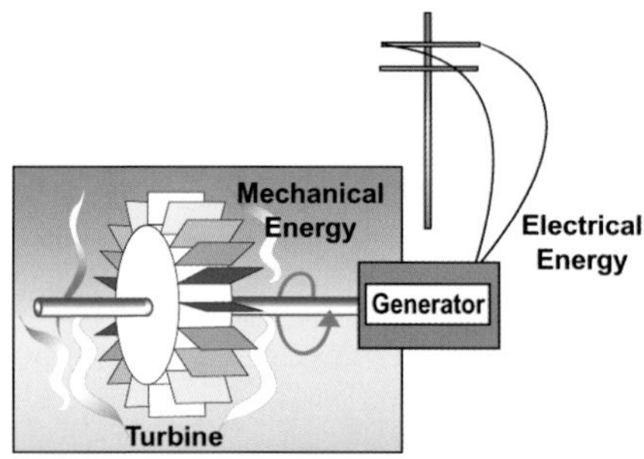

Figure 10.19: *A power plant generator contains a turbine that turns magnets inside loops of wire, generating electricity.*

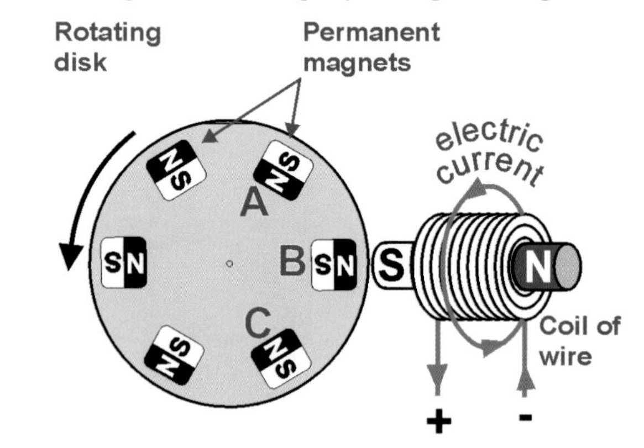

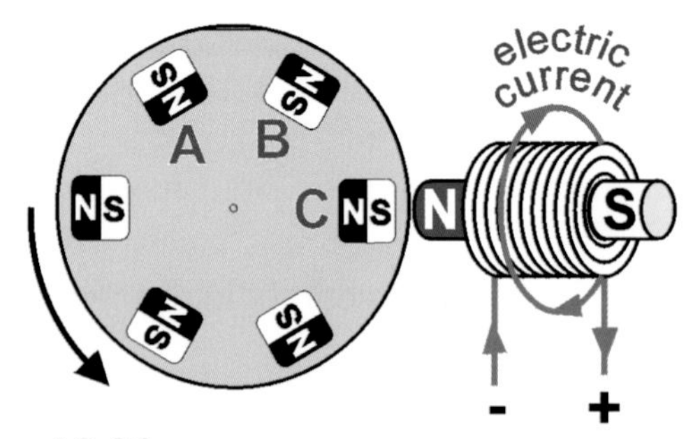

Figure 10.20: *How a generator works. In the top sketch the north pole on the disk induces a south pole in the electromagnet, causing current to flow one way. When the disk rotates, the magnetism in the coil is reversed, and the electric current generated also reverses.*

Chapter 10 Review

Vocabulary review

Match the following terms with the correct definition. There is one extra definition in the list that will not match any of the terms.

Set One

1. permanent magnet
2. magnetic north pole
3. magnetic south pole
4. magnetic forces
5. lodestone

a. A naturally occurring magnetic material

b. A material that is magnetic; it has a north and a south pole, and interacts with other magnets

c. The large magnet located inside the Earth

d. The end of a magnet that will point north if suspended in air near the surface of the Earth

e. The end of a magnet that will point south if suspended in air near the surface of the Earth

f. The forces that magnets exert on each other

Set Two

1. compass
2. magnetic field
3. electromagnet
4. electric motor
5. commutator

a. A device that uses electricity and magnets to turn electrical energy into rotating mechanical energy

b. The movement of electrons that causes them to act like tiny atomic magnets

c. A magnet that is created from current through a wire

d. The part of an electric motor that switches the electromagnets from north to south

e. Magnets create this in the space around them and it exerts forces on other magnets

f. A device that uses magnets to tell direction

Set Three

1. generator
2. electromagnetic force
3. electromagnetic induction
4. alternating current
5. turbine

a. The process by which a moving magnet creates voltage and current in a loop of wire

b. A device to float a train above the track

c. A mechanical wheel that might work with steam or water to turn a generator

d. The force that exists between electric charges; often described as electrical force or magnetic force depending on how charges interact

e. Electrical current flowing back and forth

f. A device that uses electromagnetic induction to make electricity

Concept review

1. Name two examples of naturally occurring magnetic materials.
2. What is the first known application of magnetism?
3. Explain the origin of the terms "north pole" and "south pole" used to describe the two ends of a magnet.
4. Explain why a compass points north.
5. Describe the types of forces that magnetic poles exert on each other.
6. What are three ways you can increase the strength of an electromagnet?
7. Explain why an electromagnet usually has a core of iron or steel.
8. Name two examples of machines that use electromagnets. Explain the purpose of the electromagnet in each machine.
9. In your own words, explain how atoms give rise to magnetic properties in certain materials.
10. Which picture shows the correct location of the north and south poles of the electromagnet? Choose A or B and explain how you arrived at your choice.

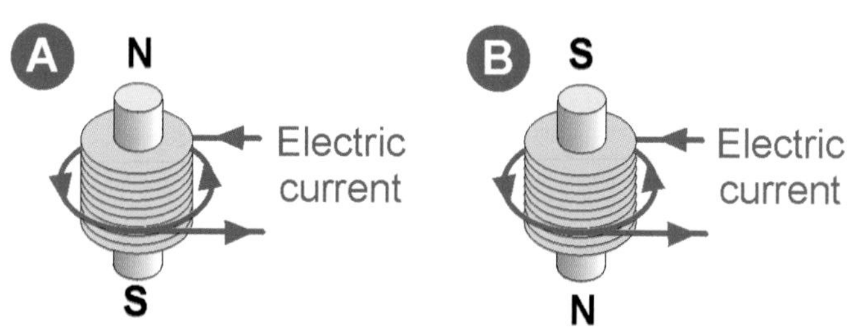

11. An electric generator is constructed that uses a rotating disk of magnets that spin past a coil of wire as shown in the diagram. Which of the following statements are TRUE?

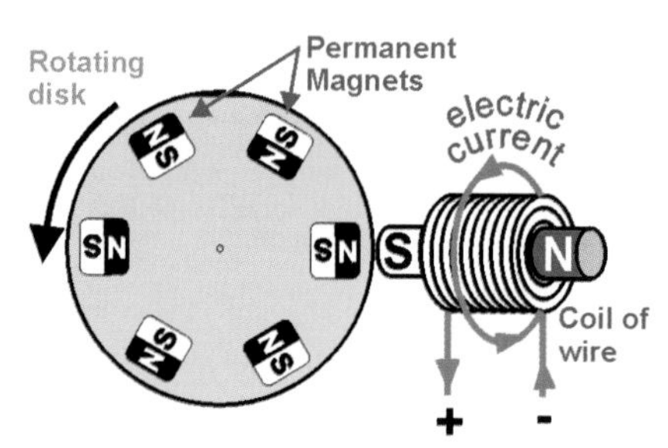

    a. Turning the disk 2 times faster generates 4 times as much electricity.
    b. Turning the disk 2 times faster generates 2 times as much electricity.
    c. Doubling the number of magnets generates 2 times as much electricity.
    d. Doubling the number of magnets and spinning twice as fast generates 4 times as much electricity.

12. The amount of electricity generated by a magnet moving through a coil of wire can be INCREASED by:

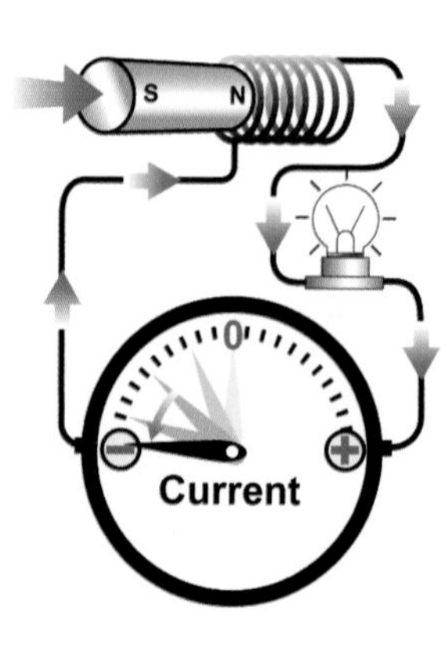

    a. Using a stronger magnet and holding the magnet stationary in the coil.
    b. Moving the magnet through the coil faster.
    c. Adding more turns of wire to the coil.
    d. Moving the magnet more slowly through the coil so the coil has time to feel the effects of the magnetic force.

Problems

1. A student knocked a ceramic magnet off her desk and it shattered when it hit the floor. Copy the broken pieces and label the north and south poles on each one.

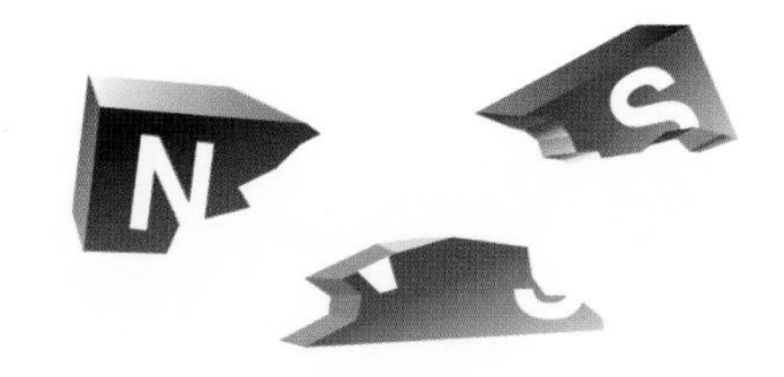

2. A student placed two magnets with opposite poles facing each other. He slowly brought the two magnets closer and observed the distance at they first interacted with each other. The student observed that one magnet could move the other at a distance of 33 millimeters.
   a. Next, he placed the two north poles facing one another. Predict the distance at which he would observe one magnet moving the other through repelling forces.
   b. The student put one of his magnets on his wooden desk with the north pole down. If the desk top is 2.5 centimeters thick, do you think he could move the top magnet by sliding another magnet under the desk? Explain how the observed data supports your answer.

3. The atoms of a permanent magnet can't move, and the electrons in the atoms are lined up so that a magnetic field is created around the magnet. The atoms in iron or steel can move. Describe what you think happens to the atoms of a steel paperclip when the paperclip is near a permanent magnet.

4. A magnet attracts a pin, as shown in the picture. The pin has become a temporary magnet. Copy the picture and then, using what you know about magnetic forces, label the north and south poles of the pin.

5. A horseshoe magnet is shown at right. Copy the picture and then draw the magnetic field lines between the north and south poles of the magnet.

6. Draw an electromagnet. Label all parts including the magnetic poles.

7. What property of matter gives rise to both electricity and magnetism?

8. A working electric motor needs to have three things. Which of the following are the three?
   a. A device to switch the electromagnets at the right time.
   b. A moving element with magnets.
   c. An even number of magnets.
   d. A stationary element with magnets.

9. An electric motor running from a single 1.5-volt battery draws a current of 1 amp. How much electric power does the motor use in watts?

10. Describe the function of the commutator in an electric motor.

Applying your knowledge

1. You read that Ptolemy Philadelphos (367-283 BC) covered the entire surface of a temple in Egypt with magnetite, a magnetic stone capable of attracting iron. He was hoping to suspend a statue of himself in midair. Ptolemy's experiment did not work, but you can suspend something using magnets. Build a device like the diagram below and see if you can make the lower magnet float. See how much weight you can hang from the lower magnet by changing the distance between the upper and lower magnets.

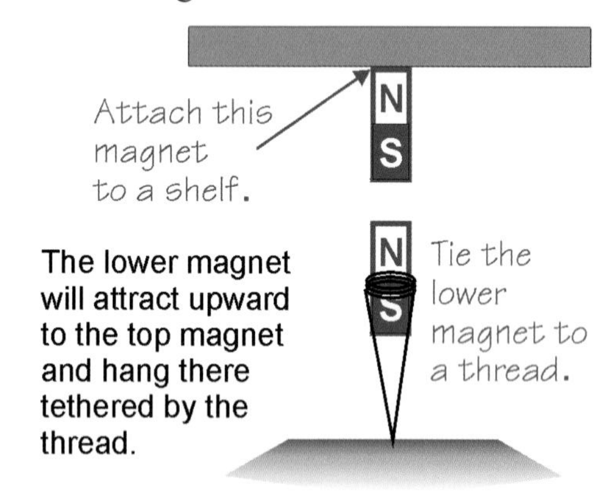
Attach this magnet to a shelf.
N
S
N
S
The lower magnet will attract upward to the top magnet and hang there tethered by the thread.
Tie the lower magnet to a thread.

2. Speakers and microphones use electromagnets to turn electric currents into sound, and vice versa. Research how electromagnets are used in sound systems. Draw a diagram that shows the location of permanent magnets and electromagnets in a speaker. How does the electromagnet produce vibrations that create sound?

3. A bicycle light generator is a device that you place on the wheel of your bike. When you turn the wheel, the generator powers a light. When you stop, the light goes out. Explain how you think the bike generator makes electricity.

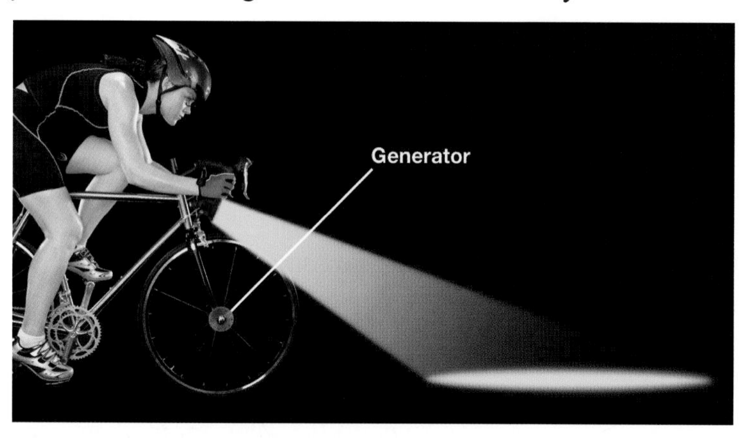
Generator

4. A clever inventor claims to be able to make an electric car that makes its own electricity and never needs gas or recharging. The inventor claims that as the car moves, the wind created by its motion spins a propeller that turns a generator to make electricity and power the wheels. Do you believe the car can work, and why (or why not)? (Hint: Think about conservation of energy.)

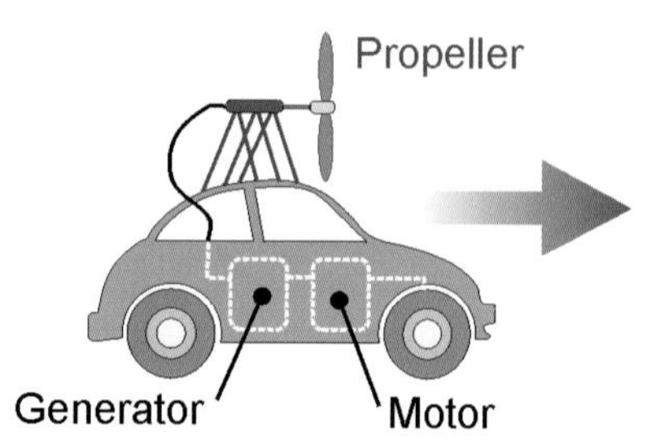
Propeller
Generator
Motor

UNIT 4 Sound and Waves

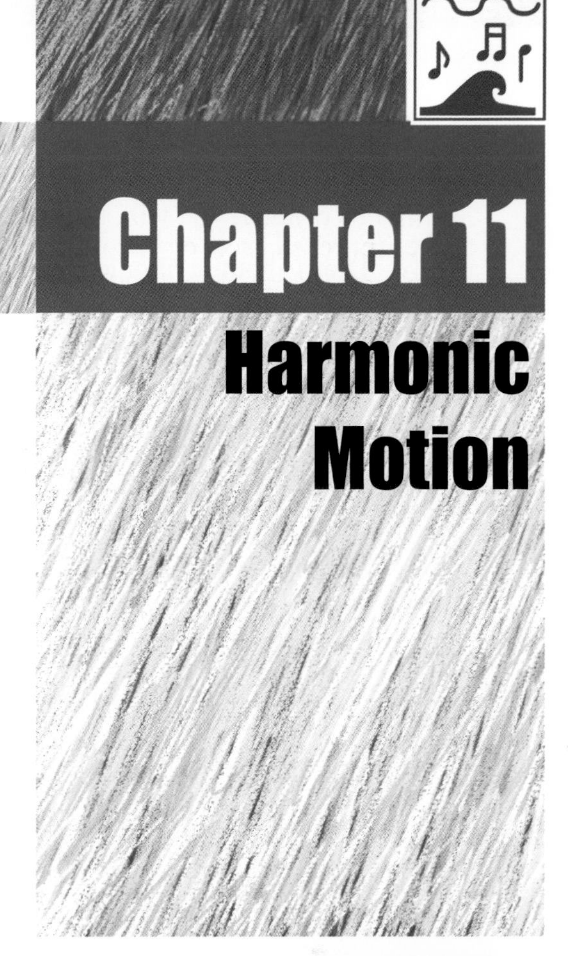

Chapter 11 Harmonic Motion

Introduction to Chapter 11

The motion we have studied so far has been from one place to another. In this chapter we will investigate harmonic motion, which is motion that repeats in cycles. From the orbit of the Earth to the rhythmic beating of your heart, harmonic motion is fundamental to our understanding of nature.

Investigations for Chapter 11

11.1	Harmonic Motion	*How do we describe the back and forth motion of a pendulum?*

The pendulum is an ideal start for investigating harmonic motion. The objective for this Investigation is to design a clock that can keep accurate time using a pendulum.

11.2	Graphs of Harmonic Motion	*How do we make graphs of harmonic motion?*

Graphs tell us much about straight-line motion. This Investigation will apply graphing techniques to oscillators. Learn how to read a heartbeat from an EKG and how to read the seismogram of a powerful earthquake!

11.3	Simple Mechanical Oscillators	*What kinds of systems oscillate?*

Many things in nature oscillate. Guitar strings, trees in the wind, and stretched rubber bands are all examples of oscillators. In this Investigation we will construct several simple oscillators and learn how to adjust their frequency and period.

Learning Goals

In this chapter, you will:

- ✔ Learn about harmonic motion and how it is fundamental to understanding natural processes.
- ✔ Use harmonic motion to keep accurate time using a pendulum.
- ✔ Learn how to interpret and make graphs of harmonic motion.
- ✔ Construct simple oscillators.
- ✔ Learn how to adjust the frequency and period of simple oscillators.
- ✔ Learn to identify simple oscillators.

Vocabulary

amplitude	harmonic motion	period	system
cycle	hertz	periodic motion	
frequency	oscillator	phase	

11.1 Harmonic Motion

As you watch moving things, you see two different kinds of motion. One kind of motion goes from one place to another. This is called *linear motion*. The concepts of distance, time, speed, and acceleration come from thinking about this kind of motion.

The second kind of motion is motion that repeats itself over and over. We call motion that repeats over and over **harmonic motion** and that is what you will learn about in this section. The word comes from *harmony* which means "multiples of." Swinging back and forth on a swing is a good example of harmonic motion (Figure 11.1). Many moving things have both kinds of motion. A bicycle moves forward but the wheels and pedals go around and around in harmonic motion (Figure 11.2).

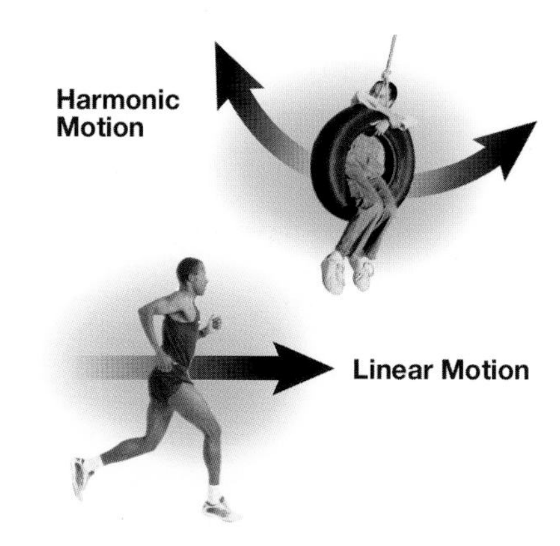

Figure 11.1: *Linear motion goes from one place to another without repeating. Harmonic motion repeats over and over the same way.*

Cycles, systems, and oscillators

What is a cycle? The **cycle** is the building block of harmonic motion. A cycle is a unit of motion that repeats over and over. All harmonic motion is a repeated sequence of cycles. The cycle of the pendulum is shown below.

The cycle of a pendulum

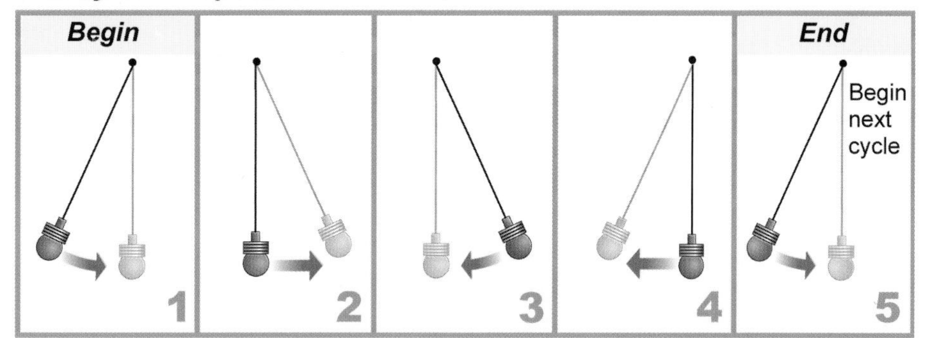

Finding the cycle When investigating harmonic motion we start by identifying the basic cycle. A cycle has a beginning and ending. Between beginning and end, the cycle has to include all the motion that repeats. The cycle of the pendulum is defined by where we choose the beginning. If we start the cycle when the pendulum is all the way to the left, the cycle ends when the pendulum has returned all the way to the left again. If we choose the cycle correctly, the motion of the pendulum is one cycle after the next with no gaps between cycles.

Figure 11.2: *Real-life situations can include both linear motion and harmonic motion.*

Harmonic motion in nature

Choosing a system

In science we often refer to a system. A system is a group we choose that includes all the things we are interested in. Choosing the system helps us concentrate on what is important and exclude what is not important. For the pendulum, the system is the hanger, string, and weight. We don't need to include the floor or the table, since these are not directly important to the motion.

We might choose the system differently depending on what we want to investigate. If we wanted to see how gravity affected the pendulum, we would have to include Earth's gravity as part of the system.

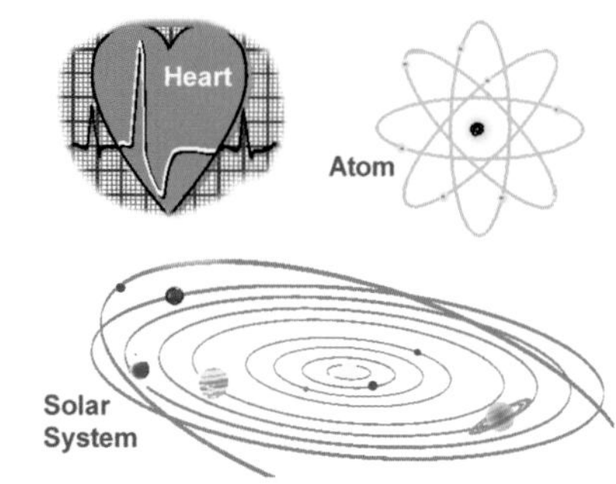

Figure 11.3: *The pendulum is an oscillator. Other examples of oscillators are an atom, your beating heart, and the solar system.*

An oscillator is a system with harmonic motion

A system that shows harmonic motion is called an **oscillator**. The pendulum is an example of an oscillator. So is your heart and its surrounding muscles (Figure12.4). Oscillators can be very small. The electrons in the atom make harmonic motion, so an atom is an oscillator. Oscillators can also be very large. The solar system is an oscillator with each of the planets in harmonic motion around the sun. We are going to study oscillators using simple models, but what we learn will also apply to more complex systems, like a microwave communications satellite.

Earth is part of several systems in harmonic motion

Earth is a part of several oscillating systems. The Earth/sun system has a cycle of one year, which means Earth completes one orbit around the sun in a year. The Earth/moon system has a cycle of approximately one month. Earth itself has several different cycles (Figure 11.4). It rotates around its axis once a day making the 24-hour cycle of day and night. There is also a wobble of Earth's axis that cycles every 22,000 years, moving the north and south poles around by hundreds of miles. There are cycles in weather, such as the El Nino and La Nina oscillations in ocean currents that produce fierce storms every decade or so. Much of the planet's ecology depends on cycles.

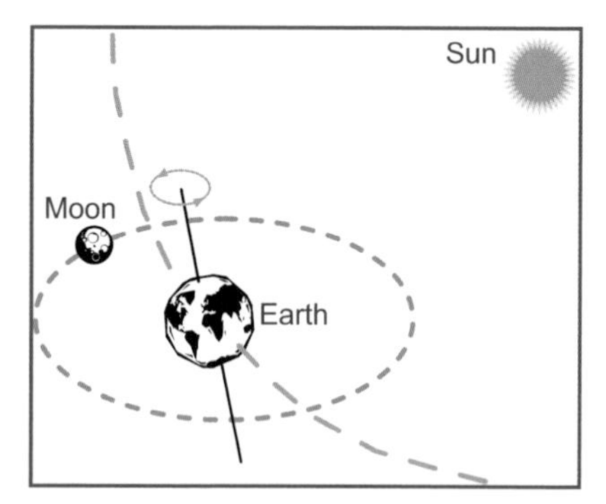

Figure 11.4: *The Earth/sun/moon system has many different cycles. The year, month, and day are the result of orbital cycles.*

Harmonic motion in art and music

Music comes from oscillations

Both light and sound come from oscillations. Music and musical instruments are oscillators that we design to create sounds with specific cycles that we enjoy hearing. Sound is an oscillation of the air. A moving speaker pushes and pulls on the air creating a small oscillation in pressure (Figure 11.5). The oscillation travels to where it hits your eardrum. Your vibrating eardrum moves tiny bones in the ear setting up more oscillations that are transmitted by nerves to the brain. There is harmonic motion at every step of the way, from the musical instrument to the perception of sound by your brain.

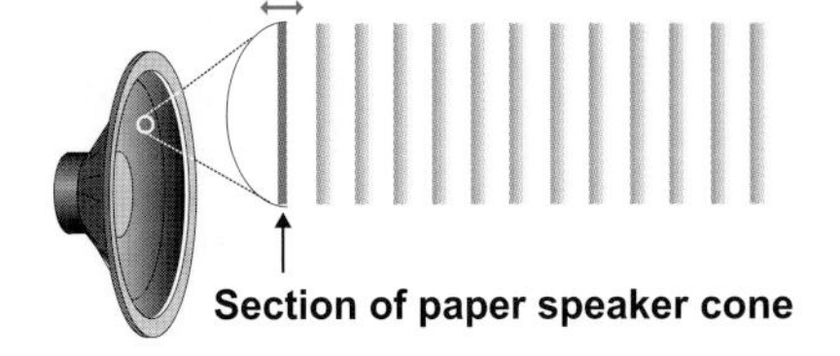

Figure 11.5: *A moving speaker oscillates back and forth, making sound that you can hear.*

Color comes from oscillations

We see colors in light waves, which are oscillations of electricity and magnetism. Faster oscillations make blue light while slower oscillations make red light. When painting a picture, each color of paint contains different molecules that absorb and reflect different colors of light. The colors you see come from the interaction between the oscillations of light and the oscillations of the electrons in the pigment molecules.

Figure 11.6: *The cordless phone you use has an electronic oscillator at millions of cycles per second.*

Harmonic motion in technology

Oscillators are used in communications

Almost all modern communication technology relies on fast electronic oscillators. Cell phones use oscillators that make more than 100 million cycles each second (Figure 11.6). FM radio uses oscillators between 95 million and 107 million cycles per second. When you tune a radio you are selecting the frequency of the oscillator you want to listen to. Each station sets up an oscillator at a different frequency. Sometimes, you can get two stations at once when you are traveling between two radio towers with nearly the same frequency.

Oscillators are used to measure time

The cycles of many oscillators always repeat in the same amount of time. This makes harmonic motion a good way to keep time. If you have a pendulum that has a cycle one second long, you can count time in seconds by counting cycles of the pendulum. Grandfather clocks and mechanical watches actually count cycles of oscillators to tell time (Figure 11.7). Even today, the world's most accurate clocks keep time by counting cycles of light from a cesium atom oscillator. Modern atomic clocks are so accurate they lose only one second in 1,400,000 years!

Figure 11.7: *Clocks and watches use oscillators to keep time. This works because many oscillators have precisely stable cycles.*

Investigating harmonic motion

Period is the time for one cycle

What makes harmonic motion useful for clocks is that each cycle takes the same amount of time. The time for one cycle is called the **period**. Some clocks have a pendulum with a period of exactly two seconds. The gears in the clock cause the minute hand to move 1/60 of a turn for every 30 swings of the pendulum. The period is one of the important characteristics of all harmonic motion (Figure 11.8).

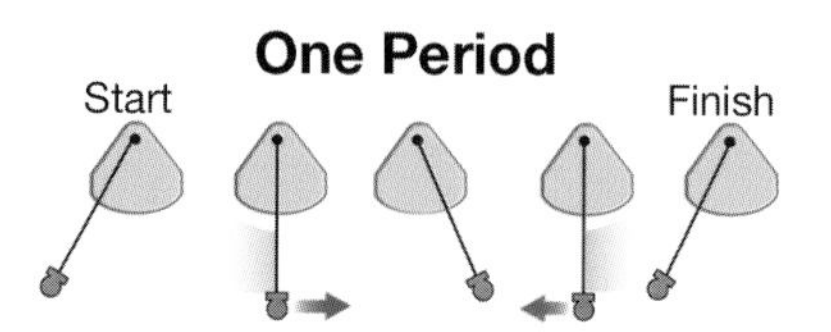

Figure 11.8: *The period is the time it takes to complete one cycle.*

Frequency is the number of cycles per second

Frequency is closely related to period. The **frequency** of an oscillator is the number of cycles it makes per second. Every day, we experience a wide range of frequencies. FM radio uses frequencies between 95 million and 107 million cycles per second (the FM standing for frequency modulation) (Figure 11.9). Your heartbeat probably has a frequency between one-half and two cycles per second. The musical note "A" has a frequency of 440 cycles per second. The human voice contains frequencies mainly between 100 and 2,000 cycles per second.

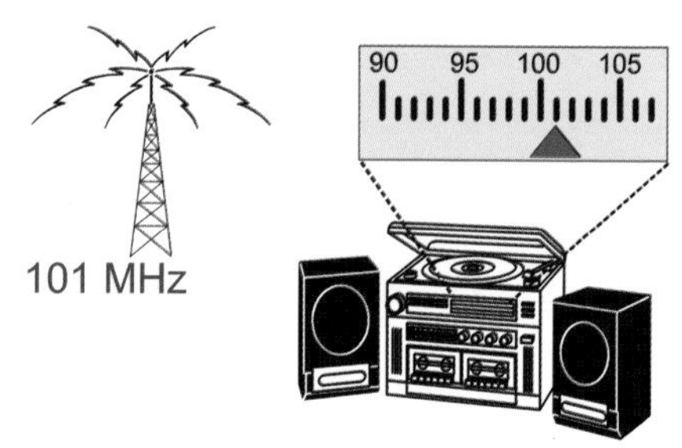

Figure 11.9: *When you tune a radio to receive a station, you are matching frequencies between receiver and transmitter.*

Frequency is measured in hertz

The unit of one cycle per second is called a **hertz**. A frequency of 440 cycles per second is usually written as 440 hertz, or abbreviated 440 Hz. The Hz is a unit that is the same in English and metric. When you tune into a station at 101 on the FM dial, you are actually setting the oscillator in your radio to a frequency of 101 megahertz, or 101,000,000 Hz. You hear music when the oscillator in your radio is exactly matched to the frequency of the oscillator in the transmission tower connected to the radio station.

Period and frequency

$$T = \frac{1}{f} \qquad f = \frac{1}{T}$$

Period (seconds) → T; Frequency (hertz) → f

Frequency (hertz) → f; Period (seconds) → T

Frequency and period are inversely related. The period is the time per cycle. The frequency is the number of cycles per time. If the period of a pendulum is 1.25 seconds, its frequency is 0.8 cycles per second (0.8 Hz). If you know one, you can calculate the other.

Example:

Calculate the frequency of a pendulum that has a period of 1/4 second.

Solution:

(1) You are asked for frequency.

(2) You are given the period.

(3) The relationship you need is F=1/T.

(4) Plug in numbers.

F = 1 / (0.25 sec)

= 4 Hz

Amplitude

Amplitude describes the size of a cycle

Another important characteristic of a cycle is its size. The period tells how long the cycle lasts. The **amplitude** describes how big the cycle is. The diagram below shows a pendulum with small amplitude and large amplitude. With mechanical systems (such as a pendulum), the amplitude is often a distance or angle. With other kinds of oscillators, the amplitude might be voltage or pressure. The amplitude is measured in units appropriate to the kind of oscillation you are describing.

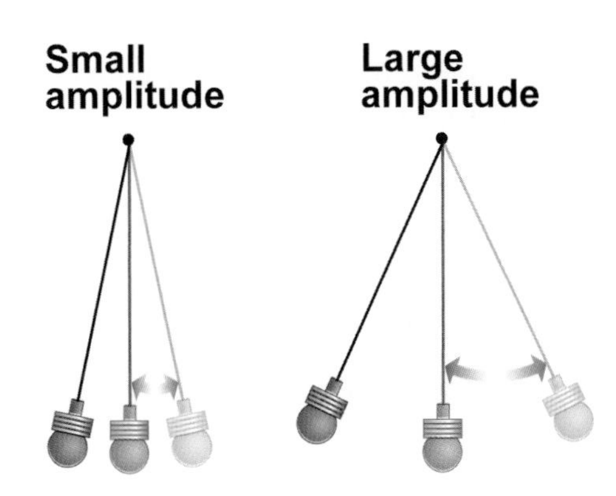

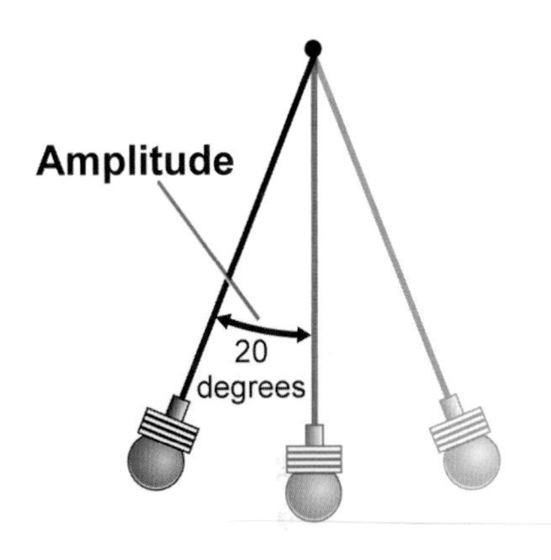

Figure 11.10: *A pendulum with an amplitude of 20 degrees swings 20 degrees away from the center.*

How do you measure amplitude?

The amplitude is the maximum distance the motion moves away from the average. For a pendulum, the average is at the center. The pendulum spends as much time to the right of center as it does to the left. For the pendulum in Figure 11.10, the amplitude is 20 degrees, because the pendulum moves 20 degrees away from center in either direction.

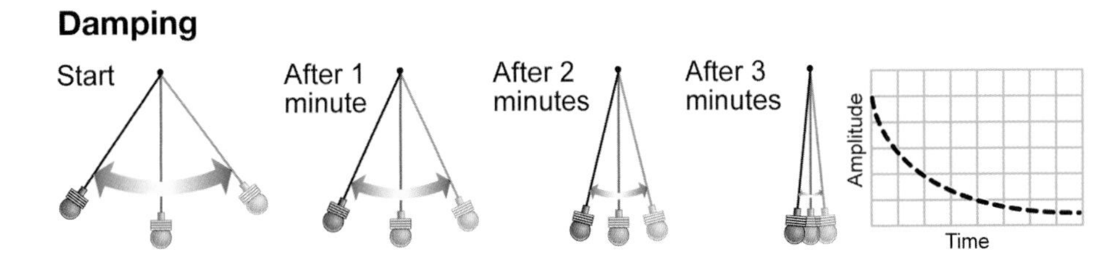

Damping

Friction slows a pendulum down, as it does all oscillators. That means the amplitude slowly gets reduced until the pendulum is hanging straight down, motionless. We use the word **damping** to describe the gradual loss of amplitude of an oscillator. If you wanted to make a clock with a pendulum, you would have to find a way to keep adding energy to counteract the damping of friction.

11.2 Graphs of Harmonic Motion

Harmonic motion graphs show cycles. This is what makes them different from linear motion graphs (Figure 11.11). The values of the period and amplitude can be read from the graphs. If you know the period and amplitude, you can quickly sketch a harmonic motion graph.

Typical Linear Motion Graphs

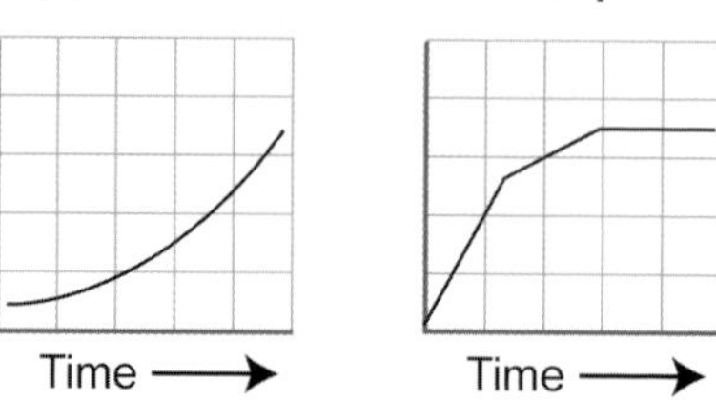

Typical Harmonic Motion Graphs

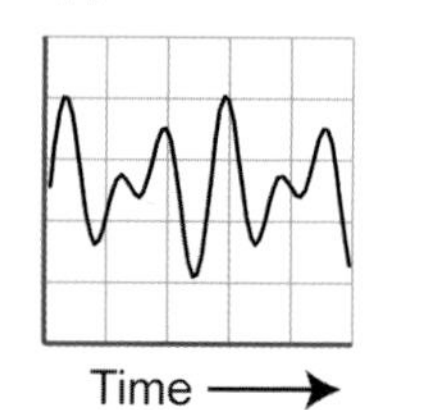

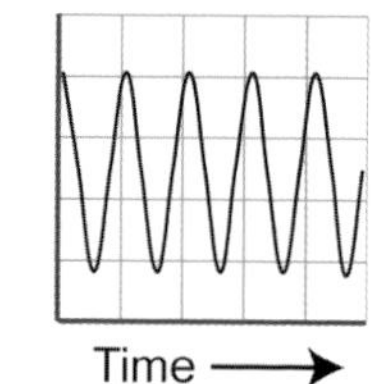

Figure 11.11: *Typical graphs for linear motion (top) and harmonic motion (bottom). Harmonic motion graphs show cycles.*

Reading harmonic motion graphs

Cycles and time

Most graphs of harmonic motion show how things change with time. The pendulum is a good example. The diagram below shows a graph of position vs. time for a pendulum. The graph shows repeating cycles just like the motion. Seeing a pattern of cycles on a graph is an indication that harmonic motion is present.

Using positive and negative numbers

Harmonic motion graphs often use positive and negative values to represent motion on either side of center. We usually choose zero to be at the equilibrium point of the motion. Zero is placed halfway up the *y*-axis so there is room for both positive and negative values. The graph alternates from plus to minus and back. The example graph below shows a pendulum swinging from +20 centimeters to -20 centimeters and back. The amplitude is the maximum distance away from center, or 20 centimeters.

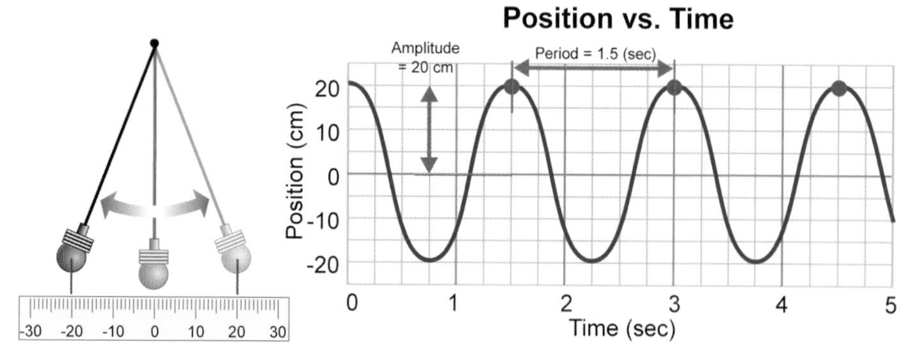

Harmonic graphs repeat every period

Notice that the graph (above) returns to the same place every 1.5 seconds. No matter where you start, you come back to the same value 1.5 seconds later. Graphs of harmonic motion repeat every period, just as the motion repeats every cycle. Harmonic motion is sometimes called periodic motion for this reason.

Determining amplitude and period from a graph

Calculating amplitude from a graph

The amplitude is half the distance between the highest and lowest points on the graph. For the example in Figure 11.12, the amplitude is 20 centimeters, as illustrated by the calculation below. The difference between the highest and lowest value of the graph is the *peak-to-peak* value.

$$\text{Amplitude} = \frac{1}{2}(\text{high} - \text{low}) = \frac{1}{2}(20 - (-20)) = 20 \text{ cm}$$

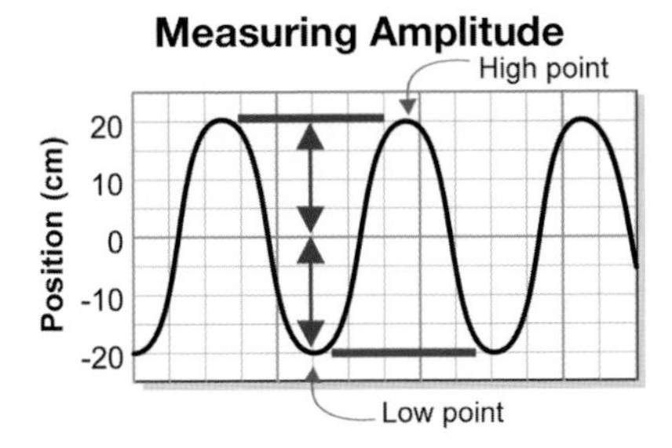

Figure 11.12: *The amplitude of a wave is one-half the peak-to-peak distance. In this graph of harmonic motion, the amplitude of the wave is 20 centimeters.*

Calculating period from a graph

To get the period from a graph, start by identifying one complete cycle. The cycle must begin and end in the same place on the graph. Figure 11.13 shows how to choose the cycle for a simple harmonic motion graph and for a more complex one. Once you have identified a cycle, you use the time axis of the graph to determine the period. The period is the time difference between the beginning of the cycle and the end. Subtract the beginning time from the ending time, as shown in the example below.

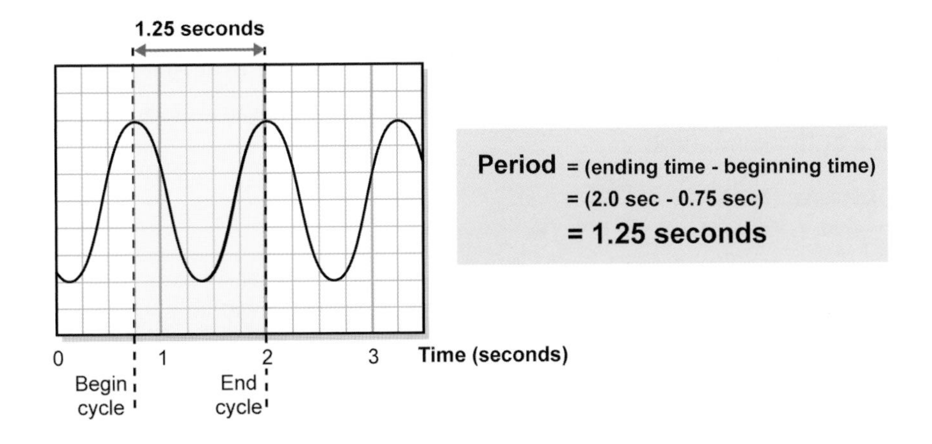

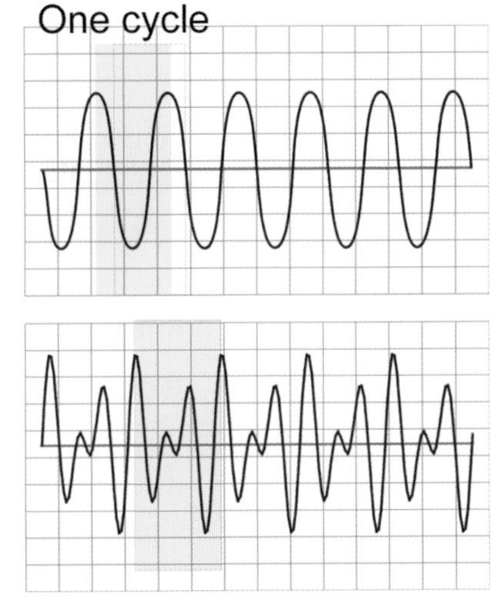

Figure 11.13: *The cycle is the part of the graph that repeats over and over. The gray shading shows one cycle for each of the graphs above. Before you can find the period, you need to identify the cycle.*

Circles and harmonic motion

Circular motion

Circular motion is very similar to harmonic motion. For example, a turning wheel returns to the same position every 360 degrees. Rotation is a cycle, just like harmonic motion. One key difference is that cycles of circular motion *always* have a length of 360 degrees. It does not matter how big the wheel is, each full turn is 360 degrees.

Figure 11.14 shows a shadow of a peg on a rotating wheel. As the wheel rotates, the shadow of the peg goes back and forth on the wall. If we make a graph of the position of the shadow, we get a harmonic motion graph. The period of the cycle is exactly the time it takes the wheel to turn 360 degrees.

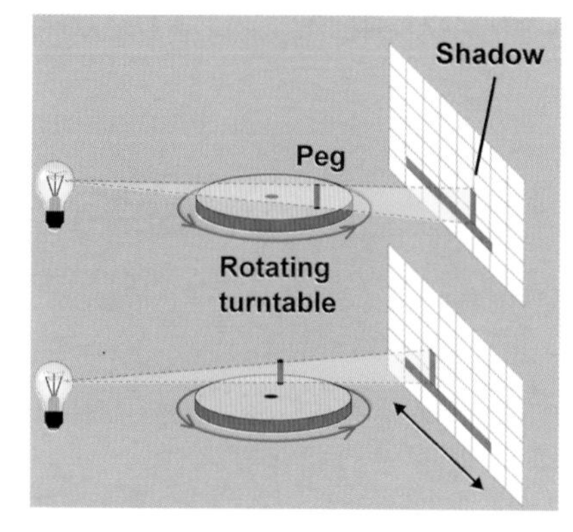

Figure 11.14: *The shadow of a peg moves back and forth on the wall as the turntable rotates. The shadow itself appears to be in harmonic motion.*

The phase of an oscillator

We often use degrees to tell us where we are within the cycle of an oscillator. For example, how would you identify the moment when the pendulum was one-tenth of the way through its cycle? If we let one cycle be 360 degrees, then one-tenth of that cycle is 36 degrees. Thirty-six degrees is a measure of the **phase** of the oscillator. The word "phase" means where the oscillator is in the cycle.

What do we mean by "in phase"?

The concept of phase is important when comparing one oscillator with another. Suppose we have two identical pendulums, with exactly the same period. If we start them together, their graphs would look like the picture below. We describe the two pendulums as being *in phase* because cycles are aligned. Each oscillator is always at the same place at the same time.

Both pendulums in phase

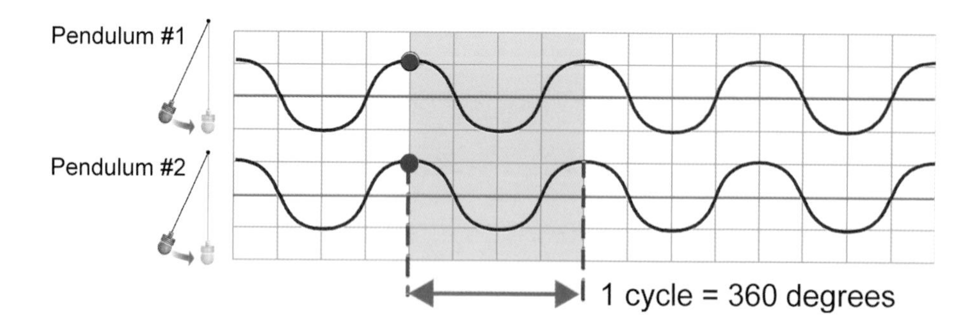

Out of phase by 90 degrees

If we start the first pendulum swinging a little before the second one, the graphs look like the diagram to the right. Although, they have the same cycle, the first pendulum is always a little ahead of the second. The graph shows the lead of the first pendulum as a phase difference. Notice that the top graph reaches its maximum 90 degrees *before* the bottom graph. We say the two pendulums are *out of phase* by 90 degrees, or one-fourth of a cycle.

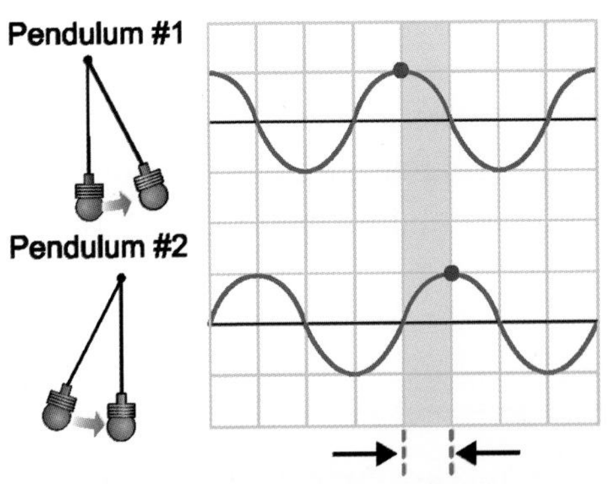

Out of phase by 180 degrees

When they are out of phase, the relative motion of the oscillators may differ by a little or by as much as half a cycle. Two oscillators 180 degrees out of phase are one-half cycle apart. The next diagram (right) shows that the two pendulums are always on opposite sides of the cycle from each other. The concepts of in phase and out of phase will be very important to our Investigations with waves and sound.

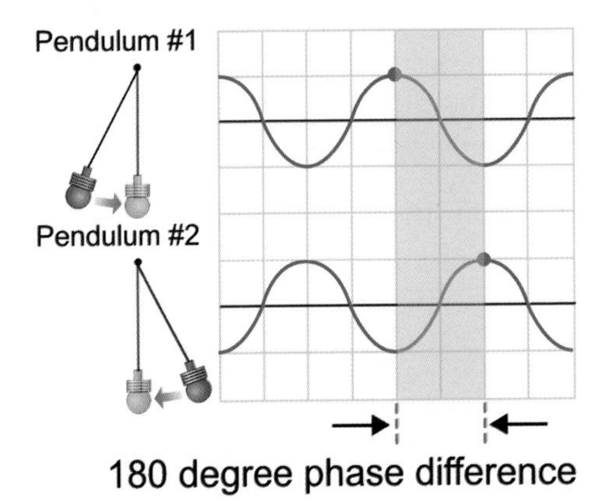

Katherine Johnson

Katherine G. Johnson was born in 1918 in White Sulphur Springs, West Virginia. Her parents were determined to provide their children with high-quality education, traveling across the state so that Katherine and her siblings could attend a laboratory high school at West Virginia State College.

Johnson earned degrees in French and math from West Virginia State. She taught high school while pursuing graduate study in math and physics. In the early 1950's, she was hired as a mathematician by the government agency that later became NASA.

At NASA, Johnson worked out complicated math problems that determined the trajectories (paths) for manned and unmanned spacecraft. She was instrumental in planning the Apollo missions and helped develop their emergency navigation systems. She also worked on determining orbits for spacecraft like the Earth Resources Satellite.

Johnson received the Group Achievement Award presented to NASA's Lunar Spacecraft and Operations team, an Honorary Doctor of Laws degree from SUNY Farmingdale, and West Virginia State College Outstanding Alumnus of the Year award.

11.3 Simple Mechanical Oscillators

Harmonic motion is so common that it would be impossible to list all the different kinds of oscillators you might find. Fortunately, we can learn much about harmonic motion by looking at just a few examples. Once we understand some basic oscillators, we will have the experience needed to figure out more complex ones.

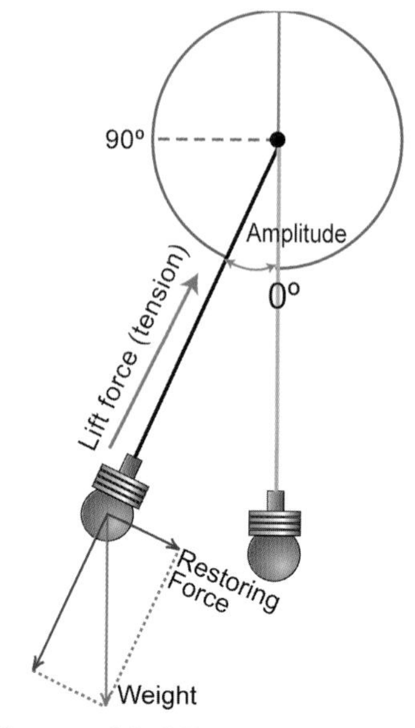

Figure 11.15: *The forces acting on the pendulum. The weight (gravity) points straight down.*

Examples of oscillators

The pendulum The simplest pendulum is a weight hanging from a string. The weight swings back and forth once it is pulled away and released. The force that always pulls the pendulum back to center comes from its weight (Figure 11.15). If you swing a pendulum to one side, the string causes it to lift slightly.

The period of a pendulum does not change much, even when its amplitude is changed. This is because two opposite effects occur. First, if you make the amplitude large, the pendulum has a greater distance to travel, which increases the period. But remember that by releasing it from a high position, it also starts with more energy. More energy means the pendulum goes faster and higher speed decreases the period. The effect of higher speed almost exactly cancels the effect of longer swing distance.

A mass on a spring If you have ever been in a car with worn-out shock absorbers, you have experienced another common oscillator. The system of a car and shock absorbers is an example of a mass on a spring. Springs resist being extended or compressed. Figure 11.16 shows how the force from a spring always acts to return to equilibrium. A mass attached to a spring adds inertia to the system. If the mass is given an initial push, the mass/spring system oscillates.

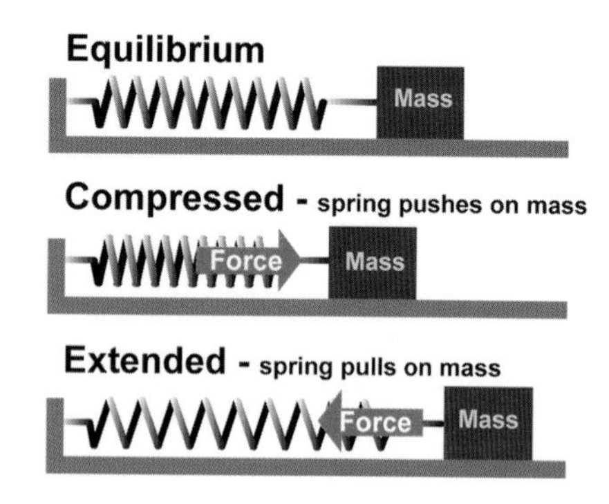

Figure 11.16: *A mass on a spring oscillator. When the spring is compressed or extended, it pushes the mass back toward equilibrium.*

A vibrating string Vibrating strings are used in many musical instruments. A stretched rubber band is a good example. If you pull the rubber band to one side, it stretches a bit. The stretching creates a restoring force that tries to pull the rubber band back straight again. Inertia carries it past being straight and it vibrates. Vibrating strings tend to move much faster than springs and pendulums. The period of a vibrating string can easily be one-hundredth of a second (0.01) or shorter.

Chapter 11 Review

Vocabulary review

Match the following terms with the correct definition. There is one extra definition in the list that will not match any of the terms.

Set One

1. harmonic motion
2. cycle
3. system
4. oscillator
5. hertz

a. A system in harmonic motion
b. A unit of one cycle per second
c. Back and forth or repeating motion
d. A part of motion that repeats over and over
e. A group of things we think are important to consider when analyzing something
f. Motion that goes from one point to another without repeating

Set Two

1. period
2. frequency
3. amplitude
4. damping
5. phase

a. The number of cycles per second
b. The size of a cycle
c. A way to identify where an oscillator is in its cycle
d. The time it takes to complete one cycle
e. Any process that causes cycles to get smaller and smaller in amplitude
f. A unit of one cycle per second

Concept review

1. Name three objects or systems around you that have cycles.
2. What is the relationship between frequency and period?
3. Which pictures show only periodic motion?

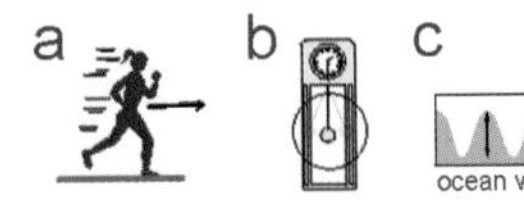

   a. A girl running a race.
   b. The swinging pendulum of a clock.
   c. An ocean wave rising and falling.
   d. A boy swinging.
   e. A car moving down the street.

4. If the length of the rope on a swing gets longer, the period of the swing will:
   a. Get longer.
   b. Get shorter.
   c. Stay the same.
   d. I need more information to answer.

5. In a pendulum experiment, the ____________ is the maximum angle that the pendulum swings away from center. (Pick one.)
   a. cycle
   b. amplitude
   c. period
   d. speed
6. Oscillations have something to do with the answers to which of the following questions? (You can pick more than one.)
   a. What color is it?
   b. How much mass does it have?
   c. How long is it?
   d. How loud is that noise?
   e. What radio station is this?
7. A clock is made using a pendulum to count the time. The weight at the bottom of the pendulum can be adjusted to make the length of the pendulum longer or shorter. The clock runs too fast, meaning it counts 50 minutes as one full hour. What should you do to correct the clock?
   a. Move the weight upward, making the pendulum shorter.
   b. Move the weight downward, making the pendulum longer.
   c. Add more weight to make the pendulum heavier.
8. Which of the graphs clearly shows harmonic motion? You may choose more than one.

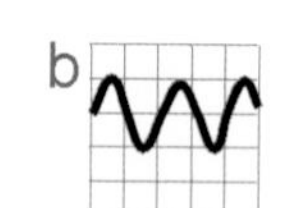

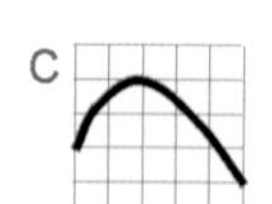

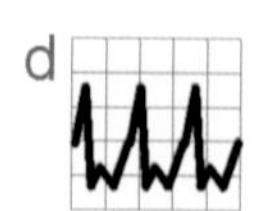

9. The measurement of 2.5 seconds could be:
   a. The frequency of an oscillator.
   b. The period of an oscillator.
   c. The mass of an oscillator.
   d. The system where we find an oscillator.
10. A measurement of 1 meter could be:
    a. The frequency of an oscillator.
    b. The amplitude of an oscillator.
    c. The mass of an oscillator.
    d. The system where we find an oscillator.
11. An oscillator is made with a rubber band and a block of wood, as shown in the diagram. What happens to the oscillator if we make the block of wood heavier?
    a. The frequency increases.
    b. The period increases.
    c. The frequency stays the same.
    d. The period stays the same.

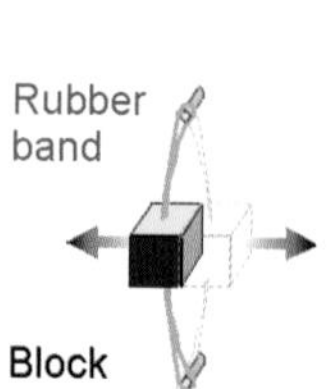

12. If the amplitude of a pendulum is doubled, which of the following will be true?
    a. It will swing twice as far away from center.
    b. Its period will be twice as long.
    c. Its frequency will be twice as high.
    d. It must have twice the mass.

Problems

1. A person's heartbeat is measured to be 65 beats per minute. What is the period between heartbeats in seconds?

    a. 65 seconds

    b. 65 Hertz

    c. 0.92 seconds

    d. 1.08 seconds

2. A pendulum has a period of 1.5 seconds. How many cycles do you have to count to make one minute?

3. A string vibrates back and forth 30 times per second. What is the period of the motion of the string?

4. The graph shows the motion of an oscillator that is a weight hanging from a rubber band. The weight moves up and down. Answer the following questions using the graph.

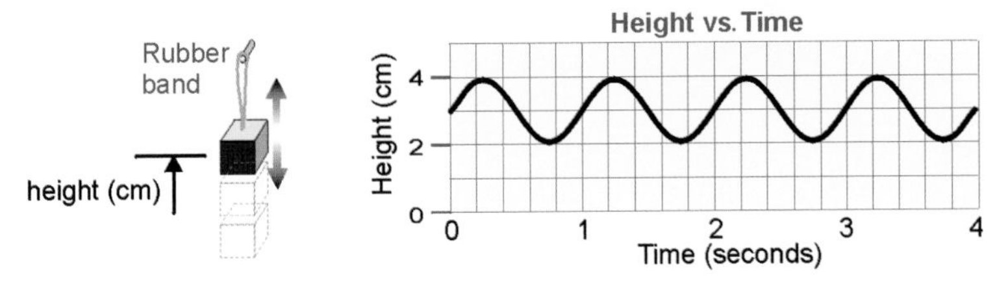

    a. What is the period?

    b. What is the amplitude?

    c. If you counted for 5 seconds, how many cycles would you count?

5. Four different groups of students make measurements of the period of a pendulum. Each group hands in a lab with no names on it. Can you tell which lab group was working with which pendulum? Match the letter of the pendulum to the number of the lab group.

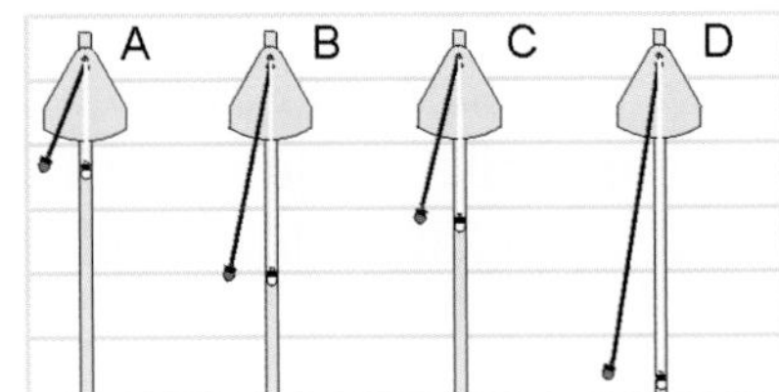

Group	Period	Pendulum
1	1.0 sec	
2	1.2 sec	
3	1.4 sec	
4	1.7 sec	

Questions 6, 7, and 8 refer to the three graphs below. Distance in these graphs means displacement of the oscillator.

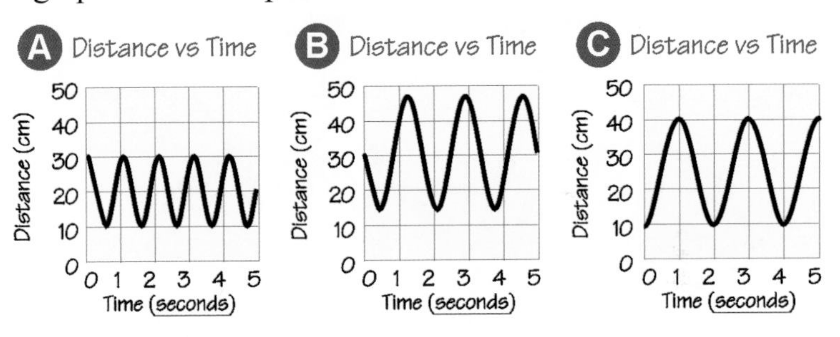

6. Which graph shows exactly 3 cycles?

7. Which graph has a period of 2 seconds?

8. Which graph has an amplitude of 10 centimeters?

Applying your knowledge

1. What is the period of the rotation of the Earth that gives us day and night?
2. An animal research scientist films a small bird and counts 240 beats of the bird's wings in 2 minutes. What is the frequency of the motion of the bird's wings?
3. The Earth, moon, and sun make a system with many cycles. Give at least two examples of cycles that relate to the Earth, moon, or sun and also give the period of each example you find.

4. You invent a bicycle speedometer that counts how many spokes of the wheel pass by each second. You ride your bicycle to test the speedometer and measure 2,160 spokes pass in one minute.
   a. What is the frequency of spokes passing your sensor in hertz?
   b. The wheel has 36 spokes. How many turns per minute does the wheel make?
5. The human heart is both strong and reliable. As a demonstration of how reliable the heart is, calculate how many times your heart beats in one day. Start by measuring the frequency of your pulse in beats per minute and use the result for your calculation.

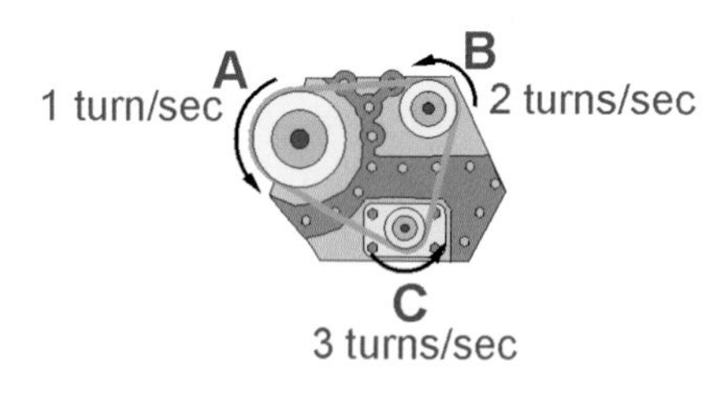

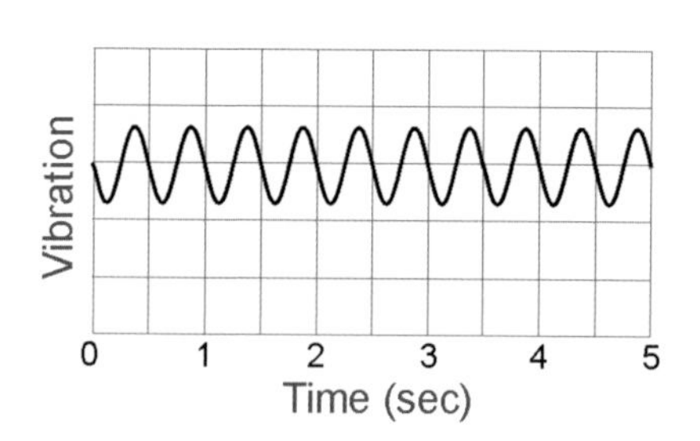

6. Frequency can be a clue to finding problems in engines before they cause serious damage. Suppose the engine has three spinning parts (A, B, C), each turning at a different speed. Since the speed of each part is different, the frequency of each is also different. If one part starts to wear out, it will vibrate more than it should. By looking at the frequency of vibration for the whole engine, you can spot which part is the problem by looking for vibrations at its characteristic frequency.
   The graph shows the vibration of the whole engine, including all three spinning parts. From the graph, can you tell which part is making too much vibration, and is therefore likely to fail?

UNIT 4

Chapter 12

Waves

Introduction to Chapter 12

Waves carry energy and information over great distances. A cell phone conversation is carried on waves that travel for thousands of miles. Waves on the ocean also travel thousands of miles before they splash at your feet on the beach. In this chapter, you will learn how to measure and control waves so that you can use them for music, communication, and many other useful things.

Investigations for Chapter 12

12.1	**Waves**	*How do we make and describe waves?*

A stretched string seems simple but it gets very interesting when you use it to make a wave! For this Investigation you will make wave pulses on springs and strings to see how they move and what they do at boundaries.

12.2	**Waves in Motion**	*How do waves move and interact with things?*

Waves in water are a familiar sight. In this Investigation we will use water waves to explore reflection, diffraction, and other things waves do.

12.3	**Natural Frequency and Resonance**	*What is resonance and why is it important?*

Everything has a natural frequency, and most things have more than one. When you force something to vibrate at its natural frequency you can make very large waves. In this Investigation we will use a fascinating electronic synthesizer to make waves on a vibrating string so that we can explore resonance and harmony. We will learn the foundation upon which all musical instruments are built.

Learning Goals

In this chapter, you will:

- ✔ Learn the role waves play in our daily lives, including our effort to communicate.
- ✔ Learn the parts and shapes of waves.
- ✔ Model transverse and longitudinal waves and their characteristics with a stretched string.
- ✔ Explore the properties of waves (like reflection and diffraction) with water.
- ✔ Investigate resonance and harmony using an electronic synthesizer.
- ✔ Learn how natural frequency and resonance are involved in making music.

Vocabulary

circular waves	diffraction	natural frequency	response
constructive interference	fundamental	plane waves	standing wave
continuous	harmonics	reflection	transverse wave
crest	hertz	refraction	trough
destructive interference	longitudinal wave	resonance	wave fronts

12.1 Waves

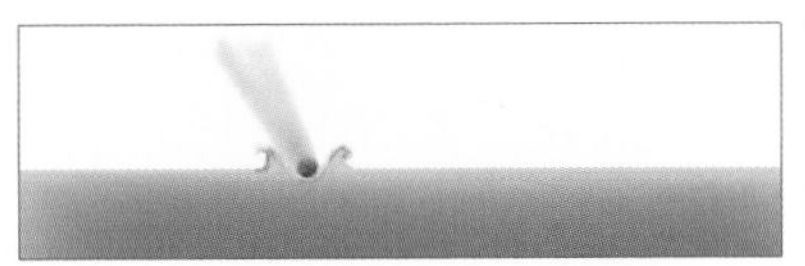
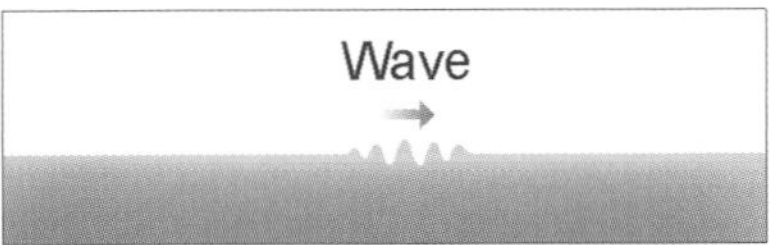

Suppose a big meteor falls into the ocean. The energy of the falling meteor creates a wave that carries the energy to distant shores. You watch a great musician on stage. The voice or instrument creates waves that carry the sound to your ears. You dial a cell phone to call a friend. A microwave comes from the antenna and carries a signal to your friend.

In this section you will learn about waves. What you learn will apply to the water waves, sound waves, and light waves you see around you all the time. What you learn will also apply to the radio waves and microwaves that are also around even though you can't feel them or see them. Even gravity has waves that astronomers believe are created when black holes crash into each other.

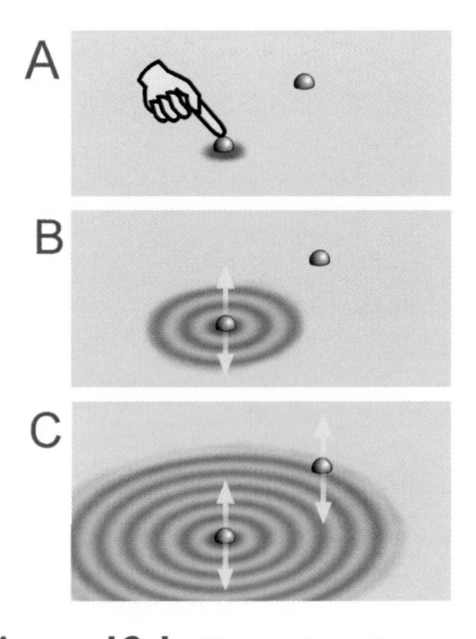

Figure 12.1: *If we poke a floating ball, it moves up and down in harmonic motion (A). The oscillating ball creates a wave (B) that travels on the surface of the water. The wave can cause oscillation of a second ball (C) placed far away from the first.*

Why learn about waves?

Waves carry oscillations from one place to another

A ball floating on the water is a good example of the difference between a wave and ordinary harmonic motion. If you poke the ball, it moves up and down. The oscillating ball creates a wave on the surface of the water that spreads outward, carrying the oscillation to other places (Figure 12.1). A second ball floating farther away also starts oscillating as soon as the wave reaches it. The wave started by an earthquake can travel around the world, reaching places far away from where it began.

Waves carry information and energy

We use waves to carry information and energy over great distances. The sound wave that travels through the air carries information about the vibration of the string from the instrument to your ear. Your ear hears the vibration as music. In a similar way, a radio wave carries sounds from a transmitter to your stereo. Another kind of radio wave carries television signals. A microwave carries cell phone conversations. Waves carry energy and information from one place to another. The information could be sound, color, pictures, commands, or many other useful things.

Waves are all around us. Waves are part of everyday experience. We might not recognize all the waves we see, but they are there. Consider standing on the corner of a busy street. How are you affected by waves?

- The stoplight that you see with your eyes is a wave.
- The sounds that you hear are waves.
- The ripples in a puddle of water are waves.
- The electricity flowing in the wires attached to the street lights is a wave.
- Waves carry radio and TV and cell phone transmissions through the air around you.

There are waves *inside* the atoms that make up everything we see. By understanding how waves work we can learn about nature and also about technology (Figure 12.2).

Figure 12.2: *The same system can support more than one kind of wave at the same time. Sound waves and light waves travel through water so dolphins can hear and see. At the same time, a boundary wave travels on the surface. Three of our five senses (sight, hearing, touch) respond to waves.*

How do you recognize a wave? All waves have things in common. When you see the things in this list, you should suspect that there is some kind of wave involved.

Evidence for suspecting there are waves:

- Anytime you see a vibration that moves, there is a wave.
- Anything that makes or responds to sound uses waves.
- Anything that makes or responds to light uses waves.
- Anything that transmits information through the air (or space) without wires uses waves. This includes cell phones, radio, and television.
- Anything that allows you to "see through" objects uses waves. This includes ultrasound, CAT scans, MRI scans, and X rays (Figure 12.3).

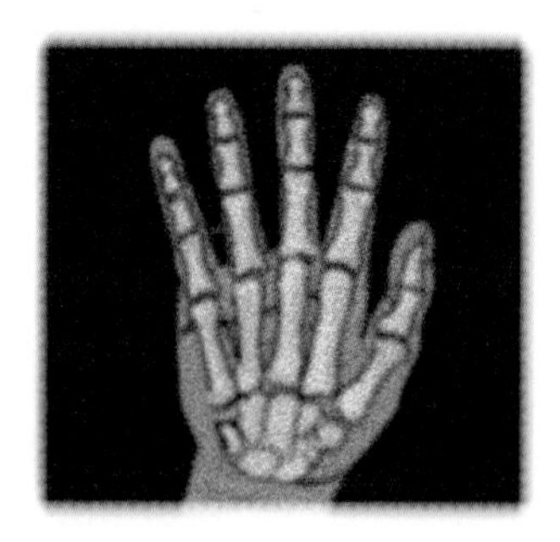

Figure 12.3: *X rays use light waves to make images that show bones under the skin.*

Where can we find waves? We will usually find waves whenever information, energy, or motion is transmitted over a distance without anything obviously moving. The remote control on a TV is an example. To change the channel you can use the remote or get up and push the buttons with your finger. Both actions carry information (the channel selected) to the TV. One uses physical motion and the other uses a wave that goes from the remote control to the television. Your knowledge of physics and waves tells you there must be some kind of wave because information traveled from one place to another, and nothing appeared to move. The wave is actually an infrared light wave, which is invisible to the eye.

Transverse and longitudinal waves

Waves spread through connections

A wave moves along a string because the string is **continuous**. By continuous we mean it is connected to itself. Waves spread through connections. If we were to break the string in the middle, the wave would not spread across the break. Whenever you have an extended body that is all connected to itself, you get waves. The ocean is an example: Waves can travel all the way across because the water is continuous from one shore to another.

Transverse waves

A **transverse wave** has its oscillations perpendicular to the direction the wave moves. The wave moves from left to right. The oscillation is up and down. Water waves are also transverse waves because the up and down oscillation is perpendicular to the motion of the wave.

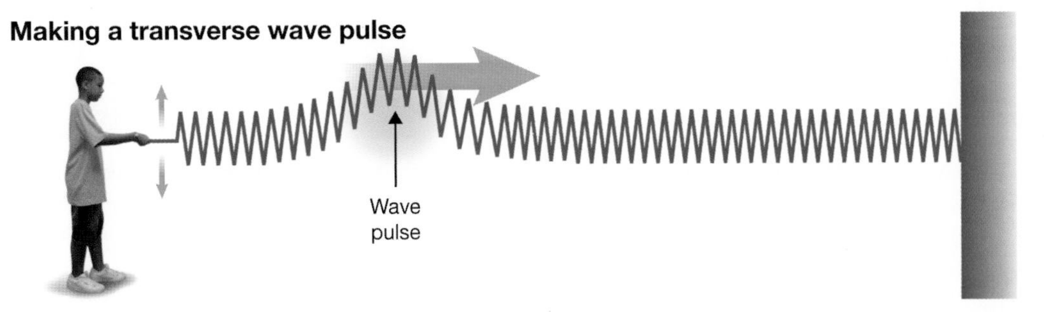

Longitudinal waves

A **longitudinal wave** has oscillations in the same direction as the wave moves. Stretch a fat Slinky with one end fastened to the wall. Give the free end a sharp push toward the wall and pull it back again. You see a compression wave of the Slinky that moves toward the wall. The compression wave on the Slinky is a longitudinal wave because the compression is in the direction the wave moves.

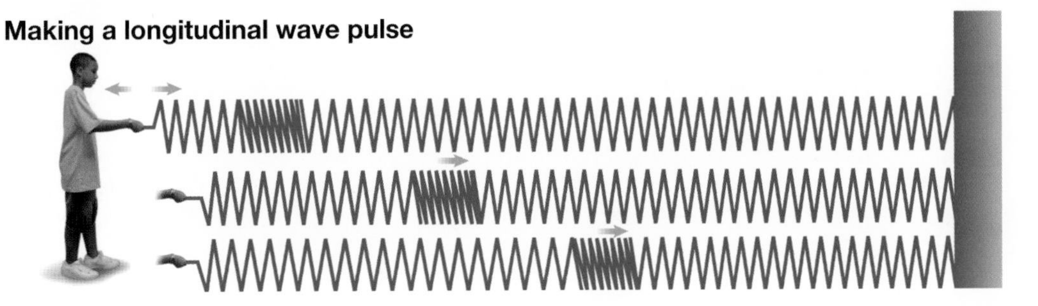

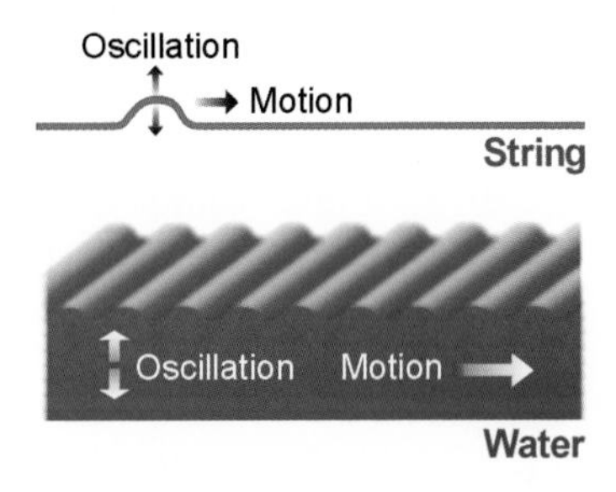

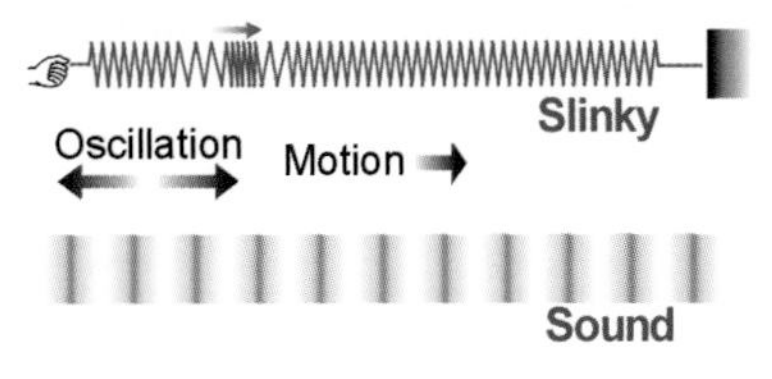

Figure 12.4: *Transverse waves oscillate perpendicular to the direction the wave moves. Strings and water are examples.*

Longitudinal waves oscillate in the same direction the wave moves. The Slinky and sound waves are examples.

Frequency, amplitude and wavelength

Basic properties Waves have cycles, frequency, and amplitude, just like oscillations. Because waves are spread out and move, they have new properties of wavelength and speed. Also, because waves are spread out, we have to be careful how we define and measure frequency and amplitude.

Frequency The frequency of a wave is a measure of how often it goes up and down (Figure 12.5). To measure the frequency, we look at one place as the wave passes through. The frequency of the oscillating motion of one point is the frequency of the wave. The wave also causes distant points to oscillate up and down *with the same frequency.* A wave carries its frequency to every area it reaches.

Frequency is measured in Hz Wave frequency is measured in **hertz** (Hz), just like any oscillation. A frequency of one hertz (1 Hz) describes a wave that makes everything it touches go through a complete cycle once every second. Your laboratory-size water waves typically have low frequencies, between 0.1 and 10 hertz.

Amplitude The amplitude of a wave is the largest amount that goes above or below average (Figure 12.6). You can also think of the amplitude as one-half of the distance between the highest and lowest places.

Wavelength Wavelength is the length of one complete cycle of a wave (Figure 12.7). For a water wave, this would be the distance from a point on one wave to the same point on the next wave. You could measure the wavelength from crest-to-crest or from trough-to-trough. For the vibrating string, the wavelength is the length of one complete "S" shape. We use the Greek letter "lambda" to represent wavelength. You write a lambda like an upside down "y."

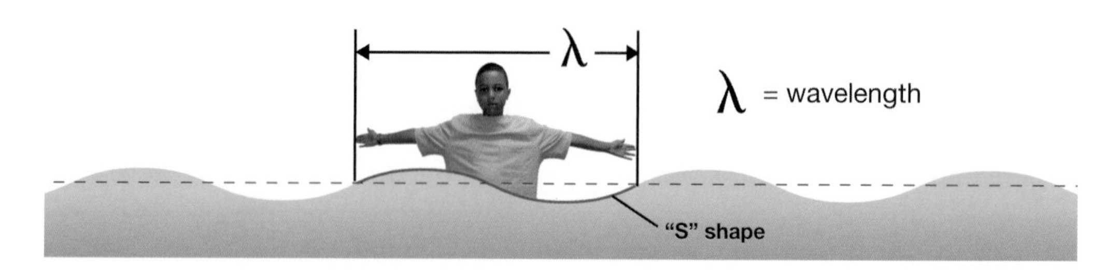

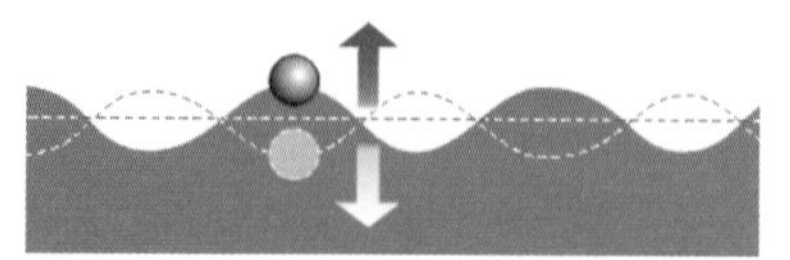

Figure 12.5: *The frequency of a wave is the frequency at which every point on the wave oscillates. The floating ball oscillates up and down at the frequency of the wave.*

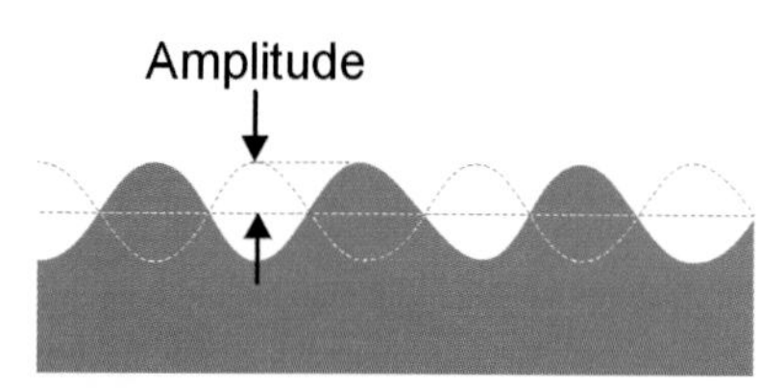

Figure 12.6: *The amplitude of a water wave is the maximum distance above the level surface. This is the same as half the distance between the lowest and highest places.*

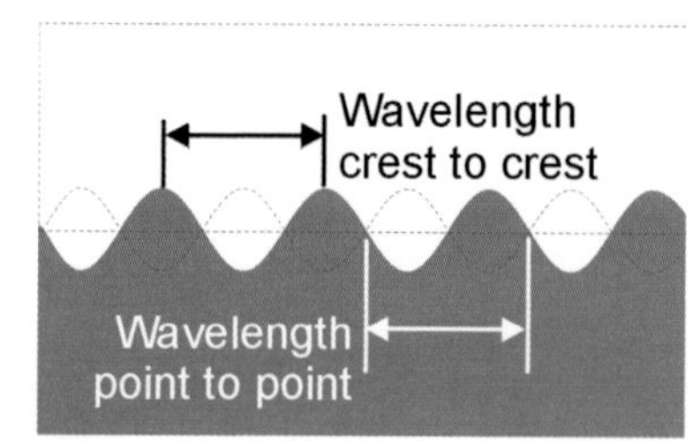

Figure 12.7: *The wavelength of a water wave can be measured from crest to crest. This is the same as the distance from one point on a wave to the same point on the next wave.*

Speed The speed of a wave describes how fast the wave can transmit an oscillation from one place to another. Waves can have a wide range of speeds. Most water waves are slow; a few miles per hour is typical. Light waves are extremely fast—186,000 miles per *second*. Sound waves travel at about 660 miles per hour, faster than water waves and much slower than light waves.

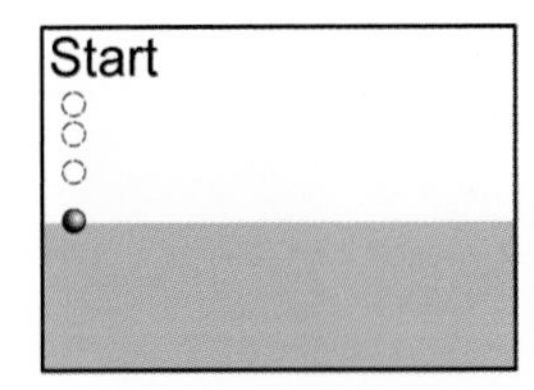

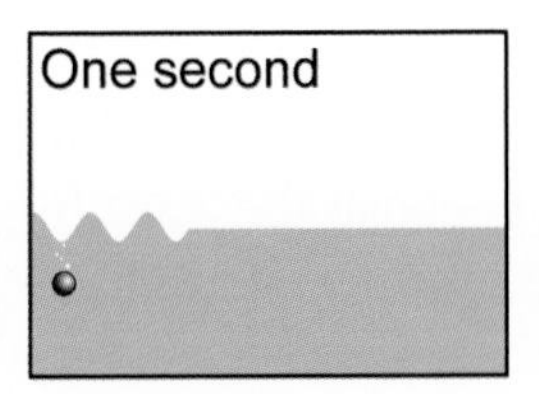

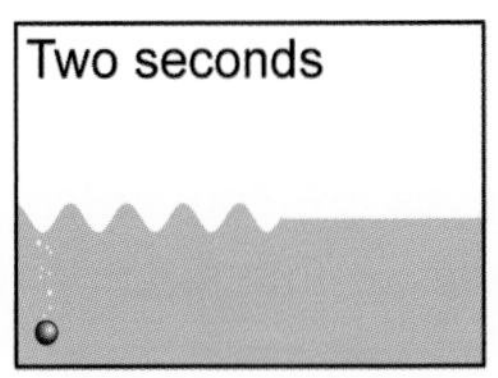

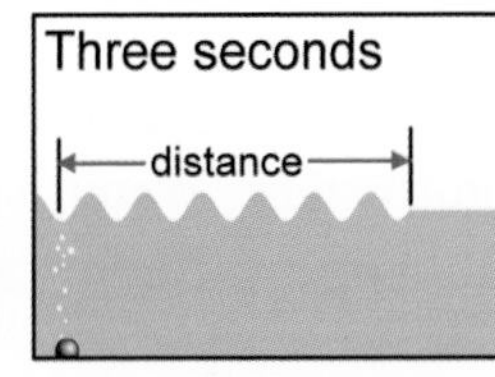

What is the speed of a wave? The speed of a wave is different from the speed of whatever the wave is causing to move. In a water wave, the surface of the water moves up and down. You could measure the up-down speed of the water surface, but that would NOT be the speed of the wave. The speed of the wave describes how quickly a movement of one part of the water surface is transmitted to another place. To measure the speed of the wave, you would have to start a ripple in one place and measure how long it takes the ripple to affect a place some distance away.

Speed is frequency times wavelength In one complete cycle, a wave moves forward one wavelength (Figure 12.8). The speed of a wave is the distance traveled (one wavelength) divided by the time it takes (one period). Since the frequency is the inverse of the period, it is usually easier to calculate the speed of the wave by multiplying wavelength and frequency. The result is true for sound waves, light waves, and even gravity waves. Frequency times wavelength is the speed of the wave.

$$\text{Speed} = \frac{\text{Distance Traveled}}{\text{Time Taken}} = \frac{\text{Wavelength}}{\text{Period}} = \text{Wavelength} \times \left(\frac{1}{\text{Period}}\right)$$

$$\text{Speed} = \text{Wavelength} \times \text{Frequency}$$

The speed of a wave

$$v = f\lambda$$

Speed (m/sec) → v; Frequency (hertz) → f; Wavelength (meters) → λ

A wave moves one wavelength in one cycle.

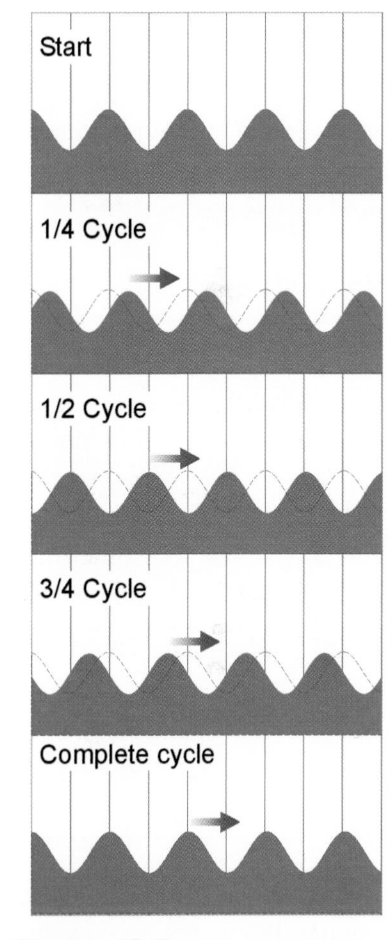

Figure 12.8: *A wave moves a distance equal to one wavelength in one cycle. Since a cycle takes one period, the speed of the wave is the wavelength divided by the period.*

12.2 Waves in Motion

In what shapes do we find waves?

What happens when a wave hits something?

You will learn the answers to these questions in this section. We start with waves in water, because these are easy to make and observe. The shape of wave fronts, and the explanation for reflection, diffraction, and other interesting things, can be seen in the lab. Almost every process we see with water waves also occurs with sound and light waves. Water waves are convenient because they are big and slow, so we can see the details of what happens. Light waves, on the other hand, are small and fast, and sound waves are invisible.

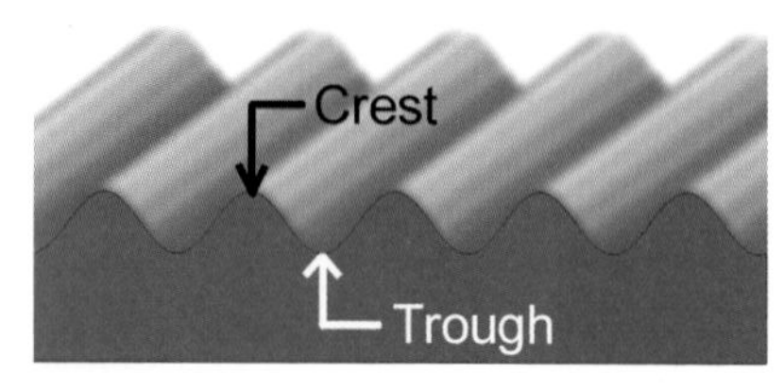

Figure 12.9: *The crest is the highest point on the wave. The trough is the low point.*

Wave shapes

Crests, troughs, and wave fronts

Since a wave extends over a large area, to talk about the motion of a wave we need to pick a reference point. You can think of a wave as a series of high points and low points. A crest is the shape of the high points of the wave, a trough is the low points. When we describe the shape and motion of wave, it is useful to think in terms of the crests. As the wave moves, the crests move. The crests of a wave are sometimes called wave fronts. You can think of the crest as the front of a wave if it helps you to remember the definition of a wave front (Figure 12.9).

Plane waves and circular waves

The shape of a wave is determined by the shape of the wave fronts. You can make waves in all shapes but plane waves and circular waves are easiest to create and study (Figure 12.10). The crests of a plane wave look like straight lines. The crests of a circular wave are circles. A plane wave is started by disturbing the water in a line. A circular wave is started by disturbing the water at a single point. A fingertip touched to the surface will start a circular wave.

Determining the direction the wave moves

The shape of the wave front determines the direction the wave moves. Circular waves have circular wave fronts that move outward from the center. Plane waves have straight wave fronts that move in a line perpendicular to the wave fronts. To change the direction the wave moves, you have to change the shape of the wave front. In later chapters, we will see that this is exactly how lenses work.

Plane waves

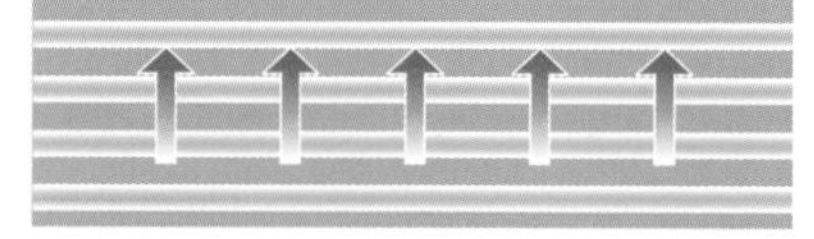

Circular waves

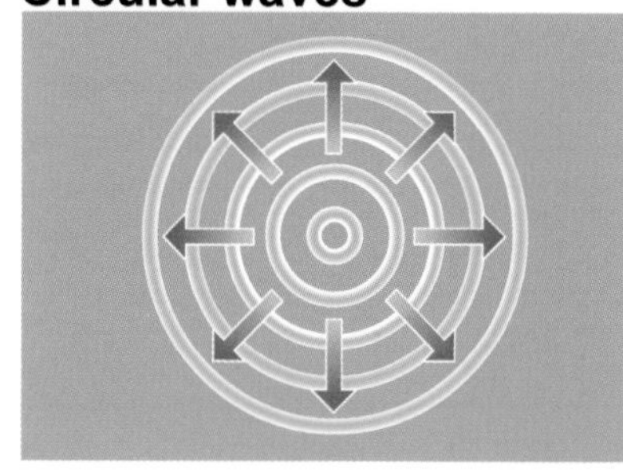

Figure 12.10: *Plane waves and circular waves. Plane waves move perpendicular to the wave fronts. Circular waves radiate outward from the center.*

What happens when a wave hits something?

The four wave interactions

Waves can do different things when they hit an obstacle (Figure 12.11).

Reflection	The wave can bounce off and go in a new direction.
Refraction	The wave can pass straight into and through the obstacle.
Diffraction	The wave can bend around or through holes in the obstacle.
Absorption	The wave can be absorbed and disappear.

Sometimes, the wave can do all those things at once, partly bouncing off, partly passing through, partly being absorbed, and partly going around. You may have noticed the radio in a car sometimes loses the station as you enter a tunnel. Part of the wave that carries the signal bends around the entrance to the tunnel and follows you in. Part is absorbed by the ground. The deeper in the tunnel you go, the weaker the wave gets until the radio cannot pick up the signal at all and you hear static. Simple things like mirrors and complex things like ultrasound or X rays all depend on how waves act when they encounter objects.

Boundaries

Waves are affected by boundaries where conditions change. The first three interactions (reflection, refraction, diffraction) usually occur when a wave crosses a boundary. Absorption can also occur at a boundary, but often happens within the body of a material.

Reflection

When a wave bounces off an obstacle we call it reflection. If you make water waves travel toward a wall they will be reflected. The wave that reflects is like the original wave but moving in a new direction. The wavelength and frequency are usually unchanged. The reflection of a wave happens at a boundary (or edge) where the wave has to pass from one condition to another. Mirrored sunglasses are a good example. The lenses reflect some light so they look like mirrors. The boundary is the surface of the lens where the light wave crosses from air to glass. Abrupt changes in material will almost always cause reflections.

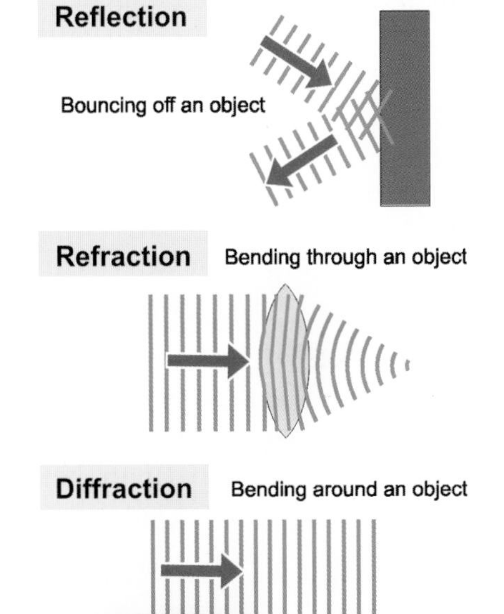

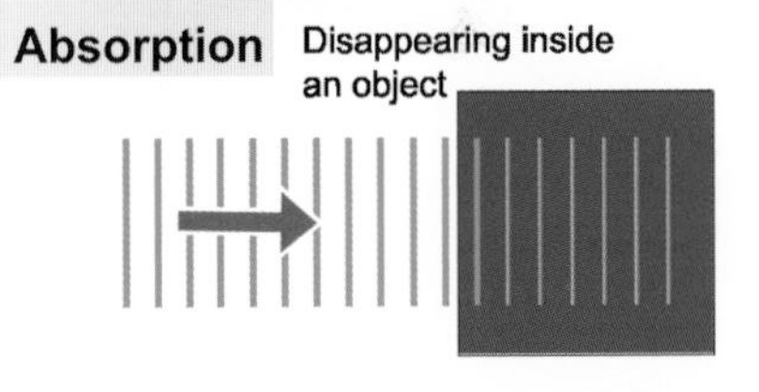

Figure 12.11: *The four processes for waves interacting with boundaries.*

Refraction Waves can cross boundaries and pass into or through objects. Placing a thin plate on the bottom of ripple tank creates a boundary where the depth of the water changes. If you look carefully, you see that waves are bent as they cross the boundary. The wave starts in one direction and changes direction as it crosses. We call it **refraction** when a wave bends as it crosses a boundary. We say the wave is *refracted* as it passes through the boundary. Refraction is useful because it allows us to shape and control waves. Eyeglasses are a very good example where refraction is used to change light waves. Glasses help people to see by bending the light waves into an easier shape for some people's eyes to focus.

Absorption Waves can be absorbed as they pass through objects. Absorption is what happens when the amplitude of a wave gets smaller and smaller as it passes through a material. Some objects and materials have properties that absorb certain kinds of waves. A sponge can absorb a water wave while letting the water pass. A heavy curtain absorbs sound waves. Theaters often use heavy curtains so the audience cannot hear backstage noise. Dark glass absorbs light waves, which is how some kinds of sunglasses work.

Diffraction through a small opening turns plane waves into circular waves.

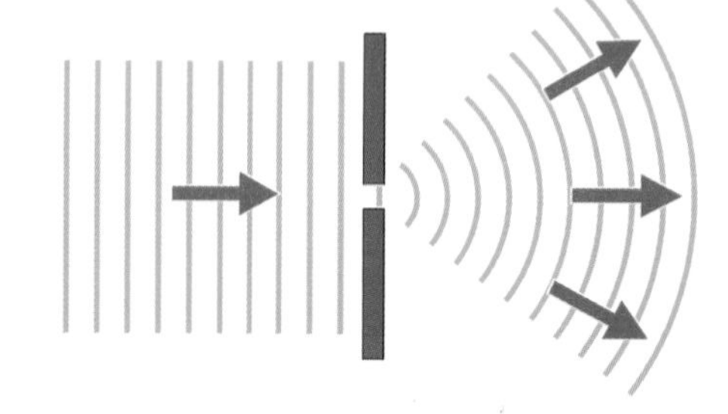

Diffraction Waves can bend around obstacles and go through openings. The process of bending around corners or passing through openings is called **diffraction**. We say a wave is *diffracted* when it is changed by passing through a hole or around an edge. Diffraction usually changes the direction and shape of the wave. Diffraction turns a plane wave into a circular wave when the wave passes through a narrow opening. Diffraction explains why you can hear someone even though a door is only open a tiny crack. Diffraction causes the sound wave to spread out from the crack.

Seismic waves

Seismic waves are generated when Earth's crust slips in an earthquake. Two kinds of seismic waves travel through Earth: primary waves (P-waves) and secondary waves (S-waves).

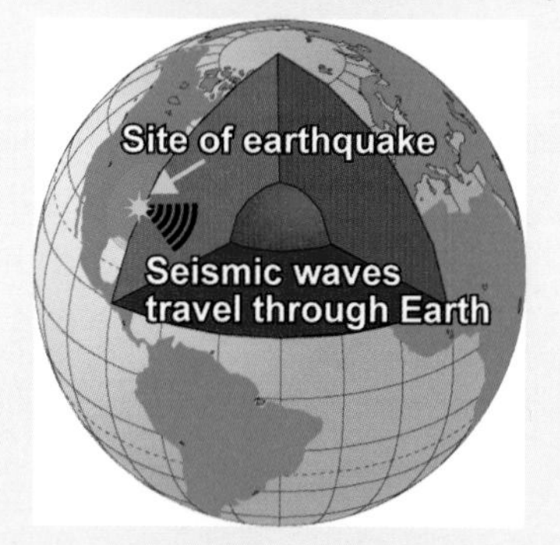

P-waves are longitudinal. S-waves are transverse and cause powerful, sideways shaking of the ground. As the P-waves and S-waves encounter layers in the Earth, they refract and reflect. By studying the patterns of waves that are recorded after an earthquake, geologists have identified the parts of Earth's internal structure.

12.3 Natural Frequency and Resonance

Theoretically, waves can extend forever. Realistically, they are limited by the size of the system. Boundaries create conditions that favor special frequencies or wavelengths. Just as the length of the string set the period of the pendulum, the boundaries and properties of the system make certain waves much more powerful than others. The concepts of *resonance* and *natural frequency* apply to a huge range of natural and human-made systems. These two powerful ideas are the key to understanding the tides of the ocean, the way our ears separate sound, and even how a microwave oven works.

Natural frequency

The natural frequency is the frequency at which a system oscillates when it is disturbed.

Natural frequency

What is natural frequency?

If you pluck a guitar string in the middle it vibrates back and forth. If you pluck the same string 10 times in a row and measure the frequency of vibration you find that it is always the same. When plucked, the string vibrates at its natural frequency. The pendulum also had a natural frequency.

Why natural frequency is important

The natural frequency is important for many reasons:

1. All things in the universe have a natural frequency, and many things have more than one.
2. If you know an object's natural frequency, you know how it will vibrate.
3. If you know how an object vibrates, you know what kinds of waves it will create.
4. If you want to make specific kinds of waves, you need to create objects with natural frequencies that match the waves you want.

Microwave ovens, musical instruments, and cell phones all use the natural frequency of an oscillator to create and control waves. Musical instruments work by adjusting the natural frequency of vibrating strings or air to match musical notes. The A string on a guitar has a natural frequency of 440 hertz.

Figure 12.12: *A guitar uses the natural frequency of the strings to make the correct notes. Once it is tuned, the A string, when plucked, will always vibrate at 440 hertz.*

Changing the natural frequency

The natural frequency depends on many factors, such as the tightness, length, or weight of a string. We can change the natural frequency of a system by changing any of the factors that affect the size, inertia, or forces in the system. For example, tuning a guitar changes the natural frequency of a string by changing its tension.

Resonance

The response of an oscillator

To keep a system oscillating, we apply an oscillating force. For example, if you want to get a jump rope going, you shake the end up and down. What you are really doing is applying an oscillating force to the rope. The response of the rope is to oscillate up and down with the same frequency of your applied force.

If you try this, you notice that at certain frequencies your force is noticeably more effective at making the rope oscillate. For example, shaking the end up and down twice per second (1.6 Hz) results in an amplitude of a few centimeters. Slowing down to once per second (1 Hz) makes an amplitude of more than a meter! Slowing even more, to once every two seconds (0.5 Hz), causes the amplitude to drop back down again. Your experiment shows that the frequency of 1 hertz is *many times* more effective than any other frequency.

Resonance

The extra-strong response at 1 hertz is an example of **resonance**. You can think of resonance as having the natural frequency of the system exactly in tune with your force. Each cycle of your force exactly matches each cycle of the system. As a result, each push adds to the next one and the amplitude of the oscillation grows (Figure 12.13). Resonance happens when something is vibrated at its natural frequency (or a multiple of the natural frequency). Resonance is an important idea because it is used to transfer power into all kinds of waves from lasers to microwave ovens to musical instruments.

A swing is a good example of resonance

The example of a swing (that you might sit on at the park) is one of the best ways to describe resonance. With a swing, small pushes applied over time build up a large amplitude of motion. This happens because each push is synchronized to the natural motion of the swing. A forward push is always given when the swing is as far back as it can go. The swing is like a pendulum, which has a natural frequency. By applying small pushes at a frequency matched to the natural frequency, we are able to create a large motion. The interaction of the repeating pushes and the natural motion of the swing is what creates resonance. The effect of the resonance is that the swing's motion gets large even though the pushes are small. Resonance is not a single thing. Resonance is an interaction between a wave, a driving force, and the boundaries of the system.

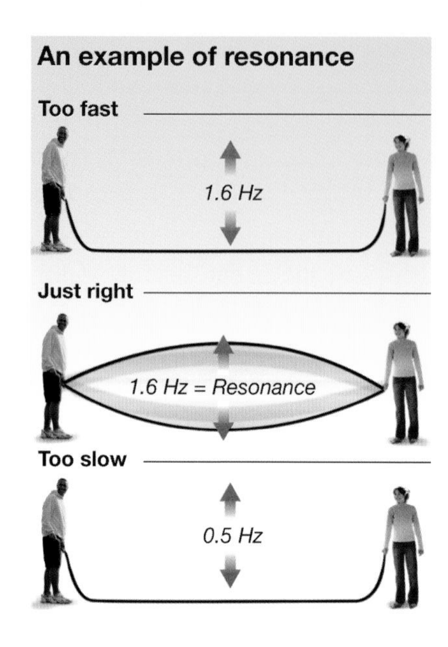

Figure 12.13: *A jump rope is a good experiment for resonance. If you shake it at the right frequency, it makes a big wave motion. If your frequency is not just right, the rope will not make the wave pattern at all.*

Standing waves on a string

What is a standing wave? Although waves usually travel, it is possible to make a wave stay in one place. A wave that is trapped in one spot is called a **standing wave**. It is possible to make standing waves of almost any kind, including sound, water, and even light. A vibrating string is a great example for doing experiments with standing waves. Vibrating strings are what make music on a guitar or piano.

Harmonics are multiples of the natural frequency of a standing wave

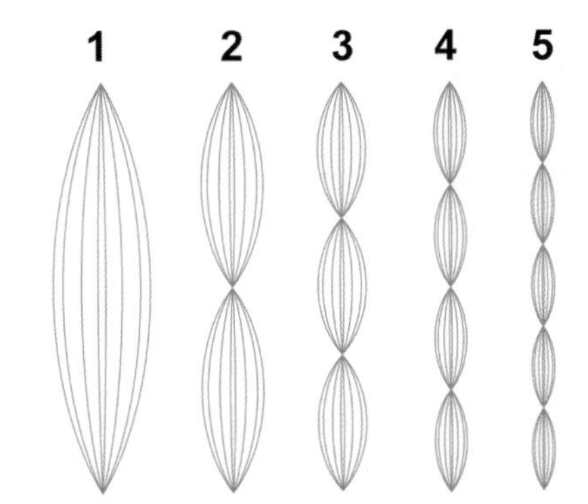

The first five harmonics of the vibrating string

Standing waves occur at frequencies that are multiples of the **fundamental**, which is the natural frequency of the string. The fundamental and multiples of its frequency are called **harmonics**. The diagram to the left shows the first five harmonics. You can tell the harmonic number by counting the number of "bumps" on the wave. The first harmonic has one bump, the second has two bumps, the third has three, and so on. If the frequency of the first harmonic is 10 hertz, then the second will be at a frequency of 20 hertz, the third will be at 30 hertz, and so on.

Wavelength A vibrating string moves so fast that your eye averages out the image and you see a wave-shaped blur (Figure 12.14). At any one moment the string is really in only one place within the blur. The wavelength is the length of one complete "S" shape on the string. Higher frequency waves have shorter wavelengths.

Why are standing waves useful? Standing waves are useful because we can control their frequency and wavelength. Because the wave is trapped, it is easy to put power into it and make large amplitudes. In your microwave oven, there is a device called a magnetron. Inside the magnetron is a standing wave driven by electricity. A small hole in the boundary lets some of the wave's energy out to cook food. The shape of the magnetron forces the standing wave to oscillate at exactly 2.4 billion cycles per second (2.4 gigahertz). Energy that leaks out at the same frequency is perfectly matched to heat water molecules in food.

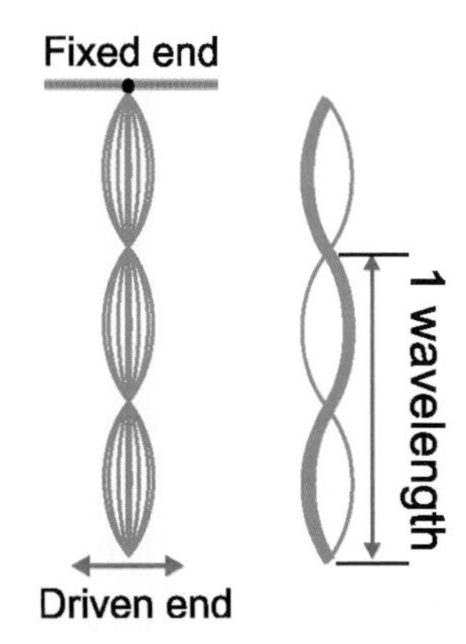

Figure 12.14: *A standing wave on a vibrating string. The wavelength is the length of one complete **S** shape of the wave.*

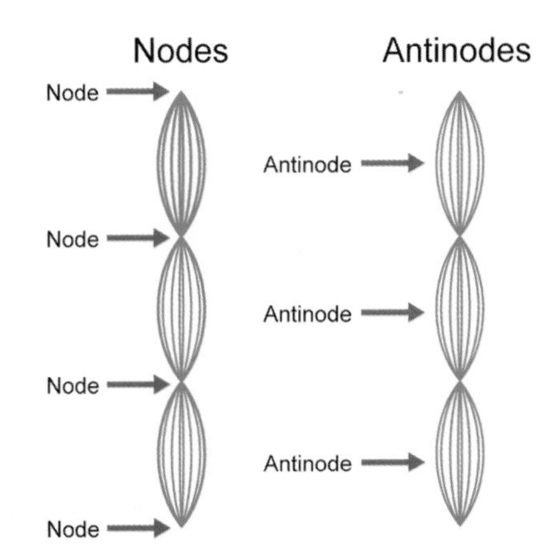

Figure 12.15: *Nodes and antinodes for the third harmonic of the vibrating string. Nodes are points where the string does not move. Antinodes are points of the greatest amplitude.*

Interference

What is interference? Interference happens when two or more waves come together. Because there are so many waves around us, they often interfere with each other. In fact, radio and television use the interference of two waves to carry music and video. The resonance of a vibrating string can be understood using the interference of waves. Sometimes on the ocean, two big waves add up to make a gigantic wave that may only last a few moments but is taller than ships, and can have a terrible impact.

Constructive interference Suppose you make two wave pulses on the stretched spring. One comes from the left and the other comes from the right. When they meet in the middle, they combine to make a single large pulse. This is called constructive interference. Constructive interference occurs when waves add up to make a larger amplitude (Figure 12.16).

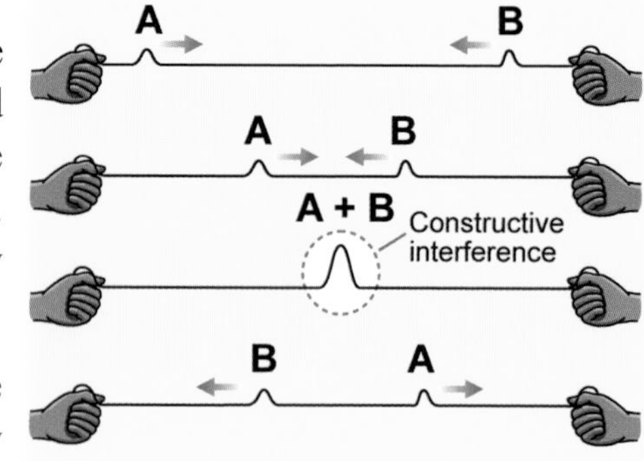

Figure 12.16: *Two wave pulses on the same side add up to make a single, bigger pulse when they meet. This is an example of constructive interference.*

Destructive interference There is another way to launch the two pulses. If we make pulses on opposite sides of the cord, something different happens. When the pulses meet in the middle they cancel each other out! One wants to pull the string up and the other wants to pull it down. The result is that the string is flat and both pulses vanish for a moment. This is called destructive interference. In destructive interference waves add up to make a smaller amplitude (Figure 12.17).

After they interfere, both wave pulses separate again and travel on their own. This is surprising if you think about it. For a moment, the middle of the cord is flat in the example of destructive interference. A moment later, two wave pulses come out of the flat part and race away from each other. Waves still store energy, even when they interfere.

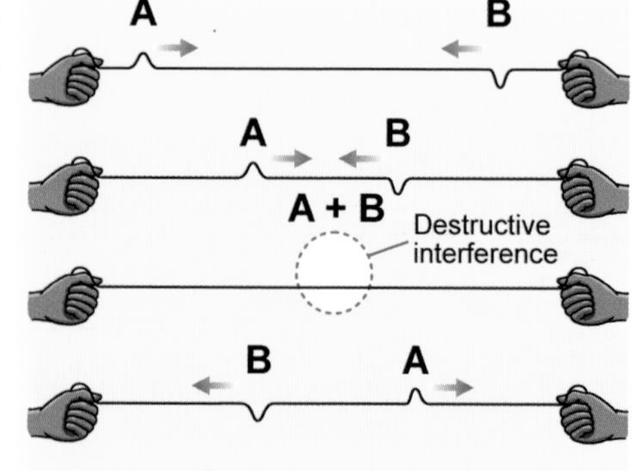

Figure 12.17: *Two equal wave pulses on opposite sides subtract when they meet. The upward movement of one pulse exactly cancels with the downward movement of the other. For a moment there is no pulse at all. This is an example of destructive interference.*

Waves at the atomic level Down at the scale of atoms, there are many extremely strong waves. Because there are so many and they are tiny and random, they interfere destructively on average. We don't see the wavelike nature of atoms because of large-scale destructive interference. In special cases, like with a magnetic resonance imaging (or MRI) machine, or a laser, we create constructive interference of atomic waves. The result is very powerful and useful technology.

Chapter 12 Review

Vocabulary review

Match the following terms with the correct definition. There is one extra definition in the list that will not match any of the terms.

Set One

1. wave	a. A short length of wave that travels
2. vibration	b. A wave where the oscillation is perpendicular to the direction of motion
3. wave pulse	c. An oscillation that travels
4. transverse	d. A wave where the oscillation is in the same direction as the direction of motion
5. longitudinal	e. A word that means the same as oscillation
	f. The time it takes to complete one cycle

Set Two

1. wavelength	a. A place where a wave changes suddenly
2. natural frequency	b. The interaction of two or more waves with each other
3. resonance	c. A special frequency (or frequencies) at which objects vibrate if they are disturbed
4. interference	d. A special condition where the frequency you push matches the natural frequency of the system, resulting in large amplitude waves
5. boundary	e. The length of one complete wave
	f. A unit of one cycle per second

Set Three

1. reflection	a. The process where a wave gets smaller and smaller
2. refraction	b. The process of bouncing a wave off a boundary
3. diffraction	c. The process of bending a wave as it crosses a boundary
4. absorption	d. What happens when a wave bends around obstacles or through holes
	e. A word that means the same as oscillation

Set Four

1. node	a. A wave whose frequency is a multiple of another wave
2. antinode	b. A point on a wave where there is no motion
3. harmonic	c. A wave that is trapped between boundaries
4. standing wave	d. The place on a wave where the amplitude is largest
	e. The length of one complete wave

Concept review

1. A wave which vibrates at 60 Hz has a higher ______ than a wave that vibrates at 30 Hz.

   a. wavelength   b. frequency

   c. amplitude   d. transverse

2. Which of the following things must involve a wave? You may choose more than one. Explain each of your choices.

   a. A bulldozer is moving the dirt for a highway.
   b. A person is talking to someone on a cell phone.
   c. An earthquake in the Pacific Ocean causes the floor of a house to shake in Texas.
   d. A car is going 70 miles per hour on a highway.
   e. Two people stop to listen to a jet plane passing overhead.
   f. A doctor makes an X ray to check for broken bones.
   g. An explorer shines a flashlight to see a passage in a cave deep underground.

3. Which of the following pictures shows a correct measure of the wavelength? You may choose more than one.

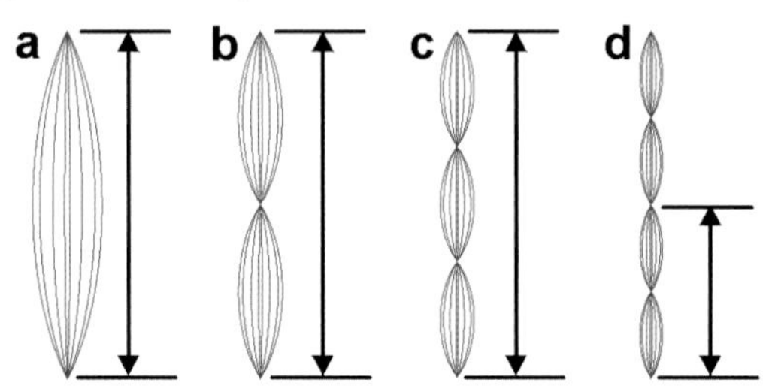

4. A wave is moving toward a hole in a wall. What will the wave look like as it passes through the wall?

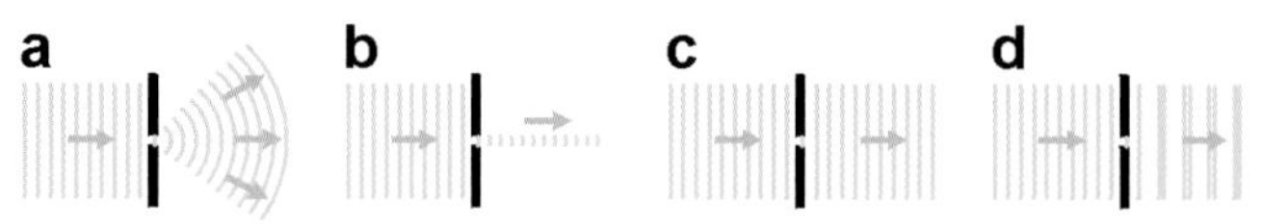

5. Which of the following best describes what happens when a water wave hits a solid wall?

   a. reflection   b. refraction

   c. diffraction   d. absorption

6. An elastic string is attached to a wall on one end. A wave pulse traveling on the string reflects off the wall and comes back:

   a. On the same side of the string as it started.
   b. On the opposite side of the string from where it started.
   c. Split equally between both sides of the string.

7. A transverse wave is:

   a. A wave with a very high frequency, like light.
   b. A wave that oscillates perpendicular to the direction it moves.
   c. A wave that oscillates along the direction it moves.
   d. A wave with a frequency that is a multiple of another frequency.

8. A string with natural frequency of 15 Hz will likely show resonance when wiggled at which frequency.

   a. 20 Hz   b. 40 Hz

   c. 30 Hz   d. 50 Hz

Problems

1. You find the pattern in the picture at a frequency of 40 Hz. Answer the following questions.
   a. What is the period?
   b. At what frequency will you find the third harmonic?
   c. At what frequency will you find the eighth harmonic?
   d. How many antinodes are in the wave in the picture?

40 Hz

2. A group of students shows you sketches in their lab book of four patterns they found on a vibrating string. You suspect that one of the pictures is either a fake, or a mistake. Which picture is the fake (or mistake) and how did you know?

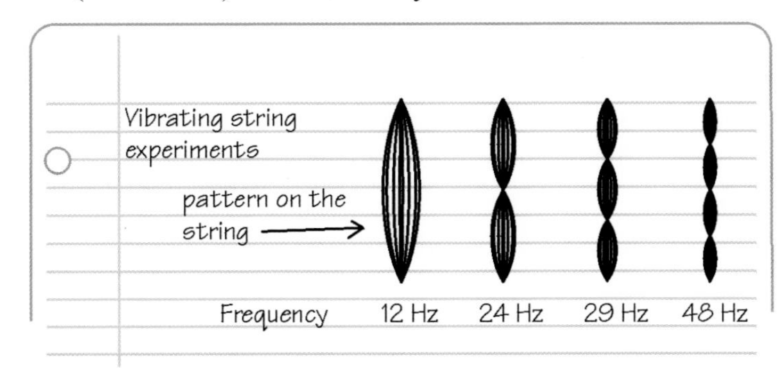

3. The wave in the picture has how many nodes?

   a) Two
   b) Three
   c) Four
   d) None

4. The wavelength of a wave on a string is 25 centimeters and the frequency is 20 Hz. Calculate the speed of the wave.

5. A wave has a frequency of 5 Hz and a wavelength of 2 meters. What is the speed of the wave?
   a. 10 m/sec
   b. 0.4 m.sec
   c. 2.5 m/sec
   d. 7 m/sec

6. You are doing a vibrating string experiment and observe the seventh harmonic at a frequency of 63 Hz. At what frequency will you find the third harmonic?
   a. 21 Hz
   b. 27 Hz
   c. 189 Hz m/sec
   d. 9 Hz

7. You are doing a vibrating string experiment and observe a resonance that looks like the picture below. You measure a frequency of 22 Hz. Fill in the rest of the data table with the frequency and wavelengths you would expect to find in an experiment. Note: Harmonics 6 and 8 are not included on the table.

2

Harmonic	Frequency	Wavelength
1		
2	22 Hz	1 meter
3		
4		
5		
7		
9		

1 3 4 5 7 9

Applying your knowledge

1. A guitar string is divided by frets. When you hold your finger on each fret, you make the length of the string shorter. This makes the wavelength shorter. If the wavelength gets shorter, the frequency must get higher to compensate.

   You know that multiplying frequency and wavelength for a vibrating string always gives you the same number. Suppose your guitar string is 68 centimeters long and vibrates with a natural frequency of 120 Hz. What length of string would you need to make it vibrate at 180 Hz, which is 1.5 times higher?

2. Marching is when many people walk exactly in step with each other. Tromp, tromp, tromp, every foot falls at exactly the same moment with a steady frequency. It has been known since early times that troops should never march across a bridge. When soldiers cross a bridge they all walk with a different pace. Discuss why marching across a bridge is a bad idea, knowing what you learned in this chapter.
3. Waves in the ocean are created by the wind acting on the surface of the water. It is suspected that many ships have been wrecked by the interference of two waves. Discuss how the meeting of two waves might sink a ship that could easily ride over a single wave.
4. Earthquakes make vibrations of the ground that can literally shake buildings to pieces. Buildings are not completely stiff, and tall buildings sway quite a bit. Swaying is a form of oscillation, and all buildings have at least one natural frequency. What do you think happens if the natural frequency of a building matches the frequency of an earthquake? How might you change the natural frequency of a building?

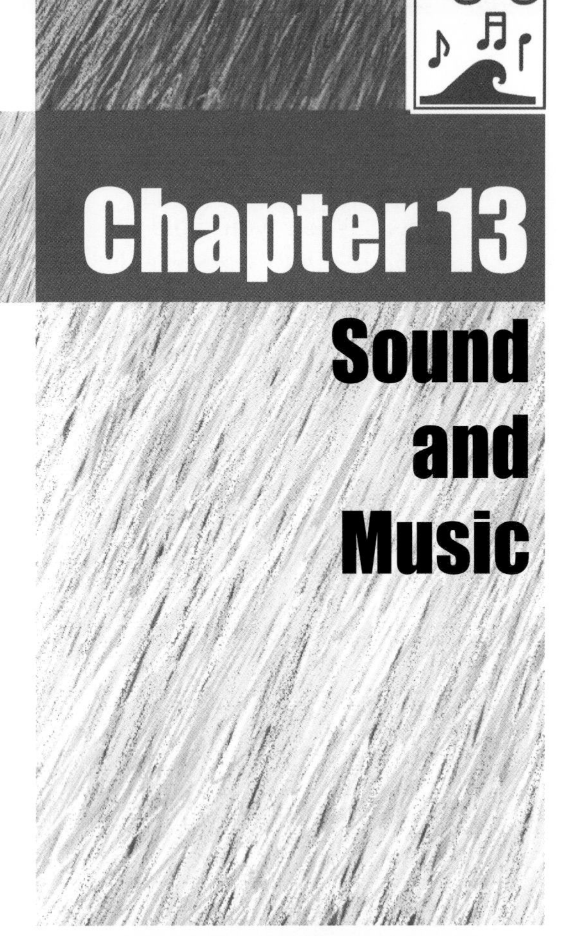

Introduction to Chapter 13

Sound is one of the richest of our five senses. In this chapter you will explore a field of study that includes everything from making computers that can understand speech to building concert halls and speaker boxes. The end of the chapter provides an introduction to music, truly a universal language that humans have always enjoyed.

Investigations for Chapter 13

13.1	Sound	*What is sound and how do we hear it?*

The first investigation explores the perception of sound. Humans hear frequencies between 20 Hz and 20,000 Hz, a range that varies widely with people. You will measure the sensitivity of your own ears as well as those of your classmates.

13.2	Properties of Sound	*Does sound behave like other waves?*

Using an electronic synthesizer, you will create resonance, beats, and interference of sound waves. The evidence you collect will dramatically demonstrate that sound is a wave, and show you how to control sound waves for useful purposes.

13.3	Music	*What is music and how do we make music?*

The musical scale was known to humans 20,000 years before anyone invented writing. Musical sounds are derived from an elegant mathematical foundation of simple fractions and ratios. Once you know the ratios, you can design and build your own musical instruments.

Learning Goals

In this chapter, you will:

- ✔ Learn how we hear sound.
- ✔ Learn how your brain interprets sound to understand words and music.
- ✔ Learn what kinds of sounds we can hear, and what kinds we cannot hear.
- ✔ Learn what a sound wave is and how it travels.
- ✔ Learn how the loudness of sound is measured.
- ✔ Learn the basics of acoustics as applied to the design of buildings and musical instruments.
- ✔ Learn to read a sonogram and how a computer recognizes spoken words.
- ✔ Learn what *supersonic* means.
- ✔ Learn why a musical scale sounds good, or why it sounds bad.
- ✔ Learn how we tell voices and instruments apart from each other.

Vocabulary

acoustics	dissonance	pitch	sonogram
beat	harmonics	pressure	supersonic
cochlea	musical scale	reverberation	white noise
consonance	beats	ultrasound	decibel
pitch	harmony	sound	rhythm

13.1 Sound

Sound is one of the most important of our senses. We use sound to express the whole range of human emotion. In this section you will learn about sound and sound waves. Scientifically, sound is one of the simplest and most common kinds of waves. But what a huge influence it has on our everyday experience! Sound is a rich and beautiful palette from which musicians create works of joy, excitement, and drama. We know sound is a wave because:

1. Sound has a frequency that we hear as higher or lower pitch.
2. Sound has a wavelength that we can construct experiments to show.
3. The speed of sound is frequency times wavelength.
4. Resonance happens with sound.
5. Sound can be reflected, refracted, and absorbed.
6. Sound shows evidence of interference and diffraction.

How do we hear a sound wave?

Hearing sound

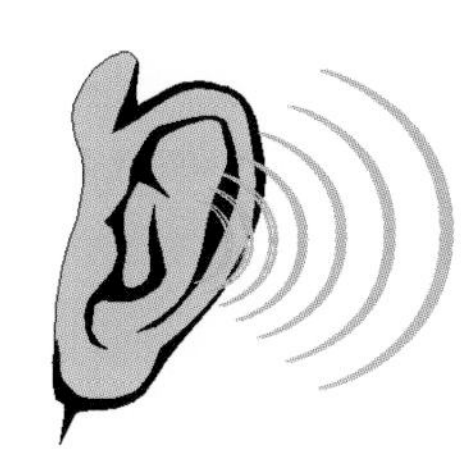

We get our sense of hearing from the cochlea, a tiny fluid-filled organ in the inner ear (Figure 13.1). The inner ear actually has two important functions: providing our sense of hearing and our sense of balance. The three semicircular canals near the cochlea are also filled with fluid. Fluid moving in each of the three canals tells the brain whether the body is moving left-right, up-down, or forward-backward.

How the cochlea works

The perception of sound starts with the eardrum. The eardrum vibrates in response to sound waves in the ear canal. The three delicate bones of the inner ear transmit the vibration of the eardrum to the side of the cochlea. The fluid in the spiral of the cochlea vibrates and creates waves that travel up the spiral. The spiral channel of the cochlea starts out large and gets narrower near the end. The nerves near the beginning see a relatively large channel and respond to longer wavelength, low-frequency sound. The nerves at the small end of the channel respond to shorter wavelength, higher-frequency sound.

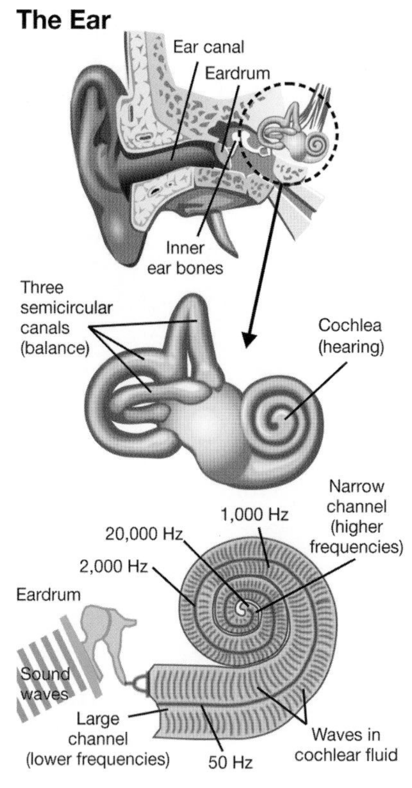

Figure 13.1: *The structure of the inner ear. When the eardrum vibrates, three small bones transmit the vibration to the cochlea. The vibrations make waves inside the cochlea, which vibrates nerves in the spiral. Each part of the spiral is sensitive to a different frequency.*

The range of human hearing

The range of human hearing is between 20 Hz and 20,000 Hz (20 kHz). The combination of the eardrum, bones, and the cochlea all contribute to the limited range of hearing. You could not hear a sound at 50,000 Hz, even at 100 decibels (loud). Animals such as cats and dogs can hear much higher frequencies because they have more sensitive structures in their inner ears.

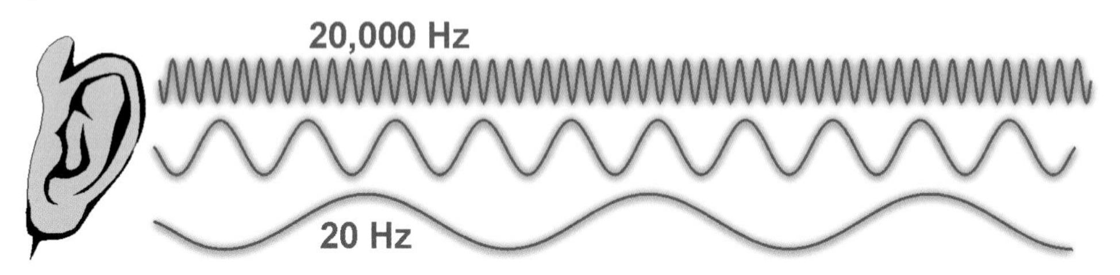

Figure 13.2: *Hearing protection is recommended when working in loud environments.*

Hearing ability changes with time

Hearing varies greatly with people and changes with age. Some people can hear very high frequency sounds and other people cannot. People gradually lose high frequency hearing with age. Most adults cannot hear frequencies above 15,000 Hz, while children can often hear to 20,000 Hz.

Hearing can be damaged by loud noise

Hearing is affected by exposure to loud or high-frequency noise. The nerve signals that carry sensation of sound to the brain are created by tiny hairs that shake when the fluid in the cochlea is vibrated. Listening to loud sounds for a long time can cause the hairs to weaken or break off. Before there were safety rules about noise, people who worked in mines or other noisy places often became partly deaf by the time they retired. It is smart to protect your ears by keeping the volume reasonable and wearing ear protection if you have to stay in a loud place (Figure 13.2). Many musicians wear earplugs to protect their hearing when playing in concerts!

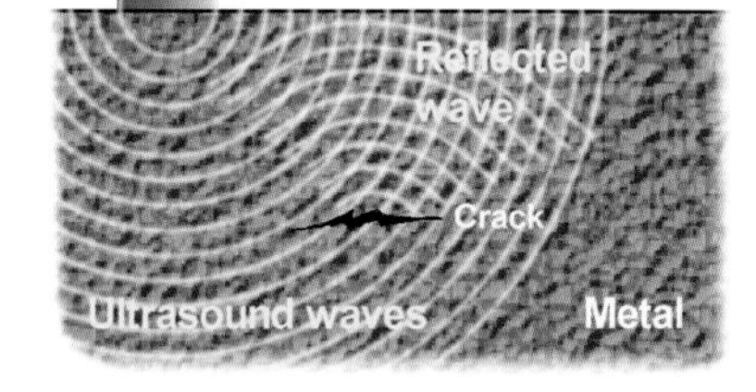

Figure 13.3: *Ultrasound can be used to find tiny cracks in metal. The crack reflects the sound wave. The reflection can tell the engineer the depth and size of the crack.*

Ultrasound

It is possible to make sound of much higher frequency than the human ear can hear. Ultrasound is sound that has very high frequency, often 100,000 Hz or more. We cannot hear ultrasound, but it can pass through the human body easily. Medical ultrasound instruments use the refraction and reflection of sound waves inside the body to create images. Doctors often take ultrasound pictures of a beating heart or a baby in the womb. Ultrasound is also used to find cracks in materials (Figure 13.3). If you pass ultrasound through a solid material, any small cracks create reflections that can be detected by instruments. Ultrasound examinations are routinely done on the structural frames of aircraft.

13.2 Properties of Sound

Like other waves, sound has the fundamental properties of frequency, wavelength, amplitude, and speed. Because sound is such a part of human experience, you probably already know its properties, but you know them by different names. For example, you will rarely hear someone complain about the high amplitude of sound. What you hear instead is that the sound is too *loud*.

What is sound?

Air pressure Air, like any other gas, is made of free molecules whizzing around and bumping into each other (Figure 13.4). The molecules in a gas have lots of space around them. Because of the extra space it is easy to squeeze molecules together to fit more in a given volume. Squeezing more into the same volume makes the pressure of the gas go up (Figure 13.5). Pressure is a measure of the force felt by the walls of the container holding the gas. If there are more molecules bouncing off the walls, there is more pressure.

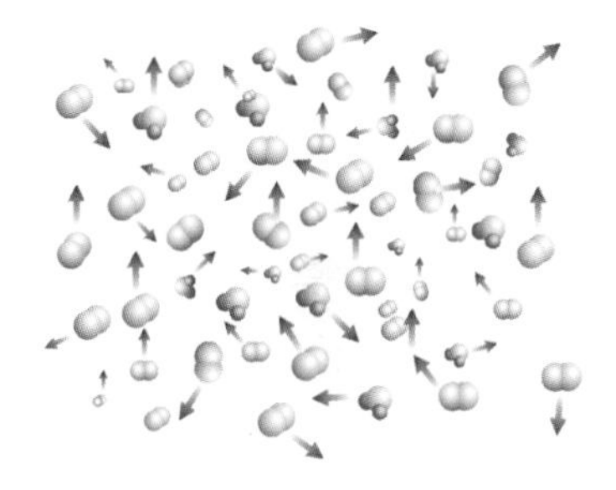

Figure 13.4: *Air is made of molecules in constant random motion, zooming around, bumping off each other and the walls of their container. There is a great deal of empty space between molecules.*

We can also lower the pressure. If we expand the volume, but don't let any molecules in or out, the pressure will go down. The pressure goes down because for every unit of area of our container there are fewer molecules bouncing off the walls.

We can also heat the gas up so the molecules move a little faster. Faster means they bang into the walls faster and bounce off with more force. Raising the temperature is a second way to increase pressure. For sound waves, however, we are mostly concerned with changes in density, or number of molecules per unit of volume.

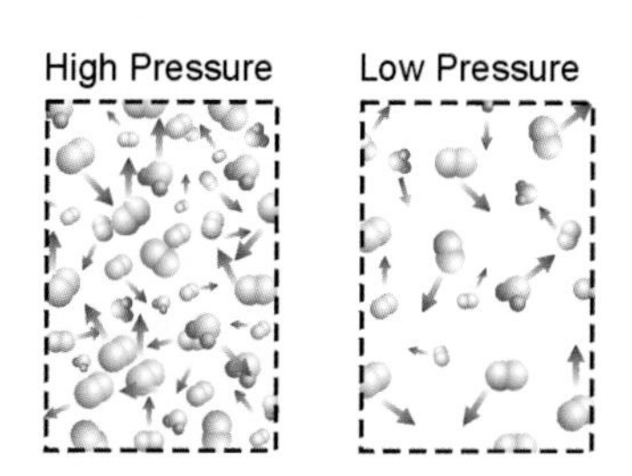

Figure 13.5: *More molecules per unit volume makes pressure go up. Fewer molecules makes pressure go down.*

Pressure is a restoring force The pressure of a gas is a type of restoring force. If we increase the pressure in one place, the natural tendency is for the atoms to spread back out again, lowering the pressure. Conversely, if we reduce the pressure in one spot, other atoms nearby rush in to fill in the extra open space and raise the pressure. Atoms have mass, and therefore inertia. Pressure provides a restoring force. The combination of inertia and restoring force results in harmonic motion and waves. The harmonic motion is an oscillation in pressure and the wave is a sound wave.

Close-up look at a sound wave

Figure 13.6 shows a greatly magnified illustration of a speaker, a sound wave and the oscillation of pressure. If you touch the speaker surface you can feel the vibration. Imagine looking at the air very close to the speaker. The surface of the speaker is going back and forth. When the surface moves forward it pushes on the air touching the surface, compressing it and raising the pressure. The speaker then moves back and lowers the pressure. The back and forth motion of the speaker creates alternating layers of high and low pressure. The pressure waves travel away from the speaker as a sound wave.

A sound wave is a wave of alternating high pressure and low pressure regions of air. Anything that vibrates in air creates a sound wave. The wave travels away from the source and eventually reaches our ear, where it vibrates the eardrum and we hear the sound.

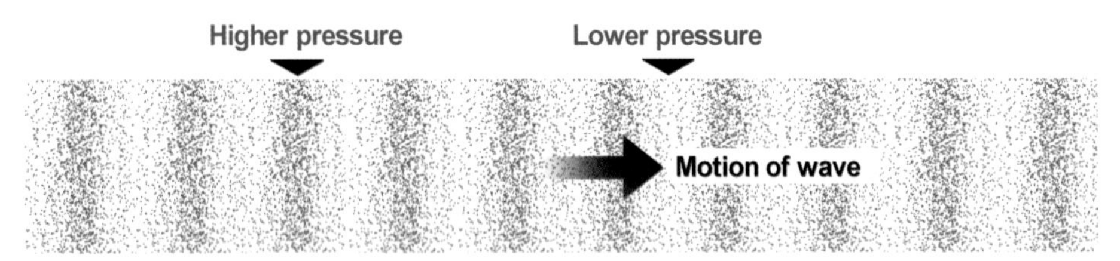

The pressure waves are small

It is hard to feel the pressure directly because the amplitude of the pressure wave is very small for most ordinary sounds. The vibrations of most sounds are also too fast for nerves in the skin to react. However, for very low frequency sounds you can feel the vibration with your skin. If you put your fingertips very close (but not touching) a speaker, you can feel the vibrating air for frequencies lower than about 100 Hz. Anyone who has listened to a loud bass guitar will confirm that sound is a vibration that you can feel at low frequencies!

Sound is a longitudinal wave

Sound waves are longitudinal because the air is compressed in the direction of travel. You can think of a sound wave like the compression wave on the Slinky. Anything that vibrates creates sound waves as long as there is air or some other material. Sound does *not* travel in space. Science fiction movies always add sound to scenes of space ships exploding. If the scenes were real, there would be total silence because there is no air in space to carry the sound waves.

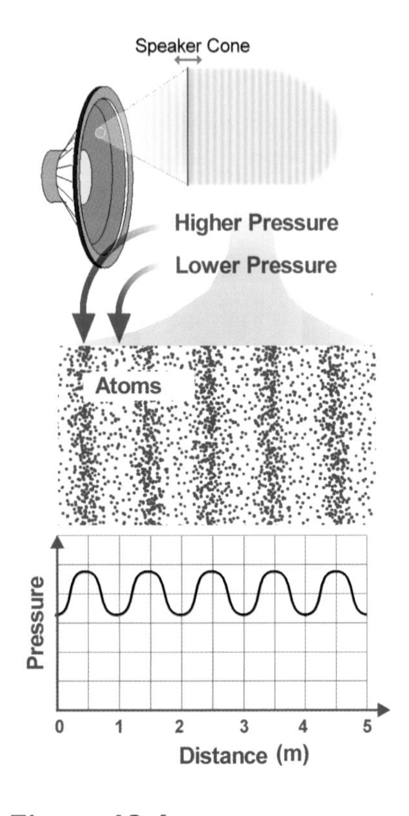

Figure 13.6: *What a sound wave might look like if you could see the atoms. The effect is greatly exaggerated to show the variation. In an actual sound wave, the difference in pressure between the highest and lowest is much smaller, less than one part in a million. From the graph you can tell the wavelength of this sound is about a meter.*

The loudness of sound

The decibel scale

The loudness of sound is measured in decibels (dB). As you might expect, loudness is related to the amplitude of the sound wave. The amplitude of a sound wave is one half of the difference between the highest pressure and the lowest pressure in the wave. Because the pressure change in a sound wave is very small, almost no one uses pressure to measure loudness. Instead we use the decibel scale. Most sounds fall between 0 and 100 on the decibel scale, making it a very convenient number to understand and use. The graphic below shows where some sounds fall on the decibel scale.

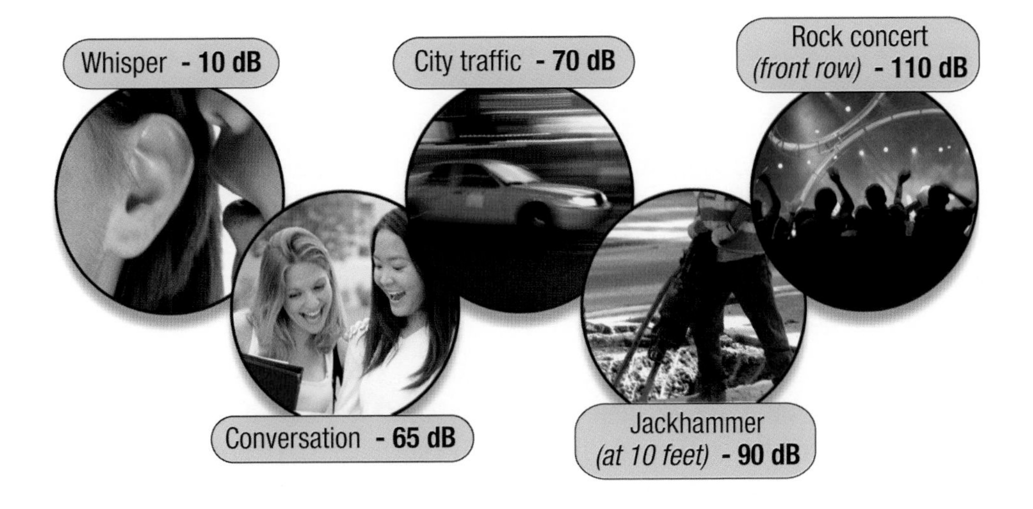

What is a decibel?

The decibel scale is a *logarithmic* measure of sound pressure. This is different from linear measures you are familiar with. Every increase of 20 dB means the pressure wave has 10 times greater amplitude.

Logarithmic scale	Linear Scale
Decibels (dB)	**Amplitude**
0	1
20	10
40	100
60	1,000
80	10,000
100	100,000
120	1,000,000

We use the decibel scale because our ears can hear such a wide range of amplitudes. Our ears also hear changes in loudness proportional to dB and not to amplitude. Every 20 dB increase sounds about twice as loud.

The sensitivity of the ear

The actual oscillations in pressure from a sound wave are very small (Figure 13.7). Table 13.2 gives some examples of the amplitude for different decibel levels. As you can see, the human ear is very sensitive. We can easily hear a pressure wave that is only 2 parts different out of 100 million! If you were looking at a pile of a million coins, you could never notice one missing. Yet our ears can detect a change in pressure of less than one part in a 100 million! This exquisite sensitivity is why hearing can be damaged by listening to very loud noises for a long time.

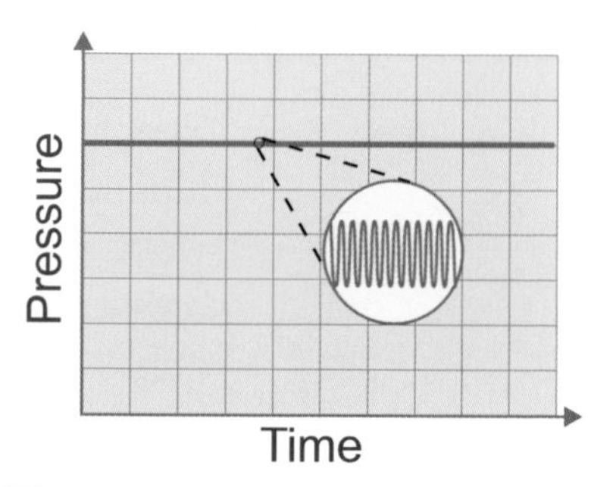

Figure 13.7: *The amplitude of a sound wave is very small. Even an 80 dB noise (quite loud) creates a pressure variation of only a few millionths of an atmosphere.*

Table 13.1: ***Loudness and amplitude of sound waves in air***

Loudness in Decibels	Amplitude of Pressure Wave (fraction of 1 atmosphere)
20 dB	2 / 1,000,000,000
40 dB	2 / 100,000,000
80 dB	2 / 1,000,000
120 dB	2 / 10,000

Acoustics

Reducing the loudness of sound is important in many applications. For example, a library might want to absorb all sound to maintain quiet. A recording studio might want to block sound from the outside from mixing with sound from the inside. **Acoustics** is the science and technology of sound. Knowledge of acoustics is important to many careers, from the people who design stereo speakers to the architects who designed your school.

Soundproofing

Because the ear is so sensitive, it is difficult to block sound. Sound can be transmitted through materials or through gaps in walls and around doors (Figure 13.8). Sound can also be reflected from hard surfaces. A good soundproofing design addresses all ways that sound can travel. To stop transmitted sound, we use dense, thick wall materials such as concrete or brick. Careful sealing around doors and openings stops sound from leaking through cracks. Thick curtains and carpets help absorb reflected sound on floors and walls. Acoustic tiles are used to reduce the loudness of sound reflected off the ceiling. Music is often recorded in studios with good soundproofing so only music inside the studio is recorded and not sounds from outside.

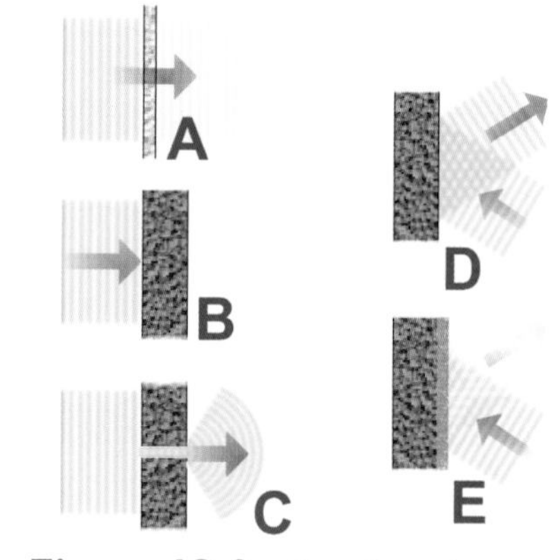

Figure 13.8: *Soundproofing requires careful attention to the way sound behaves.*
(A) It can pass through thin walls.
(B) It is stopped by dense walls.
(C) It goes through cracks.
(D) It reflects from hard surfaces.
(E) Carpet reduces reflection of sound.

The frequency of sound

Frequency and pitch

We hear the different frequencies of sound as having different pitch. A low-frequency sound has a low pitch, like the rumble of a big truck. A high-frequency sound has a high pitch, like a whistle or siren. The range of frequencies that humans can hear varies from about 20 Hz to 20,000 Hz.

The sensitivity of the ear

How we respond to the loudness of sound is affected by the frequency of the sound as well as by the amplitude (Figure 13.9). High-frequency sounds seem louder than low-frequency sounds, even if the decibel level is the same. This is because our ears are more sensitive to sounds between 100 and 2,000 Hz than to sounds outside this range. Most of the frequencies that make up speech are between 100 and 2,000 Hz.

Sound can have more than one frequency

Most sound that we hear contains many frequencies, not just one. A good analogy is to think of sound as having a recipe. The different frequencies are like different ingredients. To make the sound of a guitar you add a bunch of one frequency, a bit of a few different frequencies, and a pinch of a few others (Figure 13.10). The opposite process also works. You can take a complex sound and break it down into different amounts of pure frequencies.

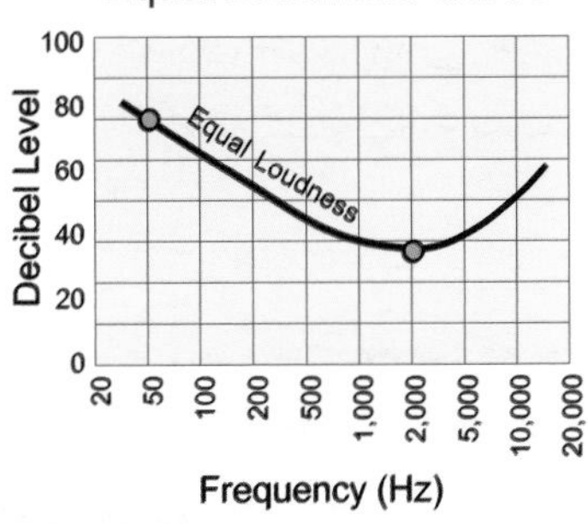

Figure 13.9: *How loud we perceive sound to be depends on the frequency as well as the amplitude. The ear is most sensitive to sounds around 2,000 Hz. The solid line on the graph represents sounds that are heard as equally loud. From the graph you can tell that an 80 dB sound at 50 Hz seems just as loud as a 38 dB sound at 2,000 Hz.*

Complex sound is made from many frequencies

You can add up single frequencies to make a complex sound.

264 Hz
330 Hz
396 Hz

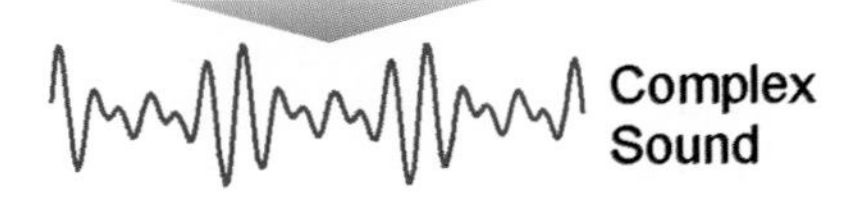

You can take a complex sound and break it down into single frequencies.

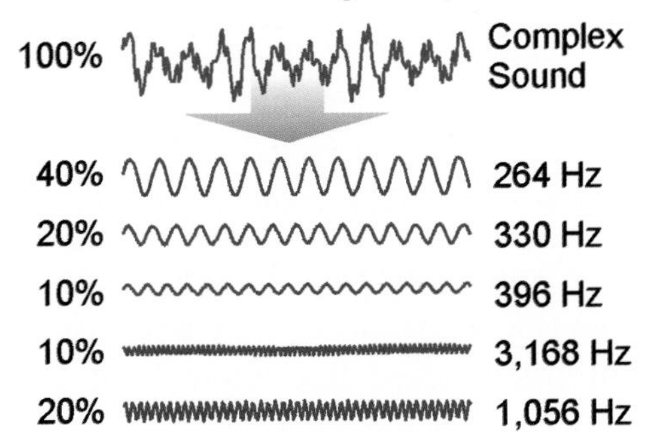

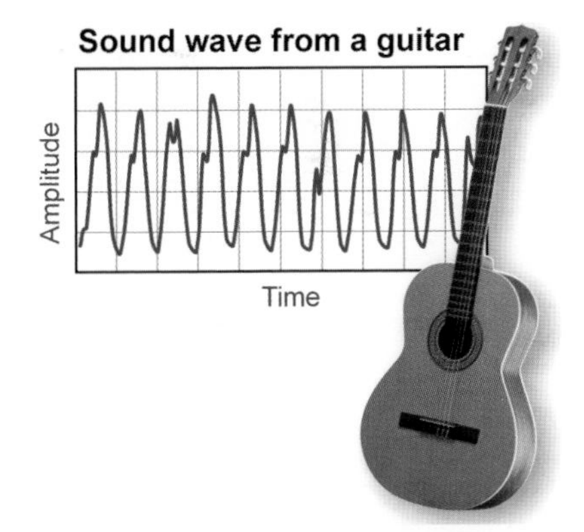

Figure 13.10: *The sound wave from a guitar playing the note E. Several frequencies are present because the graph is not a simple wave.*

Finding meaning in sound

Each nerve in the ear responds to a different range of frequency. One nerve might hear 330 Hz while another hears 800 Hz. Our brain has learned to assemble all the different frequencies and attach meanings to different patterns. The spoken word "hello" has a characteristic sound that contains a pattern of frequencies. We are taught to recognize the pattern and interpret the sound to be a word with meaning.

Think about reading one single word from a story. You recognize the word, but it does not tell you much about the story. When you read the whole story you put all the words together to get the meaning. The brain does a similar thing with different frequencies of sound. A single frequency by itself does not have much meaning. The meaning comes from patterns in many frequencies together.

Reading a sonogram

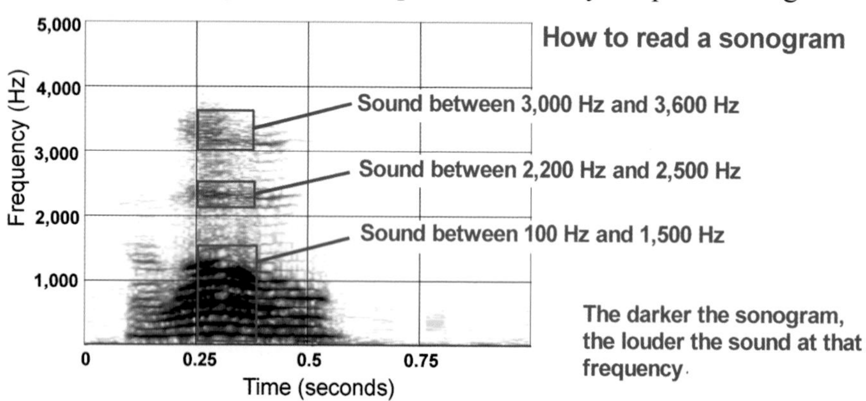

Sonograms

A sonogram is a special kind of graph that shows how loud "sound" is at different frequencies. The sonogram above is for a male voice saying "hello." The word lasts from 0.1 seconds to about 0.6 seconds. You can see lots of sound below 1,500 Hz and two bands of sound near 2,350 Hz and 3,300 Hz. Every person's sonogram is different, even when saying the same word.

White noise

Sometimes you do not want to hear meaning in sound, like when you want to go to sleep. Many people find white noise to be a relaxing sound. White noise is an equal mixture of all frequencies, like white light is a mixture of all colors. Because all frequencies are at the same level there is no pattern the brain can recognize. The lack of pattern is helpful for relaxing because it can drown out more distracting noises, like people talking or a television.

Talking to computers

Today there are programs that allow you to speak while the computer types what you say. Many people see a day when we talk to our computers rather than type at a keyboard.

Voice recognition programs have to be trained. The program gives you a story to read. The program knows every word in the story. You read the story into the microphone and the computer learns to recognize words from the frequency patterns of your voice.

Since everyone's voice is different, voice programs work only for the person who trained them! The computer types nonsense if you talk into a program trained to someone else's voice.

The wavelength of sound

Bass and treble speakers

Speakers that have great bass (low frequency) are large. Speakers that have good treble (high frequency) are usually much smaller. This is because of the wavelength and energy of the different frequencies of sound (Figure 13.11). The chart below gives some typical frequencies and wavelengths for sound in air.

Table 13.2: *Frequency and wavelength for some typical sounds*

Frequency (Hz)	Wavelength	Typical Source
20	17 meters	rumble of thunder
100	3.4 meters	bass guitar
500	70 cm (27”)	average male voice
1,000	34 cm (13”)	female soprano singer
2,000	17 cm (6.7”)	fire truck siren
5,000	7 cm (2.7”)	highest note on a piano
10,000	3.4 cm (1.3”)	whine of a jet turbine
20,000	1.7 cm (2/3”)	highest pitched sound you can hear

Why the wavelength of sound is important

Although we usually think about different sounds in terms of frequency, the wavelength can also be important. If there are boundaries or objects similar in size to the wavelength we will get resonance. Resonance makes certain sounds much louder. If you want to make sound of a certain wavelength, you often need to have a vibrating object that is similar in size to the wavelength (Figure 13.12). This is the reason organ pipes are made in all different sizes. Each pipe is designed for a specific wavelength of sound.

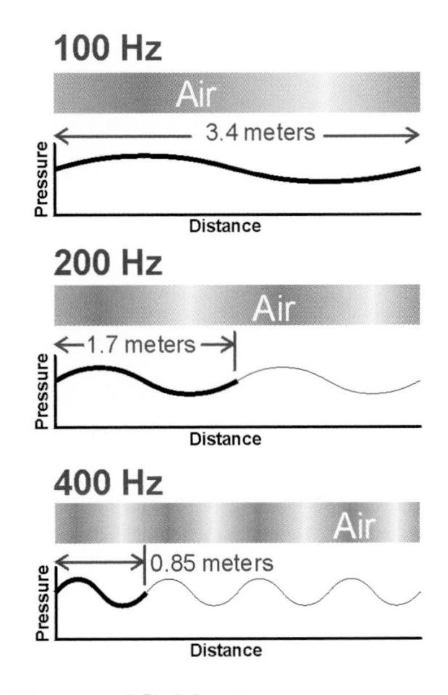

Figure 13.11: *The frequency and wavelength of sound are inversely related. When the frequency goes up, the wavelength goes down proportionally.*

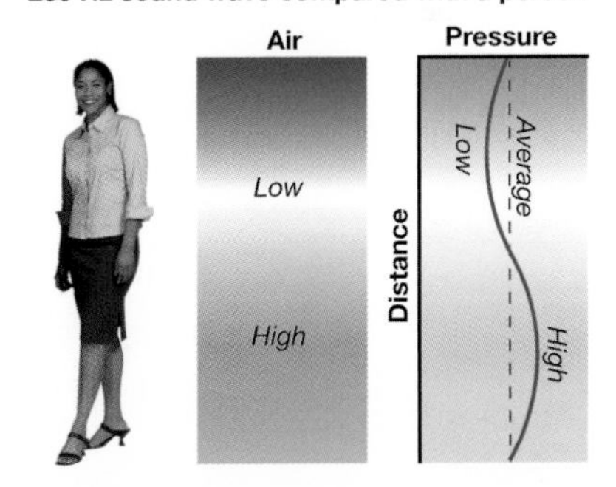

Figure 13.12: *A 200 Hz sound has a wavelength about equal to the height of a person.*

The speed of sound

Sound is fast, about 340 meters per second

Sound moves faster than most motion you are familiar with. Under average conditions the speed of sound is about 340 meters per second (660 mph). Ordinary passenger jets fly slower than sound, usually around 400 to 500 miles per hour. We use the term **supersonic** to describe motion that is faster than sound. Only one kind of passenger jet (the Concorde) is supersonic (Figure 13.13). If you were on the ground watching the Concorde flying toward you, there would be silence. The sound would be *behind* the plane, racing to catch up. You would hear the sound after the plane passed overhead. You would also hear a deafening sonic boom when the sound finally reached your ears.

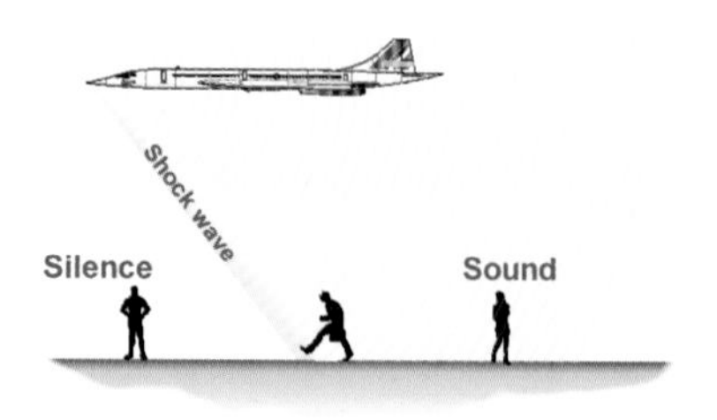

Figure 13.13: *The Concorde is a supersonic jet. If one flew overhead, you would not hear the sound until the plane was far beyond you. The boundary between sound and silence is called a shock wave. It is almost as if all the sound were compressed into a thin layer of air. The person in the middle hears a sonic boom as the shock wave passes over him. Because the sonic boom can shatter windows, planes are not allowed to fly over cities at supersonic speeds.*

The speed depends on pressure and temperature

The speed a sound wave travels in air depends on how fast the molecules in the air are moving. If the molecules are moving slowly (cold), sound does not travel as fast as when they are moving fast (hot). The kind of molecules also affects the speed of sound. Air is made up of mostly of oxygen (O_2) molecules and nitrogen (N_2) molecules. Lighter molecules, like hydrogen (H_2), move faster for a given temperature. Because of the speed difference, sound travels faster in hydrogen than in air.

Like other waves, the speed of sound also depends on the strength of the restoring force. High pressure creates larger restoring forces and increases the speed of sound. Lower pressure decreases the restoring force and decreases the speed of sound.

Sound in liquids and solids

Sound can also travel through liquid and solid materials, like water and steel (Figure 13.14). The speed of sound in other materials is often faster than in air. The restoring forces in solid steel (for example) are much stronger than in a gas. Stronger restoring forces tend to raise the speed of sound. People used to listen for an approaching train by putting an ear to the rails. The sound of the approaching train travels much faster through the steel rails than through the air.

Material	Sound speed (m/sec)
Air	330
Helium	965
Water	1530
Wood (average)	2000
Gold	3240
Steel	5940

Figure 13.14: *The speed of sound in various materials (helium and air at 0°C and 1 atmospheric pressure).*

How sound waves are affected by surfaces

Reverberation

Sound waves reflect from hard surfaces. In a good concert hall the reflected sound adds to the direct sound. You hear a multiple echo celled reverberation. The right amount of reverberation makes the sound seem livelier and richer. Too much reverberation and the sound gets muddy from too many reflections. Concert hall designers work hard on the shape and surface of the walls and ceiling to provide the best reverberation. Some concert halls even have movable panels that can be raised or lowered from the ceiling to help with the sound.

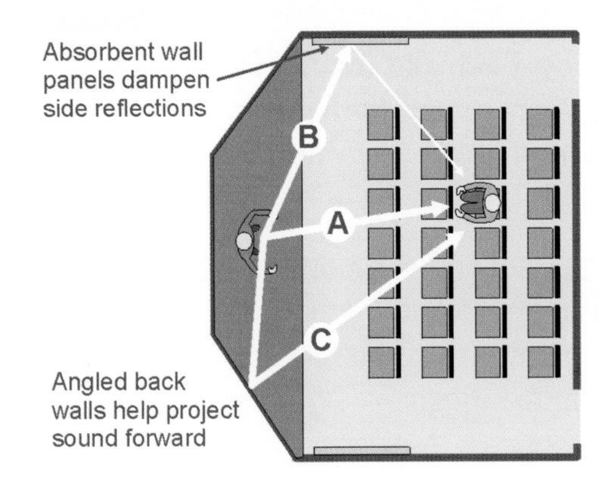
Absorbent wall panels dampen side reflections
B
A
C
Angled back walls help project sound forward

Making a good concert hall

Direct sound (**A**) reaches the listener along with reflected sound (**B, C**) from the walls. The shape of the room and the surfaces of the walls must be designed so that there is some reflected sound, but not too much.

Interference can also affect sound quality

Reverberation also causes interference of sound waves. When two waves interfere, the total can be louder or softer than either wave alone. The diagram above shows a musician and an audience of one person. The sound reflected from the walls interferes as it reaches the listener. If the distances are just right, one reflected wave might be out of phase with the other. The result is that the sound is quieter at that spot. An acoustic engineer would call it a *dead spot* in the hall. Dead spots are areas where destructive interference causes some of the sound to cancel with its own reflections. It is also possible to make very loud spots where sound interferes constructively. Good concert halls are designed to have even sound, not too lively, but not too quiet, either.

Diffraction

Because sound is a wave, it can be diffracted. This means that sound can bend around objects and pass through openings of any size.

Avery Fisher Hall

New York's Philharmonic Hall opened in 1962, and it was an acoustic disaster. The building was beautiful but the sound quality in the hall was awful, with loud spots, dead spots, and muddy reflections. How did some of the best architects and acoustic experts go wrong?

The hall was redesigned in 1976 by Cyril Harris, an acoustical specialist from Columbia University. Professor Harris altered almost all of the interior, changing wall shapes, and adding or moving many absorbing and reflecting panels. The sound quality was greatly improved and the building was renamed Avery Fisher Hall.

13.3 Music

Music is a combination of sound and rhythm that we find pleasant. The kinds of sounds and rhythms can be very different for different styles of music. Some people like music with a heavy beat and strong rhythm. Other people like music where the notes rise and fall in beautiful melodies. Music can be slow or fast, loud or soft, happy or sad, comforting or scary. In this chapter we will learn what kinds of sounds music is made from.

Pitch and rhythm

Pitch The pitch of a sound is how high or low we hear its frequency. Pitch and frequency usually mean the same thing. However, because pitch depends on the human ear and brain, sometimes pitch and frequency can be different. The way we hear a pitch can be affected by the sounds we heard before and after.

Rhythm Rhythm is a regular time pattern in a sound. Rhythm can be loud and soft, tap-tap-TAP-tap-tap-TAP-tap-tap-TAP. Rhythm can be made with sound and silence or with different pitches. People respond naturally to rhythm. Cultures of people are distinguished by their music and the special rhythms used in the music.

The musical scale Most of the music you listen to is made from a set of frequencies called a **musical scale**. The scale that starts on the note C is show in the diagram below.

C major scale								
Note	C	D	E	F	G	A	B	C
Frequency (Hz)	264	297	330	352	396	440	495	528
Ratio to C-264	1/1 (264/264)	9/8 (297/264)	5/4 (330/264)	4/3 (352/264)	3/2 (396/264)	5/3 (440/264)	15/8 (495/264)	2/1 (528/264)

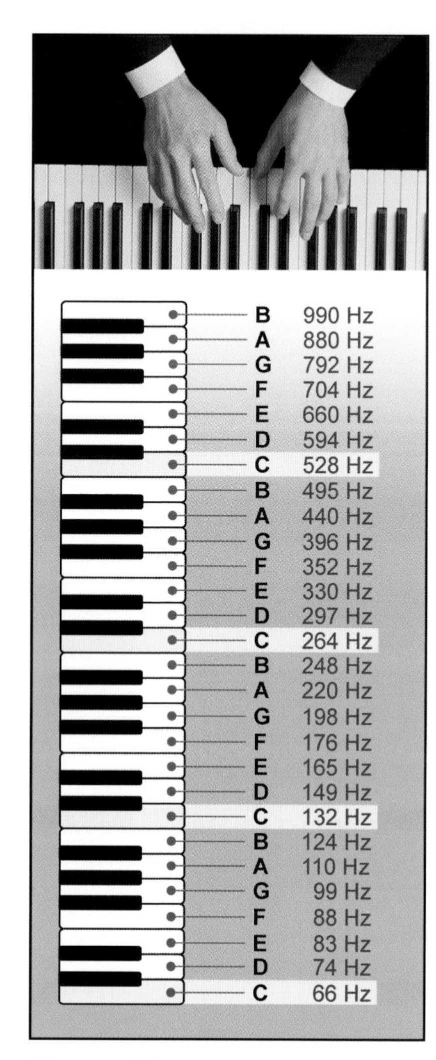

Figure 13.15: *A portion of a piano keyboard showing the frequencies of the notes*. Four octaves are shown. A grand piano has 88 keys and covers seven octaves. (*tuned to perfect C major scale)*

Consonance, dissonance, and beats

Harmony Music can have a profound effect on people's mood. The tense, dramatic soundtrack of a horror movie is a vital part of the audience's experience. Harmony is the study of how sounds work together to create effects desired by the composer. Harmony is based on the frequency relationships of the musical scale.

Beats An interesting thing happens when two frequencies of sound are close, but not exactly the same. The phase of the two waves changes in a way that makes the loudness of the sound seem to oscillate or **beat**. Sometimes the two waves are in phase, and the total is louder than either wave separately. Other times the waves are out of phase and they cancel each other out, leaving periods of silence. The rapid alternations between loudness and silence are referred to as beats. Most people find beats very unpleasant to listen to. Out-of-tune instruments make beats. The frequencies in the musical scale are chosen to reduce the occurrence of beats.

Beats come from adding two waves that are only slightly different in frequency

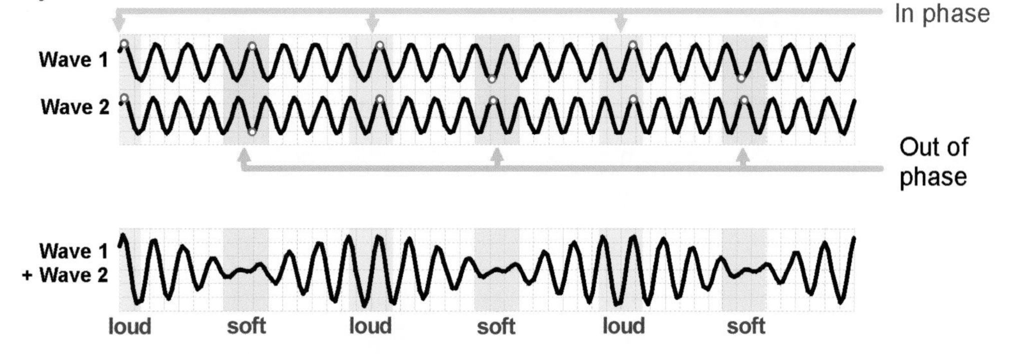

Consonance and dissonance When we hear more than one frequency of sound and the combination sounds good, we call it **consonance**. When the combination sounds bad or unsettling, we call it **dissonance**. Consonance and dissonance are related to beats. When frequencies are far enough apart that there are no beats, we get consonance. When frequencies are too close together, we hear beats that are the cause of dissonance. Dissonance is often used to create tension or drama. Consonance can be used to create feelings of balance and comfort.

Echolocation and beats

Bats "see" at night using ultrasound waves instead of light. A bat's voice is like a "sonic flashlight" shining a beam of sound. A bat emits bursts of sound that rise in frequency, called "chirps." When the sound reflects from a bug, the bat's ears receive the echo. Since the frequency of the chirp is always changing, the echo comes back with a slightly different frequency. The difference between the echo and the chirp makes *beats* that the bat can hear. The beat frequency is proportional to how far the bug is from the bat. A bat triangulates the bug's position by comparing the echo from the left ear with that of the right ear.

Harmonics and the "color" of sound

The same note can sound different

The same note sounds different when played on different instruments. As an example, suppose you listen to the note C-264 Hz played on a guitar and the same C-264 Hz played on a piano. A musician would recognize both notes as being C because they have the same frequency and pitch. But the guitar sounds like a guitar and the piano sounds like a piano. If the frequency of the note is the same, what gives each instrument its characteristic sound?

Instruments make mixtures of frequencies

The answer is that the sound we hear is not a single pure frequency. If the piano and the guitar both made a pure 264 Hz sound, we could not tell the difference. We can tell because real instruments make sounds with many frequencies. The most important one is still the fundamental note (for example, C-264 Hz). The variation comes from the **harmonics**. Remember, harmonics are frequencies that are multiples of the fundamental note. We have already learned that a string can vibrate at many harmonics. The same is true for all instruments. A single C from a grand piano might include 20 or more different harmonics.

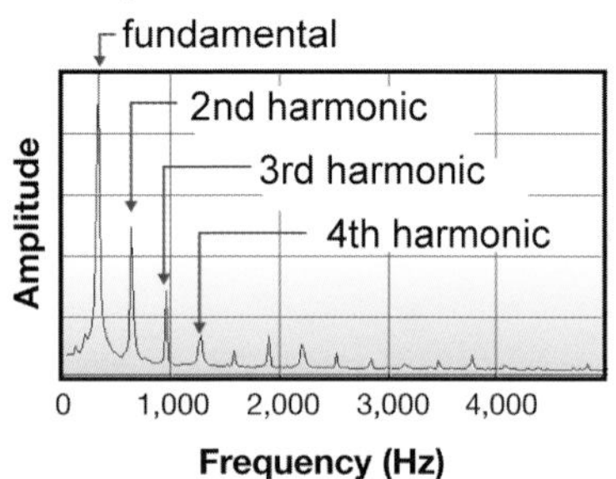

Figure 13.16: *This graph shows the frequencies in a guitar playing an E note. Notice how many harmonics there are!*

Recipes for sound

A good analogy is that each instrument has its own *recipe* for sound. The "guitar" sound shown in Figure 13.16 has a mix of many harmonics. For this guitar, the fundamental is twice as big as the 2nd harmonic. There are strong 3rd, 4th and 5th harmonics. The piano recipe would have a different mix.

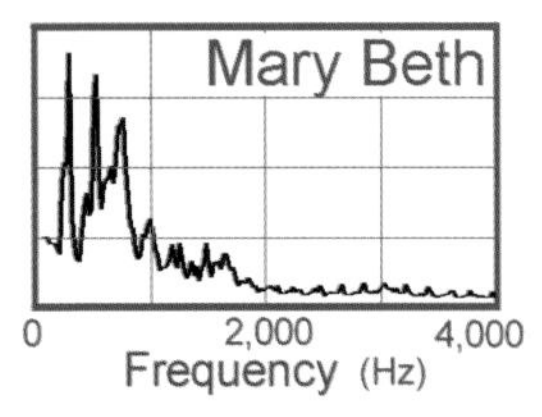

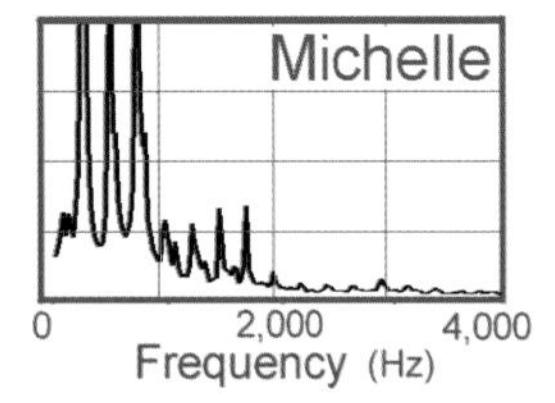

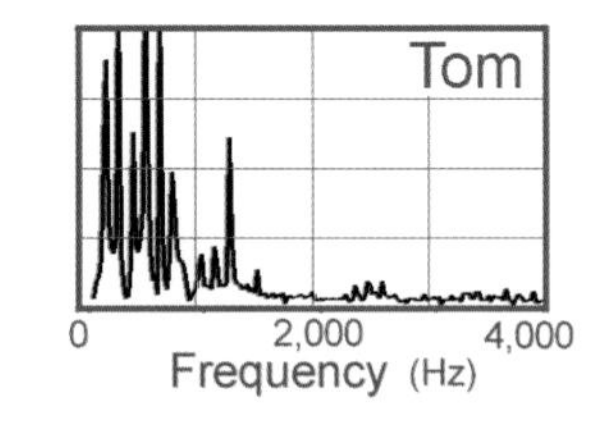

Human voices

The human voice also has harmonics. We recognize different people's voices by the patterns in frequency. The diagrams above show the frequencies of male and female voices saying the word "hello." The frequencies range from 100 Hz to about 4,000 Hz. The peaks in the diagrams indicate the harmonics in the voices. Each voice has a unique set of harmonics. This is why it is possible to identify someone by their voice even if you only hear that person say "hello."

Chapter 13 Review

Vocabulary review

Match the following terms with the correct definition. There is one extra definition in the list that will not match any of the terms.

Set One

1. sound
2. pressure
3. soundproofing
4. cochlea
5. decibel

a. The force of molecules colliding with each other and the walls of a container
b. A scale to measure the loudness of sound
c. A pressure wave we hear with our ears
d. Building and designing ways to control sound
e. The highest frequency of sound
f. The part of the ear that senses sound

Set Two

1. ultrasound
2. acoustics
3. pitch
4. sonogram
5. white noise

a. The technology of making and using sound
b. How we hear different frequencies of sound
c. A graph showing frequency, loudness, and time
d. An equal mixture of all frequencies of sound
e. Sound of frequencies too high for the human ear to hear
f. The speed of sound

Set Three

1. supersonic
2. reverberation
3. rhythm
4. musical scale
5. octave

a. The time pattern in sound
b. A set of frequencies that we find pleasant to listen to
c. The effect of multiple echoes in a room
d. A speed faster than the speed of sound
e. A nerve in the ear that is sensitive to sound
f. The interval between a frequency and double the frequency

Set Four

1. note
2. beats
3. consonance
4. dissonance
5. harmony

a. The artistic mixing of sounds of many different frequencies
b. When two or more sounds are pleasant to hear together
c. When two or more sounds are unpleasant to hear together
d. The loudness of sound
e. A frequency of sound that is part of a musical scale
f. An oscillation in loudness that occurs when two frequencies of sound are close but not equal

Concept review

1. A string that vibrates at 150 Hz creates a sound wave of:

   a. 150 cycles/sec b. 150 decibels
   c. 150 m/sec d. 150 meters

2. Which of the following is evidence that sound is a wave? You may choose more than one.

   a. Sound has a frequency we hear as differences in pitch.
   b. Some sounds are represented by special symbols.
   c. The speed of sound is the product of frequency times wavelength.
   d. We observe interference and diffraction of sound.

3. Which frequencies can most people hear? You may choose more than one.

   a. 300 Hz b. 10,000 Hz
   c. 2,500 Hz d. 100,000 Hz
   e. 5 Hz f. 50,000 Hz

4. Ultrasound is used for:

   a. Making images of the body for medical purposes.
   b. Extremely loud music.
   c. Making digital recordings for music CDs.
   d. Creating scary soundtracks for horror movies.

5. Air pressure is affected by (you may choose more than one):

   a. The movement of atoms and molecules.
   b. The temperature of a gas.
   c. Sound waves.
   d. Light waves.

6. The decibel scale is a measure of the ______ of a sound wave?

   a. frequency
   b. wavelength
   c. amplitude
   d. speed

7. The human voice contains only one frequency of sound at a time. True or false?

8. We recognize people's voices by patterns in the frequency of sound. True or false?

9. The frequency of sound has no effect on how loud we hear the sound. True or false?

10. A sonogram is a graph that shows how patterns of frequency change over time, as when someone is speaking. True or false?

11. If you wanted to create a very quiet room, you would do what (you may choose more than one):

    a. Cover the walls and ceilings with a hard surface like paneling.
    b. Cover surfaces with materials like carpet and foam.
    c. Seal doors and windows to eliminate cracks.

12. Arrange the following in order of the speed of sound in the material: air, wood, steel, water, helium.

Fastest Slowest

13. Beats are caused by:
    a. Two frequencies of sound that are close but not identical.
    b. Two frequencies of sound that are consonant.
    c. Two frequencies of sound that are exactly one octave apart.
    d. Two frequencies of sound that are exactly the same.

14. Choose *all* the following that are true of the human voice:
    a. The frequencies of female voices are usually lower than male voices.
    b. The frequencies of female voices are usually higher than male voices.
    c. Voices mostly contain frequencies between 100 Hz and 2,000 Hz.
    d. Voices mostly contain frequencies between 2,000 Hz and 10,000 Hz.

Problems

1. The speed of sound is approximately 340 m/sec. What is the wavelength of a sound wave with a frequency of 1,000 Hz?
    a. 3.4 meters
    b. 34 centimeters
    c. 340 meters
    d. 2.9 meters

2. If a sound is 20 decibels louder than another sound, the amplitude of the louder sound is:
    a. 20 times the amplitude of the softer sound.
    b. 10 times the amplitude of the softer sound.
    c. 20 pounds per square inch more than the softer sound.
    d. 2 times the amplitude of the softer sound.

3. What is the loudest frequency shown in the graph?
    a. The fundamental.
    b. The second harmonic.
    c. The third harmonic.
    d. The fourth harmonic.

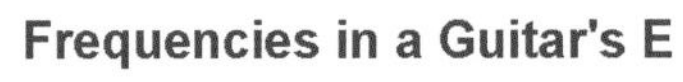

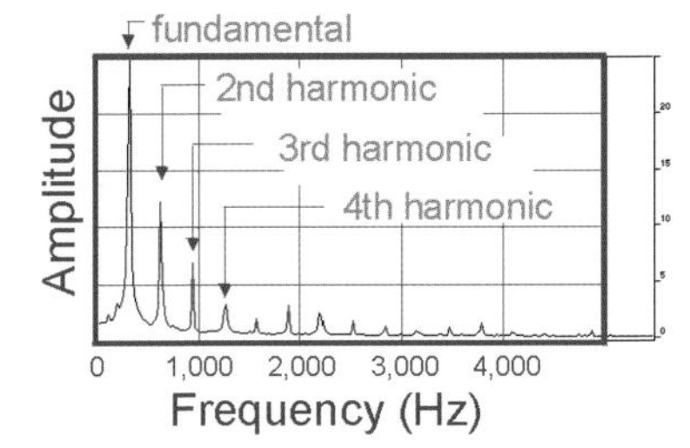

4. Suppose you stand in front of a wall that is 170 meters away. If you yell, how long does it take for the echo to get back to you if the speed of sound is 340 m/sec?

5. The sonogram shows:

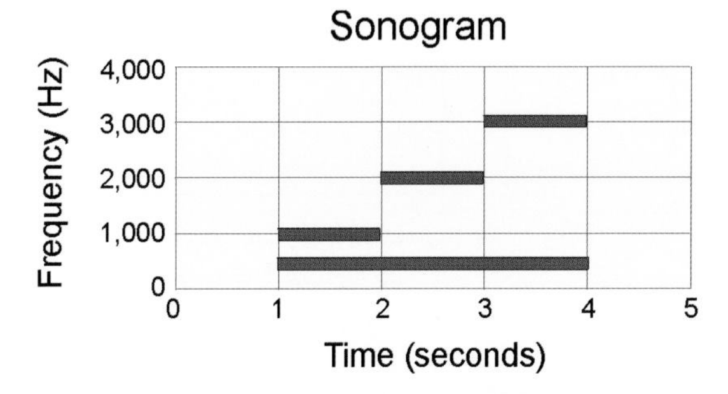

    a. A frequency of 1,000 Hz that lasts for 1 second.
    b. A frequency of 1,000 Hz that lasts for 2 seconds.
    c. A frequency of 1,500 Hz that lasts for 1 second.
    d. A frequency of 1,500 Hz that lasts for 2 seconds.

Applying your knowledge

1. Resonance applies to sound waves in boxes just like it does to strings. However, in a box there are three dimensions: length, width, and height. Each dimension can support a wave, so there can be three different wavelengths (a, b, c) that are resonant in a box.

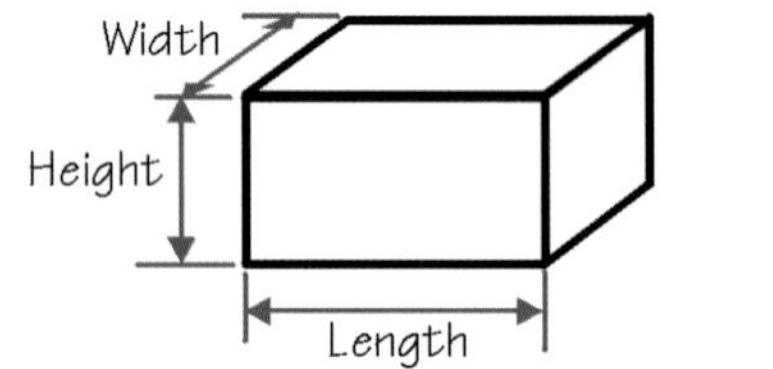

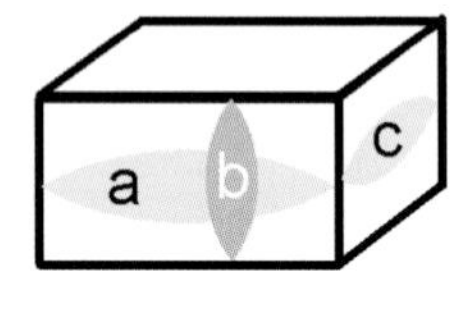

Suppose you are designing stereo speakers and you don't want resonance. Resonance would make some wavelengths (frequencies) of sound always be louder than others. This is usually bad for music. You want speakers to reproduce sound as it was recorded, and not make some sounds louder than others.

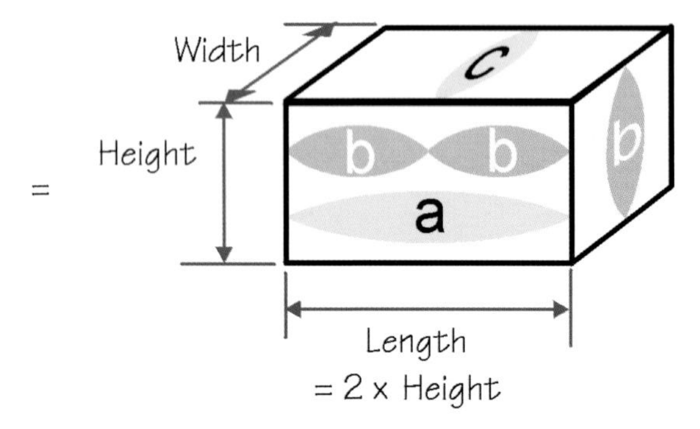

You can't escape some resonance. But suppose one side of your box was exactly twice another side. Then the second harmonic of one resonance (a) would be the same as the first harmonic of another resonance (b) and your sound problem would be twice as bad. Can you think of a rule for the three dimensions of a speaker box that would make sure that none of the three resonances, or their lower harmonics, would ever overlap?

2. Railroad engineers could always tell when a train was coming long before they could hear it. They would put their ear to the track and listen to the steel rails. Compare the speed of sound in steel to the speed of sound in air and explain why listening to the rails was a smart thing to do.

3. When it was first invented, the telephone was a marvel. The electronics of Alexander Graham Bell's days were much less sophisticated than we have today. Today, stereo makers claim they can reproduce frequencies over the whole range of human hearing from 20 Hz to 20,000 Hz. The early telephones could not deliver such a range. Look back at the graphs of frequencies of voices in the chapter. What is the minimum range of frequencies that telephones had to cover to make people's voices understandable? Have you ever noticed that a voice on the telephone never sounds like a real person's voice? Why do you think that is?

UNIT 5

Light and Optics

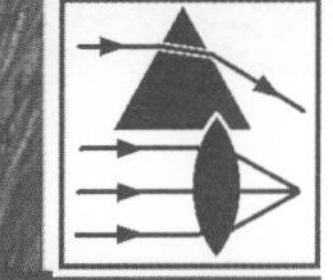

Chapter 14

Light and Color

Introduction to Chapter 14

We live in a world where light and color play a pivotal role in the very survival of life on this planet. Plants use sunlight to make sugar. Our ability to see helps us gather food. These processes and many others hinge on the unique properties of light. This chapter will introduce you to some of light's unique characteristics.

Investigations for Chapter 14

14.1	**Introduction to Light**	*How can you make light and how can you study it?*

In this Investigation you will look through a diffraction grating at a light source to see all the different colors that make up light. This leads us to the question "What makes different colors?" The different colors of light will be explained in terms of the energy of electrons falling from higher energy to lower energy inside atoms. Different atoms have different energy levels and produce different colors.

14.2	**Color**	*What happens when you mix different colors of light?*

All of the colors of light that you see are really a combination of three primary colors: red, blue and green. In this Investigation, you will discover how to make all colors of light by mixing the three primary colors. You will also use a tool called a spectrometer to analyze light. This instrument allows you to break light into its "fingerprint" wavelengths.

Learning Goals

By the end of this chapter, you will be able to:

- ✔ Describe the atomic origin of light.
- ✔ Explain the difference between incandescence and fluorescence.
- ✔ Identify uses for the other categories of electromagnetic energy.
- ✔ Compare the speed of sound to the speed of light.
- ✔ Identify the parts of the eye that see black and white, and color.
- ✔ Describe the physical reason for different colors in terms of the wavelength and energy of light.
- ✔ Identify and explain the RGB color model.
- ✔ Identify and explain the CMYK color model.
- ✔ Understand the mixing of light and pigment.
- ✔ Compare how a color printer makes color and how a color monitor makes color.

Vocabulary

chemical reaction	fluorescent	photoluminescence	subtractive primary colors
cone cells	incandescence	pixel	terahertz
cyan	magenta	polarizer	visible light
electromagnetic spectrum	nanometers	rod cells	yellow

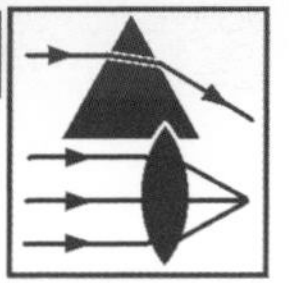

14.1 Introduction to Light

What is light? How do we see? These questions intrigue us because, from infancy through adulthood, we are drawn to bright, flashing lights and brilliant, sparkling colors. "Bright and shiny" is a common phrase that refers to this attraction. Although light is only a small part of the sensory energy around us, many people would say sight is the most important of our five senses.

We see objects by their reflected light

What is light?

Light is a wave that we see

Light is a wave that we can see with our eyes. Besides helping us to see the world around us, light has many other qualities that we use.

- Light can carry heat and warmth.
- Light has color.
- Light can be bright or dim.
- Light travels almost unimaginably fast and far.
- Light travels in straight lines, but can be bent by lenses or reflected by mirrors.

How do we see?

What happens when you see a car? Sunlight bounces off the car and into your eyes. Your eyes send signals to your brain, which creates an *image* of the car. Because the brain is so important in forming images, different people see things differently. This is one reason why paintings and drawings of a landscape or person are not the same when created by different people.

There are forms of "light" we cannot see

The light we see, visible light, is only one part of the *electromagnetic spectrum*. Radio waves, ultraviolet rays, microwaves, and X rays are also *electromagnetic waves*. Although we can't see them, these waves are used in a variety of ways including food preparation (microwaves), communication (radio waves and microwaves), medicine (X rays), and space exploration (see sidebar, right).

George Carruthers

After earning a Ph.D. in aeronautical and astronomical engineering from the University of Illinois in 1964, Dr. George Carruthers began working for the Naval Research Laboratory in Washington, D.C. There, he developed new tools to study space using ultraviolet rays. Using his tools, astronomers detected molecular hydrogen in deep space, leading to a better understanding of the total amount of matter in the universe.

In 1972, a special camera that Carruthers invented was used on the Apollo 16 mission to the moon. Called the Far-Ultraviolet Camera/Spectrograph, it took pictures that revealed important new information about deep space objects and Earth's outer atmosphere.After the mission, NASA awarded Carruthers its Exceptional Scientific Achievement medal.

Carruther's inventions have been used to study comets, stars, nebula, and other deep space objects. He was inducted into the National Inventors Hall of Fame in 2003.

What makes light?

Atoms make light

We know of many things that give off light: the sun, fireflies, lightning, fire, incandescent and fluorescent bulbs are a few examples. But what actually makes the light? The thing that is common to all these different sources of light is that they are made up of atoms. Almost everything that creates light is made of atoms.

Atoms, electrons, and energy levels

You may remember that each atom contains smaller particles within it: a nucleus made up of protons and neutrons at the center of the atom and electrons at the outside edge of the atom. The electrons are always arranged in *levels*, like layers of onion skin. The electrons in each level have a different amount of energy. The farther away the electrons are from the nucleus, the more energy they have. Electrons can gain energy and rise to a higher level in the atom. When this happens, they can also fall back to a lower level in the atom and release energy.

Glow-in-the-dark stuff

Consider an amazing but very common material, glow-in-the-dark plastic. If this material is exposed to light, it soon gives off its own light. What is happening?

An example of making light

Embedded in glow-in-the-dark plastic are atoms of the element *phosphorus*. When light hits phosphorus atoms, some of the electrons absorb the light, rise to a higher energy level and then stay up there. Slowly, the electrons fall back down and give off their stored light. Because the electrons fall back over a long period of time, glow-in-the-dark stuff gives off light for many minutes. When all the electrons have finally fallen to the lowest levels, no more light comes out. To "recharge" your glow-in-the-dark material, you have to expose it to light again.

When phosphorus gives off light the process is called photoluminescence. The word "photo" means light and the word "luminescence" means glowing. Light energy has led to the production of light by something else.

Energy is required to raise electrons to higher levels.

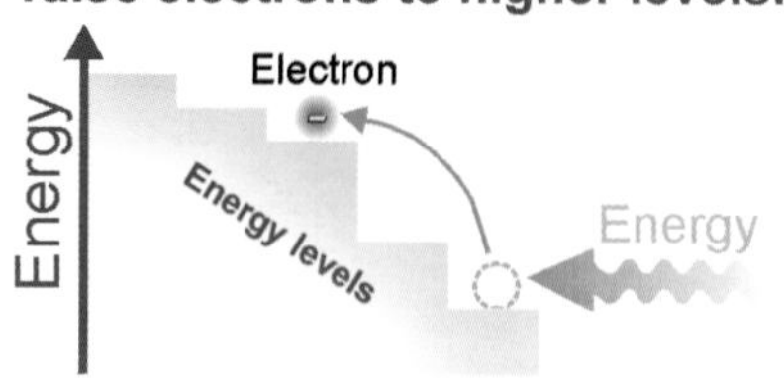

Energy is given off when electrons drop levels.

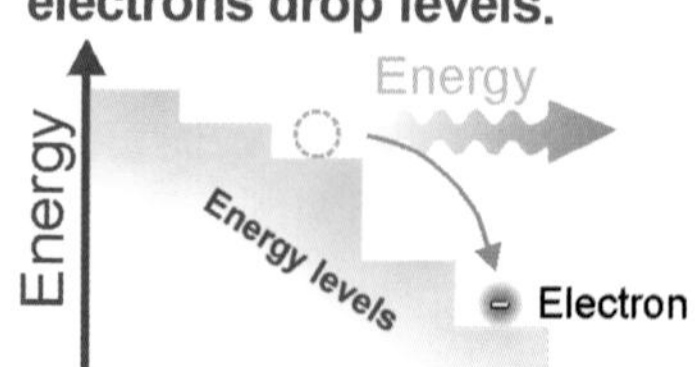

Glow sticks

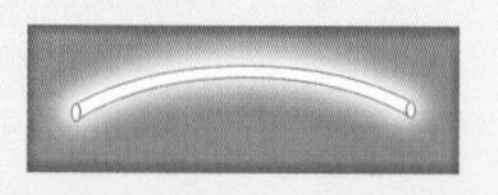

Glow sticks are a great example of atoms emitting light. When you bend a glow stick, two chemicals are mixed. The active chemical is called Luminal. When Luminal mixes with the other chemicals in the glow stick, a reaction takes place, causing electrons to fall from high energy levels to lower levels.

The energy released is almost completely in the form of light. After all the electrons have fallen to their lowest energy levels, the light stick stops glowing. You can slow the reaction down by cooling the chemicals in cold water or the freezer.

If you activate two glow sticks and put one in hot water and the other in ice water, you can graphically see how reaction rate is linked to temperature.

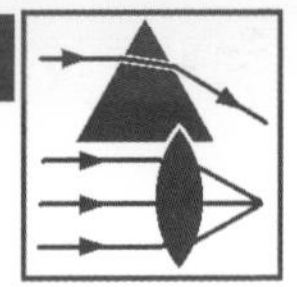

More about energy levels and light

What is an energy level? Think about Earth orbiting the sun. Earth is attracted to the sun by the force of gravity, but it is not pulled into the sun because it has kinetic energy from moving in its orbit. Electrons in atoms also have kinetic energy. The energy of electrons keeps them in stable energy levels, like orbits (Figure 14.1). That is why they don't fall into the nucleus.

Why are there energy levels? The question "Why are there energy levels?" is hard to answer. When we look at nature and study atoms, we find energy levels. Niels Bohr built a model of the atom to help us understand how energy levels work. He used something called quantum mechanics to explain his model. We know that the energy of electrons in atoms comes in levels. We can use quantum mechanics to calculate what the energy levels are. We know how to use our knowledge of energy levels to make lasers and TV screens. But, fundamentally, we don't know *why* quantum mechanics works or why there are energy levels. Maybe someday you will find out and win the Nobel Prize!

Light from chemical reactions If an atom has some electrons in a high energy level and they somehow fall into a lower energy level, the atom will give off energy that our eyes might see. This happens all the time. When wood is burning, a chemical reaction takes place between the atoms in the wood and the atoms of oxygen in the air. Chemical reactions move electrons around. If any electrons move to lower levels, light can come out. The warm flickering light from a candle comes from trillions of tiny electrons falling down energy levels as the wick combines with oxygen and burns.

Light from lightning and the sun When electricity moves through the air, it can cause the atoms in the air to rearrange their electrons. This can also produce light, which we call lightning. We cannot see the electricity (although we could certainly feel it), but we can see the light that is created. The light from the sun comes from moving electrons in the sun's very hot outer layers. Because reactions inside the sun release a lot of energy, the sun makes several kinds of electromagnetic waves, including infrared light, visible light, and ultraviolet (UV) light. These waves move through space and reach the Earth, sustaining life by bringing heat and light.

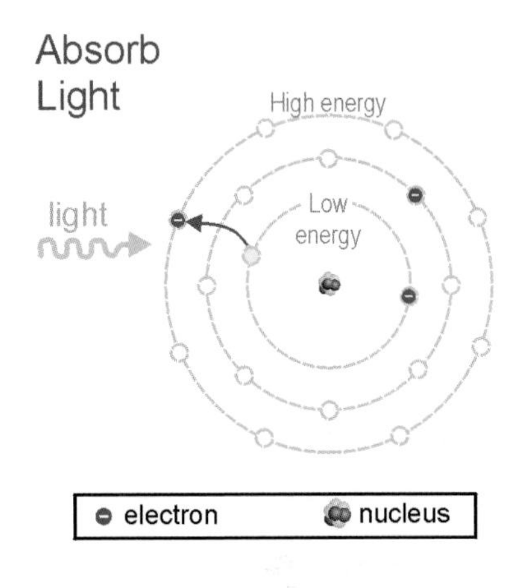

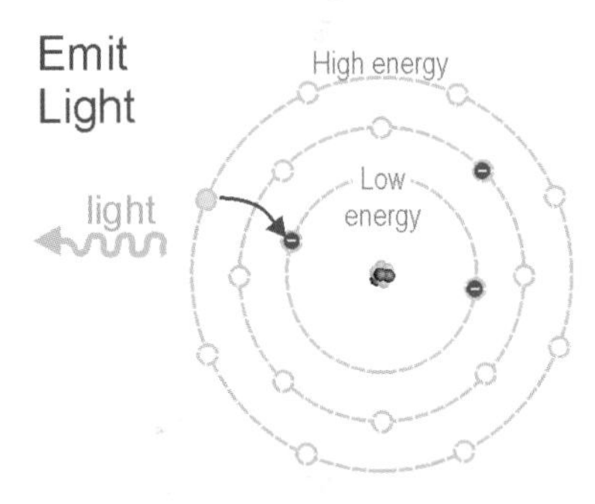

Figure 14.1: *If we want an atom to give off light, we need at least one electron that can fall back down to an empty spot at lower energy.*

1) We can have an atom absorb some light and move an electron to high energy.

2) We can let the electron fall back down and the atom emits light.

Electric lights

Incandescent light bulbs

The light we use at night or indoors is usually made with electricity. When electricity passes through materials, it heats them up. If the atoms get hot enough, some of the energy moves electrons from low energy levels to higher ones. The electrons fall back down immediately and give off energy as light. The process of making light with heat is called **incandescence**. This is how incandescent light bulbs work. The filament in the light bulb is heated white-hot by electricity. The hot filament emits light. These bulbs actually produce more heat energy than light energy. (Heat, not light, is why these bulbs are used to help chicken eggs hatch!)

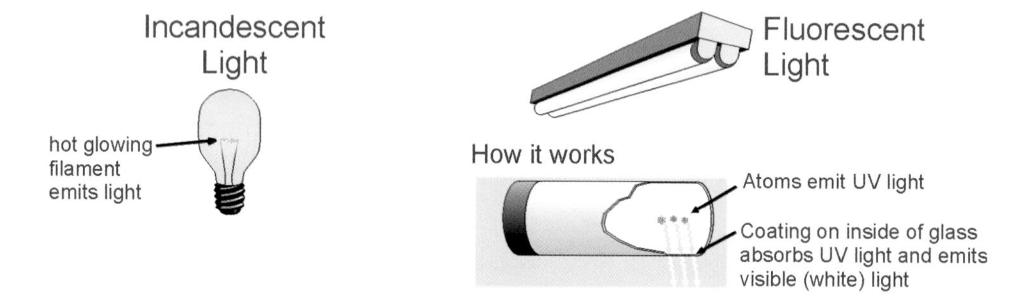
Incandescent Light
hot glowing filament emits light
Fluorescent Light
How it works
Atoms emit UV light
Coating on inside of glass absorbs UV light and emits visible (white) light

Fluorescent light bulbs

The other common kind of electric light bulb is the **fluorescent** bulb. We are seeing many more fluorescent bulbs today because they are much more efficient. Compared with a standard (incandescent) bulb, you get four times as much light from a fluorescent bulb for the same amount of electricity! The reason is that not as much energy is lost as heat. In a fluorescent bulb, high-voltage electricity energizes atoms in a gas with a diffuse spark, much like lightning. Much more of the electrical energy is used to raise electrons and less is used to heat the atoms.

Getting useful light from a fluorescent bulb is actually a two-step process. The light emitted by the electrons in the gas is mostly ultraviolet, which we cannot see. In a fluorescent bulb the ultraviolet light hits a white coating on the inside surface of the bulb. The coating absorbs the UV light and emits it again as white light. You can buy fluorescent bulbs with different coatings to make the light more blue or more yellow, like natural sunlight.

Please turn out the lights when you leave!

There are about 285,000,000 people living in the United States. If an average house has four light bulbs per person, it adds up to 1,140,000,000 light bulbs. The average bulb uses 100 watts of electricity. Multiplying it out gives an estimate of 114,000,000,000 watts, just for light bulbs.

A big electric power-plant puts out 2,000,000,000 watts. That means 67 big power plants are burning up resources just to run your light bulbs. If everyone were to switch their incandescent bulbs to fluorescent lights we would save 75 percent of this electricity. That means we could save 50 big power plants' worth of pollution and wasted resources!

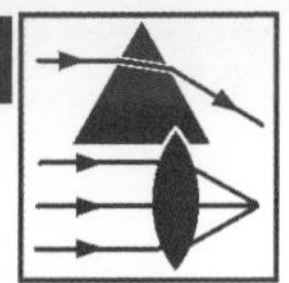

Light waves and the electromagnetic spectrum

The amount of energy given off by atomic electrons can be tiny or huge. The light we can see, visible light, is only a small part of the possible energy range. The whole range is called the electromagnetic spectrum and visible light is in the middle of it. On the low energy end of the spectrum are radio waves with wavelengths billions of times longer than those of visible light. On the high energy end are gamma rays. These have wavelengths millions of times smaller than those of visible light. We will see that visible light, with a medium energy range, is perfectly suited for sustaining life. That is why our eyes are so well adapted to this part of the spectrum.

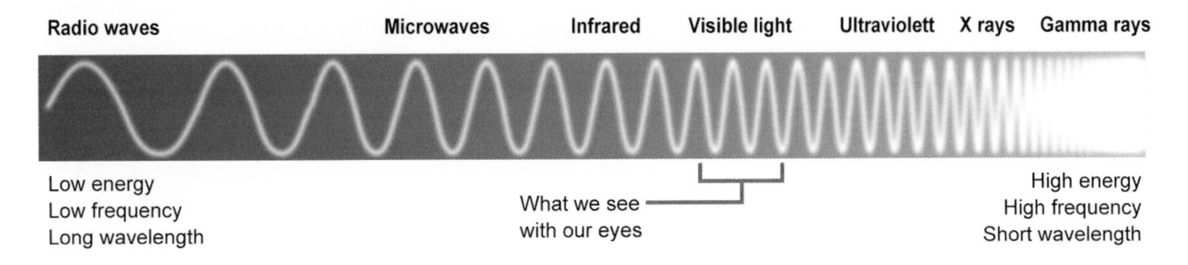

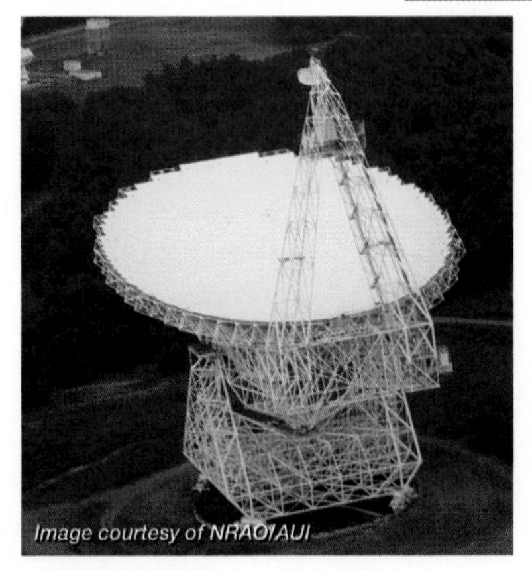

Figure 14.2: *The 140-foot-diameter radio telescope at Green Bank, West Virginia. The giant reflecting mirror is so large because the wavelength is large. Mirrors for optical telescopes can be smaller because the wavelength of visible light is smaller.*

Radio waves Radio waves are used to transmit radio and television signals. Radio waves have wavelengths that range from hundreds of meters down to less than a centimeter. Radio broadcast towers are so tall because they have to be at least 1/4 wavelength long. Your clock radio uses the length of wire that plugs into the wall socket as its antenna. If your station doesn't come in properly, you should untangle that wire. FM radio waves are shorter than AM radio waves so a radio must have two antennas; one is a coil of wire inside the unit, and the other is the expanding metal rod that you pull out when you want to use FM.

Microwaves Microwave wavelengths range from approximately 30 centimeters (about 12 inches) to about one millimeter (the thickness of a pencil lead). In a microwave oven, the waves are tuned to frequencies that can be absorbed by the water in food. The food absorbs the energy and gets warmer. Microwaves are also used for cell phone transmissions.

Figure 14.3: *Cell phones use microwaves to transmit signals.*

Infrared waves Infrared is the region of the spectrum with a wavelength of about one millimeter to approximately 700-billionths of a meter. Infrared waves include thermal radiation. For example, burning charcoal may not give off very much light, but it does emit infrared radiation which is felt as heat. Infrared images obtained by sensors in satellites and airplanes can yield important information on the health of crops and can help us see forest fires even when they are covered by clouds of smoke.

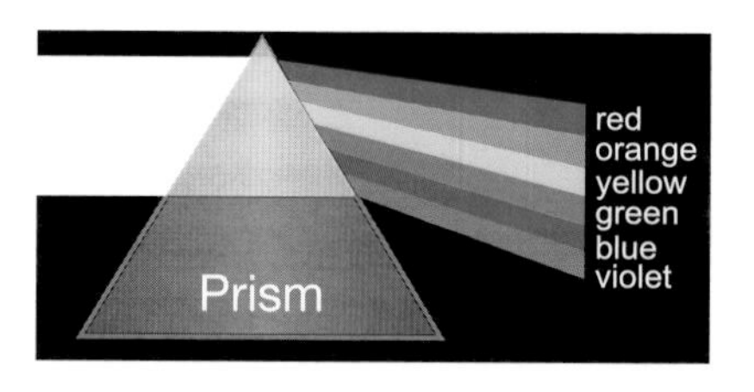

Figure 14.4: *Light carries information about color.*

Visible light The rainbow of colors we know as visible light is the part of the spectrum with wavelengths between 700-billionths and 400-billionths of a meter (700 to 400 nanometers). When people talk about "light" in ordinary conversation, they are usually talking about visible light. When scientists talk about "light" they could be referring to any part of the electromagnetic spectrum from microwaves to X rays.

Ultraviolet waves Ultraviolet radiation has a range of wavelengths from 400-billionths of a meter to about 10-billionths of a meter. Sunlight contains ultraviolet waves that can burn your skin. A small amount of ultraviolet radiation is beneficial to humans, but larger amounts cause sunburn, skin cancer, and cataracts. Most ultraviolet light is blocked by ozone in the Earth's upper atmosphere. Scientists are concerned that damage to the Earth's ozone layer could allow more ultraviolet light to reach the surface of the planet, creating problems for humans, plants, and animals.

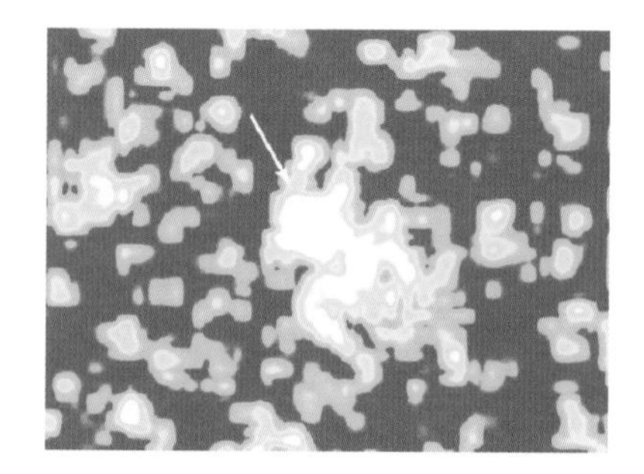

Figure 14.5: *Gamma rays are given off in nuclear reactions on Earth and also in stars. Astronomers are searching for explanations for unusually strong gamma rays that appear and disappear in space. The bright spots show regions of the sky with strong gamma ray emissions.*

X rays X rays are high-energy waves which have great penetrating power and are used extensively in medical applications. They are also used to detect faults in the metal welds that hold equipment (like airplanes) together. Their wavelength range is from about 10-billionths of a meter to about 10-trillionths of a meter.

Gamma rays Gamma rays have wavelengths of less than about 10-trillionths of a meter. Gamma rays are generated by radioactive atoms, in nuclear reactions, and are used in many medical applications. Gamma rays have even higher energy than X rays. The energy is so high that it can push electrons right out of the atom and break chemical bonds, including the chemical bonds holding the molecules in your body together. You do not want to be around strong gamma rays without a heavy shield!

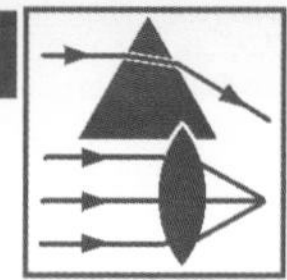

The speed of light

Seeing lightning and hearing thunder

How does light get from one place to another? This is a question that has intrigued people for many hundreds of years. Lightning and thunder actually happen at the same time. You see a bolt of lightning and then hear the thunder a few seconds later because light travels much faster than sound.

Measuring the speed of sound

Sound (the thunder) travels so slowly that you could almost time it yourself with a stopwatch. If you stood 170 meters from a large building and shouted at the building, you would hear your own echo about one second later. The sound traveled the 170 meters to the wall, bounced and traveled the 170 meters back to you in one second (Figure 14.6). The speed of sound in air is about 340 meters per second.

Measuring the speed of light

Trying this trick with light is much more difficult. Suppose you shine a light at a mirror 170 meters away (Figure 14.7). You wouldn't even begin to push down on the stopwatch before you saw the reflected light. It only takes light about a millionth of a second to get to your mirror and back. When scientists did eventually come up with a way to measure the speed of light, they used mirrors more than 20 miles apart. Even with such a long distance they needed a fancy spinning mirror to measure the speed of light.

Using this spinning mirror, scientists discovered that the speed of light is about 300 million (300,000,000) meters *per second*. If you were to walk around the earth at the widest part, you would have to walk about 12,756 km, or 12,756,000 meters. It would take you a very long time to walk that far, but since light travels so fast, a beam can circle the earth about 7.5 times in one second!

The universal speed limit

The speed of light is special because nothing in the universe travels faster than light. This idea forms part of Albert Einstein's theory of relativity. This brilliant theory explains that space and time are tied together. One of the ways that Einstein developed his theory was by asking himself about how light behaves. He wondered what light would look like if it were to stop and stand still (he imagined himself observing a beam of light while traveling as fast as light himself). Using what he knew about light, Einstein showed that it was impossible to stop light or even to observe a stationary beam of light.

Sound echo

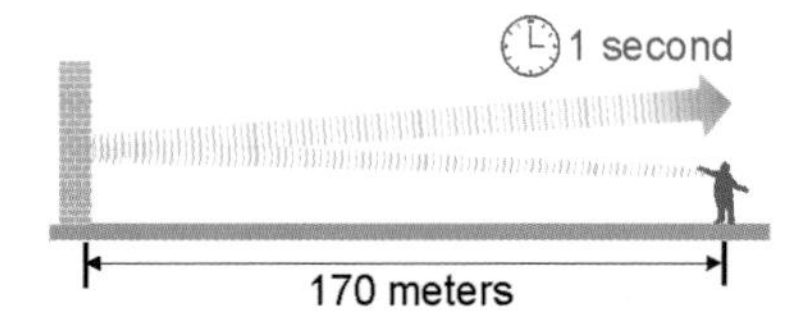

Figure 14.6: *A sound echo takes about one second from a wall that is 170 meters away.*

Light echo

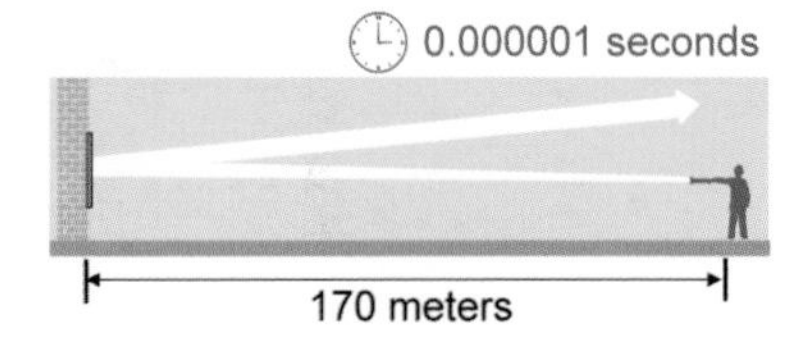

Figure 14.7: *The reflection of light from a mirror 170 meters away reaches you in 0.000001 seconds. Light travels much faster than sound.*

Polarization

Polarization

Polarization is a useful property of light waves. Light is a transverse wave of electricity and magnetism. To understand polarization, think about shaking a taut string up and down to make a vertical wave. We say a light wave with an up-down electrical pattern is "polarized" in the vertical axis. If you vibrate the string side to side, you create a horizontal wave. A light wave with a side-to-side electrical pattern is "polarized" in the horizontal axis. Polarization at an angle between vertical and horizontal can be understood as being part vertical and part horizontal, like the sides of a triangle. Each atom usually emits light at a different polarization; therefore, most of the light you see is a mixture of polarizations. We call this light "unpolarized" since no single polarization dominates the mixture.

How we use polarization of light

A **polarizer** is a partially transparent material that lets only one polarization of light through. Microscopically, polarizers behave like a grid of tiny wires. Light that is electrically aligned with the wires can pass through. A vertical polarizer only lets light with vertical polarization pass through. Horizontally polarized light is blocked. At different angles, a polarizer allows different polarizations of light to pass through (Figure 14.8).

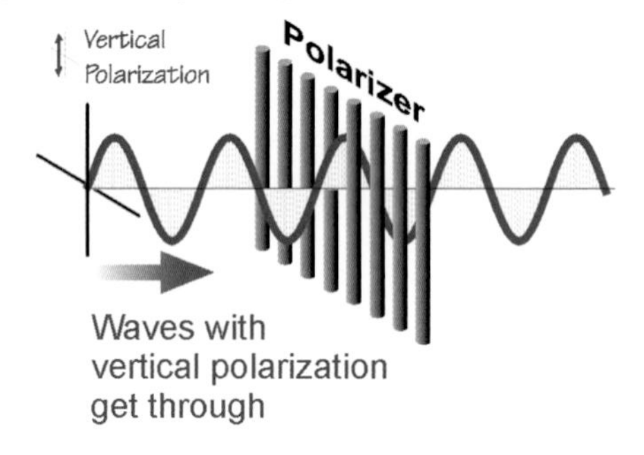

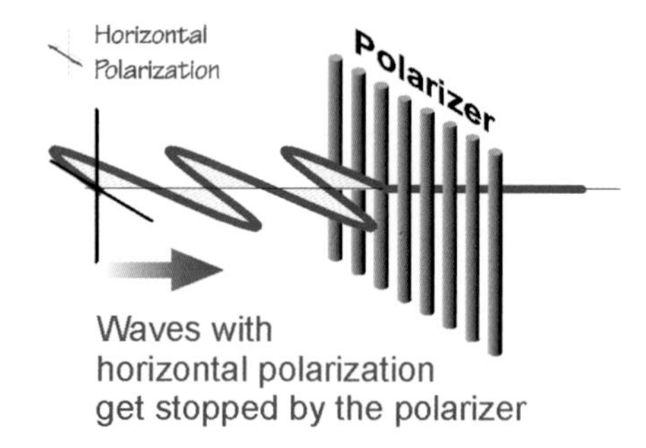

Using two polarizers

If you use two polarizers, you can control the flow of light (Figure 14.8). Light coming through the first one is polarized in a known direction. If the axis of the second polarizer is in the same direction, the light gets through. If the second polarizer is not in the same direction, some or all of the light cannot get through. You can control how much light gets through by adjusting the angle of the second polarizer relative to the first one.

A vertical polarizer polarizes the light by letting through only the light that is vertically oriented (about 50%).

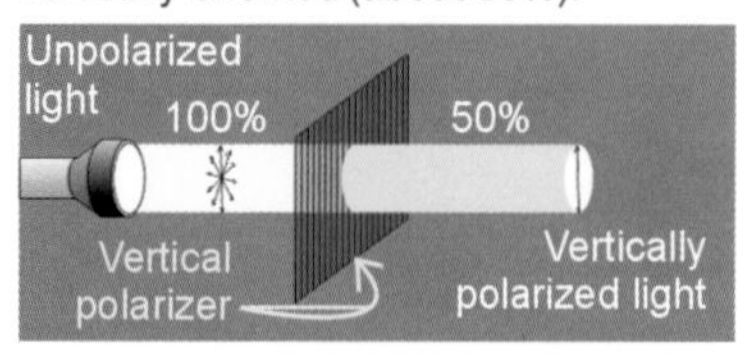

The vertically polarized light gets through a second vertical polarizer.

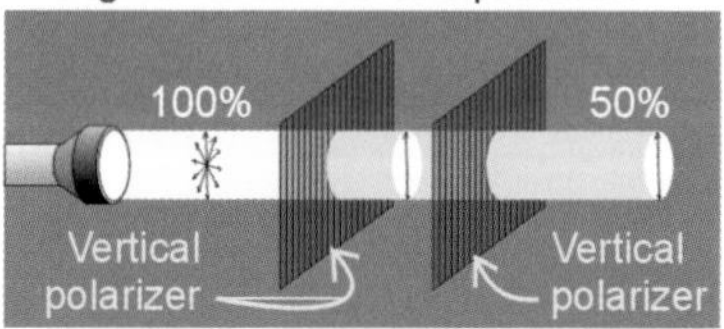

A second polarizer at 45 degrees cuts out half of the vertically polarized light.

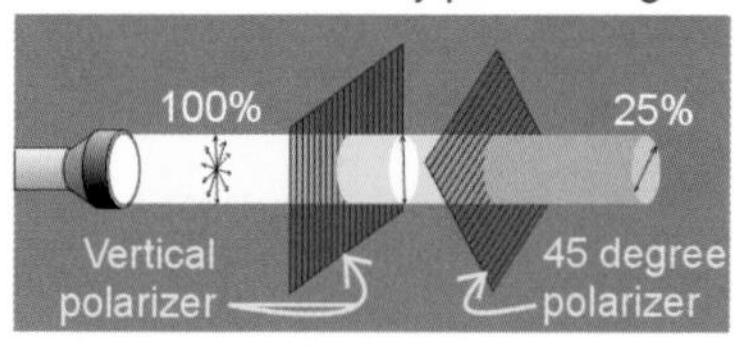

A second polarizer that is horizontal (90°) stops all vertically polarized light.

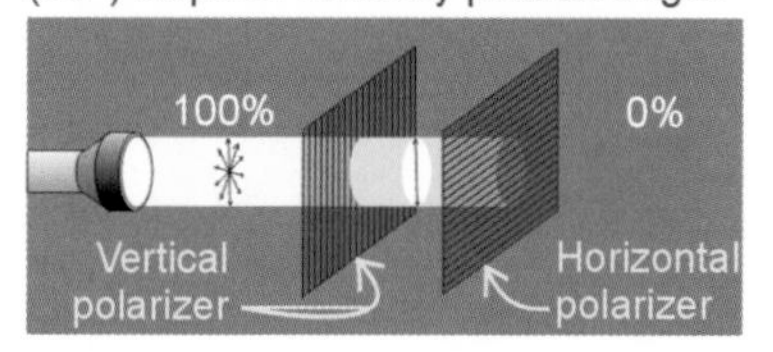

Figure 14.8: *A single polarizer polarizes light by letting through only the portion of the original light that has the right polarization. You can use two polarizers to filter some or all of the light.*

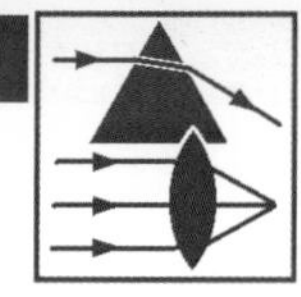

How polarizing sunglasses work

Polarizing sunglasses are used to reduce the glare of reflected light. Light that reflects at low angles from horizontal surfaces is polarized mostly horizontal. Polarizing sunglasses are made from a vertical polarizer. The glasses block light waves with horizontal polarization. Because glare is horizontally polarized, it gets blocked much more than other light which is unpolarized.

Polarizing filters for cameras

Photographers often use polarizing filters on camera lenses. The filters allow them to photograph a river bed or ocean bottom without the interfering glare of reflected light. Polarizing filters are used in landscape photography to make the sky appear a deeper blue color. Can you explain why a polarizer has this effect?

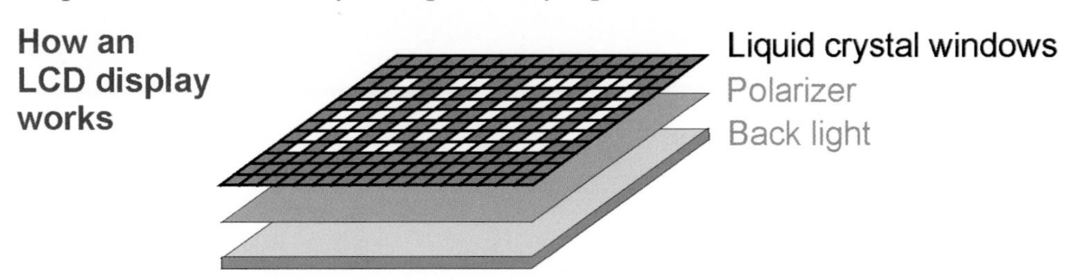

How an LCD computer screen works

The LCD (liquid crystal diode) screen on a laptop computer uses polarized light to make pictures. The light you see starts with a lamp that makes unpolarized light. A polarizer then polarizes all the light. The polarized light passes through thousands of tiny pixels of liquid crystal that act like windows. Each liquid crystal window can be electronically controlled to act like a polarizer, or not. When a pixel is NOT a polarizer, the light comes through, like an open window and you see a bright dot. The polarization direction of the liquid crystal is at right angles to the first polarization direction. When a pixel becomes a polarizer, the light is blocked and you see a dark dot. The picture is made of light and dark dots.

Because the first polarizer blocks half the light, LCD displays are not very efficient, and are the biggest drain on a computer's batteries. New technologies are being developed to make more efficient flat-panel displays.

Glare reflected from the water

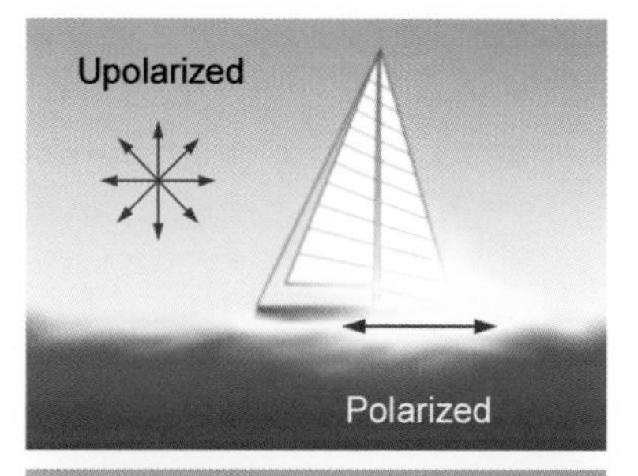

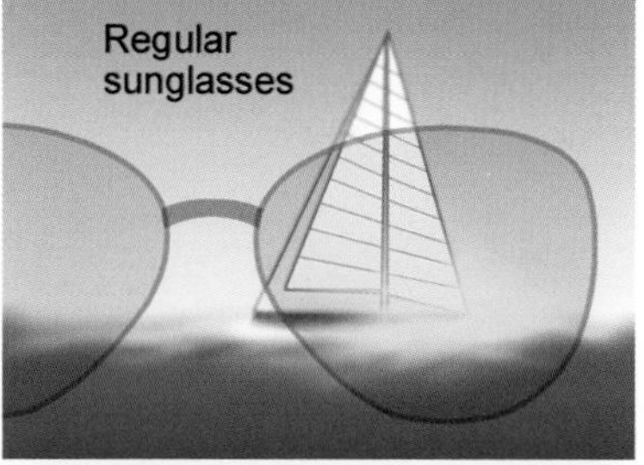

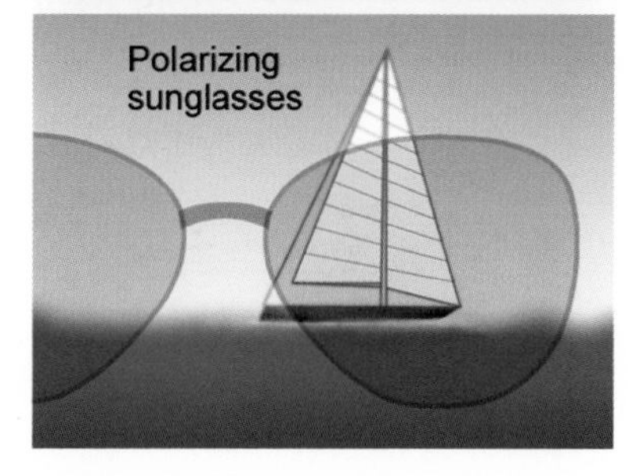

Figure 14.9: *Reflected glare is partly polarized, while the rest of the light you see is usually unpolarized. Regular sunglasses block all the light equally. Polarizing sunglasses block the polarized glare more than other light, enhancing what you see.*

14.2 Color

Color adds much richness to the world. The rainbow of colors our eyes can see ranges from deep red, through the yellows and greens, up to blue and violet. Just as we hear different frequencies of sound as different notes, we see different frequencies of light as different colors. Artists through the ages have sought recipes for paints and dyes to make vivid colors for paintings and clothing. In this section we will explore some of the ways we make and use colors.

Where does color come from?

Frequency and wavelength

To understand color we need to look at light as a wave. Like other waves, light has frequency and wavelength.

Frequency 4.6×10^{14} to 7.5×10^{14} Hz

Wavelength 4×10^{-7} to 6.5×10^{-7} meters

The frequency of light waves is incredibly high: 10^{14} is a 10 with 14 zeros after it! Red light has a frequency of 460 trillion, or 460,000,000,000,000 cycles per second. Because the frequency is so high, the wavelength is tiny. Waves of red light have a wavelength of only 0.00000065 meters (6.5×10^{-7}m). More than 200 wavelengths of red light fit in the thickness of a human hair! Because of the high frequency and small wavelength, we do not normally see the true wavelike nature of light (table 14.1). Instead, we see reflection, refraction, and color.

Table 14.1: ***Wavelength and frequency of light***

Energy	Color	Wavelength (nanometers)	Frequency (THz)
Low	Red	650	462
	Orange	600	500
	Yellow	580	517
	Green	530	566
	Blue	470	638
High	Violet	400	750

Figure 14.10: *The wavelength of visible light is much smaller than the thickness of a hair! The drawing is greatly exaggerated. In reality more than 200 wavelengths of red light would fit in the thickness of a single hair.*

Big and small numbers

The wavelength of light is so small that we use nanometers to describe it. One nanometer is one-billionth of a meter.

The frequency is so large we need units of terahertz (THz). One terahertz is equal to one trillion cycles per second.

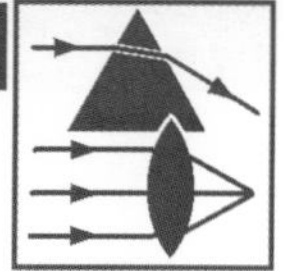

How does the human eye see color?

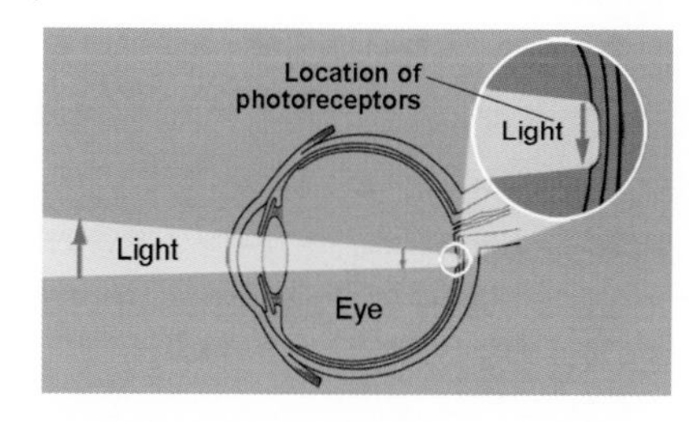

Figure 14.11: *The photoreceptors that send color signals to the brain are at the back of the eye.*

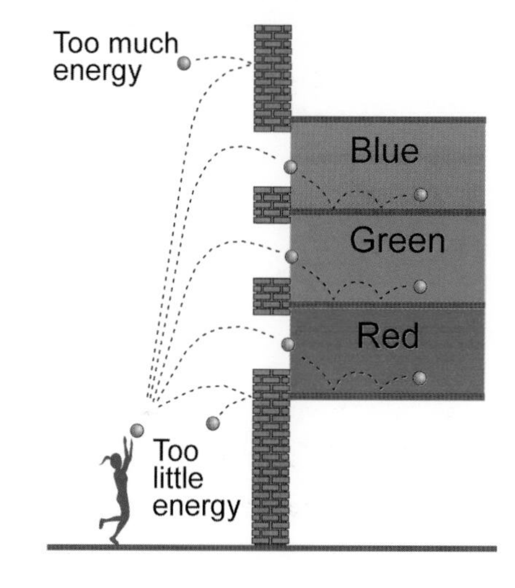

Figure 14.12: *Imagine trying to throw a basketball up into a window. If you get the energy right, it will go in. The three photoreceptors are like windows of different heights. If the light has a certain energy, it lands in the RED window. Higher energy and you get the GREEN window. Even higher energy falls into the BLUE window. If the energy is too low or too high, we don't see the light at all.*

Energy Scientists discovered something rather interesting near the turn of the 20th century. A German physicist, Max Planck, thought that color had something to do with the energy of light. Red light was low energy and violet light was high energy. Albert Einstein was awarded the 1921 Nobel Prize for proving the exact relationship between energy and color. When light hits some metals, electrons are ejected. If more light is used, more electrons come out, but the energy of each electron does not change. Einstein showed that the energy of an ejected electron depends on the frequency of the light, not the amount of light. His observation proved that the energy of light is related to its frequency, or color.

Energy and color All of the colors in the rainbow are really light of different energies. Red light has low energy compared with blue light. The closer to violet, the higher the energy. Low energy means lower frequency so waves of red light oscillate more slowly than waves of blue light. We see the different energies of light as different colors.

How we see color Scientists have discovered cells in the retina of the eye that contain **photoreceptors** (Figure 14.11). That fancy phrase means that they receive light and release a chemical. When light hits a photoreceptor cell, the cell releases a chemical signal that travels down the optic nerve to the brain. In the brain, the signal is translated into a perception of color.

Rods and cones Our eyes have two different types of photoreceptors, called **rod cells** and **cone cells**. Cone cells respond to color, and there are three kinds. One kind only gives off a signal for red light. Another kind only works with green light and the last kind only works for blue light. Each kind of cone cell is tuned to respond only to a certain energy range of light (Figure 14.12). We get millions of different colors from just three primary colors: red, green, and blue.

Rod cells see black and white The rod cells respond only to differences in brightness. Rod cells essentially see in black, white, and shades of gray. The advantage is that rod cells are much more sensitive and work at very low light levels. At night, colors seem washed out because there is not enough light for your cone cells to work. When the overall light level is very dim, you are actually seeing "black and white" images from your rod cells.

How do we see colors other than red, green, and blue?

How we perceive color

The human eye allows us to see millions of different colors. When the brain receives a signal *only* from the red cone cells, it thinks *red*. If there is a signal from the green cone cells (Figure 14.13) and neither blue nor red, the brain thinks *green*. This seems simple enough.

The additive color process

Now consider what happens if the brain gets a signal from both the red and the green cone cells *at the same time*? These energies add together and the sensation created is different from either red or green. It is what we have learned to call *yellow*. If all three cone cells are sending a signal to the brain at once, we think *white*. This is called an *additive* process because new colors are formed by the addition of more than one color signal from cone cells to the brain.

The additive primary colors

The **additive primary colors** are red, green, and blue (shown in Figure 14.15 on the next page). In reality, our brains are receiving all three color signals just about all of the time. If so, then why aren't we seeing everything in white? Two reasons: There are lots of different places in our field of vision, such as top, bottom, left, and right. The other reason is that the *strength* of the signal matters too. It's too simple to say that red and green make yellow. What if there's a lot of red and only a little green, like in Figure 14.14 (strong red signal, weak green signal)? As you might guess, you will see a color that is quite orange (maybe like the color of orange juice.) There are an unlimited number of adjustments you can make to the strengths of the signals by changing the proportions of red, green, and blue. Thus, you can get millions of different colors.

Color blindness

Some people don't have all three types of cone cells. The condition of color blindness is caused by one or more missing types of cone cells. The most common type of color blindness is the one in which the person lacks the red cone cells. This would imply that everything they see would be in shades of blue, green, cyan, and black, of course. We have to be very careful not to assume too much. Perhaps a person who has this form of color blindness can look at *cyan* (blue-green) and have the same sensation or experience that a person who has normal color vision has when they see white. But then, perhaps not. We really don't know. The *sensation* of color is quite subjective.

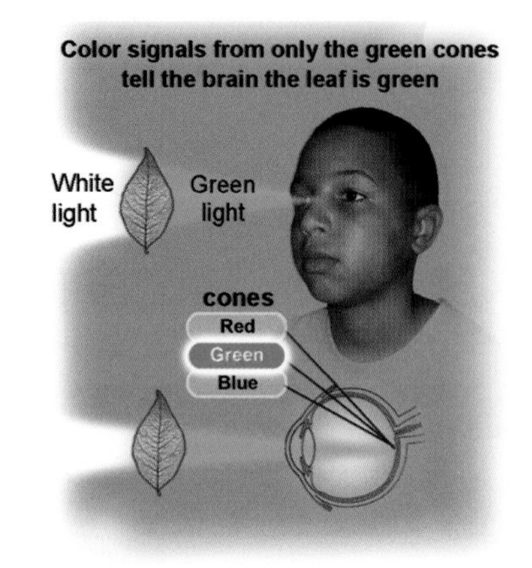

Figure 14.13: *If the brain gets a signal ONLY from the GREEN cone cells, we see "green."*

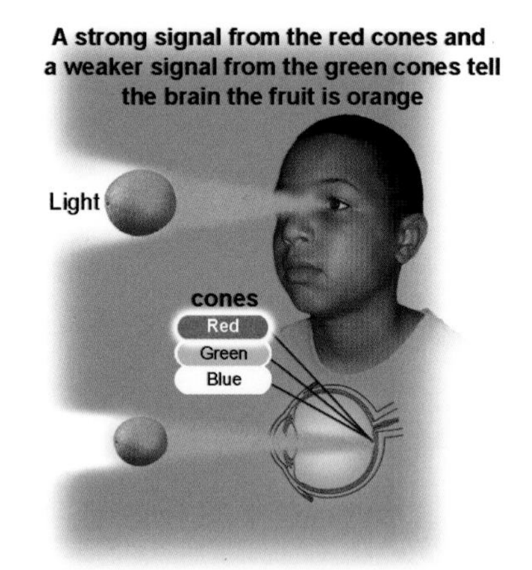

Figure 14.14: *If there is a strong RED signal and a weak GREEN signal, we see orange. All the range of colors can be made from combinations of red, green, and blue at different strengths.*

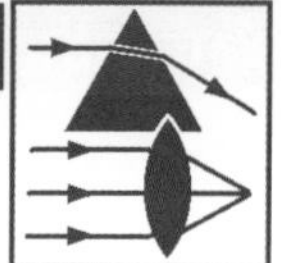

More on color

Not all animals see the same colors

To the best of our knowledge, primates, (such as chimpanzees and gorillas) are the only animals with three-color vision similar to that of humans. Birds and fish—in particular, tropical varieties—have three or more kinds of photoreceptors. Some birds and insects can also see ultraviolet light which humans cannot detect. Dogs, cats, and some squirrels are thought to have at least two color photoreceptors. Although both squid and octapi can change color better than any other animal, they cannot detect color.

We see mostly reflected light

When we see an object, the light that reaches our eyes can come from two different processes.

1 The light can be emitted directly from the object, like a light bulb or glow stick.

2 The light can come from somewhere else, like the sun, and we only see because of the light that is reflected off of them.

Most of what we see is actually from reflected light. When you look around you, you are seeing light originally from the sun (or electric lights) that has been reflected from people and objects around you. To convince yourself of this, turn off the lights in a room with no windows. You don't see anything. If you remove the source of light, there isn't any light to reflect, so you see nothing.

What gives objects their color?

When we look at a blue piece of cloth, we believe that the quality of blue is in the cloth, which is not actually true. The reason the cloth looks blue is because the pigments in the cloth have taken away (absorbed) all the frequencies of light for colors *other than blue* (Figure 14.16). Since blue vibrations are all that is left, they are the ones that are reflected to our eyes. The blue was never *in the cloth*. The blue was hidden or mixed in with the other colors in white light even before it first hit the piece of cloth. The cloth unmasked the blue by taking away all the other colors and sending only the blue to our eyes.

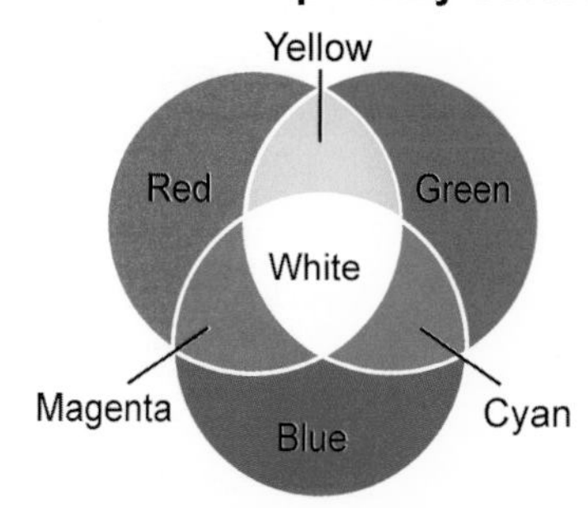

Figure 14.15: *White light is a mixture of all colors. You can make white light by mixing the additive primary colors: red, green, and blue. Thus, when the red, green, and blue cone cells are all equally stimulated, we see white light.*

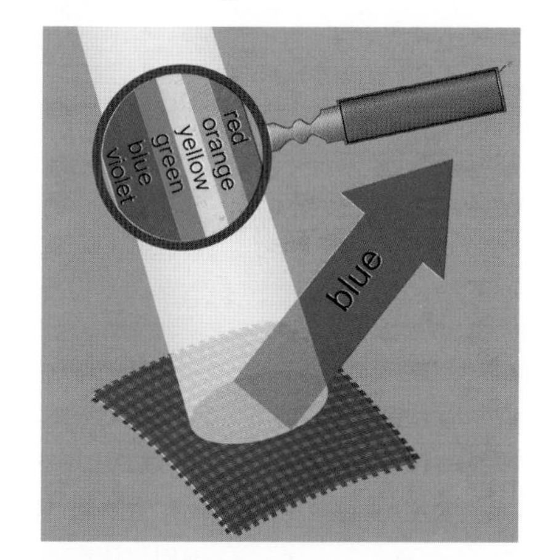

Figure 14.16: *You see blue cloth because the dyes in the fabric absorb all colors EXCEPT blue. The blue is what gets reflected to your eyes so you see the cloth as blue.*

The subtractive color process

Colored fabric gets color from a *subtractive* process. The dyes subtract out colors by *absorption* and *reflect* the colors you actually see. It works because white light is a mixture of red, orange, yellow, green, blue, indigo, and violet. But actually, you need just three primary colors—red, green, and blue—to make white light. How, then, does this work?

The subtractive primary colors

To make all colors by subtraction we also need three primary dyes. We need one that absorbs blue, and reflects red and green. This color is called yellow. We need another dye that absorbs only green, and reflects red and blue. This is a kind of pink-purple color called magenta. The last one absorbs red and reflects green and blue. The third color is called cyan, and is a greenish kind of light blue. Magenta, yellow, and cyan are the three subtractive primary colors. By using different combinations of the three we can make paper look any color because we can vary the amount of red, green, and blue reflected back to your eyes.

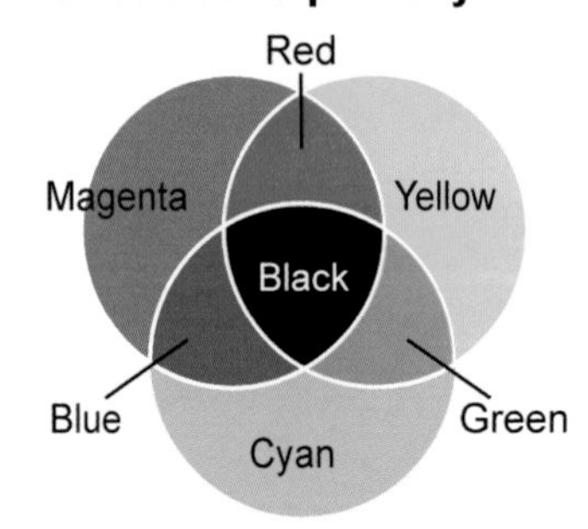

Black

You see black when no light is reflected. If you add magenta, cyan, and yellow you have a mixture that absorbs all light so it looks black. Some electronic printers actually make black by printing cyan, magenta, and yellow together. Because the dyes are not perfect, you rarely get a good black this way. Better printers have a black ink to make black separately.

How to mix green paint

Suppose you want to make green paint. White light falling on your paint has equal parts red, green, and blue. To reflect only the green you need to get rid of the red and blue light. Starting from white paint, you need to add cyan and yellow. The cyan absorbs red, leaving blue and green. The yellow absorbs the blue, leaving only the green, just as you wanted.

Color printers

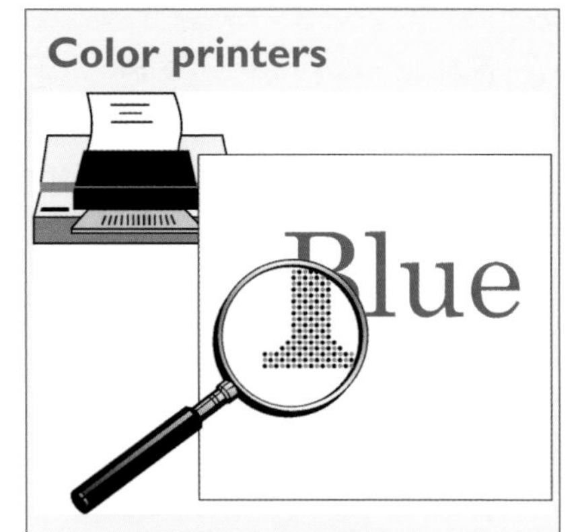

Color printers work by putting tiny dots on paper. The dots use four colors, cyan, magenta, yellow, and black. Printers refer to these as CMYK where the letter K stands for black.

The dots are so tiny that you see them as a single color. By using only the three subtractive primary colors, printers can reproduce a very wide range of reflected colors. The smaller the dots, the sharper the overall image. Newspapers print about 150 dots per inch (dpi), resulting in photographs being a little blurry. Good color printers print as many as 1,200 dpi.

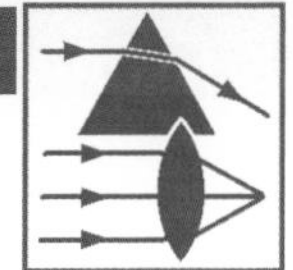

Why are plants green?

Light is necessary for photosynthesis

Plants are green because of how they use visible light. In a very unique way, plants absorb physical energy in the form of light and convert it to chemical energy in the form of sugar. The process is called photosynthesis. The graph in Figure 14.17 shows the wavelengths of visible light that plants absorb. The *x*-axis on the graph represents the wavelengths of visible light. The *y*-axis on the graph represents the amount of light absorbed by plant pigments for photosynthesis.

Chlorophyll

The green pigment, chlorophyll *a*, is the most important light-absorbing pigment. You can see on the graph that chlorophyll *a* absorbs light at each end of the spectrum. In other words, it reflects most of the green light and uses blue and red light. Plants are green because they reflect green light. In fact, plants will not grow well if they are placed under pure green light!

Why leaves change color

Notice that chlorophyll *b* and carotenoids (orange pigments) absorb light where chlorophyll *a* does not. These extra pigments help plants catch more light. Leaves change color in the fall when chlorophyll *a* breaks down and these pigments become visible. They are the cause of the beautiful bright reds and oranges that you see when leaves change color in the fall.

Plants reflect some light to keep cool

Why don't plant pigments absorb all wavelengths of visible light? The reason for this has to do with why you might want to wear light colored clothes when it is really hot outside. Like you, plants must reflect some light to avoid getting too hot!

Visible light has just the right energy for life

Visible light is just a small part of the electromagnetic spectrum. Why do living things see and use this part the most? In other words, why can't plants grow in dark places? Why can't we see ultraviolet or infrared light?

Visible light, it turns out, is just right for living things to use. The other parts of the electromagnetic radiation spectrum are not as useful. Ultraviolet light, for example, has too much energy. It can break bonds in important molecules. Infrared radiation is mostly absorbed by water vapor and carbon dioxide in the atmosphere. Therefore, this longer wavelength light is not as available as visible light for living things to use.

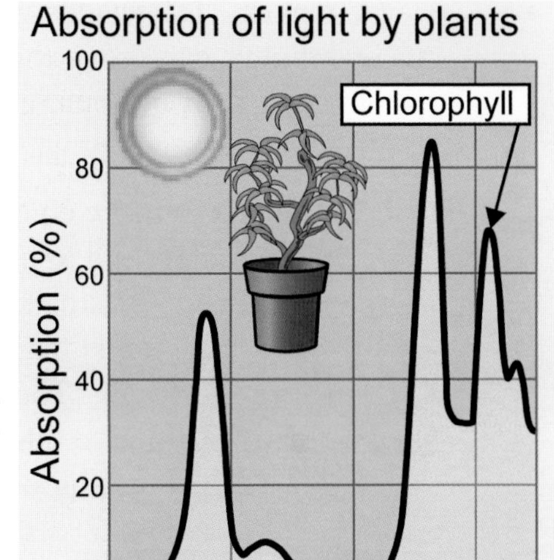

Figure 14.17: *The lines in the graph show which colors of light are absorbed by plant pigments for photosynthesis. Chlorophyll a is used in photosynthesis. Chlorophyll b and carotenoids help absorb light for photosynthesis. The graph shows that blue light and red light are absorbed (two peaks) and green light is not absorbed (flat center). Plants are green because green light is reflected by the pigments in the leaves and other green parts of the plant.*

How does a color TV work?

TV makes its own light

Televisions give off light. They do not rely on reflected light to make color. You can prove this by watching a TV in a dark room. You can see light from the TV even if there are no other sources of light in the room. Computer monitors and movie projectors are similar. All these devices make their own light.

The RGB color process

To make color with a TV you can use red, green, and blue (RGB) directly. You do not need to use the subtractive colors. Take a magnifying glass and look closely at a television screen while it is running. You will notice something interesting. The screen is made of tiny red dots, green dots, and blue dots! Each of the dots gives off light. The colored dots are separated by very thin black lines. The black lines help give intensity to the resultant colors and help make the darker colors darker. By turning on the different dots at different intensities TV sets can mix the three colors to get millions of different colors. From far away, you can't see the small dots. What you see is a nice smooth color picture (Figure 14.18).

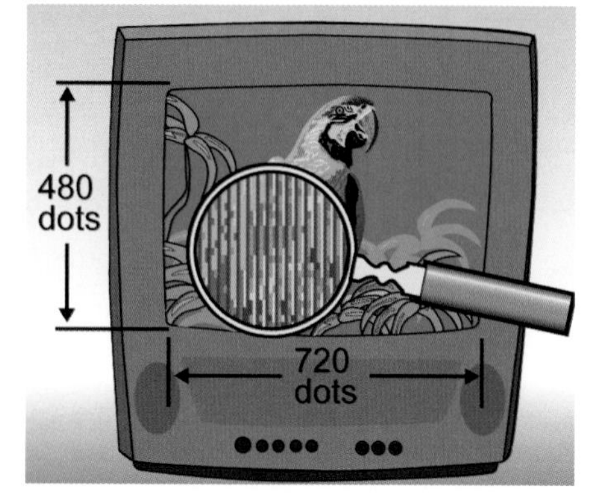

Figure 14.18: *Television makes color using tiny glowing dots of red, green, and blue. All devices that make their own light (like TV) use the RGB color model to make color.*

If you see a big screen at a sporting event it looks just like a color television. Looking closer, you see that image is actually made up of small colored light bulbs. The bulbs are red, green, and blue, just like the dots in the television screen.

Two complementary color processes

All devices that make their own light use the RGB (red, green, blue) color model. They create millions of colors by varying the strengths of each of the three primaries. Anything that relies on reflected light to make color uses the CMYK (cyan, magenta, yellow, black) color process. This includes printing inks, fabric dyes, and even the color of your skin.

How computers make color

Computers use numbers to represent the values for red, green, and blue. Every **pixel**, or dot, on your computer screen has three numbers that tell it what color to make. Each color can go from 0 to 256, with 256 being the brightest. The value RGB = (0,0,0) is pure black, no color. Setting RGB = (255, 255, 255) gives pure white, or equal red, green, blue. Using this model, computers can represent 256 x 256 x 256 or 16,777,216 different colors. More than 16 million colors can be made from just three numbers!

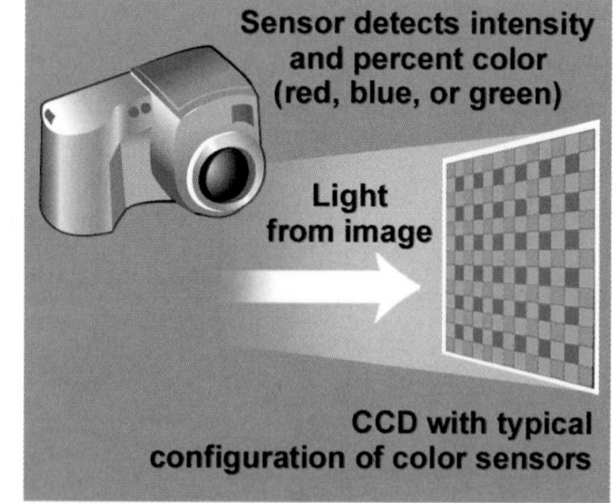

Figure 14.19: *Digital cameras have a device called a CCD that is an array of tiny light sensors, just like the human eye. A 1-megapixel camera has a million of each red, green, and blue sensors on a chip smaller than a dime.*

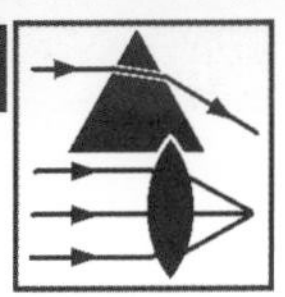

Chapter 14 Review

Vocabulary review

Match the following terms with the correct definition. There is one extra definition in the list that will not match any of the terms.

Set One

1. light	a. A property of electrons inside atoms
2. electromagnetic spectrum	b. A wave we don't necessarily see with our eyes
3. energy level	c. Heating something up so hot it gives off light
4. incandescence	d. Stimulating atoms to emit light using light of another energy
5. fluorescence	e. The range of waves that includes radio waves, light, and X rays
	f. The interaction of two or more waves with each other

Set Two

1. radio waves	a. Electromagnetic waves that we feel as heat
2. infrared	b. Electromagnetic waves that have very high energy and come from nuclear reactions
3. ultraviolet	c. Electromagnetic waves that have very low energy and wavelengths of many meters
4. X rays	d. Electromagnetic waves that can pass through skin and make images of the body
5. gamma rays	e. Electromagnetic waves with more energy than visible light and that cause sunburns
	f. Electromagnetic waves that we see with our eyes

Set Three

1. polarization	a. How we perceive different frequencies of light within the visible range
2. color	b. Making all colors as mixtures of red, green, and blue light
3. photoreceptors	c. Red, green, and blue
4. primary colors	d. A way of aligning the direction of light wave vibration by blocking some of the waves
5. RGB model	e. Nerves in the eye that are sensitive to light
	f. The wavelength of X rays

Set Four

1. magenta	a. A dye that absorbs red light
2. yellow	b. A dye that absorbs green light
3. cyan	c. Making all colors with cyan, magenta, yellow, and black pigments
4. photosynthesis	d. The process plants use to get energy from light
5. CMYK model	e. A dye that absorbs blue light
	f. A wavelength absorbed by the ozone layer

Concept review

1. What does photoluminescence mean?

2. What does incandescence mean?

3. What must happen to an electron in order for an atom to emit light?

   a. Move from a lower energy level to a higher energy level.

   b. Stay in a high energy level.

   c. Move from a high energy level to a low energy level.

   d. Stay in a low energy level.

4. Identify which of the following produces electromagnetic waves in the gamma ray part of the spectrum.

   a. A nuclear reaction

   b. A cell phone

   c. A radio transmitter

   d. A flashlight

5. Identify which of the following devices uses microwaves. You may choose more than one.

   a. an oven for heating food

   b. a cell phone

   c. a satellite transmitter

   d. a small flashlight

6. A polarizer is:

   a. A filter that separates light.

   b. An ink that absorbs green light.

   c. A sensor in the eye that detects blue light.

   d. A device for creating diffraction.

7. Infrared radiation belongs where in the electromagnetic spectrum diagram below? (Choose a, b, c, or d)

Radio waves | Microwaves | Visible light | X rays | Gamma rays

a | b | c | d

8. Which of the following would produce the sensation of white light?

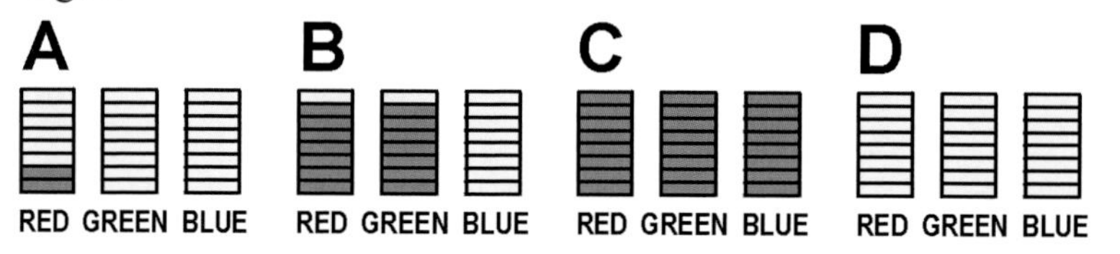

9. Which of the following would produce the sensation of yellow light?

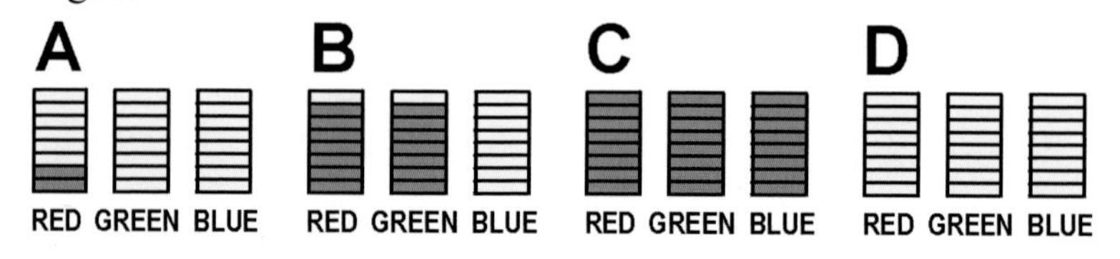

10. What are the three primary colors of light?

    a. red, green, and blue

    b. red, yellow, and blue

    c. magenta, cyan, and yellow

    d. orange, green, and violet

11. What are the three primary colors of pigments?

    a. red, green, and blue

    b. red, yellow, and blue

    c. magenta, cyan, and yellow

    d. orange, green, and violet

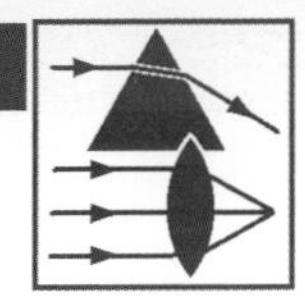

Problems

1. Arrange the following in order of speed from fastest to slowest:

   a. Sound waves b. Light waves c. Water waves

2. What color is obtained when the three primary colors of light are combined in equal strengths?

3. Which photochemical receptors in our eyes are stimulated when we see the color yellow?

4. If you wanted to make green paint, you would use which combination of dyes?

   a. cyan and magenta
   b. cyan and yellow
   c. magenta and yellow
   d. magenta only

5. What does a piece of blue cloth do to the colors in white light that falls upon it?

   a. It absorbs blue light and reflects all the rest of the colors to our eyes.
   b. It absorbs all the colors except blue and reflects only blue light to our eyes.
   c. It absorbs all of the colors in the white light.
   d. It absorbs none of the colors in the white light.

6. What happens to the light energy that is shined upon a black object?

7. Name the four colors used by color computer printers.

8. What are the primary colors used to construct the image on a color TV monitor?

9. When a store clerk adds more colorants (pigments) to a can of white paint, what will be the result?

   a. More colors are taken away from the light we use to view the paint.
   b. More colors are added to the light we use to view the paint.
   c. Fewer colors are taken away from the light we use to view the paint.
   d. No change occurs in the light we use to view the paint.

10. Describe wavelength and frequency of green light and why using only green light would not allow plants to grow.

11. Arrange the following in order from LOWEST energy to HIGHEST energy: Gamma rays, visible light, X rays, microwaves, radio waves, infrared light, ultraviolet light.

12. Calculate how much money you would save in one year by changing from an incandescent bulb to a fluorescent bulb. Assume electricity costs 10 cents per kilowatt hour and that the bulb is on all the time for the whole year. The two bulbs in the picture produce the same amount of light.

Incandescent Bulb — 100 watts

Compact Fluorescent Bulb — 23 watts

Applying your knowledge

1. Why does fire give off light?
2. Why would putting out a fire with water stop it from giving off light?
3. How many different kinds of photochemical receptors are found in the eyes of most people? What colors of light do these photochemical receptors respond to? To what location does a photochemical receptor send its signal?
4. What is different about the photochemical receptors in the eyes of people with color blindness?
5. What may be different about the photochemical receptors in the eyes of other animals?
6. Research color blindness using your library or the Internet. How many different kinds of color blindness are there? Find out what kinds of receptors are missing in the eyes of people with the various kinds of color blindness. Find out which tasks are more difficult for them and which ones are actually easier.
7. Design an improvement to a common product to make it easier for color blind people to use. Suggest ways that people with normal color vision can avoid making life unnecessarily difficult for people with color blindness.
8. How do we know anything about the color vision of animals? Look up the studies done on honeybees and report on the experimental methods. Design your own study to find out if dogs or cats can tell one color from another.
9. What makes the colors on a computer screen different from the colors in paint? How can you get red, green, and blue from both?
10. Computer graphic artists use two different color models to represent color. The RGB model has three numbers that represent the strengths of red, green, and blue. The CMYK model uses four numbers that represent the strength of cyan, magenta, yellow, and black.
    a. What are the maximum and minimum values for the numbers that determine color on a computer?
    b. Find a table of colors and identify the numbers you need to make orange in both RGB and CMYK systems.
       RBG: R = _____ B = _____ G = _____
       CMYK: C = _____ M = _____ Y = _____ K = _____
    c. If a picture contains 1,000 pixels, or dots, how much computer memory is needed to store the picture in RGB and CMYK models? Assume that each number takes 8 bits of memory to store.
11. Why is ice sometimes clear and sometimes cloudy white? Experiment with freezing ice in your home freezer. Find out how you can control the transparency of ice.

UNIT 5 Light and Optics

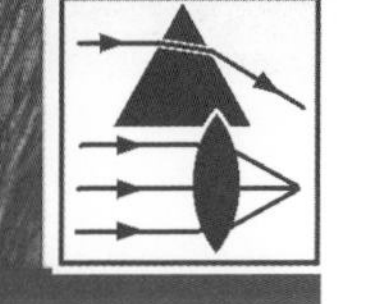

Chapter 15 Optics

Introduction to Chapter 15

Cameras, telescopes, and our eyes are all optic devices. Rays of light are everywhere and optic devices bend and bounce these rays to produce all the colors and images that you can see. This chapter will introduce you to the science of optics.

Investigations for Chapter 15

15.1	Seeing an Image	*What does magnification really mean and how do you plot a reflected image?*

We see images based on what happens to light. In this Investigation you will discover how light can be bent by a lens to magnify an image, or bounced by a mirror to produce a reflected image. Plotting the rays of light from an object will allow you to understand what a mirror or lens is doing.

15.2	The Human Eye	*How does a lens form an image?*

A lens can bend light to create amazing images. The actual bending of the light in our eye is caused by a clear lens that can change shape slightly. The shape-changing lens in the eye allows us to see close up or far away. In this Investigation, you will work with lenses to focus light and create images

15.3	Optical Technology	*How are optics used in everyday life?*

Fiber optics are becoming one of the most important and versatile aspects of optical technology. Fiber optics work on a simple principle. If light is traveling in a material like glass or water, and enters into air, it can become trapped in the material. In this Investigation you will explore total internal reflection, the process that makes fiber optics possible.

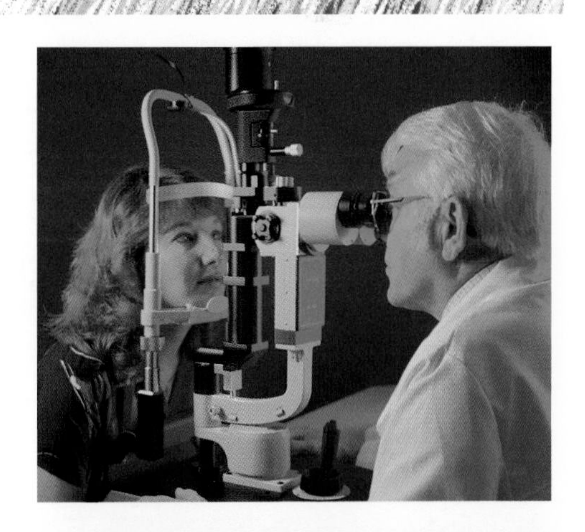

Learning Goals

By the end of the lesson, you will be able to:

- ✔ Describe the function of the human eye.
- ✔ Describe the difference between objects and images.
- ✔ Describe and demonstrate the formation of an image.
- ✔ Draw a ray diagram for a lens.
- ✔ Calculate the magnification of a lens.
- ✔ Describe the index of refraction and explain how it is applied in the making of lenses.
- ✔ Identify the characteristics of reflection.
- ✔ Draw a reflected ray.
- ✔ Predict how light will bend when its speed changes.
- ✔ Understand internal reflection.
- ✔ Identify uses of fiber optics.

Vocabulary

converging	focal length	index of refraction	real image
converging lens	focal point	lens	reflected ray
diverging	focus	normal	refraction
diverging lens	image	optics	total internal reflection
critical angle	incident ray	ray diagrams	virtual image

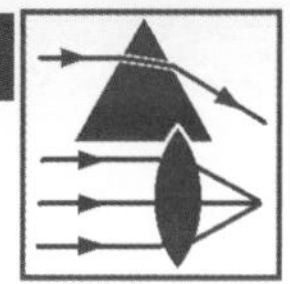

15.1 Seeing an Image

Try this quick experiment: Take a magnifying lens and look through it at your thumb. You can adjust the distance until the thumb is big. You are actually seeing a big thumb. You are bending the light that is coming from your thumb, so that you *see* a huge thumb. Imagine how big your hand would be if your thumb really was that big. It would be a giant hand!

Imagine that a few cells of your thumb were under a microscope. You can see the individual cells of your skin. You can see parts of the cell and they look big. Now imagine how big your thumb would be if all the cells were actually that big. Wow! You would have the hand of super giant! Of course, your hand is actually the same size it always was though what you see is a super giant hand. One branch of optics is the study of how to manipulate light to create images that are different from the original object.

Figure 15.1: *A magnifying glass makes your thumb look as big as if you were a giant!*

What is optics?

Definition of optics

The study of how light behaves is called **optics**. Optics deals with the collection and use of light to create **images**. The category of optics covers devices that direct light like lenses, mirrors, cameras, telescopes, and microscopes. It includes events of light like rainbows, sunsets, and eclipses. Ultimately, all of the light from these sources gets to your eye. We will see that the eye itself is an optical instrument.

Lenses, mirrors, and prisms

Your eye contains a lens. A lens is one kind of optical device that is used to bend light. By bending the light so that it comes together (**converging**), you can magnify an image and by bending the light so that it spreads apart (**diverging**), you can get a smaller image.

A mirror is a familiar optic device; you probably used one this morning. Mirrors reflect light and allow us to see ourselves. Flat mirrors show a true-size image. Curved mirrors cause light to come together or spread apart. A fun house at the circus uses curved mirrors to make you look thin, wide, or upside down. Curved mirrors distort images. The curved side-view mirror on a car, for example, makes the cars behind you look farther away than they really are.

A prism is another optic device that can cause light to change directions. Traditionally, a prism is used to separate the colors of light and to demonstrate how light bends (**refracts**) as it travels through different media (Figure 15.2).

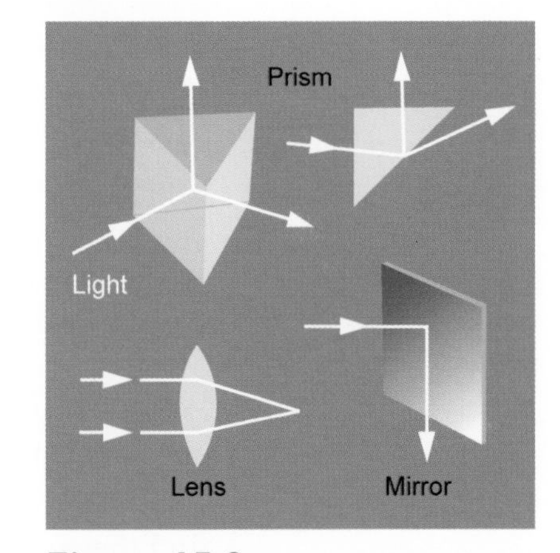

Figure 15.2: *Lenses, mirrors, and prisms are part of the study of optics.*

Light rays

What is a light ray?

It is convenient to think about light in terms of rays. A ray of light can be considered an imaginary arrow that follows a single beam of light. This simplification allows us to analyze where the light travels. We only need to follow the rays. Very often we will need to follow several rays of light to determine what will happen.

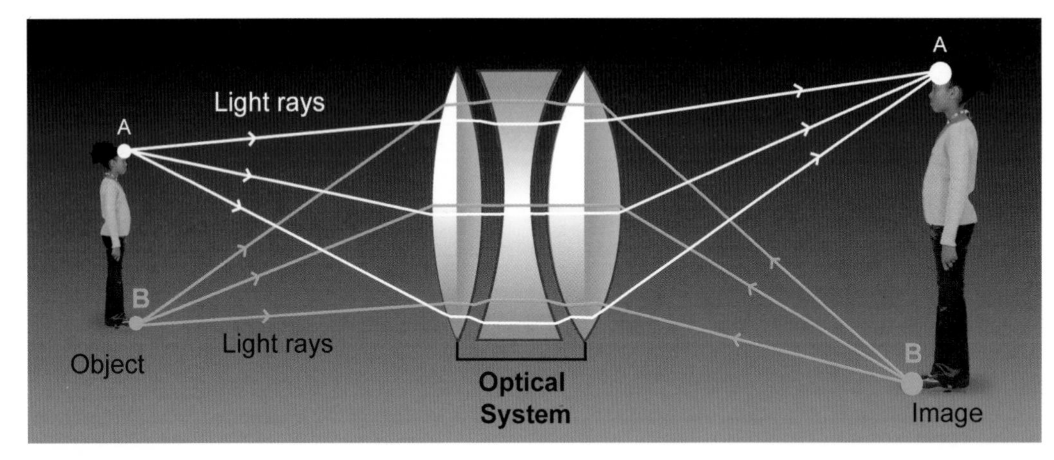

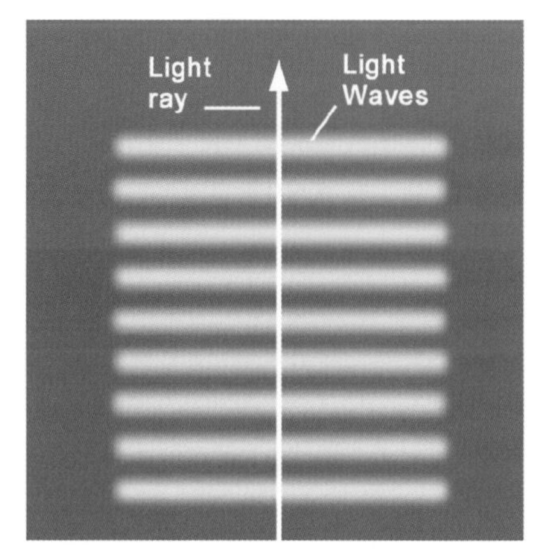

Figure 15.3: *The relationship between rays and wave fronts. The ray is the path of the wave.*

Drawing light rays in diagrams

Light waves are like the waves you see in the ocean as they move continually toward the beach. Rays are represented by lines that are **perpendicular** to the wave fronts. The lines have arrows that show you which way the light is moving. When you see a ray drawn on a diagram, you should know that technically, the ray isn't really one ray of light but a series of light waves. Figure 15.3 uses an arrow to represent which way the light waves are moving.

Rays come from objects

When we see an object, every point on the object reflects many rays of light. Let's consider an example to demonstrate what this means. Look at the clock in your classroom, and focus on the number seven. If you walk around the room, you will find that you can still see the number seven. This demonstrates how light from a single point (in this case, the number seven) can be seen from different angles. This is true because light is reflected to all angles in the room. Figure 15.4 is an illustration of how light rays are reflected off a vase.

Figure 15.4: *Every point on an object is the source of many light rays that come at all angles to the viewer.*

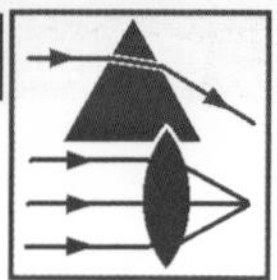

Images

Rays come together in an image

Suppose you could collect all the rays from one point on an object, bringing them all together again. You would have created an image. An image is a place where many rays from the same point on an object meet together again in a point. A camera works by collecting the rays from an object and bending them so they form an image on the film.

Objects and images

It is helpful to think about optics in terms of objects and images. Objects are any real physical things that give off or reflect light rays. Images are "pictures" of objects that are formed in places where light rays from the object meet. The focus is the place where all the light rays from the object meet to form the image.

Light travels in straight lines

Normally, light travels in straight lines. Most of the time, when you see an object, it is because the light traveled in a straight line from the object to your eye. As long as nothing is in the way, you can be sure the object is precisely where you perceived it to be. This is because the light rays did not bend.

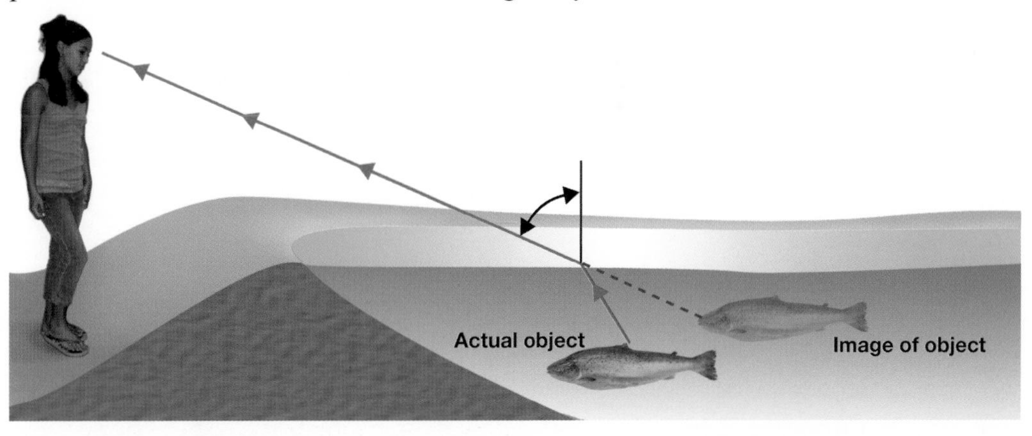

Light rays can be bent

To make images, we often need to bend light rays. Light is sometimes bent *between* an object and your eye. This bending will usually make the image appear different from the object in size or location. A good example is seeing a fish under water. The light waves from the fish bend as they travel from the water to the air. Due to the bending rays, the *image* of the fish appears in a different place from where the fish is actually swimming.

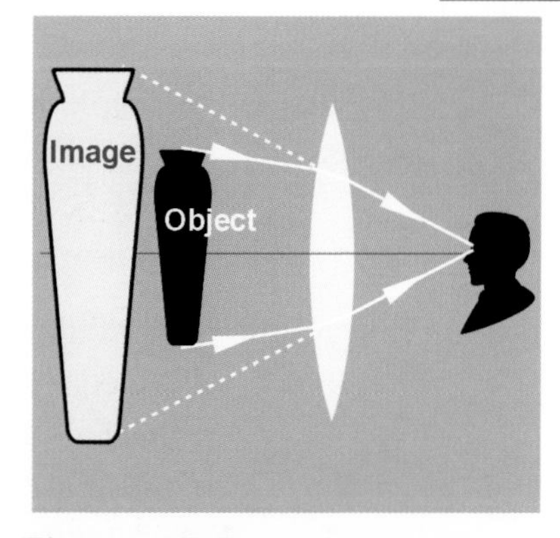

Figure 15.5: *The difference between objects and images.*
The light rays from the object are bent when they go through the lens. Our brain does not know the rays were bent. We "see" the rays as having traveled in straight lines.
The image appears larger because the lens has bent the light rays so they appear to come from a larger object. This is the principle of the magnifying glass.

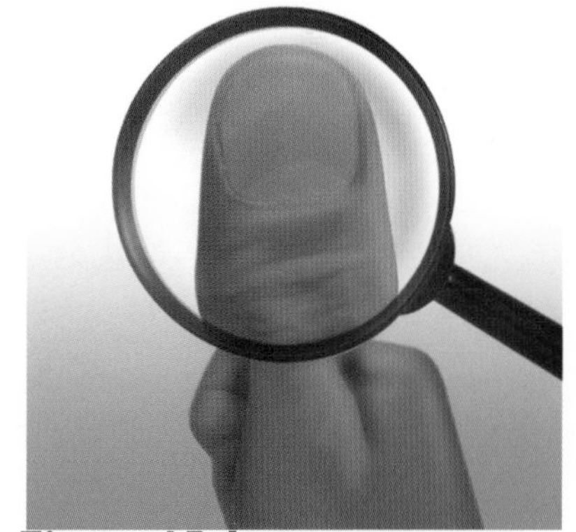

Figure 15.6: *A magnifying glass makes a virtual image that appears larger than the object.*

Optical systems

What is an optical system? An optical system collects light and uses refraction and reflection to form an image. When we use an optical system, we do not see the actual object. What we really see is an image. When light is bent through an optical system before it gets to our eyes, the image we see might not represent the actual object as it truly is.

Refraction Refraction is the bending of light that occurs when light crosses a boundary between two different substances. Usually one is air and the other is a clear material such as glass, plastic, or even water. A lens is a special shape of clear solid material that uses refraction to cause light to come together or spread apart. A magnifying glass on a sunny day can be used to illustrate how one type of lens works (Figure 15.7).

Reflection A mirror reflects rays of light so that they change their path. Reflection happens when objects or waves can "bounce" off a surface. Whenever a wave strikes a surface, part of the energy is reflected. By changing the shape of a mirror you can also cause light to come to a focus, just like with a lens (Figure 15.8).

The telescope A telescope is a collection of lenses that can magnify an image. When you look through a telescope, the rays of light are bent and appear as if they were coming from an image much closer than the actual object. A telescope is an optical system that makes objects appear larger than they are, and sometimes upside down!

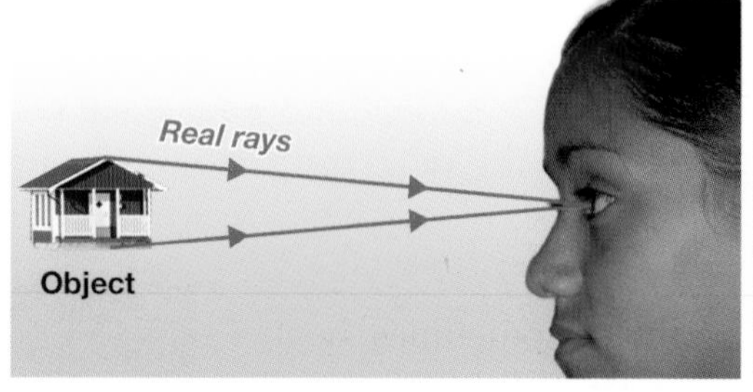

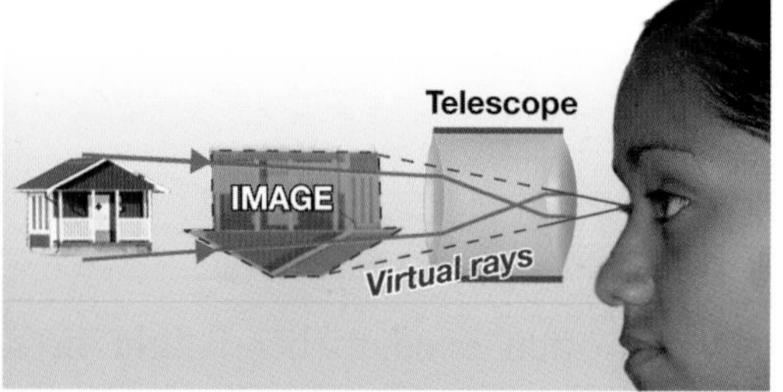

Why we see magnified images The illusion created by a telescope happens because we perceive that light travels in a straight line. If the device bends light so that it appears to have come straight from a large object, then we see a magnified image.

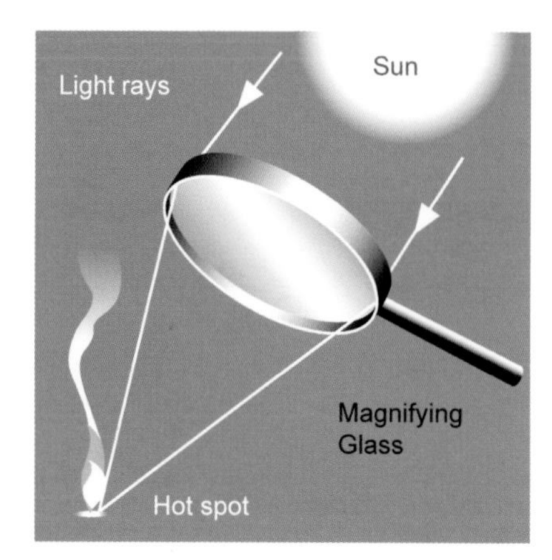

Figure 15.7: *A magnifying glass can bend many rays to come together at a focus. On a sunny day the focus can be quite hot!*

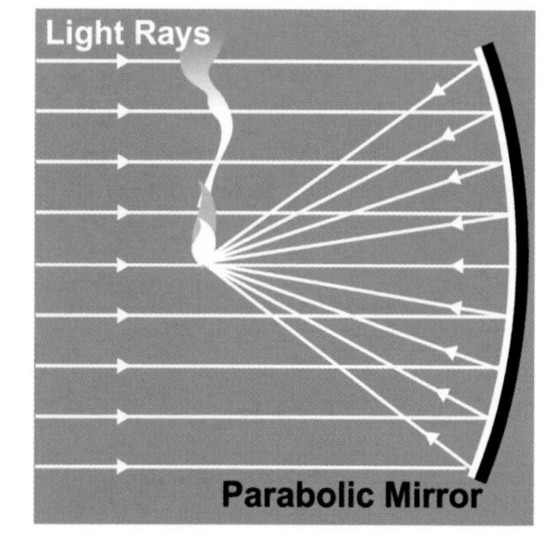

Figure 15.8: *Mirrors also change the direction of light rays. A curved mirror can make light rays from the sun change direction and meet at a focus, just like a lens. This is how solar ovens work.*

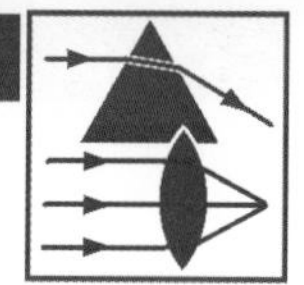

The functions of an optical system

Most optical devices have two important functions.

1. They collect light rays.
2. They bend the collected light rays to form an image.

Both functions are important. Those of you who like astronomy might be interested to know that most of the things in the night sky don't produce enough light for our eyes to see. Not only does a telescope make things appear larger, it also collects more light so we can see fainter objects more clearly.

The ray diagram

To figure out how an optical system works we often draw ray diagrams. Ray diagrams trace how several light rays behave as they go through the system. The rays come straight from an object and are bent or bounced as they encounter a lens or mirror. By tracing the rays through the system we are usually looking to find what kind of image will be produced.

Some typical questions that we use ray diagrams to answer are:

1. Where is the focus (or is there a focus)?
2. Will the image be magnified or reduced in size?
3. Will the image be upside down or right side up?
4. Will the image be inverted left to right?

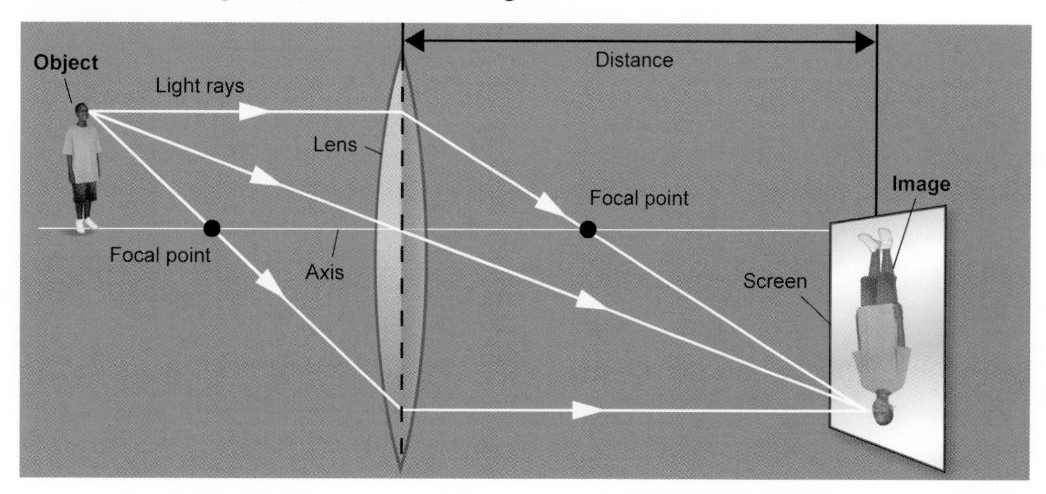

A plastic bag lens

Water is capable of bending light. Take a clear plastic bag and fill it with water. Now look through it. What you see is called an image. The shape of the optic device determines the shape of the image. Squeeze the bag in different places and see how the image changes.

Reflection and mirrors

Mirrors create a virtual image

When you look in a mirror, you see an image. The image appears to be behind the mirror and is reversed from left to right. For example, if you hold a sign in front of a mirror, the letters appear backward. Why does this occur?

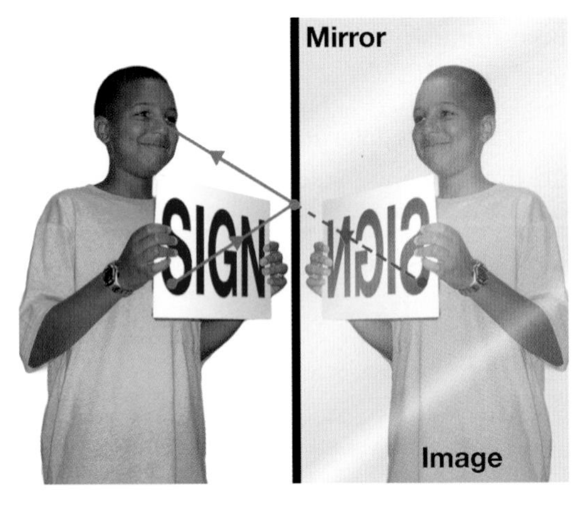

The light rays that travel from the "S" in the sign hit the mirror at an angle and are reflected back to your eye at an equal but opposite angle.

Your brain assumes that this reflected ray traveled to your eye in a straight line from an "object" behind the mirror. As a result, the image of the "S" appears to have come from the opposite direction as the actual letter on the sign.

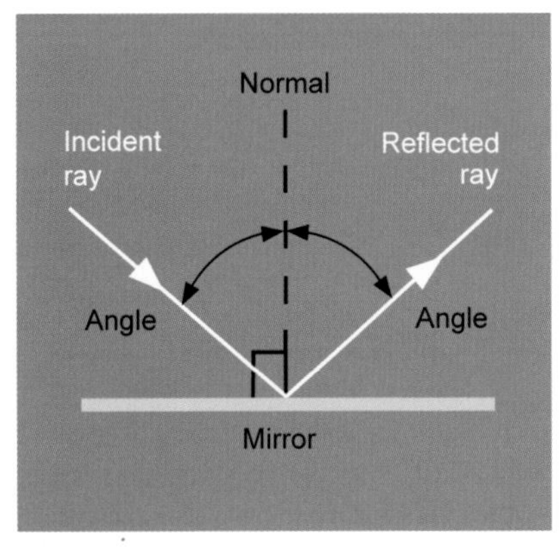

Figure 15.9: *The normal is a line perpendicular to the mirror. The incident ray is the ray that comes in to the mirror. The reflected ray is the ray that bounces off the mirror.*

Incident and reflected rays

To investigate mirrors further, we will talk about incident and reflected rays. The **incident ray** is the ray that comes from the object and hits the mirror. The **reflected ray** is the ray that bounces off the mirror (Figure 15.9). There is a rule that tells us how to predict the direction of the reflected ray once we know the incident ray's direction.

The law of reflection

The rule that determines the reflected ray is called the *law of reflection*. This law is very simple: Light rays bounce off a mirror at the same angle at which they arrive. The only tricky part is defining the angles. To keep things clear we always define angles relative to the **normal**. In optics, the normal is a line perpendicular to the mirror (Figure 15.10).

If a light ray comes in at an angle of 30 degrees from the normal, it bounces off at the same angle, 30 degrees. If a ray comes in at zero degrees (straight on) it also bounces back at zero degrees. In other words, the light comes in and reflects out on the same normal.

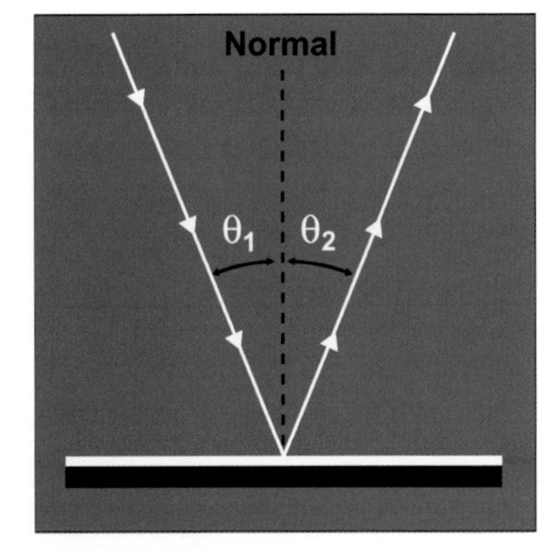

Figure 15.10: *The law of reflection states that the angle of incidence (θ_1) is equal to the angle of reflection (θ_2). How could you throw a ball against a wall to demonstrate that $\theta_1 = \theta_2$?*

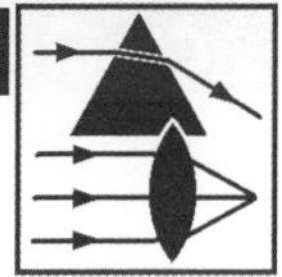

Refraction and lenses

Refraction When light crosses the boundary between two different (transparent) materials the rays may bend. We call the bending **refraction**. Refraction happens because the wave fronts move more slowly in materials other than air (Figure 15.11). As we already learned, if we change the shape of wave fronts we can turn a wave.

What is a lens? A **lens** is a shape of transparent material, like glass, that is used to bend the light rays. Figure 15.12 shows how the curved surface of a lens works. We choose the shape of the lens depending on how strongly we want to bend the light. Lenses come in many different shapes and strengths.

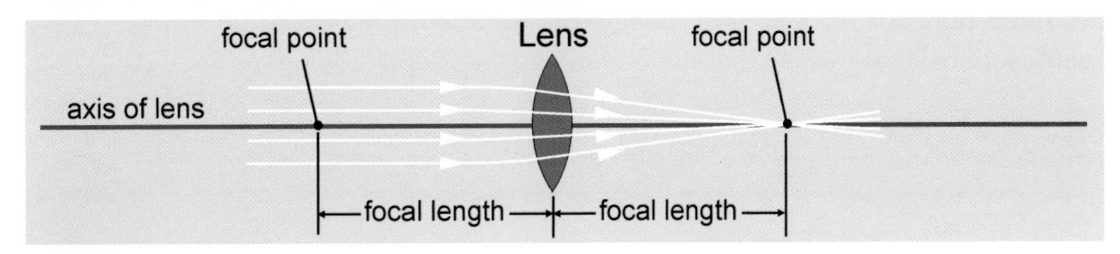

Focal point and focal length Almost all lenses are shaped to have a very useful property. Light rays that enter a lens **parallel** to its axis will bend to meet at a point called the **focal point**. The distance from the center of the lens to the focal point is called the **focal length**. The focal length of a lens determines how powerful the lens is and how it can be used to focus light.

Converging and diverging lenses There are two kinds of lenses we will examine. **Converging lenses** bend the parallel light rays passing through them inward toward the focal point. **Diverging lenses** bend the parallel light rays passing through them outward away from the focal point. A parallel beam coming into a diverging lens is bent away from the focal point.

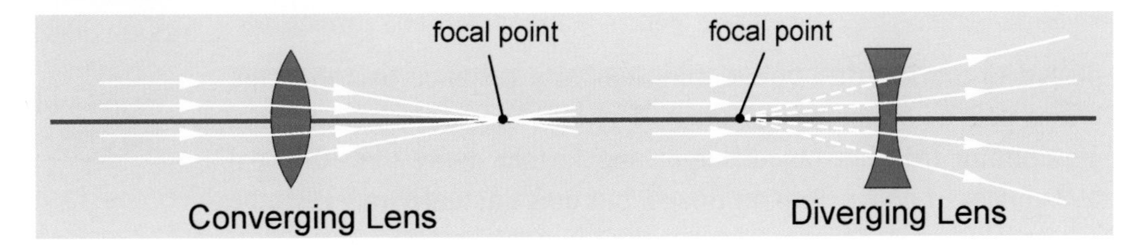

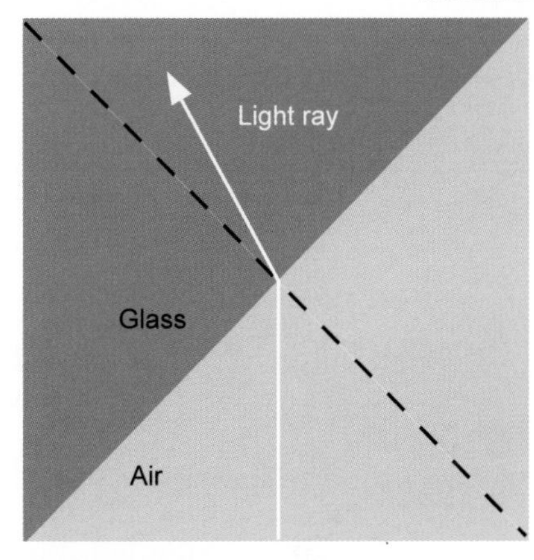

Figure 15.11: *A ray of light is refracted (bent) when it crosses from one material into another.*

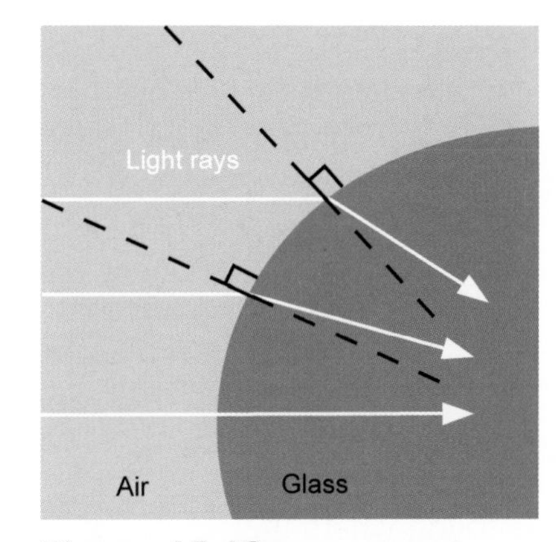

Figure 15.12: *For a curved surface, the amount the ray bends depends on where it hits the surface and the type of material. Rays farther out are bent the most. If the surface is curved just right, all the rays that hit the lens are bent so they meet at the focus.*

Forming images with lenses

Why are lenses useful?

Lenses are used in eyeglasses, microscopes, telescopes, and other devices to form images. An image, as you have learned, forms when light rays emitted or reflected from one point on an object meet at a point again. Ray diagrams can be used to show where the image will form, how large the image will appear, and whether it is upside down or right side up.

What kinds of images are formed?

If an object is placed to the left of a converging lens at a distance greater than the focal length, an inverted image is formed on the right-hand side of the lens. We call this image a **real image**. Real images can be projected on a smooth surface, like photographic slides onto a wall. Since real images are inverted, slides must be loaded into the carousel upside down, so that the picture appears right side up!

Example: A lens has a focal length of 10 centimeters. An object is placed 15 centimeters to the left of the lens. Trace the rays and predict where the image will be. Is the image bigger, smaller, or inverted?

Step 1: Draw the axis and focal points.

Step 2: Draw three rays from the object's tip.

Step 3: The image of the object's tip is found where the three rays meet.

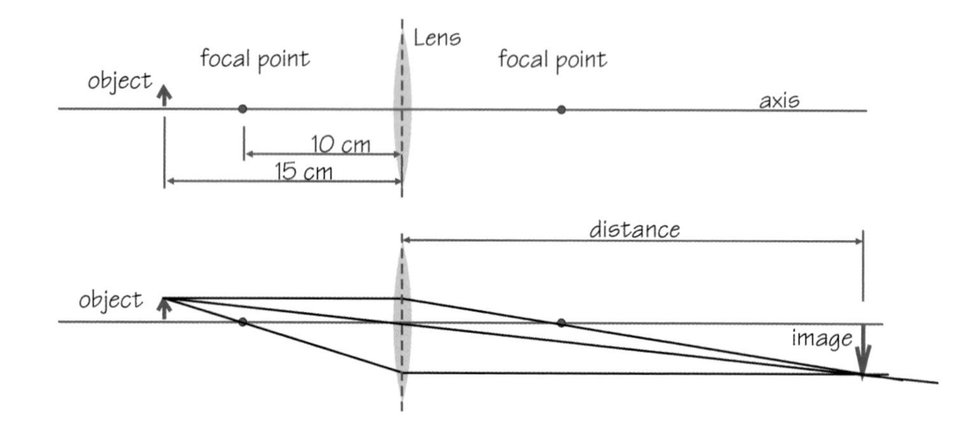

The image is formed 30 cm to the right of the lens. It is magnified and inverted.

If an object is placed to the left of a converging lens at a distance less than the focal length, the lens acts as a magnifying glass. The lens bends the rays so that they appear to be coming from an object larger and farther away than the real object. These rays appear to come from an image, but don't actually meet, so the images are called **virtual images**. Mirrors create virtual images.

Galileo and the telescope

Lenses were being made as early as the 13th century to help people see. Galileo did not invent the telescope, but he learned of it around 1608. He was the first to use it as a tool for astronomy, and by 1609 he had created an improved telescope of far better magnification than any in existence.

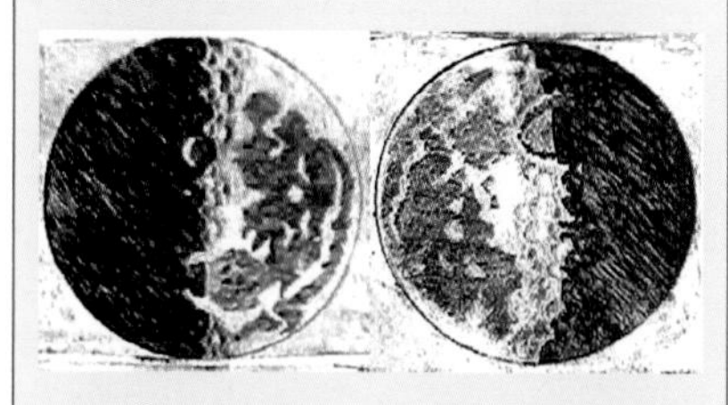

One of the first things Galileo saw was that the line between dark and light on the Moon was not smooth, but jagged. Galileo correctly recognized that the jagged line was due to tall mountains on the moon casting shadows onto the lighter side. His 400-year- old sketches show incredible detail including craters and the lunar maria (seas).

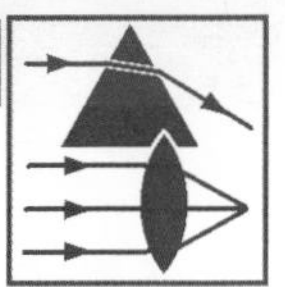

The index of refraction

The index of refraction Light waves travel at a slower rate through glass and other transparent materials than through air. This is because the wave has to constantly be absorbed and reemitted by all the atoms in a material (Figure 15.13). Since not all atoms are alike, you might expect different materials to slow the light by different amounts. This is indeed true, and we have a ratio called the index of refraction that tells how much the speed of light is reduced when it passes through a material.

The index of refraction is a ratio of the speed of light in a vacuum (or air) compared with its speed in a material. The number is always greater than one because light travels fastest in a vacuum. We use the letter n to represent the index of refraction.

Higher index means more bending The higher the index of refraction, the more a light wave bends when crossing in or out of the material. Figure 15.14 gives some typical values of n for common materials. Light waves are strongly bent by a diamond. It is the high index of refraction that gives diamonds their sparkle and beautiful rainbows of color.

The prism A prism is a polished shape of glass that you can use to investigate refraction. A common shape for a prism is a triangle. Light coming into any face of the prism is bent by refraction. The light is bent again when it comes out of the prism.

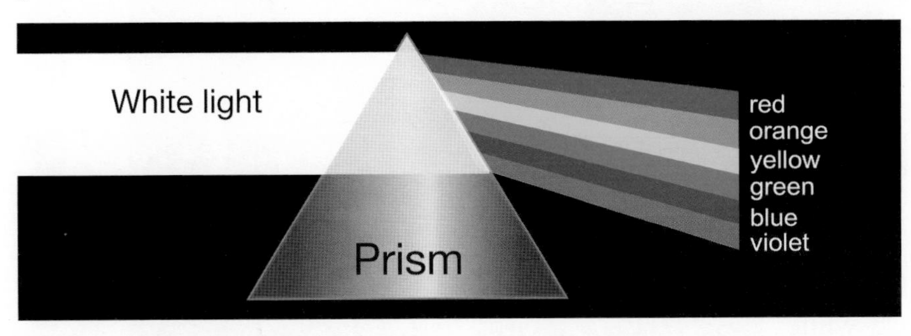

Splitting colors with a prism The index of refraction varies slightly depending on the color of the light. Blue light is bent more strongly than red light. Because of this you can use a prism to split white light up into different colors. Blue light is on one end of our visible spectrum. Red light is on the other end.

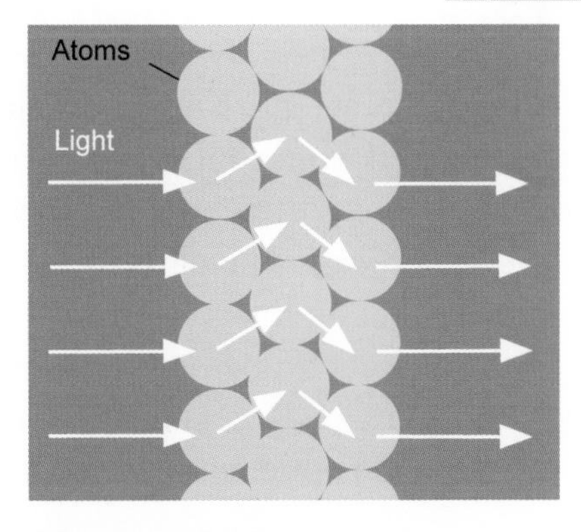

Figure 15.13: *Light travels slower through glass because it is continually absorbed and reemitted by each atom it passes through.*

The index of refraction (n)

$$n = \frac{\text{speed of light in air}}{\text{speed in material}}$$

Material	Index (n)
Air	1.00
Ice	1.31
Water	1.33
Ethyl alcohol	1.36
Fused quartz	1.46
Crown glass	1.52
Cubic zirconia	2.20
Diamond	2.41

Figure 15.14: *Index of refraction (n) for some common materials.*

15.2 The Human Eye

Your eye is an entire optical system that works together with the optic nerve and your brain to help you see images. Some scientists even consider the eye to be part of the brain itself. Everything we have learned about refraction and images applies to the eye. The parts of your eye work together to help you see objects. The parts of the eye are shown in the graphic to the right. The *cornea* and *lens* focus light so that an image forms on a special layer of cells at the back of the eye called the *retina*. The *iris* is a circular opening in front of the lens that can change in size to let more or less light into the eye (Figure 15.15). The *rod and cone cells* that make up the retina sense the images and transmit them via the optic nerve to the brain.

Nerves

What is a nerve? Nerves are made up of wire-like cells that transmit signals throughout your body. They are linked together in a network throughout your body. Some nerves respond to sensation like pressure, heat, cold, pain, or light, and others transmit signals to and from the brain. When you touch something, nerves in your finger link to other nerves and send a message to your brain. In your ear you have nerves that can detect sound.

Your eye also has nerve cells The rod and cone cells in your eye are special nerve cells called *photoreceptors*. Rod cells respond to light intensity only, so they see black, white, and shades of gray. Cone cells are sensitive to color but need brighter light. Your cones are located closer to the center of your eye. If somebody were to bring an object from the side of your vision slowly into your line of sight, you could detect the object but not the color.

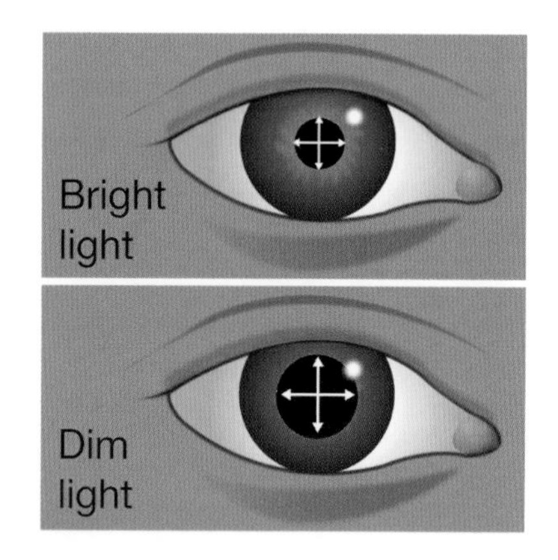

Figure 15.15: *The pupil of the eye is really the opening created by the iris. When there is a lot of light the iris constricts and the pupil gets smaller. When the light level is dim, the iris opens up and the pupil gets larger.*

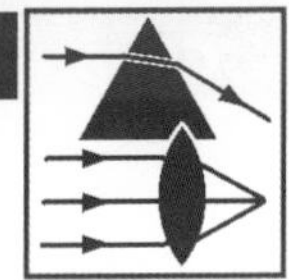

Forming an image

The image on the retina The lens focuses light on the retina at the back of the eye. Since it is a single lens, ray tracing tells you that the image is upside down! Of course, our brains have learned to flip the image right side up, so we don't notice.

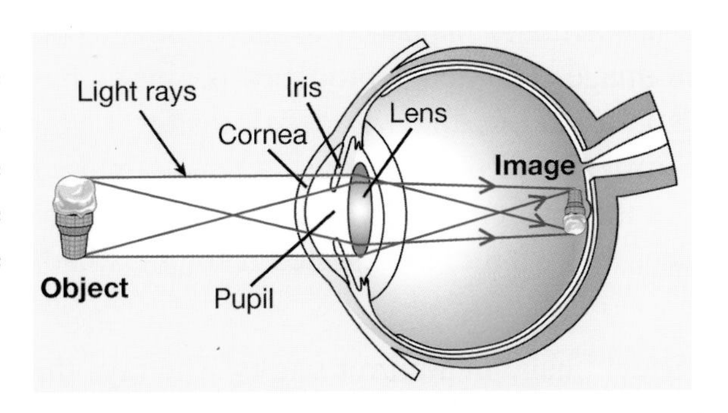

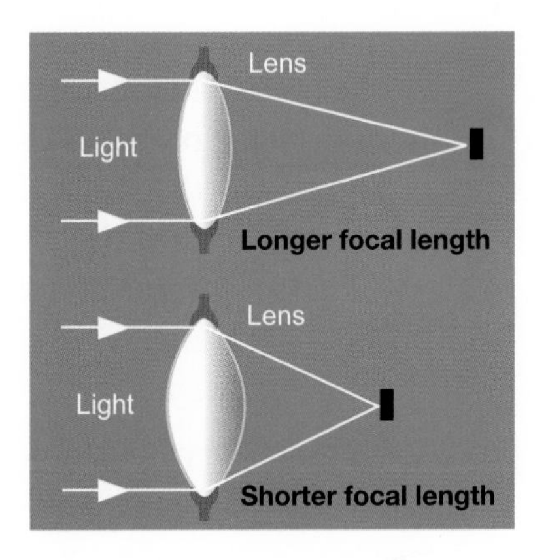

Figure 15.16: *The lens of the eye can change its shape to focus at different distances. The lens is quite tiny, about 4 millimeters thick and 9 millimeters in diameter.*

The lens can change focal length The lens in your eye also has a unique feature which makes it different from the lenses you use in the lab. The lens of your eye is flexible. Small muscles around the edge can stretch it and change its shape. This allows you to focus on objects close by and also focus on objects far away (Figure 15.16). As you get older the lens loses some of its flexibility. Many people wear contact lenses or glasses that adjust the light before it gets to their eye. Bifocal glasses have two regions; one to help you see close and the other to help you see far.

How the eye makes an image The spot on the retina where an image forms is called the fovea. For the average human eye, the fovea has about 120 million rod cells and another 5 million cone cells. Each of these cells contributes one dot, or pixel, to the image received by the brain. The brain puts all the pixels together to perceive an image. This is much like a computer monitor creates images from pixels.

Comparing the eye to a computer monitor Let's examine a computer monitor that is 1,600 pixels wide and 1,200 pixels high. Multiplying 1,600 times 1,200 gives a total of 1.9 million pixels. By comparison, the image created by the eye is equivalent to a computer screen 8 times bigger, 13,000 pixels wide, and 9,600 pixels high! The optic nerve carries 64 times more data than a high-resolution computer graphics display.

Stereoscopic vision and depth perception Stereoscopic vision means that the brain receives two images of the same object, one from each eye. The brain interprets small differences between the images. We use this information to determine distances between objects and how far they are from us. Our ability to judge distances is called depth perception.

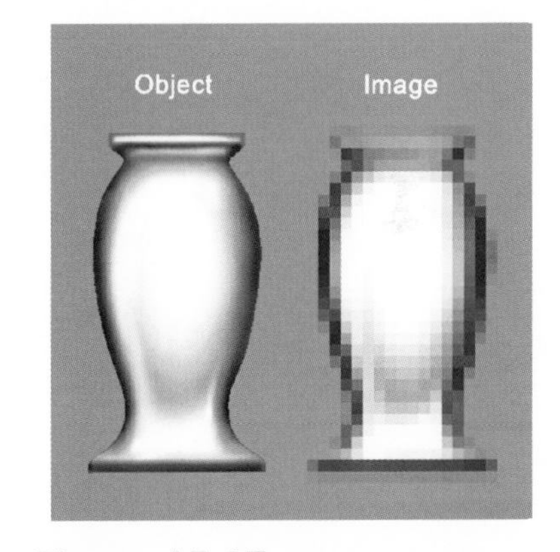

Figure 15.17: *The eye senses images in pixels. Each of the 125 million rod and cone cells sends one dot. The brain assembles the dots into the perception of an image.*

Optical illusions

The brain interprets the image

No matter what has actually happened to the light entering our eyes, our brains produce a single image. The image produced is always based on the assumption that light travels in a straight line. It doesn't matter if you use funny mirrors to bend light in all different directions or use a lens to make rays of light appear to come from places they weren't really coming from. The brain always creates an image of an object that would have existed if the rays had come straight to your eye.

The virtual image in a mirror

This is why a virtual image in a mirror works. The rays that reach your eye after bouncing off the mirror travel along lines that seem to come from the virtual image. Your brain places the image where the rays appear to come from. If you are standing three feet in front of a mirror, you see a virtual image standing three feet behind the mirror (six feet from you).

Optical illusions

There are many well-known optical illusions where the brain interprets an image to be something that it is not. Such illusions trick the brain by using cues such as light and shadow. For example, how is your brain tricked by the drawing show to the right? The elephant may look normal at first glance. However, clever shading and lines create an image that cannot exist in reality. The artist M.C. Escher, was famous for creating "impossible" images that trick the brain into seeing a three-dimensional object that is physically impossible.

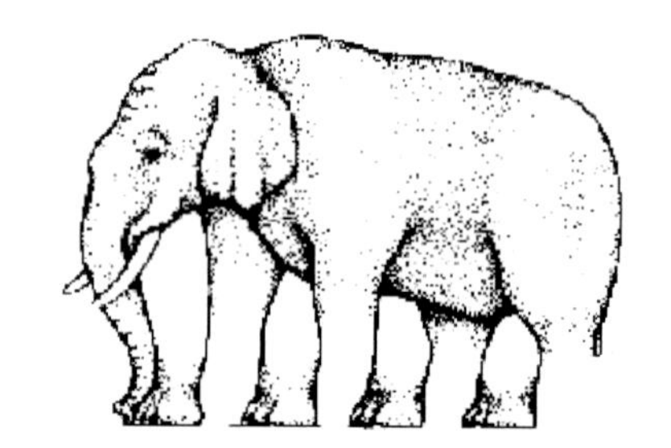

Lotfi Merabet

The cornea, iris, and lens of the eye work together to form an image on the retina. But what happens if the rod and cone cells of the retina get damaged? The retina can't transmit information about the image to the brain, and blindness results.

What if an electronic device could replace the damaged cells? This question intrigues members of the Boston Retinal Implant project. Dr. Lotfi Merabet and Dr. Joseph Rizzo have worked with a team of scientists and engineers to create a device to help restore sight.

The implant they have developed is thinner than a human hair! For the implant to work, the blind person wears special glasses containing a small camera. The camera sends signals to the implant using wireless technology. The implant stimulates nerve cells at the back of the eye to send messages to the brain—taking over the damaged rod and cone cells' job.

The research team hopes that with the implant, people with damaged rod and cone cells will one day be able to recognize shapes and colors and get around on their own in unfamiliar places.

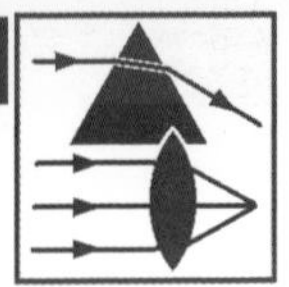

15.3 Optical Technology

We use a wide range of optical technology every day. Glasses and contact lenses are obvious examples. Light-emitting diode (LED) lights and remote controls are other examples. Internet and telephone signals are transmitted using optical fibers and lasers. Your compact disc player uses a laser and a sophisticated miniature optical system. People are even trying to build optical computers that use light rather than electricity. It is very likely that your future will keep you in daily contact with optical technology.

Fiber optics

Bouncing a rock off the water

Have you ever skipped a stone on a pond? First, you need to find a flat stone. Now you hold the stone between your thumb and forefinger. Pull your arm back and throw the stone. If you throw it just right, the stone will bounce off the surface of the water! To be successful, you have to throw the stone at a very large angle of incidence. It's amazing that you can throw a rock at water and have the water bounce the rock back into the air. You don't usually think of water being able to bounce a rock but, if the angle is right, the rock bounces instead of sinks.

When light enters glass, it bends toward the normal

Light, which would normally go through glass, can also be made to bounce off. The key is to get the angle of incidence large enough. If light is traveling in a material with a low index of refraction (air: $n = 1.00$), and it goes into a material with a higher index of refraction (glass: $n = 1.50$), it will bend so that the angle of refraction is less than the angle of incidence. Figure 15.18 shows how a light ray bends toward the normal when going into a material with a higher index of refraction.

When light exits glass, it bends away from the normal

On the other hand, if the light is already in the glass and it is going into air, it will bend so that the angle of refraction is greater than the angle of incidence. This means the light bends away from the normal. In a window, both conditions occur. The light bends toward the normal when it enters and away from the normal when it leaves. That is why light going through a flat sheet of glass comes out in the same direction it went in. We see images through windows almost perfectly clearly because the surfaces are flat.

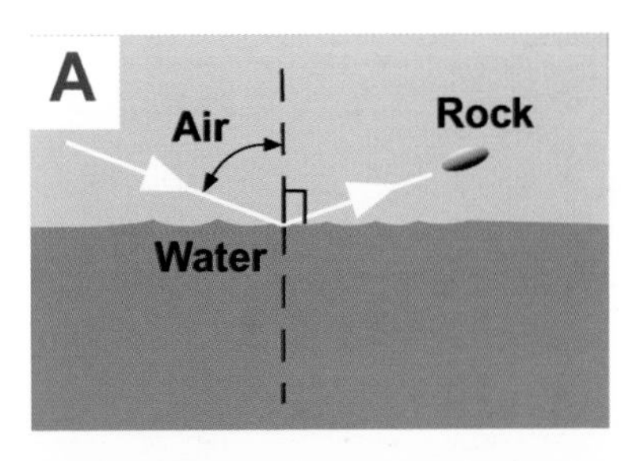

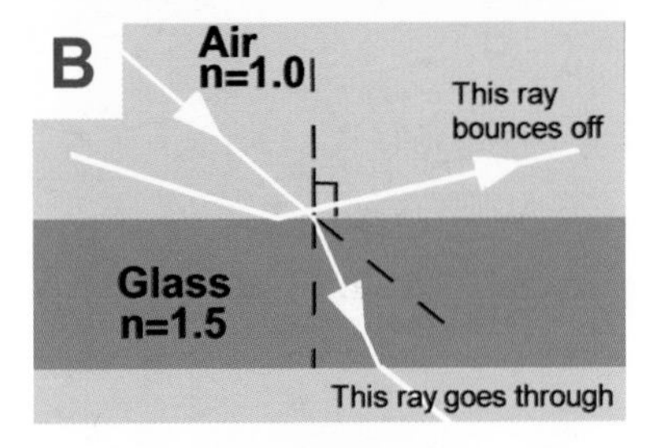

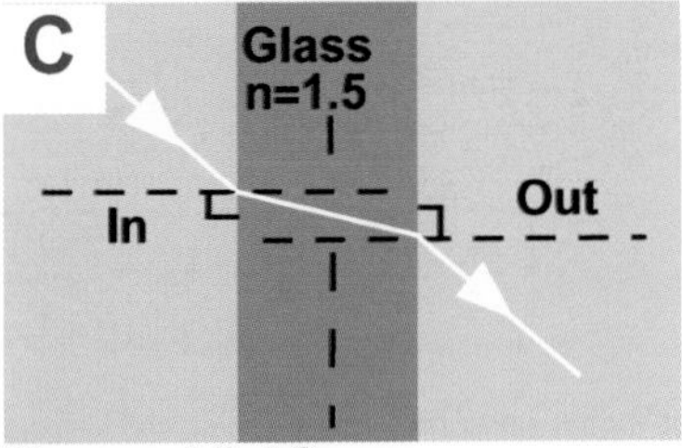

Figure 15.18:
A *You can skip a rock off the surface of water if you throw it at a large angle of incidence.*
B *A light ray bounces off glass if it encounters the surface at a large angle of incidence. A light ray will enter glass if it encounters the surface at a small angle of incidence.*
C *With a flat sheet of glass, the refraction going in exactly cancels the refraction going out and the light comes out in the same direction.*

Total internal reflection

If the angle of incidence is great enough, light enters but does not leave a material because all the light is reflected back into the material. The angle of incidence is called the **critical angle**, and it depends on the index of refraction. If light approaches the surface at greater than the critical angle, it reflects back. This is called **total internal reflection**. The critical angle for glass is about 41 degrees.

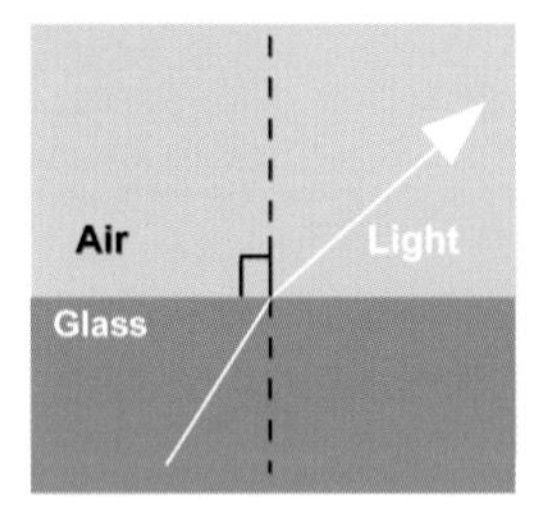

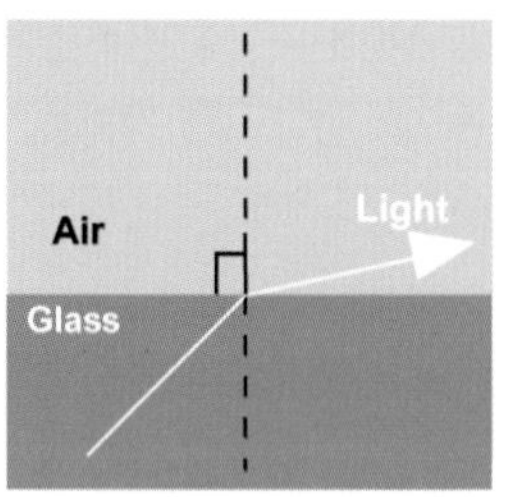

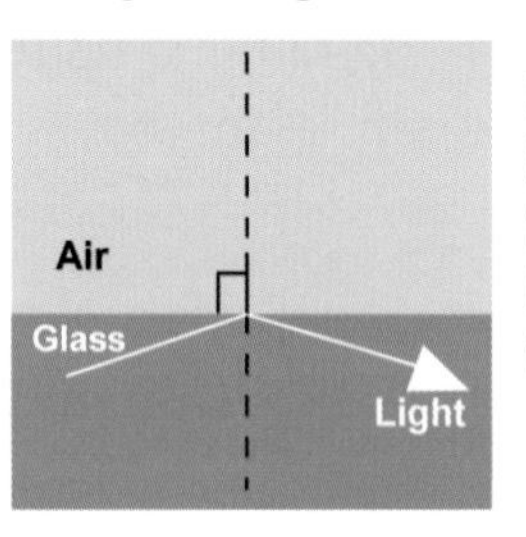

Past a certain angle, light is reflected from the surface instead of being transmitted

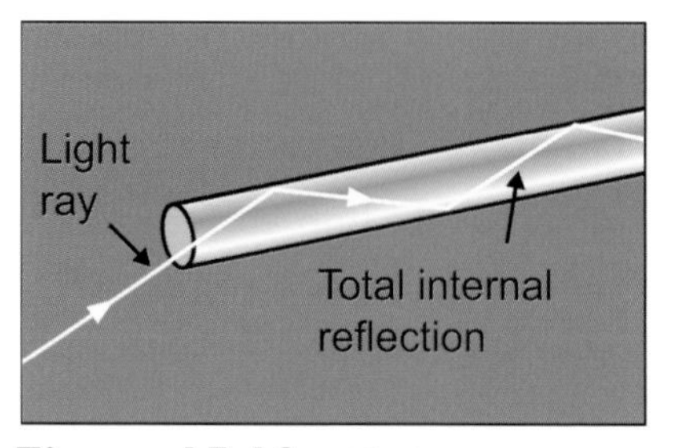

Figure 15.19: *A light pipe traps light by total internal reflection. The light always approaches the wall at greater than the critical angle.*

A pipe for light

Suppose you have a tube of glass and you send light into the end at greater than the critical angle. The light reflects off the wall and bounces back. It then reflects off the opposite wall as well. In fact, the light always approaches the wall at greater than the critical angle so it always bounces back into the tube. You have constructed a light pipe! Light goes in one end and comes out the other. Fiber optics use total internal reflection to trap light into a flexible glass fiber. To connect a fiber optic, you must be careful to feed light in along a cone of the right angle (Figure 15.20). Any light outside the cone will leak out the edges because it will not be internally reflected.

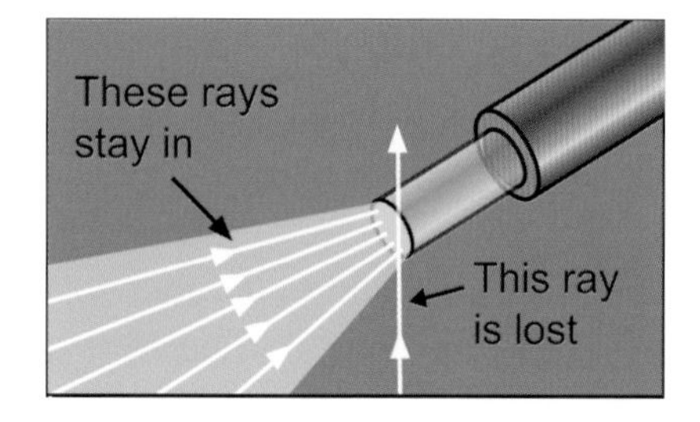

Figure 15.20: *A fiber optic is a thin light pipe that is flexible. Any light that enters the fiber outside a certain angle will be lost since internal reflection of this light will not occur.*

Carrying images on a fiber

Bundles of fiber optics can transmit an image without lenses. If all the fibers at one end of a bundle are perfectly aligned at the other end, then they will send an image through the fiber, even if the fiber is tied in a knot!

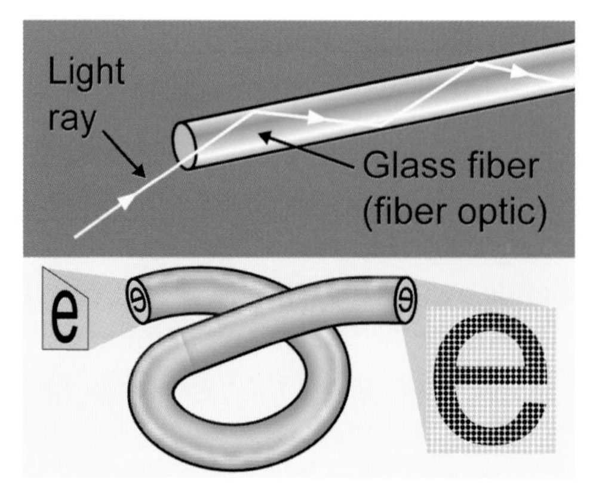

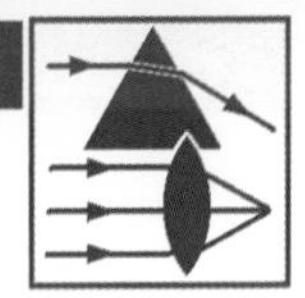

Fiber optics technology

Imagine you invented a code to signal a far-off friend with a flashlight. You tell your friend to look for a light pulse every second. Two "on" pulses followed by an "off" might mean the letter "a" for example. You could invent a different code for every letter. This is essentially how light wave communications work. The light pulses are carried through very thin, glass fibers and can travel great distances. Most long-distance telephone calls today are carried on these fibers. This kind of technology is called *fiber optics*. Computers that communicate over fiber optic links can exchange data much faster than using any other means.

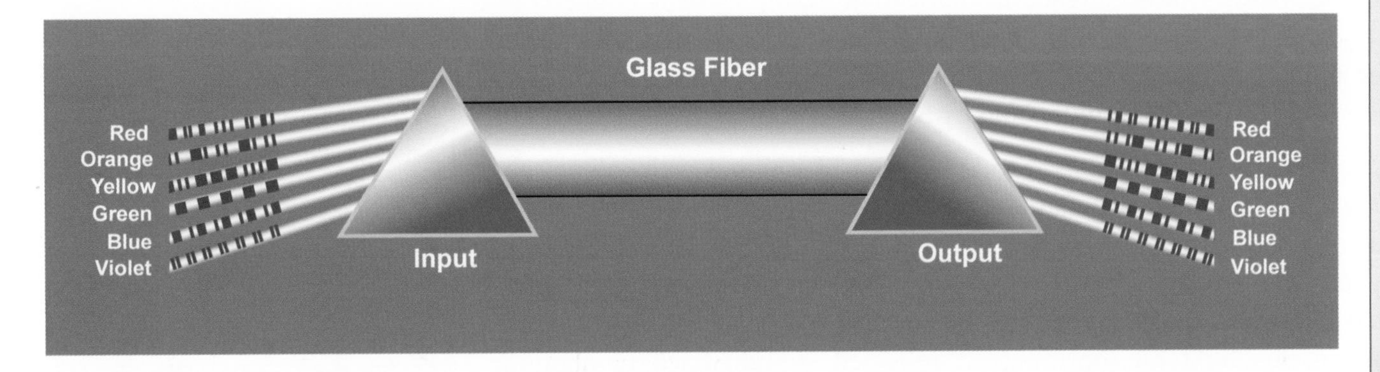

Each color carries a signal

Many different colors of light can go through a glass fiber without interfering with each other. In the graphic above, the dark bands represent the pulses of each color. A single glass fiber can carry as many as 64 different signals. Each signal is given its own frequency (color) of light. The light from all signals is first combined using a prism and sent through the fiber. At the other end of the fiber, the signal is split into different colors, also using a prism. Each color is then decoded separately.

The Internet

Almost all Internet data communication is carried through fiber optic networks that stretch between cities and between important buildings. Most long-distance telephone communication is also carried through fiber optics. The only part that is still carried on copper wires is the link from your home or desk to the main telephone company station near where you live. Once the signal reaches the telephone station, it is converted to light using lasers. When you make a long distance call, your voice makes a journey thousands of miles over fiber optics.

Fiber optics and the future

Someday, a fiber optic cable will come right to your house or apartment. Your telephone, computer, radio, and TV stations will all ride the light waves down the fiber. This is possible because light has such a high frequency. The higher the frequency, the more information you can send. One fiber optic cable can carry more information than used to be carried by a thousand copper wires.

Lasers

What is a laser? A *laser* is a special type of flashlight. Lasers typically have a special material. When energized in a specific way, electrons in a laser material move into a higher energy level. Like electrons in the "glow-in-the-dark stuff," electrons in a laser material do not fall to a lower energy level right away. The operator of a laser can cause electrons in the laser material to be energized or to fall at the same time. If all the electrons fall at the same time, then the light waves that are created are very unique. All the waves will be aligned in phase. The resulting light is one color because all the waves are the same frequency. This light is also very bright because the aligned waves do not spread out quickly. (The term LASER is an acronym; it stands for Light Amplification by Stimulated Emission of Radiation.)

The first laser The first laser was made using a short rod made out of synthetic ruby. The ruby rod was surrounded by a special flash bulb that was shaped like a coil. Mirrors were placed at each end of the ruby rod. The light from the flash caused electrons in the ruby to rise to an excited orbit. Any energy that was traveling straight down the ruby rod would cause other electrons to fall and add to the energy that was moving. When this light hit the mirror it reflected straight back to continue collecting more and more energy from falling electrons. One mirror was slightly less reflective than the other. When the light was bright enough it would escape.

Helium neon lasers The lasers you may see at school look like long narrow boxes. They have a gas tube inside of them instead of a ruby rod. The tube is filled with helium and neon gases. These helium neon lasers produce red light and use high voltage electricity to energize the electrons instead of a flash lamp.

Diode lasers *Diode lasers* are becoming the laser of choice because of their low cost, reliability, low voltage, and safety. If you have ever played with a laser pointer, you have used a diode laser. Supermarket scanners also use diode lasers. A diode laser can be smaller than a pinhead and can make light from a tiny amount of electricity. There are diode lasers that make red, green, and blue light. Researchers are trying to put red, green, and blue lasers together to make a "laser TV" that could project bright color images.

Narinder Kapany

Narinder Kapany grew up in northern India, where his high school physics teacher told the class that light travels only in straight lines. Kapany took this statement as a challenge: He wondered if he could figure out a way to bend light.

Kapany tested his idea that light could be transmitted through glass fibers. He spent months experimenting with different types of glass. In 1954 he published his report of successfully transmitting images through fiber optical bundles. Due to this groundbreaking report, Kapany is widely known as the "father of fiber optics."

Kapany received his Ph.D. from the University of London in 1955 and then moved to the United States. He used to be a professor at the University of California-Santa Cruz. His research interests and inventions include fiber-optic communications, lasers, biomedical instruments, solar energy, and pollution monitoring. He has over 100 patents!

Dr. Kapany is also a sculptor and art collector. He is the founding chairman of the Sikh Foundation, which runs programs celebrating Sikh heritage, culture, and art.

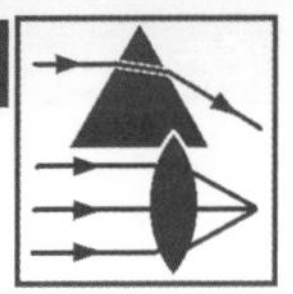

Chapter 15 Review

Vocabulary review

Match the following terms with the correct definition. There is one extra definition in the list that will not match any of the terms.

Set One

1. optics
2. lens
3. mirror
4. prism
5. light ray

a. A device that uses reflection to bend light to form an image
b. A device that bends different frequencies of light to separate colors
c. The study of how light behaves
d. An imaginary arrow used to show the path of a single beam of light
e. A device that uses refraction to bend light to form an image

Set Two

1. refraction
2. reflection
3. telescope
4. real image
5. virtual image

a. An image formed by rays of light coming together on a surface like the retina of the eye
b. The bouncing of light rays from a surface
c. Bending of light rays that results as light crosses a boundary between two different substances
d. An image formed when light rays seem to come from a point other than where the object exists
e. A device (used by Galileo) that uses a collection of lenses to magnify an image

Set Three

1. normal
2. incident ray
3. reflected ray
4. angle of incidence
5. angle of reflection

a. The ray of light that bounces off a mirror
b. The angle measured from the normal to the incident ray
c. A line drawn perpendicular to the surface of a mirror or any surface
d. The angle measured between the normal and the reflected ray
e. The ray of light that strikes a mirror
f. The ray of light that passes through a mirror

Set Four

1. retina
2. lens
3. stereoscopic vision
4. total internal reflection
5. fiber optics

a. A device that uses the stimulation of electrons to create an amplified emission of radiation
b. The back of a human eyeball where an image is formed
c. A light pipe that uses total internal reflection to carry light and signals from one point to another
d. This part of the human eye bends the light that comes into it
e. This process happens when light inside a glass of water tries to get out but is reflected back into the material
f. The process by which humans use two eyes to see things with depth

Concept review

1. A ray of light falls on a lens made of glass. Which of the following (a, b, or c) best describes the path of the light ray leaving the lens?

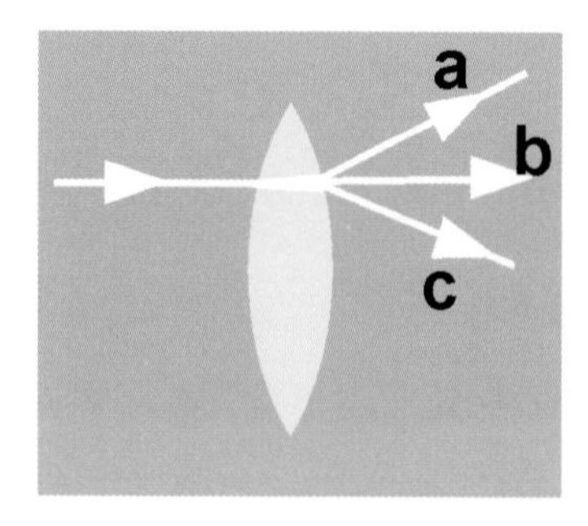

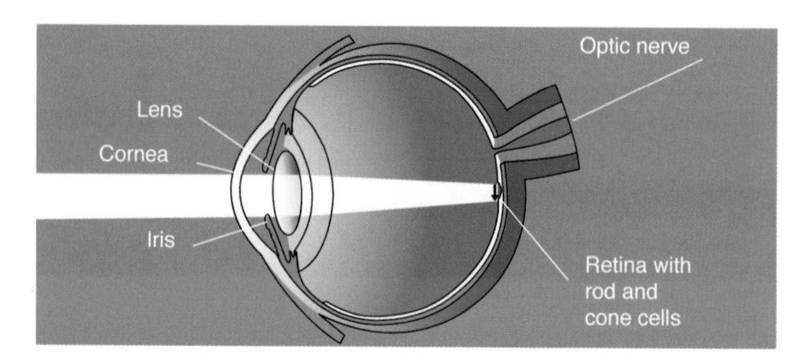

2. An image is best described as:
   a. A place where light rays leaving one point on an object come together again.
   b. A light source that creates objects.
   c. The splitting of white light into different colors.
   d. A group of light rays leaving from the same point on an object.

3. A ray of light falls on a mirror. Which of the following (a, b, c, or d) best describes the path of the light ray leaving the mirror?

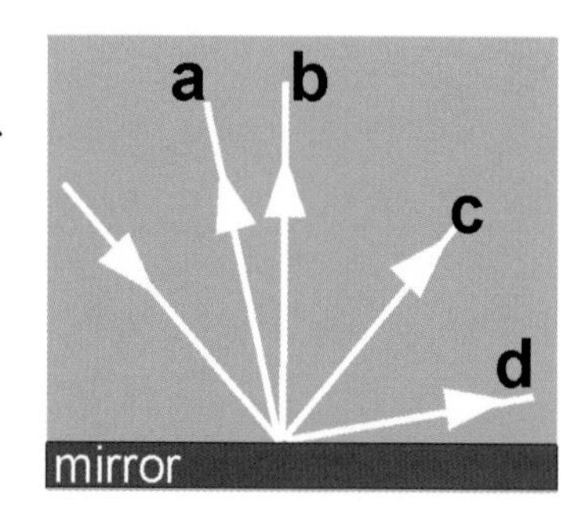

4. Total internal reflection happens when light comes from air and strikes the surface of water.
   a. True b. False

5. What is the purpose of the iris in the eye?

6. What is the purpose of the optic nerve in the eye?

7. What is the purpose of a rod or cone cell in the eye?

8. What is the purpose of the lens in the eye?

9. Identify which of the following kinds of electromagnetic waves are used by the bar-code scanner at a grocery store.
   a. microwaves
   b. visible light
   c. radio waves
   d. X rays

10. Identify which of the following kinds of electromagnetic waves are transmitted through fiber optics.
    a. microwaves
    b. visible light
    c. radio waves
    d. X rays

11. Which creature must take total internal reflection and refraction into account when hunting in its natural environment?
    a. An eagle
    b. A tiger
    c. An alligator
    d. A wolf

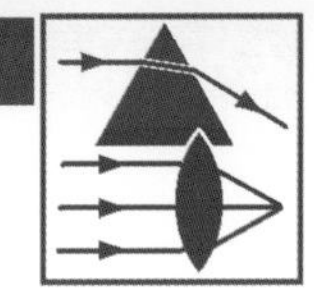

12. Why do you use a ruler to draw rays of light?
    a. The ruler makes the picture look more professional.
    b. The ruler has light that comes out of it.
    c. The ray of light has marks every centimeter like a ruler.
    d. The ray of light travels in a perfectly straight line.

13. How many rays of light do you need to draw to find where an image is located?
    a. Only one ray is needed.
    b. Three rays are needed, but they must be flashing.
    c. A minimum of two rays is needed to find an image.

Problems

1. What does the term ***normal*** mean?
   a. Average
   b. The middle
   c. Perpendicular
   d. All of these are correct

2. The angle between the incident ray and the reflected ray is 60°. What is the angle of reflection?
   a. 10°
   b. 20°
   c. 30°
   d. 40°

3. How do you measure the incident angle?
   a. The angle between the incident ray and the normal.
   b. The angle between the incident ray and the surface of the mirror.
   c. The angle between the surface of the mirror and the normal.
   d. The angle between the reflected ray and the surface of the mirror.

4. Which of the arrows in the diagram shows the path taken by a light ray as it travels through the lens?

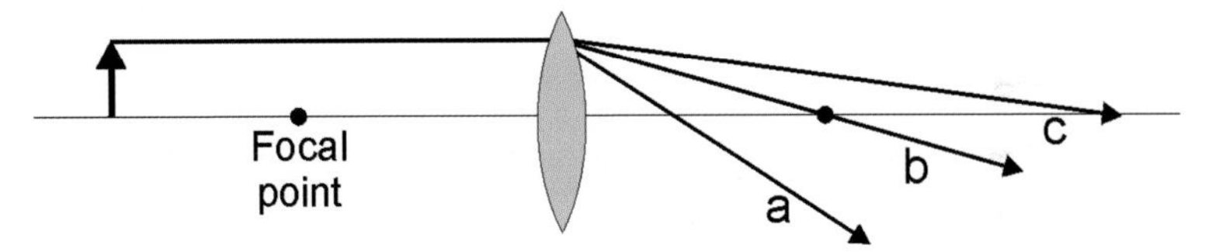

5. As light goes from air into glass the angle of refraction is:
   a. The same as the angle of incidence.
   b. Less than the angle of incidence.
   c. Greater than the angle of incidence.
   d. Is not related to the angle of incidence.

6. As light goes from glass into air the angle of refraction is:
   a. The same as the angle of incidence.
   b. Less than the angle of incidence.
   c. Greater than the angle of incidence.
   d. Not related to the angle of incidence.

Applying your knowledge

1. Sketch an eyeball. Draw and label all the major parts of the eye.
2. A microscope is a tool scientists use to magnify cells and very small objects. Find a drawing of a microscope and make a sketch of how many lenses there are. What do the following words mean when talking about a microscope?
    a. Eyepiece
    b. Objective
    c. Magnification
3. A telescope can be used for looking at objects on Earth as well as in the sky. What do the following words mean when used to describe the working of a telescope?
    a. Aperture
    b. Magnification
    c. Reflector
    d. Refractor
4. Explain how glow-in-the-dark material works.
5. Explain the things that happen to an atom that cause it to give off light.
6. The rear view mirror on some cars has a message, "Objects may be closer than they appear," painted on the mirror surface. Explain why car manufacturers thought it was necessary to put this message there.

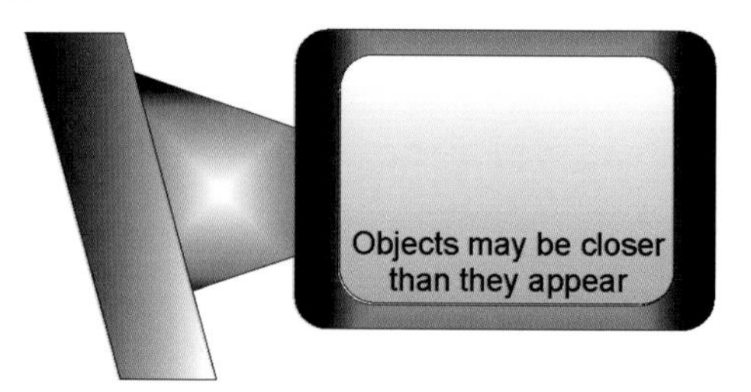

UNIT 6 Properties of Matter

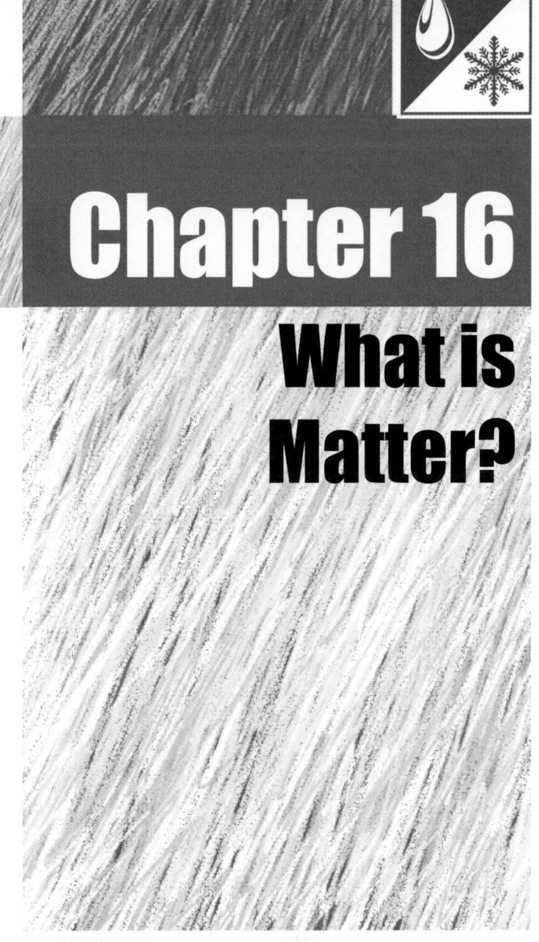

Chapter 16 What is Matter?

Introduction to Chapter 16

What do a silver necklace, a glass of orange juice, a helium-filled balloon, and a star have in common? All of these objects are made of matter. In this chapter, you will learn how matter is classified and how it undergoes changes of state. All matter can exist as a solid, liquid, or gas. Changes in temperature and atmospheric pressure can cause changes in state.

Investigations for Chapter 16

16.1	Classifying Matter	*How can a homogeneous mixture be separated?*

In this Investigation, you will use a technique called paper chromatography to separate water-soluble ink (a homogeneous mixture) into its components.

16.2	Measuring Matter	*How is matter measured?*

In this Investigation, you will demonstrate your ability to measure the mass and volume of liquids, and of regular and irregular solids using a variety of techniques.

16.3	States of Matter	*How fast can you melt an ice cube?*

In this Investigation, you will attempt to influence the rate at which 15 milliliters of water changes from solid to liquid. Next, you will measure the average kinetic energy of water molecules as they undergo a change of state and analyze the transfer of energy that occurred.

Learning Goals

In this chapter, you will:

- ✔ Classify samples of matter from everyday life as heterogeneous mixtures, homogeneous mixtures, compounds, or elements.
- ✔ Measure volume using the displacement technique.
- ✔ Measure mass with scales and balances.
- ✔ Use an indirect technique to infer mass from density measurements.
- ✔ Identify the states of matter.
- ✔ Classify the states of matter in order of energy.
- ✔ Recognize changes in state as a physical change in matter.
- ✔ Explain the states of matter in terms of molecular motion.
- ✔ Identify and investigate the law of conservation of mass.

Vocabulary

atom	heterogeneous mixture	matter	substances
compounds	homogeneous mixture	mixtures	
elements	law of conservation of mass	molecule	

16.1 Classifying Matter

What is matter? Matter is easier to describe than to define. Your book, your desk, your lunch, the air that you breathe and the water you drink are all made of matter. Matter is a term used to describe anything that has mass and takes up space. Different kinds of matter have different characteristics, such as boiling and melting temperatures, hardness, and elasticity. In this section, you will learn how matter is classified. By the end of the section, you should be able to define mixture, homogeneous mixture, heterogeneous mixture, substance, element, and compound.

How do scientists classify matter?

Mixtures contain more than one kind of matter

Matter can be divided into two categories: mixtures and substances. Mixtures contain more than one kind of matter. For example, cola is a mixture that can be separated into carbonated water, corn syrup, caramel color, phosphoric acid, natural flavors, and caffeine.

Homogeneous mixture is the same throughout

A homogeneous mixture is the same throughout. In other words, all samples of a homogeneous mixture are the same. For example, an unopened can of cola is a homogeneous mixture. The cola in the top of the unopened bottle is the same as the cola at the bottom. Once you open the can, however, carbon dioxide will escape from the cola making the first sip a little different from your last sip. Brass is another example of a homogeneous mixture. It is made of 70 percent copper and 30 percent zinc. If you cut a brass candlestick into ten pieces, each piece would contain the same percentage of copper and zinc.

Two samples of a heterogeneous mixture could be different

A heterogeneous mixture is one in which different samples are not necessarily made up of exactly the same proportions of matter. One common heterogeneous mixture is chicken noodle soup: One spoonful might contain broth, noodles, and chicken, while another contains only broth.

Figure 16.1: *Carbonated soft drinks are homogeneous mixtures.*

Figure 16.2: *Chicken noodle soup is a heterogeneous mixture.*

Mixtures can be separated by physical means

All mixtures, whether homogeneous or heterogeneous, share one common property: They can be separated into different types of matter by physical means such as sorting, filtering, heating, or cooling. Chicken noodle soup, for example, could be separated into its components by using strainers and filters of different sizes. The separation process does not change the characteristics of each component. You still have broth, noodles, and chicken.

Substances cannot be separated by physical means

Substances, on the other hand, cannot be separated into different kinds of matter by physical means such as sorting, filtering, heating, or cooling. Some substances, like silver, contain only one kind of matter. These substances are called elements. Other substances contain more than one kind of matter, but the different kinds cannot be separated without changing the substance. For example, table salt is made up of two elements, sodium and chlorine. If you could separate table salt into its two elements, you would no longer have a crystallized substance that you sprinkle onto french fries and other foods. Instead, you would have sodium, a soft metal that can cause an explosion if dropped into water, and chlorine, a yellowish, poisonous gas.

All substances are either elements or compounds

Table salt and other substances that are made of two or more elements that cannot be separated by physical means are called compounds. Figure 16.3 shows some examples of compounds.

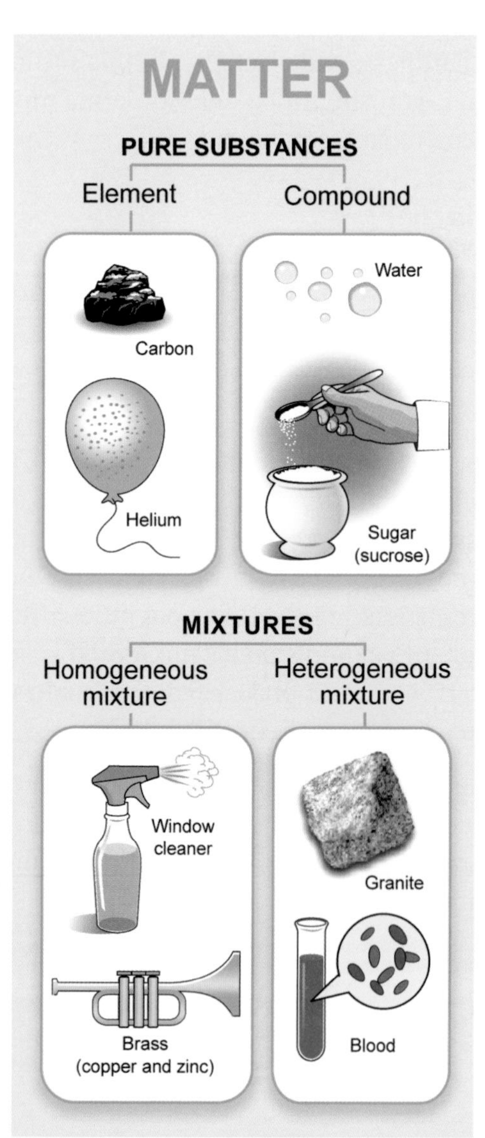

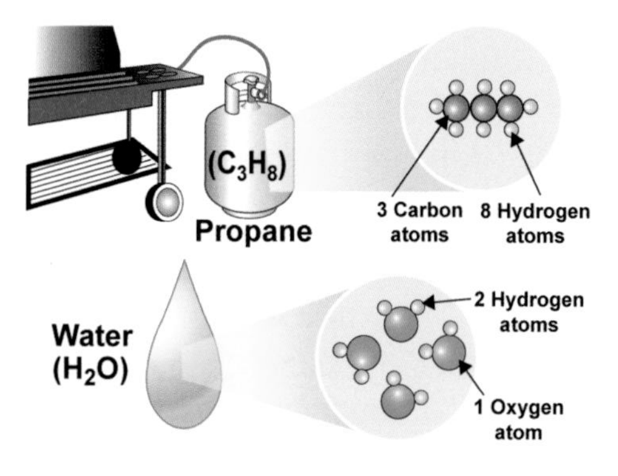

Figure 16.3: *Sodium, a soft metal, and chlorine, a toxic gas, react to form the very edible and useful compound table salt (NaCl).*

How can you separate mixtures into substances?

Separating mixtures into substances is a very important part of scientific work. Medical researchers try to isolate the substances in plants that may help heal diseases. Forensic scientists try to match evidence from the scene of a crime with substances found with a suspect. Nutritionists evaluate the amount of carbohydrates, fats, proteins, vitamins, and minerals in various foods.

Separating mixtures is not always an easy task. In this unit you will learn about a variety of physical properties that can be used to identify substances in a mixture. Later, you will learn how chemists work to break down substances even further, so that they can separate compounds into elements.

Element
One single kind of atom

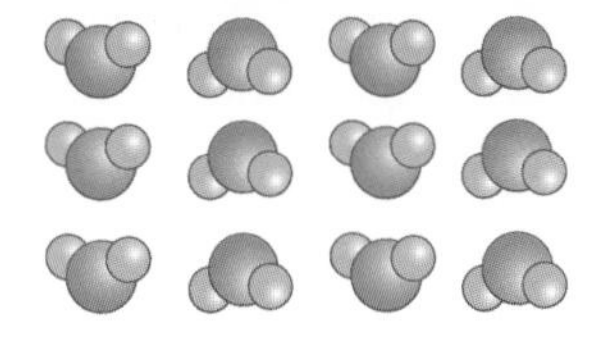

Compound
One type of molecule

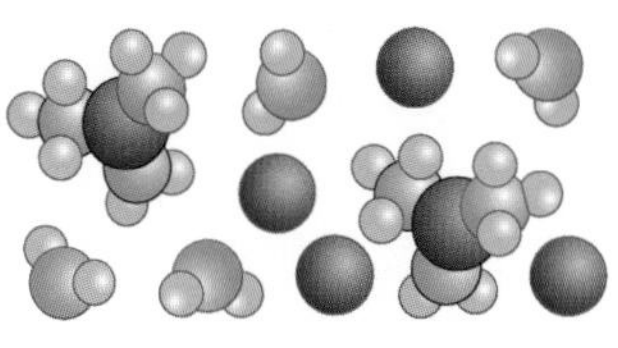

Mixture
Combination of different compounds and/or elements

Table 16.1: *Summary of the types of matter*

Type of matter	Definition	Examples
Homogeneous mixture	A mixture that contains more than one type of matter and is the same throughout.	soda pop, air, chocolate ice cream
Heterogeneous mixture	A mixture that contains more than one type of matter and is not the same throughout.	chicken soup, soil, fudge ripple ice cream
Element	A substance that contains only one type of atom.	copper metal, oxygen gas, liquid nitrogen
Compound	A substance that contains more than one type of atom.	table salt, rust (iron oxide), carbon dioxide gas

Petroleum is a heterogeneous mixture

Petroleum is a very old and complex mixture that we extract from the Earth. Formed millions of years ago, petroleum contains 100,000 to 1,000,000 different molecules! A use has been found for just about every component of this heterogeneous mixture. Important petroleum products include fuel, oils, asphalt, and waxes. Refining petroleum is a process that is used to separate the specific components to make each product. Refining includes physical processes (like distillation) and chemical reactions to isolate the components of petroleum.

16.2 Measuring Matter

How many gallons of gasoline do I need to fill the tank of this car? Do I have enough sugar to make a batch of brownies? Will this suitcase fit in the airplane's overhead compartment? Every day, people need to measure various amounts of matter. In this section, you will review how to measure the mass and volume of matter, and become proficient at using the displacement method to find the volume of irregular objects.

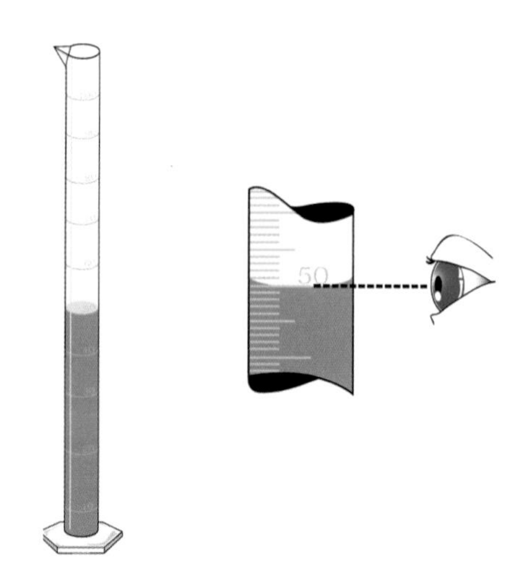

Figure 16.4: *The meniscus of water curves downward. Read the mark at the bottom of the curve.*

Measuring volume and mass

Read volume marks at eye level for accuracy

Measuring the volume of liquid matter is easy. You simply pour it into a marked container such as a measuring cup, graduated cylinder, or beaker, and read the volume mark. To get the greatest accuracy, there are two things to keep in mind. First, read the mark at eye level. Second, you may notice that the surface of the liquid forms a curve (like a hill or a valley), rather than a straight line. This curve is called the meniscus. If the surface curves downward, (liquid water does this) read the volume at the bottom of the curve. A few liquids, like mercury, will form an upward curve. In this case, read the volume mark at the top of the curve.

You can calculate the volume of solids using a formula

You have probably already learned to measure the volume of some solid shapes. The volume of a rectangular solid (a shoebox shape), for example, is found by multiplying length times width times height. Some common volume formulas are shown in table 16.2.

Table 16.2: *Volume Formulas*

Shape	Formula in words	Formula in symbols
rectangular solid and cube	length × width × height	$l \times w \times h$
cylinder	pi ×radius^2 × height	$\pi r^2 \times h$
cone	1/3 × pi × radius^2 × height	$1/3 \times \pi r^2 \times h$
sphere	4/3 × pi × radius^3	$4/3 \times \pi r^3$

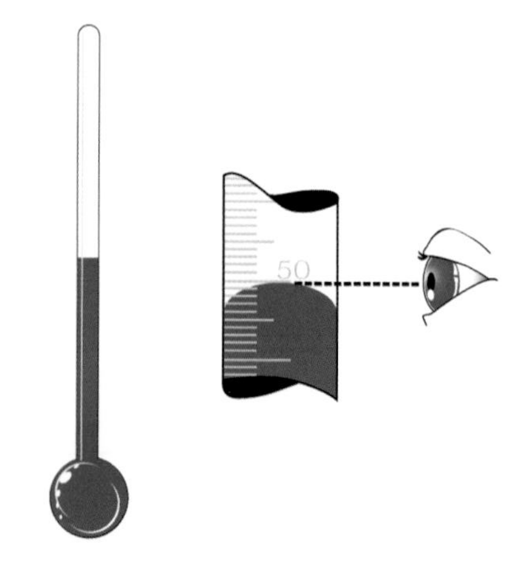

Figure 16.5: *The meniscus of mercury curves upward. Read the mark at the top of the curve.*

The displacement method

We can find the volume of an irregular shape using a technique called displacement. To displace means to "take the place of" or to "push aside." You can find the volume of an irregularly shaped object by submerging it in water and measuring how much water the object displaces or pushes aside.

How you make the measurement

You can use this method to find the volume of an ordinary item like a house key. Fill a 100-milliliter graduated cylinder with 50 milliliters of water (Figure 16.6). Gently slide the key into the water. The water level in the container will rise, because the key displaced, or pushed aside, some water. If the level now reads 53.0 milliliters, you know that the key displaced 3.0 milliliters of water. The volume of the key, or of any object you measured in this way, is equal to the volume of the water it displaced. The key has a volume of 3.0 milliliters, or 3.0 cubic centimeters (cm^3).

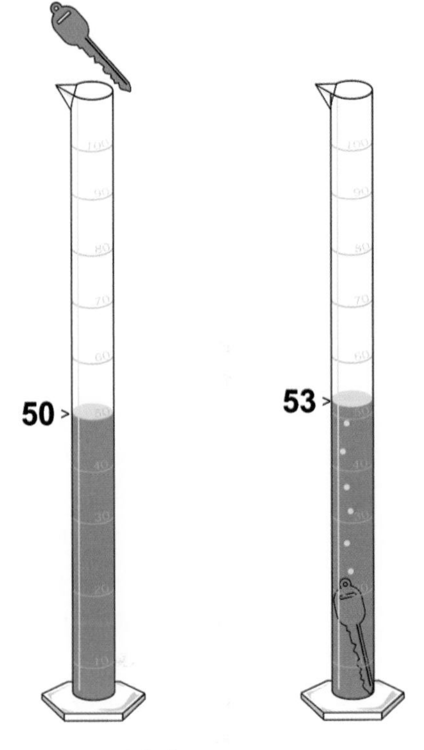

Figure 16.6: *The key displaced 3.0 milliliters of water.*

Mass is the amount of matter in an object

Sometimes we are more concerned about the quantity of matter we have, rather than the space it takes up. Breakfast cereal, for example, isn't sold by volume. As boxes of cereal are shipped from plant to warehouse to store, the contents "settle." By the time the cereal is purchased by the consumer, the container may appear only three-fourths full. For this reason, cereal is measured in grams. An equal mass of cereal is placed into each container at the factory.

How does a scale work?

A scale measures the gravitational force between an object and Earth. This means that a scale that reads in grams or kilograms has actually measured *weight* and calculated the mass from the weight.

How does a balance work?

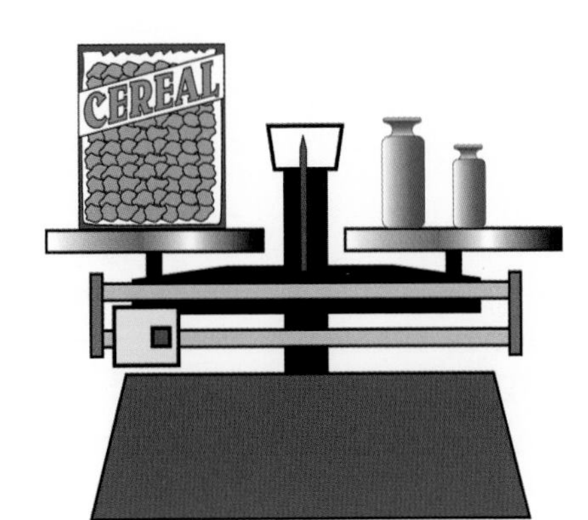

A balance measures the mass of an object (like a quantity of cereal) by comparing it with objects whose masses are known. Since a balance measures by comparing standard masses, it is not affected by changes in gravity.

Would a balance function correctly on the moon? Why or why not?

Measuring very large or very small quantities of matter

How could you measure a quantity of matter that is too large for a balance or displacement tank? Read on to find out how a citizen's group solved this problem.

How could you measure the mass of an asphalt tennis court?

After years of watching a tennis court fall into disrepair at a local park, a group of neighbors got together to discuss what could be done with the site. They voted to approach the town council to see if a children's play structure could be built there.

The town council asked the group to provide a budget for the renovation. It was easy for the group to find prices for new play structures; but first, the tennis court would have to be taken down and the asphalt removed. The group learned that the fee for disposing of construction or demolition debris was 5 cents per kilogram. How did they figure out the cost of asphalt disposal?

Indirect measurement

The group used a technique called *indirect measurement* to estimate the disposal cost. First, they picked up a palm-sized chunk of loose asphalt from the tennis court. They used displacement to find its volume: 1,687 cubic centimeters. Using a balance, they found that the chunk had a mass of 1.94 kilograms.

Next, they measured the tennis court: 36.51 meters by 18.29 meters. They estimated the asphalt to be 0.075 meters thick. By multiplying length × width × depth, they found that the court contained 50.08 cubic meters of asphalt.

Set up a proportion

Now they could set up a proportion:

$$\frac{\text{mass of chunk}}{\text{volume of chunk}} = \frac{\text{mass of court}}{\text{volume of court}}$$

The volume of the chunk was converted to cubic meters so that the units would match. The group solved their equation for the mass of the court, and found that the asphalt had a mass of 57,590.5 kilograms.

At 5 cents per kilogram, the disposal fee came to $2,879.52.

How to measure very small objects

Indirect measurement can also be used to measure very small quantities. If you put one sunflower seed on a balance, the balance still reads 0.0 grams. This means that the mass of the seed is less than 0.1 gram! It might be 0.04 grams or 0.00964 grams, but how could you find out? Use indirect measurement by finding the mass of 100 sunflower seeds and then dividing it by 100.

Figure 16.7: *When the old tennis court asphalt is removed, a child's playground can be built in its place.*

1. equation

$$\frac{\text{mass of chunk}}{\text{volume of chunk}} = \frac{\text{mass of court}}{\text{volume of court}}$$

2. rearrange variables

$$\text{mass of court} = \frac{(\text{mass of chunk}) \times (\text{volume of court})}{(\text{volume of chunk})}$$

3. plug in data and cancel units

$$\text{mass of court} = \frac{(1.94\ \text{kg}) \times (50.08\ \cancel{\text{m}^3})}{(0.001687\ \cancel{\text{m}^3})}$$

4. solve

mass of court = 57,590.5 kg

16.3 States of Matter

Suppose your teacher gave each student a teaspoon of salt and offered a reward to the person who could separate out the smallest piece. How would you do it? You might start by sprinkling a few grains onto a piece of dark paper. Perhaps you could isolate one grain. Next, you might try to smash that grain into smaller particles with a hammer. If you were able finally to divide the grain of salt into particles as small as a speck of dust, you might have won the contest, but your bit of salt would still be about 100 trillion times as large as the smallest possible piece! In this section, you will learn about the smallest whole particles of matter, atoms and molecules. By the end of the section, you should be able to describe how those particles move in solids, liquids, and gases.

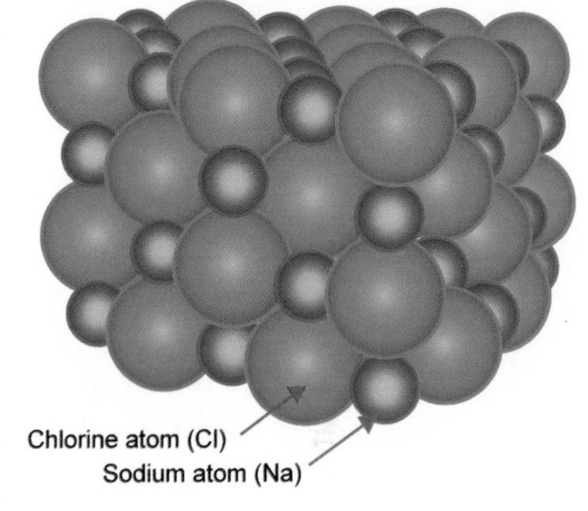

Figure 16.8: *A single crystal of sodium chloride (table salt) is a cube. The molecules are arranged in the crystal so that each sodium atom is surrounded by six chlorine atoms, and six sodium atoms surround each chlorine atom.*

Atoms and molecules

Molecules and atoms

Scientists call the smallest possible particle of a compound that retains the properties of the compound a molecule. The smallest possible particle of an element is called an atom. Atoms and molecules are more than a trillion times smaller than a human cell, a bacterium, and everything else that can be seen with an optical microscope. We know they exist because we can describe and predict how they will act in various substances and mixtures.

Movement of molecules

Let's examine a very common compound, water. Water is one of the most important substances on the planet. It covers more than 70 percent of the Earth's surface. Without it, life would not be possible. We need water for our bodies to function properly and for plants to grow. We use ice to preserve food. Steam-powered turbines and hydroelectric dams provide electricity for homes and businesses.

Atoms and molecules are always in motion

Each tiny water molecule contains one oxygen atom and two hydrogen atoms. A single drop of water is made up of more than 3×10^{21} molecules. These molecules are always in motion. At higher temperatures, they move faster and bump into one another with more force. At lower temperatures, they move with less energy.

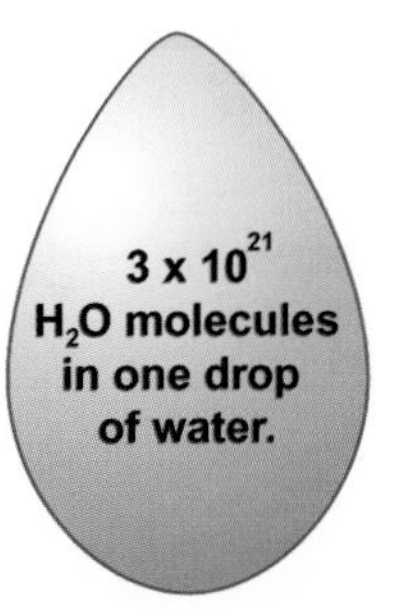

Changes of state

Molecules in solids, liquids and gases vibrate differently

At temperatures below 0°C, water is a solid called ice. In the solid state, molecules constantly vibrate, but cannot switch places with other molecules (Figure 16.9, top). Between zero and 100°C, water is a liquid. Molecules in a liquid move faster and slip out of position (Figure 16.9, middle). Liquids flow because the molecules can move. At temperatures above 100°C, water becomes a gas. At this high temperature molecules move so fast that they bounce out of the liquid state and become a gas. In the gaseous state, molecules are widely separated (Figure 16.9, bottom).

What is temperature?

Temperature influences changes of state. Temperature measures the average energy of a certain amount of molecules, and is related to the average velocity of the molecules. The higher the temperature, the faster (on average) the molecules move.

Melting and boiling

The temperature at which the water changed from solid to liquid is called its melting point. The temperature at which it changed from liquid to gas is called the boiling point. Different substances change from solid to liquid and from liquid to gas at different temperatures. Iron, for example, melts at 1538°C (2800°F) and boils at 2861°C (5182 °F). These changes are called changes of state.

What is evaporation?

Fast-moving molecules in a liquid can escape to become a gas. The word *evaporation* describes the transformation from the liquid to gas. Evaporation is a cooling process. For example, when you step out of a shower, you often feel cold. The reason is that when water evaporates from the surface of your skin, the highest energy molecules are the ones that jump from liquid to gas. Lower energy molecules are left behind. The high energy molecules that leave take away energy so your body feels cooler!

What is condensation?

The evaporation of water is an important part of the Earth's water cycle. Water in the oceans, lakes, ponds, and rivers becomes part of the Earth's atmosphere when it evaporates. Once water vapor is part of the atmosphere, some molecules will collect to form small droplets. Clouds are large formations of water droplets. The process of transforming from a gas to a liquid is called condensation. When water droplets in a cloud get too big, they fall back to the Earth as rain.

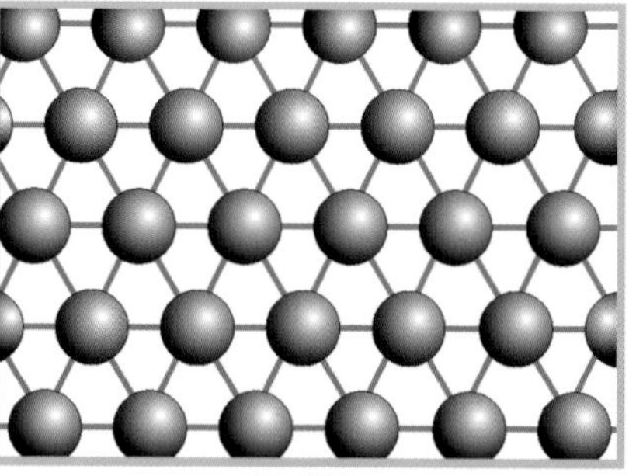

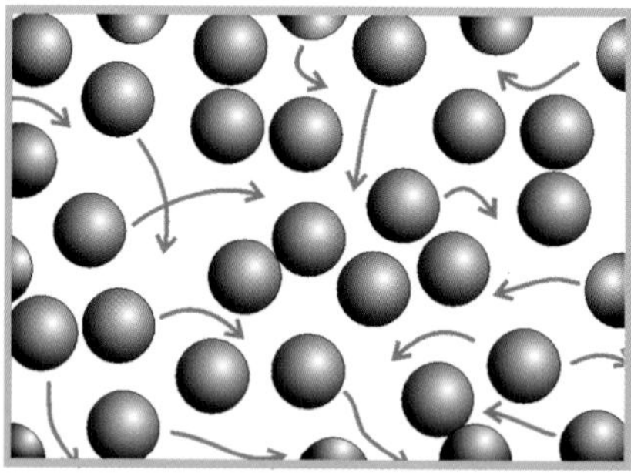

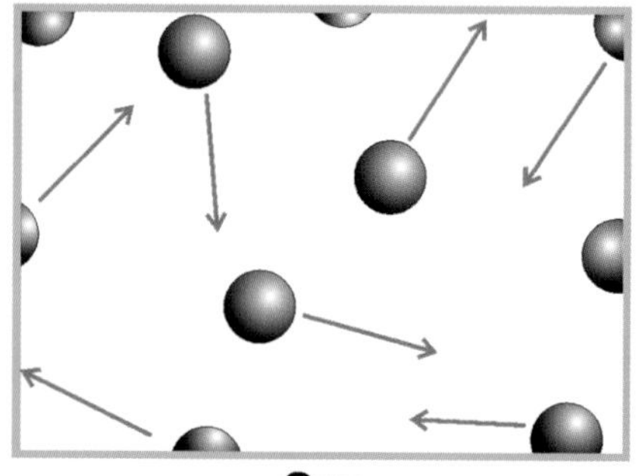

Figure 16.9: *Molecules in the solid, liquid, and gas states.*

A solid can sometimes change directly into a gas

Have you ever noticed that ice cubes sometimes seem to shrink when they have been in the freezer for a long period of time? Sometimes a solid can change directly to a gas when heat energy is added. This process is called *sublimation*. Solid iodine is a substance that readily undergoes sublimation at room temperature. This is evident by a the formation of a purple cloud above the crystals.

States of matter

All substances can exist as a solid, liquid, or gas

On Earth, elements and compounds are usually found as solids, liquids, or gases. These are called states of matter. Each substance can exist in each of the three states, and each substance has a characteristic temperature and pressure at which it will undergo a change of state.

Table 16.3: *Changes of state at 1 atm (normal atmospheric pressure)*

Substance	Melting/freezing point	Boiling/condensing point
helium	-272°C	-269°C
oxygen	-218°C	-183°C
mercury	-39°C	357°C
water	0°C	100°C
lead	327°C	1749°C
aluminum	660°C	2519°C

A solid retains its shape and size

Although we cannot easily see the molecules of a substance moving around, we can describe the resulting characteristics of the matter in each state. When a substance is in a solid state, the molecules vibrate, but they cannot change position. As a result, a solid retains its shape and size. For example, steel nails do not change shape so that you can fit more in a jar (Figure 16.10).

A liquid has definite size, but not shape

In the liquid state, molecules of a substance can move over and around each other. Therefore, the liquid has a definite volume, but no definite shape. Instead, it will take on the shape of whatever container it is poured into (Figure 16.11).

Figure 16.10: *Steel nails are an example of a solid.*

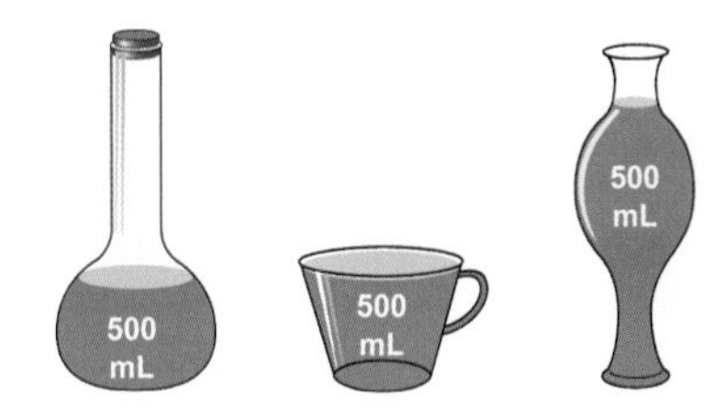

Figure 16.11: *Liquids flow to take the shape of the container but keep their volume.*

Figure 16.12: *A gas expands to fill its container, such as a balloon.*

A gas has no definite shape or size

In the gas state, molecules move around freely and separate from one another. In this state, a substance has neither a definite size nor shape. It will spread out evenly throughout its container.

Change of state and mass

When a substance undergoes a change of state, only the movement of the molecules changes. The number of molecules does not change. The mass of the substance remains the same whether it is in the solid, liquid, or gas state.

Plasma is a fourth state of matter

The most common state of matter in the universe is a state rarely found on Earth: plasma. Matter enters the plasma state when it is heated to such a high temperature that some of the atoms actually begin to break apart. They lose their outer layer of electrons. For most materials this requires temperatures of more than 10,000 degrees.

Where do you find plasma?

Our sun and other stars are made of plasma. Scientists believe the core of the sun has a temperature of about 15 million degrees. The surface of the sun is about 5,000 degrees. A type of plasma is used on Earth to make neon and fluorescent lights. Instead of heating the gases to an extremely high temperature, an electrical current is passed through them. The current strips the electrons off the atoms, producing plasma. You also see a plasma every time you see lighting.

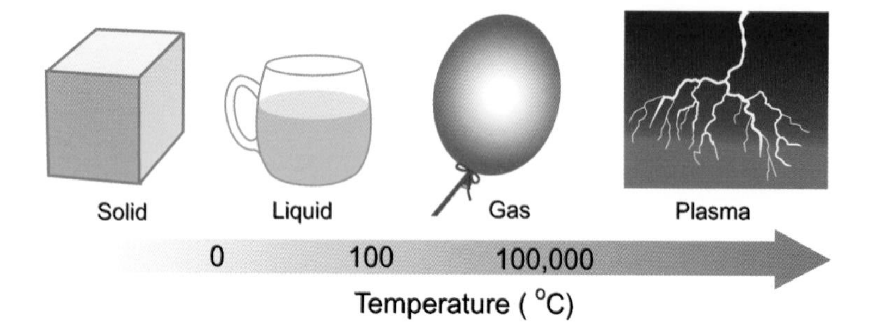

The four familiar states of matter

Matter has four states that we experience. In order of increasing energy they are: solid, liquid, gas, and plasma. Since temperature is a measure of energy, matter changes from one phase to another as its temperature is increased.

Exotic super-hot states of matter

If an atom of a substance keeps getting hotter, eventually even the nucleus of the atom comes apart. Some very exotic states of matter exist in particle accelerators that heat matter up to trillions of degrees and more.

High-altitude cooking

Did you know that the freezing and boiling points of a substance change as the air pressure changes? At a lower air pressure, it is easier for water molecules to escape from liquid into the air. Therefore, water will boil at a lower temperature. This is why cake mixes often have high-altitude directions. The lower air pressure at high altitudes allows the water in the mix to begin to turn to gas at a lower temperature, so it leaves the mix earlier. To prevent the cake from drying out, extra water is added to the mix.

Chapter 16 Review

Vocabulary Review

Match the following terms with the correct definition. There is one extra definition in the list that will not match any of the terms.

Set One

1. matter
2. homogeneous mixture
3. heterogeneous mixture
4. element
5. compound

a. Two samples of this material might contain different kinds of matter
b. A pure substance which contains only one kind of matter
c. Any material that contains at least two kinds of matter
d. Anything that has mass and takes up space
e. Contains two or more kinds of matter that cannot be separated by physical means
f. Every sample of this material is the same

Set Two

1. substance
2. mixture
3. meniscus
4. displacement
5. indirect measurement

a. Very tiny; microscopic
b. Calculating size of very large or small objects through use of proportional relationships
c. Measuring volume by placing an object in water and recording the change in water level
d. The curve formed by the surface of a liquid
e. A sample of matter that cannot be separated by physical means; may contain only one or several kinds of matter
f. A sample of matter that contains two or more kinds of particles that can be separated by physical means

Concept review

1. What are the two major categories of matter?
2. Name three foods that would be classified as heterogeneous mixtures, and three foods that are homogeneous mixtures.
3. Explain the difference between the two kinds of substances.
4. Explain the difference between an atom and a molecule.
5. Describe the movement of atoms or molecules in solid form.
6. Describe the movement of atoms or molecules in liquid form.
7. Describe the movement of atoms or molecules in gas form.
8. A liquid takes the shape of its container, but why doesn't a liquid expand to fill the container completely?
9. List at least two similarities between mass and volume and at least two differences.
10. Evaporation and boiling can be referred to at the same time as vaporization. Describe the difference between vaporization and sublimation.

Problems

1. How could you use indirect measurement to find the mass of a large boulder?
2. How could you use indirect measurement to calculate the thickness of one index card?
3. As you know, the Earth is a watery planet. About 70 percent of the Earth's surface is covered by water. There is water underground, and even in the atmosphere. What is water's state at each of the following temperatures?
   a. temperatures below zero degrees Celsius
   b. temperatures between zero and 100 degrees Celsius
   c. temperatures above 100 degrees Celsius

Applying your knowledge

1. Design a poster to illustrate the classification of matter. Provide examples of everyday objects that belong in each category.
2. Construct a three-dimensional model that could be used in a fourth-grade classroom to explain how molecules move in the solid, liquid, and gaseous states.
3. Land surveyors measure and map land. One of their jobs is to figure out the dimensions of land features and formations. Interview a surveyor to learn how indirect measurement is used to calculate precise distances. Prepare a five-minute report for your class.
4. Look around your classroom or home and name an object that has a relatively large mass, but has a relatively small volume. Name an object that has a relatively small mass, but has a relatively large volume.
5. Write a brief procedure for determining:
   a. the volume of a rock; and
   b. the mass of a small amount of orange juice.
6. How could you determine the percentage of empty space in a square cleaning sponge?
7. Design a poster or model to summarize for your classmates the difference between a solid, liquid, gas, and plasma.
8. Create a chart that illustrates the state changes: melting, boiling, freezing, evaporation, condensation, and sublimation.
9. Plasmas, or ionized gases as they are sometimes called, are of great interest both physically and technologically. Do some research to find out why plasmas are of great interest to scientists and manufacturers. Describe at least two current uses of plasmas, and describe one way scientists and engineers hope to use plasmas in the future.

UNIT 6

Properties of Matter

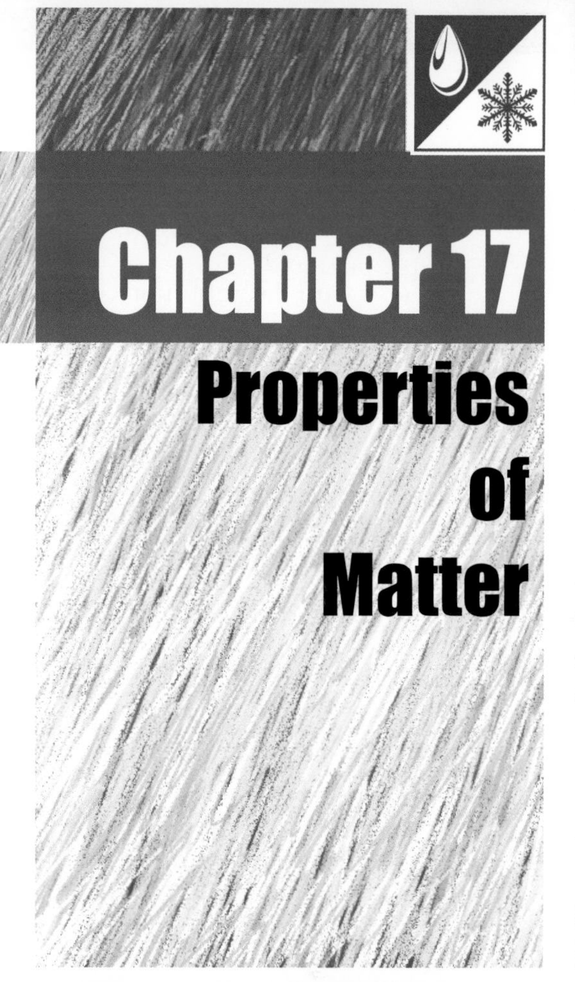

Chapter 17

Properties of Matter

Introduction to Chapter 17

In this chapter, you will learn how to describe matter—both solids and fluids. Solids are characterized by their hardness or malleability, for example. Terms that apply to fluids include buoyancy and viscosity. Density is a property of matter that can change with temperature.

Investigations for Chapter 17

17.1	Properties of Solids	*How can you find the density of a solid?*

In this Investigation, you will measure the mass and volume as a means to determine the density of a set of objects. Using your understanding of density, you will solve a historical problem—whether or not the U.S. Congress passed a law to change the metal composition of a penny.

17.2	Density of Fluids	*Can you create a stack of liquids?*

In this Investigation, you will use a density column to estimate the density of a few solids. You then will use this estimate to predict the density of rubber.

17.3	Buoyancy of Fluids	*Can you make a clay boat float?*

In this Investigation, you will discover how the shape of an object influences whether it sinks or floats. You will explore the relationship between the weight of an object and the weight of the water the object displaces.

17.4	Viscosity of Fluids	*How can viscosity be measured?*

In this Investigation, you will learn how to measure the viscosity of fluids. You will set up a "viscometer" to measure the velocity of a marble as it travels through fluids of different viscosities.

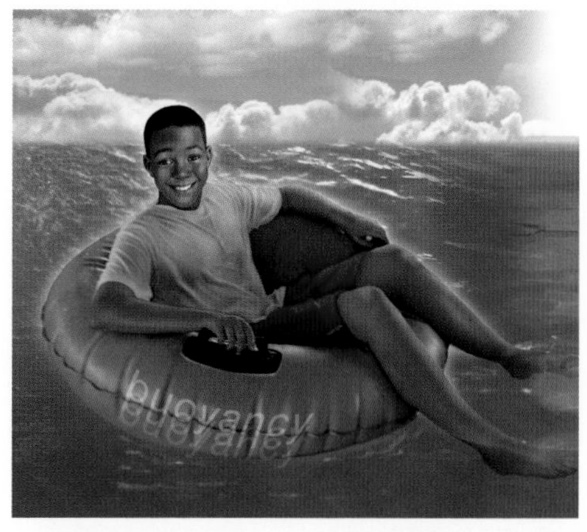

Learning Goals

In this chapter, you will:

- ✔ Learn the definitions of terms used to describe properties of matter.
- ✔ Learn how to calculate the density of solids.
- ✔ Learn how to find the density of liquids and use your understanding to make a density column.
- ✔ Use a density column to predict the density of a solid.
- ✔ Investigate how the shape of an object can determine whether it floats or sinks.
- ✔ Compare the weight of an object with the weight of the water it displaces.
- ✔ Learn why certain fluids are more viscous than others.
- ✔ Measure the viscosity of fluids using a viscometer.
- ✔ Compare the properties of fluids: viscosity and density.

Vocabulary

Archimedes' principle	Charles' law	hardness	pressure
Boyle's law	density	malleability	tensile strength
brittleness	elasticity	pascal	viscosity
buoyancy			

17.1 Properties of Solids

Different types of matter have different characteristics. They melt and boil at different temperatures. They might be different colors or have different odors. Some can stretch without breaking, while others shatter easily. These and other properties help us distinguish one kind of matter from another. They also help us choose which kind of material to use for a specific purpose. In this section, we will concentrate on the properties of matter in its solid form. By the end of this section, you should be able to understand and explain these terms: density, hardness, elasticity, brittleness, and malleability.

Elasticity Elastic materials deform without breaking

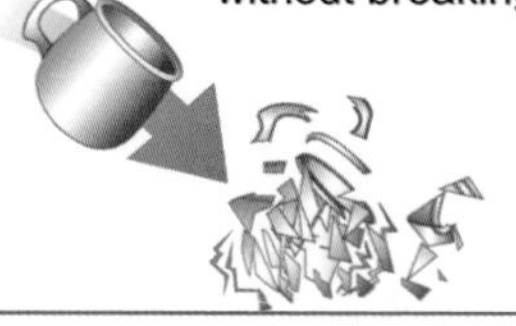

Brittleness Brittle materials break instead of deforming (much

Figure 17.1: *Elasticity and brittleness are properties of solids*

Density

What is density?

Earlier in this unit, you learned two different ways to measure matter: You can find its mass or its volume. **Density** is a property that describes the relationship between these two measurements. If the matter is a homogeneous mixture or a substance, each cubic centimeter (cm^3) or milliliter will have the same mass. For example, one cubic centimeter of silver has a mass of 10.5 grams. Three cubic centimeters of silver have a mass of 10.5 + 10.5 + 10.5 grams, or 31.5 grams. Ten cubic centimeters of silver have a mass of 105 grams.

Density

$$D = \frac{m}{V}$$

Density (g/cm^3) → D; Mass (g) → m; Volume (cm^3) → V

Density can be found by dividing mass by volume

The density of a homogeneous material or substance is expressed as a ratio of grams per cubic centimeter. The density will stay the same no matter how large or small the sample of material. For example, a steel paper clip and a steel bicycle brake cable have the same density.

	Mass	Volume	Density
paper clip	0.36 grams	0.046 cm^3	7.8 g/cm^3
bicycle brake cable	19.8 grams	2.53 cm^3	7.8 g/cm^3

What is a cubic centimeter?

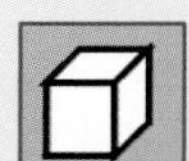

The formula for the volume of a rectangular solid or a cube is length times width times height. If all the sides were measured in centimeters, the unit for this volume would be in cubic centimeters. A shorthand way of writing cubic centimeters is "cm^3." One cubic centimeter will hold 1 milliliter of liquid. In other words, one cubic centimeter = 1 cm^3 = 1 milliliter.

Samples of heterogeneous mixtures will not always have the same density. Suppose you divide a chocolate chip cookie into three pieces and find the density of each. Why might one piece have a greater density than the others?

Density describes how tightly packed the atoms or molecules are in a substance

Density gives us information about how tightly the atoms or molecules of a particular material are "packed." Lead, for example, has many atoms squeezed very close together in one cubic centimeter of space. This gives it a relatively high density of 11.3 g/cm^3. Paraffin, or wax, doesn't have nearly as many molecules packed into each cubic centimeter. Its density is a much lower: 0.87 g/cm^3.

Figure 17.2: *Why do pieces of a chocolate chip cookie have different densities?*

Hardness

What is hardness?

Hardness measures a solid's resistance to scratching. Diamond is the hardest natural substance found on Earth. Geologists sometimes classify rocks based on hardness. Given six different kinds of rock, how could you line them up in order of increasing hardness?

Elasticity

What is elasticity?

If you pull on a rubber band, its shape changes. If you let it go, the rubber band returns to its original shape. The ability of rubber bands to stretch around things and hold them together is due to the property of **elasticity**. Elasticity is the measure of a solid's ability to be stretched and then return to its original size. This property also gives objects the ability to bounce and to withstand impact without breaking. Based on the property of elasticity, which would you rather play basketball with: a bowling ball or a volleyball?

Figure 17.3: *Which ball would you rather play basketball with?*

Brittleness

What is brittleness?

Brittleness measures a material's tendency to shatter upon impact. Brittleness is considered a hazardous property in the automobile industry, where, for instance, shattering glass can cause serious injuries.

Safety glass

The first "safety glass," designed to reduce the brittle tendencies of regular glass, was discovered by accident. In 1903, a French chemist named Edouard Benedictus dropped a glass flask in the lab. The flask was full of cracks, but surprisingly, the pieces did not scatter across the floor. The shape of the flask remained intact.

The glass had been used to store a chemical called cellulose nitrate. Although the chemical had evaporated, it left a plastic film on the inside of the glass.

Initially, Benedictus had a hard time selling his shatter-resistant glass to automobile manufacturers. During World War I, he did sell it for use in gas mask lenses. Soon after the war, the auto industry began using his glass.

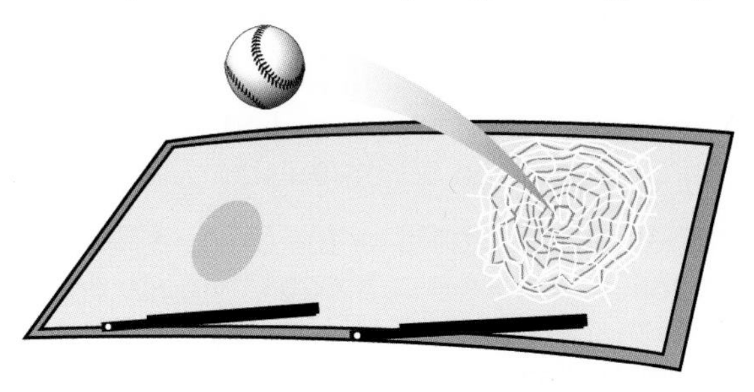

Enhanced Protective Glass is shatter-resistant

Materials scientists have continued to seek better materials for safety glass. Solutia Inc. of St. Louis, Missouri, recently began marketing a new glass product called enhanced protective glass (EPG) with Saflex. It consists of a sheet of a material called polyvinyl butyral (PVB) sandwiched between two pieces of glass under high heat and pressure. EPG with Saflex is so shatter-resistant that it can prevent occupants from being ejected from a vehicle in a collision. Because it is so hard to shatter, it is marketed as a deterrent to thieves as well. The material has another significant benefit: It is a sound insulator, reducing highway noise by about six decibels, resulting in a noticeably quieter ride.

Cellulose nitrate

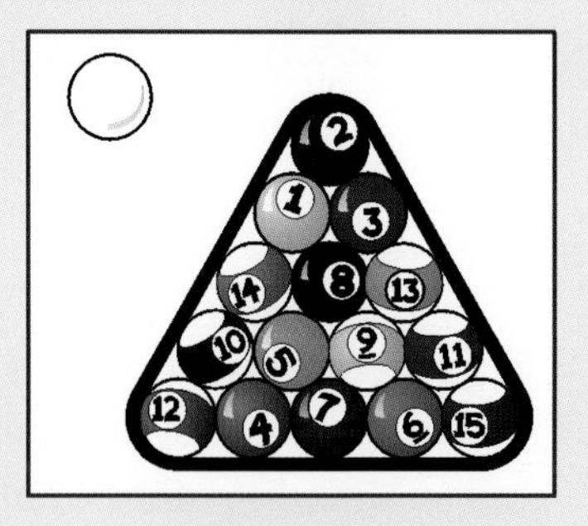

Cellulose is a polymer made by plants. Wood, paper, cotton, and plant fibers are all made of cellulose. When cellulose reacts with nitric acid, cellulose nitrate is produced.

In addition to being used to make safety glass, cellulose nitrate has been used to make billiard balls. Billiard balls used to be made of ivory from African elephants' tusks. The invention of cellulose nitrate created an excellent substitute for ivory. Elephants are now a protected species. Ivory is rare and it is no longer used to make billiard balls.

Malleability

What is malleability?

Malleability measures a solid's ability to be pounded into thin sheets. Aluminum is a highly malleable metal. Aluminum foil and beverage cans are two good examples of how manufacturers take advantage of the malleability of aluminum.

Tensile strength

What is tensile strength?

Tensile strength is a measure of how much pulling, or tension, a material can withstand before breaking. It is an important property of fibers, as it determines the strength of ropes and fabrics. It is also crucial to the manufacture of cables and girders used to support bridges.

Figure 17.4: *Bullet-resistant vests and tennis racquets are often made from KEVLAR®. This product is used when manufactured goods need to be strong, lightweight, and long-lasting.*

KEVLAR® is a registered trademark of E.I. du Pont de Nemours and Company.

Inventing new materials: DuPont KEVLAR® brand fiber

What has five times the tensile strength of steel on an equal weight basis, and can be used to make canoe hulls, windsurfer sails, tennis racquets, and, of a lifesaving nature, motorcycle helmets, cut-resistant gloves, and bullet-resistant vests?

It's KEVLAR® brand fiber, a synthetic fiber manufactured by the DuPont Company. It was invented in 1964 by Stephanie Kwolek, a chemist who was trying to dissolve polymers, which are chains of molecules that are hooked together like the boxcars of a train. Kwolek found that when the polymers were placed in certain solvents, they formed liquid crystal fluids. This means that the chains of polymers were lined up in neat, repeating patterns.

She decided to spin one of her solutions to see if a fiber would form—and it did! She tested the tensile strength and stiffness of her new fiber and found that, although the fiber was very lightweight, it was extremely strong.

Kwolek and a team of researchers studied the properties of this new fiber, enabling them to modify the chains of molecules in order to make them even stronger. Kwolek has been the author or coauthor of 17 U.S. patents on polymers, polycondensation processes, liquid crystalline solutions, and fibers.

17.2 Density of Fluids

What is a fluid? A fluid is defined as any matter that is able to flow. Liquids, as you know, can be poured from one container to another. They flow. Gases exhibit this property as well. You may have noticed cool air flow into a room when a window was opened, or a waft of perfume drifting your way. In this section, we will investigate the first of three important properties of fluids: density.

Density

How could you find the density of *liquid* silver? A piece of pure silver in the shape of a candlestick has the same density as a pure silver ring. Size and shape do not change a material's density (Figure 17.5). But what if you heated the silver until it completely melted? Could you measure its density in liquid form? Would the density change?

Figure 17.5: *The density of pure silver is the same, whether in the form of a ring or a candlestick. Decorative "silver" items are often made of sterling silver, which is a mixture of 93 percent silver and 7 percent copper. Adding the copper creates a harder, more durable metal.*

Measuring mass You could find the mass of your liquid silver using a balance. The amount of silver would not change when the candlestick melted. Therefore, the mass should not have changed.

Atoms in liquid form tend to take up more space The volume of the liquid silver, however, is greater than the volume of the solid silver! The atoms or molecules in a solid, as you remember, are fixed in position. Although the silver atoms in the candlestick were constantly vibrating, they could not switch places with another atom. They were neatly stacked in a repeating pattern. The atoms in the liquid silver are less rigidly organized. They can slide over and around each other. Because they are not as neatly stacked, they tend to take up more space.

Why liquids are less dense than solids The silver atoms in solid form could be compared to a brand-new box of children's wooden blocks. When you open the box, the blocks are tightly packed in an organized, repeating pattern. Now imagine that you empty the box of blocks into a large container, and then try to pour them back into their original box. Although the blocks would still be touching one another, they would not fit entirely inside the box. The blocks would now resemble the arrangement of silver atoms in liquid form (Figure 17.6).

Figure 17.6: *Toy blocks arranged in a tight, repeating pattern take up less space than those in a random arrangement.*

The density of liquid silver

How does the density of the silver in liquid form compare with its density in solid form? Remember, the mass stayed the same but the volume increased. The same mass divided by a larger volume results in a smaller value for density. Therefore, liquid silver is less dense than solid silver.

Table 17.1: *Density of solid and liquid silver*

	Mass	Volume	Density
Candle holder (at 20°C)	1313 g	125 cm^3	10.5 g/ cm^3
Melted candle holder (962°C)	1313 g	141 ml	9.31 g/ml

Temperature and solid density

The density of solids usually decreases slightly as temperature increases because solids expand when heated. As the temperature of the solid silver increases, the volume increases slightly, even before the silver melts. This is due to the increased vibration of the silver molecules.

Water is less dense in solid form

Most materials are more dense in their solid phase than in their liquid phase. Water is a notable exception. Ice is less dense than liquid water! When water molecules freeze into ice crystals, they form a pattern that has an unusually large amount of empty space (Figure 17.7). The molecules are more tightly packed in water's liquid form!

Because ice is less dense than liquid water, it floats on the surface in winter (Figure 17.8). If the ice were denser than the liquid, it would sink to the bottom. If you woke up one morning, and ice were denser than water, there would be serious consequences for life on Earth.

What would happen if solid water was more dense?

For example, each winter, more ice would sink to the bottom of rivers, lakes, or oceans. In some places, the water would be too deep for the sun's rays to reach the ice. Consequently, the ice would not melt in the summer. Many aquatic plants could no longer grow. Frogs and turtles that burrow in the mud at the bottom of ponds could not complete their life cycles. The climate of cities along the Mississippi River, the Great Lakes, and other large bodies of water would become much cooler.

Figure 17.7: *Because of the spacing, ice forms hexagonal crystals which give us the beautiful six-pointed shapes of snowflakes.*

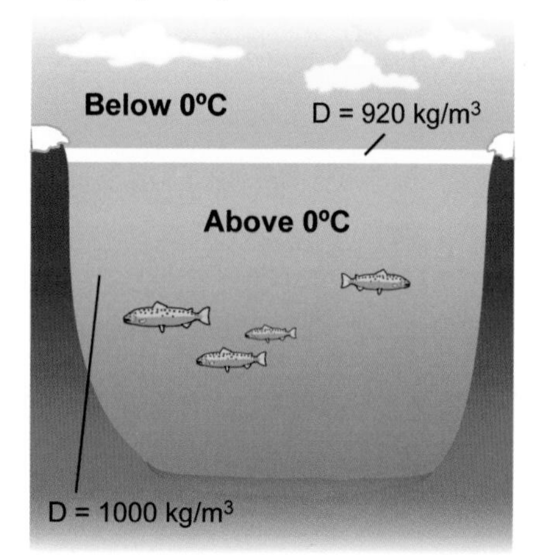

Figure 17.8: *Ice floats keeping the water below from reaching freezing temperatures.*

17.3 Buoyancy of Fluids

Have you ever noticed how easy it is to do a push-up to lift yourself up and out of a swimming pool? It's much easier than doing push-ups on land. That's because the water is exerting an upward force on you. In this section, you will learn more about the force that fluids exert on an object. By the end of the section, you should be able to define buoyancy and explain Archimedes' principle. You should also be able to explain how gases exert forces when they are confined in a container.

What is buoyancy?

A simple experiment can be used to demonstrate the upward force of water you can feel in a swimming pool. A piece of string is tied to a rock, and its weight is measured with a spring scale. The rock weighs 2.25 newtons. Next, the rock is immersed in water, but not allowed to touch the bottom or sides of the container. Now the spring scale measures 1.8 newtons. The water has exerted a force of 0.45 newtons on the rock. We call this force *buoyancy*. **Buoyancy** is a measure of the upward force a fluid exerts on an object, which is created by the pressure differences.

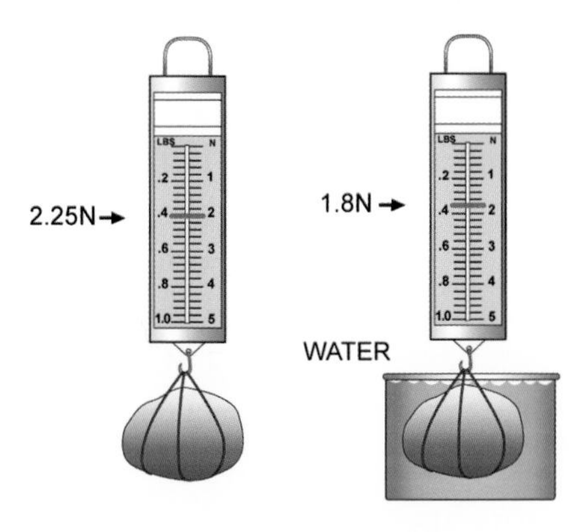

Figure 17.9: *Measuring the weight of a rock in newtons (N). When the rock is suspended in air, it weighs 2.25 N. In water, it weighs 1.8 N.*

What is Archimedes' principle?

In the third century BC, a Greek mathematician named Archimedes made an important discovery about the buoyant force. He realized that the force exerted on an object in a liquid is equal to the weight of the fluid displaced by the object. We call this relationship **Archimedes' principle**.

Archimedes' principle tells us that the water displaced by the rock in the experiment above had a weight of 0.45 newtons.

Do all fluids exert the same buoyant force on an object?

Archimedes' principle can be used to find the buoyant force of liquids other than water. For example, we could immerse the rock from the previous experiment in glycerin, which has a density of 1.26 g/cm^3.

The rock will always displace the same volume of liquid, in this case, about 43 milliliters. Forty-three milliliters of glycerin weigh 0.53 newtons. Therefore, the glycerin exerts a buoyant force of 0.53 newtons on the rock.

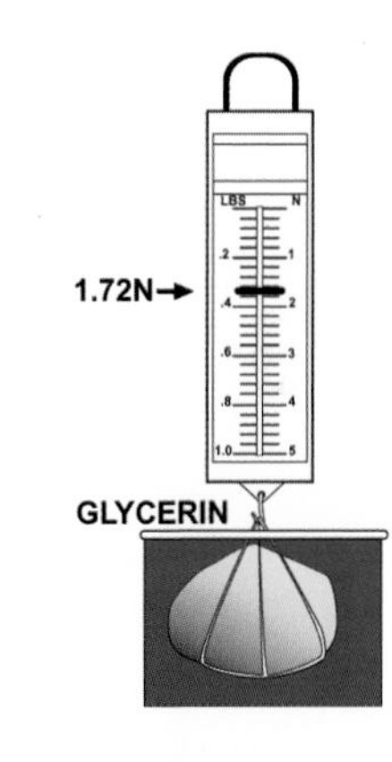

Figure 17.10: *When the rock is suspended in glycerin, it weighs 1.72 N.*

Why objects sink and float

Buoyancy helps explain why some objects sink and others float. If the buoyant force is greater than its weight, the object floats. In the example above, we would need a buoyant force greater than 2.25 newtons to make our rock float.

If the buoyant force is less than its weight, then the object will sink. Neutral buoyancy occurs when the buoyant force is equal to the weight of the object. When an object is neutrally buoyant, it will stay immersed in the liquid at the level where it was placed. Scuba divers use weights and a buoyancy control device (BCD) to help them maintain neutral buoyancy. When a scuba diver is neutrally buoyant he or she can swim and move underwater without rising to the top or sinking.

Why does a block of steel sink, but a steel boat float?

Archimedes' principle explains why a substance in one shape will float and in another shape will sink. A cubic meter of steel has a weight of 76,400 newtons. When placed in water, the block would displace one cubic meter of water. The water would have a weight of 9,800 newtons. The weight of the steel block is much greater than the weight of the displaced water. As expected, the block sinks (Figure 17.11).

Why a steel boat floats

Imagine the same block of steel flattened into a thin sheet, its sides bent up into the shape of a boat. That original block of steel, now shaped to be hollow inside, might occupy 10 cubic meters of space instead of one. Ten cubic meters of displaced water has a weight of 98,000 newtons. Now the displaced water weighs *more* than the steel, which still weighs 76,400 newtons (Figure 17.12).

When placed in the water, your steel boat would settle in the water until it reached a level where it displaced 76,400 newtons of water. Then the upward force exerted by the water would equal the downward force exerted by the boat (Figure 17.13).

Can you make a clay boat float?

You can try a similar experiment with a stick of clay and a bucket of water. Drop the stick of modeling clay into the bucket and observe what happens. Now mold the clay into a boat shape. Can you make a clay boat float?

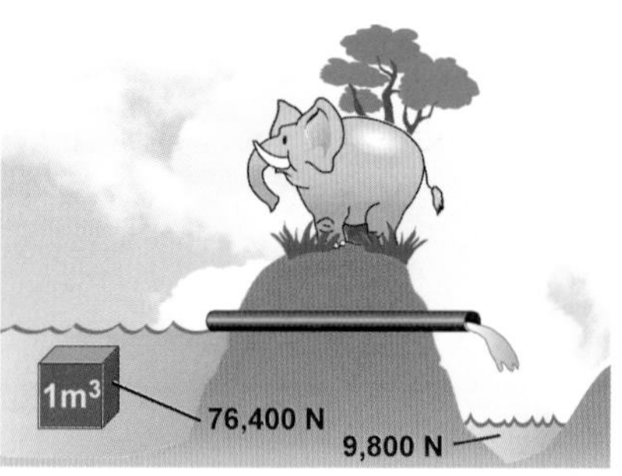

Figure 17.11: *A solid cubic meter of steel weighs 76,400 N. It displaces 9,800 N of water.*

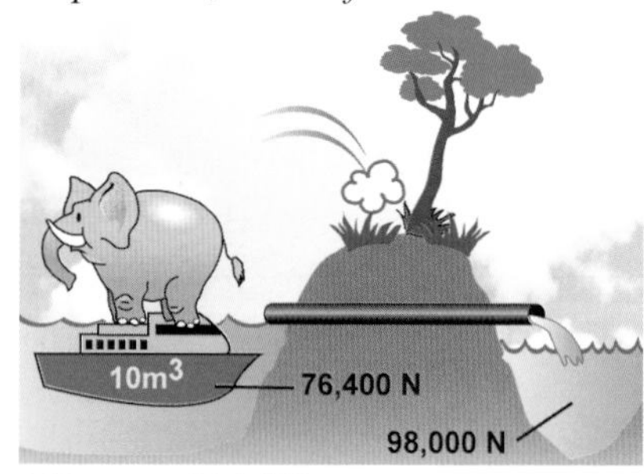

Figure 17.12: *The same amount of steel, shaped into a 10-cubic-meter boat, is held just under the surface by an elephant. Now it displaces 98,000 N of water.*

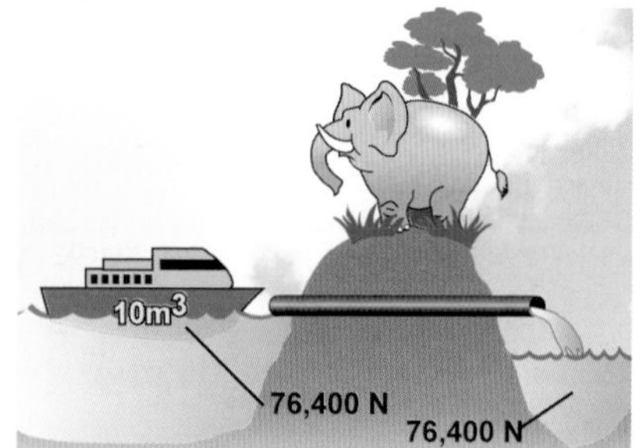

Figure 17.13: *When the boat floats, it displaces 76,400 N of water—which is equal to the boat's own weight.*

Buoyancy and gases

Figure 17.14: *A balloon uses the buoyancy of hot air to lift off.*

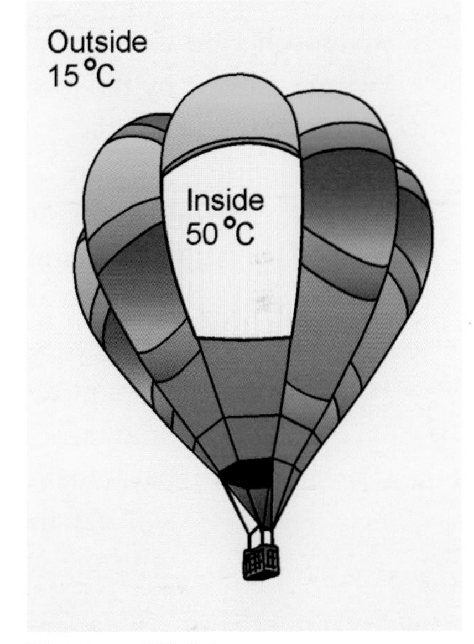

Figure 17.15: *To help objects like hot-air balloons take up a lot of space, air is heated to make it much less dense than the surrounding air.*

Why do hot air balloons float?

Buoyancy is a property of gases as well as liquids. A helium balloon floats because it displaces a very large volume of air. This volume of air weighs *more* than the total weight of the balloon, the gondola (the basket that the balloon carries), and the people in the gondola. The hot-air balloon floats because it weighs *less* than the volume of air displaced.

The relationship between the temperature and volume of a gas

So how can you get a hot-air balloon to take up a lot of space? You probably know the answer to this question. "Hot air" is important. To get their balloons to take flight, balloonists use a torch to heat the air molecules inside the balloon. Heated molecules move with greater energy. As they collide with each other and the sides of the balloon, they take up more space. In effect, the air in the balloon expands. This illustrates an important relationship, known as Charles' law, which was discovered by Jacques Charles in 1787. According to Charles' law, the volume of a gas increases with increasing temperature. The volume of a gas shrinks with decreasing temperature.

Charles' law

The volume of a gas increases with increasing temperature proportionately.
The volume of a gas decreases with decreasing temperature proportionately.

The buoyancy of hot air

Charles' law helps explain why the air inside the balloon becomes much less dense than the air outside the balloon. Because it is less dense, a hot-air balloon will rise in the atmosphere until the density of the air displaced by the balloon matches the average density of the air inside the balloon and the matter of the balloon itself. Stated another way, the weight of the air displaced by the balloon provides buoyant force to keep the balloon in flight.

Gases and pressure

What is pressure? Have you ever pumped up a bicycle tire? What is happening inside of the tire? As you pump more air into the tire, more and more particles of air are pushed into the tire, increasing the **pressure** inside. On a microscopic level, each particle of air collides with the inside walls of the tire, exerting a force which pushes the inner surface of the tire outward. As you pump more air into the tire, there are more particles that can exert forces on the inside walls of the tire. The forces of all of the particles of air inside the tire add together to create pressure (Figure 17.16).

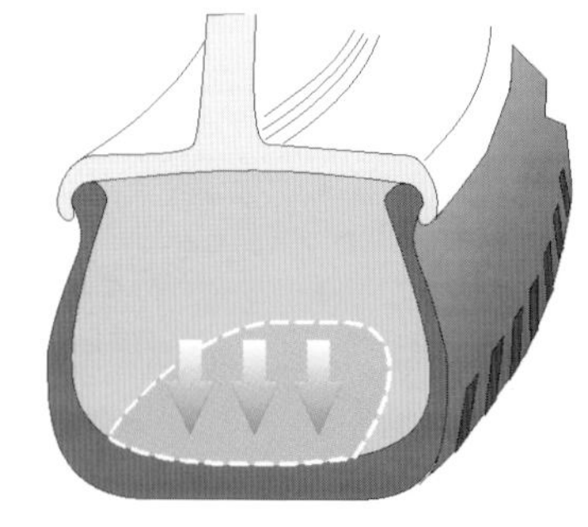

Figure 17.16: *The forces of all of the particles inside the tire add together to create pressure. The pressure inside the tire is what holds a car up.*

Units of pressure Pressure is the force acting on a unit area of surface. You may have noticed that tire pressure is usually measured in units of pound per square inch (psi). A typical bicycle tire should be inflated to about 60 psi. The SI unit for pressure is called a **pascal** (Pa). One pascal is equal to one newton of force acting on one square meter of surface area.

What is atmospheric pressure? The air you breathe is made of many different gases including carbon dioxide, oxygen, and nitrogen. The Earth's air, known as the atmosphere, is held in place by the force of gravity on the air particles. Without the force of gravity, the air you breathe would escape into space. At the Earth's surface, the atmosphere exerts a pressure of 101,300 pascals, or 101,300 newtons of force per square meter—about the weight of an elephant! Atmospheric pressure decreases with altitude. This is why the atmospheric pressure on top of a mountain is less than the atmospheric pressure at sea level. Does this explain why your ears pop when you fly in a plane?

How are pressure and volume related? Suppose you pump five liters of air into a beach ball. If you pump the same amount of air into a basketball *half* the size of the beach ball, which has a greater amount of pressure? Assuming that the temperature remains constant, the basketball has *twice* as much pressure as the beach ball. This is because if you squeeze the same amount of gas into a smaller container, the gas particles collide with the walls of the container *more* often, increasing the pressure. On the other hand, the gas particles inside of the beach ball occupy *twice* as much volume so they collide with the walls *less* often. This property of gases, called **Boyle's law**, was discovered by Robert Boyle in 1662.

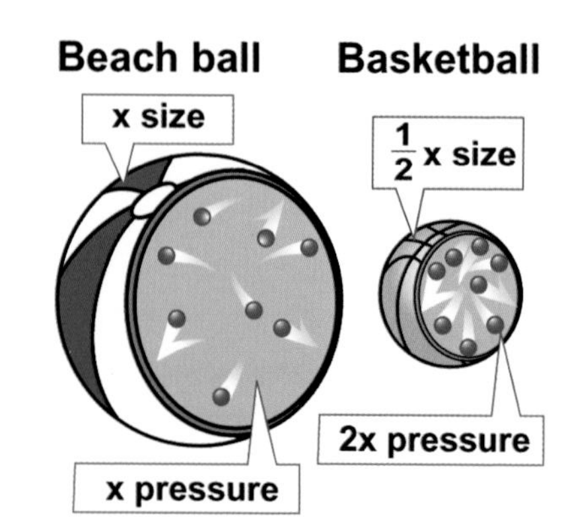

Figure 17.17: *The beach ball and basketball each contain the same amount of air. The basketball has greater pressure than the beach ball because the air particles are squeezed into a smaller space and collide with the walls more often.*

Boyle's law

As the pressure of a gas increases, its volume decreases proportionately.
As the pressure of a gas decreases, its volume increases proportionately.

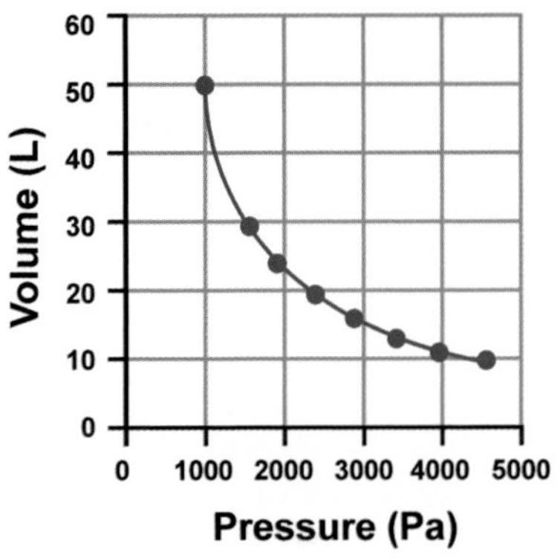

Figure 17.18: *The graph shows the relationship between the pressure and volume of a gas when the temperature does not change.*

Boyle's law equation

The relationship between pressure and volume for a gas, when temperature remains constant, is evident in the graph in Figure 17.18. This relationship can also be expressed by the following equation:

Boyle's law

Initial volume; Initial pressure; New pressure; New volume

$$P_1V_1 = P_2V_2$$

This equation shows that the product of the *initial* pressure and volume of a gas is equal to the product of the *final* pressure and volume of a gas when either pressure or volume is changed. The example below shows how to solve a problem using the equation.

Example problem

A kit used to fix flat tires consists of an aerosol can containing compressed air and a patch to seal the hole in the tire. Suppose 5 liters of air at atmospheric pressure (101.3 kilopascals) is compressed into a 0.5 liter aerosol can. What is the pressure of the compressed air in the can?

What do you know? The equation for Boyle's law is: $P_1V_1 = P_2V_2$

$P_1 = 101.3$ kPa; $V_1 = 5$ L; $P_2 =$ unknown; $V_2 = 0.5$ L

Rearrange the variables: Solve for P_2 and the equation is: $P_2 = \frac{P_1 \cdot V_1}{V_2}$

Plug in the numbers: $P_2 = \frac{101.3 \text{ kPa} \times 5.0 \text{ L}}{0.5 \text{ L}}$

Solve the problem: The pressure inside the aerosol can is 1,013 kPa.

Atmospheric pressure

The pressure exerted by the Earth's atmosphere at sea level is 101,300 pascals (Pa). Since pascals are very small, other units of pressure are often used. The pressure of the Earth's atmosphere at sea level is also equal to:

- 101.3 kilopascals (kPa)
- 1.00 atmosphere (atm)
- 14.7 pounds per inch^2 (psi)
- 760 millimeters of mercury (mm Hg)

17.4 Viscosity of Fluids

Viscosity is another important property of fluids. It is a measure of the material's resistance to flow. High-viscosity fluids take longer to pour from their containers than low-viscosity fluids. Ketchup, for example, has a higher viscosity than tomato juice. Tomato juice has a higher viscosity than water. In this section, you will learn how the size and shape of a molecule influences a liquid's viscosity, and how an increase in temperature changes the viscosity of a fluid.

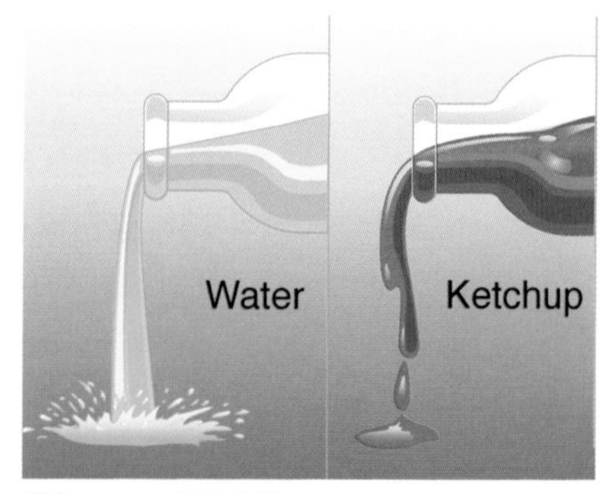

Figure 17.19: *Water is less viscous than ketchup.*

Why does viscosity matter?

Thick substances are very viscous

Viscosity is an important consideration in food production. Fast-food restaurants advertise that their chocolate shakes are thicker than the competitor's. Special ingredients such as carrageenan, which is made from seaweed, are used to bring yogurts, puddings, and pasta sauces to the viscosity that consumers prefer. One company even based a large advertising campaign on the fact that its brand of ketchup was so viscous, a spoon would stand up in a cupful.

Substances like motor oil need to have the right viscosity to work effectively

Viscosity is also an important property of motor oils. If an oil is too thick, it may not flow quickly to the parts of an engine, leaving them vulnerable to excess wear. However, if the oil is too thin, it may not provide enough "cushion" to protect any part of the engine from the effects of friction. A motor oil must function properly when the engine is started on a very cold day, and when the engine is operating at high temperature. As a result, manufacturers make very careful choices about which types of molecules will be included in their formulas for motor oil.

Figure 17.20: *Numbers on the side of a quart of motor oil are based on a scale established by the Society of Automotive Engineers (SAE). The first number indicates the lowest temperature at which the oil will work well (-10°F in this case). The "W" means the oil works well in cold weather. The second number is a grade for the oil: "50" is best for summer driving, "30" for winter driving, and "40" for mild weather temperatures.*

Large, bumpy molecules create more friction than small, smooth molecules

Viscosity is determined in large part by the shape of the molecules in a liquid. If the molecules are large and have bumpy surfaces, a great deal of friction will be created as they slide past each other. The liquid will flow at a slower rate than liquids made up of small molecules with a smoother surface.

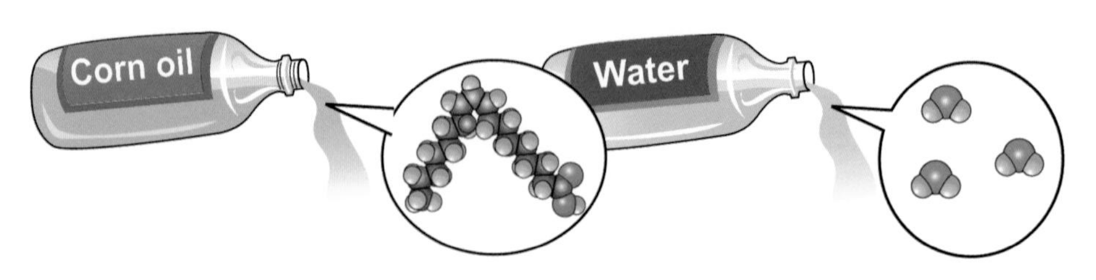

How does temperature effect viscosity?

As a liquid gets warmer, its viscosity decreases

As the temperature of a liquid is raised, the viscosity of the liquid decreases. In other words, warm liquids have less viscosity than cold liquids. Warmed maple syrup or hot fudge, for example, is much easier to pour than the same syrup chilled. Why does this happen? Remember from your study of states of matter that when energy is added to a liquid, the movement of the molecules increases. The increasing speed allows the molecules to slide past each other with greater ease. As a result, the viscosity decreases.

The viscosity of a liquid is related to its temperature

The viscosity of some liquids changes a great deal as the temperature increases. Olive oil, for example, is more viscous at 20°C than 60°C. The oleic acid molecules that are in olive oil are made up of carbon, hydrogen, and oxygen atoms. At lower temperatures, the hydrogen atoms in the oleic acid molecules tend to form loose connections called "hydrogen bonds" with oxygen atoms in other oleic molecules. These connections make it hard for the individual oleic acid molecules to slide around. However, as molecular speed increases with an increase in temperature, some of the hydrogen-oxygen connections between neighboring molecules break apart. As a result, the oil's viscosity decreases significantly.

As a gas gets warmer, its viscosity *increases*

It is interesting to note that gases exhibit the opposite property. As you raise the temperature of a gas, it becomes *more* resistant to flow. This is due to the fact that gas molecules are spaced far apart, so they do not have to slide over one another very often in order to flow. Increasing the temperature increases the number of collisions between the molecules. Therefore, the net effect is an increase in friction and a corresponding increase in viscosity.

Figure 17.21: *Heating fudge makes it easier to pour. The viscosity of the fudge decreases with increased temperature.*

Fun with Physical Science: Silly Putty®— Solid or Liquid?

Silly Putty—it's been a popular party favor for more than fifty years. Your parents probably played with it when they were kids. Some people call it America's longest lasting fad. It's easy to understand why people like Silly Putty. Roll it into a ball, and you can bounce it around the room. Pull on it slowly and it will stretch out like a long lazy snake. Give it a quick yank and it will break with a satisfying *snap*. Have you ever tried to smash a ball of Silly Putty with a hammer? It keeps its shape every time. However, if you gently press on it with your thumb, you can flatten it easily. If you leave a ball of Silly Putty on your dresser overnight, in the morning you'll see that it flattened out by itself while you were sleeping.

Silly Putty isn't easy to categorize. It holds it shape when hammered, yet flows into a puddle when left alone overnight. No wonder the people who make Silly Putty call it "a real solid liquid." Rheologists (scientists who study how matter flows and/or deforms) have another term for Silly Putty: it's a viscoelastic liquid.

Viscoelastic is a compound word (like snowman). The visco- part comes from the word viscous, which means "resistant to flow." Thick, gooey, slow-flowing liquids like hot fudge sauce are viscous. Silly Putty is like that. You're probably already familiar with the second half of the word. Elastic, in physics terms, describes a material that returns to its original shape when deformed. So, rheologists describe Silly Putty as a slow-flowing, elastic liquid.

It's not too surprising that Silly Putty bounces, because it was accidentally invented by a chemist looking for a substitute for rubber. In 1943, James Wright, a researcher for General Electric, dropped some boric acid into silicone oil, creating a gooey compound. This compound, first called "nutty putty," was sent to engineers around the world—but no practical uses were found. In 1949, a man named Peter Hodgson decided to sell it as a toy. He borrowed $147 to buy a batch from General Electric, divided the batch into one-ounce lumps, and placed each lump into a plastic egg. He renamed the compound "Silly Putty" after the main ingredient, silicone. A New Yorker magazine reporter wrote an article about Silly Putty in 1950, and afterward Hodgson received 250,000 orders in three days. Silly Putty was a hit!

The silicone oil used to make Silly Putty is known to chemists as polydimethylsiloxane, or PDMS. PDMS is a polymer, which means each molecule is made up of long chain of identical smaller molecules.

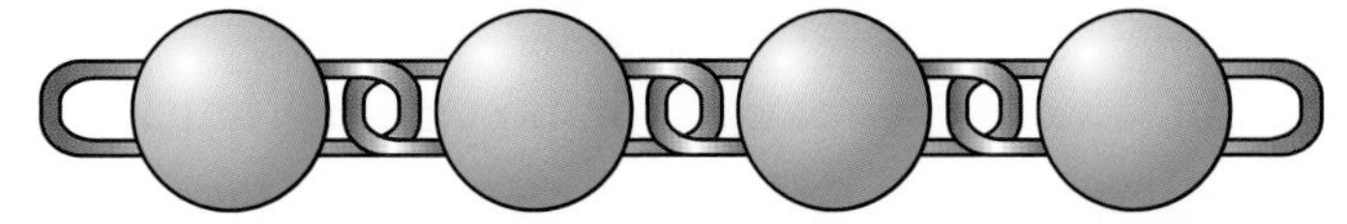

When boric acid is added to the long chains of PDMS, boron crosslinks begin to form. This means that the boron hooks chains of PDMS molecules together like this:

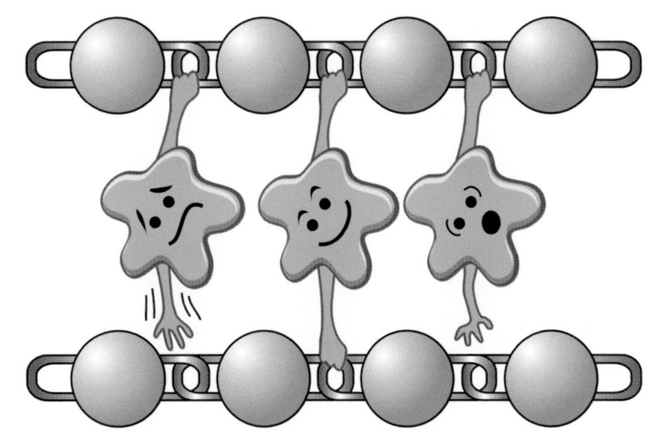

These boron crosslinks are not very strong. Remember that molecules in solids and liquids are always in motion. This motion breaks boron crosslinks, but over time new crosslinks form. This action is called dynamic (changing) crosslinking. Because of this dynamic crosslinking, Silly Putty reacts one way to quick forces and another way to long-acting forces.

When you strike Silly Putty with a hammer, the Silly Putty reacts like an elastic solid: it bounces back. That's because most of the boron crosslinks remain in place during the split second of the hammer's strike. When you leave a ball of Silly Putty untouched overnight, the boron crosslinks that help Silly Putty hold its shape have about eight hours to break down. Over that time, molecular motion breaks many of the original crosslinks. Gravitational force constantly pulls the PDMS molecules downward, and in the morning you're left with a Silly Putty puddle.

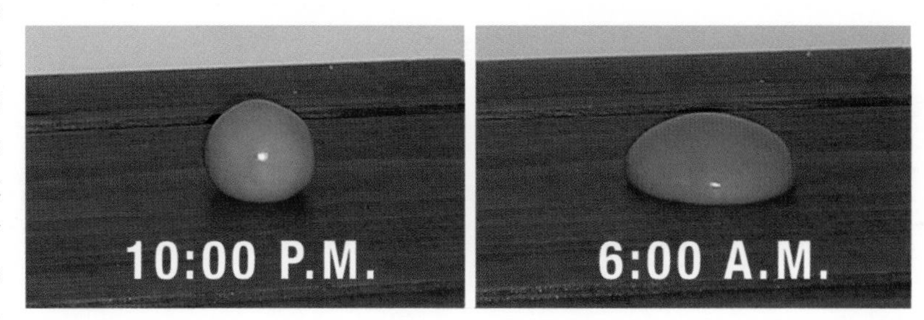

Chapter 17 Review

Vocabulary review

Match the following terms with the correct definition. There is one extra definition in the list that will not match any of the terms.

Set One

1. density
2. hardness
3. brittleness
4. elasticity
5. malleability

a. A measurement of how easily a solid can be pounded into thin sheets
b. A measurement of the "compactness" of a substance; the ratio of its mass to volume
c. A measure of a solid's ability to return to its original shape after it is stretched or squeezed
d. A measurement of how easily a solid will shatter
e. A measurement of how easily a solid can be scratched
f. A measurement of how well a solid resists breaking when it is under tension

Set Two

1. tensile strength
2. fluid
3. buoyancy
4. Archimedes' principle
5. viscosity

a. The upward force of a liquid or gas upon an object immersed in it
b. Any material that flows; commonly refers to matter in the liquid or gas state
c. A measure of a fluid's resistance to flow
d. A measurement of how well a solid resists breaking when it is pulled on
e. The force exerted on an object in a fluid is equal to the volume of the displaced fluid
f. The force exerted on an object in a fluid is equal to the weight of the displaced fluid

Concept review

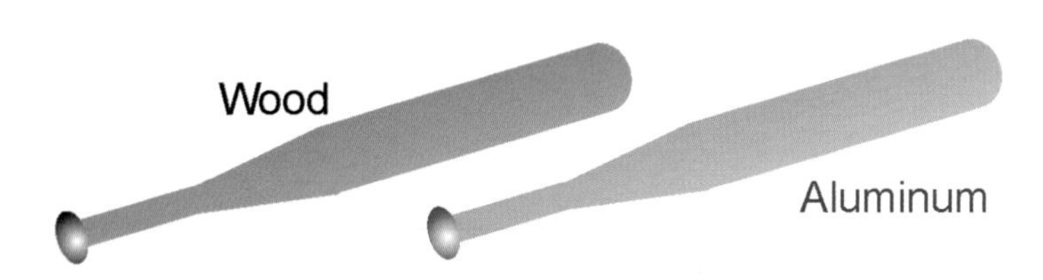

1. A wooden baseball bat and an aluminum bat have the exact same shape, size and mass. Aluminum is much denser than wood. Explain how the two bats could be the same size and mass.

2. At 20°C, the density of copper is 8.9 g/cm^3. The density of platinum is 21.4 g/cm^3. What does this tell you about how the atoms are "packed" in each material?

3. You are an engineer who must choose a type of plastic to use for the infant car seat that you are designing. Name two properties of solids that would help you decide, and explain why each is important.

4. Would a cube of solid silver sink or float in liquid silver? How do you know?

5. The Dead Sea is a body of water that lies between Israel and Jordan. It is so salty that almost no organisms other than a few types of bacteria can survive in it. The density of its surface water is 1.166 g/ml. Would you find it easier to float in the Dead Sea or in a freshwater lake? Give a reason for your answer.

6. You pump your soccer ball up with a certain volume of air the night before a game. The next morning, you wake up and go outside to get your ball. You notice that it is much colder outside than the night before. When you pick up the ball, you notice that it appears to need more air. Assuming that the ball does not have a leak, can you explain why it appears that the volume of air in the ball may have decreased?

Problems

1. The density of gasoline at 20°C is 0.7 g/ml. What is the mass of 4 liters of gasoline?

2. Your teacher gives you two stainless steel ball bearings. The larger has a mass of 25 g and a volume of 3.2 cm^3. The smaller has a mass of 10 g. Calculate the volume of the smaller ball bearing.

3. Ice has a density of 0.92 g/cm^3. What is the volume of 100 grams of ice? If the ice completely melted, what would the volume of the water be? (The density of water is 1.00 g/ml).

4. A chunk of pure gold weighs 2.00 N. Its volume is 10.6 cm^3.
   a. If the gold is immersed in water at 20°C, find the weight of the displaced water. Hints: 1 cm^3 of water = 1 g; 1 g = 0.0098 N.
   b. If the gold were attached to a spring scale and suspended in the water, how much would it appear to weigh?

5. Six liters of helium gas held at 2,500 kilopascals are pumped into a balloon that holds 1 liter. What is the pressure inside the balloon? Assume that the temperature does not change.

Applying your knowledge

1. Ancient peoples learned to make tools out of bronze before they learned to make iron. Bronze is harder than copper, but not as hard as iron. Bronze is a homogeneous mixture made up of 90 percent copper and 10 percent tin. At 20°C, the density of pure copper is 8.9 g/cm^3 and the density of tin is 7.3 g/cm^3. What is the density of bronze at 20°C?

2. Scientists believe that if the density of ice were greater than that of water, the states of Michigan, Wisconsin, Ohio, and New York would be much colder in the summer than they currently are. Why? Research this phenomenon and create a poster presentation to explain your findings.

3. In the reading, you learned that the Earth's atmosphere exerts a pressure of about 101,300 newtons per square meter of surface—about the weight of an elephant. Why doesn't this pressure crush you? What conditions need to exist so that atmospheric pressure does not crush you?
   a. Research how humans (and other organisms that live on land) are adapted to live in this atmospheric pressure. Make a list of these adaptations and an explanation of each.
   b. Some organisms are adapted to life in the depths of the ocean. Research the amount of pressure these organisms need to be able to withstand. Make a list of their adaptations to life under tremendous pressure, and explain your findings.

4. Hardness is a property of matter that is easy to confuse with toughness or durability. Look around your classroom, your home, or outside, and name one object that has high hardness but low durability and one object that has low hardness but high durability.

5. Observe the world around you and find different objects or materials that fit each of the following descriptions:
   a. has both high elasticity and high tensile strength
   b. has both high hardness and low malleability
   c. has both high hardness and high brittleness
   d. has some elasticity but low tensile strength

6. JAN FEB MAR The Roman architect Vitruvius (first century B.C.) is the source of a story of how Archimedes discovered that a golden crown commissioned by Hiero II, the king of Syracuse, wasn't 100 percent gold! The crown would have been in the form of a wreath, like the picture at right. The crown/wreath would have been placed on an important statue. Suspecting that the goldsmith might have mixed silver with gold to make the crown, Hiero asked Archimedes to determine whether the wreath was pure gold without destroying the wreath in any way. In other words, Archimedes had to perform nondestructive test.

   The way to test the wreath occurred to Archimedes when he stepped into his bath and caused it to overflow. Based on his observation, he decided to put a weight of gold equal to the crown and known to be pure into a bowl that was filled with water to the brim. Then the gold would be carefully removed from the water and the king's crown put in its place. An alloy of lighter silver would increase the bulk of the crown and cause the bowl to overflow. However, if the wreath was pure gold, the water would rise back to the level it was at when the pure gold bar was in the water.

   Explain whether you think Archimedes' method would work in identifying whether or not the crown was pure gold.

7. Quite a number of studies have been done on the viscosity of lava from various volcanic eruptions around the world. Do some research to find out how scientists determine the viscosity of lava, and discover if there is much variation in the viscosity of different lava flows.

UNIT 6

Properties of Matter

Chapter 18

Atoms and Elements

Introduction to Chapter 18

What does matter look like at its most basic level? This question has intrigued people for thousands of years. In this chapter, you will learn about atoms, how they are put together, how many kinds of atoms exist, and how people keep track of the different kinds of atoms.

Investigations for Chapter 18

18.1	**Atomic Structure**	*How was the size of an atom's nucleus determined?*

You will use indirect measurement to find the radius of a circle, and compare your work with the classic experiment used to find the radius of an atomic nucleus.

18.2	**Comparing Atoms**	*What are atoms and how are they put together?*

You will construct models of several kinds of atoms using the atom-building game.

18.3	**The Periodic Table of Elements**	*What does atomic structure have to do with the periodic table?*

You will learn how different kinds of atoms (the elements) are arranged in the periodic table of elements. You will play Atomic Challenge, a game that will test your skills in reading the periodic table.

Learning Goals

In this chapter, you will:

- ✔ Use indirect measurement to determine the radius of a circle.
- ✔ Build models of atoms.
- ✔ Research one of the historical atomic models.
- ✔ Understand how atoms of each element differ.
- ✔ Describe the forces that hold an atom together.
- ✔ Use the concept of electron shells to arrange electrons in atomic models.
- ✔ Understand how elements are organized in the periodic table.
- ✔ Use the periodic table to identify the atomic number and mass numbers of each element.
- ✔ Calculate the numbers of protons and neutrons in each stable isotope of an element.

Vocabulary

atomic mass	electron	mass number	proton
atomic mass units	energy levels	neutron	strong nuclear force
atomic number	group of elements	nucleus	subatomic particles
atomic theory	isotopes	periodic table of elements	valence electrons
chemical symbol			

18.1 Atomic Structure

All matter is formed from atoms. Atoms, by themselves or combined with other atoms in molecules, make up everything that we see, hear, feel, smell, and touch. An individual atom is so small that one cell in your body contains 100 trillion atoms, and a speck of dust contains many more atoms than that. As small as they are, atoms and molecules are the building blocks of every type of matter. A few hundred incredibly tiny atoms of gold have the same density as a bar of gold. A few hundred very tiny molecules of water have the same density as a cup of water. In this section you will find out about atoms and learn about the historical experiments that helped scientists understand atomic structure.

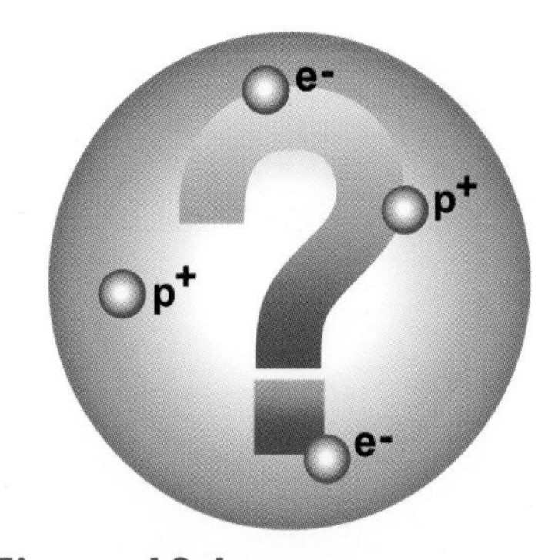

Figure 18.1: *What do atoms look like? What are they made out of? These questions have been asked by scientists ever since 400 BC, when Democritus (a Greek philosopher) proposed the existence of atoms.*

Inside an atom

Protons, neutrons, and electrons

Atoms and molecules are called the building blocks of matter because if you attempt to break down an atom, you no longer have gold or water or any other recognizable substance. If broken apart, almost all atoms contain three smaller particles called **protons**, **neutrons**, and **electrons**. Because these particles are even smaller than an atom, they are called **subatomic particles**. These three types of particles are arranged in an atom as shown in Figure 18.2.

How are protons, neutrons, and electrons arranged within an atom?

Protons and neutrons cluster together in the atom's center, called the **nucleus**. The electrons move in the space around the nucleus. No one is able to say exactly where an electron is at any one time. A useful analogy is that electrons buzz around the nucleus much like bees around a hive. Some people describe each electron as a wave; just as the vibration of a guitar string exists all along the string, the electrons exist at all the shaded points in Figure 18.2.

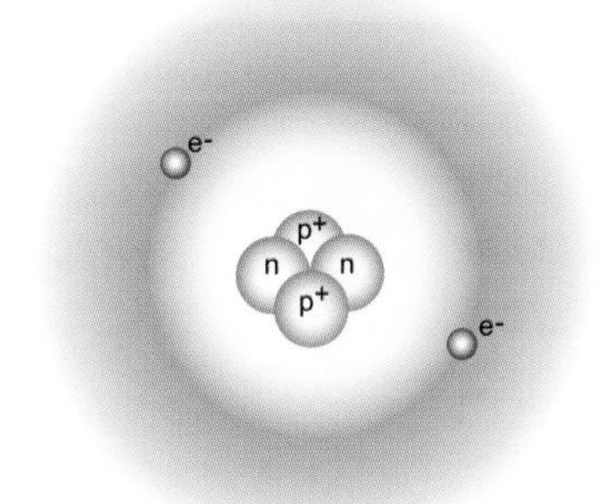

Figure 18.2: *An atom has a nucleus with one or more protons and neutrons and one or more energy levels occupied by electrons. The shaded area around the outside of the atom represents the places the electrons might be. A good analogy is that electrons "buzz" around the nucleus in energy levels like bees around a hive.*

Subatomic particles

Protons, neutrons, and electrons are called subatomic particles. The proton is positive, the electron is negative, and the neutron is electrically neutral. Protons and neutrons have about the same mass. Each is about 2,000 times the mass of an electron. Since protons and neutrons exist in the nucleus, almost all the mass of an atom is concentrated there. These properties helped scientists figure out the atomic structure.

How big are atoms?

Atoms are very small

An atom and its parts are much smaller than a meter. The diameter of an atom is 10^{-10} (0.0000000001) meter, whereas an electron is smaller than 10^{-18} (0.000000000000000001) meter. Comparatively, this means that an electron is 10 million times smaller than an atom! The diameter of a nucleon (a proton or neutron) is a distance that is equal to one fermi. This unit (equal to 10^{-15} meter) is named for Enrico Fermi, an Italian-born physicist who studied the nucleus of the atom. For his work with neutrons, he received the Nobel Prize for physics in 1938.

Most of the atom is empty space

You may be surprised to learn that most of the atom is actually empty space: If the atom was the size of your classroom, then the nucleus would be the size of a grain of sand in the center of the room.

Particle	Diameter (meters)
atom	10^{-10}
nucleus	10^{-14}
proton	10^{-15}
neutron	10^{-15}
electron	10^{-18}

Figure 18.3: *Diameters of an atom and its subatomic particles.*

John Dalton and the atomic theory

As early as 400 BC, Greek philosophers proposed the atomic theory. This theory states that all matter is composed of tiny particles called atoms. Many centuries later, English chemist and physicist John Dalton (1766-1844) was one of the first scientists to set out to gather evidence for the idea. Dalton was a remarkable person. Born into a family too poor to send him to school, young John educated himself and, at age 12, became a schoolteacher. He grew to be one of the leading scientists of his time.

In 1808, Dalton published a detailed atomic theory that contained the following important points:

1 Each element is composed of extremely small particles called atoms.
2 All atoms of a given element are identical.
3 Atoms of different elements have different properties, including mass and chemical reactivity.
4 Atoms are not changed by chemical reactions, but merely rearranged into different compounds.
5 Compounds are formed when atoms of more than one element combine.
6 A compound is defined by the number, type (element), and proportion of the constituent atoms.

Dalton's atomic theory laid the groundwork for later atomic models, and over time, his original theory has been expanded and updated.

Weather & atomic theory

One of John Dalton's interests was weather (he kept detailed records for 57 years), and that led him to study gases. He studied the evaporation of water into the air and was able to understand that the process increased gas pressure. From these observations of pressure, and from other experiments, he gathered evidence about the structure of matter.

The changing model of the atom

The current model of the atom represents our current understanding of atomic structure. This model is one of a series of models constructed by people as they learned new information about atoms. New information enabled people to update and change their ideas about how the atom is constructed.

The name *atom* comes from Democritus, a Greek philosopher (circa 460-370 BC) who proposed that matter is made up of small particles, which he called atoms (from the Greek word *atomos,* or indivisible). His model describes atoms as small particles that differ in size and shape, that combine in different configurations, and that are constantly in motion. Many of Democritus' ideas were based on logical thinking.

The idea that theories need to be supported by evidence—often gathered in carefully controlled experiments—became important in the 1600s. Then scientists began to design experiments to support or disprove ideas proposed by earlier thinkers such as Democritus. John Dalton (see previous page) was a chemist who experimented with different gases. His careful measurements gave him repeatable evidence that matter is made up of atoms. His model of the atom is a tiny hard sphere.

The idea that atoms might contain smaller particles came about through a series of observations of cathode ray tubes, devices that were early versions of fluorescent and neon lights. Julius Plucker, a German physicist (1801-1868), and William Crooks, an English physicist and chemist (1832-1919), and his countryman and fellow physicist Joseph John Thomson (1856-1940) conducted many of these experiments. They showed that different gases placed in the tubes generated streams of particles and conducted current.

From these experiments Thomson identified the electron, which carries a negative charge. Thomson knew that atoms were electrically neutral, so he proposed that the atom was a positive sphere with negative electrons embedded in it like raisins in a roll or bun (Figure 18.4). The positive sphere and the negative electrons had an equal and opposite amount of charge, so the atom was neutral.

In 1911 in England, physicists Ernest Rutherford (1871-1937), Hans Geiger (1882-1945), and Ernest Marsden (1889-1970), used high-speed, lightweight atoms called alpha particles (generated by radioactive material), to bombard very thin pieces of gold foil. Most of the alpha particles passed through the foil and hit a screen behind it. But surprisingly, some of them bounced back ((Figure 18.5). They must have hit areas of the foil with greater density!

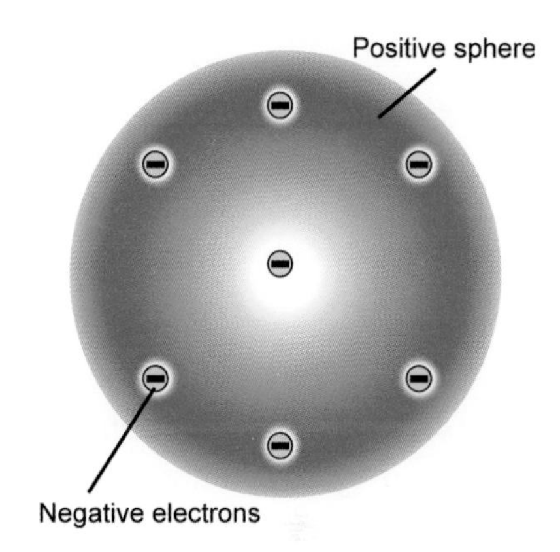

Figure 18.4: *The Thomson model of the atom. The atom is a positive sphere with negative electrons embedded in it.*

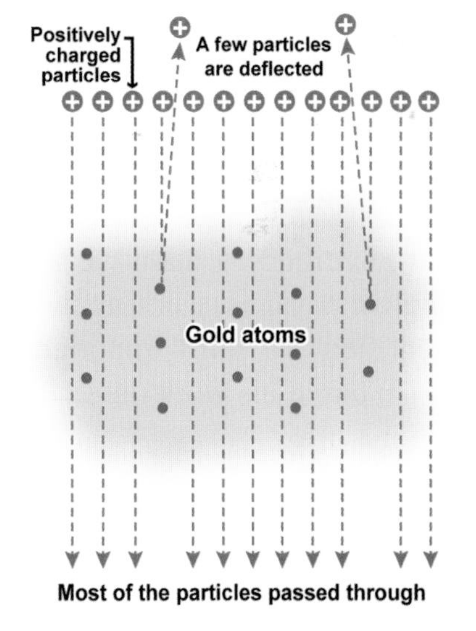

Figure 18.5: *An illustration of Rutherford's experiment.*

Rutherford hypothesized that an atom must be made up of mostly empty space, allowing most of the alpha particles to pass through the foil. In the center of the atom, he suggested, was a tiny core called a nucleus, which contained positively-charged protons. This is where most of the mass must be found. The lighter electrons occupied the area between the nucleus and the edge of the atom. However, Rutherford did not have enough information to describe the electrons' location more fully.

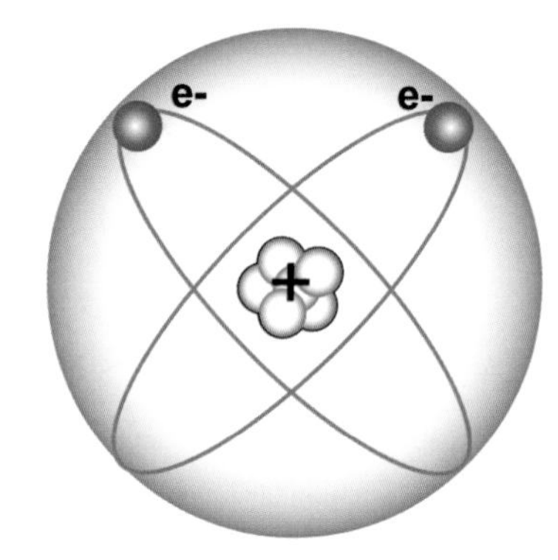

Figure 18.6: *The Bohr model of the atom. Electrons move around the nucleus in fixed orbits.*

Danish physicist Niels Bohr (1885-1962) used information about the nature of the emission of light by heated objects to update Rutherford's model. He described electrons as moving around the nucleus in fixed orbits that have a set amount of energy (Figure 18.6). Bohr's model of the electron orbits is still used in many analyses of the atom. However, other 20th century experiments have shown that radiating waves can behave like particles in motion, and particles in motion can behave like waves (Figure 18.7).

In 1923, Louis de Broglie (1892-1987), a French physicist, showed how to analyze a moving particle as a wave. In 1926, Austrian physicist Erwin Schrödinger (1887-1961) built on de Broglie's work and treated electrons as three-dimensional waves. He developed a mathematical description of electrons in atoms that is called the quantum mechanical model of the atom. It is also called the electron cloud model, because his mathematical description cannot be described easily either in words or pictures, so a cloud represents the probability of electron position.

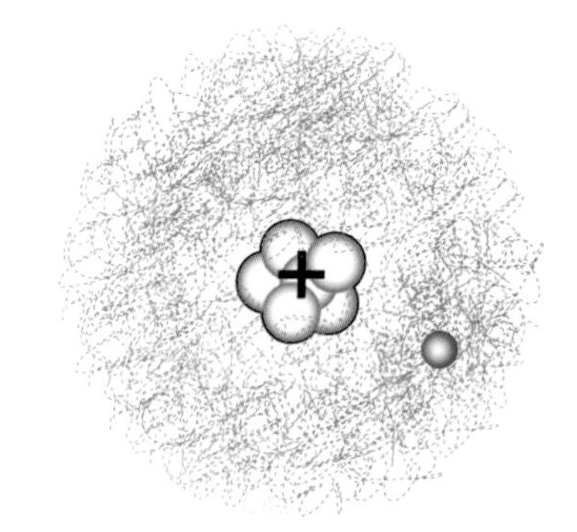

Figure 18.7: *Electrons in the Schrodinger model of the atom. This model is also called the electron cloud model. The cloud represents the probable location of an electron.*

There still remained a serious problem with the atomic model, a problem Rutherford had identified so many years earlier: missing mass. In 1932, James Chadwick, an English physicist working in Rutherford's laboratory, finally solved the problem. He identified the third important subatomic particle, the neutron. Chadwick (1891-1974) based his work on earlier experiments by French physicists Irene and Frederic Joliot-Curie.

Understanding what is inside an atom has motivated many thousands of scientists and thinkers. What some of them discovered along the way changed the world, influencing not only theoretical spheres such as many of the sciences, philosophy, logic, and other areas, but also those subjects' practical applications. So many new technological developments of the late 20th century have been made possible by atomic research that the present era is often referred to as the "atomic age."

18.2 Comparing Atoms

As you know, some substances are made up of only one kind of atom and these substances are called elements. You already know something about a number of elements—you've heard of hydrogen, helium, silver, gold, aluminum, copper, lead, and carbon, for example.

Exactly how does one element differ from another? This information is important. Over the centuries chemists, physicians, technologists, and inventors have used this knowledge to create everything from better medicines to beautiful jewelry.

How people figured out *why* the elements are different from each other is one of the most fascinating stories in science. It brings together the work of physicists, who studied the structure of the atom, and chemists, who studied how elements react and combine.

Figure 18.8: *How does one kind of atom differ from another?*

Atomic number

The number of protons determines an element

Remember that atoms are themselves composed of protons, electrons, and neutrons. Through intense study of the structure of the atom, people discovered that it is the *number of protons* that distinguishes an atom of one element from the atom of another element.

Can you change the number of protons?

All atoms of the same element will have the same number of protons, and atoms of different elements will have different numbers of protons. Adding or removing a proton from an atom usually takes (or releases) huge amounts of energy. Therefore, most atoms are very stable. Even if atoms bond or break apart during chemical reactions, the number of protons in each atom always remains the same. The atoms themselves are only rearranged in different combinations.

What is the atomic number?

Because the number of protons in an atom remains the same during physical and chemical changes, we can refer to each element by the number of protons its atoms contain. This unique number is called the **atomic number**.

Atomic numbers start at 1, with the element hydrogen, and go up by one until 111, the element unununium. The heaviest elements (those with the highest atomic numbers) have been created in a laboratory and have not been seen in nature.

Atomic number: The number of protons

Figure 18.9: *Look at the periodic table in the back cover of this book. The atomic number tells you the number of protons in an atom.*

Atomic mass, mass number, and isotopes

Mass number In addition to the atomic number, every atomic nucleus can be described by its mass number. The **mass number** is equal to the total number of protons plus neutrons in the nucleus of an atom. Recall that atoms of the same element have the same number of protons. Atoms of the same element *can* have different numbers of neutrons.

What does the atomic mass tell you? Chemists arrange the elements in a table called the **periodic table of elements**. If you look at the periodic table in the back cover of this book, you will notice that the atomic number increases by one whole number at a time. This is because you add one proton at a time for each element. The atomic masses however, increase by amounts greater than one (Figure 18.10). This difference is due to the neutrons in the nucleus. Neutrons add mass to the atom, but do not change its atomic number (or charge).

Mass number and neutrons The total number of protons and neutrons in the nucleus of an atom is called the mass number. Sometimes, the mass number of an element is included in the symbol. By convention, the mass number is written as a superscript above the symbol and the atomic number as a subscript below the symbol (Figure 18.11). You can find the number of neutrons by subtracting the atomic number from the mass number. How many neutrons does the carbon atom in Figure 18.11 have?

What are isotopes? Many elements have atoms with different numbers of neutrons. These different forms of the same element are called isotopes. **Isotopes** are atoms of the same element that have different numbers of neutrons. Because of this, the notation shown in Figure 18.11 is called *isotope notation*.

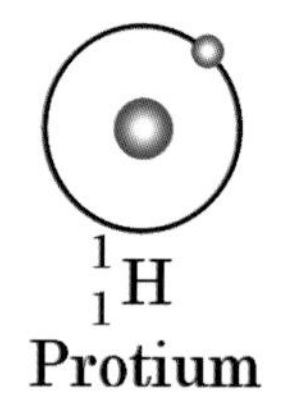

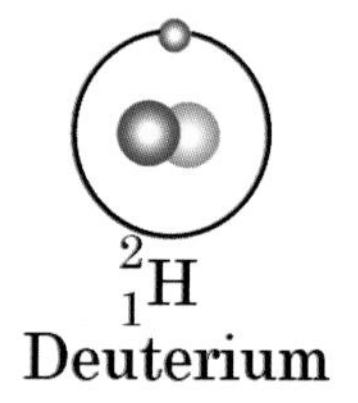

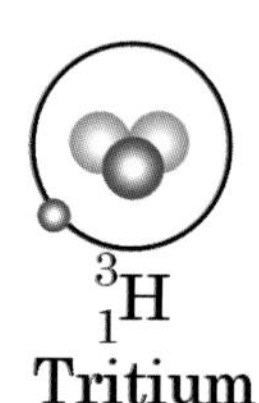

The three isotopes of hydrogen are shown here.

Figure 18.10: *The difference between the atomic number and atomic mass is due to the number of neutrons.*

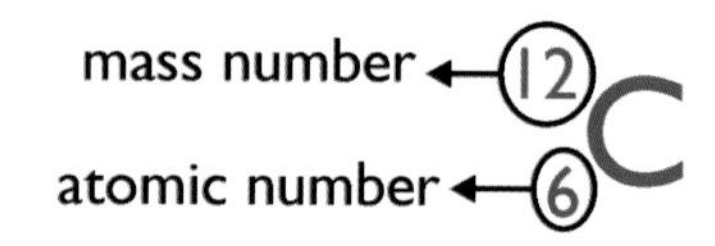

Figure 18.11: *The isotope notation for carbon-12.*

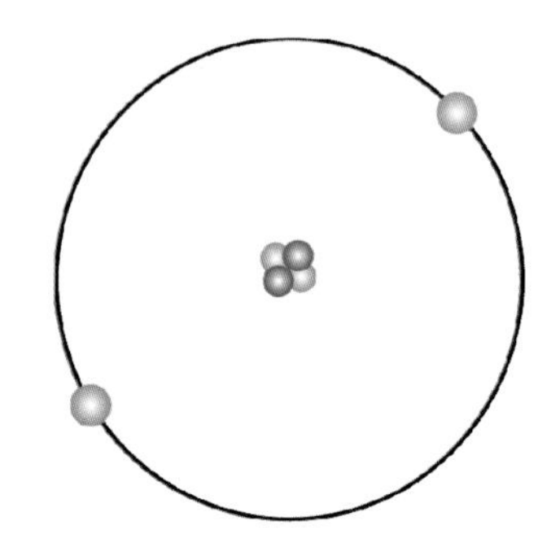

Figure 18.12: *This atom has 2 protons and 2 neutrons. What is the element? What is its mass number?*

Example: finding the number of neutrons

Example: How many neutrons are present in an atom of carbon that has a mass number of 14?

Solution: The mass number is the number of protons plus the number of neutrons.

(1) You are asked for the number of neutrons.

(2) You are given that it is carbon-14. Carbon has 6 protons.

(3) The relationship is $n + p = \text{mass number}$

(4) Solve for n

$n = \text{mass number} - p$

(5) Plug in numbers and get answer

$n = 14 - 6 = 8$

There are 8 neutrons in a carbon-14 nucleus.

How many different elements are possible?

Why aren't there infinite numbers of elements?

Why aren't there infinite numbers of elements, each with an atomic number greater than the one before it? The answer may lie in the forces that keep a nucleus together. Remember that positive charges repel each other. In the nucleus, however, positive protons and neutral neutrons sit side by side. Because the protons are repelling each other, they (and the nucleus) should fly apart!

What holds the nucleus of an atom together?

The nucleus stays together because there is another force acting that is stronger than the repulsion of the protons for each other. Because it is stronger than the electromagnetic force, scientists call it the **strong nuclear force**. Unlike gravity, which can reach millions of miles, the strong force only acts on very short distances. The effective distance for the strong force is so short, we do not feel it outside the nucleus of an atom.

What holds the nucleus together?

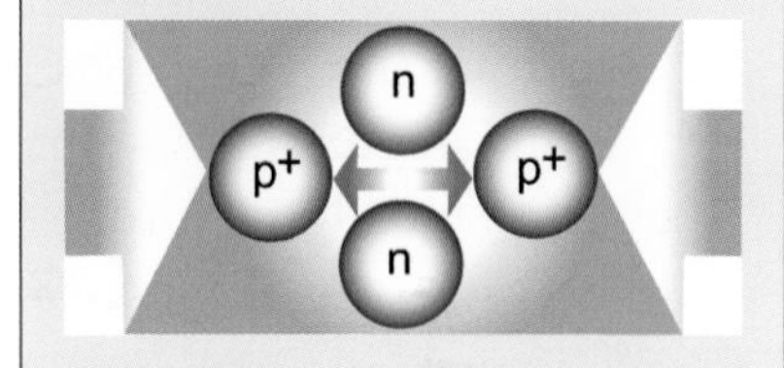

Protons in the nucleus both repel and attract each other. The repulsions are due to electromagnetic force and the attractions are due to the strong nuclear force. The strong nuclear force only acts over very short distances, about the size of an atomic nucleus. Neutrons and protons also attract each other because of the strong nuclear force.

How are electrons arranged in atoms?

Neutral atoms have the same number of electrons as protons

Atoms are electrically neutral. An atom of helium has an atomic number of 2 and two protons in its nucleus. A neutral atom of helium would therefore have two electrons, which stay close to the nucleus because the positive protons and the negative electrons attract each other. An atom of silver has an atomic number of 47 and 47 protons in its nucleus. A neutral atom of silver would therefore have 47 electrons. Are these electrons randomly placed or are they organized in some way?

Electrons are found in the electron cloud

Electrons are never all in one place at the same time. Instead, they literally buzz around the nucleus at a very fast rate, or frequency. Because of this behavior, we can refer to the entire space that electrons occupy as the *electron cloud* (Figure 18.13).

The electron cloud is divided into energy levels

The current model of the atom describes the area of the electron cloud that each electron occupies as an *energy state*. The farther away from the nucleus the electron is found, the higher its energy state. Therefore, the electron cloud is divided into *energy levels*. The first energy level is closest to the nucleus and has the lowest energy. Electrons that occupy this level are at a lower energy state than electrons that occupy the second energy level, which is farther from the nucleus. Each energy level can hold up to a certain number of electrons (Figure 18.14). Sometimes, when an atom absorbs enough energy, some of its electrons "jump" to a higher energy level. When they fall back to their normal energy level, light is released with a frequency equal to the amount of energy the atom absorbed.

Like the layers of an onion, as the energy levels extend farther from the nucleus, they get larger in diameter and can hold more electrons. The maximum number the first four levels can hold is shown in Figure 18.14.

Energy levels can overlap

It is important to note that some energy levels can overlap. In fact, each energy level is subdivided into smaller regions called *orbitals*. Some orbitals in the third energy level may have higher energy than some in the fourth and so on. Scientists have found out exactly which orbitals are occupied, and by how many electrons, in all 111 elements. You will explore this concept in greater detail in future chemistry courses.

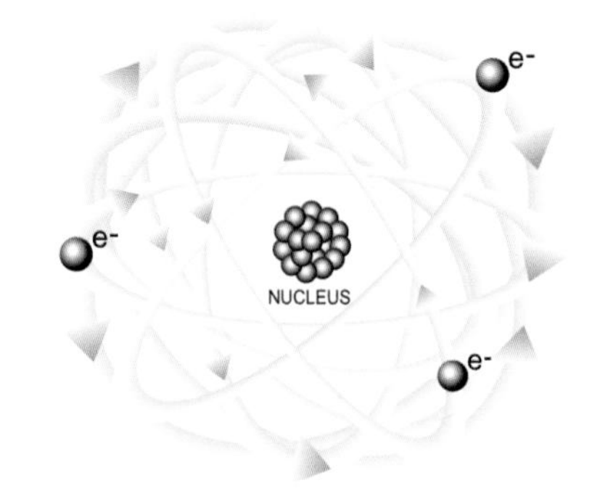

Figure 18.13: *Electrons buzz around the nucleus at a very fast rate.*

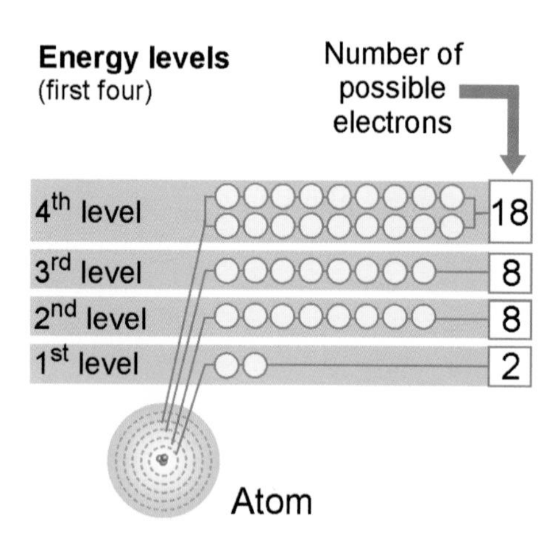

Figure 18.14: *Electrons occupy energy levels around the nucleus. The farther away an electron is from the nucleus, the more energy it possesses.*

Fireworks and electron energy levels

Almost everyone enjoys the bright colors, noise, and drama of fireworks. The loud noises are caused by a black powder that explodes when burned. What causes the colors? The answer to this question is directly related to energy levels and the strict rules that govern how electrons act around a nucleus.

Electrons will fill up the lowest energy level first, because they are attracted to the nucleus. But just as we can lift a marble to the top of a hill, energy can be used to move an electron farther away from the nucleus. When fireworks burn at a high heat, the energy provided by the heat is absorbed by the atoms and the electrons jump up to higher energy levels. This process is called *electron excitation*.

When an electron falls back down to its original position, energy is released in the form of electromagnetic radiation, including light. The release of electromagnetic energy that occurs when the electrons fall down into a lower-energy position is called *emission*.

Because electromagnetic radiation is a wave, it comes in different frequencies. Some frequencies we can see with our eyes and we call those frequencies light. As you remember from the last unit, light of different frequencies we see as different colors.

Because of the arrangement of the energy levels surrounding an atom, excited electrons can release electromagnetic radiation in a range of frequencies. The trick in building fireworks is to find materials that release radiation at the right frequency for us to see. These materials are metal salts, which are combinations of metal ions with other ions. With energy input, these metal ions release electromagnetic radiation at wavelengths that we see as colors. The colors we see from different elements are listed in Figure 18.16.

The fact that different elements, when heated, can release different colors of light tells us that energy levels in an atom have specific amounts of energy. For example, the wavelengths for different colors are approximately: 610 nanometers for red; 579 for yellow; 546 for green; 436 for blue; and 405 for purple.

The discovery around 1900 that electrons exist at set energy levels changed the way people looked at the physical world. Before then, people believed that objects could have any amount of energy.

The idea that electrons exist at set energy levels has redefined the field of physics and led us to a much deeper understanding of the way the physical universe works. This idea is known as *quantum theory.*

Figure 18.15: *What causes all the different colors in fireworks? Electrons!*

Metal	Color
copper	green
barium	yellow-green
sodium	yellow
calcium	red-orange
strontium	bright red

Figure 18.16: *Metals used in fireworks.*

18.3 The Periodic Table of Elements

Before people understood the internal structure of the atom, they were able to identify elements by how they acted chemically. In this section, you will learn how chemists summarize the properties of elements in the *periodic table of elements*, and how an element's chemistry and structure are related.

Groups of elements

Elements and compounds

In 1808, John Dalton published his theory that all materials were made up of atoms, and that atoms can bond together in different combinations. He supported his theory with experimental results. This work provoked two important questions. Which substances were *elements*, made up of only one kind of atom? Which substances were *compounds*, made up of combinations of atoms?

How many elements are there?

In the 18th through 20th centuries, new theories, technologies, and scientific discoveries motivated chemists to find and catalog all the elements that make up our universe. To do so, they had to carefully observe substances in order to identify them, and then try to break them apart by any possible means. If a substance could be broken apart, then they had even more work to do: They observed and tried to break apart each of those materials. If a substance could not be further broken apart, then it most probably was an element.

We now know of 111 different kinds of elements, and the search for new ones continues. Scientists try to build elements with even more protons (called *superheavy elements*) to determine the limits of the internal structure of the atom.

Elements that are part of the same group act alike

As chemists worked on determining which substances were elements, they noticed that some elements acted very much like other elements. For example, one atom of some metals always reacts with two atoms of oxygen. Chemists called these similar elements a **group of elements**.

By keeping track of how each element reacted with other elements, chemists soon identified a number of groups. At the same time, they also began figuring out ways to determine the relative masses of different elements. Soon chemists were organizing this information into tables. The modern *periodic table of elements* is descended from the work of these early chemists.

JD Garcia

JD Garcia grew up in a small village called Alcalde in northern New Mexico. JD attended a boarding high school about 30 miles from home, in Santa Fe. There he recognized the importance of learning new things—especially in math and science.

Garcia enrolled in New Mexico State University on a cooperative student scholarship. The scholarship required him to go to school for half the year and work in a job in his chosen field for the remaining six months. The combination worked well for Garcia and he excelled in school and at work. After graduation, Garcia went to Germany for a year as a Fulbright scholar. He enjoyed working with some of the famous scientists he had studied in college. Then he went on to earn his doctorate at the University of Wisconsin, Madison, in 1966.

Dr. Garcia is a professor at the University of Arizona. His research focuses on subatomic particles. He smashes atoms together and studies the resulting pieces. He wants to learn more about the forces that make atoms move and form molecules, what keeps an atom together, and how stars form.

Source: SACNAS.org

The periodic table of elements

If you read across the rows of the table, the elements are listed in order of increasing atomic number and weight. Each row indicates how many electrons are in each region of the electron cloud. As you remember, the electrons of an atom are found in an electron cloud around the nucleus. The electron cloud is divided into energy levels. By looking at the row number, you can figure out how many energy levels are filled and how many electrons are partially filling each region of the energy levels. For example, carbon, in row 2, has a filled energy level 1 and four electrons in energy level 2. You know that carbon has four electrons in energy level 2 because it is the fourth element in row 2. Recall that higher energy levels overlap, so this system becomes more complex the higher you go up on the periodic table. The outermost region of the electron cloud contains the valence electrons and is called the *valence shell*.

Number of valence electrons

Periodic table of the elements

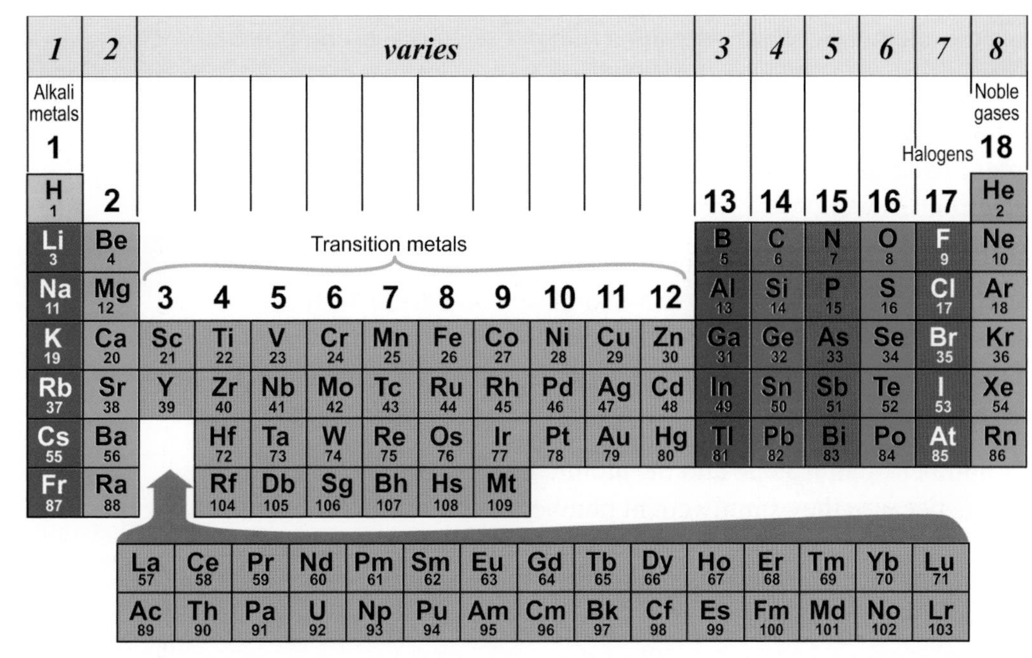

Because the most stable forms of atoms have either full or empty valence shells, the groups of elements relate to the way the valence shells of each element are filled. For example, the last column contains the group known as the *noble gases*. They don't react easily with any other elements, because this group has atoms with completely filled valence shells. We will study valence electrons in the next chapter.

The periodic table

In 1871, the Russian chemist Dimitri Mendeleev (1834-1907) organized information about all the known elements in a table that visually organized the similarities between them. It became known as the periodic table of elements.

Mendeleev placed each element on the table in a certain row and column based on its properties. Each column represents a group of elements with similar chemical behavior. For example, copper, silver, and gold are in the same column. How are these elements similar?

Reading the periodic table

As you just learned, the arrangement of each element in the periodic table conveys a lot of information about it. The individual listing can tell us even more about the element. A periodic table may show some, or, as in Figure 18.17, all of the information for each element.

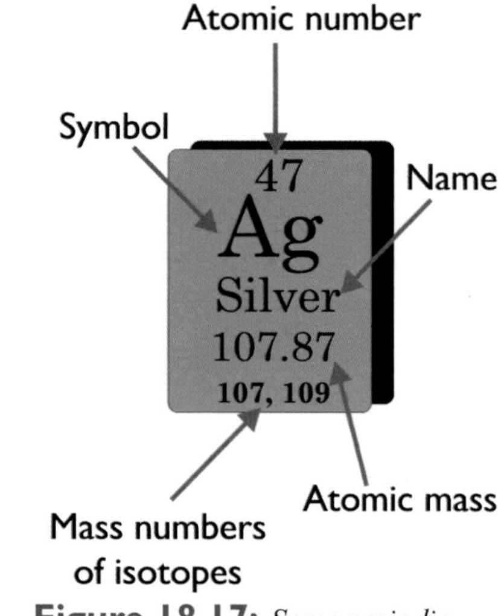

Figure 18.17: *Some periodic tables give you the information shown above.*

Chemical symbol — The chemical symbol is an abbreviation of the element's name. Unlike the abbreviations for a U.S. state, these symbol-abbreviations are not always obvious. Many are derived from the element's name in a language such as Latin or German. In Figure 18.17, Ag is the chemical symbol for the element silver. Its symbol comes from the Latin word for silver, *argentum*. Note that the first letter in the symbol is upper case and the second is lower case. Writing symbols this way allows us to represent all of the elements without getting confused. There is a big difference between the element cobalt, with its symbol Co, and the compound carbon monoxide, written as CO. What is the difference between Si and SI?

Atomic number — As you learned in the last section, the atomic number is the number of protons all atoms of that element have in their nuclei. If the atom is neutral, it will have the same number of electrons as well.

Mass numbers — The mass number of an element is the total number of protons and neutrons in the nucleus. In Figure 18.17, you see that silver has two mass numbers, 107 and 109. This means that there are two types of silver atoms, one that has 47 protons and 60 neutrons, and one that has 47 protons and 62 neutrons. Forms of the same element with different mass numbers are called isotopes.

Atomic mass — Although the mass number of an isotope and the atomic number of an element are always whole numbers because they simply count numbers of particles, the atomic mass of an element is not. The atomic mass is the average mass of all the known isotopes of the element. It takes into consideration the relative abundance of the various isotopes. The atomic mass of an element is expressed in atomic mass units, or amu. *Each atomic mass unit is defined as the mass of 1/12 the mass of a carbon-12 atom* (6 protons and 6 neutrons in the nucleus, plus 6 electrons outside the nucleus). Since carbon consists of a mixture of naturally occurring isotopes, the atomic mass of carbon is not exactly 12 amu. You will learn more about how atomic mass is determined in the next chapter.

element	symbol	origin
copper	Cu	*cuprium*
gold	Au	*aurum*
iron	Fe	*ferrum*
lead	Pb	*plumbum*
potassium	K	*kalium*
silver	Ag	*argentum*
sodium	Na	*natrium*
tin	Sn	*stannum*

Figure 18.18: *The symbols for some elements don't always obviously match their names.*

Chapter 18 Review

Vocabulary review

Match the following terms with the correct definition. There is one extra definition in the list that will not match any of the terms.

Set One

1. proton
2. neutron
3. electron
4. subatomic particles
5. nucleus

a. Particle with no charge that exists in nucleus of most atoms
b. Negatively charged particle that exists in nucleus of atom
c. Center of atom, contains most of atom's mass
d. Negatively charged particle that exists in space surrounding an atom's nucleus
e. Positively charged particle that exists in nucleus of atom
f. Tiny bits of matter that are the building blocks of an atom

Set Two

1. atomic number
2. strong nuclear force
3. energy levels
4. atomic mass
5. atomic mass unit

a. Equal to $^1/_{12th}$ the mass of a carbon-12 atom
b. A way to refer to an element; describes the number of protons in the nucleus
c. The reason that an atom's protons don't break its nucleus apart
d. The process that moves electrons away from the nucleus
e. How electrons are arranged around an atom
f. The average mass of all of the known isotopes of an element

Set Three

1. group of elements
2. periodic table
3. chemical symbol
4. mass number
5. isotope

a. Atoms of the same element which have different numbers of neutrons in the nucleus
b. A unit equal to one-twelfth of the mass of carbon-12
c. Elements with similar properties, listed in a single column on the periodic table
d. The total number of protons and neutrons in the nucleus of an atom
e. A chart of the elements, arranged to provide information about each element's behavior
f. The abbreviation for the name of an element

Concept review

1. Draw a pictorial model of an atom that has 5 protons, 5 neutrons, and 5 electrons. Label the charge of each subatomic particle. What element is this?
2. Two atoms are placed next to each other. Atom A has 6 protons, 6 neutrons, and 5 electrons. Atom B has 6 protons, 7 neutrons, and 6 electrons. Are atoms A and B different elements? How do you know?
3. Why don't the protons in a nucleus repel each other and break the atom apart?
4. Do scientists suspect that there is an infinite number of elements, just waiting to be discovered? What evidence might they give to support such a hypothesis?

Problems

1. How many electron shells would be completely filled by a neutral atom of calcium? How many electrons would be left over?
2. How many electron shells would be completely filled by a neutral xenon atom? How many electrons would be left over?
3. Which element is more likely to combine with other elements, calcium or xenon? How do you know?
4. Use the periodic table on the inside cover of your textbook to answer the following questions:
   a. A magnesium atom will react with two chlorine atoms to form magnesium chloride, $MgCl_2$. Name two other elements that are likely to react with chlorine in a similar manner.
   b. How many completely full electron shells do the elements in the third row contain? Are there any exceptions?
5. For each of the nuclei shown below, do the following:
   a. Name the element.
   b. Give the mass number.
   c. Show the isotope notation.

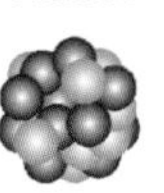

Atom B

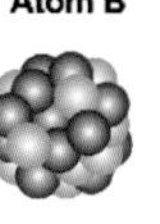

Atom C

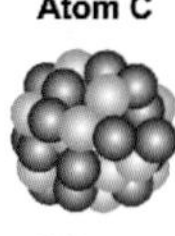

Atom D

Applying your knowledge

1. Make a poster illustrating models of the atom scientists have proposed since the 1800s. Explain how each model reflects the new knowledge that scientists gained through their experiments. When possible, comment on what they learned about charge, mass, and location of subatomic particles.
2. Choose an atom and make a three-dimensional model of its structure, using the Bohr model. Choose different materials to represent protons, neutrons, and electrons. Attach a key to your model to explain what each material represents.

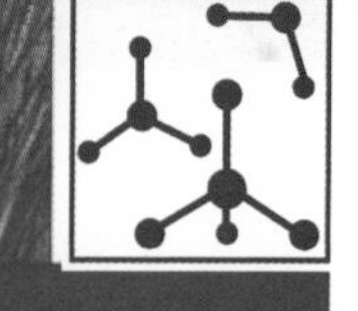

UNIT 7 Changes in Matter

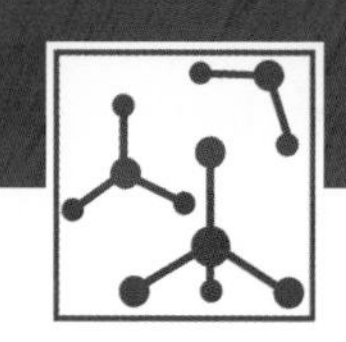

Chapter 19 Molecules and Compounds

Introduction to Chapter 19

Elements are made up of one type of atom. Compounds are made up of molecules which consist of more than one type of atom. Why is it that most of the substances found on earth are compounds? Why do atoms usually associate with other atoms instead of existing alone? In this chapter, you will explore why atoms form chemical bonds to make molecules and compounds.

Investigations for Chapter 19

19.1	**Chemical Bonds**	*Why do atoms form chemical bonds?*

In this Investigation, you will build models of atoms and discover one of the fundamental ideas in chemistry: How electrons are involved in the formation of chemical bonds.

19.2	**Chemical Formulas**	*Why do atoms combine in certain ratios?*

In this Investigation, you will discover how the arrangement of electrons in atoms is related to groups on the periodic table. You will also learn why atoms form chemical bonds with other atoms in certain ratios.

19.3	**Comparing Molecules**	*How can you determine the chemical formula of a compound?*

Atoms combine in whole number ratios to form chemical compounds. In fact, the same two elements may form several different compounds by combining in different ratios. Chemical formulas show the ratios in which elements combine to form a compound. In this Investigation, you will use nuts and bolts to illustrate the meaning of chemical formulas.

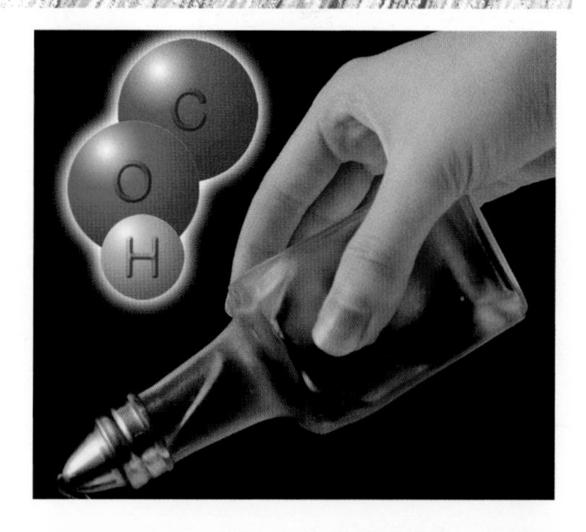

Learning Goals

In this chapter, you will:

- ✔ Relate the chemical behavior of an element, including bonding, to its placement on the periodic table.
- ✔ Explain how elements form chemical bonds and the identify the role of electrons in bonding.
- ✔ Predict the chemical formulas of compounds made up of two different elements.
- ✔ Write chemical formulas for compounds made up of many different types of elements.
- ✔ Calculate the formula mass of a compound and compare different compounds based on their formula masses.
- ✔ Identify the environmental and economic impact of recycling plastics.

Vocabulary

Avogadro number	diatomic molecule	ion	polymer
chemical bond	energy level	monoatomic ion	react
chemical formula	formula mass	octet	subscript
covalent bond	ionic bond	polyatomic ion	valence electron

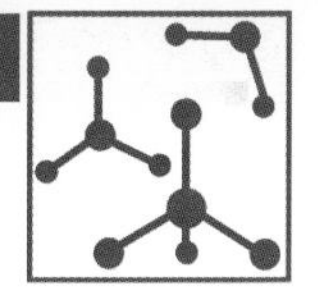

19.1 Chemical Bonds

Most of the matter around you and inside of you is in the form of compounds. For example, your body is about 80 percent water. You learned in the last unit that water, H_2O, is made up of hydrogen and oxygen atoms combined in a 2:1 ratio. If a substance is made of a pure element, like an iron nail, chances are (with the exception of the noble gases) it will eventually react with another element or compound to become something else. Why does iron rust? Why is the Statue of Liberty green, even though it is made of copper? The answer is simple: Most atoms are unstable unless they are combined with other atoms. When atoms of different elements combine to make compounds, they form chemical bonds. A chemical bond forms when atoms exchange or share electrons.

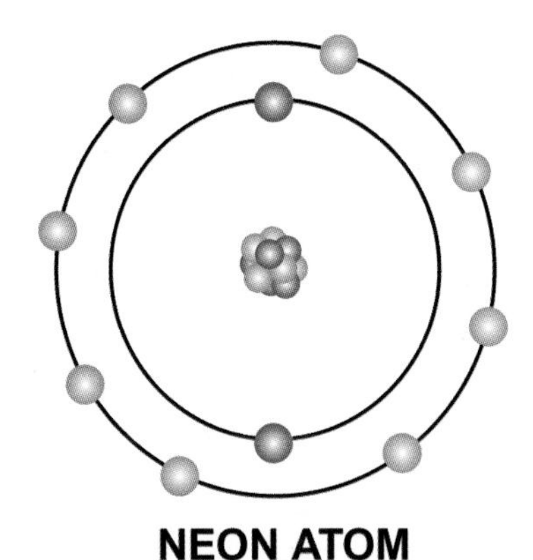

Figure 19.1: *A neon atom has a complete octet, or eight valence electrons.*

Valence electrons and the octet rule

The outer electrons are involved in bonding

Electrons in atoms are found in energy levels surrounding the nucleus in the form of an electron cloud. The higher the energy level, the more energy is required in order for an electron to occupy that part of the electron cloud. The outermost energy level contains the valence electrons and is called the *valence shell.* The maximum number of valence electrons that an atom can have is *eight.* The exception to this rule is the first energy level, which only holds *two* electrons. *Valence electrons are the ones involved in forming chemical bonds.*

The octet rule

When an atom has eight valence electrons, it is said to have an octet of electrons. Figure 19.1 shows neon with a complete octet. In order to achieve this octet, atoms will lose, gain, or share electrons. An atom with a complete octet, like neon has lower energy and is more stable than an atom with an incomplete octet, like sodium (Figure 19.2). Atoms form chemical bonds with other atoms by either sharing electrons, or transferring them in order to complete their octet and move to a lower energy state. This is known as the octet rule.

Atoms form chemical bonds with other atoms by sharing or transferring electrons to have a complete set of eight valence electrons.

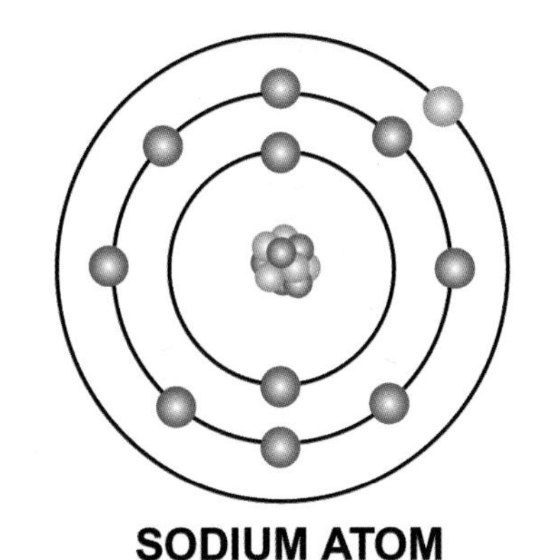

Figure 19.2: *A sodium atom an incomplete octet with only one valence electron.*

Exceptions to the octet rule

Some atoms are an exception to the octet rule. Why? Remember, the first energy level only needs two electrons, not eight. Hydrogen, with only one electron, needs only one more to fill its valence shell. Helium, with two electrons, has a full valence shell (Figure 19.3). This means that helium is chemically stable and does not bond with other atoms.

Stable atoms have full valence shells

What about lithium? It has three electrons. This means that its first shell is full but there is one extra electron in the second shell. Would it be easier for lithium (Figure 19.4) to gain seven electrons to fill the second shell—or to lose one electron? You probably would guess that it is easier to lose one electron that gain seven. You would be correct in your guess, for lithium loses one electron when it bonds with other atoms. Table 19.1 shows the number of valence electrons and the number needed to complete the octet for the first 18 elements.

Table 19.1: ***Elements, number of valence electrons, and number needed to complete the octet***

element	valence electrons	number needed	element	valence electrons	number needed
H	1	1	Ne	8	0
He	2	0	Na	1	7
Li	1	7	Mg	2	6
Be	2	6	Al	3	5
B	3	5	Si	4	4
C	4	4	P	5	3
N	5	3	S	6	2
O	6	2	Cl	7	1
F	7	1	Ar	8	0

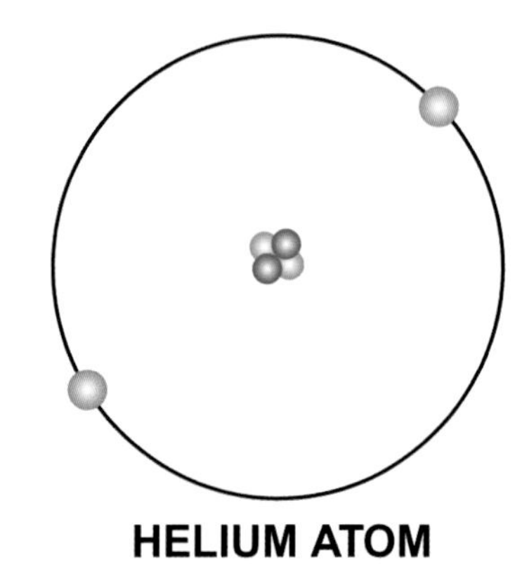

Figure 19.3: *Helium atoms have only two electrons, both of which are in the outermost level. Helium is an exception to the octet rule.*

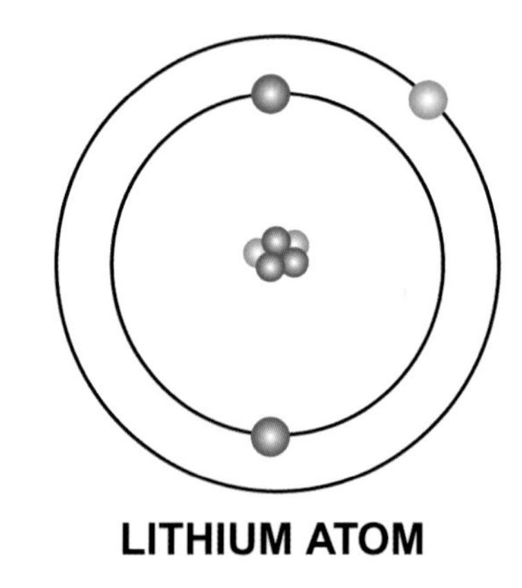

Figure 19.4: *Lithium atoms have three electrons. Since the first energy level only holds two electrons, lithium has one valence electron. If lithium loses that electron, it will have a full valence shell with two electrons.*

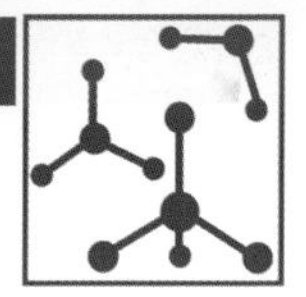

Electrons and the periodic table

Valence and the periodic table

The periodic table arranges elements from left to right by the number of valence electrons. The alkali metals (group 1) have one valence electron. Group 2 elements have two valence electrons. Group 17 elements have seven valence electrons. These elements are called *halogens*. The halogens are very reactive since they only need to gain one electron to get to eight valence electrons. The *noble gases* (group 18) have no valence electrons and do not form chemical bonds with other atoms.

Transition metals

The elements in groups 3 to 12 are called the **transition metals**. These elements have electrons in the fourth and fifth energy levels. The bonding patterns for transition metals are more complex because of the large number of electrons in the highest unfilled level.

Number of valence electrons

Periodic table of the elements

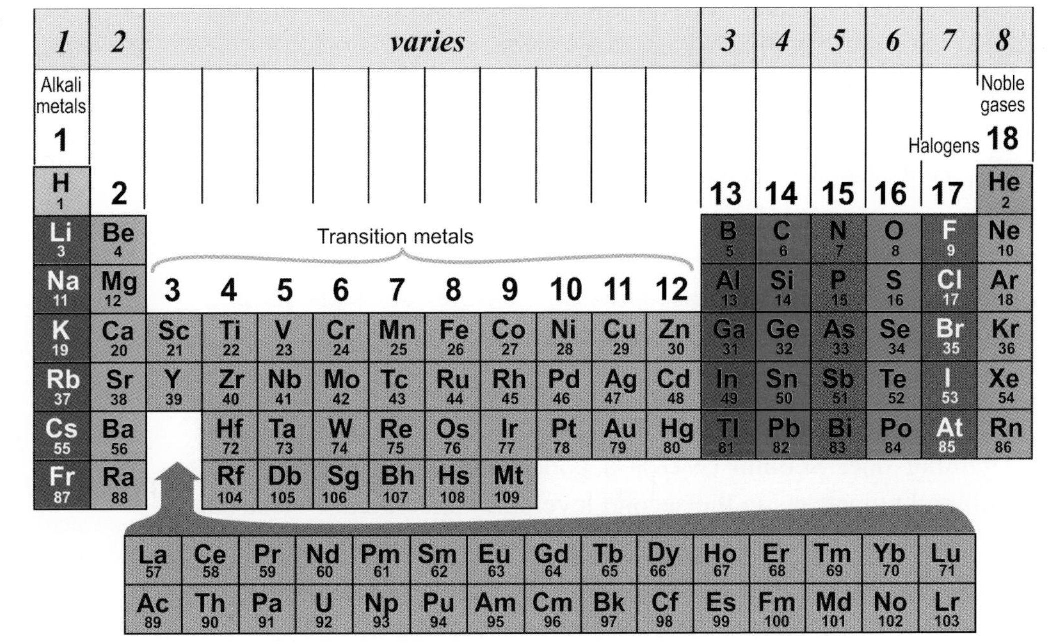

Noble gases are useful

Argon, a noble gas, is used in welding metal because it makes no chemical bonds. When metal is hot, it reacts quickly with oxygen in the air to form oxides, like rust. The oxides greatly reduce the strength of the metal.

A Metal Inert Gas (MIG) welder uses a flow of argon gas to keep oxygen away. The argon gas flows through a tube around the tip of the welder's rod. The hot area around the tip of the welding rod is kept free of oxygen and strong welds can be made without oxides.

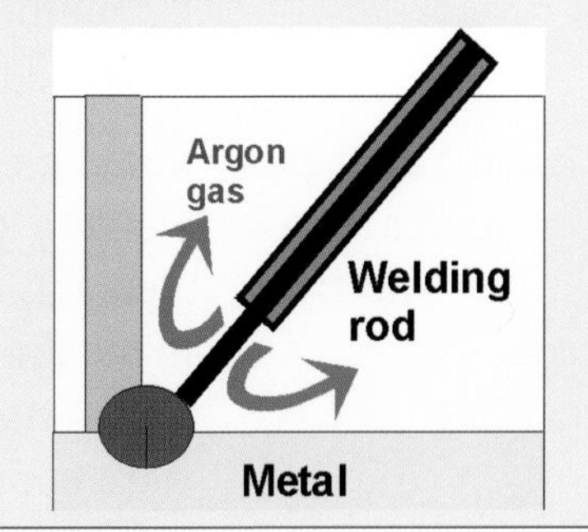

Why chemical bonds form

Atoms form bonds to reach lower energy

Chemical bonds are a form of potential energy. Imagine pulling adhesive tape off a surface. It takes energy to separate atoms that are bonded together just like it takes energy to pull tape off a surface. If it takes energy to separate bonded atoms, then the same energy must be released when the bond is formed. This is a direct consequence of the law of conservation of energy. Energy is released when atoms form chemical bonds. The atoms in matter are usually chemically bonded to other atoms because chemically bonded atoms have lower energy than free atoms. Like a ball rolling downhill, systems in nature tend to settle into the configuration of lowest energy.

Atoms bond to get eight valence electrons

Atoms are most stable when they have either 2 or 8 valence electrons. The noble gases already have eight, so they are stable and do not form bonds with other atoms. Other atoms form chemical bonds so that they can share electrons to reach that stable number of eight. The Lewis dot diagram (Figure 19.5) shows the element symbol surrounded by one to eight dots representing the valence electrons. Carbon has four dots, hydrogen one. One carbon atom bonds with four hydrogen atoms because this molecule (methane) allows the carbon atom to have eight valence electrons—four of its own and four shared with hydrogen atoms.

Molecules with oxygen

Oxygen has six valence electrons. That means oxygen needs two more electrons to get to eight. One oxygen atom bonded with two hydrogen atoms (water) is one way to make eight. One oxygen atom can also bond with one beryllium atom to make eight. Beryllium has two valence electrons. Complex molecules are formed by multiple atoms sharing valence electrons so that each one can achieve the required number of eight.

Some elements prefer to lose electrons

Some elements can achieve the stable eight electrons more easily by losing an electron than by gaining one. Sodium (Na) is a good example of this type of element. It has a full eight electrons in the second level, and one valence electron in the third level. If the single valence electron is given away, sodium is left with a stable eight electrons in the (full) second level. For this reason, sodium tends to form bonds that allow it to give up its single valence electron.

Lewis dot diagrams

Neon	8 valence electrons	:Ne:
Fluorine	7 valence electrons	:F·
Oxygen	6 valence electrons	:O·
Nitrogen	5 valence electrons	:N·
Carbon	4 valence electrons	·C·
Boron	3 valence electrons	·B·
Beryllium	2 valence electrons	Be
Lithium	1 valence electron	Li
Hydrogen	1 valence electron	H

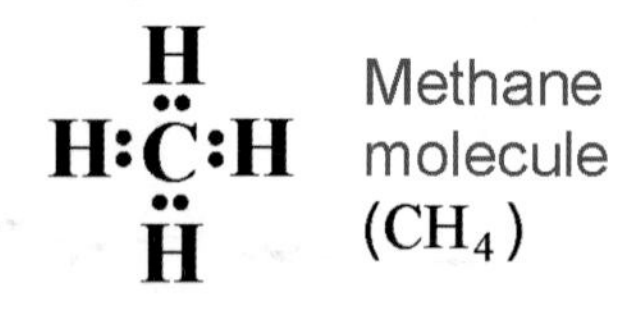

Figure 19.5: *Lewis dot diagrams show valence electrons as dots around the element symbol. Atoms form bonds to get eight valence electrons by sharing with other atoms.*

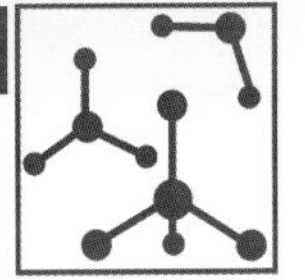

Ionic and covalent bonds

Ionic bonds

Most chemical bonds fall into two categories, depending on whether the valence electrons are transferred or shared. Electrons in an **ionic bond** are transferred from one atom to another. Atoms that either gain or lose an electron become **ions**. Ions may have either positive or negative electric charge. The atom which takes the electron acquires an overall negative charge. The positive and negative ions are attracted to each other, creating the bond. Ionic bonds tend to form between more than one pair of atoms at a time. The bond between sodium (Na) and chlorine (Cl) in sodium chloride (salt) is a good example of an ionic bond. In a crystal of salt each sodium ion is attracted to all the neighboring chlorine ions (Figure 19.6).

Covalent bonds

In a **covalent bond** the electrons are *shared* between atoms. The bonds between hydrogen and carbon in a methane molecule are covalent bonds. The electrons in a covalent bond act like ties between the two atoms. An important difference between covalent and ionic bonds is that covalent bonds act only between the atoms in a single *molecule*, while ionic bonds act between all adjacent atoms (ions).

Alkali metals tend to form ionic bonds

Whether a covalent or ionic bond is formed depends on how close each atom is to the stable number of eight valence electrons. The alkali metals with one valence electron have a high tendency to give up an electron. The halogen elements with seven valence electrons have a high tendency to take an electron. If you put an alkali (Na) with a halogen (Cl), you get an ionic bond because one atom *strongly* wants to lose an electron and the other *strongly* wants to gain one.

Examples of covalent bonds

Elements that have two to six valence electrons tend to form covalent bonds with each other since the tendency to take or receive electrons is more matched. For example, all the bonds in silicon dioxide (glass) are covalent bonds between silicon and oxygen atoms. Diamonds are the hardest substance known. A diamond is a pure carbon crystal in which every carbon atom is joined to four other carbon atoms by a covalent bond (Figure 19.7). The hardness of diamonds is due to the fact that four covalent bonds must be broken to move each carbon atom.

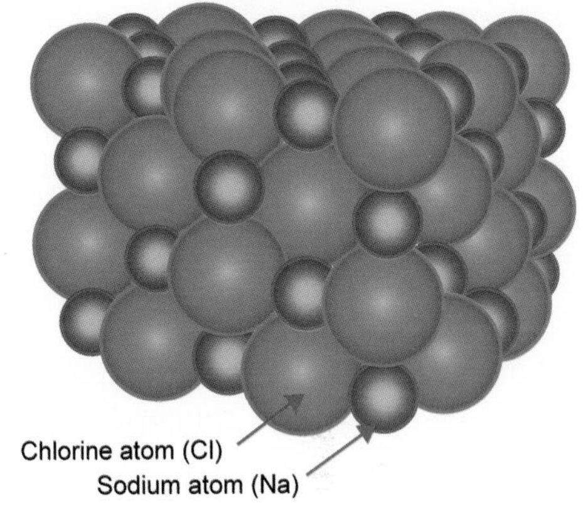

Figure 19.6: *The ionic bonds in a salt crystal (NaCl) come from electrical attraction between negative chlorine ions and positive sodium ions.*

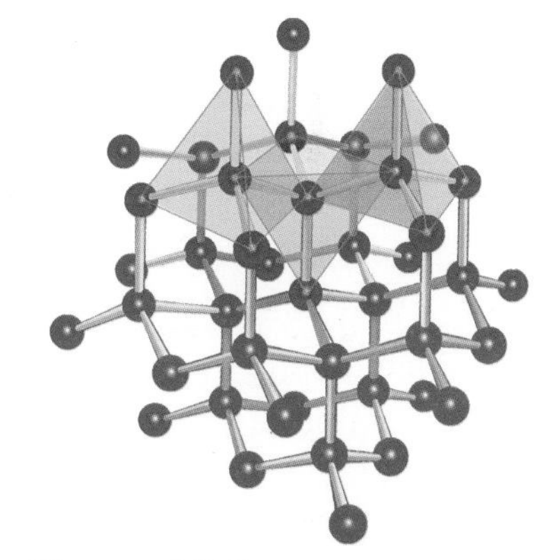

Figure 19.7: *A diamond crystal is made of pure carbon connected by a strong network of covalent bonds.*

The formation of bonds

Chemical bonds make compounds with different properties

Sodium is a soft, silvery metal that is so reactive, it must be stored so it does not come in contact with the air. Chlorine exists as a yellowish-green gas that is very poisonous. When atoms of these two elements chemically bond, they become the white crystals that you use to make your food taste better—salt! This compound is also known as sodium chloride. When atoms form chemical bonds, the properties of the resulting compound are usually very different than the properties of the elements from which they are made.

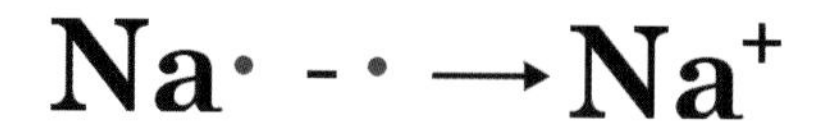

Figure 19.8: *When a sodium atom loses its valence electron, its net electric charge is +1.*

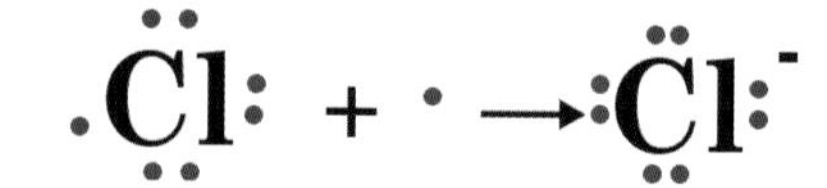

Figure 19.9: *When a chlorine atom gains one electron, its net electric charge is -1.*

The formation of an ionic bond

A neutral sodium atom has 11 positively charged protons and 11 negatively charged electrons. When sodium loses one electron, it has 11 protons (+) and 10 electrons (-) and becomes an ion with a net charge of +1. This is because it now has one more positive charge than negative charges (Figure 19.8). A neutral chlorine atom has 17 protons and 17 neutrons. When chlorine gains one electron to complete its stable octet, it has 17 protons (+) and 18 electrons (-) and becomes an ion with a charge of -1. This is because it has gained one negative charge (Figure 19.9).

Opposites attract

Because the sodium ion has a positive charge and the chlorine ion has a negative charge, the two atoms become attracted to each other and form an ionic bond. Recall that opposite charges attract. When sodium, with its +1 charge, comes into contact with chlorine, with its -1 charge, they become electrically neutral as long as they are together. This is because +1 and -1 cancel each other out. This also explains why sodium and chlorine combine in a 1:1 ratio to make sodium chloride (Figure 19.10).

Figure 19.10: *When a sodium ion and a chlorine ion form an ionic bond, the net electric charge is zero (neutral).*

Covalent bonds and diatomic molecules

Covalent bonds can form between two different types of atoms, or between two or more atoms of the same type. For example, chlorine, with seven valence electrons, sometimes shares an electron with another chlorine atom. With this configuration, both atoms can share an electron through a covalent bond to become more stable (shown left). Many elemental gases in our atmosphere exist in pairs of covalently bonded atoms. The gases nitrogen (N_2), oxygen (O_2) and hydrogen (H_2) are a few examples. We call these covalently bonded atoms of the same type **diatomic molecules**.

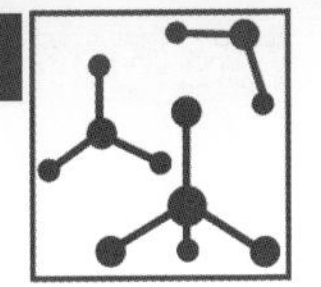

Environmental Issue: Paper or plastic?

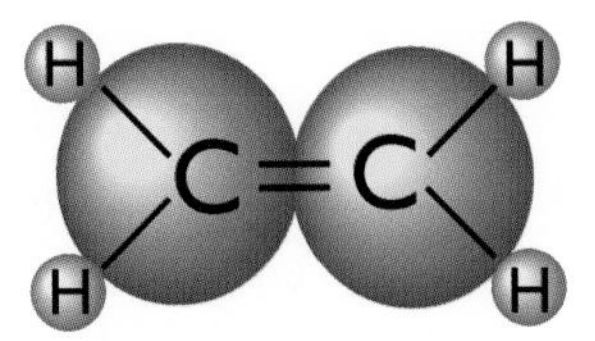

Figure 19.11: *The ethylene molecule is the building block, or subunit, of synthetic plastics. That is why plastics are often referred to as "polyethylenes."*

What is plastic?

Plastics are polymers. You may already know that the prefix *poly-* means "many" and the suffix *-mer* means "unit." A polymer is a large molecule that is composed of repeating smaller molecules. The building block or subunit of synthetic plastics is a molecule called ethylene (Figure 19.11). Paper is made out of a natural polymer called cellulose. Cellulose, the most abundant polymer on Earth, is made out of many subunits of glucose molecules. The difference between a natural polymer like cellulose, and the man-made polymer that is used to make a bag or a soda bottle is that cellulose is easily digested by microorganisms. In contrast, synthetic plastics are not easily broken down. For this reason, when you throw a plastic cup away, there isn't much chance it will decompose quickly or at all.

Why can't microorganisms digest plastic?

In order for microorganisms to be able to break down a plastic molecule, they must have access to an exposed end or side branch of the molecule. Because synthetic plastics are such long chains of carbon surrounded by hydrogens, there are no places for microorganisms to begin "biting" on the molecule. Since most plastics we use are man-made, microorganisms are not able to consume them.

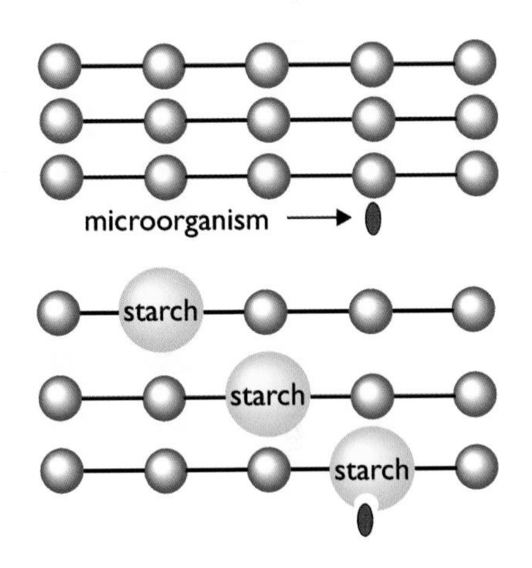

Figure 19.12: *Inserting starch molecules into the polyethylene chain provides a place for microorganisms to begin breaking it down.*

Biodegradable plastics

One way to approach the plastics problem is to make them *biodegradable*. This means that microbes such as bacteria and fungi can "eat" the plastic. Making biodegradable plastics involves creating exposed ends on the molecules so microbes can get a start. This is done by inserting a food item that microbes readily eat into a plastic. For instance, starch can be inserted in the polyethylene molecule (Figure 19.12). Once microbes have eaten the starch, two ends of polyethylene are exposed. Many plastic grocery bags contain starch.

Recycling plastics

You may be familiar with the recycling symbols on the bottoms of plastic bottles. Those symbols allow you to sort the different plastics that make up each kind of plastic. Choosing the kind of plastic that is used for a certain product is a careful decision. Think about the wide variety of plastic containers (and don't forget their lids) that are used for certain products. In order to recycle plastic, you need to melt it so that it can be remolded into new containers or extruded into a kind of fabric that is used for sweatshirts.

19.2 Chemical Formulas

In the previous section, you learned how and why atoms form chemical bonds with one another. You also know that atoms combine in certain ratios with other atoms. These ratios determine the chemical formula for a compound. In this section, you will learn how to write the chemical formulas for compounds. You will also learn how to name compounds based on their chemical formulas.

Chemical formulas and oxidation numbers

Ionic compounds

Recall that sodium atoms form *ionic bonds* with chlorine atoms to make sodium chloride. Because sodium chloride is a compound made out of ions, it is called an ionic compound. The chemical formula for sodium chloride is NaCl. This formula indicates that every formula unit of sodium chloride contains one atom of sodium and one atom of chlorine, a 1:1 ratio.

Why do sodium and chlorine combine in a 1:1 ratio? When sodium loses one electron, it becomes an ion with a charge of +1. When chlorine gains an electron, it becomes an ion with a charge of -1. When these two ions combine to form an ionic bond, the net electrical charge is zero. This is because (+1) + (-1) = 0.

All compounds have an electrical charge of zero; that is, they are neutral.

Oxidation numbers

A sodium atom always ionizes to become Na+ (a charge of +1) when it combines with other atoms to make a compound. Therefore, we say that *sodium has an oxidation number of 1+*. An oxidation number indicates how many electrons are lost, gained, or shared when bonding occurs. Notice that the convention for writing oxidation numbers is the opposite of the convention for writing the charge. When writing the oxidation number, the positive (or negative) symbol is written *after* the number, not *before* it.

What is chlorine's oxidation number? If you think it is 1-, you are right. This is because chlorine gains one electron, one negative charge, when it bonds with other atoms. Figure 19.14 shows the oxidation numbers for some of the elements.

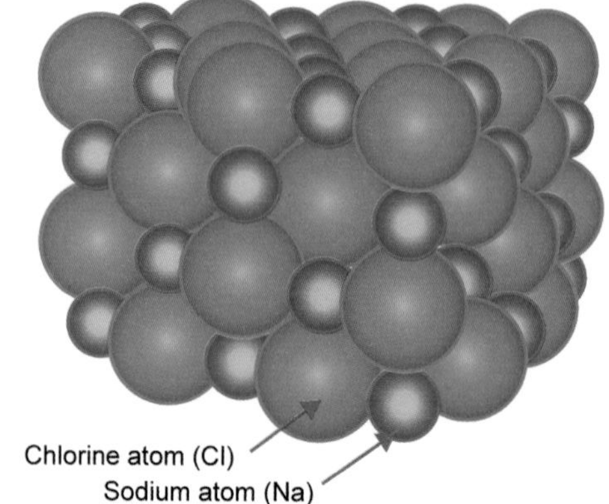

Figure 19.13: *All compounds have en electrical charge of zero. In the case of sodium chloride, sodium ions (+1) and chlorine ions (-1) combine in a 1:1 ratio. This means that there is one sodium ion for every chlorine ion in the compound.*

atom	electrons gained or lost	oxidation number
K	loses 1	1+
Mg	loses 2	2+
Al	loses 3	3+
P	gains 3	3-
Se	gains 2	2-
Br	gains 1	1-
Ar	loses 0	0

Figure 19.14: *Oxidation numbers of some common elements.*

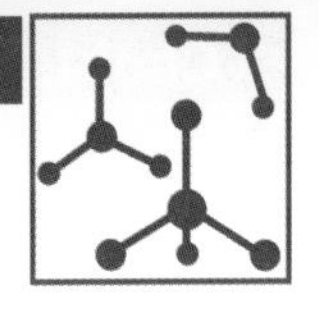

Predicting oxidation numbers from the periodic table

In the last section, you learned that you can tell how many valence electrons an element has by its placement on the periodic table. If you can determine how many valence electrons an element has, you can predict its oxidation number. For example, locate beryllium (Be) on the periodic table below. It is in the second column, or Group 2, which means beryllium has two valence electrons. Will beryllium get rid of two electrons, or gain six in order to obtain a stable octet? Of course, it is easier to lose two electrons. When these two electrons are lost, beryllium becomes an ion with a charge of +2. Therefore, the most common oxidation number for beryllium is 2+. In fact, the most common oxidation number for all elements in Group 2 is 2+. Table 19.2 shows some common oxidation numbers.

Table 19.2: ***Some oxidation numbers***

atom	electrons gained or lost	oxidation number
K	loses 1	1+
Mg	loses 2	2+
Al	loses 3	3+
P	gains 3	3-
Se	gains 2	2-
Br	gains 1	1-
Ar	loses 0	0

The periodic table below shows the most common oxidation numbers of most of the elements. The elements known as transition metals (in the middle of the table) have variable oxidation numbers.

1+	2+	Most common oxidation number										3+	4+	3-	2-	1-	
																	He 2
Li 3	Be 4											B 5	C 6	N 7	O 8	F 9	Ne 10
Na 11	Mg 12											Al 13	Si 14	P 15	S 16	Cl 17	Ar 18
K 19	Ca 20	Sc 21	Ti 22	V 23	Cr 24	Mn 25	Fe 26	Co 27	Ni 28	Cu 29	Zn 30	Ga 31	Ge 32	As 33	Se 34	Br 35	Kr 36
Rb 37	Sr 38	Y 39	Zr 40	Nb 41	Mo 42	Tc 43	Ru 44	Rh 45	Pd 46	Ag 47	Cd 48	In 49	Sn 50	Sb 51	Te 52	I 53	Xe 54

NOTE: Many elements have more than one possible oxidation number.

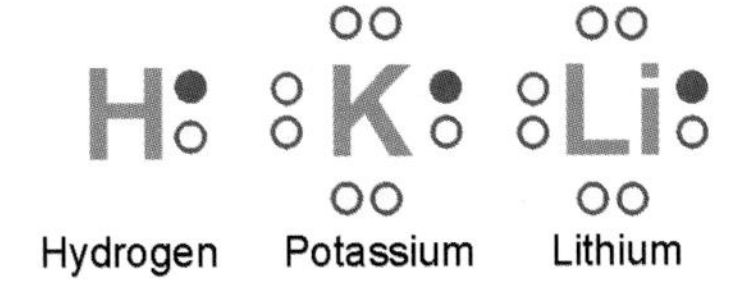

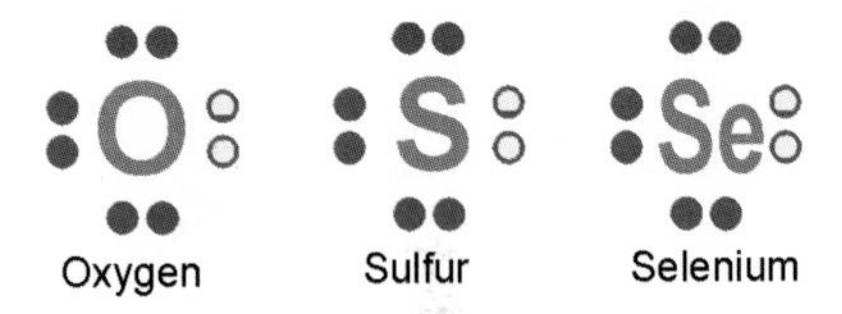

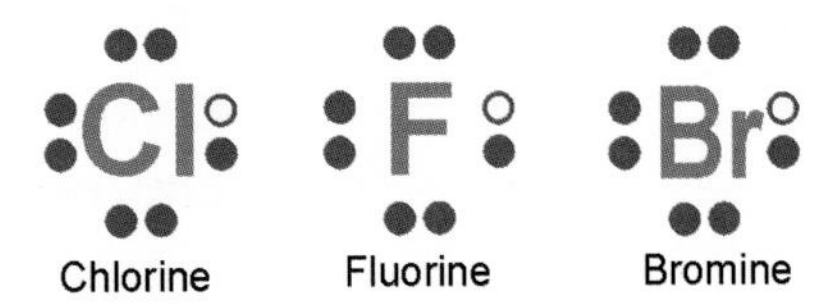

Figure 19.15: *Oxidation number corresponds to the need to gain or lose electrons.*

Writing the chemical formulas of ionic compounds.

Monoatomic ions

Both sodium and chlorine ions are monoatomic ions, that is, ions that consist of a single atom. It's easy to write the chemical formula for compounds made of monatomic ions, if you follow these rules:

1	Write the symbol for the monoatomic ion that has a ***positive*** charge first.
2	Write the symbol for the monatomic ion that has a ***negative*** charge second.
3	Add subscripts below each element symbol so that the sum of the positive and negative oxidation numbers is equal to zero—a neutral compound, remember? Subscripts tell you how many atoms of each element are in the compound.

Some elements have more than one oxidation number. In this case, roman numerals are used to distinguish the oxidation number. Figure 19.16 shows a few of these elements.

element	oxidation number
copper (I)	Cu^+
copper (II)	Cu^{2+}
iron (II)	Fe^{2+}
iron (III)	Fe^{3+}
chromium (II)	Cr^{2+}
chromium (III)	Cr^{3+}
lead (II)	Pb^{2+}
lead (IV)	Pb^{4+}

Figure 19.16: *Elements with variable oxidation numbers.*

Example: Writing a chemical formula

Write the formula for a compound that is made of iron (III) and oxygen.

1. Find the oxidation numbers of each element in the compound.

Iron (III) is a transition metal. The roman numbers indicate that it has an oxidation number of 3+. Its formula is Fe^{3+}.

Oxygen is in group 16 of the periodic table and has an oxidation number of 2-. Its formula is O^{2-}.

2. Determine the ratios of each element and write the chemical formula.

If one iron (III) ion bonds with one oxygen ion, will the compound be neutral? No, since 3+ added to 2- equals 1+. If you have two iron (III) ions for every three oxygen ions, what happens? 2(3+) added to 3(2-) is equal to 0. This means that three iron (III) ions bond with two oxygen ions to get a neutral compound.\

The formula for a compound of iron (III) and oxygen is Fe_2O_3.

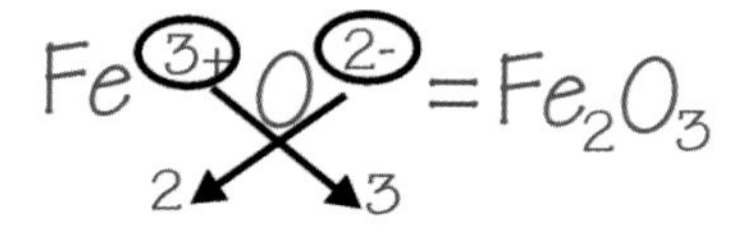

Figure 19.17: *The criss-cross method is a simple way to determine the chemical formula of a compound.*

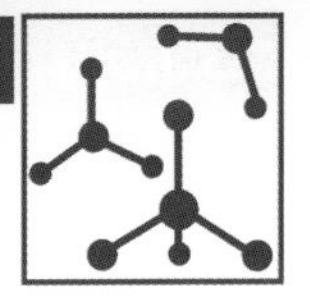

Ionic compounds made of more than two types of atoms

Not all compounds are made of only two types of atoms

Have you ever taken an antacid for an upset stomach? Many antacids contain calcium carbonate, or $CaCO_3$. How many types of atoms does this compound contain? You are right if you said three: calcium, carbon, and oxygen. Some ionic compounds contain **polyatomic ions**. Polyatomic ions contain more than one type of atom. The prefix *poly* means "many." Table 19.3 lists some common polyatomic ions.

Table 19.3: *Polyatomic ions*

oxidation no.	name	formula
1+	ammonium	NH_4^+
1-	acetate	$C_2H_3O_2^-$
2-	carbonate	CO_3^{2-}
2-	chromate	CrO_4^{2-}
1-	hydrogen carbonate	HCO_3^-
1+	hydronium	H_3O^+
1-	hydroxide	OH^-
1-	nitrate	NO_3^-
2-	peroxide	O_2^{2-}
3-	phosphate	PO_4^{3-}
2-	sulfate	SO_4^{2-}
2-	sulfite	SO_3^{2-}

The positive ion is Ca^{2+} This is a *monoatomic* ion. You can determine its oxidation number by looking at the periodic table.
The negative ion is CO_3^{2-} This is a *polyatomic* ion. You can determine its oxidation number by looking at the ion chart (Table 19.2).

Figure 19.18: *Which ions does $CaCO_3$ contain?*

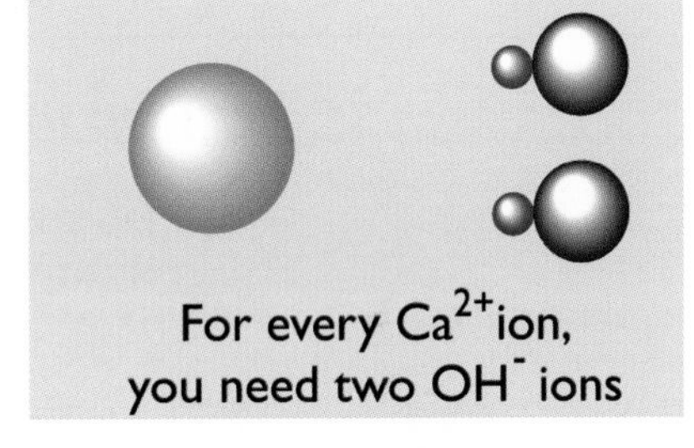
For every Ca^{2+} ion,
you need two OH^- ions

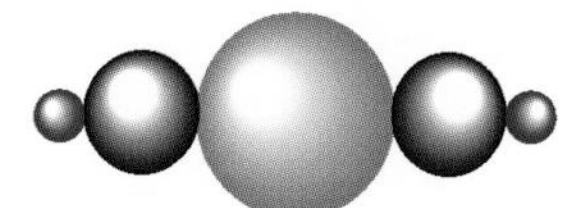

to make a neutral compound
$Ca(OH)_2$

Figure 19.19: *How to write the chemical formula for calcium hydroxide.*

Rules for writing chemical formulas of ionic compounds that contain polyatomic ions

1. Write the chemical formula and oxidation number of the positive ion. If the positive ion is monoatomic, you can find its oxidation number from the periodic table. If the positive ion is polyatomic, use table 19.3 to find the oxidation number of the polyatomic ion.
2. Write the chemical formula and oxidation number for the negative ion. Again, use the periodic table if the negative ion is monoatomic, or table 19.3 if the negative ion is polyatomic.
3. Add the oxidation numbers of the positive and negative ions. Do they add up to zero? If yes, write the formula for the positive ion first and the negative ion second. Do not include the oxidation numbers in the chemical formula. Be sure to write the subscripts!
4. If the oxidation numbers do not add up to zero, figure out how many of each ion you will need so that the oxidation numbers add up to zero. (**Hint:** *Find the least common multiple between the two oxidation numbers. The number that you have to multiply each oxidation number by to equal the least common multiple tells you how many of each ion you need).*

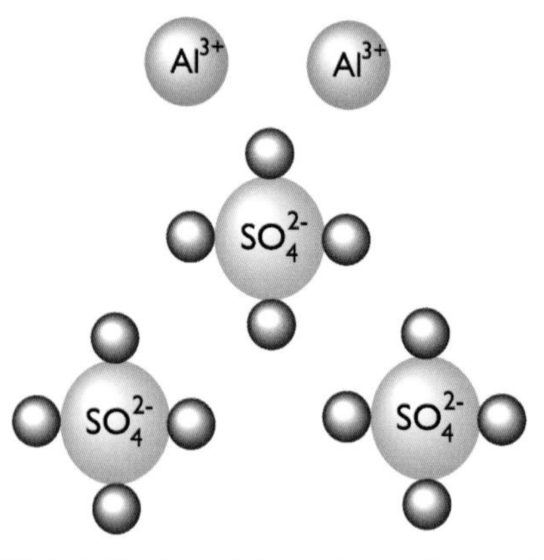

Figure 19.20: *This diagram shows how to determine the chemical formula for aluminum sulfate. How many of each ion does the formula indicate? How many atoms of each element are in one formula unit of aluminum sulfate?*

Example: Writing the chemical formula for *aluminum sulfate*

1. Find the formula and charge of the positive ion.

The positive ion is always the first ion in the name. Where can you find the chemical formula for the aluminum ion? Aluminum is monoatomic and its formula is Al. You can find its oxidation number from the periodic table. Al is in group 13 and contains three valence electrons. When it loses those, its charge becomes +3. Therefore, the oxidation number for Al is 3+.

Chemical formula and oxidation number = Al^{3+}

2. Find the formula and charge of the negative ion.

Sulfate is the negative ion. Where can you find the chemical formula and oxidation number for the sulfate ion? Since sulfate is a polyatomic ion, you must consult an ion chart, unless you can remember the formulas and oxidation numbers for all ions!

Chemical formula and oxidation number = SO_4^{2-}

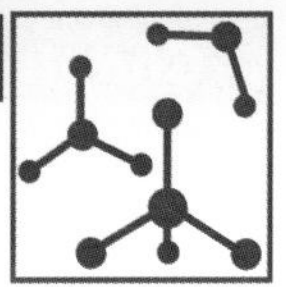

Example, continued

3. Determine how many of each ion are needed so the charges are equal to zero.

The oxidation numbers of (3+) and (2-) add up to (1+), not zero. (3+) + (2-) = (1-)
You need 2 aluminum ions and 3 sulfate ions to make the charges add up to zero.
$(Al^{3+}) \times (2) = (6+)$ $(SO_4^{2-}) \times (3) = (6-)$

4. Write the chemical formula for the compound.

Write the formula, enclosing sulfate in parentheses. Do not change subscripts in the ion.

$Al_2(SO_4)_3$

Example: Name BaF_2

1 The first element is barium.
2 The second element is fluorine.
3 The compound's name is barium fluoride.

Figure 19.21: *How to name an ionic compound that is made of two monoatomic ions.*

How do you name ionic compounds?

Compounds with only monoatomic ions

Naming compounds with only monoatomic ions is very simple if you follow the rules below. Figure 19.21 shows an example.

1 Write the name of the first element in the compound.
2 Write the root name of the second element. For example, ***chlor-*** is the root name of ***chlorine***. Simply subtract the ***-ine*** ending.
3 Add the ending ***-ide*** to the root name. ***Chlor-*** becomes ***chloride***.

Compounds that contain polyatomic ions

To name a compound that contains polyatomic ions, follow these steps.

1 Write the name of the positive ion first. Use the periodic table or an ion chart to find its name.
2 Write the name of the negative ion second. Use the periodic table or an ion chart to find its name.

1 The positive ion, Mg^{2+}, is **magnesium**.
2 The negative ion, CO_3^{2-}, is **carbonate**.
3 The name of the compound is **magnesium carbonate**.

Figure 19.22: *How to name a compound with the chemical formula $MgCO_3$.*

Covalent compounds

Covalent compounds consist of molecules

Compounds that are formed through covalent bonds (shared electrons) are called covalent compounds. Covalent compounds are sometimes referred to as *molecular compounds* because covalent bonding produces molecules. Ionic bonding does not produce molecules but groups of positively- and negatively-charged ions that attract each other. Each individual group is called a *formula unit*.

Naming covalent compounds

Covalent compounds that are made of more than two types of elements have their own special naming system that you will learn about in more advanced chemistry courses. Naming covalent compounds that consist of only two elements, often called binary compounds, is fairly straightforward. This naming is very similar to the methods used in naming ionic compounds that contain only two elements described on page 342. However, in this case, the *number* of each type of atom is specified in the name of the compound. Figure 19.23 shows how to name a binary covalent compound.

The Greek prefixes in Figure 19.24 are used in naming binary covalent compounds. If the molecule contains only one atom of the first element, the prefix *mono-* is not used. It is used in the name of the second element in the compound as in the example below:

CO carbon monoxide

CO_2 carbon dioxide

Empirical and molecular formula

The simplest whole-number ratios by which elements combine are written in a form called the empirical formula. The actual number of atoms of each element in the compound is written in a form called the molecular formula. For some compounds, the empirical formula and the molecular formula are the same as is the case with water, H_2O. A molecule of the sugar glucose has a molecular formula of $C_6H_{12}O_6$. To find the empirical formula of glucose, calculate the simplest whole number ratio of the atoms. The empirical formula for glucose is CH_2O.

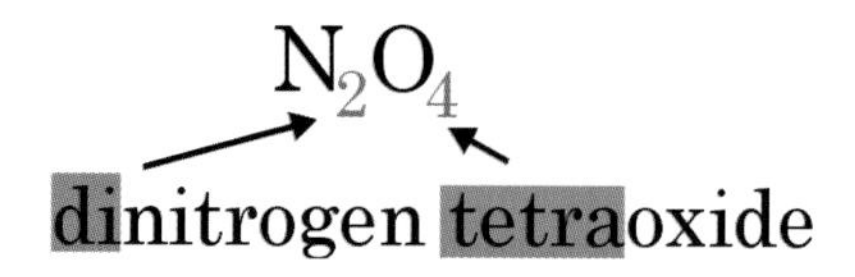

Figure 19.23: *To name a binary covalent compound, specify the number of each type of atom using a Greek prefix. The ending of the name of the second element in the compound is modified by adding the suffix -ide.*

prefix	meaning
mono-	1
di-	2
tri-	3
tetra-	4
penta-	5
hexa-	6
hepta-	7
octa-	8
nona-	9

Figure 19.24: *Greek prefixes used in naming binary covalent compounds.*

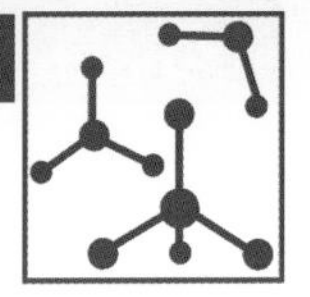

19.3 Comparing Molecules

If you have ever bought paper, you know that it is sometimes sold in a package of 500 sheets called a *ream*. Do you think someone in a factory counts individual sheets of paper and packages them for sale? Instead of counting individual sheets, the paper is packaged according to *mass*. Knowing the mass of 500 sheets of paper allows the paper to be packaged quickly and efficiently by machines. If the machines that make the paper suddenly started making sheets that were twice as heavy, what would happen to the number of sheets in a package? "Counting" by mass is a useful way to deal with large numbers of objects that are uniform in size—like atoms in an element or molecules in a compound. In this section, you will learn how to quantify atoms and molecules using mass.

Figure 19.25: *Paper in a factory is packaged by mass instead of by counting.*

Comparing a water molecule to a formula unit of calcium carbonate

A water molecule has a different mass than a unit of calcium carbonate

Does a molecule of *water* (H_2O) have the same mass as a group of atoms (called a *formula unit*) that make up the ionic compound *calcium carbonate* ($CaCO_3$)? Figure 19.26 shows the comparative sizes of each. This question seems difficult to answer at first because atoms are so small that you cannot see them. However, you *can* use what you have learned so far to answer the question. You know that atoms of different elements have different *atomic masses*. You also know that compounds are made of different numbers and types of atoms. Based on this knowledge, you can logically conclude that a molecule of water would have a *different* mass than a formula unit of calcium carbonate.

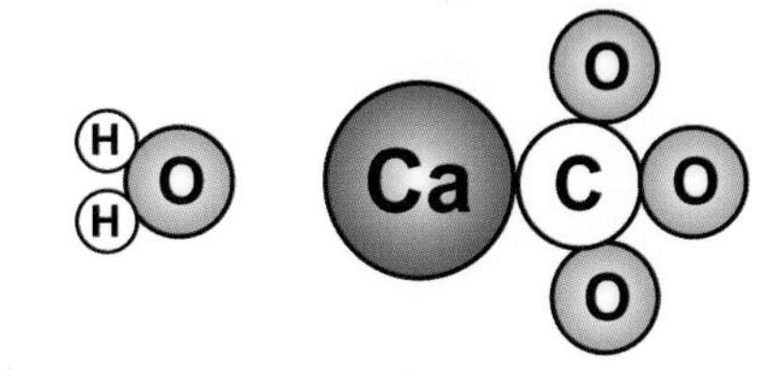

Figure 19.26: *Do you think that a molecule of water has the same mass as a formula unit of calcium carbonate?*

Atomic mass units

All atoms are assigned a unit of relative mass known as the *atomic mass unit,* or amu. Atomic mass units allow us to compare quantities of matter even though we can't see the molecules and atoms that we want to count or measure.

How is atomic mass determined?

Carbon atoms are used as a standard for determining the atomic mass units for the other elements on the periodic table. One carbon atom is equivalent to 12.01 atomic mass units. Because one hydrogen atom is about 1/12 the mass of one carbon atom (Figure 19.27), it is represented as having 1.01 atomic mass units. The actual mass of one atomic mass unit is 1.6606×10^{-24} grams—a very small amount!

Figure 19.27: *One hydrogen atom is 1/12th the mass of one carbon atom.*

Chemical formulas and formula mass

Different objects can be compared by using relative mass

We can use an analogy to explain how the concept of relative mass can be used. Let's say that we have the same number of gumdrops and jawbreakers, and that we will use the variable "*x*" to represent this number. The sample of *x* gumdrops has a mass of 100 grams, and the sample of *x* jawbreakers has a mass of 400 grams. This means that an individual gumdrop has a mass that is 1/4, or 25 percent of, the mass of a jawbreaker. Twenty-five percent can be represented by the number 0.25. This number represents the relative mass of a gumdrop compared with a jawbreaker. Let's call the jawbreaker unit of mass a jmu, for "jawbreaker mass unit." Now, if a single jawbreaker has a mass of 1.0 jmu, then a gumdrop would have a mass of 0.25 jmu. How many jawbreaker mass units would *x* number of candy bars be if they weighed 800 grams? They would have a mass of 2 jmu.

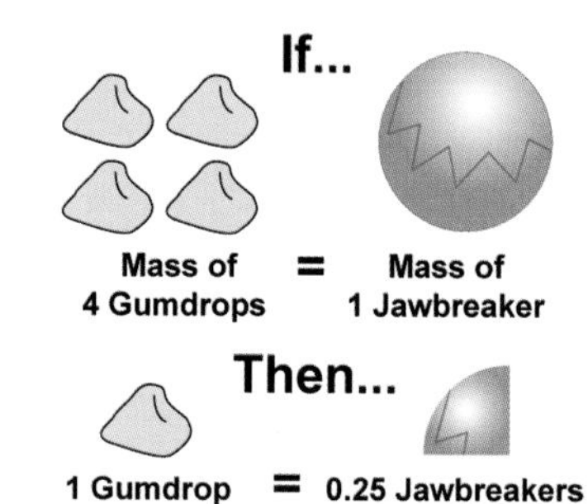

Figure 19.28: *If a single jawbreaker has a mass of 1 jmu (jawbreaker mass unit), what would the mass of 1 gum drop be in jmu?*

Chemical formulas

A chemical formula for a compound gives you three useful pieces of information. First, it tells you which types of atoms and how many of each are present in a compound. Second, it lets you know if polyatomic ions are present. Remember that polyatomic ions are distinct groups of atoms with a collective oxidation number. For example, NO_3^- is a polyatomic ion called nitrate with an oxidation number of 1-. As you practice writing chemical formulas, you will start to recognize these ions.

What is formula mass?

Third, a chemical formula allows you to calculate the mass of one unit of the compound *relative* to the mass of other compounds. Formula mass, like atomic mass, is a way to compare the masses of units of different compounds. The formula mass of a compound is determined by adding up the atomic masses of all of the atoms in the compound as shown in Figure 19.29.

Figuring formula mass

The formula for water is H_2O. This means that there are two hydrogen atoms for every one of oxygen in a molecule of water. Using the periodic table, you can see that the atomic mass of hydrogen is 1.007 amu. For our purposes, we will round all atomic masses to the hundredths place. Using 1.01 amu for hydrogen, we can multiply this number by the number of atoms present to determine atomic mass of hydrogen in a water molecule. The atomic mass of oxygen, rounded off, is 16.00. Using this information, the formula mass for water is calculated.

$LiNO_3$

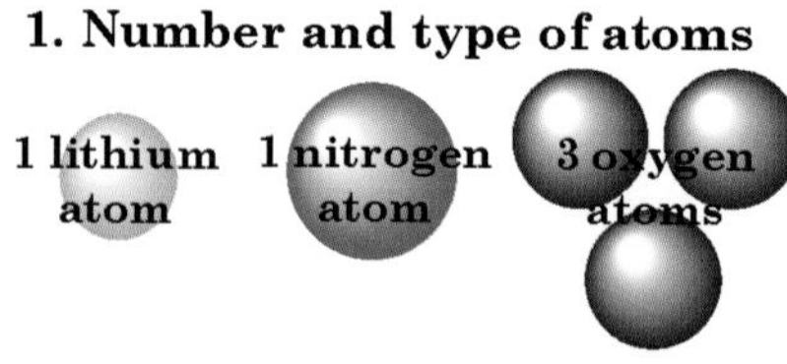

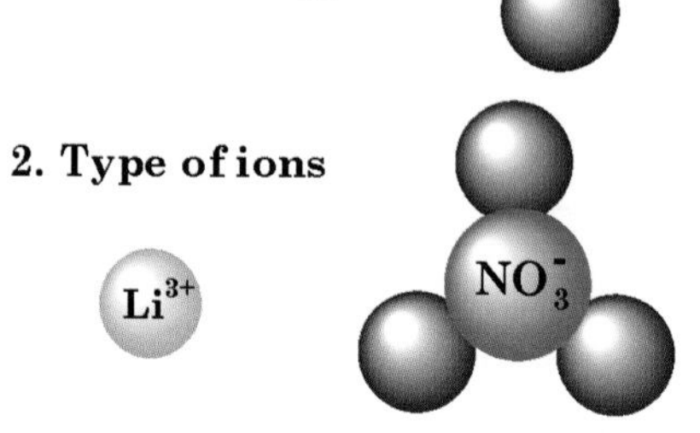

3. Formula mass

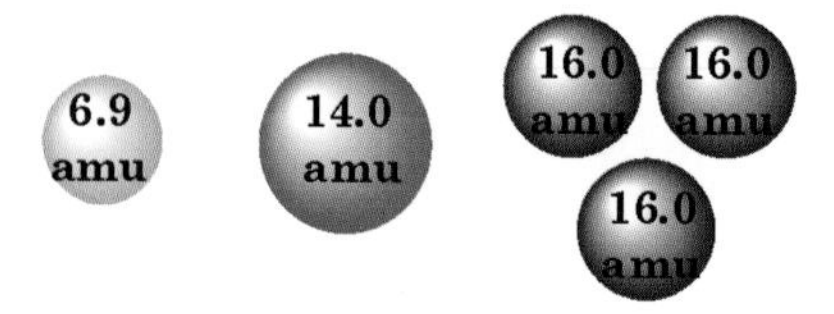

$(6.9) + (14.0) + (3 \times 16.0) = 68.9$ amu

Figure 19.29: *What does a chemical formula tell you?*

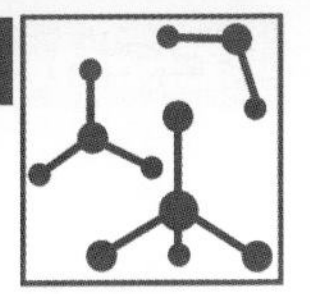

How do we make atomic mass units useful to work with?

Atomic mass units and grams

Working with atomic mass units would be very difficult because each atomic mass unit has a mass of 1/12th the mass of a carbon atom. In order to make atomic mass units useful for conducting, using, and evaluating chemical reactions, it would be convenient to set the value of one amu to equal one gram. One gram is, after all, an amount of matter that we can see! For example, one paper clip has a mass of about 2.5 grams.

How do you relate molecules, atomic mass units, and grams?

The mass of one water molecule in atomic mass units is 18.02. How many molecules of water would be in 18.02 *grams* of water? To find out, we need to come up with a *number* of molecules or atoms in a sample that is equal to the atomic mass, in grams. From here forward, we will say that 18.02 grams of water contains the Avogadro number of molecules. This number is 6.02×10^{23}—a very, very large number of molecules! Look at the relationships in Figure 19.30 to help you understand the Avogadro number.

The Avogadro number

The Avogadro number is the number of atoms in the atomic mass of an element or the number of molecules in the formula mass of a compound when these masses are expressed in grams. One set of 6.02×10^{23} atoms or molecules is also referred to as a mole of that substance. The term mole is used to talk about a number of atoms or molecules just like the term *dozen* is used to talk about quantities of eggs, doughnuts, or cans of soda.

The number, 6.02×10^{23}, was named in honor of Count Meadow Avogadro (1776 - 1856), an Italian chemist and physicist who first thought of the concept of the molecule. A German physicist actually discovered the Avogadro number nine years after Avogadro's death.

Comparing different compounds

If 6.02×10^{23} water molecules has a mass of 18.02 grams, how much does the same number of formula units of calcium carbonate (an ionic compound) weigh in grams? If we calculate the mass of the same number of molecules or formula units of each substance, we can compare the relative mass of each molecule or unit as shown on the next page.

The formula mass of H_2O is 18.02 amu

18.02 amu = 1 molecule of H_2O

18.02 grams = 6.02×10^{23} molecules of H_2O

Figure 19.30: *The relationship between formula mass, atomic mass units, and grams.*

Science Facts: How large is the Avogadro number?

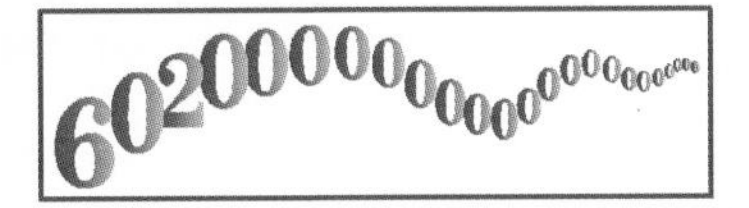

Imagine that every person on Earth was involved in counting the Avogadro number of atoms. How long do you think it would take? If all 6 billion people counted 3 atoms per second, it would take 1 million years to count 6.02×10^{23} atoms!

Example: Calculating the formula mass of a compound

What is the formula mass of calcium carbonate to the nearest hundredth?

1. Write the chemical formula for the compound.

calcium: Ca^{2+} carbonate: CO_3^{2-}

chemical formula: $CaCO_3$

2. List the atoms, number of each atom, and atomic mass of each atom.

atom	number	atomic mass	total mass (number x atomic mass)
Ca	1	40.08	40.08
C	1	12.01	12.01
O	3	16.00	48.00

3. Add up the values for each type of atom to calculate the formula mass.

40.08 + 12.01 + 48.00 = 100.09 amu

The formula mass of calcium carbonate is 100.09 amu.

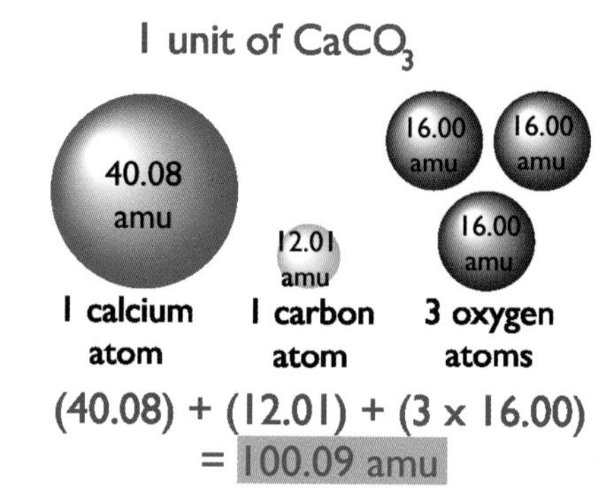

Figure 19.31: *Calculating the formula mass of calcium carbonate.*

How do you compare samples of substances?

The Avogadro number of formula units of calcium carbonate would have a mass of 100.09 grams. In other words, if you used a balance to weigh 100.09 grams of calcium carbonate, there would be 6.02×10^{23} formula units of calcium carbonate in the sample. Likewise, if you used a balance to weigh 18.02 grams of water, there would be 6.02×10^{23} molecules of water in the weighed sample (Figure 19.32).

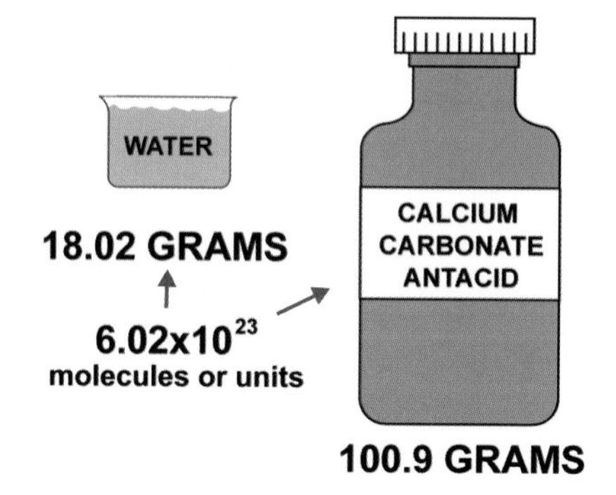

Figure 19.32: *100.09 g of $CaCO_3$ contains 6.02×10^{23} formula units of calcium carbonate. 18.02 g of H_2O contains 6.02×10^{23} molecules of water.*

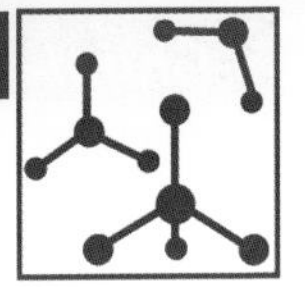

Hydrates and the chemical formulas

Hydrates are ionic compounds that contain precise numbers of water molecules

Have you ever bought a product that contained in the packaging a packet that was labeled: "Silica gel — do not eat"? These packets are often found inside boxes containing electronics equipment—like a DVD player or a stereo receiver. They are found inside shoeboxes, too. What is the purpose of these packets?

The presence of moisture in the packaging of certain products can be a problem. Manufacturers added packets of silica gel to absorb any such water. Ionic compounds like silicon oxide have the ability to incorporate water molecules as part of their structure. Water molecules become chemically bonded to their ions. A hydrate is a compound that has water molecules chemically bonded to its ions. Different compounds can absorb different numbers of molecules of water, as table 19.3 shows.

Table 19.3: ***Common hydrates***

Name	Formula
Silicon oxide monohydrate	$SiO_2 \cdot H_2O$
Barium chloride dihydrate	$BaCl_2 \cdot 2H_2O$
Calcium nitrate tetrahydrate	$Ca(NO_3)_2 \cdot 4H_2O$
Cobalt chloride hexahydrate	$CoCl_2 \cdot 6H_2O$
Magnesium sulfate heptahydrate	$MgSO_4 \cdot 7H_2O$
Iron (III) nitrate nonahydrate	$Fe(NO_3)_3 \cdot 9H_2O$

Note that the chemical formula of a hydrate shows the ionic compound times a certain number of water molecules. This denotes a ratio of the number of molecules of water absorbed for each formula unit of the compound. Note also that the name for each compound is followed by a Greek prefix indicating the number of water molecules and the word "hydrate." Figure 19.33 lists some Greek prefixes and their meanings.

prefix	meaning
mono-	1
di-	2
tri-	3
tetra-	4
penta-	5
hexa-	6
hepta-	7
octa-	8
nona-	9

Figure 19.33: *Greek prefixes.*

Getting rid of the water molecules

You can remove the water molecules from a hydrate by heating it. When all the water leaves the hydrate through evaporation, it is anhydrous, a term that means "without water." Now that you know why packets of silica gel are included with some products, how could you *reuse* a packet of silica gel? How would you know when the packet of silica gel was anhydrous?

How do you calculate the formula mass of a hydrate?

It's easy to calculate the formula mass of a hydrate. First, calculate the formula mass of the ionic compound, then add the formula mass of water times as many molecules of water as are present. The example below shows you how to do this step by step.

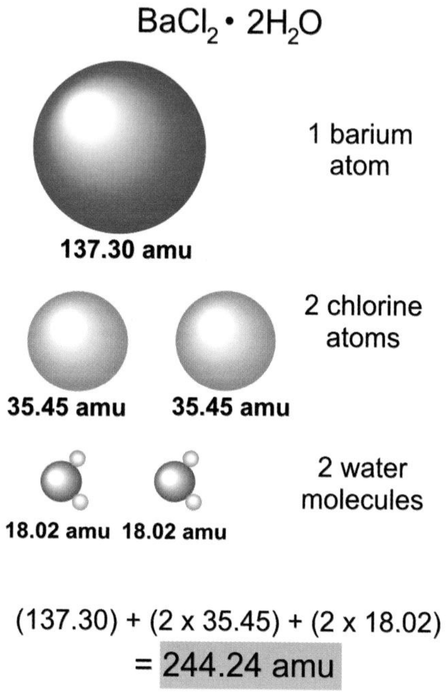

Example: Calculating the formula mass of a hydrate

What is the formula mass of $BaCl_2 \cdot 2H_2O$?

1. Calculate the formula mass of the ionic compound

The ionic compound is $BaCl_2$. To calculate its formula mass:

1 Ba atom × 137.30 amu = 137.30 amu

2 Cl atoms × 35.45 amu = 70.90 amu

137.30 amu + 70.90 amu = 208.20 amu

2. Calculate formula mass of the water molecules

The formula mass for water is:

2 H atoms × 1.01 = 2.02 amu

1 O atom × 16.00 = 16.00 amu

2.02 + 16.00 = 18.02 amu

There are 2 molecules of water in the hydrate. The total formula mass is:

2 molecules H_2O × 18.02 = 36.04 amu

3. Calculate the formula mass of the hydrate

$BaCl_2 \times 2H_2O$ = 208.20+ 36.04 = 244.24 amu

$BaCl_2 \cdot 2H_2O$

1 barium atom

137.30 amu

2 chlorine atoms

35.45 amu 35.45 amu

2 water molecules

18.02 amu 18.02 amu

(137.30) + (2 x 35.45) + (2 x 18.02)
= 244.24 amu

Figure 19.34: *Calculating the formula mass of a hydrate.*

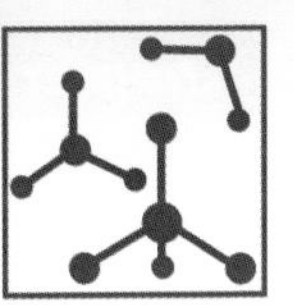

Chapter 19 Review

Vocabulary review

Match the following terms with the correct definition. There is one definition extra in the list that will not match any term.

Set One	
1. covalent bond	a. The electrons involved in chemical bonding
2. ionic bond	b. Most atoms need eight valence electrons to be stable
3. octet rule	c. A bond between atoms in which electrons are lost or gained
4. valence electrons	d. A number that represents the number of electrons that are lost or gained in bonding
	e. A bond between atoms in which electrons are shared

Set Two	
1. Binary compound	a. An ion like Na+, K+, or Cl-
2. Monoatomic ion	b. Electrons that are involved in bonding
3. Oxidation number	c. An ion like CO_3^{2-} or OH^-
4. Polyatomic ion	d. A number that indicates how many electrons will be gained or lost during bonding
	e. A molecule composed of two monatomic ions

Concept review

1. Why do atoms tend to combine with other atoms instead of existing as single atoms?
2. Why are atoms in Group 18 considered to be chemically stable?
3. How can you determine the number of valence electrons by looking at the periodic table?
4. What conditions are met when an atom is chemically stable?
5. What is the major difference between ionic and covalent bonds?
6. Provide one general rule for predicting whether or not a bond will be ionic. (Hint: use the periodic table in your rule.)
7. What are polymers? Give an example of a natural polymer and a synthetic polymer.
8. What is an oxidation number? How can you determine an element's oxidation number by looking at the periodic table?
9. In a chemical formula, what do subscripts tell you?
10. What is the relationship between the formula mass of a compound, the Avogadro number of molecules of that compound, and the mass in grams of the compound?

Problems

1. Fill in the table below.

Element	Atomic number	Valence electrons	Lewis dot diagram
Fluorine			
Oxygen			
Phosphorus			
Carbon			
Beryllium			
Nitrogen			
Sulfur			
Neon			
Silicon			

2. Identify which of the following bonds are ionic and which are covalent. Justify your answer with a sentence.
   a. C-C
   b. Na-Br
   c. C-N
   d. C-O
   e. Ca-Cl

3. Fill in the table below.

Element	Number of valence electrons	Electrons gained or lost during ionization	Oxidation number
Potassium			
Aluminum			
Phosphorus			
Krypton			

4. Which group number on the periodic table is represented by each description?
   a. These atoms form compounds with ions that have an oxidation number of 1^-.
   b. The oxidation state of the atoms in this group is 3^-.
   c. Atoms in this group have four valence electrons in the outermost energy level. The atoms in this group form compounds with ions like H^+, Na^+ and Li^+.
   d. If these ions combined with Al^{3+}, you would need three of them and two aluminum ions in the formula.
   e. Atoms in this group lose two electrons during ionization.

5. Which of the following would be a correct chemical formula for a molecule of N^{3-} and H^+?
   a. HNO_3
   b. H_3N_6
   c. NH_3
   d. NH

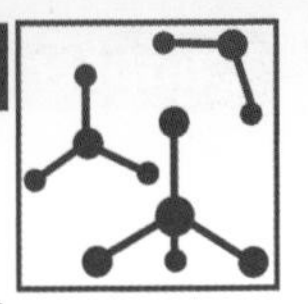

6. What is the simplest ratio of carbon to hydrogen to oxygen in a molecule of glucose ($C_6H_{12}O_6$)?
   a. 1:2:1
   b. 6:12:6
   c. 2:4:2
   d. 6:2:6

7. What is the correct name for the compound $NaHCO_3$?
   a. sodium carbonide
   b. sodium hydrogen carbonate
   c. sodium hydrogen carboxide
   d. bicarbonate

8. Which of the following ion pairs would combine in a 1:2 ratio?
   a. NH^{4+} and F^-
   b. Be^{2+} and Cl^-
   c. sodium and hydroxide
   d. hydrogen and phosphate

9. For each of the compounds below, (1) state whether it is an empirical or molecular formula; and (2) write the empirical formula (if it is not already an empirical formula).
   a. CH_2O
   b. $(CH_2)_2(OH)_2$
   c. $C_7H_5NO_3S$
   d. $C_{10}H_8O_4$

10. Name each of the following binary covalent compounds.
    a. N_4O_6
    b. SiO_2
    c. S_2F_{10}
    d. $SbCl_5$

11. Write the chemical formula for the following compounds. Consult Table 19.3, "Polyatomic ions," on page 343 when needed.
    a. Sodium acetate
    b. Aluminum hydroxide
    c. Magnesium sulfate
    d. Ammonium nitrate
    e. Calcium fluoride

12. Calculate the formula mass for the following household compounds. Use the periodic table on the inside back cover.
    a. Lye drain cleaner, NaOH
    b. Epsom salts, $MgSO_4$
    c. Aspirin, $C_9H_8O_4$
    d. Plant fertilizer, $Ca(H_2PO_4)_2$
    e. Dampness absorber, $CaCl_2 \cdot 6H_2O$

13. Give the scientific name of compounds (a), (b), and (e) in question 10. Consult Table 19.3 on page 343.

Applying your knowledge

1. Many of the atoms on the periodic table have more than one oxidation number. You can figure out the oxidation number for these elements if you know at least one of the oxidation numbers in the compound. You only need to figure out what the oxidation number would be to make the molecule neutrally charged. Fill in the oxidation numbers for each of the following molecules.

Chemical formula of compound	Oxidation number for positive ion	Oxidation number for negative ion
SiO_2		2-
PBr_3		1-
$FeCl_3$		1-
CuF_2		1-
N_2O_3		2^-
P_2O_5		2^-

2. Suppose you are working in the lab with the following compounds: NaCl and Al_2O_3.
    a. Would the same number of molecules of each compound have the same mass? Explain your reasoning.
    b. Explain how you would measure out Avogadro's number of molecules (6.02×10^{23}) of each compound.
    c. Why is there a difference in the mass of the exact same number of molecules of each compound?

3. Find out about recycling plastics in your community. Prepare a pamphlet or bulletin board for your school that provides information on how to recycle plastics. The pamphlet or bulletin board should include practical information about recycling plastics including: how to get involved in community organizations, and what types of plastics are recycled. If your school does not recycle plastics, see if you can form a committee to develop and implement a plan.

4. Examine the household chemicals that are used in your own home. Make a list of the products your family uses, the names of the chemicals in each product and the hazards associated with each chemical. Research environmentally friendly alternatives to some of the products your family uses and prepare a brief presentation for your class.

UNIT 7

Changes in Matter

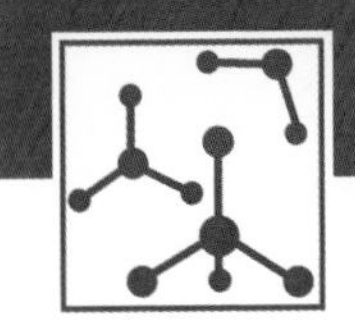

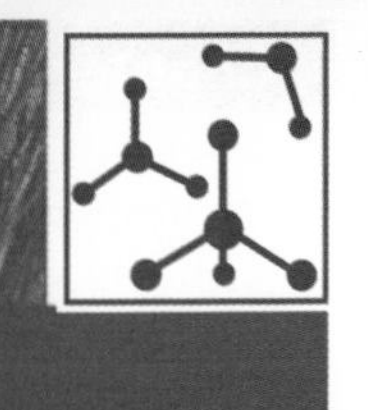

Chapter 20

Chemical Reactions

Introduction to Chapter 20

When you drive a car, the engine is using oxygen and gasoline to produce carbon dioxide and water vapor. This is a chemical reaction that you depend upon to go places. In this chapter, you will learn what happens during a chemical reaction and how chemical reactions obey the laws of conservation.

Investigations for Chapter 20

20.1	**Chemical Changes**	*What is the evidence that a chemical change has occurred?*

You will make a list of the evidence for chemical change by carefully observing a series of chemical reactions.

20.2	**Chemical Equations**	*How do you balance chemical equations?*

You will use the Periodic Table Tiles to learn how to balance chemical equations so that the number and type of atoms that react balance with the number and type of atoms that are produced in a reaction.

20.3	**Conservation of Mass**	*How can you prove that mass is conserved in a chemical reaction?*

You will design your own experiment to prove that what you put into a reaction can be accounted for in the products that are produced.

20.4	**Using Equations as Recipes**	*How can you predict the amount of product in a reaction?*

You will discover an important mathematical relationship that will allow you to predict the amount of product based on the amount of one of the reactants.

Learning Goals

In this chapter, you will:

- ✔ Distinguish between physical and chemical changes in matter using examples from everyday life.
- ✔ Write and balance chemical equations.
- ✔ Investigate and identify the law of conservation of mass.
- ✔ Use chemical equations to predict the amount of product that will be produced in a reaction.
- ✔ Design an experiment to prove conservation of mass.
- ✔ Identify the mathematical relationship between the mass in grams of reactants and products, the coefficients in a balanced equation, and the formula masses of the reactants and products.
- ✔ Identify economic and environmental reasons for recycling tires.

Vocabulary

balance	coefficient	limiting reactant	product
chemical change	conservation of atoms	percent yield	reactant
chemical equation	conservation of mass	physical change	
chemical reaction	excess reactant	polymer	

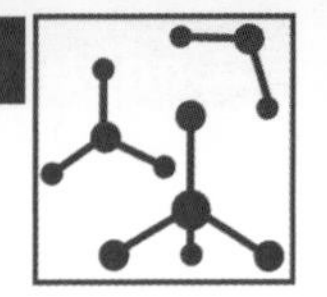

20.1 Chemical Changes

Have you ever tried to watch rust forming on a car? You have probably noticed a patch of rust getting larger as weeks or months pass, but chances are, you did not actually *see* the rust form. Can you watch an ice cube melt? Yes, but this process happens much faster than a car rusts. Changes in matter are occurring all around you, all of the time. There are different types of changes in matter that happen. The rusting of a car is much different from the melting of ice. We can classify changes in matter as either chemical changes or physical changes.

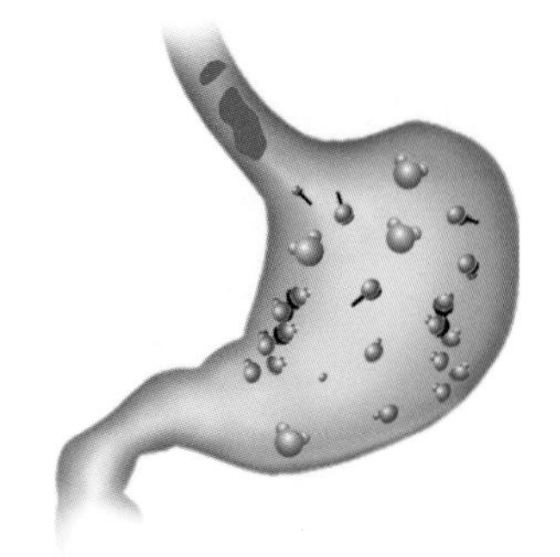

Figure 20.1: *The process of digestion involves both physical and chemical changes to the food. Chewing breaks food into smaller pieces causing a physical change. In the stomach, acids are produced which cause chemical changes.*

Physical changes

You are what you eat "*You are what you eat.*" You have heard this many times, but have you ever thought about what it means? How does the food you eat become part of your body? How does the food you eat give you energy? The answer is that the food you eat goes through many *changes* as it passes through your body. The process of breaking food down so that your body can use it is called *digestion*. It involves many different changes to the food, both physical changes and chemical changes.

Physical changes If you take a bite out of an apple, have you changed the chemical composition of the apple? Of course not. You have only removed a small piece of the apple. Once the piece of apple is in your mouth, you begin to chew it. Chewing does not alter the chemical composition of the apple either. It only breaks the apple into smaller pieces so that you can swallow it easily. Chewing causes a physical change in the apple. A **physical change** is a change that affects only the physical properties of a substance. Those properties include size, shape, and state.

Energy and physical changes You can change the physical properties of ice by crushing it or by simply letting it melt. In both cases, energy is added to the ice. The only difference between solid water (ice), liquid water, and water vapor is the amount of energy involved in each state. Water vapor is the most energetic form of water. Ice, liquid water, and water vapor all have the exact same chemical composition.

Figure 20.2: *Physical changes affect only the physical properties of a substance.*

Chemical changes

Chemical changes

Is the function of chewing only to make the pieces of apple smaller so that you can swallow them? In fact, another function of chewing is to create lots of available surface area for special chemicals called *enzymes* to cause chemical changes in the apple. A **chemical change** is a change in a substance that involves breaking and reforming of chemical bonds to make one or more different substances. When you begin chewing, glands in your mouth produce *saliva*. An enzyme in your saliva called *amylase* immediately gets to work to break down complex carbohydrate molecules into simpler carbohydrate molecules by breaking bonds. This causes a chemical change in the apple, altering its chemical composition. Your body actually begins the process of digestion in your mouth.

Chemical reactions

After you swallow the bite of apple, it travels to the next digestion site, the stomach. There, more enzymes and acid further break down the food you have swallowed. The whole process of digestion is very dependent upon chemical changes. Although physical changes are necessary to break any food into bits, chemical changes help release important energy and nutrients from the food you consume. Chemical changes are the result of *chemical reactions*, that is, the breaking of bonds in one or more substances, and the reforming of new bonds to create new substances.

How do you know when a chemical change has occurred?

You know a chemical change has occurred when one or more starting substances are mixed and you get products that appear to be different from those starting substances. This is because chemical changes involve changes in the chemical bonds that hold substances together. Chemical reactions also involve energy. Therefore, when you see any evidence that energy has been released or absorbed, a chemical change has probably occurred. You can use your powers of observation to determine that a chemical change has taken place. However, sometimes you need to make sure that the chemical properties of the new substances are different from the ones you started with. If you had never seen ice or water before, would you know that they were the same thing?

Try this...

Place a saltine cracker in your mouth. Hold it there for about 10 minutes. Then, how does it taste? Is this evidence of a chemical or physical change?

Figure 20.3: *When your body "burns" food for energy, carbon dioxide and water are released. This process is called respiration. You need oxygen for this process to occur. Where do the carbon dioxide and water come from?*

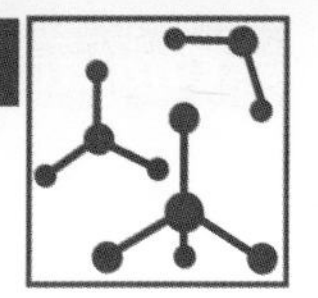

Environmental Issue: Recycling tires

How many tires are thrown away each year?

The next time you travel in a car, think about the tires you are riding on. Did you know that more than 275 million discarded tires are dumped annually into landfills in the United States? Around the world, over 5 million tires are thrown away each day! As the number of cars on the road increases each year, so do the number of tires discarded. For many years, the only alternatives were to throw used tires into landfills, or burn them, which caused air pollution. Today, scientists and engineers are coming up with ways to put a new spin on the discarding of tires. Reusing and recycling scrap tires requires the use of both physical and chemical changes.

What are tires made of?

A typical automobile tire is about 65 percent rubber, 25 percent steel, and 10 percent fiber (plastic). The rubber found in tires is *vulcanized*, or chemically treated to increase the number of sulfur bonds. While this process produces a rigid, strong, and puncture-resistant substance, it also makes it harder to *chemically* break the rubber down into useful substances. Because of this combination of materials, some specialists say that reclaiming the original components from discarded tires is like trying to recycle a cake back to its original ingredients.

How are tires recycled?

Tires can be recycled in two ways: (1) processing them, and (2) using them whole. Whole tire recycling involves using the old tire as is for other purposes, such as landscape borders, playground structures, bumpers, and highway crash barriers. Processing tires for recycling involves chopping them up into pieces, and then separating the rubber and fiber from the steel. While this initial processing is only a *physical change* to the materials found in a tire, it is very challenging because of the way tire manufacturers put the materials together.

An expensive, but very effective way to separate the rubber, fiber, and steel involves cooling the small pieces of tire with liquid nitrogen. This releases the steel, rubber, and fiber pieces from sticking to each other. Next, magnets are used to take out the steel. The pieces of rubber can then be separated from the fiber using density techniques.

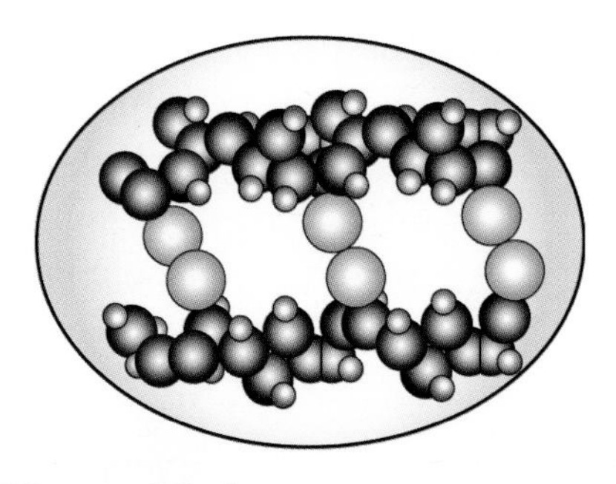

Figure 20.4: *Vulcanized rubber is chemically treated to increase the number of sulfur bonds. This makes the tire harder and more puncture-resistant.*

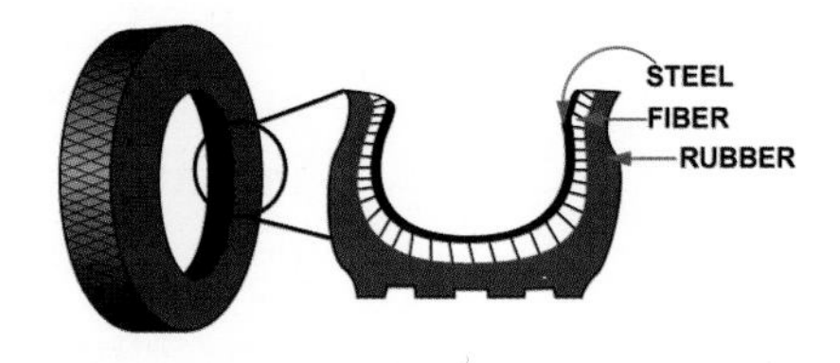

Figure 20.5: *The components of a typical radial tire.*

Use your head...

Based on what you learned in the last unit, can you explain how to separate rubber and fiber using the physical property of density?

Uses for scrap rubber and steel

The small particles of rubber can be used immediately as a substitute for new rubber in products such as footwear, carpet underlay, and waterproofing compounds. It can be mixed with asphalt to make safe and durable road surfaces. In fact, it has been found that adding scrap rubber to the asphalt used to pave roads can significantly decrease braking distances! Asphalt-scrap rubber mixtures are also considered the superior choice for track and field grounds, equestrian tracks, and paved playgrounds.

The steel that is recovered from tires is used to make new steel. In fact, almost everything we make out of steel contains some percentage that is recycled. For nearly as long as steel has been made, recycling has been part of the process.

Recycling 1 ton of steel conserves...
2,500 lbs of iron ore
1,400 lb. of coal
120 lbs of limestone
11 million Btu's of energy

Figure 20.6: *Recycling steel*

Chemically changing rubber

Like plastic, rubber is a polymer. A **polymer** is a molecule that consists of long chains of repeating combinations of atoms. Rubber is a polymer that is very difficult to break down—especially vulcanized rubber. Recent advances in technology have created an environmentally friendly process for breaking the carbon-carbon, carbon-sulfur, and sulfur-sulfur bonds in order to produce smaller molecules. These smaller molecules can be used to make liquid and gaseous fuels, ingredients for other polymers, lubricating oils, and a charcoal that can be used to decontaminate water or soil.

A shortage of discarded tires?

Currently, there are so many uses for discarded tires that a better question seems to be, why not recycle *all* of our discarded tires? Perhaps in the near future, instead of an overabundance of discarded tires, there will be a shortage!

Exploring further...

- Interview someone from a company that makes asphalt about using scrap rubber from tires.
- Research further about using recycled tires as a fuel source.
- Find out what happens to discarded tires in your community.

For discussion

1. What are the advantages and disadvantages to whole-tire recycling?
2. Describe the physical changes that are used in processing tires for recycling.
3. What are the advantages and disadvantages to chemically changing scrap rubber?
4. How do you think technological advances in tires could present additional challenges to the recycling process?

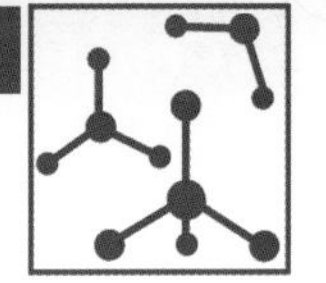

20.2 Chemical Equations

All of the chemical changes you observed in the last Investigation were the result of chemical reactions. A chemical reaction involves breaking the chemical bonds in one or more reactants and reforming chemical bonds into one or more products. All chemical reactions involve breaking and/or forming chemical bonds and all involve energy.

What happens during a chemical reaction?

Did a chemical change take place?

In the last Investigation, you observed several chemical reactions. For example, in one of the reactions, you mixed vinegar with baking soda. When you mixed these two substances, you observed a fairly violent bubbling as the baking soda appeared to dissolve into the vinegar. You may have noticed a drop in temperature as the reaction proceeded. These observations provide *evidence* that a chemical change has occurred (Figure 20.7).

Proving chemical change

In order to prove that a chemical change has occurred, you need to be able to confirm that the chemical and physical properties of one or more of the products are different from those of the reactants. For example, when methane (natural gas) is burned, it reacts with oxygen to form carbon dioxide and water. This is a common reaction used to heat homes, cook food—or heat up chemistry experiments! Upon careful examination, you would conclude that carbon dioxide has different chemical and physical properties from methane.

Methane + Oxygen ⟶ Carbon Dioxide + Water

Reactants — substances that change

Products — substances that are formed

Where does the new substance come from?

In ordinary chemical reactions, atoms are rearranged through the breaking and reforming of chemical bonds. In the methane reaction, the bonds between carbon and hydrogen in methane are broken. Carbon reforms a bond with the oxygen to form carbon dioxide, one of the products. Hydrogen also forms a bond with additional oxygen atoms to produce water. In addition, heat and light are produced.

Bubbling

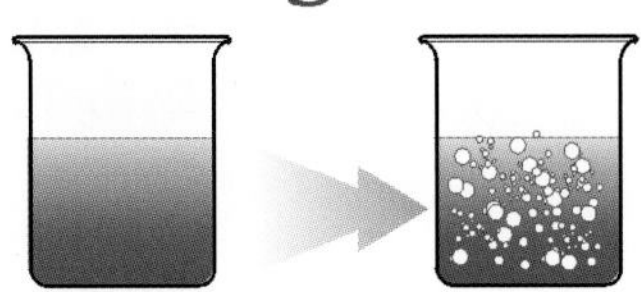

A new gas is forming?

Turns cloudy

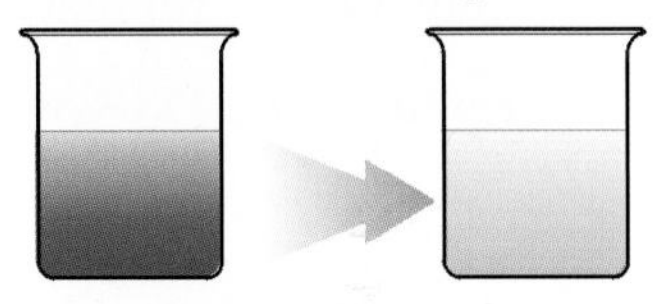

A new solid is forming?

Temperature change

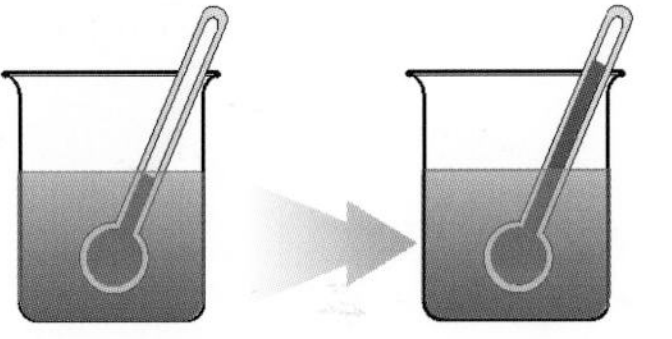

Chemical bonds are changing?

Color change

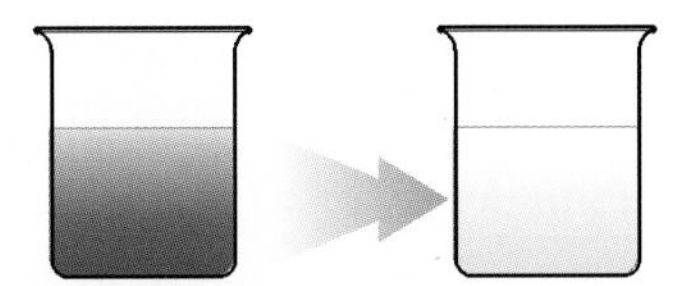

A new substance is forming?

Figure 20.7: *Different kinds of evidence that chemical reactions are occurring.*

How are chemical reactions written?

Chemical reactions as sentences

We could simply write chemical reactions as sentences. For example, we could write the reaction of methane and oxygen as follows:

Methane gas reacts with oxygen gas to produce carbon dioxide and water.

Chemical formulas are more convenient

It is more convenient to use chemical formulas that correspond to the elements and compounds in the reaction. When we use chemical formulas and symbols to represent a reaction instead of using words, it is called a chemical equation.

Remember diatomic molecules?

Do you remember why oxygen is O_2 instead of just O? Recall from the last unit that in nature, most elemental gases do not exist as single atoms (with the exception of the noble gases). Oxygen is called a diatomic molecule, meaning there are two atoms in the molecule. Table 20.1 below shows some of the elements that exist as diatomic molecules.

Using formulas and symbols, the chemical equation for the reaction of methane with oxygen can be written as:

$$CH_4 + O_2 \longrightarrow CO_2 + H_2O$$

Table 20.1: *Elements that exist as diatomic molecules*

Hydrogen, H_2	Nitrogen, N_2	Oxygen, O_2
Fluorine, F_2	Chlorine, Cl_2	Bromine, Br_2

Chemical equations should show that atoms are conserved in a reaction

The chemical equation above is not completely correct. It does not agree with an important principle in chemistry called conservation of atoms. This principle says that the number of each type of atom on the reactants side of a chemical equation must be equal to the number of each type of atom on the products side of the equation. In other words, you get out of a reaction what you put into it, nothing more, nothing less. If you count the number and type of each atom in the chemical equation above, do they add up on both sides of the equation equally? If you count them carefully, you'll find that the answer is no.

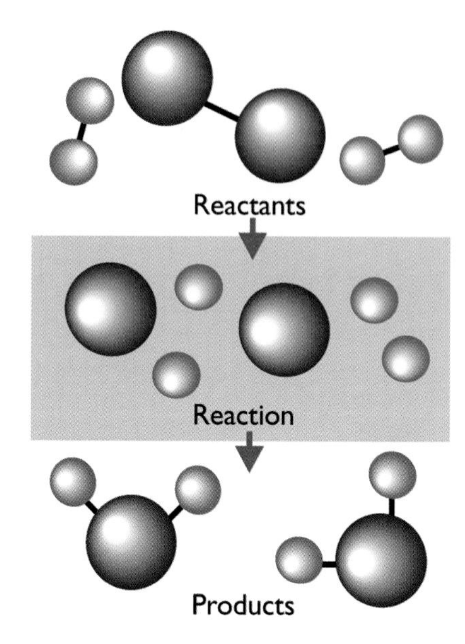

Figure 20.8: *In a chemical reaction, chemical bonds are broken and reformed to make new products.*

substance	chemical formula
methane	CH_4
oxygen	O_2
carbon dioxide	CO_2
water	H_2O

Figure 20.9: *Chemical formulas for substances in the methane reaction.*

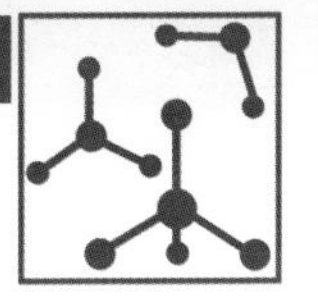

How do you write a chemical equation that shows conservation of atoms?

Numbers and types of atoms must balance

Since only whole atoms can react—not fractions of an atom—it is necessary to **balance** the number and type of atoms on the reactants and products sides of the equation. Furthermore, by balancing the numbers and types of atoms, you are not allowed to change the chemical composition of any of the substances on the reactants or products sides. To learn about how to balance chemical equations, let's take another look at that methane reaction.

$$CH_4 + O_2 \longrightarrow CO_2 + H_2O$$

The arrow in the chemical equation is read as:

- "to produce" or
- "to yield"

Subscripts below the symbols for elements tell you how many of each type of atom there are in a molecule.

Figure 20.10: *Helpful hints for reading chemical equations.*

Count the number and type of each atom on both sides of the chemical equation

Once again, count the number of each type of atom on both sides of the reaction. The table below summarizes the numbers:

type of atom	total on reactants side	total on products side	balanced?
C	1	1	yes
H	4	2	no
O	2	3	no

When an equation is unbalanced

The chemical equation is not balanced because the number of hydrogen atoms and oxygen atoms are different on both sides of the equation. To make them equal and balance the equation, you must figure out what number to multiply each compound by in order to make the numbers add up. Remember: You cannot change the number of individual atoms in a compound. That would change its chemical formula and you would have a different compound. You can only change the number of molecules of that compound.

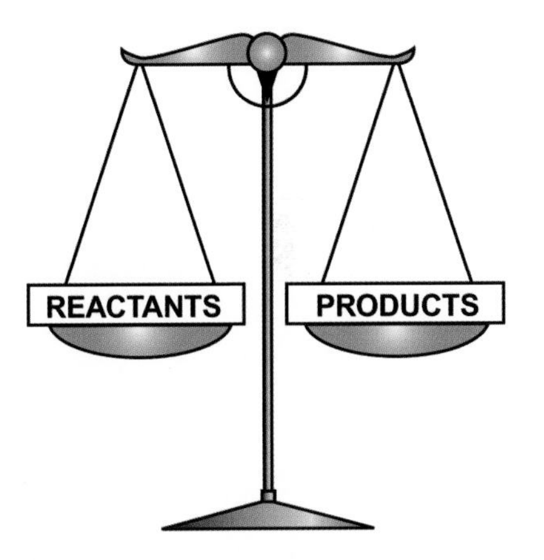

Figure 20.11: *In a chemical equation, the number and type of atoms on both sides of the equation must be equal.*

Balancing equations involves adding coefficients

To change the number of molecules of a compound, you can write a whole number coefficient in front of the chemical formula. When you do this, all of the types of atoms in that formula are multiplied by that number. For example:

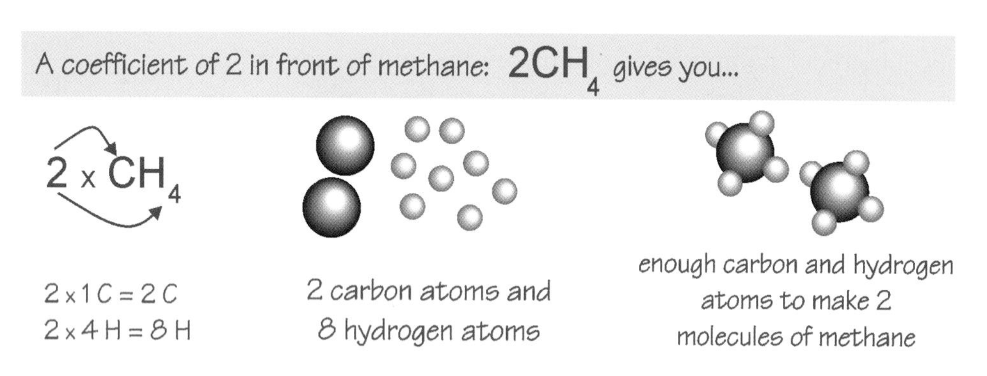
A coefficient of 2 in front of methane: 2CH4 gives you...
2 x CH4
2 x 1 C = 2 C
2 x 4 H = 8 H
2 carbon atoms and
8 hydrogen atoms
enough carbon and hydrogen
atoms to make 2
molecules of methane

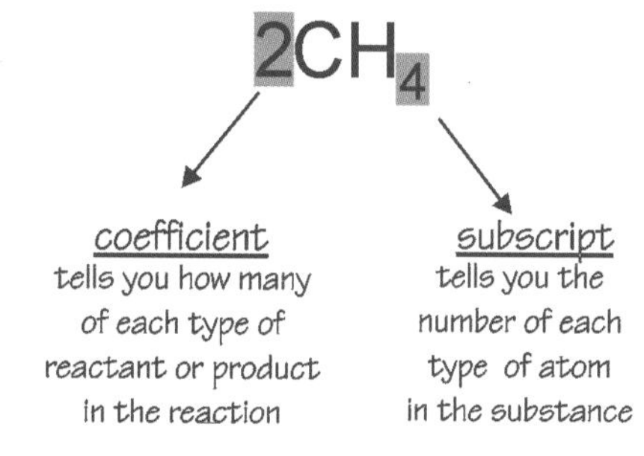
2CH4
coefficient
tells you how many
of each type of
reactant or product
in the reaction
subscript
tells you the
number of each
type of atom
in the substance

Figure 20.12: *What do coefficients and subscripts mean?*

Multiplying molecules with coefficients

Figuring out where to place coefficients to multiply the numbers of atoms in a chemical formula is largely a process of trial and error. Let's look at the methane reaction after the correct coefficients have been added:

$$CH_4 + 2O_2 \longrightarrow CO_2 + 2H_2O$$

Counting the atoms on both sides again, we see that the equation is balanced.

atom	total on reactants side	total on products side
C	1	1
H	4	2 × 2 = **4**
O	2 × 2 = **4**	2 + (2 × 1) = **4**

How do you read a balanced equation?

The balanced equation above can be read as follows:

One molecule of methane reacts with two molecules of oxygen

to produce

one molecule of carbon dioxide and two molecules of water.

1. Make sure you have written the correct chemical formula for each reactant and product.
2. The subscripts in the chemical formulas of the reactants and products cannot be changed during the process of balancing the equation. Changing the subscripts will change the chemical makeup of the compounds.
3. Numbers called coefficients are placed in front of the formulas to make the number of atoms on each side of the equation equal.

Figure 20.13: *Things to remember when balancing chemical equations.*

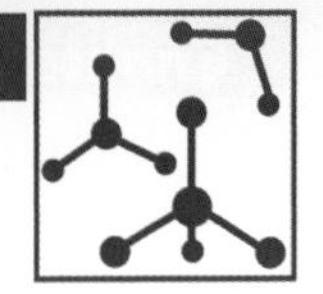

Example: Balancing a common reaction

What happens when you take an antacid?

Hydrochloric acid is a substance your stomach normally produces to help you break down food. Sometimes, if you eat spicy foods or worry excessively about studying chemistry, your stomach produces too much hydrochloric acid and you get acid indigestion. Most people take antacids to relieve this painful condition. Many antacids contain calcium carbonate which neutralizes the hydrochloric acid. The products formed are calcium chloride, carbon dioxide, and water. How do you write and balance the chemical equation for this reaction? The following steps outline this process for you:

1. Write the word form of the equation.

Hydrochloric acid reacts with calcium carbonate to produce calcium chloride, carbon dioxide, and water.

2. Write the chemical equation

Consult an ion chart for some of the chemical formulas. The ion chart on page 343 is useful for solving problems of this type. You need to get the chemical formula for each chemical that appears. The chemical equation for this reaction is:

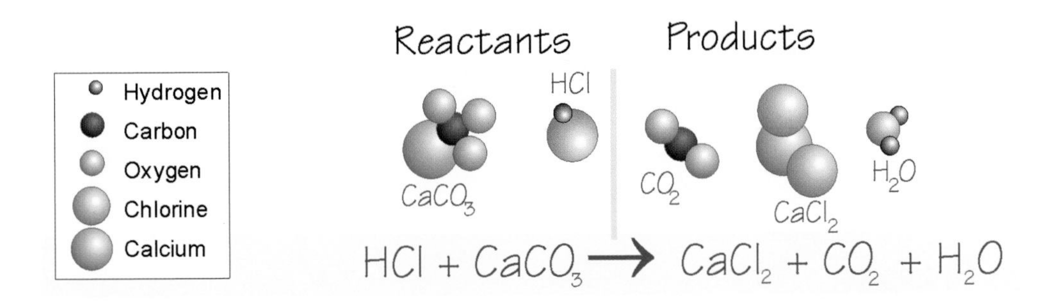

What coefficients mean

- A coefficient placed in front of O_2 means that the reaction will require two oxygen molecules for every methane molecule.
- A coefficient placed in front of H_2O means that two molecules of water will be produced for every one molecule of carbon dioxide.
- No coefficient in front of a chemical formula indicates one molecule.

Figure 20.14: *What is a coefficient?*

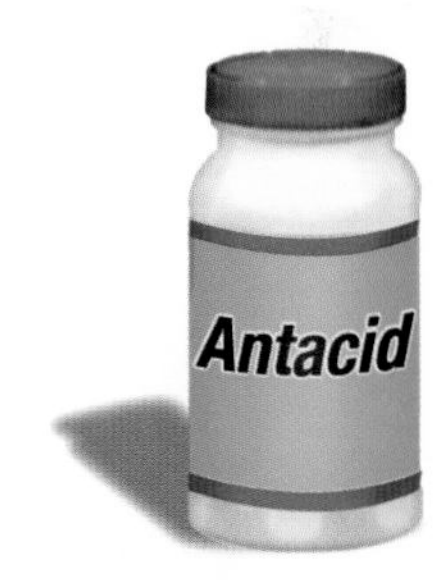

3. Count the number of each type of atom on both sides

The table below summarizes how many atoms of each type are on the reactants' and products' sides of the chemical equation. Notice that there is an extra hydrogen and an extra chlorine on the products' side. These two extra atoms have to come from somewhere. We need to add something to the reactants that will give us an extra chlorine and hydrogen.

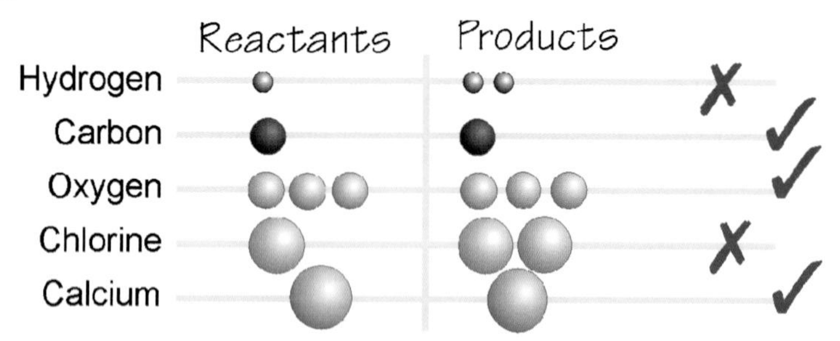

hydrochloric acid	HCl
calcium carbonate	$CaCO_3$
calcium chloride	$CaCl_2$
carbon dioxide	CO_2
water	H_2O

Figure 20.15: *Chemical formulas for each compound in the reaction.*

4. Add coefficients to balance the equation

Fortunately, one of the reactants is HCl so we can add one more molecule of HCl to the reactants side. In the equation we put a '2' in front of the HCl to indicate that we need 2 molecules. You cannot change the subscripts. In this case, you just need to put a coefficient of 2 in front of HCl to balance the equation.

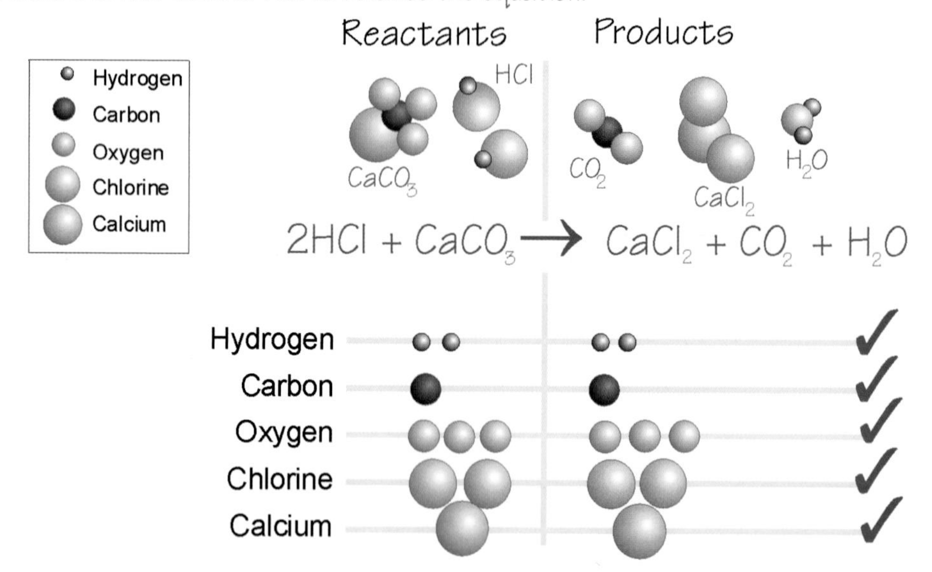

atom	reactants	products
H	1 × 2 = **2**	2
Cl	1 × 2 = **2**	2
Ca	1	1
C	1	1
O	3	3

Figure 20.16: *Is the equation balanced after adding a coefficient of 2 in front of HCl?*

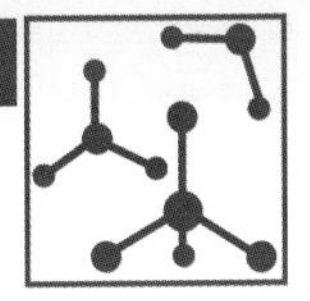

20.3 Conservation of Mass

Have you ever been to a campfire? What happens to the pile of wood after it is finished burning? Of course, it is reduced to a pile of ashes. What happened to the wood? Did it just disappear into the atmosphere? The burning of wood is a chemical reaction. So far, you have learned that every atom in a chemical reaction is accounted for. If this is so, what happened to the mass of the wood in that pile? In this section, you will learn why the mass of the reactants is equal to the mass of the products in any chemical reaction.

Conservation of mass

What is the law of conservation of mass?

In the eighteenth century, chemical reactions were still a bit of a mystery. A French scientist, Antoine Laurent Lavoisier (1743-94), established an important principal based on his experiments with chemical reactions. He stated that the total mass of the products of a reaction is equal to the total mass of the reactants. This statement is known as the law of conservation of mass. Lavoisier's law of conservation was not obvious to many other scientists of the time.

How can you prove the law of conservation of mass?

You already know that when wood is burned, a chemical reaction is taking place, but do you know what happens to the mass of the wood after it has burned? By now, you also know that much of the mass of the burning wood is converted into a gas such as carbon dioxide. This gas then escapes into the atmosphere. How can you prove that the mass of the reactants is equal to the mass of the products in the reaction of burning wood? Lavoisier showed that a *"closed" system* must be used when studying chemical reactions. When chemicals are reacted in a closed container, you can show that the mass before and after the reaction is the same.

An example of how mass is conserved in a reaction

In one of his experiments, Lavoisier placed 10.0 grams of mercury (II) oxide into a sealed container. He heated the container so that the mercury (II) oxide reacted to produce oxygen and mercury. As he observed the reaction, the white, powdery mercury (II) oxide bubbled, and turned into a smaller amount of a silvery liquid. In the reaction, 10.0 grams of mercury (II) oxide reacted in the presence of heat to produce 0.7 grams of oxygen gas and 9.3 grams of mercury. How does this data prove the law of conservation of mass?

Antoine Lavoisier

Born in 1743, Antoine Lavoisier was one of the best known French scientists of his time, and an important government official. As a student he stated "I am young and avid for glory." He demonstrated with careful measurements that it was not possible to change water into soil, but that the sediment observed from boiling water came from the container. He also burned sulfur in air and proved that the products of the reaction weighed more than the reactants and that the weight gained came from the air. Despite his contributions to chemistry, he believed that the existence of atoms was philosophically impossible. He became suspicious to leaders of the French Revolution and was beheaded in 1794.

Conservation and petroleum

Why are we in danger of running out of natural resources like petroleum?

In a chemical reaction, *atoms* are conserved, not necessarily molecules. Petroleum is a mixture of many different molecules. Furthermore, the rate of production of these molecules in nature is very small compared to the rate at which we use them. The United States uses many millions of barrels of petroleum each day in a variety of different chemical reactions. Since the mass of petroleum on earth is limited, how long do you think it will take before we run out?

What is petroleum?

Petroleum is our most important *nonrenewable* resource. From it we obtain fuels to burn in our cars, homes and power plants. It also provides us with the chemicals used to manufacture many different products we use every day. Petroleum is a mixture containing hundreds of different compounds, called *hydrocarbons*, that have two important chemical properties. First, when these compounds burn in oxygen, they release large amounts of energy. Second, molecules of these compounds can be modified in a variety of ways to produce useful materials such as plastics, drugs, explosives and even perfumes! It is no wonder that petroleum is often called "black gold."

What are hydrocarbons?

Hydrocarbons are compounds that consist of many carbon atoms bonded together to form a backbone know as a *carbon chain*. Hydrogen atoms are attached to this chain (Figure 20.17). Do you see where the name "hydrocarbon" comes from? The chemical formulas for some of the hydrocarbons found in petroleum are given in Figure 20.18.

How was petroleum formed?

The formation of petroleum is a chemical reaction that takes millions of years to complete. Many scientists believe that the petroleum we use today originated from animals and plants that lived in the ocean millions of years ago. As these organisms died, they settled to the bottom and were covered with sediments. The plant and animal material was digested by microscopic organisms and, as more sediments piled up on top of them, pressure and heat converted the organic material into petroleum that is now trapped in porous rocks, deep under the earth. While it is likely that petroleum is continuously being formed, its rate of formation is too slow for it to be considered a *renewable* resource.

A short list of petroleum products...

- Aspirin
- Make-up
- Synthetic rubber
- Chewing gum
- Saccharin
- Fibers for clothing
- Artificial flavors
- Fertilizers
- Plastics

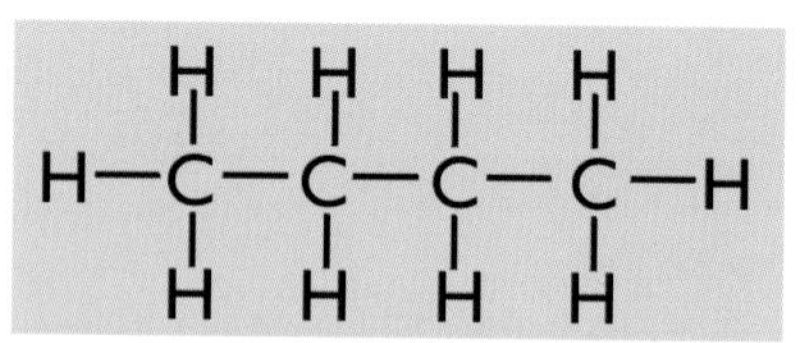

Figure 20.17: *A hydrocarbon*

name	formula
methane	CH_4
ethane	C_2H_6
propane	C_3H_8
butane	C_4H_{10}
pentane	C_5H_{12}
hexane	C_6H_{14}
heptane	C_7H_{16}
octane	C_8H_{18}

Figure 20.18: *Some of the hydrocarbons found in petroleum.*

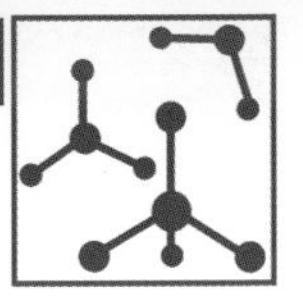

20.4 Using Equations as Recipes

Have you ever tried to make something from a recipe—say, a chocolate cake—and it didn't turn out quite the way you hoped? Some recipes require you to follow directions and add the correct amounts and types of ingredients. If you left out the eggs, for example, your cake wouldn't turn out at all. A balanced chemical equation is just like a recipe. It tells you the ingredients needed and the amount of each. It also tells you how much of each product will result if the precise amount of reactants are added. In this section, you will learn what chemical equations tell you and how to use them much like you would a recipe for a chocolate cake, although your products won't be as tasty!

Figure 20.19: *What happens when you leave out an ingredient in a recipe?*

What can a chemical equation tell you?

Recipe #1: Chocolate Cake	**Recipe #2: Water**
1 cup flour 1/2 cup cocoa powder 1/2 cup butter 1 tsp vanilla 1 cup sugar 1 teaspoon baking powder 1/2 cup milk 1 egg	2 molecules of hydrogen gas 1 molecule of oxygen gas $2H_2 + O_2 \longrightarrow 2H_2O$ 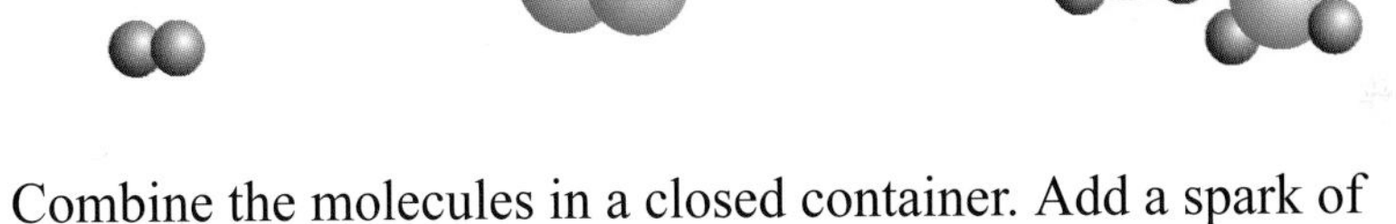
In a bowl, combine flour, sugar, cocoa powder, and baking power. Add butter, milk, vanilla, and egg. Mix until smooth. Bake in a 350°F oven for 35 minutes. *Makes 8 servings*	Combine the molecules in a closed container. Add a spark of electricity. *Makes two molecules of water.*

Chemical equations are like recipes

How are the two recipes above alike? How are they different? Both recipes give you the ingredients needed, the instructions, and the product that will be produced. Both recipes also give you the *quantities* of ingredients (reactants) needed and the *quantities* of products that are produced.

Recipes tell you the ratios of ingredients

The recipe for chocolate cake shows the *ratios* among the various ingredients needed to make eight servings. If you double the ingredients, you will make twice as many servings. Suppose you only had half a cup of flour. Could you still make eight servings? If you tried it, the cake would probably not turn out like the recipe intended. What would you need to do to make the same final product? Of course, you would use half as much of the rest of the ingredients since you only have half as much flour.

Figure 20.20: *If you had half as much flour, you could only make half the amount of cake.*

Proportional relationships in balanced equations

Just like recipes which show the ratios of the amounts of each ingredient, balanced equations show the ratios of the number of molecules of reactants needed to make a certain number of molecules of products. *The ratios are determined by the coefficients of the balanced equation.* In the formation of water, two molecules of H_2 react with one molecule of O_2 to produce two molecules of H_2O. If you reacted four molecules of H_2 with two molecules of O_2, you would produce four molecules of H_2O instead of two. Doubling the number of each reactant doubles the amount of product formed. What happens if you only double the number of H_2 molecules and not the number of O_2 molecules? How many H_2O molecules could you make? Would you have anything left over? (Figure 20.21)

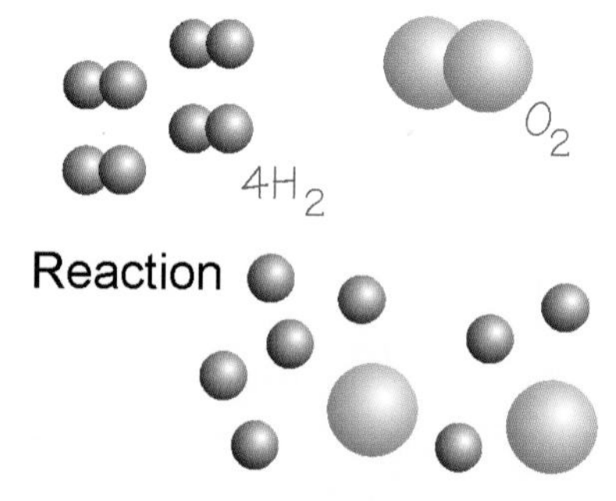

Products

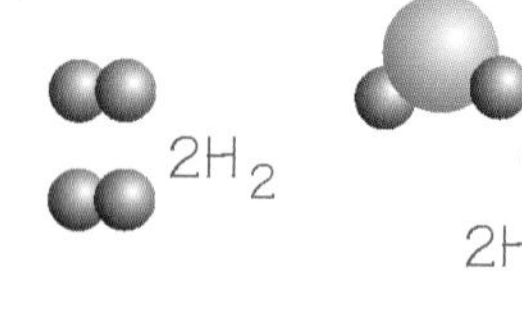

Figure 20.21: *What happens if you double the number of hydrogen molecules in the reaction for the formation of water?*

Balanced equations also show the ratio of relative masses

You have learned that the formula mass of a substance is *relative* to the formula mass of another substance. This is because individual atoms of different elements have an atomic mass relative to the size of their nuclei. Both atomic and formula mass are measured in atomic mass units, or amu. You should also remember that the avogadro number (6.02×10^{23}) of atoms or molecules is equal to the mass of the substance, in grams. For example, the formula mass of water is 18.02 amu. If you had a beaker with 6.02×10^{23} molecules of water, the water would have a mass of 18.02 grams. You have also learned that the coefficients in a balanced equation tell you the ratio of each substance in the equation. If you have a coefficient of 2 in front water in an equation, this means that you have two times the amount of water molecules. Therefore, the molecular mass of water would be 36.04 amu's and 2 x (6.02×10^{23}) molecules would have an actual mass of 36.04 grams.

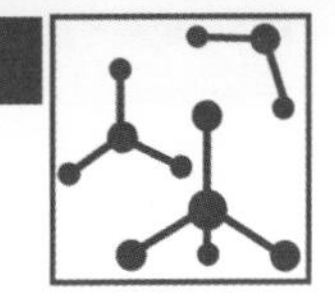

Let's take a closer look at the formation of water using this logic:

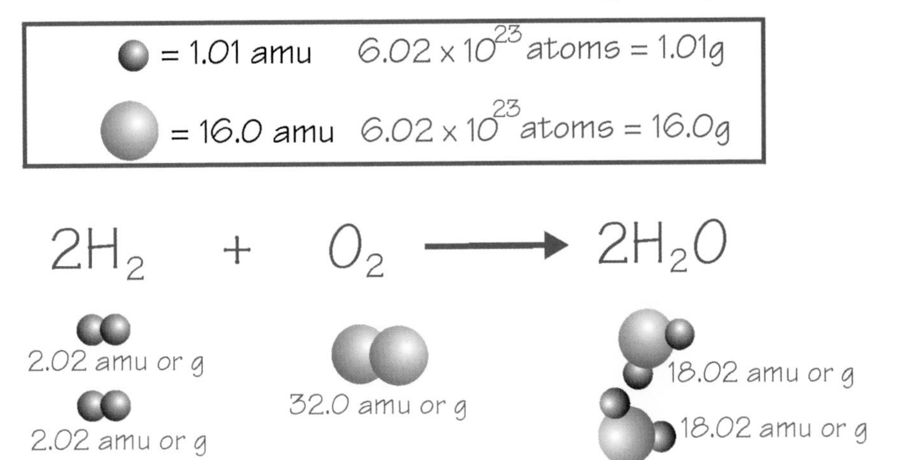

total reactants: 36.04 amu or g = total products: 36.04 amu or g

Balanced equations show how mass and atoms are conserved

As you can see from the balanced equation of the formation of water, there are an equal number of hydrogen and oxygen atoms in the reactants and products. By adding up the atomic masses, you can determine the formula mass in atomic mass units. You can also see that the masses in atomic mass units are equal on both sides of the equation. Therefore, if you have 6.02×10^{23} of each molecule represented in the diagram, a total of 36.04 grams of reactants, will produce 36.04 grams of water—providing all goes as planned. Can you see how a balanced equation can be used like a recipe?

What doesn't a balanced equation tell you?

It is important to note that a balanced equation does not describe the exact conditions under which a reaction will occur. For example, simply putting hydrogen and oxygen molecules together does not always produce water. A jolt of energy will usually result in the formation of water. Many reactions require specific conditions to occur and these are not shown in the balanced equation. Some reactions may not occur at all, even though you can write a balanced equation for them. If this were the case, we could make just about anything we need! Most of the reactions that are used in science and industry are the result of research and experimentation.

Dr. Shirley Ann Jackson

Shirley Ann Jackson grew up in Washington DC in the 1950's and '60's. As a child, she was fascinated with how things work. She and her sister raced go-carts which their Dad helped them build. She spent hours figuring out how to make hers go faster.

Dr. Jackson excelled in her high school classes and won a full scholarship to MIT. She was one of 43 women in her freshman class of 900, and one of 10 African-Americans out of 4,000 undergraduates. Sometimes she felt isolated and lonely. She volunteered in a hospital pediatric ward and tutored children at a local YMCA. This, she says, helped her keep perspective.

In 1973, Dr. Jackson became the first African-American woman to receive a Ph.D. from MIT. Afterward, she researched subatomic particles in government and international labs, and worked on semiconductors and other systems at AT&T Bell laboratories.

In 1995, Dr. Jackson was appointed the Chairman of the U.S. Nuclear Regulatory Commission by President Bill Clinton. She worked to increase nuclear plant safety in the U.S. and with international organizations to enhance worldwide nuclear safety.

Dr. Jackson became president of Rensselaer Polytechnic Institute in 1999. In 2005 she was described by Time Magazine as "Perhaps the ultimate role model for women in science."

What happens if one reactant is used up before another?

If a cookie recipe calls for two eggs and you only have one, can you make a whole batch of cookies? Of course you could only make half as many. The fact that you only have one egg *limits* the amount of cookies you can make. The same is true of chemical reactions. When a chemical reaction occurs, the reactants are not always present in the exact ratio indicated by the balanced equation. In fact, this is rarely the case unless the reaction is performed in a lab with specific amounts of reactants measured. The reaction will run until the reactant that is in short supply is used up.

The reactant that is in short supply is called the limiting reactant

The reactant that is used up first is called the limiting reactant because it is used up first and thus, limits the amount of product that can be formed. A reactant that is not completely used up is called an excess reactant because some of it will be left over when the reaction is complete.

Because it is used up first, the limiting reactant determines the amount of product formed.

Do reactions always turn out as expected?

Not all reactions turn out exactly as planned. In other words, if you use a specific amount of a limiting reactant and expect the exact amount of product to be formed, you will usually be disappointed. There are many factors involved in the occurrence of reactions that affect the amount of product formed. Usually the amount of product that is formed is less than the amount you would expect. If you can measure the amount of product produced in a reaction, you can determine the percent yield. The percent yield is the actual yield divided by the predicted yield and then multiplied by one hundred as in the equation below:

$$\text{percent yield} = \left(\frac{\text{actual yield}}{\text{predicted yield}}\right) \times 100$$

The predicted yield can be determined from the balanced equation for the reaction. The actual yield is determined by simply measuring the mass, in grams, of the product produced in the actual reaction.

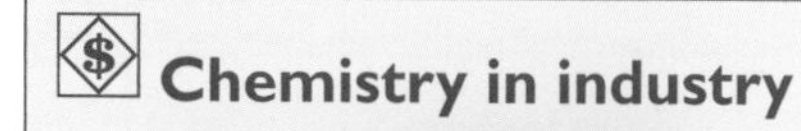

Chemistry in industry

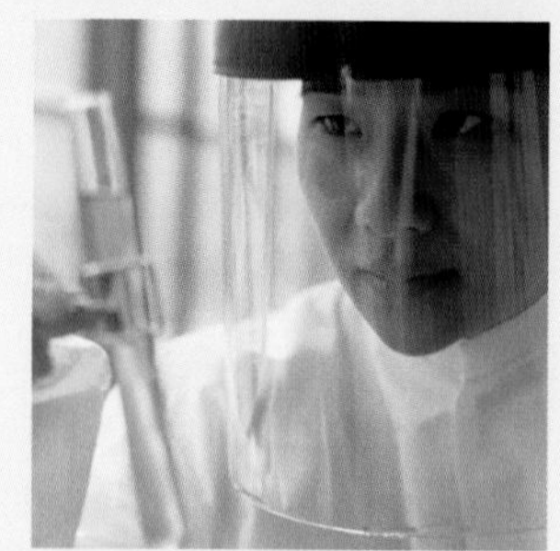

When a chemical reaction is carried out by an industry, the more expensive reactant is usually the limiting reactant and the cheaper one is the excess reactant. For example, in the manufacture of artificial flavorings such as vanillin (artificial vanilla) or artificial almond flavoring, acetic acid is reacted with a chemical called an ester to produce the desired flavor. There are many different types of esters that are used, but all of them are more expensive than acetic acid (found in vinegar). Which chemical do you think is used for the limiting reactant?

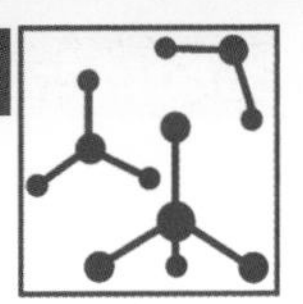

Chapter 20 Review

Vocabulary review

Match the following terms with the correct definition. There is one extra definition that will not match any of the terms.

Set One	
1. chemical change	a. The type of bonding that an element typically undergoes is an example of this kind of property
2. polymer	b. The state, size, or shape of a substance
3. physical change	c. What happens when two substances react to produce entirely different substances
4. physical property	d. Ice melting is an example of this kind of change
	e. A molecule that consists of long chains of repeating combinations of atoms

Set Two	
1. balanced equation	a. The "3" in $CaCO_3$
2. coefficient	b. The "6" in $6H_2O$
3. subscript	c. An equation with an equal number of atoms in the reactants and products
4. Law of conservation of mass	d. The number that represents the number of electrons the atom will lose or gain
	e. You cannot create or lose mass in a reaction

Set Three	
1. actual yield	a. The reaction that uses carbon dioxide and water to make sugar
2. limiting reactant	b. The amount of product that should be produced in a chemical reaction
3. percent yield	c. The reactant that is in short supply for a chemical reaction
4. predicted yield	d. The numerical relationship between two objects or substances
5. ratio	e. The ratio of actual yield to predicted yield times 100
	f. The amount of product that you can measure after a chemical reaction

Concept review

1. How can you tell the difference between a physical change and a chemical change?
2. List three examples of a physical change.
3. List three examples of a chemical change.
4. List two differences and two similarities between a recipe for a food item and a chemical reaction.
5. What happens to chemical bonds during a chemical reaction?
6. What is meant by the phrase, "atoms are conserved in chemical reactions"?
7. Describe the contributions of Antoine Laurent Lavoisier to our current knowledge of chemical reactions.
8. Describe three things you can tell from a chemical equation.
9. What is the difference between a limiting reactant and an excess reactant?
10. Give three reasons the actual yield for a product in a reaction is usually lower than the predicted yield.

Problems

1. The process of digestion involves:
   a. Only chemical changes.
   b. Only physical changes.
   c. Both physical and chemical changes.
2. How are ice, liquid water, and water vapor *different* from each other?
   a. Each is a physical state of water.
   b. A chemical change has to occur for ice to become liquid and then for liquid water to become water vapor.
   c. Each of these states of water has a different amount of energy.
3. Which of the following events is *not* evidence that a chemical change has occurred?
   a. When you eat and breathe in oxygen, you have energy and breathe out carbon dioxide.
   b. You mix two solutions and a bright yellow precipitate appears.
   c. You notice that your grandmother's silver is very dark in places and needs polishing.
   d. Your cup of hot chocolate gives off steam.
4. Which of the following events is *not* evidence that a physical change has occurred?
   a. When you accidentally leave a soft contact lens on the bathroom sink overnight, it becomes dry and brittle.
   b. When you mix baking soda and vinegar, the two substances fizz and produce bubbles.
   c. When you take the cap off a soda bottle for the first time, bubbles suddenly appear and rush to the surface of the soda.
   d. Baby food carrots no longer look like carrots because the carrots have been nearly liquefied.

5. Fill out the table for this reaction: $Al + Br_2 \rightarrow AlBr_3$

type of atom	total on reactants side	total on products side	balanced? (yes or no)
Al			
Br			

6. Which of the following equations is balanced?
   a. $Al + Br_2 \rightarrow 2AlBr_3$
   b. $2Al + 2Br_2 \rightarrow 3AlBr_3$
   c. $2Al + 3Br_2 \rightarrow 2AlBr_3$
   d. $Al + Br_2 \rightarrow AlBr_3$

7. How would you express the following combustion of ethane, C_2H_6, as a sentence: $2C_2H_6 + 7O_2 \rightarrow 4CO_2 + 6H_2O$?
   a. Two ethane molecules combine with oxygen to produce carbon dioxide molecules and six water.
   b. Two ethane molecules combine with seven oxygen molecules to produce four carbon dioxide molecules and six water molecules.
   c. Ethane combusts to produce carbon and water.
   d. Four carbon dioxide molecules and six water molecules can be mixed to make oxygen and ethane.

8. Which of the following reactions is balanced?
   a. $CS_2 + 3O_2 \rightarrow CO_2 + SO_2$
   b. $2N_2O_5 + NO \rightarrow 4NO_2$
   c. $P_4 + 5O_2 \rightarrow P_2O_5$
   d. $4Fe + 3O_2 \rightarrow 2Fe_2O_3$

9. What coefficient for oxygen would balance the equation below?

   $4Fe + \_\_\_\_ O_2 + 6H_2O \rightarrow 2(Fe_2O_3 \cdot 3H_2O)$

10. Balance the following equations. If an equation is already balanced, say so in your answer.
    a. $Cl_2 + Br \rightarrow Cl + Br_2$
    b. $CaO + H_2O \rightarrow Ca(OH)_2$
    c. $Na_2SO_4 + BaCl_2 \rightarrow BaSO_4 + NaCl$
    d. $ZnS + O_2 \rightarrow ZnO + SO_2$

11. Balance these chemical equations:
    a. $Cl_2 + KBr \rightarrow KCl + Br_2$
    b. $NH_3 + O_2 \rightarrow NO + H_2O$

12. Calculate the formula mass for each of the molecules listed in the *balanced* equation for 11b (above). Hint: Multiply the coefficient for each molecule times the formula mass for the molecule.

    a. NH_3 __________ amu   c. NO __________ amu
    b. O_2 __________ amu   d. H_2O __________ amu

13. If you had the Avogadro number of each molecule in question 12, what would the masses of these molecules be? Include the coefficient from question 11b in your calculation. Hint: You don't need a calculator for this question!

    a. NH_3 __________ g   c. NO __________ g
    b. O_2 __________ g   d. H_2O __________ g

14. If oxygen was the limiting reactant in equation 11b and you had only 20 grams of oxygen, what would be the predicted yield of water in this reaction? Be sure to show your work.

15. In the equation to the right, the actual yield of bromide (Br_2) was 19.8 grams when the reaction was performed with 10 grams of chlorine (Cl_2). Calculate the predicted yield for the reaction and then calculate the percent yield.

$$Cl_2\,(g) + KBr \longrightarrow KCl(aq) + Br_2$$

Applying your knowledge

1. List the steps for preparing and eating a salad. Identify which steps have chemical changes and which have physical changes.
2. Identify whether or not a chemical reaction has occurred or will occur in the following situations.
   a. By activating a heat pack, you generate heat to warm your hands.
   b. An orange precipitate forms when two solutions are mixed.
   c. A glass of water turns red when you add dye to it.
   d. The recipe calls for adding sugar and butter to flour.
   e. When you add an effervescent tablet to water, it immediately starts to fizz.
3. Aspirin can be made in the laboratory through a series of reactions. If the actual yield for aspirin was 461.5 grams when the reactions were performed, and the predicted yield was 500 grams, what was the percent yield?
4. The source of fuel in a science lab is methane gas, CH_4, which burns in oxygen gas, O_2, to produce carbon dioxide, CO_2, and water, H_2O. The equation for this reaction is:

   $$CH_4 + 2O_2 \longrightarrow CO_2 + 2H_2O$$

   If you have ever heated glassware in the lab, you may have noticed a black soot forming on the surface of the glass. This happens when there is insufficient oxygen and not all of the carbon combines with oxygen to form carbon dioxide.
   a. Which element do you think makes up the soot?
   b. Which substance is the limiting reactant in this reaction?
   c. Which substance is the excess reactant?
5. A chocolate sundae is prepared by combining 1/2 cup of ice cream, 2 ounces of chocolate sauce and 1 cherry. Assume you have 10 cups of ice cream, 25 ounces of chocolate sauce and 10 cherries.
   a. What is the maximum number of sundaes you can make?
   b. Which ingredient is the limiting component of the system?
   c. What quantities of the other two "reactants" will be left over when you are finished?
6. Look for situations that demonstrate chemical change. List each situation and describe the evidence of chemical change that you observe. Try to identify the reactants and products.
7. Identify an industry in your community that uses chemical reactions (Actually, it would be more difficult to find one that does not use them!) Examples include: hospitals, sewage or water treatment plants, dry cleaners, photo developers and manufacturers of any product. Research the chemical reactions the facility uses. Write balanced equations for each reaction you identify.

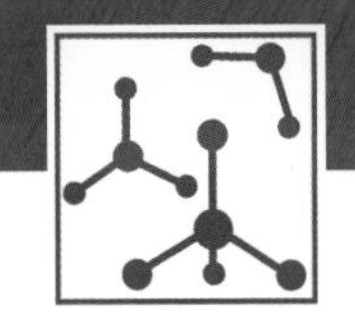

UNIT 7

Changes in Matter

Chapter 21

Types of Reactions

Introduction to Chapter 21

There are many different types of reactions that occur around you all of the time. For example, when you breathe you take in oxygen, which reacts with the sugar in your cells to carbon dioxide and water. It also releases energy for your cells to use or store. This type of reaction is called a combustion reaction. In this chapter you will learn how to classify reactions based on the reactants and products, and whether or not they produce or use energy.

Investigations for Chapter 21

21.1	**Classifying Reactions**	*How can you predict the products in a reaction?*

A double-displacement reaction is a chemical reaction in which the ions from the two reactants change places. One of the new compounds formed is sometimes insoluble and forms a cloudy precipitate. In this Investigation, you will develop a set of rules for precipitate formation that will allow you to make predictions about the types of products in double-displacement reactions.

21.2	**Energy in Reactions**	*How can you classify reactions based on energy?*

You will measure the energy changes in reactions and classify reactions according to how they use or produce energy.

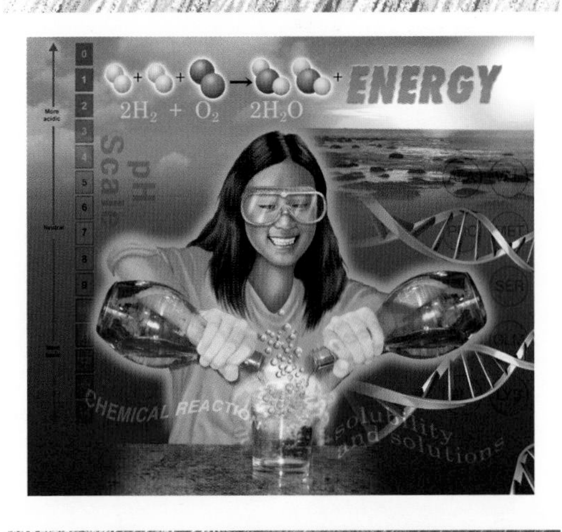

Learning Goals

In this chapter, you will:

- ✔ Distinguish between different types of reactions.
- ✔ Given the reactants, identify the type of reaction that will occur and predict the products that will be formed.
- ✔ Analyze energy changes that accompany chemical reactions and classify them as exothermic or endothermic.
- ✔ Observe reactions of household chemicals to develop a set of rules for precipitate formation. Use these rules to make predictions.
- ✔ Demonstrate safe practices during laboratory investigations.

Vocabulary

addition reaction	dissolution reaction	exothermic reaction	precipitate
combustion reaction	double-displacement reaction	insoluble	single-displacement reaction
decomposition reaction	endothermic reaction	polymerization	

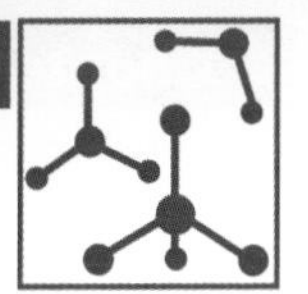

21.1 Classifying Reactions

Most of the products you use every day are the result of chemical reactions. How do manufacturers know which chemical reactions to use when they make their products? In this section, you will learn how to classify reactions. Being able to recognize the types of reactions will help you predict what types of substances will be produced.

Addition reactions

Compounds are made in addition reactions

In an addition reaction, two or more substances combine to form a new compound. A good example of an addition reaction is the formation of rust:

$$Fe_{(s)} + O_{2(g)} \longrightarrow Fe_2O_{3(s)}$$

A general equation for addition reactions is:

$$A + B \longrightarrow AB$$

A and B are elements or compounds, and AB is a compound.

Acid rain

Some fossil fuels, like coal, contain sulfur. When these fuels are burned, the sulfur reacts with oxygen in the air to form sulfur dioxide in the following addition reaction:

$$S_{(s)} + O_{2(g)} \rightarrow SO_{2(g)}$$

In air polluted with sulfur dioxide, acid rain is produced in the reaction below:

$$SO_{2(g)} + H_2O_{2(g)} \rightarrow H_2SO_{4(aq)}$$

H_2O_2 is hydrogen peroxide, a substance that is produced in clouds in a reaction between oxygen and water.

Figure 21.1 explains the meaning of the symbols in parenthesis.

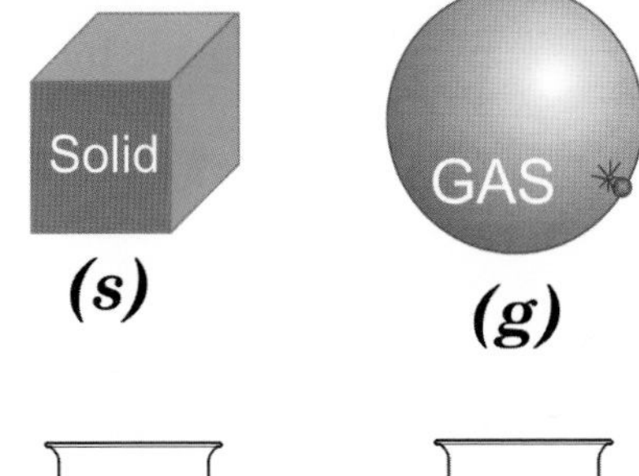

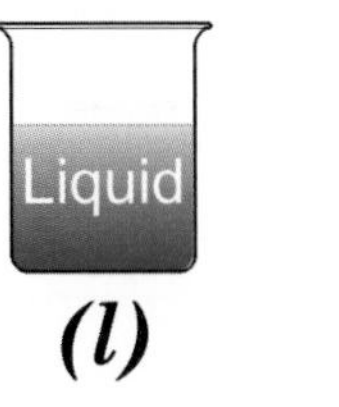

symbol	meaning
(s)	substance is a solid
(l)	substance is a liquid
(g)	substance is a gas
(aq)	substance is dissolved in solution (aqueous)

Figure 21.1: *What do the symbols shown in parentheses mean in equations?*

Polymerization is an addition reaction

In the last chapter, you learned that polymers are large molecules made up of repeating segments. Polymerization, or the formation of polymers, is a series of addition reactions taking place to produce a very large molecule. Polymers are made by joining smaller molecules called monomers.

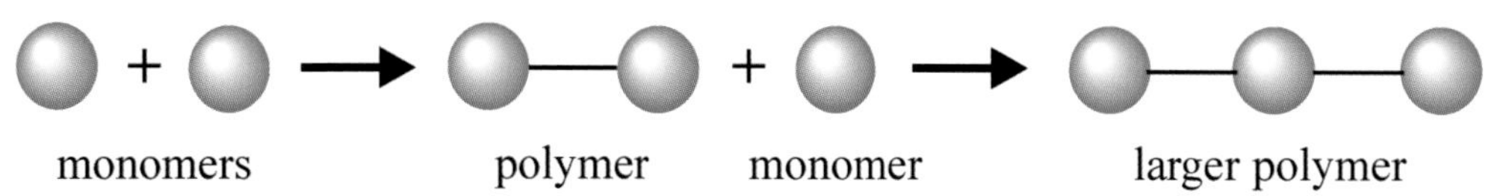

polymer	products
polystyrene	foam containers
polyethylene	food packaging
polyester	clothing
polyvinyl chloride	plumbing (PVC pipes)
polyvinyl acetate	chewing gum

Figure 21.2: *Here are some examples of polymers you may find around your house.*

Decomposition reactions

Compounds are broken down in decomposition reactions

A chemical reaction in which a single compound is broken down to produce two or more smaller compounds is called a decomposition reaction. The simplest kind of decomposition is the breakdown of a binary compound into its elements, as in the decomposition of water into hydrogen and oxygen with electricity:

$$2H_2O_{(l)} \longrightarrow 2H_{2(g)} + O_{2(g)}$$

Larger compounds can also decompose to produce other compounds, as in the decomposition of baking soda with heat:

$$2NaHCO_{3(s)} \xrightarrow{heat} CO_{2(g)} + Na_2CO_3 + H_2O$$

The general equation for decomposition is:

$$AB \longrightarrow A + B$$

AB is a compound, and A and B are elements or compounds.

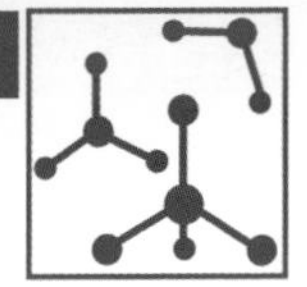

Single-displacement reactions

In single displacement reactions, one element replaces another in a compound

In single-displacement reactions, one element replaces a similar element in a compound. For example, if you place an iron nail into a beaker of copper (II) chloride, you will begin to see reddish copper forming on the iron nail. In this reaction, iron *replaces* copper in the solution and the copper *falls out* of the solution as a metal:

$$Fe_{(s)} + CuCl_{2\,(aq)} \longrightarrow FeCl_{2(aq)} + Cu_{(s)}$$

Single-displacement reactions can be represented with the general equation:

$$AX + B \longrightarrow BX + A$$

Where AX is a compound, B is an element, BX is a compound, and A is an element.

Reactants

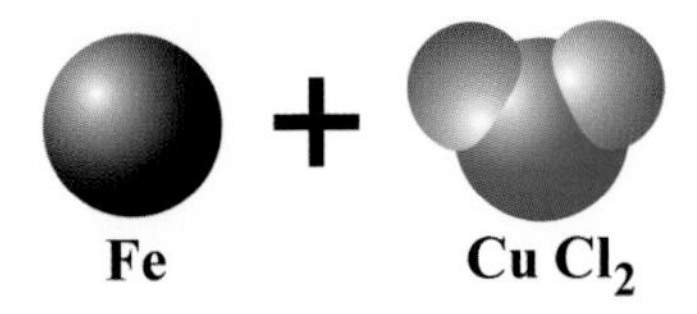

Products

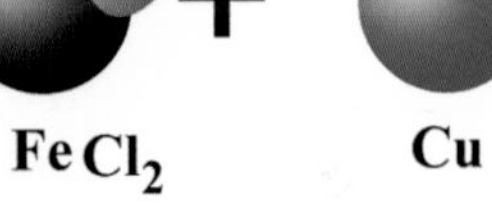

Figure 21.3: *The reaction between iron and copper chloride is a single-displacement reaction.*

Double-displacement reactions

In double-displacement reactions, ions switch places

In double-displacement reactions, ions from two compounds in solution exchange places to produce two new compounds. One of the compounds formed is usually a precipitate that settles out of the solution, a gas that bubbles out of the solution, or a molecular compound such as water. The other compound formed often remains dissolved in the solution.

The general formula for a double-displacement reaction is:

$$AB + CD \longrightarrow AD + CB$$

Where AB and CD are ionic compounds in a solution, and AD and CB are ionic compounds in a solution as well.

What is a precipitate?

The formation of a precipitate occurs when one of the compounds formed in a double-displacement reaction is insoluble, or does not dissolve in water. Precipitates are first recognizable by the cloudy appearance they give to a solution.

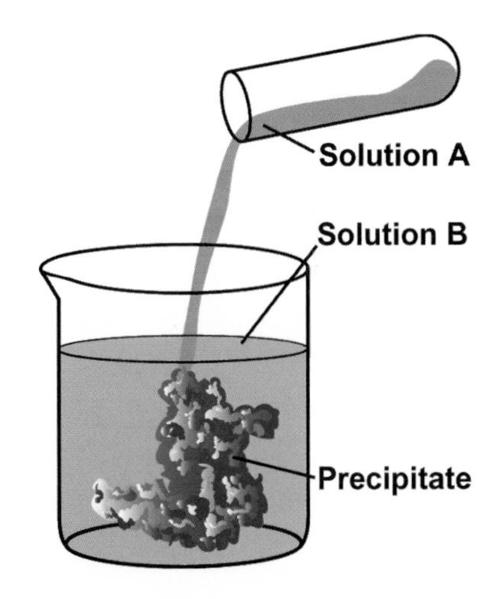

Figure 21.4: *The formation of a cloudy precipitate is evidence that a double-displacement reaction has occurred.*

If undisturbed in a beaker, a precipitate will settle to the bottom. Depending on the compound formed, the precipitate can be many different colors from white to fluorescent yellow, as in the reaction between lead (II) nitrate and potassium iodide:

$$Pb(NO_3)_{2(aq)} + 2KI_{(aq)} \longrightarrow PbI_{2(s)} + 2KNO_{3(aq)}$$

Consumer chemistry: Preserving dried fruit

Have you ever opened up a box of dried fruit such as golden raisins or apricots and smelled a slight "sulfur" odor, like a lit match? The odor is caused by *sulfur dioxide*, a gas that is used to preserve the color of dried fruits. This gas is produced in a double-displacement reaction between sodium sulfite and hydrochloric acid:

$$Na_2SO_{3(aq)} + 2HCl_{(aq)} \longrightarrow 2NaCl_{(aq)} + H_2O_{(l)} + SO_{2(g)}$$

The fruit is exposed to the gas, which is absorbed into the skin of the fruit. When you open the box for the first time, some of the gas that has escaped the fruit may not escape your nose!

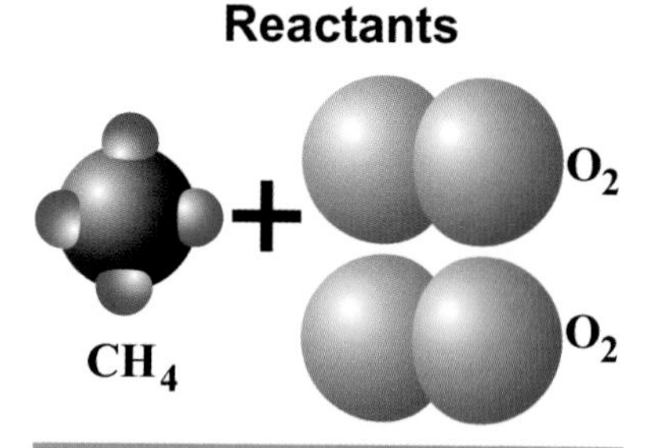

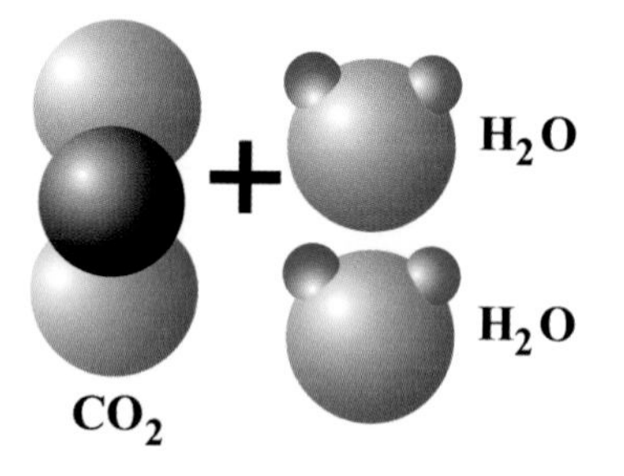

Figure 21.5: *The combustion of meathane gas, in oxygen, produces carbon dioxide and water.*

Combustion reactions

In a combustion reaction, a substance combines with oxygen to release energy

It's hard to imagine where our society would be without combustion reactions. A substance such as wood, natural gas, or propane combines with oxygen, releasing a large amount of energy in the form of light and heat, thus completing a combustion reaction. For example, in the combustion of natural gas to heat a house, methane (natural gas) combines with oxygen to produce carbon dioxide and water:

$$CH_4 + 2O_2 \longrightarrow CO_2 + 2H_2O$$

the general formula for the combustion of a carbon compound is:

$$\text{Carbon Compound} + O_{2(g)} \longrightarrow CO_{2(g)} + H_2O_{(g)}$$

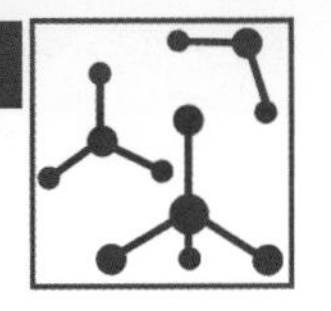

Energy and the environment: Hydrogen-powered cars

Combustion reactions that do not use carbon compounds as a reactant do not produce carbon dioxide. For example, when hydrogen gas is burned in oxygen, water is the only product:

$$2H_{2(g)} + O_{2(g)} \longrightarrow 2H_2O_{(l)}$$

Perhaps in the future, some of our cars will run by this reaction. In fact, automobile manufacturers are developing hydrogen-powered cars right now using a technology called "fuel cells."

- How would hydrogen-powered cars impact global warming?
- Do some Internet research to find out about fuel cells and hydrogen-powered cars.

George Washington Carver

George Washington Carver was born around 1864 in Missouri toward the end of the Civil War. George and his mother, a slave for Moses and Susan Carver, were kidnapped when he was an infant. Only George was found and returned to the Carvers who then raised him. Due to frail health, he spent time exploring nature and developed his talent for studying plants. He pursued plant studies in school and earned an agricultural degree from Iowa State College. He became the first African-American faculty member at the college and earned his master's degree two years later. Soon afterward, Booker T. Washington, founder of Tuskegee Institute in Alabama, contacted Carver to lead the agricultural department. There, Carver taught students and local farmers to rotate crops annually to enrich the soil. Benefits included improving the cotton crop and adding new cash crops such as peanuts and sweet potatoes. Carver is especially known for gathering a list of products and recipes that utilized the peanut plant. His many achievements include research on soy as a possible biofuel, displaying artwork at the 1893 World's Fair, and meeting with three American presidents.

Summary of the types of reactions

Table 21.1: ***Summary of the types of reactions***

Type	General equation	Example
addition	$A + B \rightarrow AB$	$2H_2 + O_2 \rightarrow 2H_2O$
decomposition	$AB \rightarrow A + B$	$2NaHCO_3 \rightarrow CO_2 + Na_2CO_3 + H_2O$
single-displacement	$AX + B \rightarrow BX + A$	$Fe + CuCl_2 \rightarrow FeCl_2 + Cu$
double-displacement	$AB + CD \rightarrow AD + CB$	$Pb(NO_3)_2 + 2KI \rightarrow PbI_2 + 2KNO_3$
combustion	carbon compound $+ O_2 \rightarrow CO_2 + H_2O$	$C_6H_{12}O_6 + 6O_2 \rightarrow 6CO_2 + 6H_2O$

Example: Predicting the products of a reaction

Can you predict the products of this reaction?

Silver becomes tarnished as time passes. Have you ever eaten something with a tarnished fork or spoon? The black tarnish is silver sulfide, the result of a reaction between the silver metal and sulfur in foods. Some products claim to be able to remove the tarnish without destroying the silver. One product contains aluminum metal in a solution. Write the complete reaction for removing tarnish with this product.

1. Write the chemical formulas for the reactants

Silver sulfide reacts with the aluminum metal in the product.

Silver = Ag^+ ion; sulfide = S^{2-} ion

The chemical formula for silver sulfide is Ag_2S

Aluminum is an element so its formula is Al

Chemical formulas for reactants: $Ag_2S + Al$

2. Identify the type of reaction

This is a *single replacement* reaction because of the general formula:

$$AX + B \longrightarrow BX + A$$

3. Predict the products and write their chemical formulas

Ag_2S is a compound and Al is an element so Al will replace Ag.

The products formed will be aluminum sulfide and silver metal.

Aluminum ion = Al^{3+}; sulfide ion = S^{2-}

Chemical formulas for products: $Al_2S_3 + Ag$

4. Write and balance the complete equation

Unbalanced equation:

$Ag_2S + Al \rightarrow Al_2S_3 + Ag$

Balanced equation:

$3Ag_2S + 2Al \rightarrow Al_2S_3 + 6Ag$

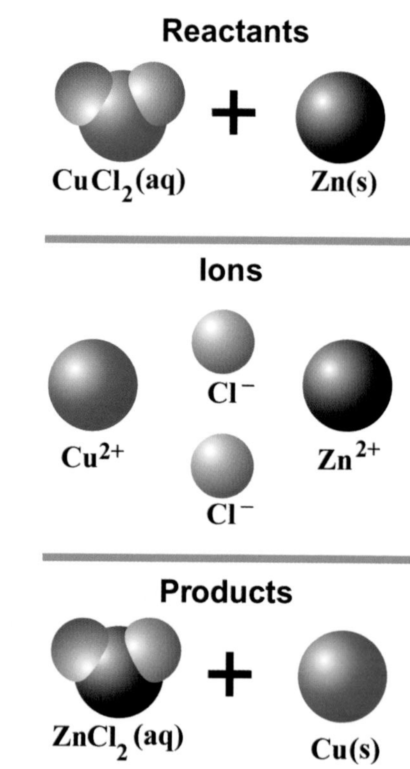

Figure 21.6: *The reaction of copper chloride (in solution) with zinc metal is another example of a single-displacement reaction.*

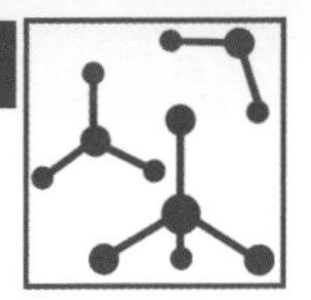

21.2 Energy in Reactions

You have learned that when most reactions take place, chemical bonds must be broken and new chemical bonds must be formed. Breaking chemical bonds requires energy. When new bonds are formed, energy is released. Why do some reactions *produce* more energy than others? Why do some reactions *use* more energy than they produce? In this section, you will learn about both these types of reactions and some ways we use them in household products.

Exothermic reactions

Exothermic reactions produce energy

In many reactions, less energy is required to break the bonds in the reactants than is released when bonds are formed to make new products. In these types of reactions, called **exothermic reactions**, some type of energy is released. The combustion of gasoline to run automobiles is an exothermic reaction. Some other exothermic reactions happen so slowly that you cannot feel the heat, like the formation of rust. Exothermic reactions can be detected by measuring a rise in temperature.

What are some useful exothermic reactions?

It is fairly obvious that we use exothermic reactions every day to heat our homes, drive our cars, and cook our food. These reactions are all combustion reactions that produce tremendous amounts of heat and light. Some other exothermic reactions may not be so obvious.

Meals ready to eat

The US Army developed a Meal, Ready to Eat (or MRE) for the 1991 Gulf War. These meals have a special sleeve placed around the food, which is wrapped in aluminum foil. When water is added to the sleeve, the resulting chemical reaction produces enough heat to cook the food inside the foil. What's in that sleeve? It is a pad that contains suspended particles of magnesium metal. When the magnesium reacts with the water to produce magnesium hydroxide, heat is released. The heat is conducted through the aluminum to heat the food. The result is a piping hot meal, ready to eat!

$$Mg_{(s)} + 2H_2O_{(l)} \rightarrow Mg(OH)_{2(aq)} + H_{2(g)}$$

Clogged drain?

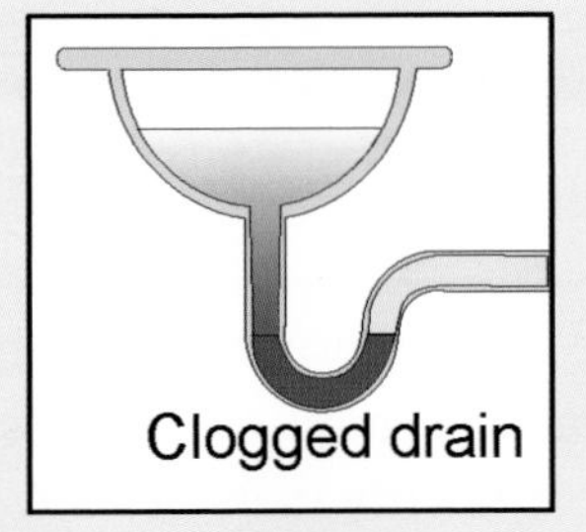

Many drain cleaners are a mixture of sodium hydroxide and aluminum filings. When these two substances mix in water, they react to produce enough heat to melt the fat in your clogged drain. The bubbles produced are hydrogen gas.

Can you write the balanced equation for this reaction?

Endothermic reactions

How does a cold pack work?

Have you ever used an "instant cold pack" as a treatment for aching muscles? These products, found in your local drugstore, use a special chemical reaction that has to do with energy. The product usually comes in a plastic bag. Inside of the bag is a packet of water surrounded by crystals of ammonium nitrate. To activate the cold pack, you squeeze the plastic bag to release the water. When the water contacts the ammonium nitrate crystals, a reaction occurs and the pack becomes icy cold.

$$NH_4NO_{3(s)} + H_2O_{(l)} \rightarrow NH_4^+{}_{(aq)} + NO_3^-{}_{(aq)}$$

The reaction gets very cold because it takes energy to dissolve the ionic bonds in the ammonium nitrate.

Endothermic reactions require more energy than they produce

Sometimes more energy is required to break the bonds in the reactants than is released from the formation of new bonds in the products. In these reactions, called **endothermic reactions**, more energy must be provided for the reaction to take place than is released. You can detect an endothermic reaction by measuring a decrease in the temperature. The cold pack reaction can be classified as an endothermic reaction.

Look at the cold pack reaction in above. Besides being endothermic, this reaction is also called a dissolution reaction. A **dissolution reaction** occurs when an ionic compound dissolves in water to make an ionic solution.

What are some useful endothermic reactions?

Most of the reactions used in industry to produce useful materials and products require more energy than they produce. This is one of the reasons sources of energy are so important to industry. For example, the refining of ores to produce useful metals frequently uses an endothermic reaction, as in the refinement of aluminum ore:

$$2Al_2O_{3(s)} \rightarrow 4Al_{(s)} + 3O_{2(g)}$$

This reaction requires the input of energy because it takes more energy to break the bonds in the aluminum oxide than is released when the products are formed.

Figure 21.7: *An instant cold pack contains ammonium nitrate crystals and a packet of water. When squeezed, the water is released and the reaction occurs.*

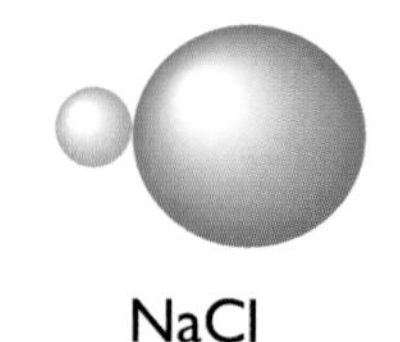

NaCl

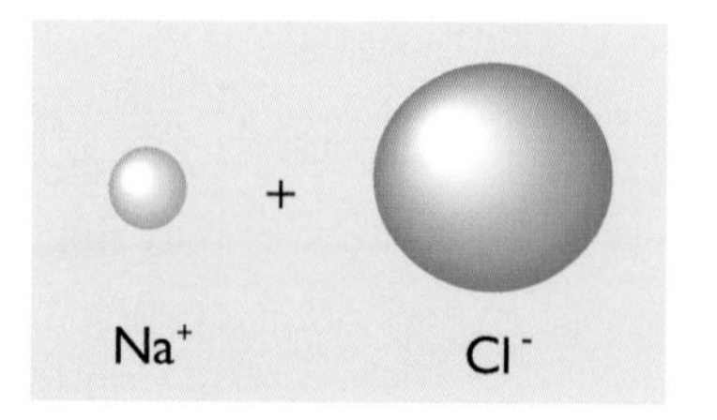

NaCl in water

Figure 21.8: *When NaCl is in water, it dissolves into positive and negative ions. This is an example of a dissolution reaction.*

Chapter 21 Review

Vocabulary review

Match the following terms with the correct definition. There is one extra definition that will not match any of the terms.

Set One	
1. combustion reaction	a. A large molecule with repeating units of smaller molecules
2. decomposition reaction	b. A molecule that is used to speed up reactions
3. double-displacement reaction	c. The process of attaching small molecule units together to make a large molecule
4. polymer	d. AB → A + B
5. polymerization	e. AB + CD → AD + CB
	f. A reaction that is used to obtain energy from fuel

Set Two	
1. precipitate	a. A reaction that uses more energy than it produces
2. single-displacement reaction	b. AB + CD → AD + CB
3. endothermic reaction	c. A + B → AB
4. addition reaction	d. AX + B → BX + A
5. exothermic reaction	e. The insoluble product of a double-displacement reaction
	f. A reaction that produces more energy than it uses

Concept review

1. Are combustion reactions usually exothermic or endothermic?
2. The formation of rust is represented by the following reaction:
   $4Fe(s) + 3O_2(g) \longrightarrow 2Fe_2O_3(s) + \text{energy}$
   a. Classify this reaction as either: single-displacement, decomposition, addition, combustion or double-displacement.
   b. Is this reaction exothermic or endothermic?
3. What conditions must be met in order for a reaction to be considered exothermic?
4. A reaction that requires more energy to break the bonds in the reactants than is released when new bonds are formed in the products is a(n):
   a. MRE reaction.
   b. endothermic reaction.
   c. silver reaction.
   d. exothermic reaction.

Problems

1. Identify the following reactions as: addition, decomposition, single-displacement, double-displacement, or combustion reactions.
   a. $NaS(aq) + ZnNO_3(aq) \rightarrow NaNO_3(aq) + ZnS(s)$
   b. $6Li(s) + N_2 \rightarrow 2Li_3N$
   c. $2KClO_3 \rightarrow 2KCl + 3O_2$
   d. $2C_3H_7OH + 9O_2 \rightarrow 6CO_2 + 8H_2O$
   e. $Mg + 2AgNO_3 \rightarrow Mg(NO_3)_2 + 2Ag$
2. Complete the reactions below. You are not required to balance this set.
   a. $H_2SO_4(aq) + BaCl(aq) \rightarrow$
   b. $ZnSO_4(aq) + Na_3PO_4(aq) \rightarrow$
   c. $HCl(aq) + K_2SO_3 \rightarrow$
   d. $SnCl_2 + Fe_2(SO_4)_3 \rightarrow$
3. Use the solubility rules to identify the precipitate, if any, for each reaction in question 2.
4. Complete the following reactions by predicting the products. Then, balance each equation.
   a. $Fe(s) + CuCl_2(aq) \rightarrow$
   b. $C_2H_6(g) + O_2(g) \rightarrow$
   c. $NaCl(aq) + NH_4OH(aq) \rightarrow$
   d. $H_2O \rightarrow$
   e. $Cu(s) + O_2(g) \rightarrow$
   f. $Al_2O_3 \rightarrow$
   g. $Mg(s) + HCl(aq) \rightarrow$
   h. $LiNO_3(aq) + MgCl_2(aq) \rightarrow$

Applying your knowledge

1. Many drain cleaners are a mixture of sodium hydroxide and aluminum filings. When these two substances mix in water, they react to produce enough heat to melt the fat in a clogged drain. The bubbles produced are hydrogen gas. The complete reaction occurs in two steps:

   step 1: $Al(s) + NaOH(aq) \rightarrow Al(OH)_3(s) + Na^+(aq)$

   step 2: $Na^+(aq) + H_2O \rightarrow Na_2O(s) + H_2(g)$

   a. Classify step 1 of the reaction as: addition, single-displacement, double-displacement or decomposition.
   b. Is this an endothermic or an exothermic reaction?
   c. Balance each equation for each step of the reaction.
2. Propane, C_3H_8, is a gas that is used by cooks and campers every day. It is burned in oxygen in order to cook food, provide heat and light, and even to run refrigerators in areas that do not have electricity. Write the complete, balanced equation for the combustion of propane.
3. Light bulb filaments are made of the element tungsten. When this metal is heated, it usually forms an oxide with the oxygen in the air. This causes the metal to become brittle and fall apart. Can you explain why the filament of tungsten inside of a light bulb does not form an oxide? (Hint: think about the structure of a light bulb.)

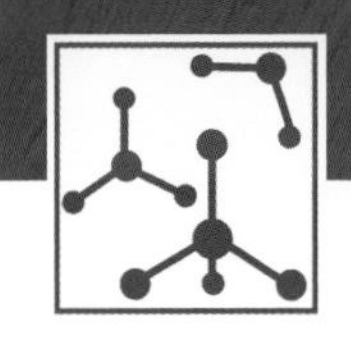

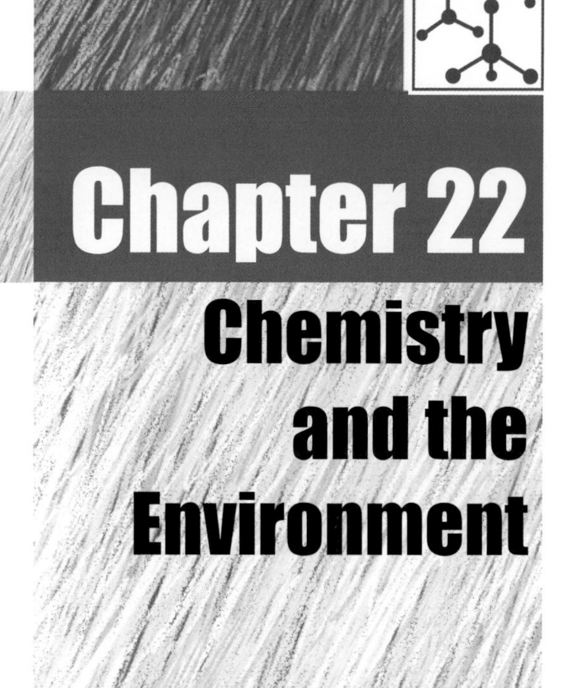

Chapter 22 Chemistry and the Environment

Introduction to Chapter 22

The reactions of elements and compounds are everywhere in the environment. In fact, the Earth's environment as we know it is the result of the reactions of organisms. Plants, for example, produce the atmospheric oxygen that we depend on. In this chapter you will learn about how nuclear reactions in the sun produce the energy that eventually leads to this oxygen production. As you learn more about nuclear and carbon reactions, you will see the role they play in improving and affecting our environment and lifestyles.

Investigations for Chapter 22

22.1	**Nuclear Reactions**	*How do you simulate nuclear decay?*

With 92 protons and 146 neutrons, the nucleus of uranium-238 has a tendency to fall apart or "decay." It emits radiation in the forms of particles and energy until it becomes an atom with a more stable nucleus. The entire radioactive decay process for uranium-238 takes about 5 billion years! In this Investigation, you will simulate the radioactive decay of an element.

22.2	**Carbon Reactions**	*How do your choices impact the environment?*

If you needed to buy a car to drive to school or work, what would you buy? How would you make your decision? In this Investigation, you will use consumer information to evaluate how your decision affects the environment and your personal finances. You will calculate how much carbon dioxide your car or truck would produce. In the last part of the Investigation, you will see how the sun's energy may be used to reduce carbon dioxide in the atmosphere.

Learning Goals

In this chapter, you will:

- ✔ Compare and contrast nuclear reactions with chemical reactions.
- ✔ Describe the environmental impact of nuclear reactions.
- ✔ Research and describe the environmental and economic impact of the end-products of chemical reactions.
- ✔ Identify how personal choices about products can have an impact on the environment.
- ✔ Evaluate the impact of scientific research on society and the environment.
- ✔ Organize data and use it to predict trends.

Vocabulary

alpha decay	emissions	half-life	radioactive
alpha particles	fission	isotope	radioactive isotope
beta decay	fossil fuels	nuclear reactions	stable
beta particles	fusion	nucleons	unstable
carbon dating	global warming	photosynthesis	

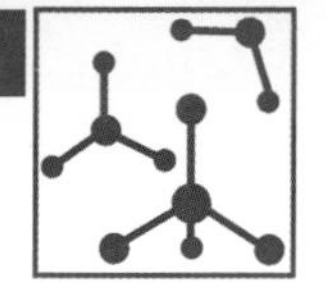

22.1 Nuclear Reactions

In the Middle Ages, individuals called alchemists spent a lot of time trying to make gold. Often, they fooled people into believing that they had made gold. Although alchemists never succeeded in making gold, their experimental techniques laid the foundation for the field of chemistry.

Gold is an element. Is it possible to make an element? What do you think?

Making an element is possible only if you can achieve a nuclear reaction, something the alchemists could not do. Nuclear reactions involve either combining or splitting the nuclei of atoms. In this section, you will learn about nuclear reactions as well as nuclear energy and radioactivity.

Figure 22.1: *Gold is a precious metal. In the Middle Ages "alchemists" tried to turn ordinary substances into gold. Using the means they had at the time, alchemists never succeeded in making gold. Today it is possible, but not economically reasonable to make gold!*

Making gold is not a simple task

Gold on the periodic table

Do you know where to find gold on the periodic table? Unlike what you might expect, its symbol is not Gd, nor Go, or Ga. The symbol comes from the Latin word ***aurum***. The Romans used this word to refer to gold, but it also meant "shining dawn."

Atoms are distinguished by number of protons

Although gold's ancient name is descriptive, an atom of gold is defined by its atomic number, 79. This number identifies how many protons an atom has in its nucleus. All atoms that have 79 protons are gold atoms. Atoms with one more proton are mercury (Hg) atoms, and atoms with one fewer proton are platinum (Pt) atoms. In these terms, it seems that it would be easy to make gold. You could simply combine nuclei (the plural form of nucleus) of different atoms until you made an atom with 79 protons. Which atoms do you think could be combined to make gold?

Fusion and fission reactions provide a way to make gold

To make gold, you would need to perform a nuclear reaction. There are two kinds of nuclear reaction: fusion and fission. The process of combining the nuclei of atoms to make different atoms is called fusion. To make gold, you could also split the nucleus of an atom that has more protons and neutrons than gold. Breaking up the nucleus of an atom is called fission. Scientists can use a special machine called a particle accelerator to bombard particles and atoms in order to achieve fusion and fission reactions. However, only a very small number of atoms can be made in this way at one time.

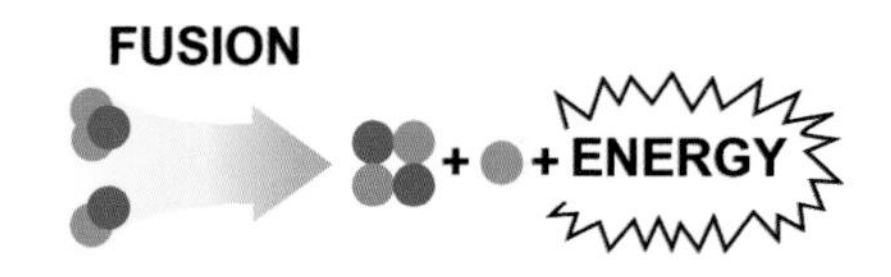

Figure 22.2: *In fusion, nuclei are "fused," a particle is emitted, and a lot of energy is released. The reaction shown above shows the fusion of hydrogen-3 (1 proton + 2 neutrons) with hydrogen-2 (1 proton + 1 neutron) to make a helium nucleus, a neutron and energy. In the graphic, the dark blue dots are protons; the lighter blue dots are neutrons.*

What is a nuclear reaction?

What are nuclear reactions? Fission and fusion are nuclear reactions. Protons and neutrons—the two most important subatomic particles in the nucleus—participate in these reactions. Collectively, the protons and neutrons in the nucleus are called nucleons. Nuclear fission can be started when a neutron (dark ball) bombards a nucleus (blue ball). A chain reaction results. A free neutron (step A) bombards a nucleus (step B) and the nucleus splits releasing more neutrons (step C). These neutrons then bombard other nuclei.

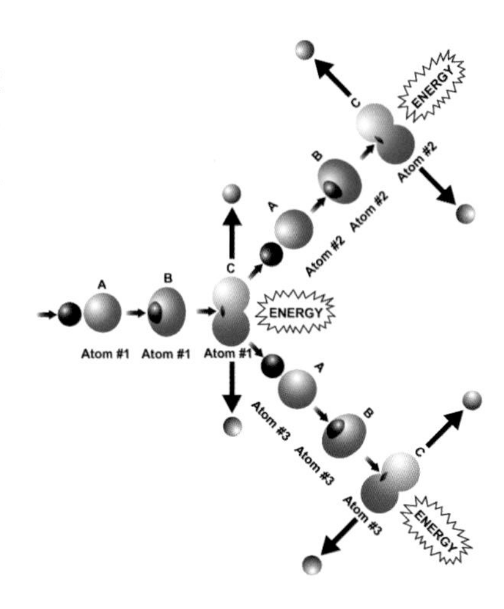

Chemical vs. nuclear reactions Chemical reactions involve only the outermost electrons of atoms. A summary of the differences between chemical and nuclear reactions is listed in the table below.

	chemical reactions	nuclear reactions
What part of the atom is involved?	Outermost electrons	Protons and neutrons in the nucleus
How is the reaction started?	Atoms are brought close together with high temperature or pressure, or catalysts, or by increasing concentrations of reactants	High temperature is required or atoms are bombarded with high-speed particles
What is the outcome of the reaction?	Atoms form ionic or covalent bonds	The number of protons and neutrons in an atom usually changes
How much energy is absorbed or released?	A small amount	A huge amount
What are some examples?	Burning fossil fuels, digesting food, housecleaning, making medicines and commercial products	Nuclear energy, taking x-rays, treating cancer, irradiating food to sterilize it, the sun generating heat and light

Chien-Shiung Wu

During World War II, Chinese-American physicist Chien-Shiung Wu played an important role in the Manhattan Project, the army's secret work to develop the atomic bomb. In 1957, she overthrew what was considered to be an indisputable law of physics, changing the way we understand the weak nuclear force.

Chien-Shiung Wu was born in 1912 near Shanghai, China. She attended a boarding high school that had two sections—a teacher training school and an academic school. Wu enrolled in the teacher training area. She graduated first in her class and was invited to attend a prestigious university in Nanjing. After earning a physics degree, Wu emigrated to the United States. She earned a Ph.D. from the University of California-Berkeley in 1940.

After working on the Manhattan Project, Wu continued research in nuclear physics at Columbia University. She won the National Medal of Science, the nation's highest award for scientific achievement, in 1975.

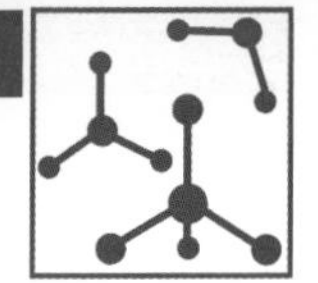

Forces in the nucleus

Opposites attract to form neutral atoms

Protons are positively charged particles. Consider an atom like boron with an atomic number of 5. The nucleus of a boron atom has five positively charged protons. What keeps these positive particles packed together? If "likes repel," shouldn't the protons fly apart from each other?

Strong nuclear force is the key

The nucleus stays together because of the *strong nuclear force*. The strong nuclear force attracts every proton and neutron to every other proton and neutron. The attractive forces from the neutrons and protons together are stronger than the electromagnetic force that cause the protons to repel each other.

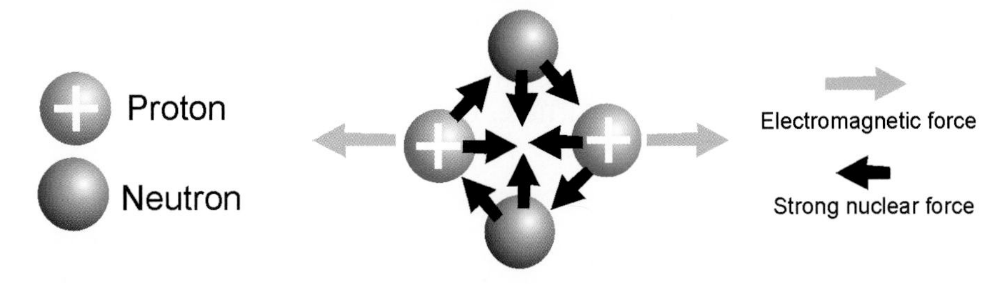

Figure 22.3: *Theoretical physicist, Hideki Yukawa (1907-1981) was the first Japanese to receive a Nobel Prize. He won the award in 1949 for his theory of strong nuclear force. This theory predicted the meson, a elementary particle that was later discovered.*

The importance of neutrons

For every atom heavier than helium there needs to be at least as many neutrons as protons to hold the nucleus together. For example, calcium-40 has 20 protons and 20 neutrons. For heavier atoms, more neutrons are needed than protons. This is because neutrons add attractive force without electromagnetic repulsion. For atoms with more than 83 protons, even the added strong nuclear force from neutrons is not enough to hold the nucleus together. Every nucleus with more than 83 protons is unstable.

Different atoms of an element can have different numbers of neutrons

You may already know that the atoms in an element can have different numbers of neutrons. For example, all carbon atoms have six protons, but some have six neutrons and some have seven neutrons. Atoms of the same element that differ in their number of neutrons are called **isotopes**. The best way to identify isotopes is by their atomic mass number. A carbon atom with six neutrons is referred to as carbon-12 and one with seven neutrons is carbon-13. The *atomic mass number* of an isotope is the number of protons plus the number of neutrons in an atom.

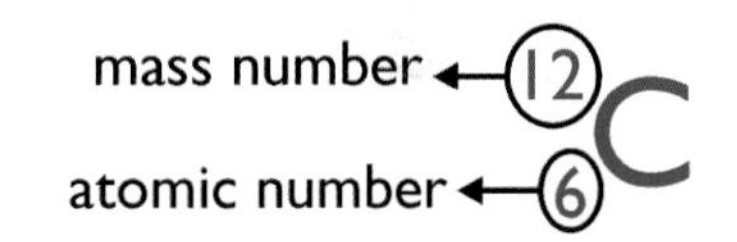

Figure 22.4: *The isotopes of carbon can written with the mass number above the atomic number. Here, we will call this format the "isotope notation." The diagram above is for carbon-12, one of the common and stable isotopes of carbon.*

What is radioactivity?

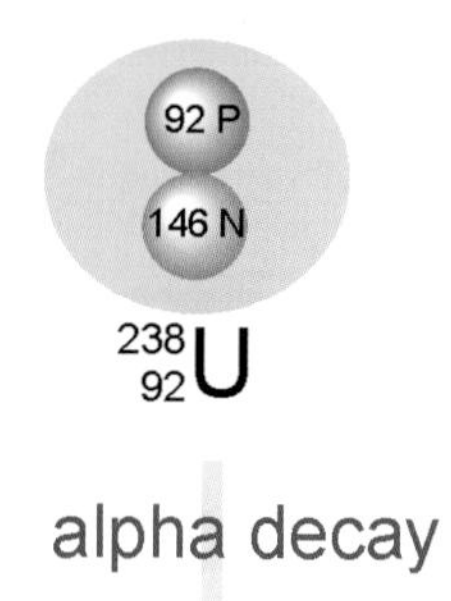

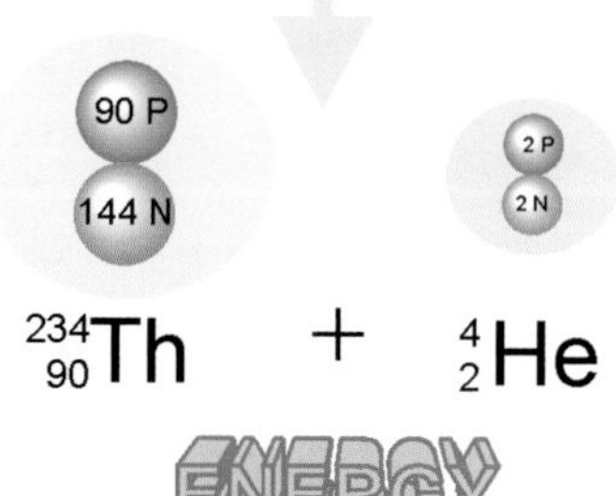

Figure 22.5: *When uranium-238 undergoes alpha decay, it becomes thorium-234 and releases a helium nucleus. Additionally, a lot of energy is released. The helium nucleus is called an alpha particle. The mass number for the elements on one side of the equation above equal the mass numbers on the other side. Nuclear reactions follow the law of conservation of mass.*

An unstable nucleus is radioactive

Radioactivity is how we describe any process where the nucleus emits particles or energy. The nucleus of a uranium-238 atom is radioactive. It emits radiation in the forms of particles and energy as it transforms itself into an atom with a more stable nucleus. In Figure 22.5, uranium-238 emits two protons and two neutrons to become a thorium-234 atom. Eventually, uranium-238 decays naturally to lead-206, which is not radioactive. The entire decay process takes about 5 billion years!

The three kinds of nuclear decay

Unstable isotopes emit three kinds of radioactive decay. These include alpha particles, beta particles, and gamma rays.

Alpha decay

In alpha decay, a particle that has two protons and two neutrons is released from an unstable nucleus. This particle is called an alpha particle. When a radioactive isotope undergoes alpha decay, it ejects an alpha particle. Uranium-238 undergoes alpha decay to become thorium-234 (Figure 22.5).

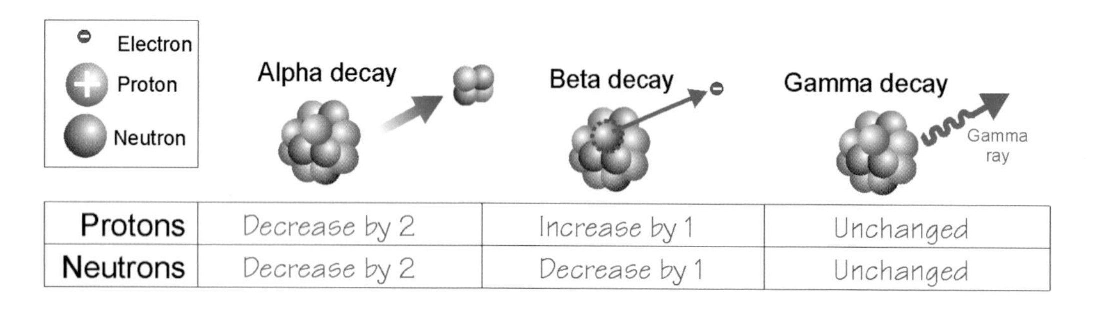

	Alpha decay	Beta decay	Gamma decay
Protons	Decrease by 2	Increase by 1	Unchanged
Neutrons	Decrease by 2	Decrease by 1	Unchanged

Beta decay

Beta decay occurs when a neutron in the nucleus of a radioactive isotope splits into a proton and an electron. The proton stays behind in the nucleus, but the electron is emitted. The electron is called a beta particle. Carbon-14 (a radioactive form of carbon) undergoes beta decay to become nitrogen-14. Why are the atomic masses of the carbon and nitrogen atoms both 14?

Gamma decay

Gamma decay involves the release of high-energy, electromagnetic radiation from the nucleus of an atom. Gamma rays have shorter wavelength than X rays and have much more energy.

Use your head...

Gold-185 decays to iridium-181. Is this an example of alpha or beta decay?

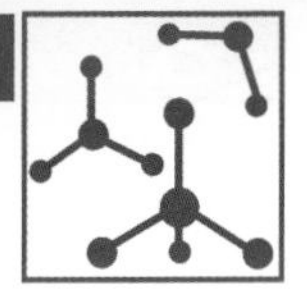

Using nuclear reactions for our energy needs

Sun power is nuclear power

Nuclear reactions are more common in everyday life than you might think. For example, consider that we all depend on the energy from the sun. We need the sun to warm us. What we and other animals eat depends on plants and algae converting energy from the sun into food. Even the fuel we use in our cars, derived from the fossil remains of plants and animals, can be attributed to the sun's energy. The huge amount of energy produced in the sun is the result of a multi-step fusion reaction in which hydrogen isotopes are forced together in the extremely hot interior of the sun to make helium.

Nuclear reactors

Some of our energy production on Earth involves nuclear reactors that use fission to produce heat. This heat is then used to generate steam for running turbines. In turn, the turbines generate electricity for homes and businesses.

Nuclear reactors produce hazardous nuclear waste

Almost all of our energy technologies also produce some harmful waste products. Burning coal and oil creates waste gasses that contribute to global warming and acid rain. Although nuclear reactors do not normally produce harmful emissions, they do produce nuclear waste. What is nuclear waste and why is it a problem?

Half-life

To understand nuclear waste, you have to understand the term half-life. All radioactive elements have a half-life. This means that there is a certain length of time after which *half* of the radioactive element has decayed. For example, the half-life of carbon-14 (one of the radioactive isotopes of carbon) is 5,730 years. This means that if you start out with 100 atoms of carbon-14, 5,730 years from now only 50 atoms will still be carbon-14. The rest of the carbon will have decayed to nitrogen-14 (a stable isotope). As a radioactive element decays, it emits harmful radiation (alpha and beta particles, and gamma rays). By breaking chemical bonds, radiation can damage cells and DNA. Exposure to radiation is particularly harmful if it is too intense or for too long a period of time.

The half-life of uranium

The radioactive element in nuclear reactor fuel is uranium. When a uranium atom breaks up (fission), giving off energy, the resulting smaller atoms are also radioactive. Many of the atoms which are decay products of uranium fission have long half-lives. That means spent fuel from a reactor stays radioactive for a long time, which is why it is dangerous.

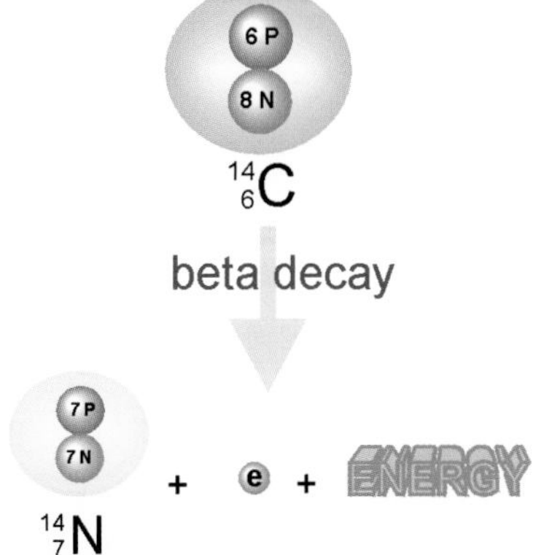

Figure 22.6: *When carbon-14 undergoes beta decay, it becomes nitrogen-14. This is because one of the neutrons in the carbon nucleus becomes a proton and an electron. The proton stays in the nucleus and an electron and energy are emitted.*

Radiation all around

Because you cannot see or feel radiation, you may not be aware that it is all around you. Many common objects contain radioactive isotopes. Exposure to radiation can come from space (radiation entering the Earth's atmosphere), having an x ray, brick or stone buildings, or brazil nuts! Fortunately, exposure to radiation from these sources is very low.

A plan for storing nuclear waste

In 1974, the U.S. Congress established the Nuclear Regulatory Commission (NRC) as a monitoring organization for nuclear fuel use and the storage of nuclear waste. There is a proposed permanent storage facility for highly radioactive nuclear waste that may be built by 2007 in Yucca Mountain, Nevada. Presently, nuclear waste is stored in special facilities around the country in containers meant to last 100 years. Storing nuclear waste is a very controversial issue. What do you think should be done about storing it?

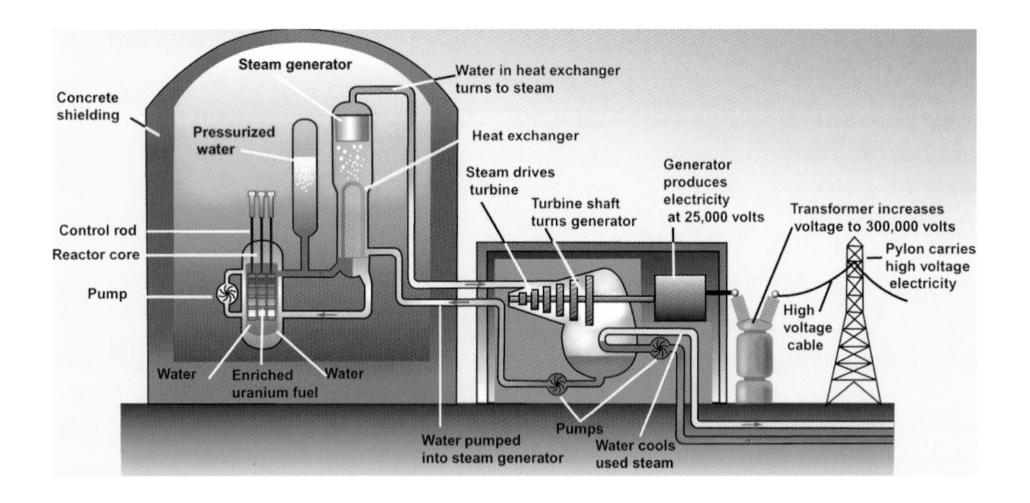

How much energy comes from nuclear reactors?

The US gets about 1/5 (20%) of its energy from nuclear fission reactors. The remaining energy comes from coal, natural gas, oil, and hydroelectric dams. Many foreign countries get more of their electricity from nuclear fission reactors. France is the most dependent on nuclear power. About 75% of electricity generated in France comes from nuclear fission. Sweden and Belgium also get more than 50% of their energy from nuclear fission.

What is nuclear fusion?

Nuclear fission is one of two ways to get energy from the atomic nucleus. The other process is called nuclear fusion. In nuclear fusion, light atoms are heated up to extremely high temperatures so their nuclei can fuse together to create heavier atoms. The process gives off tremendous amounts of energy, and is what powers the Sun and the stars.

Roscoe Koontz

Roscoe Koontz was born in 1922 in St. Louis, Missouri. During World War II, he was chosen to participate in a special Army pre-engineering program at West Virginia State college. After the war, he continued his education at Tennessee State University, where he earned a bachelor's degree in chemistry.

Koontz was invited to participate in the Atomic Energy Health Physics Fellowship Training Program at the University of Rochester in 1948. He became one of the world's first health physicists. A *health physicist* is a professional who makes sure that the risks associated with overexposure to radiation are minimized. The health physicist looks at a situation where ionizing radiation is to be used—a nuclear reactor, x-ray machine, high energy particle accelerator, or medical radiation. When Koontz entered the field, few standards existed to protect workers and the public from harmful radiation. Koontz and others developed many of the strategies currently used in radiation safety.

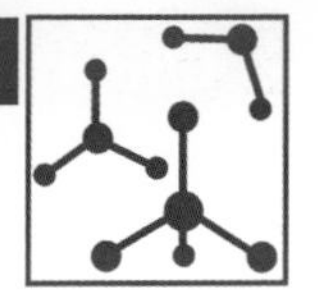

Using nuclear reactions in medicine and science

Radioactive isotopes can be used to detect problems in systems

Radioactive isotopes (also called *radioisotopes*) are commonly used as tracers in medicine and science. By adding a radioactive isotope into a system (such as the human body or an underground water supply), problems can be detected. The tracer's radiation allows it to be detected using a Geiger counter or other machine and followed as it travels through the system. In the food industry, nuclear reactions are used to sterilize packaged foods.

The age of some fossils can be determined by measuring carbon-14

It is possible to figure out the age of objects made from plants or animals that are between 50,000 and a few thousand years old using carbon dating. Plants and animals absorb carbon into their tissues. Much of the carbon they absorb is carbon-12 and carbon-13 because these are the most abundant carbon isotopes. However, some carbon-14 is also absorbed. Carbon-14 undergoes radioactive decay and has a half-life of 5,730 years. By measuring the amount of carbon-14 remaining in a plant or animal fossil, the age of the fossil can be estimated if it isn't too old. Why do you think very old fossils cannot be dated using carbon dating?

Marie Curie

The field of nuclear chemistry began when Marie Curie (1867-1934) and her husband, Pierre Curie (1859-1906), discovered radioactivity. In 1898, Marie Curie, a Polish-born chemist, coined the word "radioactivity" to describe peculiar behavior of elements she and her husband had discovered. They shared a Nobel Prize in 1903 for their discovery of radioactivity. Marie Curie was awarded a second Nobel in 1911 for her discovery of the elements radium and polonium.

Marie Curie began her career as a scientist at the University of Sorbonne in Paris. There, she was the first woman to graduate with a degree in physics (1893). Later in 1894, she received a degree in mathematics. For her work on radioactivity, she was the first woman to receive a Nobel Prize and the first person to receive two Nobel prizes. She was also the first woman professor at the University of Sorbonne. During World War I, she used her knowledge of radioactivity and her passion for applying this technology to medicine to organize mobile X-ray machines that could go from hospital to hospital. She championed radiation therapy as a treatment for cancer.

Rosalyn Sussman Yalow

Rosalyn Sussman was born in New York City in 1921. Rosalyn studied physics and chemistry in college, and then went on to the University of Illinois, where she earned her doctorate in nuclear physics. There she met and married Aaron Yalow.

In 1950, Rosalyn Yalow began researching medical uses of radioactive substances at the VA Hospital in the Bronx. She and her research partner, Solomon Berson, developed radioimmunoassay, or RIA. RIA is a technique that uses radioactive isotopes to measure tiny concentrations of biological substances and certain drugs in blood and other body fluids.

One early application of RIA was in diabetes research, which was especially significant to Yalow because her husband was diabetic. RIA's current uses include screening donated blood, determining effective doses of medicines, testing hormone levels in the blood, and treating certain children with growth hormones.

Yalow was awarded the Nobel Prize in Physiology or Medicine in 1977. She was the second woman to win in that category.

22.2 Carbon Reactions

What would the world be like without the sun? The world relies on the sun's energy more than you may realize. In fact, 99 percent of our energy needs are met by the sun. We get the rest of our energy namely by using fossil fuels—which were derived from the sun's energy millions of years ago. In this section you will learn about carbon reactions, such as the combustion of fossil fuels. Your body also happens to use a combustion reaction to get energy from the food you eat. By the end of the section, you will better understand the role of carbon reactions in food production, air pollution, and global warming.

Figure 22.7: *Whether you walk or ride in a car, you are using carbon reactions to travel from place to place.*

Photosynthesis

Plants convert the sun's energy into products we use

Recall that the sun produces its energy from a nuclear reaction called fusion. Inside the sun, hydrogen atoms "fuse" to produce helium and a lot of energy. The fusion reactions in the sun produce enough energy to illuminate and warm our planet Earth. This energy reaches the planet as visible and ultraviolet light, and infrared radiation (heat). It is easy to take all this energy for granted because is it free and clean. Most importantly, plants, using the process of photosynthesis, can Use energy from the sun to convert carbon dioxide and water into glucose, a type of sugar. Glucose in turn, is converted into more complex molecules that are used by animals—including humans. Fruits, vegetables, cotton, and wood are just some of the many plant products you may use of during a single day.

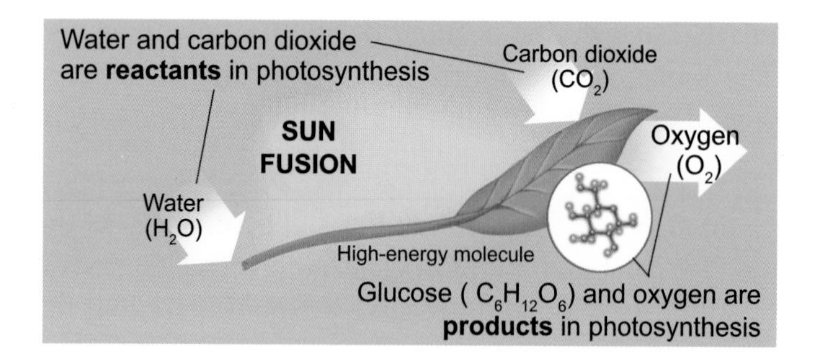

Photosynthesis

Photosynthesis is a process that is performed by plants, fresh water algae, saltwater algae, and some bacteria. In this process, special pigments absorb energy from the sun. This energy is used to convert water and carbon dioxide (CO_2) to glucose ($C_6H_{12}O_6$) and oxygen (O_2). Photosynthetic organisms (those that perform photosynthesis) produce glucose for their own energy and structural needs. Humans then use what plants produce for food, building materials, writing materials, clothing, and even medicines.

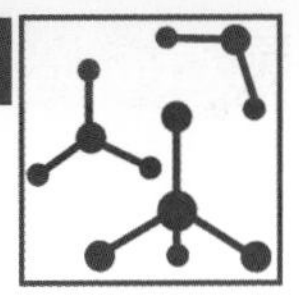

Carbon reactions and fossil fuels

Cars burn fossil fuels for energy

The sun helps make Earth very livable. More and more, however, we are requiring additional energy in the form of **fossil fuels**. The world's reliance on fossil fuels has increased steadily since the beginning of the Industrial Revolution in the mid-eighteenth century. Today, we use fossil fuels (like natural gas, kerosene, and coal) for home heating, for the production of electricity, and to run our machines. The machine we depend on most—the automobile—allows us to ride instead of walk to the places we want to go. A car converts the energy stored in fossil fuel (gasoline) into motion through a common chemical reaction called *combustion*.

Use of fossil fuels affects the environment

Unfortunately, our dependence on fossil fuels comes at a cost. When you put gasoline into a car, you are providing one of the reactants for a combustion reaction. Gasoline and oxygen react to produce carbon dioxide and water. Because combustion occurs in the engine at a high temperature and pressure, other products are produced as well. Because we can't see some of these products, it is easy to forget they are there.

Earth's atmosphere is a mixture of gases. The composition of the air is 78 percent nitrogen gas (N_2), 21 percent oxygen (O_2), 0.037 percent carbon dioxide (CO_2), 1 percent argon (an unreactive gas), traces of other gases, and some water vapor.

The atmosphere is mostly nitrogen gas

Nitrogen gas (N_2) is particularly abundant in the atmosphere because it isn't very reactive. However, nitrogen is essential for making molecules called proteins. Plants called legumes (like beans and peas) incorporate airborne nitrogen into protein for their own use. Other plants obtain nitrogen from fertilized soil. Your body obtains nitrogen for making proteins when you eat foods (vegetables and meat) that are high in protein.

O_2 comes from photosynthesis

Unlike nitrogen, oxygen (O_2) is a reactive, flammable gas. The great abundance of nitrogen (N_2) in the atmosphere effectively dilutes the O_2 so that things don't burn out of control every time a fire is started! Living plants and organisms are responsible for keeping enough oxygen in the atmosphere.

Carbon dioxide

Natural sources release about 150 billion tons of carbon dioxide each year. Much of this carbon dioxide is absorbed by natural processes, such as photosynthesis. By burning fossil fuels and clearing land for development, we put a strain on Earth's ability to manage CO_2 levels. For example, the amount of CO_2 in the atmosphere has increased by 30 percent since the beginning of the Industrial Revolution. Additionally, the average surface temperature of the planet has increased 0.6 to 1.2°F since the mid-1800s. These increases are not huge, but they are enough to have warmed the north pole and caused the sea level to rise 4 to 10 inches.

Global warming

Too much CO_2 in the atmosphere causes global warming

Compared to N_2 and O_2, there is very little carbon dioxide (CO_2) in the atmosphere. This may be surprising to you because you may have heard that increases in CO_2 in the atmosphere cause global warming. The amount of CO_2 that we have in our atmosphere is just enough to trap heat from the sun to make Earth warm and comfortable. The planet would be too warm with more CO_2 and too cold with less CO_2. When we use fossil fuels, we add more CO_2 to the atmosphere. The phrase **global warming** refers to our ability to increase the temperature of the planet's climate by increasing the amount of CO_2 in our atmosphere. In the United States, each person contributes about 6.6 tons of CO_2 every year! The world produces about 7 billion tons per year.

Car emissions are pollutants

The amount of CO_2 produced by a single car is less than that produced by a large factory or power plant. However, many of us use cars every day and carbon dioxide emissions add up. The word **emissions** refers to the airborne gases and particles that come out of the car's tailpipe when it runs. The combined CO_2 emissions and other pollution from cars on a day-to-day basis have caused many of our large cities to be noticeably hazy and smoggy.

Auto emissions	harm
carbon dioxide	major contributor to global warming
carbon monoxide	deadly gas
nitrous oxides	contribute to acid rain
ozone	irritation to eyes and lungs
hydro-carbons	cancer causing

Figure 22.8: *Ways in which automobile emissions affect air quality.*

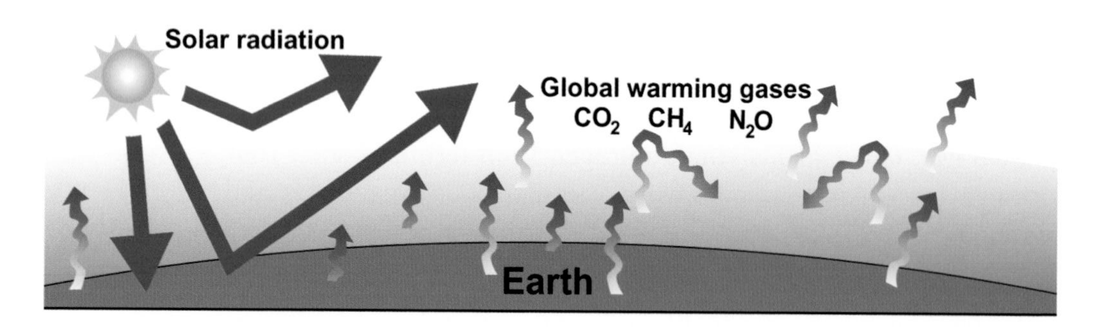

Global warming

Some of the solar radiation that reaches Earth is absorbed by its surface, and some is reflected and exits the atmosphere. However, heat that builds up within the Earth's atmospheres is trapped by global warming gases. The main global warming gases are carbon dioxide (CO_2), methane, (CH_4), and nitrous oxide (N_2O). You will learn more about global warming in chapter 26.

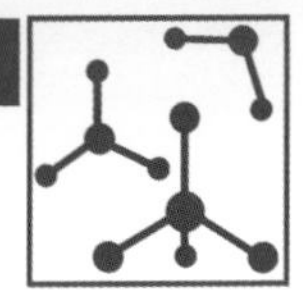

The combustion reaction in cars

Incomplete combustion means more air pollution

Fuel is a mixture of molecules called hydrocarbons. As the name suggests, these molecules only contain hydrogen and carbon. The energy of these valuable molecules is stored in the carbon-carbon and carbon-hydrogen bonds. Hydrocarbons become pollutants when they are incompletely burned during combustion or when they evaporate during refueling or from the engine while it cools. Hydrocarbons can react with nitrogen oxides and sunlight to make ozone. Both ozone and hydrocarbons are toxic pollutants.

The problems with nitrogen oxides

During combustion of fuel in a car, the high temperature and high pressure in the engine causes nitrogen in the air (which is typically unreactive) to convert to nitrogen oxides. Nitrogen oxides are reactants in the formation of ozone, a irritant to eyes and lungs. Nitrogen oxides also mix with water in the atmosphere, forming nitric acid, a component of acid rain.

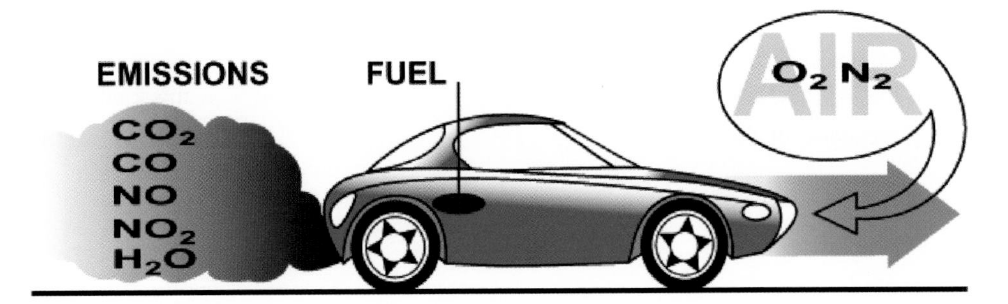

Carbon monoxide is a toxic gas

Complete combustion reactions produce only carbon dioxide. Incomplete combustion reactions also produce carbon monoxide (CO). This small molecule "looks" like oxygen to your body so your body uses CO instead of oxygen. For this reason, high concentrations of CO can be deadly. Lower concentrations found in areas with heavy traffic can be harmful to people with heart or lung disease.

The catalytic converter

The catalytic converter, introduced in the 1970s, reduces hydrocarbon and carbon monoxide emissions by converting these molecules to carbon dioxide and water. Improvements to the catalytic converter over the years have greatly reduced these emissions.

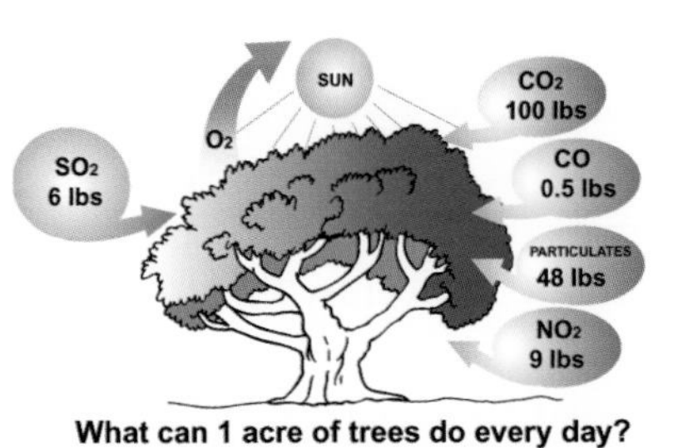

Figure 22.9: *Trees help consume carbon dioxide and other pollutants.*

.

Reducing CO_2

One acre of trees provides oxygen for about 20 people each day. This same acre can absorb emissions, including CO_2 (see Figure 22.10).

Questions to discuss with your friends:

- Trees greatly benefit our air quality, but can they solve global warming?
- Why might trees not be a good enough solution to global warming?
- What can you do to reduce how much CO_2 you produce?

Chapter 22 Review

Vocabulary review

Match the following terms with the correct definition. There is one extra definition in the list that will not match any of the terms.

Set One

1. alpha particle
2. radioactive
3. beta particle
4. radioactive decay
5. fission

a. A word to describe isotopes that undergo fission
b. The part of an atom that contains protons and neutrons
c. Two neutrons and two protons released from the nucleus of an atom
d. An electron that splits off of a neutron and is released from the nucleus of an atom
e. A nuclear reaction that involves the splitting of a heavy nucleus into a lighter nucleus
f. Radioactive isotopes experience this when they undergo fission

Set Two

1. fusion
2. gamma rays
3. half-life
4. isotope
5. nuclear reaction

a. This type of nuclear reaction occurs in the sun
b. The average time for half the amount of a radioactive element to decay
c. An atom that is distinguished by the number of neutrons in its nucleus
d. A form of electromagnetic radiation released during radioactive decay
e. The mixing of baking soda and vinegar causes this kind of reaction
f. Fission and fusion are examples of this kind of reaction

Concept review

1. In your own words, describe the difference between fusion and fission. Why do elements undergo fusion or fission spontaneously?
2. In a short paragraph, contrast nuclear reactions with chemical reactions.
3. Write the isotope notation for hydrogen-3, hydrogen-2 and hydrogen-1. List the number of neutrons, protons and electrons in each of these isotopes.
4. What are the differences between alpha decay and beta decay? Draw a labeled diagram showing each of these particles.
5. Explain how photosynthesis and respiration are related to carbon reactions. Write out these reactions in your response.
6. Describe the chemical composition of the Earth's atmosphere.
7. Explain why our use of cars can be cited as one cause of global warming.
8. List 10 products that you use or consume that are made from plants.

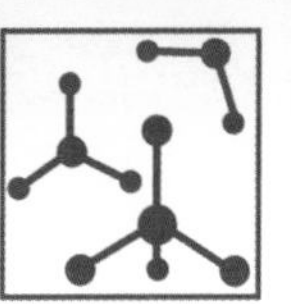

Problems

1. At the beginning of the student reading you were asked, "Which atoms could you combine to make gold?" Use a periodic table with the mass numbers of stable isotopes to write out a fusion reaction and fission reaction for gold. Use the isotope notation for referring to each isotope in the reaction (i.e., the notion for hydrogen-2 would be ${}^{2}_{1}H$). Additionally, if your reactions involve alpha or beta decay, or the gain or loss of a neutron, be sure to indicate these aspects in your written reaction.
   a. Fusion:
   b. Fission:

2. An isotope decreased to one-fourth its original amount in 18 months. What is the half-life of this radioactive isotope?

3. The decay series for uranium-238 and plutonium-240 are listed below. Above each arrow, write "a" for alpha decay or "b" for beta decay to indicate which type of decay took place at each step.

   a. ${}^{238}_{92}U \rightarrow {}^{234}_{90}Th \rightarrow {}^{234}_{91}Pa \rightarrow {}^{234}_{92}U \rightarrow {}^{230}_{90}Th \rightarrow$

   ${}^{226}_{88}Ra \rightarrow {}^{222}_{86}Rn \rightarrow {}^{218}_{84}Po \rightarrow {}^{214}_{82}Pb \rightarrow {}^{214}_{83}Bi \rightarrow$

   ${}^{214}_{84}Po \rightarrow {}^{210}_{82}Pb \rightarrow {}^{210}_{83}Bi \rightarrow {}^{210}_{84}Po \rightarrow {}^{206}_{82}Pb$

   b. ${}^{240}_{94}Pu \rightarrow {}^{240}_{95}Am \rightarrow {}^{236}_{93}Np \rightarrow {}^{232}_{91}Pa \rightarrow {}^{232}_{92}U \rightarrow$

   ${}^{228}_{90}Bi \rightarrow {}^{224}_{88}Ra \rightarrow {}^{224}_{89}Ac \rightarrow {}^{220}_{87}Fr \rightarrow {}^{216}_{85}At \rightarrow$

   ${}^{212}_{83}Bi \rightarrow {}^{212}_{84}Po \rightarrow {}^{208}_{82}Pb \rightarrow {}^{208}_{83}Bi$

4. All plants use the process of photosynthesis. However, this process wasn't always understood. In one classic experiment, a small plant and its soil were weighed. The plant was given only water for a solid year. At the end of the year, the plant weighed much more than it did at the first of the year. The soil weighed the same amount. Where did the extra weight of the plant come from?

5. Could you get rich making gold from fission and fusion reactions? Why or why not?

6. Due to radioactive decay, a sample of an isotope decreased to one-half its original amount in 6 days. What is the half-life of this radioactive isotope?

7. Answer the following:
   a. Cesium-137 is used to investigate soil erosion. This radioactive isotope naturally undergoes beta decay to become a different element. How many neutrons and protons will the different element have? What is this element?
   b. The half-life of cesium-137 is 30 years. Make a graph that shows the radioactive decay of cesium-137 over a period of 300 years. Place time on the x-axis of the graph, and amount of cesium-137 on the y-axis. The starting amount of cesium-137 is 100 atoms. Be sure to title the graph and label the axes.

Applying your knowledge

1. Mining for gold is an active industry. In order for mining companies to grow as businesses, they need to discover new sites that are rich in gold or other valuable minerals and element. Research in your library or on the Internet to find out about mining for gold. What do experts say about how much gold remains to be discovered?

2. Organize a debate in your class on the topic of nuclear energy and technology. What are the pros of using nuclear energy and technology? What are the cons? Prior to the debate, assign teams to the pro and con side and figure out with the class how the debate will be scored.

3. What is the difference between strong nuclear force and gravity? Are there other forces in the universe besides strong nuclear force and gravity? If so, what are these forces and how are they different from gravity and strong nuclear force?

4. The Earth's atmosphere differs from the atmospheres of Mars and Venus. Find out the chemical composition of the atmospheres on these planets. Explain why Earth's atmosphere is suitable for life, but the atmospheres of Mars and Venus are not.

5. Read a recent article about global warming. Write a short summary about the article and a brief paragraph explaining your opinions about the article and global warming.

6. Make a brochure that describes the causes of, the consequences of, and the solutions to global warming. Include the economic impact of global warming in your brochure. Do careful research in your library and on the Internet to make this brochure. Include quotations from individuals who are experts on this subject. Experts might be individuals who study global warming at a local college or university. Add your own color graphics to your brochure.

7. The Clean Air Act is an important piece of environmental law. The act was passed in 1970 and then amended in 1990. The purpose of this act is to reduce the number of airborne pollutants in our atmosphere. Most of these pollutants are end-products of chemical reactions that result from industrial processes and our use of gasoline-powered cars.

   Identify three chemical reactions that are used in industry that result in airborne pollutants. Find out how the Clean Air Act has regulated the industries that produce these pollutants

   .

   Obeying the Clean Air Act means that a polluting company, consumers (you), and/or tax-payers have to pay for fixing the causes of the pollutants. This could mean cleaning facilities or changing to newer, non-polluting technologies.

   List five things companies could do to reduce pollution. These costs are usually passed on to consumers through higher prices.

   List five additional problems caused by airborne pollutants that society must pay for. Is the cost of each problem paid by taxes or by the individuals affected by the pollution?

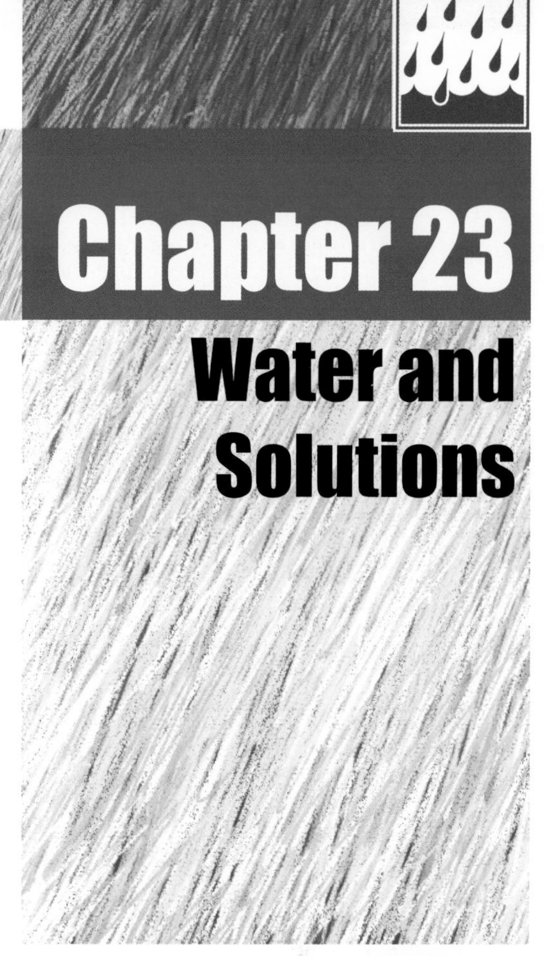

Chapter 23

Water and Solutions

Many of the foods you eat and the products you use (like shampoo) are solutions or other types of mixtures. In this chapter you will learn about water, solutions and solubility. You will also learn about two special types of solutions: acids and bases.

23.1	**Water**	*What are the properties of water?*

In this Investigation, you will conduct a series of experiments that demonstrate the properties of water.

23.2	**Solutions**	*Can you identify mixtures as solutions, suspensions, or colloids?*

You will construct an apparatus to view the Tyndall effect. The Tyndall effect is a test for determining the characteristics of a mixture. Your tests will tell you whether the mixture is a solution, colloid, or suspension.

23.3	**Solubility**	*What factors affect solubility?*

You will observe how temperature influences how fast a substance dissolves. Using your observations, you will develop an explanation for how temperature affects solubility. In addition, using carbonated water and a balloon, you will have the opportunity to explore how pressure affects the solubility of a gas in a liquid.

23.4	**Acids, Bases, and pH**	*What is pH?*

In this Investigation, a natural indicator and household chemicals are used to create a color-based pH scale. You will use your pH scale to figure out the pH of additional household chemicals and two mystery solutions.

Learning Goals

In this chapter, you will:

- ✔ Identify and describe the unique properties of water.
- ✔ Describe the shape and polarity of a water molecule.
- ✔ Discuss the nature of hydrogen bonds and their influence on the properties of water.
- ✔ Identify the components of a solution.
- ✔ Categorize mixtures as solutions, suspensions, or colloids.
- ✔ Define solubility.
- ✔ Describe saturated, unsaturated, and supersaturated solutions.
- ✔ Explain how temperature and pressure influence solubility.
- ✔ Understand solubility values.
- ✔ Interpret temperature-solubility graphs.
- ✔ Identify the characteristic properties of acids and bases.
- ✔ Relate the pH scale to examples of acids and bases.

Vocabulary

acid	electrolyte	pH	solubility value	Tyndall effect
alloy	equilibrium	pH indicator	solute	unsaturated
base	hydrogen bond	pH scale	solution	
colloid	nanometer	polar molecule	solvent	
dissociation	neutralization	saturated	supersaturated	
dissolved	nonpolar molecule	solubility	suspension	

23.1 Water

We live on a watery planet. All life on Earth depends on this combination of hydrogen and oxygen atoms. Fortunately, we have a lot of water on Earth. In fact, if you could form the water in the oceans into a giant ball, you would have a sphere that is about half the size of the moon.

While water is one of our most common substances, its combination of unique properties makes it essential to life. We cannot live without water. In fact, our bodies are made up of about 60 percent water. What are the properties of water that make it so unique?

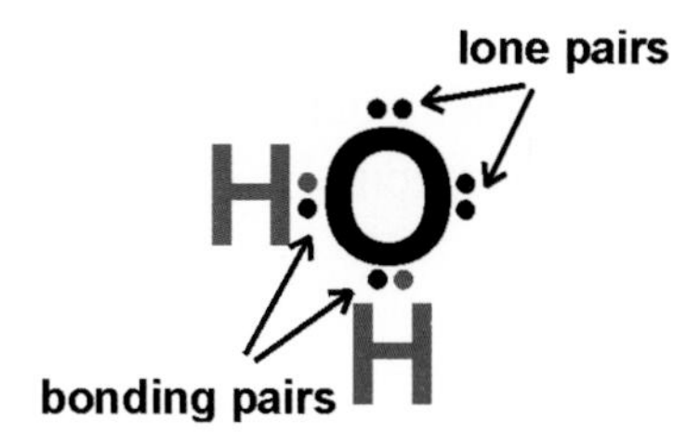

Figure 23.1: *The Lewis dot structure for water. The electron pairs involved in forming the bonds are called bonding pairs. The pairs that are not involved are called lone pairs.*

The shape of a water molecule

How a water molecule is formed

A water molecule is made of one oxygen atom that forms a chemical bond with two hydrogen atoms. Recall that oxygen has an oxidation number of 2- and has six valence electrons. Hydrogen, with an oxidation number of 1^+ has only one valence electron. When two hydrogens share their electrons with one oxygen atom, a neutral molecule is formed (shown at left). Note that the oxygen atom in the molecule now has eight valence electrons, the same number as a noble gas (as shown in Figure 23.1). Each hydrogen atom now has two valence electrons, giving them the same number of valence electrons as a helium atom.

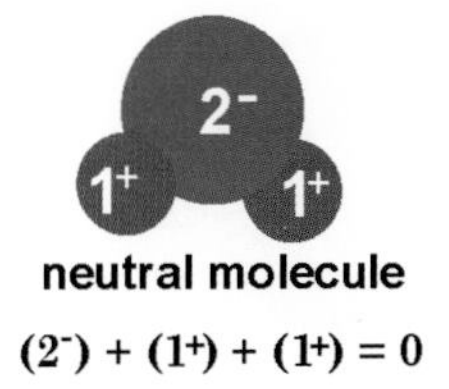

$(2^-) + (1^+) + (1^+) = 0$

The shape of a water molecule

A water molecule forms the shape of a “V.” An oxygen atom forms the point of the “V,” and the bonds with the two hydrogen atoms are the two legs. Why does a water molecule form this shape? Look at the Lewis dot structure for water (Figure 23.1). Note that there are four pairs of electrons around the oxygen atom. Only two of these pairs are involved in forming the chemical bonds. These two pairs are called *bonding pairs*. The other two pairs of electrons are not involved in forming chemical bonds and are known as *lone pairs*.

Electron pairs repel each other

Because negative charges repel, the four electrons pairs around the oxygen atom are located where they can be the farthest apart from each other. The geometric shape that allows them to be the farthest apart is called a *tetrahedron*. Since only two of the electron pairs are bonded with hydrogen atoms, the actual shape of the water molecule is a “V” (Figure 23.2).

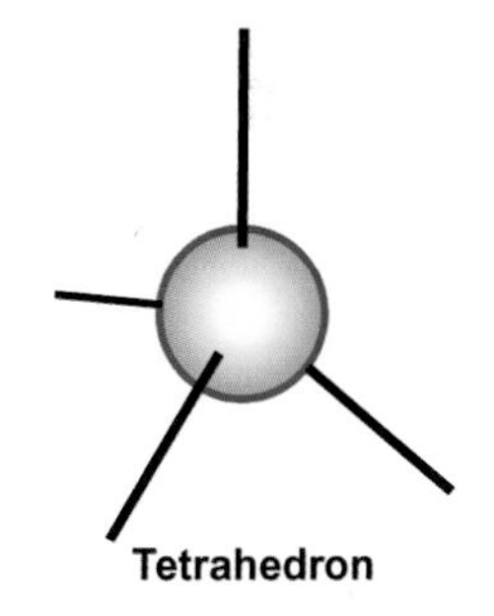

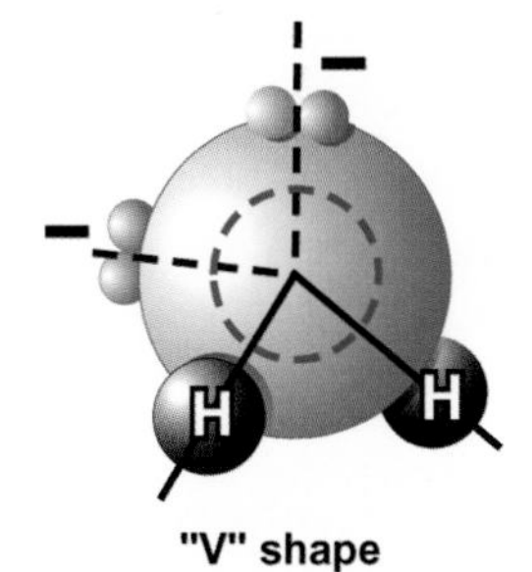

Figure 23.2: *The geometric shape that allows the electron pairs to be farthest apart is called a tetrahedron. Because only two of the pairs are involved in bonds with hydrogen, the shape of the molecule is a “V.”*

Water is a polar molecule

What is a polar molecule?

Water is a polar molecule that is, it has a *negative* end (pole) and a *positive* end (pole). In a molecule of water, the electrons are shared *unequally* between oxygen and hydrogen. This is because oxygen atoms attract electrons. Because of this, the electrons are pulled toward the oxygen atom and away from the two hydrogen atoms. The oxygen side of the molecule (the side with the lone pairs of electrons) therefore has a partially negative charge and the hydrogen side of the molecule has a partially positive charge (Figure 23.3).

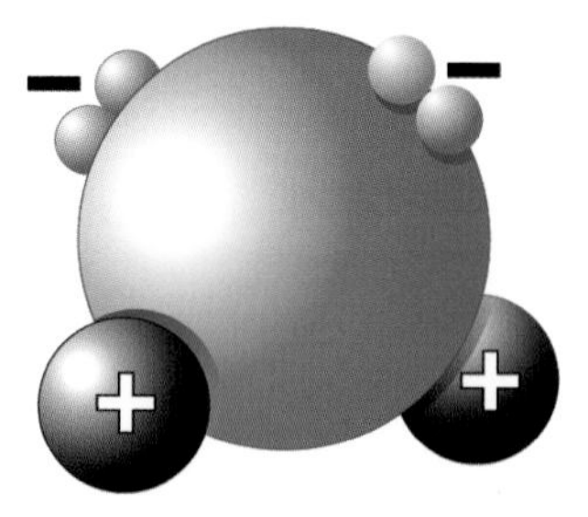

Figure 23.3: *Water is a polar molecule because it has a negative pole and a positive pole.*

Ammonia is another polar molecule

Ammonia, NH_3, is another example of a polar molecule. This molecule has one lone pair of electrons and three bonding pairs of electrons. This gives the ammonia molecule a pyramid shape. Figure 23.4 shows the shape of the molecule with the three hydrogens forming the base of the pyramid (the positive pole). The top of the pyramid is the negative pole.

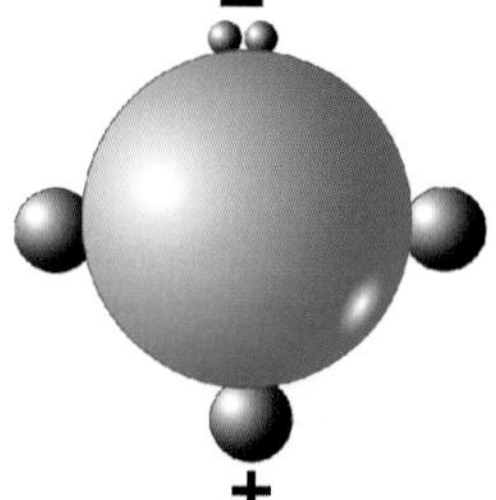

Figure 23.4: *Like water, a molecule of ammonia has a negative pole and a positive pole.*

Nonpolar molecules

Methane, CH_4, is an example of a nonpolar molecule. Nonpolar molecules do not have distinct positive and negative poles. Figure 23.5 shows a methane molecule. This molecule does not contain any lone pairs of electrons. Since there are no lone pairs of electrons, the electrons are shared equally between the carbon atom and the four surrounding hydrogen atoms.

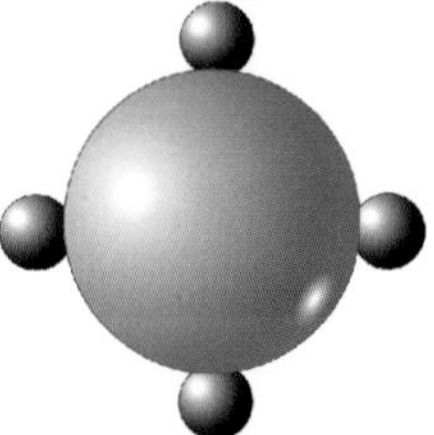

Figure 23.5: *Methane is an example of a nonpolar molecule.*

Comparing the physical properties of polar and nonpolar molecules

It takes energy to melt and boil compounds. The fact that the melting and boiling points of a polar molecule (water) are much higher than those of a nonpolar molecule (methane) provides evidence that there are attractions *between* polar molecules. This is because it takes more energy to pull apart molecules that are attracted to each other than those that have no attraction. Table 23.1 compares the melting and boiling points of water and methane. Notice that the melting and boiling points of water are much higher than those of methane.

Table 23.1: ***Comparing water, ammonia, and methane***

Compound	Melting point	Boiling point
Water	0°C	100°C
Methane	-182°C	-164°C

Attractions between water molecules

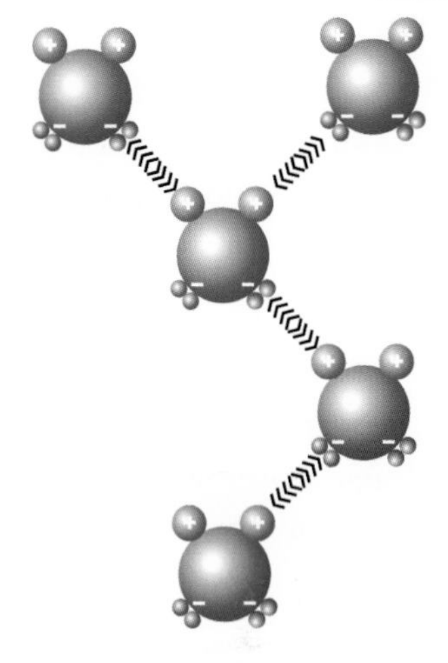

Figure 23.6: *Hydrogen bonds between water molecules.*

Water molecules behave like a group of magnets

If you place a group of magnets together, what happens? Recall that magnets have a positive side and a negative side. If you place a group of them together, you will find that they arrange themselves so that they alternate from positive to negative. The same is true if you put a group of water molecules together. The positive end of one water molecule will align with the negative end of another. When a group of water molecules is placed together, the positive and negative ends align among the molecules in the group. These *polar* attractions create organization among water molecules.

Hydrogen bonds

Figure 23.6 shows that the polar attractions in a group of water molecules are between one of the hydrogen atoms on one water molecule to the oxygen atom on another water molecule. This creates a type of chemical bond that is not as strong as the covalent bonds that hold the oxygen and hydrogen atoms in a water molecule together. The formation of a bond between the hydrogen on one molecule to another atom on another molecule is called a **hydrogen bond**. Hydrogen bonds are relatively weak. They constantly break and re-form as water molecules collide.

Water is a network of hydrogen-bonded molecules

In Figure 23.6, you can see that the oxygen atom in a water molecule has two lone pairs of electrons. Each pair of electrons is available to form a hydrogen bond with the partially positive hydrogen atom of a neighboring water molecule. Many neighboring water molecules connected by hydrogen bonds form a network of water molecules. As temperature increases, the organized structure of the hydrogen bonds among water molecules decreases. As temperature decreases, the organized structure becomes greater.

Frozen water has a honeycomb structure

Frozen water, also known as ice, has a very organized structure that resembles a honeycomb because each water molecule forms hydrogen bonds with four other water molecules (Figure 23.7). This creates a six-sided arrangement of molecules that is evident if you examine snowflakes under a microscope. As water freezes, molecules of water separate slightly from each other as a result of hydrogen bonding. This causes the volume to increase slightly and the density to decrease. This explains why water expands when it is frozen and floats. The density of ice is about 0.9 g/cm^3 whereas the density of water is about 1 g/cm^3.

Figure 23.7: *The honeycomb structure of solid water—ice. Can you identify how each molecule forms four hydrogen bonds with other molecules?*

Hydrogen bonding and properties of water

The temperature of water changes slowly

Have you ever jumped into a lake, pond or pool at night after a hot day? If so, you may have wondered why the water temperature felt warmer than the air. This is because once water heats, it cools down slowly. In fact, water cools much slower than most other substances. You may notice that water heats much slower than most other substances. This is evident if you heat a kettle of water for tea. The kettle gets hot very fast, but the water takes a long time to boil.

Hydrogen bonds cause water to resist temperature change

Because hydrogen bonds create attractions between water molecules, it takes more heat to make molecules of water move faster. Once the molecules of water begin to move faster, the temperature rises. As molecules move faster, the temperature rises more. To cool the water, the same amount of energy that was put in must be taken out again. This explains why water cools more slowly. If a large amount of energy is needed to heat water to a certain temperature, the same amount will be have to be taken away to cool it back to the starting temperature. You will learn more about this property of water, called *specific heat*, in the next unit.

Hydrogen bonding and the gaseous state

Most of the water on Earth exists in the liquid and solid states, rather than as a gas. This is because the hydrogen bonds hold the water molecules together strongly enough so that individual molecules cannot easily escape as a gas at ordinary temperatures. The hydrogen bonds in water explain why water has such a high boiling point (100 °C). In order for water to boil and turn into a gas (water vapor), enough energy must be added to separate the hydrogen bonds that hold the molecules of water together. Once these molecules are separated, they are able to enter the gaseous state (Figure 23.8).

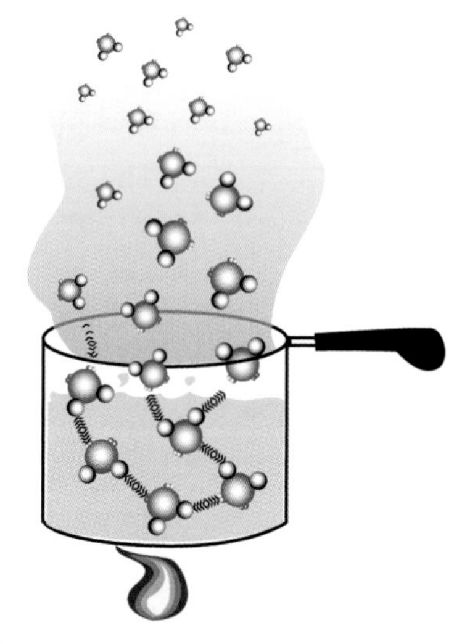

Figure 23.8: *In order for water to boil, enough energy must be added to separate the hydrogen bonds that hold the water molecules together.*

Hydrogen bonding and plants

Hydrogen bonding between water molecules is important to the function of plants. Plants obtain water from their roots. How then does a plant get water to its leaves? Plants have cells in their stems that are like soda straws. These sets of cells are microscopically thin. If a plant stem was transparent, you would see streams of water going from the roots to the leaves. As water molecules evaporate from the leaves, more water molecules are pulled into place. It is as if water molecules hold hands. If one molecule moves, the ones behind follow because they are connected by hydrogen bonds!

Figure 23.9: *Hydrogen bonds help water travel from root to stem to leaves.*

23.2 Solutions

If you walk down the beverage aisle of your local grocery store, you might see mineral water, spring water, flavored water and seltzer (carbonated water) for sale. While the labels on the bottles might call what's inside "water," each bottle contains more than just pure water. These varieties of water are actually *solutions* that also contain dissolved substances.

What is a solution?

A solution is homogeneous at the molecular level

In chemistry terms, we call different types of bottled water *solutions*. A solution is a mixture of two or more substances that is homogeneous at the molecular level. The word *homogeneous* means the particles in the water are evenly distributed. For example, in mineral water, there are no clumps of hundreds of mineral ions. The particles in a solution exist as *individual* atoms, ions, or molecules. Each has a diameter between 0.01 and 1.0 nanometer. A nanometer is one-billionth of a meter. It is represented by writing "nm."

A solution is a mixture of two or more substances that is homogeneous at the molecular level.

An alloy is a solution of two or more metals

Although we often think of solutions as mixtures of solids in liquids, solutions exist in every phase, be it solid, liquid, or gas. Carbonated water is a solution of a gas in a liquid. Fourteen-karat gold is a solution of two solids, silver and gold. "Fourteen-karat" means that 14 out of every 24 atoms in the solution are gold atoms. Likewise, ten-karat means that 10 out of every 24 atoms in the solution are gold. Solutions of two or more metals are called alloys.

A solution is a mixture of solute dissolved in a solvent

A solvent is the component of a mixture that is present in the greatest amount. The remaining components are called the solutes. When the solute particles are evenly distributed throughout the solvent, we say that the solute has dissolved (Figure 23.10). Figure 23.11 shows some other examples of solutions.

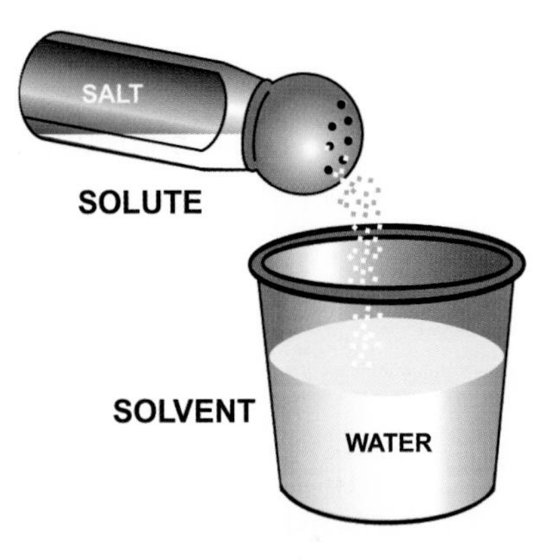

Figure 23.10: *Solutions are made when solutes dissolve in solvents. Here, salt is the solute, and water is the solvent.*

Solution	Solvent	Solute(s)
air	nitrogen (gas)	other gases
carbonated water	water (liquid)	CO_2 (gas)
saline solution	water (liquid)	salt (solid)
rubbing alcohol	alcohol (liquid)	water (liquid)
sterling silver	silver (solid)	copper (solid)

Figure 23.11: *Some examples of solutions. Notice that solutions are not always liquids.*

Colloids and suspensions are not solutions

Colloids Mixtures such as mayonnaise, egg whites, and gelatin are **colloids**. They look like solutions, but the particles in these mixtures, at one to 1,000 nanometers, are larger than those found in solutions. True solutions contain single atoms and molecules (less than 1 nanometer in size). By comparison, colloid particles are formed of *clusters* of atoms or molecules. Nevertheless, colloid particles are too small (1-1,000 nanometers) to settle to the bottom of their container. Instead, they stay evenly distributed throughout the mixture because they are constantly tossed about by the movement of the liquid particles.

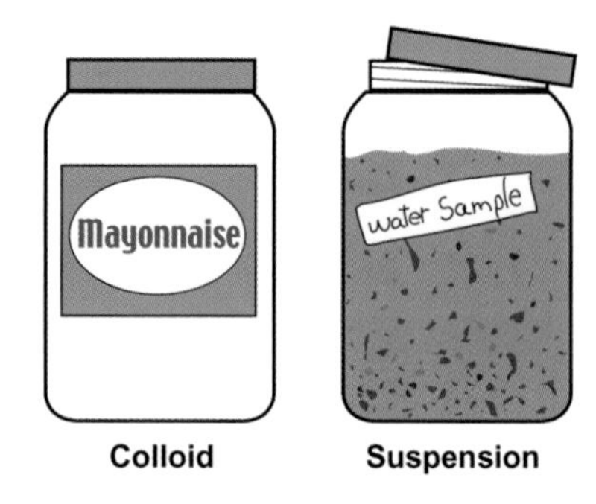

Figure 23.12: *Mayonnaise is a colloid. Water and silt make a suspension.*

Suspensions You may notice that when you step into a pond or lake to go swimming, you suddenly make the water cloudy. Your feet cause the mud on the bottom of the pond or lake to mix with the water. However, if you stand very still, eventually the water becomes clear again. This is because the individual mud particles sink. In **suspensions** like muddy water, the particles are greater than 1,000 nanometers in diameter. Atoms and molecules are much smaller than 100 nanometers. Suspensions are mixtures that settle upon standing (Figure 23.12). If you filter a suspension you can separate the different components.

The Tyndall effect It isn't easy to separate colloids by filtering. However, there is a way to visually distinguish colloids from true solutions. It is called the **Tyndall effect**. If you shine a flashlight through a jar of a translucent colloid, the particles scatter the light, making the beam visible (Figure 23.13). Fog is an example of a colloid. This is why an automobile's headlight beams can be seen on a foggy evening.

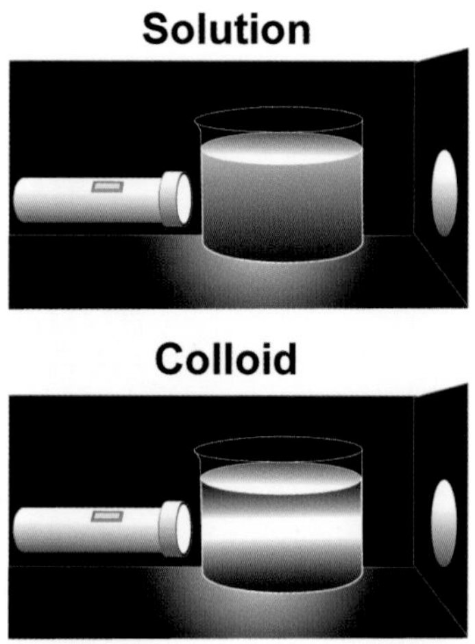

Solution

Colloid

Figure 23.13: *The Tyndall effect helps you tell the difference between colloids and solutions.*

Table 23.2: ***Properties of solutions, suspensions, and colloids***

	Approximate size of solute particles	Solute particles settle	Can be separated by filtering	Particles scatter light
solutions	0.01 - 1.0 nm	no	no	no
colloids	1.0 - 1,000 nm	no	only with special equipment	yes, if transparent
suspensions	>1000 nm	with time	yes	yes, if transparent

Why is water called the universal solvent?

Water readily dissolves many different substances

Have you ever looked at the label on a bottle of spring water? Often the label will read "bottled at the source" and will show the dissolved mineral content. In fact, most of the water you come in contact with contains many dissolved substances. For this reason, water is often called the "universal solvent." While water doesn't dissolve *everything*, it does dissolve many different types of substances such as salts and sugars. Water is a good solvent because it is a polar molecule. This gives it the ability to dissolve ionic compounds and other polar substances.

Sodium chloride is an ionic compound

Recall that sodium chloride (NaCl) is an ionic compound that is made of sodium ions (Na^+) and chlorine ions (Cl^-). If you look closely at a single crystal of NaCl, you will notice that it is a cube. Millions of sodium (Na) and chlorine (Cl) atoms, each too small to see with your naked eye, are a part of a single crystal of NaCl.

Water dissolves sodium chloride

When a sodium chloride crystal is mixed with water, a reaction occurs. The polar water molecules surround the sodium and chlorine atoms in the crystal. This causes the atoms in the crystal to *dissociate*, or separate into Na^+ and Cl^- ions. Because opposites attract, the negative ends of the water molecules are attracted to the Na^+ ions and the positive ends are attracted to the Cl^- ions. Eventually, water molecules surround the Na^+ and Cl^- ions, making a solution (Figure 23.14).

Water dissolves many ionic compounds. The process by which ionic compounds dissolve, that is, become separated into positive and negative ions is called dissociation.

The equation for the dissociation of sodium chloride

You can show the dissociation of sodium chloride as a chemical equation:

$$NaCl_{(s)} \xrightarrow{H_2O} Na^+_{(aq)} + Cl^-_{(aq)}$$

The "aq" symbol is shorthand for "aqueous" and symbolizes that the Na^+ and Cl^- ions are dissolved in water.

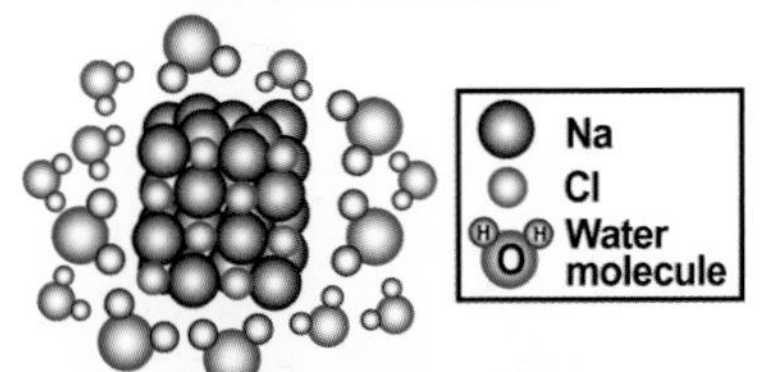

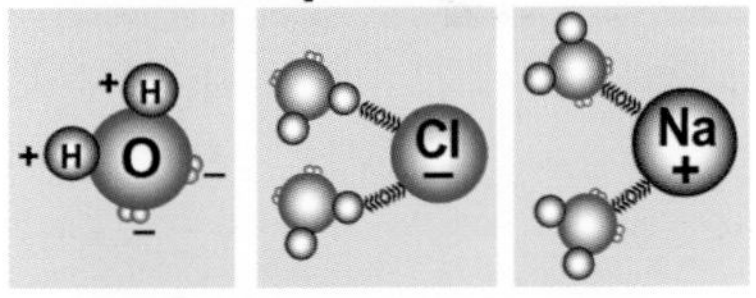

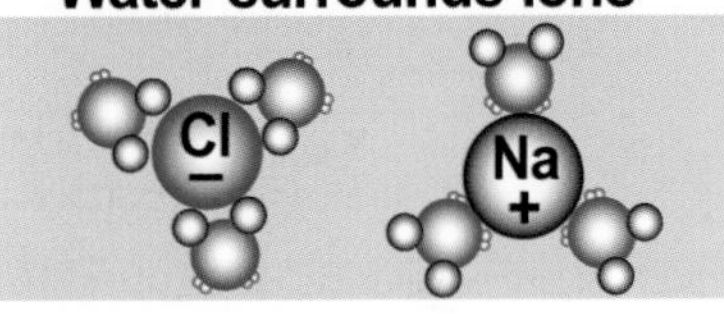

Figure 23.14: *When sodium chloride crystals come in contact with water molecules, the Na+ and Cl- ions become separated and surrounded by water molecules. This process is called dissociation.*

Water also dissolves many covalent substances

Sucrose is a covalent compound

Covalent compounds *share* electrons and are not made of ions. A good example of a covalent compound is *sucrose* ($C_{12}H_{22}O_{11}$), better known as sugar. You know that sugar dissolves easily in water if you have ever made sweetened tea. Like water, sucrose is a polar molecule because it has positive and negative ends.

Water dissolves sucrose

Like water, sucrose molecules are also held together by hydrogen bonds. In the case of sugar, these bonds hold the molecules together as crystals. When sucrose is mixed with water, the individual molecules of sucrose become separated from each other and are attracted to the opposite poles of the water molecules. Because sucrose is a covalent compound, the sucrose molecules do not dissociate into ions but remain as neutral molecules in the solution (Figure 23.15). The dissolving of sucrose in water can be represented by the following simple equation:

$$C_{12}H_{22}O_{11}\,(s) \xrightarrow{H_2O} C_{12}H_{22}O_{11}\,(aq)$$

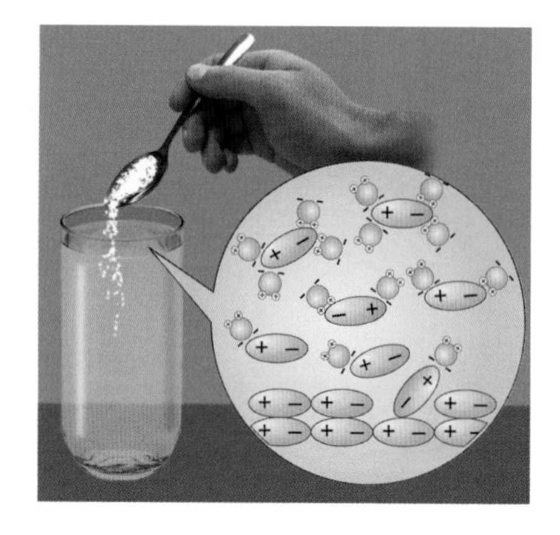

Figure 23.15: *When sucrose and water are mixed, the sugar molecules separate from each other and become surrounded by water molecules.*

Water does not dissolve oil

Have you ever tried to mix oil and water? You may have discovered that you cannot make a solution out of these two substances. Why does water dissolve sugar and not oil? The answer is because water is a polar molecule and oil molecules are nonpolar. Water dissolves sugar because they both have hydrogen bonds and their molecular interactions are *alike*. Oil is nonpolar and does not have hydrogen bonds so it is *unlike* water.

Like dissolves like

In chemistry, a good rule of thumb is that "like dissolves like." In other words, dissolving occurs when both the solute and the solvent are polar molecules, or both the solute and solvent are nonpolar molecules.

Try this at home

You can easily observe a nonpolar substance dissolving in another nonpolar substance if you mix olive oil (which is green) with soybean oil (which is nearly colorless). The two mix when you stir them together and remain mixed. You have created a solution made from two nonpolar substances.

How does soap work?

If you have ever washed greasy dishes with soap, you know that soap can make oil and water mix. The reason is that soaps have molecules with polar and nonpolar ends. The nonpolar ends surround oil molecules and the polar ends are attracted to water molecules. This causes the soap molecules to surround oil molecules. The combined oil-soap molecules become suspended in water molecules and can be rinsed away easily.

Solution concentrations

How do you express solution concentration? In chemistry, it is important to know the exact concentration of a solution—that is the exact amount of solute dissolved in a given amount of solvent. There are many ways of expressing the concentration of a solution. We'll take a look at two of the most common ways: *molarity* and *mass percent*.

Molarity The most common way of expressing concentration in chemistry is to use *molarity* (M). Molarity is equal to the moles of solute per liter of solution. Recall that one mole of a substance contains 6.02 x 10^{23} particles (atoms or molecules) and allows you to express the formula mass in grams.

$$\text{Molarity (M)} = \frac{\text{Moles of solute}}{\text{Liters of solution}}$$

Molarity example Suppose you dissolve 5.00 moles of NaCl in enough water to make 1.0 L, what is the molarity of the solution?

$$\text{Molarity (M)} = \frac{\text{5.0 moles NaCl}}{\text{1.0 L of solution}} = 5.0\text{M}$$

Mass percent The *mass percent* of a solution is equal to the mass of the solute divided by the total mass of the solution.

$$\text{Mass percent} = \frac{\text{mass of solute}}{\text{total mass of solution}} \times 100$$

Mass percent example Suppose you dissolve 10.0 grams of sugar in 100.0 grams of water. What is the mass percent of sugar in the solution?

$$\text{Mass \% sugar} = \frac{\text{10.0 g sugar}}{\text{10.0 g sugar + 100.0 g water}} \times 100 = 9.09\% \text{ sugar}$$

Concentrations in the environment

Parts per million (ppm), parts per billion (ppb), and parts per trillion (ppt) are commonly used to describe very small concentrations of pollutants in our environment. But what do these terms represent? They are measures of the amount of one material in a much larger amount of another material. For example, a pinch of salt in 10 tons of potato chips is equal to 1 part salt per billion parts chips, or a concentration of 1 ppb salt.

In the Great Lakes, the concentration of PCB (a toxic waste chemical) in drinking water is about *4 ppt* while the concentration of PCB in fish is *2 ppm*. This means that fish have about a million times more PCB than the drinking water! Which would you rather do, eat the fish or drink the water?

23.3 Solubility

Have you ever noticed that sugar dissolves more easily in a hot cup of tea than in a glass of iced tea? You may also have noticed that you can dissolve *more* sugar in a hot liquid than in a cold liquid. You can deduce that there is a relationship between the temperature of the solvent and the *solubility* of the solute. In this section you will learn about solubility and the factors that influence solubility.

Figure 23.16: *You may have already deduced that there is a relationship between temperature and solubility.*

What is solubility?

What is solubility? The term solubility means the amount of solute that can be dissolved in a specific volume of solvent under certain conditions. The solubility of a solute is influenced by several factors including the chemical nature of the solvent, the volume of solute, and temperature.

Volume affects solubility For a solute to dissolve completely, you need a specific volume of solvent. For example, to dissolve an amount of sodium chloride (NaCl) in water, you need enough water molecules to pull apart and surround all the Na^+ and Cl^- ions.

The solubility of a solid usually increases with temperature The solubility of a solid substance usually increases as temperature increases. The effect of temperature on solubility has to do with molecular motion and the energy of the solute-solvent system. At higher temperatures, molecules move faster so that there are more molecular collisions between solute and solvent molecules. The rate of collisions between these molecules is usually directly related to the rate at which the solute dissolves.

Solubility values The solubility value for table salt (NaCl) is 1 gram per 2.8 milliliters of water at 25°C. The solubility value for NaCl tells you how much can dissolve in a certain volume (or, sometimes, mass) of water as long as the water is at 25°C. Using this information, how much salt would dissolve in 280 milliliters of water at that temperature? If you said 100 grams, you are correct!

Some substances do not dissolve in water Figure 23.17 shows the solubility values for common substances. Notice that chalk and talc do not have solubility values. These substances are said to be *insoluble* because they do not dissolve in water.

Common name	Solubility at 25 °C (grams per 100 mL H_2O)
table salt (NaCl)	37.7
sugar ($C_{12}H_{22}O_{11}$)	200
baking soda ($NaHCO_3$)	approx. 10
chalk ($CaCO_3$)	insoluble
talc (Mg silicates)	insoluble

Figure 23.17: *Solubility values for common substances.*

Temperature-solubility graphs

Temperature-solubility graphs show how much substance dissolves at a given temperature

The solubility values for solutes are easily determined if you have a temperature-solubility graph. The *y*-axis on these graphs represents how many grams of solute (in this case, salts) will dissolve in 100 milliliters of water. The *x*-axis represents temperature in degrees Celsius.

You will notice in the graph that the salts (NaCl, KNO_3, $NaNO_3$) dissolve differently as temperature increases. For something to dissolve in water, the water molecules need to break the bonds between the solute molecules. Water dissolves substances differently because the chemical bond strengths between atoms found in different solutes are not the same.

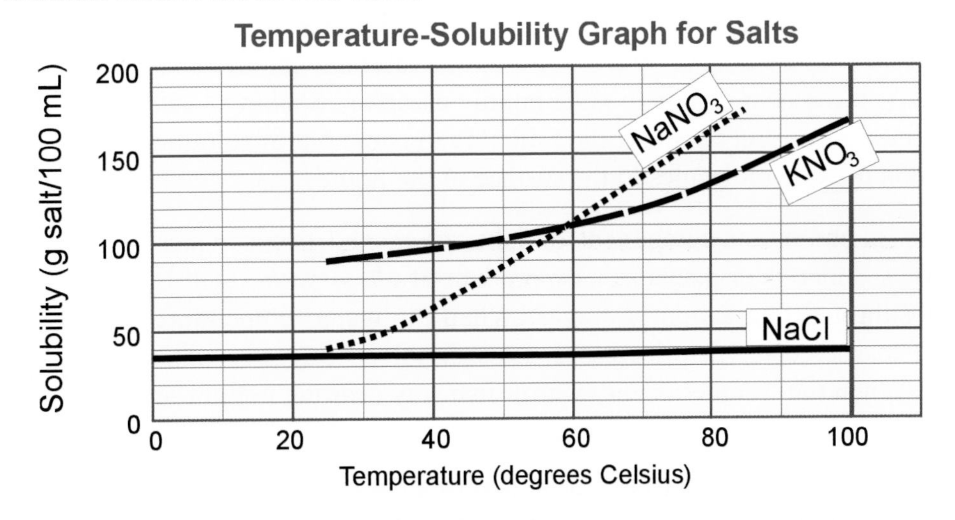

Interpreting the graph

The graph above is a temperature-solubility graph for sodium chloride (NaCl), potassium nitrate (KNO_3), and sodium nitrate ($NaNO_3$). The solubility of NaCl does not change much as temperature increases. The effect of temperature on the solubility of KNO_3 and $NaNO_3$ is more noticeable. More KNO_3 and $NaNO_3$ will dissolve in 100 milliliters of water at higher temperatures than NaCl.

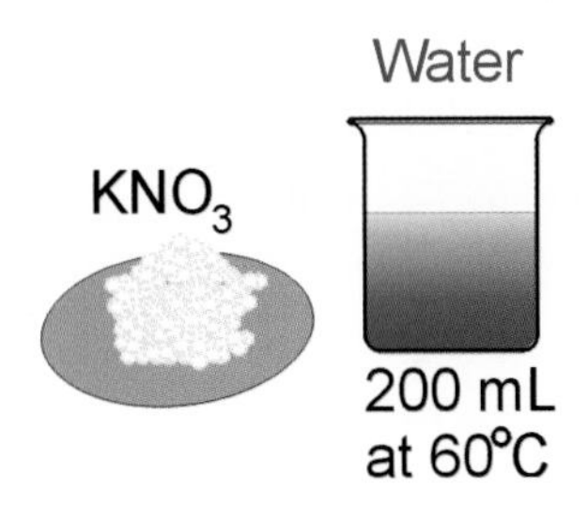

Example:

How many grams of potassium nitrate (KNO_3) will dissolve in 200 mL of water at 60°C?

Solution:

(1) You are asked for the mass in grams of solute.

(2) You are given temperature and volume.

(3) The relationship between solubility and temperature for KNO_3 can be seen on a graph to the left.

(4) From the graph, you see that 110 grams of KNO_3 dissolve in 100 mL of water at 60°C.

(5) Plug in numbers.

200 mL / 100 mL = 2

2 x 110 g = 220 g

(6) Answer:

220 grams of KNO_3 will dissolve in 200 mL of water at 60°C.

The solubility of gases

The solubility of gases in liquids decreases as temperature increases

You now know that temperature tends to increase the solubility of solids in liquids. In contrast, temperature tends *to decrease* the solubility of gases in liquids. For example, you may have noticed that a can of soda at room temperature is more likely to fizz and spill over when opened than a cold can of soda. As temperature increases, the gas and water molecules begin to move around more. The increased motion means that more dissolved gas molecules rise to the surface of the soda and escape.

Figure 23.18: *The CO_2 in a can of soda like ginger ale has been dissolved in water with the use of pressure.*

The solubility of gas also depends on pressure

The solubility of gases also depends on pressure. When you drink fizzy, carbonated beverages, you are consuming solution that contains gaseous carbon dioxide (CO_2). Soda is fizzy because the carbon dioxide has been dissolved in the liquid by using pressure (Figure 23.18). When you pop the tab on a can of soda, you release pressure. You can hear carbon dioxide rapidly escaping. Shaking a can of soda before opening it also forces some carbon dioxide to come out of solution by getting more carbon dioxide molecules to the surface of the liquid.

★ Fish need dissolved oxygen to live

Dissolved oxygen is an important component of lake, river, and ocean water. Oxygen is produced by underwater plants as a by-product of *photosynthesis*. It is mixed into the water through the action of waves. When the water temperature rises, the amount of dissolved oxygen decreases. Less dissolved oxygen means less oxygen for fish. When the weather is very warm, fish stay near the bottom of ponds and rivers where there is cooler, more oxygenated water.

How temperature affects the amount of dissolved oxygen in water

Electrical generating facilities are often built near bodies of water so that they have an inexpensive source of water for their cooling system. However, when this water is discharged back into the river or bay while it is still warm, it can significantly reduce the amount of dissolved oxygen available in the waterway. At the same time, the warming of the water increases the metabolic rate of the fish so that their need for dissolved oxygen increases. The combination of these two factors endangers fish and may cause large disturbances to the local *ecosystem*. An ecosystem is a term that describes a particular physical environment and its interconnections with plants and animals.

How did soda get its name?

In 1767, Joseph Priestly, an English chemist best known for discovering oxygen, figured out how to carbonate beverages. Initially, carbon dioxide was obtained from baking soda (sodium bicarbonate). This is why we often use the name "soda" for carbonated beverages.

How much will dissolve?

The solubility of a substance stops at equilibrium

When talking about solubility, equilibrium is the balance of solute molecules coming and going from a solution for a given set of conditions. For every set of conditions, a solute will dissolve in and come out of solution at a certain rate. When the rate of dissolving equals the rate of coming out of solution, we say equilibrium has been reached (Figure 23.12).

Equilibrium is reached when the rate of dissolving equals the rate of coming out of solution.

Saturated means the maximum amount has dissolved

A solution is saturated when the solution has dissolved all the solute it can hold at a given temperature. In other words, the solution will not dissolve any more solute under these conditions. If you raise the temperature of the system, however, you may be able to dissolve a little more solute. When the solution cools back down again, some of the dissolved solute recrystallizes (Figure 23.19).

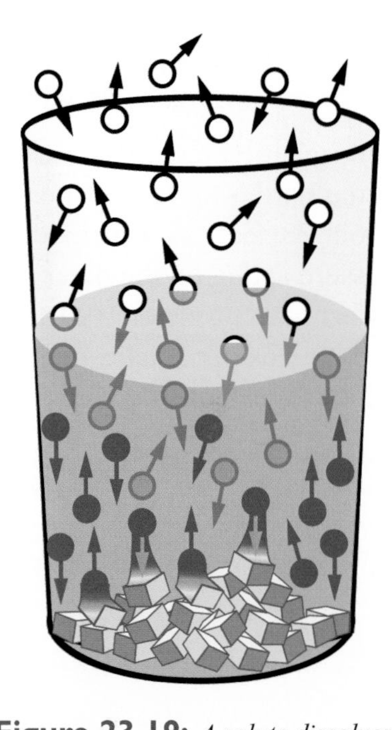

Figure 23.19: *A solute dissolves until equilibrium is reached. This diagram shows gas molecules (the open circles) dissolving and coming out of solution at the surface of the solution. At the bottom of the glass, molecules of a solid (the closed circles) are dissolving and recrystallizing.*

Unsaturated means more solute can be dissolved

Rock candy consists of large sugar crystals usually attached to a rough surface such as a piece of cotton string. The candy is made by heating water to boiling and then stirring in granulated sugar. As long as the sugar dissolves, the solution is said to be unsaturated. When no more sugar will dissolve, the solution is said to be saturated. Next, the saturated, sugar-water solution is poured into a jar with a suspended cotton string. As the solution cools, it becomes supersaturated.

Supersaturated means more is dissolved than normally possible

Supersaturated solutions are unstable. In making rock candy, if the jar of supersaturated sugar-water is jiggled, the suspended string moves even slightly, or another granule of sugar is dropped in, crystals of solute begin to form. The crystals stick to the rough surface of the string. After five to seven days, all the excess sugar returns to its solid form, and the string is covered with large crystals. The solution left behind now contains only the amount of sugar that can remain dissolved at room temperature. It is once again a *saturated* solution.

Scuba diving

You now know that gases dissolve in liquids and that pressure is an important factor in determining how much gas will dissolve in a liquid. In scuba diving, a deep descent underwater poses some problems that have to do with the solubility of gases in blood.

Atmospheric pressure is measured in units called *atmospheres*. The abbreviation of this unit is "atm." At the Earth's surface, atmospheric pressure is 1 atm. The pressure increases by 1 atm every 10 meters (about 33 feet) as a diver descends through sea water. In other words, at a depth of 10 meters, the pressure acting on the diver has doubled to 2 atmospheres, or twice what we are used to on the Earth's surface. At 30 meters (99 feet), the pressure has quadrupled to 4 atm. Because one atm is equal to 14.5 pounds per square inch (psi), at 40 meters, you would be under 72.5 psi. That's equal to about twice as much air pressure as a car tire!

A diver is under increased pressure during a dive and the concentrations of gases in the blood and tissues of the diver are higher. The diver's body can easily process the extra oxygen and carbon dioxide. However, nitrogen is an unreactive gas that stays in the tissues when a diver is in deep water. High concentrations of nitrogen in the body cause a condition called *nitrogen narcosis*. This causes divers to be either extremely carefree, or extremely suspicious and fearful. In either case, the diver loses his or her ability to function safely underwater. Diving partners (called "dive buddies") keep up constant communication to check that they are not confused because of nitrogen narcosis. The best way to treat nitrogen narcosis is to slowly rise to the water surface with a dive buddy. A slow ascent with normal breathing allows gases to come back out of the blood and tissues easily. Scuba divers should never hold their breath underwater. As a diver rises to the surface, expanding gases can rupture lung tissue!

Decompression sickness occurs when body tissues get supersaturated with nitrogen. Bubbles of nitrogen form in the bloodstream and tissues. These bubbles can block important arteries and cause a stroke or heart attack. When they are trapped in the diver's joints, back, or abdomen, the bubbles are painful. To release pressure in the back or stomach due to bubble formation, individuals with decompression sickness bend over, which is why decompression sickness is often called "the bends."

Depth (meters)	Pressure (atm)
0	1
10	2
20	3
30	4
40	5

Figure 23.20: *How pressure changes with water depth.*

How did scuba get started?

SCUBA stands for self-contained underwater breathing apparatus. A number of inventors have contributed to the development of scuba diving technology. The invention of the aqualung by Jaques-Yves Cousteau and Emile Gagnan in 1943 made scuba diving available to anyone who wanted to do underwater exploring. This device made breathing air underwater easy, safe, and reliable.

23.4 Acids, Bases, and pH

Acids and bases are among the most familiar of all chemical compounds. Some of the acids you may have encountered include acetic acid (found in vinegar), citric acid (found in orange juice), and malic acid (found in apples). You may be familiar with some bases including ammonia in cleaning solutions and magnesium hydroxide found in some antacids. The pH scale is used to describe whether a substance is an acid or a base. In this section, you will learn about the properties of acids and bases, and how the pH scale works.

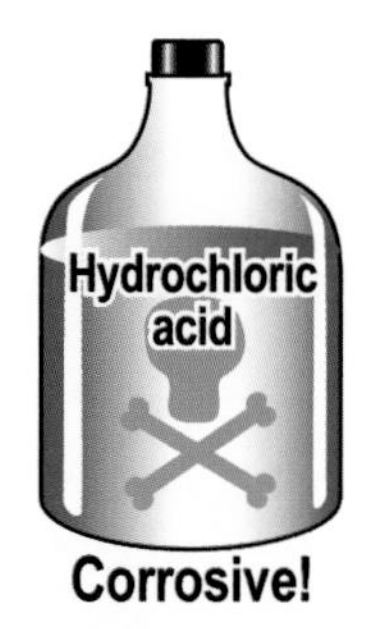

Figure 23.16: *You should NEVER taste a laboratory chemical!*

What are acids?

Properties of acids

An **acid** is any substance that produces *hydronium ions* (H_3O^+) when dissolved in water. The properties of acids include: they have a sour taste such as lemons (you should NEVER taste a laboratory chemical!); they react with metals to produce hydrogen gas (H_2); and they change the color of a plant dye (called *litmus*) from blue to red.

What are hydronium ions?

When an acid is dissolved in water, it separates, or *ionizes*, into *hydrogen ions* (H^+) and a negative ion. Hydrogen ions do not exist by themselves for very long. Each hydrogen ion is attracted to the oxygen end of a water molecule. The two combine to form hydronium ions (Figure 23.17).

HCl is an acid

When hydrochloric acid (HCl) dissolves in water, it separates into H^+ and Cl^- ions (Figure 23.17). The H^+ ions are transferred to water molecules to form hydronium ions. The Cl^- ions are left over. HCl is therefore an acid because it *transfers* H^+ ions to water molecules causing the production of hydronium ions.

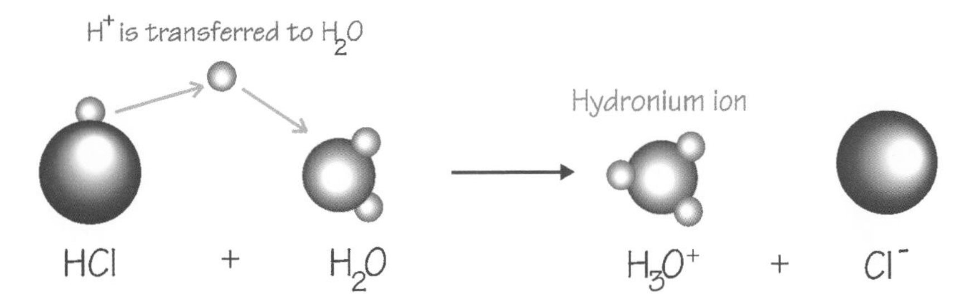

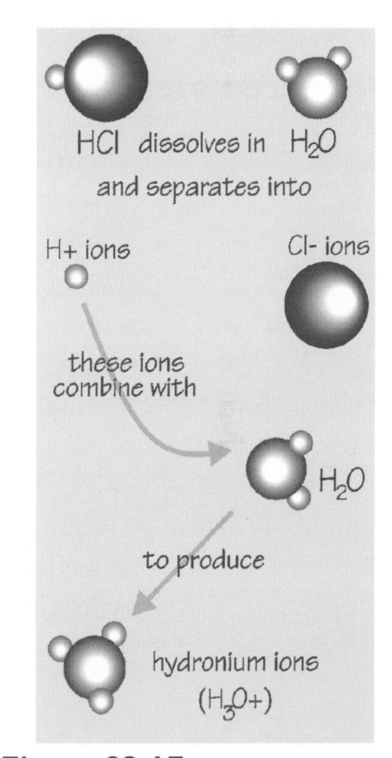

Figure 23.17: *Hydrogen ions do not exist in water for very long. They quickly become attached to water molecules to form hydronium ions.*

Strong and weak acids

HCl is a strong acid

Acids can be classified according to the degree to which they produce hydronium ions when dissolved in water. Hydrochloric acid (HCl) is a *strong acid* because no HCl molecules are present in a solution of HCl and water. This means that every molecule of HCl separates into positive (H^+) and negative (Cl^-) ions. Since all of the HCl molecules ionize, every H^+ ion becomes attached to a water molecule and all of them become hydronium ions.

Acetic acid is a weak acid

Acetic acid ($HC_2H_3O_2$), found in vinegar, is an example of a *weak acid.* This is because in a solution of acetic acid and water, most of the acetic acid molecules remain as molecules and only a small number of them ionize. This means that only a small number of hydronium ions are produced (Figure 23.18).

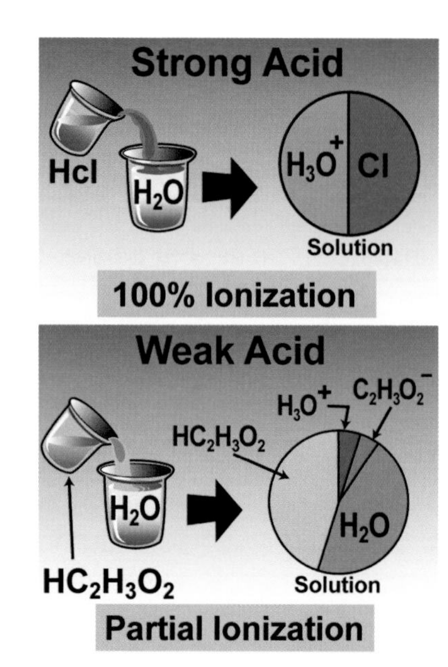

Figure 23.18: *Strong acids produce the maximum number of hydronium ions. Weak acids do not fully ionize and produce relatively smaller numbers of hydronium ions.*

What are bases?

Properties of bases

A **base** is any substance that produces *hydroxide ions* (OH^-) when dissolved in water. While you should never touch a laboratory chemical, the bases you use everyday, such as soap, have a slippery feel. Bases also have a bitter taste and they change the color of litmus from red to blue. Figure 23.19 compares bases and acids. A good example of a base is sodium hydroxide (NaOH), found in many commercial drain cleaners. This compound ionizes in water to form sodium (Na^+) and hydroxide ions:

$$NaOH \longrightarrow Na^+_{(aq)} + OH^-_{(aq)}$$

Acids	Bases
Produce H_3O^+ in water	Produce OH^- in water
Sour taste	Bitter taste
Turn blue litmus to red	Turn red litmus to blue
React with metals to produce H_2 gas	Have s slippery feel

Figure 23.19: *A quick comparison of acids and bases.*

Ammonia is also a base

Ammonia (NH_3), found in cleaning solutions, is a base because it *reacts* with water to form hydroxide ions. How is this different than NaOH? Notice that a hydroxide ion is formed when ammonia *accepts* H^+ ions from water molecules in solution as shown below.

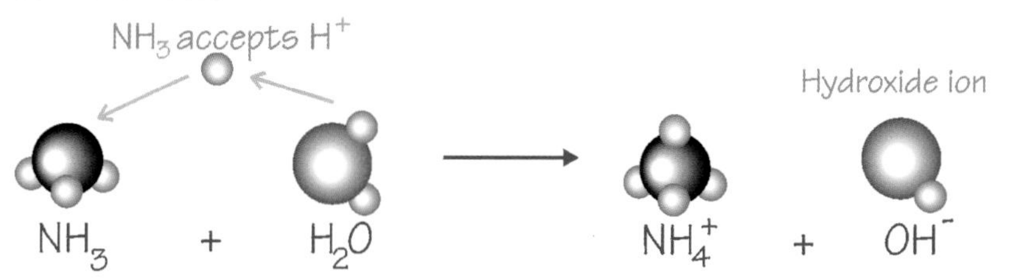

Strong and weak bases

Strong and weak bases The strength of bases depends on the relative amount of hydroxide ions (OH^-) produced when the base is mixed with water. Sodium hydroxide ($NaOH$) is considered a strong base because it ionizes completely in water to form Na^+ and OH^- ions. Ammonia (NH_3) on the other hand, is a weak base because most of its molecules do not react with water to form NH_4^+ and OH^- ions.

Weak does not mean unimportant! Just because an acid or a base is classified as weak does not mean that it is not important. Most of the acid-base chemistry that occurs inside of your body occurs through reactions involving weak acids and bases. For example, the coiling of a DNA molecule into a "double-helix" is due to hydrogen bonding between weak bases (Figure 23.20).

Hydrogen bonds

Figure 23.20: *The coiling of a DNA molecule into a double helix is due to the interactions between weak bases.*

The dissociation of water and mixing acids and bases

The dissociation of water One of the most important properties of water is its ability to act as both an acid and as a base. In the presence of an acid, water acts as a base. In the presence of a base, water acts as an acid. In pure water, the molecule ionizes to produce both hydronium and hydroxide ions. This reaction is called the *dissociation of water.*

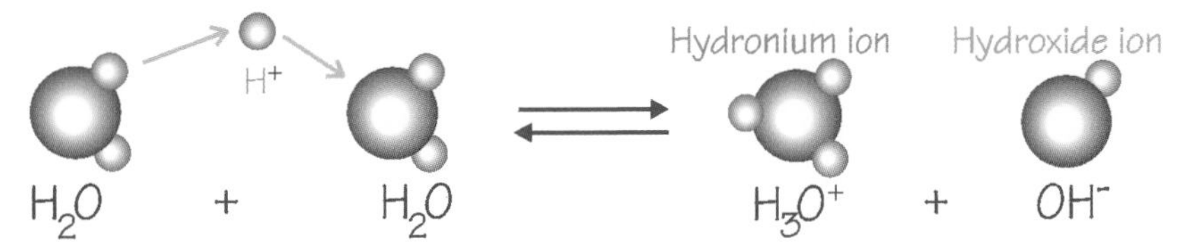

What does the double arrow mean? The double arrow in the equation means that the dissociation of water can occur in *both* directions. This means that water molecules can ionize and ions can also form water molecules. However, water ionizes so slightly that most water molecules exist whole, not as ions.

Mixing acid and base solutions When acid and base solutions are mixed in the right proportions, their characteristic properties disappear, and new ionic substances known as *salts* are formed. Water is also a product of this type of reaction, called a neutralization reaction. Figure 23.21 shows what happens when you mix hydrochloric acid solution with sodium hydroxide solution.

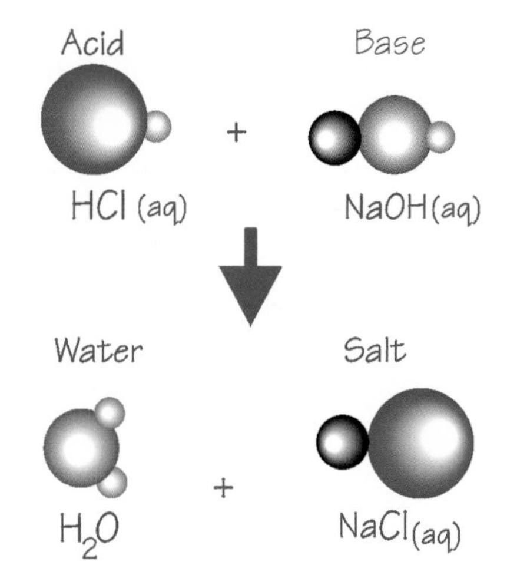

Figure 23.21: *When an acid in solution is mixed with a base in solution, the products are water and a salt. The "aq" symbol indicates that these compounds are dissolved in water and really exist as ions.*

pH and the pH scale

What is pH? Just as centimeters describe length, pH describes the exact concentration of hydronium ions in a solution. Most instruments that measure pH use a pH scale that runs from 0 to 14. At pH 1, a solution is strongly acidic and has a high concentration of hydronium ions. At pH 14, a solution is strongly basic, or *alkaline* and has a low concentration of hydronium ions.

Why do we need a pH scale? Why do we need a scale to describe the hydronium concentration of different solutions? First, the range of possible hydronium ion concentrations in a solutions is huge (from 1 M to 10^{-14} M). Second, the numbers used to measure hydronium ion concentration are very small. Is it easy to write 10^{-14} as a decimal? The pH scale allows you to represent hydronium ion concentrations using whole numbers. It was developed by S.P.L. Sørenson, a Danish biochemist, in 1909 while working on brewing beer. *pH* is an abbreviation of "the power of hydrogen." A scale of 0 to 14 is much easier to work with than a scale from 1 to 10^{-14}.

Determining pH Think about the pH numbers 0 to 14 and the range of hydronium ion concentrations 1 to 10^{-14}. You will notice that the pH value is equal to the *negative* of the exponent of the hydronium ion concentration. (In a more advanced course, you will learn that pH is equal to the negative *logarithm* of the hydronium ion concentration.) For example, a solution with a hydronium ion concentration of 10^{-9} M has a pH value of 9. Likewise, a solution with a hydronium ion concentration of 10^{-1} has a pH of 1. Since the pH value of a solution is equal to the negative of the exponent of the hydronium ion concentration, it makes sense to say that the higher the hydronium ion concentration, the lower the pH value. The lower the hydronium ion concentration, the higher the pH value (Figure 23.22).

Example: Calculating pH A solution contains a hydronium ion concentration of $10^{-4.5}$ M. What is the pH value of the solution?

pH is the negative value of the exponent of the hydronium ion concentration:

The hydronium ion concentration is $10^{-4.5}$ M. The exponent is -4.5.

pH = -(-4.5)

pH = 4.5

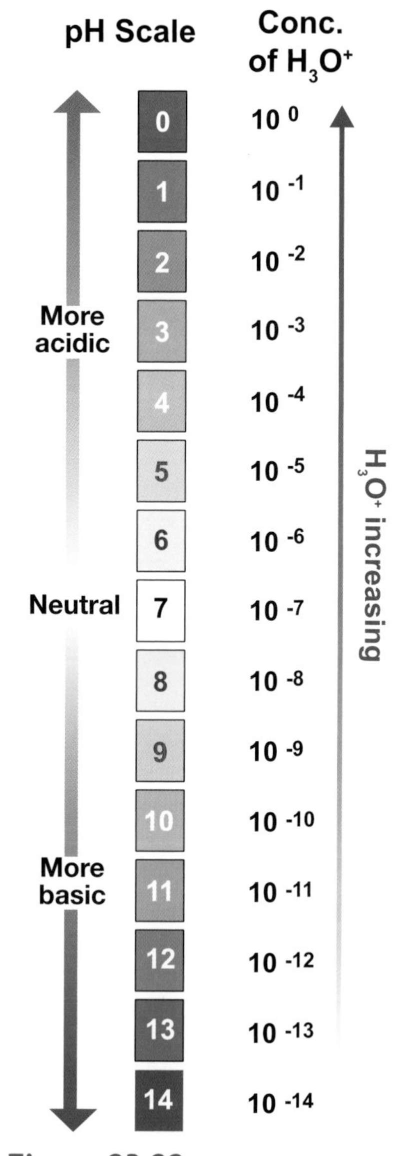

Figure 23.22: *The pH scale is based on the concentration of hydrogen ions in solution.*

The pH of common substances

Many foods are acidic and many cleaning products are basic

Table 23.3 contains a list of some common substances and their pH values. What do you notice about this list of substances? Where would you find acids in your kitchen? Where would you find bases?

Table 23.3: *The pH of some common chemicals.*

Household chemical	Acid or base	pH
lemon juice	acid	2
vinegar	acid	3
soda water	acid	4
baking soda	base	8.5
bar soap	base	10
ammonia	base	11

It turns out that many of the foods we consume or use for cooking are acidic. On the other hand, many of our household cleaning products are basic.

A pH indicator

In the investigation, you will be testing the pH of common chemicals using another item that you may find in your kitchen. You will measure pH using a pH indicator—a chemical that changes color at different pH values.

Some pH indicators are made from common foods. In the investigation, your indicator is made from the juice of a red cabbage.

Acids, bases, and taste

Our taste buds are sensitive to acids and bases. We taste acids as sour and bases as bitter. Lemon juice is strongly acidic, and soap is strongly basic. Acids that are stronger than lemon juice and bases that are stronger than ammonia are so reactive that they can harm your skin and damage clothing.

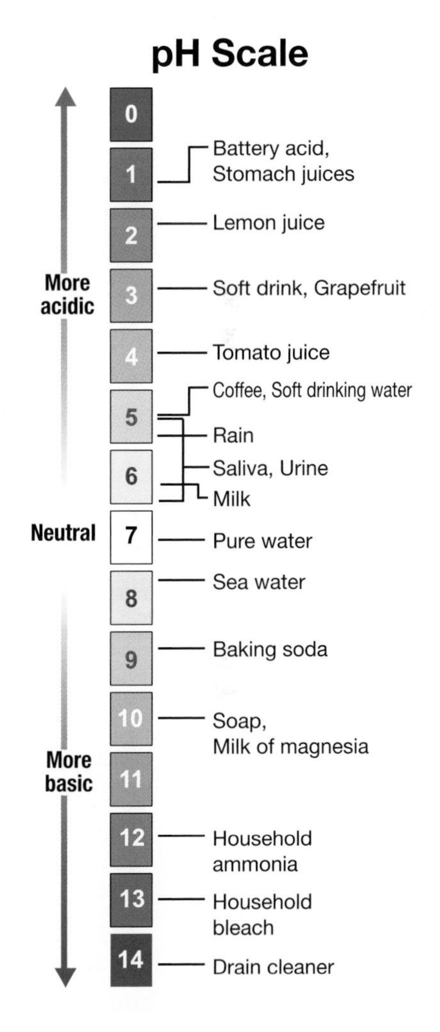

Figure 23.23: *The pH scale showing common substances.*

Acids and bases in your body

Acids and bases play a role in digestion

Many reactions, such as the ones that occur in your body, work best at specific pH values. For example, acids and bases are very important in the reactions involved in digesting food. As you may know, the stomach secretes hydrochloric acid (HCl), a strong acid (pH 1.4). The level of acidity in our stomachs is necessary to break down the protein molecules in our food so that they can be absorbed. A mucus lining in the stomach protects it from the acid produced. As food and digestive fluids leave the stomach, however, other organs in the digestive system also need to be protected from the acid. This is accomplished by two parts of the system—the pancreas and liver. These two organs secrete bicarbonate to neutralize the stomach acid before it reaches other organs.

pH and your blood

It is very important for your blood pH to stay within the normal range. At higher or lower pH values, your body does not function properly. Fortunately, you can regulate the pH of your blood simply by breathing!

Blood contains dissolved gases

Blood is a watery solution that contains many solutes including the dissolved gases carbon dioxide and oxygen. Carbon dioxide appears in your blood because it is produced by respiration. Recall that *respiration* is the combustion of sugar by your body. You breathe in oxygen to get this process going. The end products of this reaction are energy, water, and carbon dioxide.

Breathing rate controls carbon dioxide levels

The rate at which you breathe controls the concentration of carbon dioxide in your blood. For example, if you hold your breath, more carbon dioxide enters your blood. If you hyperventilate, you blow off carbon dioxide, so that significantly less is in your blood. These two processes influence blood pH. The chemical equations for the reactions are shown in Figure 23.24.

CO_2 increases the acidity of your blood

When CO_2 dissolves, H_3O^+ ions are produced in solution. Therefore, the more CO_2 in your blood, the more acidic your blood will become. If you breathe slowly, the added CO_2 makes your blood more acidic. However, if you breathe too often and too quickly (hyperventilating), the loss of CO_2 makes your blood more basic. You can offset this effect by breathing into a paper bag. This forces you to re-breathe carbon dioxide. When you breathe normally, your blood pH ranges between 7.35 and 7.45 (Figure 23.25).

Reaction 1

Carbonic acid

$$CO_2 + H_2O \rightleftharpoons H_2CO_3$$

Reaction 2

Hydronium ion

$$H_2CO_3 + H_2O \rightleftharpoons H_3O^+ + HCO_3^-$$

Figure 23.24: *An increase in carbon dioxide causes an increase in hydronium ions in the blood.*

Figure 23.25: *Some causes of low blood pH include holding your breath and producing excess lactic acid during heavy exercise. High blood pH can be caused by hyperventilating. Under normal conditions, your blood pH ranges between 7.35 and 7.45.*

Electrolytes and nonelectrolytes

Electrolytes conduct current

Current is the flow of electrical charge. When a solution contains dissolved ions (charged particles), it can conduct current. Chemicals that conduct current when dissolved in water are called electrolytes. These chemicals form ions when dissolved.

Salt dissociates in water

Ionic compounds, molecular compounds, and even atoms can contribute ions to a solution. When an ionic compound is dissolved in water, the polar ends of the water molecule attract the positive and negative ions in the solution. In previous sections, you learned how water dissolves table salt (NaCl). Recall that the attraction of the polar ends of the water molecule is strong enough to break the weak ionic bonds of NaCl. When an ionic compound is brought into solution by water it is said to *dissociate*. The term *ionization* is used if a molecular compound or atom forms an ion.

For example, when NaCl dissolves in water we say it *dissociates*. When the element Na loses an electron, it *ionizes* to Na^+.

Acids and bases are electrolytes

All acids and bases are electrolytes because they contribute ions to a solution. Some chemicals, like salt (NaCl), dissociate to form ions in solution but are not acidic or basic. Acids, bases, and salt water are examples of electrolytes.

Non-electrolytes do not have ions and are not acidic or basic

Other chemicals do not form ions when they are dissolved in solution. They are called *non-electrolytes*. Non-electrolytes are not acidic or basic. Sugar dissolved in water is an example of a non-electrolyte.

Electrical appliances and water

Because tap water contains small amounts of dissolved ions, it is an electrolyte. Remember that even a small amount of current is dangerous if it enters your body directly? Water provides a way for electric current to enter your body, so always take care when using electrical appliances near water!

Electrolytes and your body

When you perform a strenuous activity, your body cools itself by sweating. Sweat contains water and dissolved salts (or electrolytes) like sodium and potassium. Before, during, and after exercising, you can replenish fluids and your body's electrolytes by drinking diluted fruit juice, slightly salty water, or by consuming a sports drinks. The water in these fluids helps your body continue to cool itself so that you don't get overheated. By replacing electrolytes, you may be helping your body speed up resorption of fluids. Diluted fruit juice or a sports drink contains small amounts of carbohydrates to give your body the energy boost it may need during strenuous exercise.

Chapter 23 Review

Vocabulary review

Match the following terms with the correct definition. There is one extra definition in the list that will not match any of the terms.

Set One

1. polar molecule
2. nonpolar molecule
3. hydrogen bond
4. water molecule
5. lone pairs

a. A bond between the hydrogen atom on one molecule to another atom on another molecule
b. A molecule that has positive and negative ends or poles
c. An example of a polar molecule
d. A molecule that does not have positive and negative ends
e. Electrons that are involved in the formation of chemical bonds in a molecule
f. Electrons that are not involved in the formation of chemical bonds in a molecule

Set Two

1. solution
2. solvent
3. solute
4. colloid
5. suspension

a. The process by which ionic compounds dissolve
b. A mixture that will separate if left to stand for a period of time
c. The substance that is present in the greatest amount in a solution
d. A mixture that cannot be separated by filtering but does scatter light rays
e. A mixture of two or more substances that is homogeneous at the molecular level
f. A substance that is dissolved in a solution

Set Three

1. solubility
2. insoluble
3. equilibrium
4. saturated
5. unsaturated

a. Contains the maximum amount of a solute that will dissolve for a given set of conditions
b. The amount of solute that will dissolve in a given amount of solvent for a given set of conditions
c. An unstable solution containing more solute than will usually dissolve for a given set of conditions
d. Contains less than the maximum amount of solute that will dissolve for a given set of conditions
e. Substances that do not dissolve in water
f. The state of the formation of a solution in which as many molecules are dissolving as are coming back out of solution

Set Four

1. acid
2. base
3. neutralization
4. pH
5. electrolytes

a. Chemicals that form ions when dissolved in water and conduct electrical current
b. A substance that produces hydronium ions in solution
c. A substance that tells you whether or not a solution is acidic or basic
d. This occurs when acids and bases are mixed in the right proportions to produce a salt and water
e. A substance that produces hydroxide ions in solution
f. Describes the exact concentration of hydronium ions in a solution

Concept review

1. Why do hydrogen bonds form in a group of water molecules?
2. Explain why water, a polar molecule, has a higher boiling point than methane, a nonpolar molecule.
3. Give an example of a solution in which the solute is not a solid and the solvent is not a liquid.
4. Name two ways to distinguish between suspensions and colloids.
5. What would happen to the solubility of potassium chloride in water as the water temperature increased from 25°C to 100°C?
6. What happens to the solubility of oxygen in a pond as the pond temperature decreases from 25°C to 10°C?
7. When you open a can of room-temperature soda, why is it more likely to fizz and spill over than a can that has been refrigerated?
8. What happens to a supersaturated solution when more solute is added?
9. Name three ways to increase the dissolving rate of sugar in water.
10. What information goes on the *x*-axis and the *y*-axis of a temperature-solubility graph?
11. A piece of rock candy in a sugar solution is at equilibrium with the solution. What does this mean on a molecular level? In other words, what are the rock candy molecules doing, and what are the sugar molecules in solution doing? You may want to draw a picture to help answer this question.
12. Many foods are acidic. List four examples.
13. Explain the meanings of a strong acid and a weak acid. Give examples of each.
14. What is the difference between an electrolyte and a nonelectrolyte? Give an example of each.

Problems

1. Draw the Lewis dot structure for water. Label lone pairs, bonding pairs, positive pole, and negative pole.
2. One solubility value of sodium chloride is 1 gram/2.8 milliliters of water at 25°C. Use this value to figure out the following: (a) the volume of water needed to dissolve 100 grams of NaCl; (b) the mass of NaCl that would dissolve in 100 mL of water.
3. Use the temperature-solubility graph on page 419 to answer the following questions:
   a. What is the solubility value of $NaNO_3$ at 25°C?
   b. Which salt has the highest solubility value at 75°C?
   c. Temperature affects the solubility of which salt the least?
   d. Temperature affects the solubility of which salt the most?

4. What is the pH of a solution that has a hydronium ion concentration of 10^{-11} M?
5. Suppose you dissolve 6.5 moles of sugar in enough water to make 2.0 liters, what is the molarity (M) of the solution?
6. Suppose you dissolve 25.0 grams of NaCl in 50.0 grams of water. What is the mass percent of NaCl in the solution?
7. CHALLENGE! You have a 0.5L container of a 2.0 M solution of sugar dissolved in water. How many moles of sugar does the container have?
8. CHALLENGE! Suppose you have a solution that is 12.0 percent sugar by mass. The solution was mixed by dissolving a certain amount of sugar in 350.0 grams of water. How many grams of sugar were mixed with the water?

Applying your knowledge

1. Explain why ice forms on the *top* of ponds and lakes, not on the bottom. Use the following terms in your explanation: water molecules, organized structure, hydrogen bonds, and density. How does this property of water help support life in lakes and ponds?
2. When you shake a bottle of oil-and-vinegar salad dressing, the two liquids stay mixed only for a short period of time. Some food manufacturers add a substance called an emulsifying agent to help keep the oil and vinegar mixed. Emulsifying agents help keep polar and nonpolar substances (like vinegar and oil) mixed in a product. Make a list of all of the food products you can find that contain emulsifying agents. For each food, identify the name of the emulsifying agent.
3. Solutions that contain two or more metals are called *alloys*. Conduct some research on the uses of alloys. Identify 10 alloys and the metals they contain. Make a table that lists each alloy, its constituent metals, and its uses.
4. Create an interesting handout for fourth graders that explains how to make rock candy. The handout should include safety instructions, including supervision, and definitions of these words: *dissolve*, *unsaturated*, *saturated*, and *supersaturated*.
5. One remedy for an upset stomach is to take an antacid. Find out the definition of this word. Explain why an antacid might make someone's stomach feel better.
6. Blood pH values that are too high or too low indicate a health problem. Acidosis occurs when your blood pH is less than 7.4. Alkalosis occurs when your blood pH is more than 7.4. Sometimes the way your body works affects your blood pH. For instance, individuals with diabetes mellitus do not produce enough insulin to help them metabolize nutrients. This is why diabetics need to administer insulin to themselves on a regular basis. They can gauge whether they have enough insulin by testing their blood pH. If their blood is too acidic, they are producing ketone acids—a condition that occurs when their blood doesn't have enough insulin. Use the Internet or your local library to research body metabolism and ketone production as it relates to diabetes and blood pH.

UNIT 8

Water and the Environment

Chapter 24

Earth's Water Systems

Water on Earth is continuously cycled through different systems including rivers, lakes, groundwater, and the oceans. In this chapter, you will learn how water is transported through these different systems and about human impact on water systems.

24.1	The Water Cycle	*What is the quality of your local surface water?*

Your task is to meet with a local water quality official and learn how water is tested. You will monitor data for levels of coliform bacteria, pH, dissolved oxygen, biological oxygen demand, nitrate, phosphate, and turbidity. Since this data is extremely important to public health, you will summarize your findings in a report.

24.2	Water Quality	*What is the quality of your tap water?*

How pure is the water you drink? In this Investigation, you will collect hot and cold water samples at home. You will then test the pH, hardness, and levels of chlorine, copper, and iron in your water samples.

24.3	Acid Rain	*What is acid rain?*

In this Investigation, you will model the effects of acid rain on a natural ecosystem. You will observe the effect of different dilutions of an acid on the activity of water fleas (*Daphnia magna*). Water fleas are an important source of food for fish and other organisms in fresh water environments.

24.4	Oceans	*How does carbon dioxide affect the oceans?*

In this Investigation, you will simulate a chemical reaction that occurs when carbon dioxide from the atmosphere dissolves into seawater.

Learning Goals

In this chapter, you will:

- ✔ Describe the set of process through which water is continuously recycled on Earth.
- ✔ Describe how water quality is analyzed.
- ✔ Understand the cause of acid rain.
- ✔ Understand the environmental effects of acid rain.
- ✔ Demonstrate the effect of acid on a natural ecosystem.
- ✔ Explain how the oceans were formed.
- ✔ Describe the composition of seawater.
- ✔ Explain how the oceans remove carbon dioxide from the atmosphere.
- ✔ Discuss how toxic pollutants travel through marine food chains.

Vocabulary

acid rain
aquifer
carnivore
condensation
evaporation
food chain
groundwater
herbivore
hydrosphere
precipitation
producer
reservoir
salinity
surface runoff
surface water
transpiration
water cycle
watershed

24.1 The Water Cycle

The amount of water on Earth is about the same as it was during the age of the dinosaurs, 65 to 220 million years ago. With about 70 percent of its surface covered with water, Earth is truly a water planet. However, only a small amount of this water available for household use. If this is true and Earth has been around for such a long time, why haven't we run out of water?

Having water depends on the *water cycle*—an important set of processes driven by the sun that ensure that water moves from place to place. In this section, you will learn how water moves naturally around Earth so that it is available to use and appreciate.

Where is water on Earth?

The distribution of water

Of the total amount of water on Earth, less than 1 percent is available for our consumption because all the rest is either in the salty oceans—97 percent, or frozen at the planet's two poles—about 2 percent (Figure 24.2).

What is the source of water for your community?

An important role for governments is to manage water resources. Some of the water that is available for people comes from **reservoirs** (protected artificial or natural lakes), dammed rivers, and **groundwater** (water that collects underground). Moisture in the atmosphere replenishes our water supplies when it becomes rain and falls back to Earth.

The table below lists how water is distributed on Earth. Do these distribution percentages surprise you? Why or why not?

Table 24.1: ***The distribution of water on Earth***

Body of water	Description
oceans	97.1%
polar ice	2.24%
groundwater	0.61%
lakes	0.016%
moisture in the atmosphere	0.001%
rivers	0.0001%

Figure 24.1: *The amount of water on Earth is about the same as it was when dinosaurs lived on Earth 65-220 million years ago.*

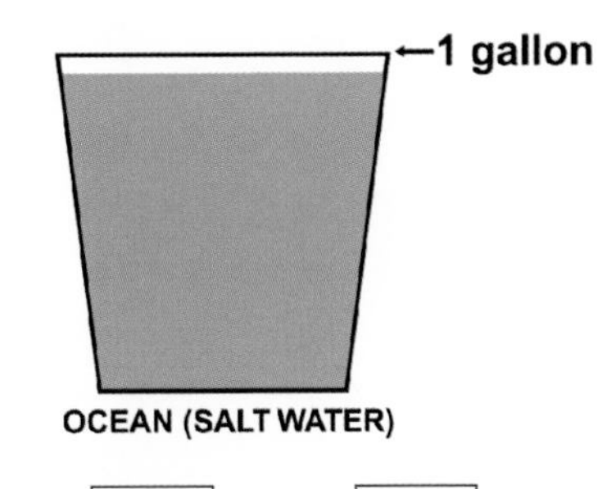

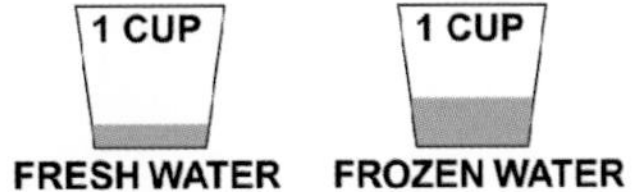

Figure 24.2: *If all the water on the Earth could fit into a one-gallon container, the amount of fresh water available for human consumption would be equal to about one-sixth of a cup!*

The water cycle

The water cycle continuously recycles and filters our water

For millions of years only a small percentage of water has been available to meet the basic needs of people, animals, and plants. Remember that our water supply today is the same as when the dinosaurs were around. Therefore, the water you drink was used by another person or organism millions of years ago. What keeps our water continuously recycled and naturally filtered is a set of processes called the **water cycle**. The sun is the source of energy that drives the water cycle. Wind, weather, and gravity are additional natural forces that keep water moving from place to place. Of course, people also play a role in transporting water on Earth.

The water cycle includes four processes

The four main processes of the water cycle are **evaporation**, **transpiration**, **condensation**, and **precipitation**. *Evaporation* and *transpiration* occur when the water molecules have enough kinetic energy to leave the liquid phase and become a gas. The source of this kinetic energy is heat from the sun. The *condensation* of water occurs when water in its gaseous state loses energy. Water vapor molecules slow down so much that they group and form droplets of liquid. When these droplets are heavy enough, they fall to Earth as *precipitation*.

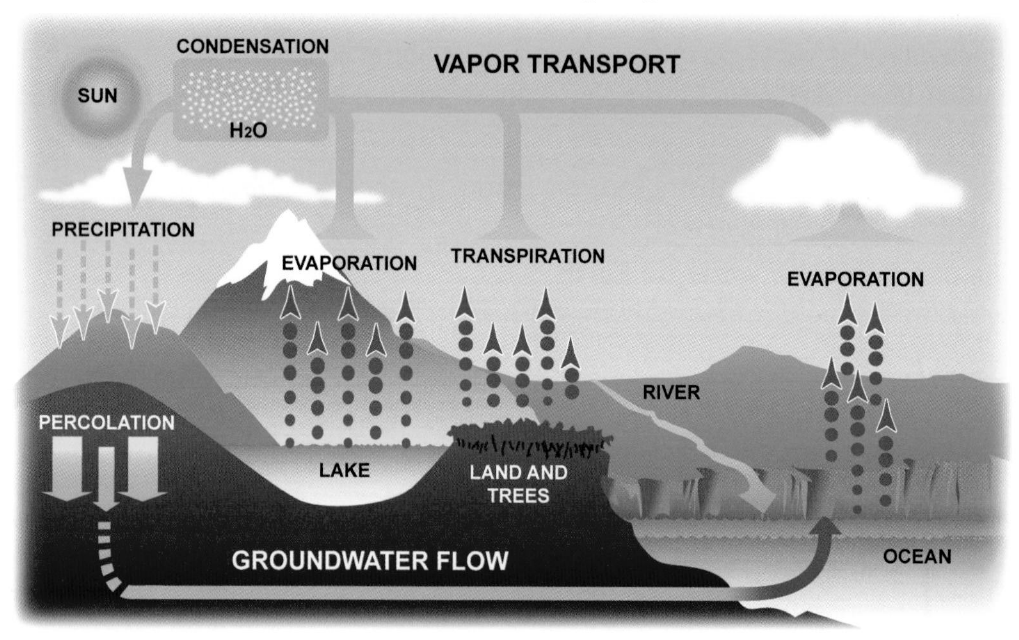

Water's journey

Water on Earth is transported from place to place through a series of processes called the water cycle. The picture below illustrates the water cycle. Trace the path of water from the ocean to groundwater and back to the ocean. Explain how the sun, wind, and gravity help move this water along on its journey. How might people get in the way of the water following a direct path through the water cycle?

How the water cycle works

Water vapor in the atmosphere comes from evaporation and transpiration

Energy from the sun causes liquid water at Earth's surface to *evaporate* and become water vapor. Water is continuously entering the atmosphere from **surface water**. Surface water includes the oceans, lakes, ponds, rivers, streams, and reservoirs. Plants also contribute water to the atmosphere. You may recall that plants need carbon dioxide (CO_2) to make sugar. Whenever plants open tiny pores on their leaves to get CO_2, they also lose some water through a process called t*ranspiration*. The water vapor in the atmosphere eventually falls back to Earth's surface as precipitation in the form of rain, hail, sleet, or snow.

Precipitation becomes surface water or ground water

Surface water is replenished when precipitation reaches Earth's surface. This water flows over land until it flows into lakes, rivers, and the oceans. The water that flows over land before reaching surface water is called **surface runoff**. As this water flows over the ground, it dissolves and collects minerals and nutrient-rich soil (thereby causing some soil erosion). Many of the nutrients in freshwater and saltwater come from surface runoff. Precipitation may also be re-evaporated or it may percolate through the soil to become groundwater.

Aquifers contain groundwater

Because soil is porous, groundwater is naturally filtered. Groundwater also contains dissolved carbon dioxide and is acidic enough to dissolve minerals. The destination of groundwater is an underground area of sediment and rocks called an **aquifer**. When groundwater is removed from an aquifer for human consumption, it takes 300 to 1,000 years to replenish the supply. Groundwater that is not collected for use will continue to flow through sediments and eventually enter the ocean, thus continuing the water cycle.

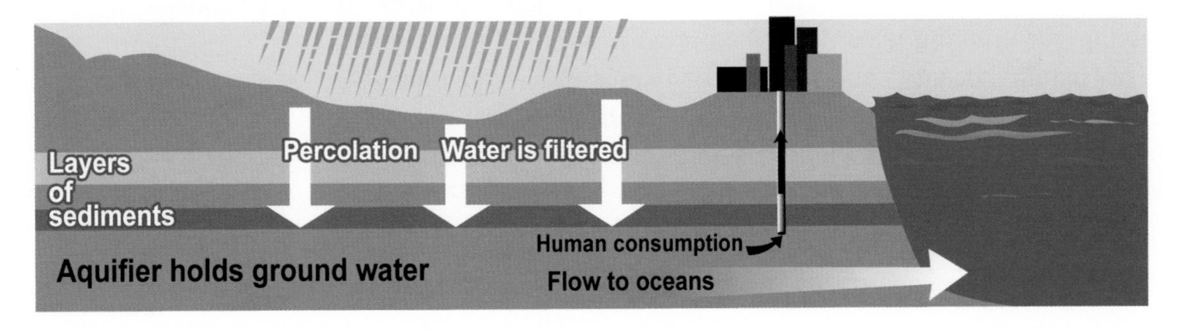

Aquifers

Aquifers are very important sources of water for communities. For example, the Florida Aquifer is very extensive with a boundary in South Carolina. Fresh water springs above ground are fed by aquifers. One-third of the major springs in the United Sates are found in Florida.

The largest aquifer in the world is the Ogallala Aquifer in the mid-western part of the United States (Kansas, Texas, Oklahoma and Nebraska) The water obtained from this aquifer has made agriculture very profitable in this otherwise dry region. However, it is expected that by 2020, a quarter of this aquifer's water supply will be depleted unless there is an effort to conserve water. It will take 1,000 years to replenish the water in this aquifer.

Watersheds

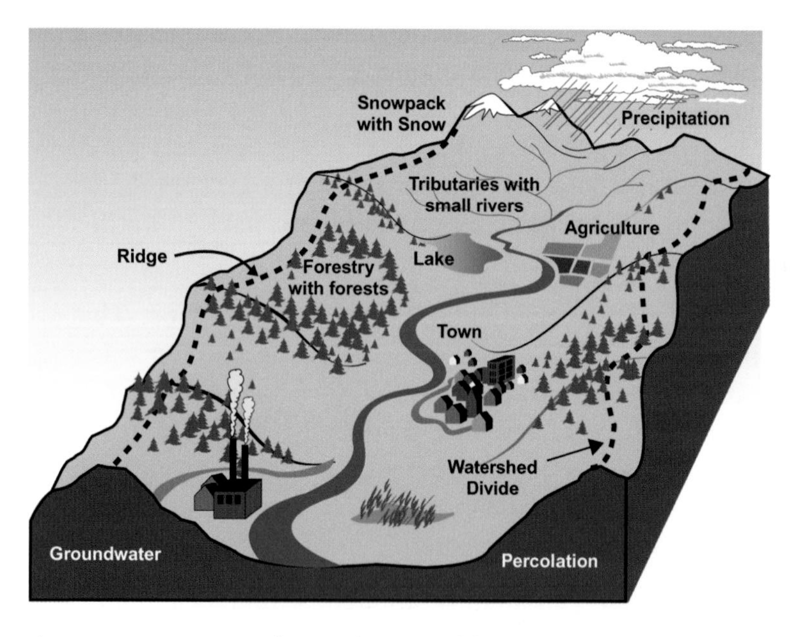

What is a watershed? The water that comes to your home is most likely from a shared source called a **watershed**. Neighboring towns often get their water from the same watershed. A watershed is an area of land that catches all rain and snow and collects it one place like a river. The boundaries of a watershed are often steep hillsides and mountain ridges. From the graphic, can you see why?

Watersheds are important natural resources Watersheds provide important resources that support and enrich our lives. In addition to supplying our drinking water, they also provide habitat for plants and animals, areas of natural beauty, and bodies of water for recreation. As communities grow and change, it is important to protect these natural resources. What is the watershed that your town uses? Is there a local organization that monitors the water quality of your watershed?

Finding out about your local watershed

The Environmental Protection Agency (EPA) website has a feature that allows you to find out about your local watershed. If you enter your zip code, you can find out the name of your watershed, and a list of links that will provide you with more information. The website address is:

www.epa.gov/surf

Find the following information about your local watershed:

- What are the major bodies of water in your watershed?
- What other communities depend on this watershed?
- Which organizations monitor the water quality?
- What are some environmental concerns or issues regarding your watershed?

24.2 Water Quality

All water on Earth is part of the water cycle. Therefore, the quality of our water—whether from a faucet or in a pond—is important. In this section, you will learn how the quality of our available water is tested and maintained.

Water quality at home

Standards are used to judge water quality

Because water is important to our health and way of living, state and federal governments have set strict standards for water quality. Water that meets these standards is safe for drinking, cooking, and other household activities.

What occurs naturally in tap water?

Calcium, magnesium, and carbon dioxide occur naturally in water that's available for human consumption. If your water has a lot of dissolved calcium and magnesium, it is called *hard water*. It is difficult to get things clean in hard water because calcium and magnesium ions interfere with how soap works. *Soft water* has very few dissolved ions. Soap works very well in this kind of water.

What else is in your tap water?

Tap water may also contain iron, zinc, and copper depending on where you live. Iron (rust), lead, and copper can dissolve into your water supply from plumbing. Additionally, the water that we drink from a faucet may be treated with sodium fluoride to prevent tooth decay and with chlorine to kill bacteria. The picture below illustrates the source of ions that are in your tap water. The variety and amount of ions in your tap water give it a certain taste.

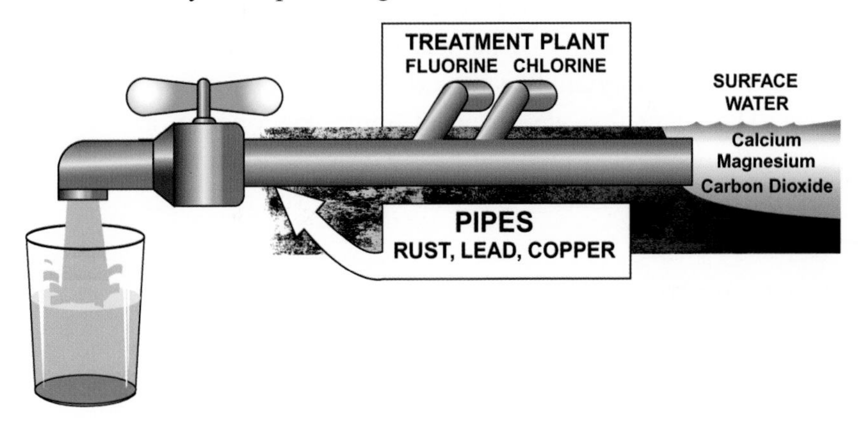

The Clean Water Act

In the past, our rivers, lakes, and oceans were used as dumping grounds for consumer and industry waste. Citizen interest in preventing further pollution of our water supply caused the United States government to pass the Federal Water Pollution Control Act Amendments of 1972.

The Clean Water Act of 1977 is the amended version of the 1972 laws. This act, which is still in use today, entitles the Environmental Protection Agency (EPA) to regulate what can be added to our water. Only within certain guidelines and with a permit can pollutants be discharged into waterways.

Table 24.2: *What is in your tap water?*

Possible component	Source	Description
acid (high H_3O^+)	Dissolved carbon dioxide from soils	Corrodes pipes; leaches lead and copper into water supply; causes deposits in pipes
base (high OH-)	Calcium and magnesium salts occurring naturally in the water supply	Components of hard water; essential minerals for human health
chlorine (Cl_2)	An additive in water treatment	Changes taste; smells; kills bacteria
fluorine (F-)	Added as sodium fluoride in water treatment	Prevents tooth decay by making teeth stronger
iron (Fe^{2+} and Fe^{3+})	Dissolved from pipes	Causes orange stains in sinks and tubs
copper (Cu^+ and Cu^{2+})	Dissolved from copper pipes	Changes taste in high concentrations; causes blue stains in sinks and tubs; trace amounts are essential to human health
lead (Pb^{2+})	Dissolved from pipes or the solder for pipes	Toxic even in very low concentrations

Analyzing water quality

Analyzing water quality is important

It is important to know the quality of your tap water because you rely on this water for drinking, cooking, and washing. The quality of natural bodies of water like rivers, streams, lakes, and ponds is also important because all the water on Earth is connected via the water cycle. The water that we obtain at home was once in a river, lake, or pond. Before that, the water was rain that resulted from moisture in the atmosphere that was evaporated from surface water (the oceans, rivers, lakes, or ponds).

You can perform water quality tests

Water quality is evaluated using a series of tests. In the Investigation for this section, you will have the opportunity to use these tests to study a pond, lake, or river near your school. These tests and the procedures for using them are explained in the next section.

Figure 24.3: *Many tests for water quality are performed by adding an indicator to a water sample. The color change that results is related to how much of a substance is in the water.*

Make observations and ask a question If you were going to analyze the water quality of a pond, river, or lake, you would first make careful observations. A way to guide observations is to ask simple questions. If you were studying a pond, you might ask, "What does the pond water look like or smell like? What animals and plants are living in the pond? Where is the pond located? Are there houses or farms nearby? Is the pond near any industry?"

Recording information It is always useful to record the time of year, date, and time that you are making your observations and testing. Describing the weather for the day and for previous days will help identify reasons why the water quality may be high or low. For example, water quality may be affected when storms or heavy rains cause soil or pollutants to be washed into the pond or lake.

Water quality testing Common tests that are used to evaluate water quality are described below. Pay attention to the methods for performing each test. For example, think about why would you want to take a sample "three or more inches below the surface of the water" (see paragraph for "Water temperature"). How would the water at the surface of the pond or river be different from water at the bottom? Also, think about why it is important to have standard procedures for water quality testing.

Water temperature Water temperature should be measured three or more inches below the surface of the water. The higher the water temperature, the less dissolved oxygen there may be in the water. Dissolved oxygen is required by all organisms living in the pond.

Dissolved oxygen test Oxygen enters surface water mainly from the air. The solubility of oxygen in water is higher at cooler temperatures. As you might expect, the quality of water in a pond is higher when levels of dissolved oxygen are high. Water samples for dissolved oxygen should be taken away from the edge of the pond and three or more inches below the surface of the water. Dissolved oxygen is measured in parts per million (or ppm) often using a special test called the *Winkler method* (see sidebar). A good level of oxygen is 9 ppm, meaning there are 9 milligrams of oxygen for every one liter of water. What would be the concentration of oxygen in parts per thousand? If you said 0.009 grams of oxygen per liter, you are correct!

Winkler Titration

Winkler titration is a method used to measure the amount of dissolved oxygen in fresh and salt water. The method works by adding a manganous sulfate solution and an alkaline-iodide solution to a water sample. These two solutions cause the formation of an insoluble oxygen-manganese complex. This precipitate is then dissolved with sulfuric acid. The result is that an amount of free iodine is released into the solution that is equal to the amount of dissolved oxygen. The method used to measure the iodine is called titration. The iodine solution is titrated with a known amount of sodium thiosulfate solution. Starch, which has a color reaction with iodine, is used as a color indicator during the titration.

Biological oxygen demand test The biological oxygen demand (BOD) test measures dissolved oxygen in two water samples taken at the same time. Oxygen is measured in the first sample when it is collected. The second sample is shielded from light (to prevent photosynthetic organisms from producing oxygen) and measured at a later time. The amount of oxygen in the first and second samples is compared to find out how much oxygen is being used by bacteria as they decompose organic material. When a pond or lake contains a lot of organic material, the bacteria consume too much oxygen and endanger other organisms, like fish, that also need oxygen.

Turbidity test The turbidity test measures the cloudiness of water. The easiest way to measure turbidity is with a Secchi disk (see Figure 24.4). The disk is lowered into the water until the black and white panels on the disk are no longer visible to a person looking into the water from above the water's surface. The rope holding the disk is marked at meter or half-meter intervals to measure the depth of the Secchi disk when it disappears from view underwater.

Nitrate test Nitrogen is used by all organisms to make protein. Nitrogen is most available to organisms when it is combined with oxygen to form nitrate (NO_3^-). Fertilizers are high in nitrates. If a pond is near a fertilized lawn or farm, the pond may have too much nitrate. Excess nitrate can cause *algal blooms*, large growths of algae in a body of water. Even though algae are plants that produce oxygen, when the plants die, they are decomposed by organisms that *use* oxygen. Algal blooms therefore reduce the amount of dissolved oxygen, harming other organisms in the water.

Phosphate test Phosphate (PO_4^{3-}) is the form in which organisms get phosphorus. Phosphorus is an essential element in DNA. Although all organisms use phosphorus, this element tends to enhance the growth of algae in particular. As with excess nitrogen, excess phosphorus in a body of water can cause algal blooms.

pH test The pH scale ranges from 0 to 14. Pure water is pH 7 (a neutral value). The pH of acids is below 7 and the pH for bases is above 7. Surface water pH ranges from 6.5 to 8.5. Most plants and animals function best when pH is nearly neutral. At the extreme ends of the pH scale, where you find strong acids and strong bases, many life processes will not occur. For example, fish have trouble reproducing when the pH of their watery environment is too acidic.

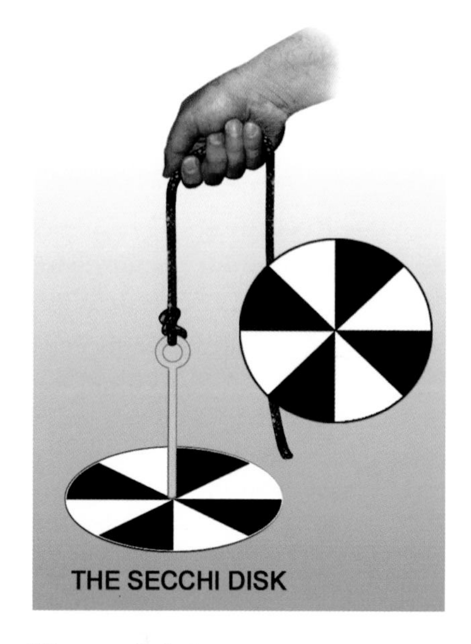

Figure 24.4: *A Secchi disk can be used to measure the turbidity of water. If water is too cloudy, sunlight is blocked. Photosynthetic organisms use sunlight to grow. These organisms are food for larger animals in the pond or lake.*
How to use a Secchi disk: The disk is lowered into the water until it is no longer visible. Then, it is pulled up slightly until it is seen again. The length of the rope between the disk and the surface of the water is related to the clarity of the water. Secchi disks usually have an alternating black and white pattern. Why is it important that a portion of the disk is white?

24.3 Acid Rain

Pollutants from industry and traffic cause acid rain. Due to weather patterns, natural places like forests or lakes can be harmed by acid rain if they are downwind from a city or industrial area. A sign that acid rain has occurred in a forest is that trees are more susceptible to disease. Also, the soil may lack calcium because acid rain dissolves calcium and carries it into the groundwater. Snails and birds need calcium. Loss of calcium for snails means that snail-eating birds do not get enough calcium. These birds lay eggs with thin shells that crack easily (Figure 24.5).

With continued exposure to acid rain, the populations of plants and animals in a forest or lake decline. In this section, you will learn what causes acid rain and how it can be prevented.

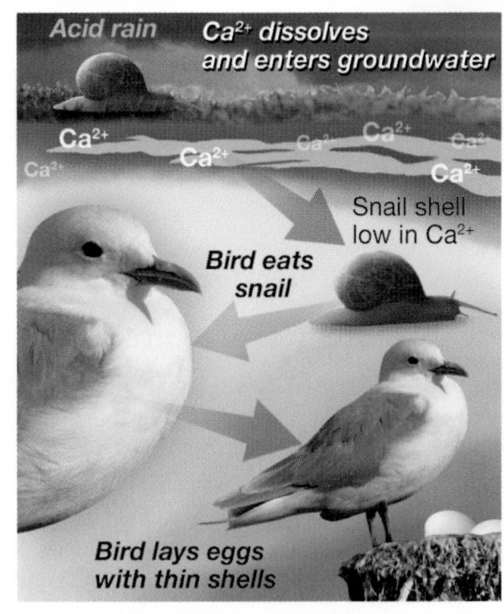

Figure 24.5: *Acid rain reduces the amount of calcium in the soil. A sign that acid rain has occurred is that some birds lay eggs with thin shells.*

What is acid rain?

The pH of acid rain is less than 5.6

All precipitation is naturally acidic because rain, snow, or fog mixes with carbon dioxide in the air and forms small amounts of carbonic acid. Before the Industrial Revolution of the 1700s, the pH of rain was around 5.6. Therefore, the normal pH of rain is 5.6. Any rain, snow, or fog that has a pH *lower* than 5.6 is called **acid rain** or *acid precipitation*.

A review of the pH scale

What does it mean to say that the pH of acid rain is lower than 5.6? pH refers to the concentration of hydronium ions (H_3O^+) in a solution. The lower the pH value, the higher the concentration of hydronium ions present. The pH scale ranges from 0 to 14. Acids range in pH from 0 to 7 and have a high concentration of hydronium ions. Bases range in pH from 7 to 14 and have a low concentration of hydronium ions. Solutions with very high or low pH are irritating and harmful. For example, strong acids are used to etch glass. In some regions that experience acid rain, the average pH of rain is 3. This is the pH of vinegar! Given this information, it is not surprising to learn that acid rain erodes statues and buildings.

Life functions when pH is nearly neutral

Acid rain is harmful to natural environments because most life and life processes function in nearly neutral environments. For example, the ideal conditions for fish are when the water pH ranges from 6 to 8. Fish have trouble reproducing when the pH of their environment is too acidic, and plants do not grow well if soil is acidified below pH 5.1 (Figure 24.6).

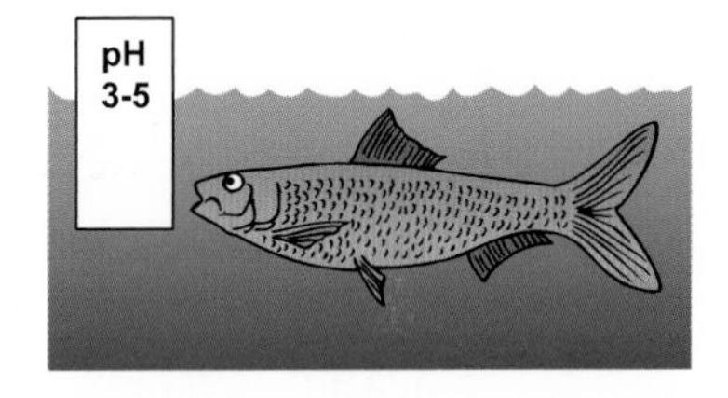

Figure 24.6: *The ideal pH of a pond or other body of water is nearly neutral. Ideally, fish require water within the 6 - 8 pH range.*

What causes acid rain?

Sulfur and nitrogen oxides cause acid rain

The chief indicators of acid rain in the atmosphere are the gases sulfur dioxide (SO_2), sulfur trioxide (SO_3), nitrogen oxide (NO), and nitrogen dioxide (NO_2). A large part of SO_2 in the atmosphere is created by the burning of coal and oil that contain sulfur, and by industrial processes such as metal purification. Nitrogen oxide is a leading by-product of fuel combustion from traffic and power plants.

Formation of sulfur and nitrogen oxides

Sulfur trioxide and nitrogen dioxide are created from the reactions of sulfur dioxide and nitrogen oxide, respectively, with oxygen-containing compounds in the atmosphere. Both of these reactions speed up due to chemicals in air-borne particles that come from traffic and industrial processes.

Formation of sulfuric and nitric acid

Sulfur dioxide in the air mixes with water, ozone, or hydrogen peroxide to form sulfuric acid (H_2SO_4). This strong acid is the number one cause of acid rain. Nitrogen oxides react with components in the atmosphere to form nitric acid (HNO_3), the second greatest cause of acid rain. Simplified equations for each reaction are shown below:

$$SO_2 \text{ (pollutant)} + H_2O_2 \text{ (hydrogen peroxide in air)} \rightarrow H_2SO_4 \text{ (acid)}$$

$$4NO_2 \text{ (pollutant)} + 2H_2O \text{ (water)} + O_2 \text{ (oxygen gas)} \rightarrow 4HNO_3 \text{ (acid)}$$

Sulfur and nitrogen gases cause health problems

Even before acid rain is formed, the four gases that cause acid rain (SO_2, SO_3, NO, and NO_2) create health problems in cities. These gases irritate the respiratory system. In particular, sulfur dioxide can cause airways to constrict in both healthy people and individuals with asthma. Exposure to either sulfur or nitrogen oxides may increase the incidence of asthma, bronchitis, or other respiratory infections and ailments in people.

Rachel Carson

Photo courtesy USFWS.

Rachel Carson was born in Pennsylvania in 1907. At age 11, Rachel submitted a story she wrote to *St. Nicholas* magazine. She won a silver medal! She hoped to have a career in writing. When Carson went to college, she enjoyed both English and biology, but she didn't know that she could be both a writer *and* a scientist.

During World War II, Carson wrote for the U.S. Fish and Wildlife Service, where she eventually became chief of publications. In her job, Carson learned of the growing problems caused by pesticides and herbicides like DDT. In 1958, Carson received a letter from a friend telling of birds killed in Massachusetts after a plane dropped DDT for mosquito control. DDT was found at toxic levels in the dead birds. Carson published a book, *Silent Spring*, in 1962, to show that DDT and other pesticides and herbicides were responsible for environmental poisoning. The book was a wake-up call that got the attention of citizens, Congress and the President. They started the Environmental Protection agency in 1970. DDT was banned in 1972.

What can be done about acid rain?

Catalytic converters

Catalytic converters in cars reduce acid rain-causing emissions. A catalytic converter is a device that converts nitrogen oxide to nitrogen gas (N_2) and oxygen (O_2) before these emissions enter the atmosphere. Nitrogen and oxygen are non-polluting gases (Figure 24.7). Catalytic converters also reduce carbon monoxide and hydrocarbon emissions. Unfortunately, catalytic converters do not reduce emissions under all driving conditions. When the accelerator is held down to accelerate quickly, the emissions by-pass the sensors that maintain the chemical conditions for the catalytic converter to work.

Scrubbing reduces power plant emissions

In the case of power plants that burn sulfur-containing coal, emissions are made less toxic by exposing them to a solution of lime (CaO). The lime reacts with sulfur dioxide (SO_2) to produce calcium sulfate ($CaSO_3$). Although this by-product of the reaction is not harmful, it is not useful and must be added to landfills. This process for treating power plant emissions is called *scrubbing*.

The diagram below shows how acid precipitation is formed.

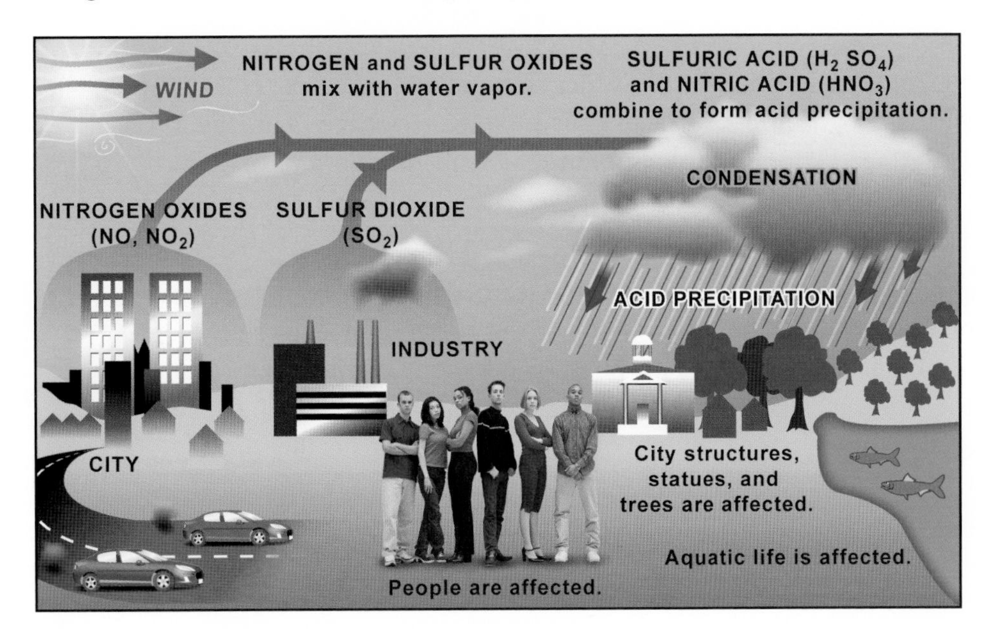
WIND
NITROGEN and SULFUR OXIDES mix with water vapor.
SULFURIC ACID (H_2SO_4) and NITRIC ACID (HNO_3) combine to form acid precipitation.
CONDENSATION
NITROGEN OXIDES (NO, NO_2)
SULFUR DIOXIDE (SO_2)
ACID PRECIPITATION
INDUSTRY
CITY
City structures, statues, and trees are affected.
Aquatic life is affected.
People are affected.

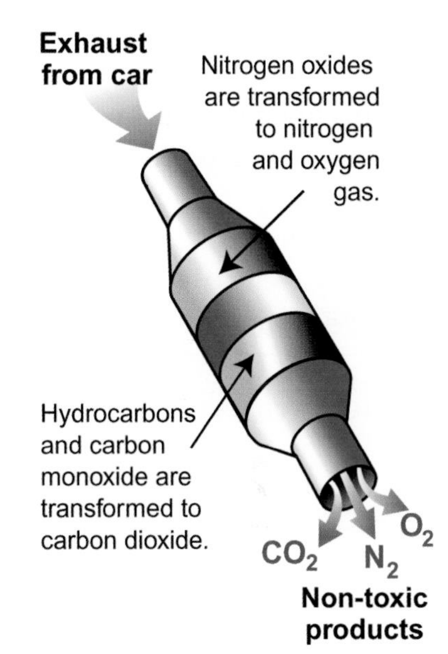
Exhaust from car
Nitrogen oxides are transformed to nitrogen and oxygen gas.
Hydrocarbons and carbon monoxide are transformed to carbon dioxide.
CO_2
N_2
O_2
Non-toxic products

Figure 24.7: *The chemical reactions that reduce emissions to non-toxic products occur in two places in the catalytic converter. Each of these has a "honeycomb" structure so that the surface area at which the reactions take place is maximized.*

24.4 Oceans

Although we can't drink ocean water, the oceans contribute to our water supply via the water cycle. The sun's energy evaporates pure water from the oceans, leaving behind salt. The resulting water vapor in the atmosphere eventually condenses to form rain. In this section, you will learn more about why the oceans are important to life on Earth. You will also learn about the chemistry of Earth's oceans, and the impact of human activities.

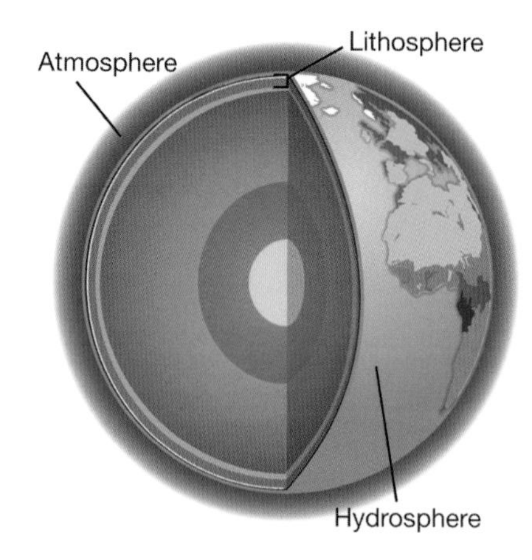

Figure 24.8: *The diagram above shows the atmosphere, lithosphere, and hydrosphere. In this section, you will learn about oceans—part of the hydrosphere.*

Where did the oceans come from?

How were the oceans formed?

Earth is about 4.6 billion years old. As our planet formed, it started out very hot and then cooled. As Earth's crust solidified during this cooling process, water vapor was released from its crust. Continual cooling then caused this atmospheric water to condense. The resulting rains filled the original ocean basins. Some of the water in our oceans is also thought to have been brought from space by large, icy comets entering our atmosphere millions of years ago. The amount of water in the oceans is about the same as it was when dinosaurs lived on Earth between 220 and 65 million years ago.

Oceans are part of the hydrosphere

Earlier, you learned that 97 percent of Earth's water is found in the oceans. Oceans are part of the water layer of Earth's surface, called the **hydrosphere**. This layer covers much of its surface. You are probably familiar with Earth's *atmosphere*. This layer of gases blankets the planet. The *lithosphere* is a thin, solid, rocky layer that covers Earth's surface (Figure 24.8).

Supply of water to the oceans

How is water supplied to the oceans today? You learned that the water cycle distributes water on Earth. This cycle carries water to the oceans and also removes it. As you can see in Figure 24.9, sources for ocean water include rivers, rain, and groundwater. These sources also bring dissolved minerals and salts into the oceans. You have just learned that the amount of water in the oceans is the same as it was many millions of years ago. It is also true that the saltiness of the oceans has also remained relatively constant for millions of years. From here forward, we will refer to ocean water as *seawater* and learn how it is different from the *freshwater* that resides in rivers, lakes, ponds, and groundwater.

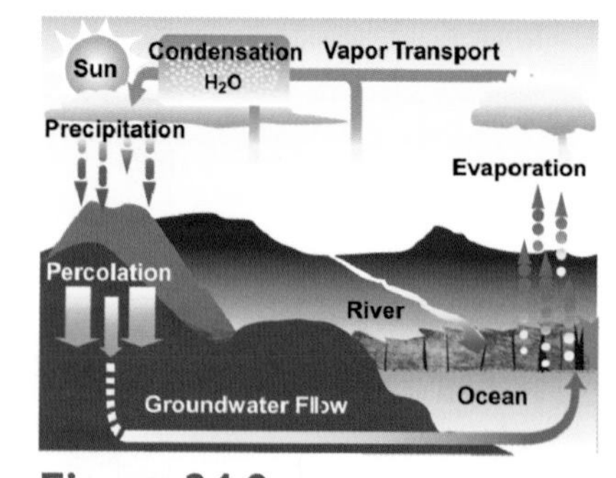

Figure 24.9: *The water cycle distributes ocean water to freshwater bodies of water, and returns freshwater to the oceans.*

What is an ocean?

Water covers about 70 percent of Earth's surface

Oceans are massive bodies of seawater that cover much of the surface of Earth. In fact, the land on which we all live covers only about 25% of Earth's surface. In comparison, the majority—about 75%—of the surface is covered with water (the hydrosphere) and much of this space is occupied by oceans. There are five major oceans on Earth.

Earth has five major oceans

The United States has boundaries on two major oceans. If you are from the east coast, you are familiar with the Atlantic Ocean. If you are from the west coast of the United States your are more familiar with the Pacific Ocean. These are two of the major oceans. The Arctic Ocean and the Indian Ocean are two smaller oceans. The Southern Ocean, the fifth ocean, was recently named as a separate ocean in 2000 by the International Hydrographic Organization (IHO). The IHO includes representatives from 68 countries that border the world's oceans.

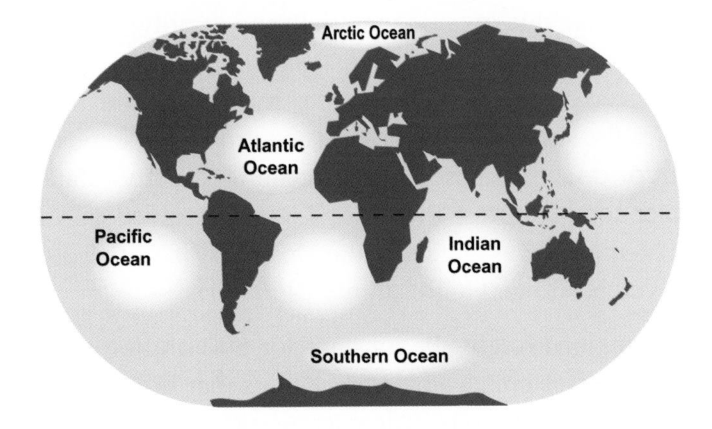

Why are oceans salty?

There are three main sources that have contributed to the saltiness of seawater over time: (1) chemical weathering of rocks on land, (2) chemical reactions between seawater and volcanic eruptions on the ocean floor, (3) volcanic eruptions on land. Weathered rocks contribute silica, sodium, calcium, potassium, and magnesium to oceans. Bicarbonate (HCO_3) is added to the oceans from rivers and comes from dissolved limestone.

Panthalassa and Pangaea

About 225 million years ago, there was one large ocean we refer to as *Panthalassa*. This ocean surrounded a single landmass we refer to as *Pangaea*. Around 200 million years ago, Pangaea began to separate into parts so that we now have seven continents and five major oceans rather than one large one. The Atlantic and Indian Oceans formed around 180 million years ago. The Pacific, Arctic, and Southern Oceans are what remain of Panthalassa.

The composition of seawater

Ions in seawater Many of the salts in seawater are dissolved, and exist as ions. There are six main ions in seawater that together account for 99% of the dissolved salts (Figure 24.10). In addition, there are more than 70 additional *trace elements* that make seawater a very complex solution. The concentration of trace elements is very low and ranges from parts per million (ppm) to parts per billion (ppb). For example, the concentration of iron in seawater is 0.06 ppb.

Ion name	Ion symbol	%
chloride	Cl^-	55
sodium	Na^+	31
sulfate	SO_4^{2-}	8
magnesium	Mg^{2+}	4
calcium	Ca^{2+}	1
potassium	K^+	1

Figure 24.10: *The six main ions in seawater.*

Salinity The term salinity describes the "saltiness" of seawater. **Salinity describes how much salt is dissolved in one kilogram of water**. On average, one kilogram of seawater has 35 grams of salt. This means there are 35 grams of salt mixed with 965 grams of water to make one kilogram of seawater. To describe the concentration of salt in the seawater, we say that the salinity is 35 parts per thousand (ppt), or 35 $^{o}/_{oo}$.

Other components of seawater Additional components of seawater include organic materials and dissolved gases. Organic materials come from marine animals and plants that live in the ocean. Dissolved gases include nitrogen, oxygen, carbon dioxide, hydrogen, and trace gases. This is not surprising since the surface of the ocean is continuously exposed to the atmosphere. The amount of dissolved gases in the ocean is directly related to water temperature. At higher temperatures, there are fewer dissolved gases. Salinity is also higher at higher temperatures. Because the Dead Sea is very warm (about 21 °C), it has few dissolved gases, and high salinity (250 ppt).

Salinity remains constant The salinity of the oceans has remained relatively constant for 600 million years because physical and chemical processes create a balance. Rivers that flow toward the oceans constantly bring in salts and minerals. Microscopic organisms remove some of these salts and minerals as they use calcium and carbonate ions or silica to build their skeletons. Excess metals (like manganese) come out of solution and form deposits on rocks on the ocean floor (Figure 24.11). Organisms also contribute to the reduction of salts when they metabolize nitrate, phosphate, and metals. As these processes reduce the amounts of salts and minerals, pure water is constantly being removed from the oceans through evaporation. The sum of these processes stabilizes the salinity of the oceans.

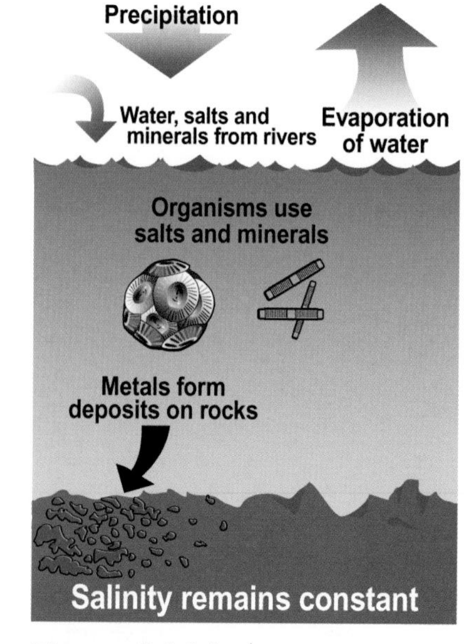

Figure 24.11: *The above diagram shows why the salinity of the oceans has remained relatively constant for 600 million years.*

The impact of increased carbon dioxide in the atmosphere

Seawater contains dissolved carbon dioxide

Some of the dissolved gases in the oceans such as oxygen (O_2) and carbon dioxide (CO_2) are produced and used by organisms in the ocean. For example, through the process of *respiration*, some organisms use O_2 and produce CO_2. These gases also enter the oceans from the atmosphere. Recall that when CO_2 dissolves in water it produces an acidic solution.

More CO_2 in the atmosphere could mean a more acidic ocean

CO_2 is a global warming gas. Global warming refers to the increase in the average temperature of Earth as a result of an increase in certain atmospheric, heat-trapping gases such as CO_2, methane (CH_4), and nitrous oxide (N_2O). Since the Industrial Revolution, the amount of CO_2 in the atmosphere has been steadily rising. As the concentration of this gas increases, more will dissolve in the oceans, which could cause the oceans to become more acidic.

Calcium carbonate buffers the ocean

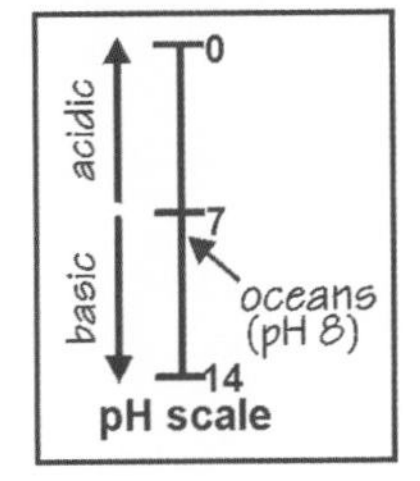

The oceans contain a natural *buffer* called calcium carbonate ($CaCO_3$). A buffer is a substance that helps maintain the pH of a solution (pH scale shown at left). $CaCO_3$ is an ingredient in the shells of many microscopic marine organisms (Figure 24.12). When these organisms die, their shells settle to the bottom of the ocean floor. The $CaCO_3$ dissociates into calcium (Ca^{2+}) and carbonate (CO_3^{2-}) ions. The ocean floor releases carbonate ions as an "antacid" in response to acidic conditions. The carbonate ions neutralize the acid and keep the pH of the oceans at around pH 8 (Figure 24.16).

Rising CO_2 levels

Is there enough $CaCO_3$ to buffer the ocean if the levels of CO_2 continue to rise in the atmosphere? Presently, the amount of CO_2 in the atmosphere is 370 ppm. Scientists project that CO_2 levels will rise to 700 ppm by 2100. If there isn't enough $CaCO_3$ to balance the increase in CO_2, the result could be an increase in the acidity of the oceans (decrease in pH).

The impact on life in the oceans

Recent scientific studies indicate that the oceans seem to be capable of handling a lot of dissolved CO_2 without experiencing a change in pH. However, in order to effectively buffer CO_2, carbonate ions are used up. This means that they are not as available to marine organisms that use these ions to make their shells. Because these organisms provide food for larger organisms, all life in the oceans could be affected by increased CO_2 levels.

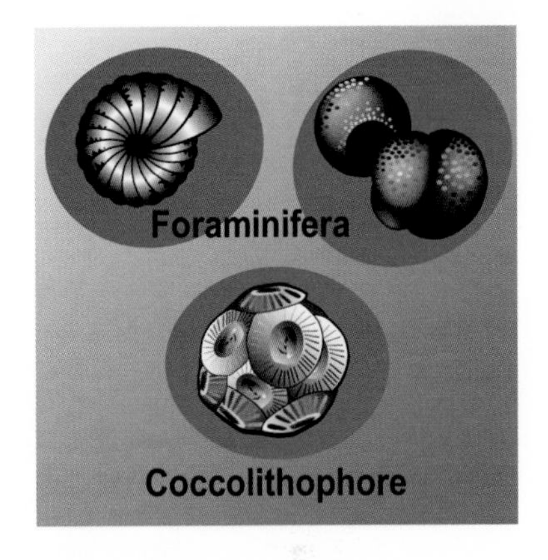

Figure 24.12: *Calcium carbonate is an ingredient in the shells of microscopic marine organisms like coccolithophores and foraminifera. When these organisms die, their shells settle to the bottom of the ocean floor.*

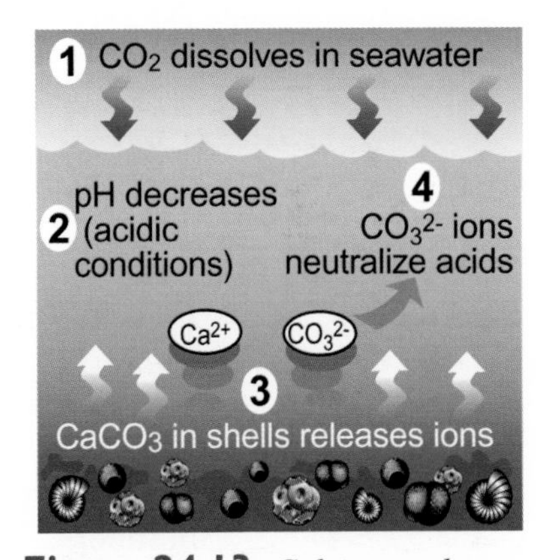

Figure 24.13: *Calcium carbonate on the ocean floor releases calcium and carbonate ions in response to acidic conditions. Carbonate ions neutralize the acid to stabilize the pH of the oceans.*

Pollution and the ocean food chain

Pollution in the oceans

Pollution is a big problem that affects the oceans. Pollution from the land enters the oceans through rivers and streams. Also, some waste materials are dumped directly into ocean water. Pollutants that enter the ocean include raw sewage, toxic chemicals (such as pesticides), heavy metals (such as mercury), and petroleum. When these substances enter the oceans, they *diffuse* (spread out) through large volumes of water and become less concentrated.

Marine organisms concentrate pollutants

The fact that pollutants become less concentrated as they spread out does not mean that they cannot harm marine organisms. In fact, some toxic pollutants become concentrated in the tissues of these organisms. High concentrations of toxins can cause problems such as slowed growth and development, decreased reproduction, reduced ability by plants to photosynthesize, and even death. To understand how this concentration occurs, you need to understand the marine *ecosystem* (the combination of living and nonliving factors present) and marine food chains.

Energy is transferred from organism to organism through a food chain.

The food chain

A food chain is a series of steps through which energy and nutrients are transferred, from organism to organism, in an ecosystem (Figure 24.14). The first step of a food chain consists of producers. Producers are plants and one-celled organisms that concentrate energy from the sun through photosynthesis. In a marine food chain, the most numerous producers are the *phytoplankton*—microscopic organisms that float near the surface. Most producers are very small.

Herbivores and carnivores

The next step on a food chain consists of herbivores. These organisms feed on producers. Herbivores are usually larger than producers, and exist in smaller numbers. There are many different species of herbivores in the oceans including "grazing" fish, snails, and organisms that "filter" phytoplankton out of the water. Many carnivores, the next step on a food chain, feed on herbivores. They are usually larger than herbivores and are less numerous. Because some carnivores eat other carnivores, there are several levels of these organisms on food chains. In marine food chains, carnivores include dolphins, sharks, and many species of fish.

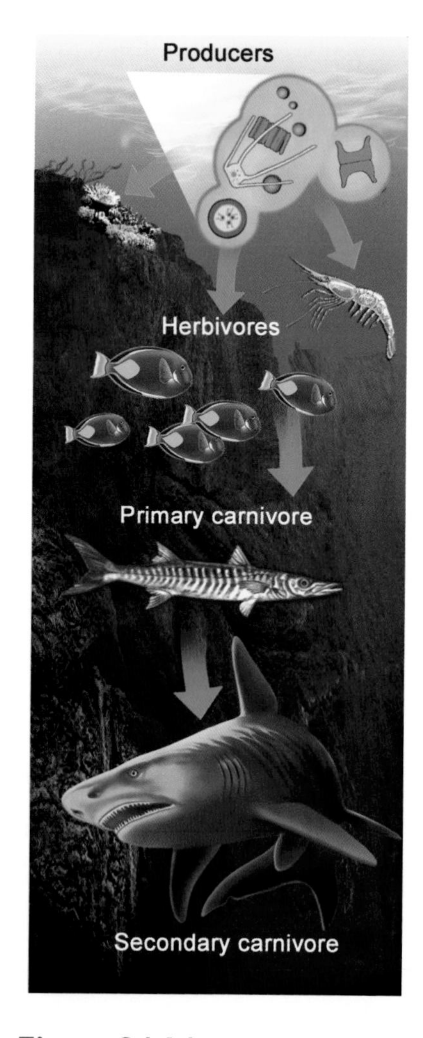

Figure 24.14: *A simple marine food chain. The arrows show the direction of energy and nutrient flow.*

The food chain as a pyramid

All living things need energy to survive. To obtain energy, herbivores eat plants and carnivores eat herbivores or other carnivores. Producers do not eat other organisms to obtain energy because they produce their own. A food chain (sometimes called a *food web* because it is more complex than a chain) can be represented as a *pyramid*, with producers forming the base, herbivores next, and carnivores at the top as shown in Figure 24.15. This arrangement represents how energy is lost in the food chain. It also explains how toxic pollutants travel through food chains and become more concentrated with each step.

Energy is lost at each level

Food chains, like other systems, obey the law of conservation of energy. So, how is energy lost at each level of a food chain? The pyramid in Figure 24.15 illustrates that the available food energy decreases moving up a food chain from producers to herbivores to carnivores. For example, an herbivore consumes large amounts of tiny, energy-rich producers. The herbivore uses the energy obtained from eating to continue to swim and search for more food. Some of the energy is also spent on growing, building a skeleton and body tissues, and reproducing. Some energy is lost as heat or waste products. When an herbivore is eaten by a carnivore, only its tissues are a source of energy. The carnivore cannot obtain energy from eating the skeleton, or recover the energy used by the herbivore for its daily activities. However, some of this lost energy can be put back in the ecosystem. *Decomposers*, like crabs, break down waste products, bones, and shells. They recycle some energy and nutrients back to the food chain. The animals that eat the decomposers also help recover some of the lost energy.

Toxic pollutants are concentrated at each level

The pyramid also shows why toxic pollutants, if present, can become highly concentrated in the tissues of top carnivores. As producers store energy, they also absorb small amounts of toxic pollutants in the water. Next, herbivores eat large numbers of producers to obtain enough energy. Because the toxins are soluble in fat, not water, they are stored in the fatty tissues of these animals and are not passed out of their bodies. When the primary carnivores eat many herbivores, they accumulate even higher levels of toxins in their tissues. Top carnivores, who prey on other carnivores, can accumulate dangerous levels of toxic pollutants. These toxins can sometimes be passed on to their young. Figure 24.16 shows how the amount of a toxic pollutant can multiply as it travels up the food chain.

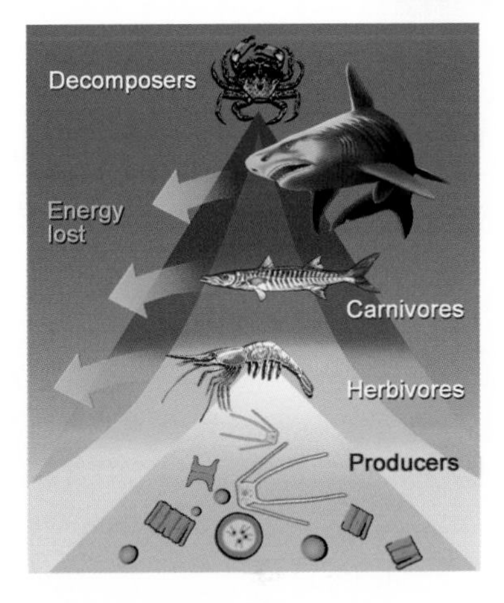

Figure 24.15: *The energy pyramid is a simple way to show how energy moves through an ecosystem.*

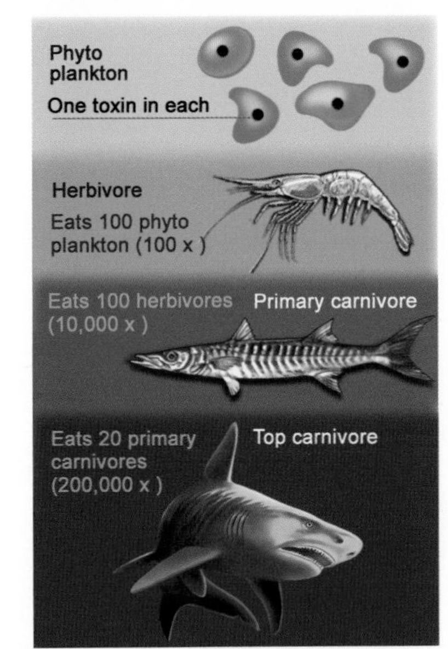

Figure 24.16: *How toxic pollutants become concentrated in the tissues of top carnivores.*

Chapter 24 Review

Vocabulary review

Match the following terms with the correct definition. There is one extra definition in the list that will not match any of the terms.

Set One

1. water cycle
2. precipitation
3. condensation
4. surface runoff
5. aquifer

a. The process by which water vapor transforms to liquid water
b. The sun-driven process by which water is moved from place to place on Earth
c. The release of water vapor from plants
d. A general term for water (in liquid or frozen form) released from clouds
e. An underground area of rock and sediment where groundwater concentrates
f. Water, usually resulting from precipitation, that flows from land to surface water

Set Two

1. surface water
2. biological oxygen demand
3. dissolved oxygen
4. turbidity
5. watershed

a. A measure of the clearness of water
b. An artificial lake that is used as a main water supply by a community
c. The concentration of oxygen in a body of water
d. The amount of oxygen consumed by bacteria in a body of water over a certain time period
e. Natural formations of water including streams, rivers, ponds, and lakes
f. The place where all a region's groundwater and surface runoff collect

Set Three

1. nitrogen oxides
2. acid precipitation
3. scrubbing
4. sulfuric acid
5. catalytic converter

a. One of the gases that cause acid rain
b. One of the acidic components of acid rain
c. Rain, snow, or fog with a pH lower than 5.6
d. The use of lime to reduce the emissions from power plants that burn sulfur-containing coal
e. A by-product of the reaction of lime with sulfur dioxide
f. A car part that is designed to reduce polluting emissions from automobile exhaust

Set Four

1. salinity
2. herbivore
3. food chain
4. producer
5. carnivore

a. An organism that eats herbivores and carnivores
b. A single huge landmass that existed on Earth 254 million years ago
c. An organism that eats only producers
d. A term that describes the environment and organisms that are associated with oceans
e. An organism that stores energy from the sun
f. A term that describes how much salt is dissolved in one kilogram of water

Concept review

1. Explain the difference between an aquifer and a reservoir. In your answer, explain where the water in each comes from.
2. Think about a water molecule in a lake. Referring to the water cycle, describe all the different things that might happen next to the molecule. How might it leave the lake? Where will it go?
3. List two dissolved substances that may be found in tap water. Explain the source of these.
4. What is the difference between hard water and soft water?
5. List two factors that you may measure to test the water quality of a pond. Explain why measuring these factors is important.
6. Explain why you would expect to find a lower level of dissolved oxygen in a warm lake than in a cold lake.
7. List the four gases formed from human activities that result in acid precipitation.
8. Identify the two most common acids found in acid rain.
9. What are the five big oceans on Earth?
10. Describe the composition of seawater. What are the six main ingredients in seawater?
11. Explain why warmer oceans usually have a higher salinity than cooler oceans.
12. Draw a simple marine food chain. Show the flow of energy in the food chain.
13. Why is energy lost in a food chain? Use the term *law of conservation of energy* in your answer.
14. Explain why toxic pollutants can become concentrated in the body tissues of top carnivores.

Problems

1. Design an original diagram to illustrate how water is distributed on Earth. Use the percentages provided in Table 24.1 to make your diagram.
2. The volume of the oceans is 1.37×10^9 km^3. One km^3 is equivalent to 1×10^{12} liters. Using these numbers, figure out how many liters of water are in the ocean. One Olympic swimming pool holds about 500,000 liters of water. How many Olympic-sized swimming pools could be filled by the oceans?
3. What does it mean to say that the pH of acid rain is 5.6?
4. You measure the oxygen content in a pond as 5 ppm. How many milligrams of oxygen are in one liter of this water? How many grams of oxygen are in one liter of water? Does this pond have a healthy amount of dissolved oxygen?
5. You measure the salinity of a seawater sample to be 33 $^{o}/_{oo}$. How many grams of salt are in this sample if the mass is 2.5 kilograms?
6. What is the salinity of a sample that you know contains 1800 grams of water and 20 grams of salt?

Applying your knowledge

1. What is the history of your community's water supply or water treatment? Go to the library to read your local newspapers or magazines from the past and present. Look for stories about the water supply or water treatment. Write a one- or two-page report about your findings.

2. Two years ago, you joined a project to study the water quality of a local pond. During the second spring, you notice that there are not as many tadpoles as there were the previous year. You want to know if the number of tadpoles is related to the pH of the pond. The records that document the water quality and frog population started 10 years ago. Describe the steps you would take to determine whether a change in pH of the pond water is affecting the population of frogs.

3. Gases that cause acid rain are all end-products of chemical reactions. These reactions are useful for our economy in that they are involved in keeping cars and industry going. However, do the economic benefits of keeping cars and industry going outweigh the economic impact of acid rain? Research this issue in your library or on the Internet and prepare a short report or presentation on the topic.

4. The Environmental Protection Agency (EPA) recommends setting limits on the amount of certain types of fish that a person consumes each month. Some marine species with recommended limits include swordfish, shark, and barracuda.
   a. Why do you think there are limits set on only certain types of fish? Why would some species of fish be more safe to eat than others?
   b. EPA limits are even more strict for pregnant women. Explain why consuming lots of swordfish, shark, or barracuda would not be safe for a pregnant woman.

5. JAN FEB MAR Many businesses, schools, and homes use the services of bottled-water companies. For a monthly fee, these companies provide drinking water and dispensers. Bottled-water services cost much more than tap water. Why do people pay for such a service? In answering this question, you will make *inferences* based on information that you collect. An inference is a statement that can be made based on observations and known facts. Inferences can be used to make a hypothesis that can be tested in an experiment.

   Collecting your data:

   a. Interview three people who use the services of a bottled-water company. Ask them why they use the service.
   b. Look in your local phone book to find advertisements for three bottled-water services. Call each company and ask them why they recommend using bottled water in your area.
   c. Perform an Internet search for information about bottled water and tap water. For example, search according to the phrase "bottled water versus tap water." Make a table that lists three reasons you *would* use a water service (pros) and three reasons you *would not* use a bottled water service (cons).
   d. Examine the data from parts 7 (a-c). Based on your data, make three inferences as to why people might purchase bottled-water services.
   e. Based on your data, make at least one inference as to why someone might *not* choose to use a bottled-water service.

UNIT 9

Energy in the Earth System

Chapter 25

Measuring Heat

Why do some substances warm up and cool down faster than others? What is the difference between temperature and heat? How is heat transferred from one place to another? In this chapter, you will learn the answers to these and other questions as you study temperature scales, specific heat, and heat transfer.

25.1	**Measuring Heat**	*How is temperature measured?*

In this Investigation you will graph the Celsius temperature scale as a function of the Fahrenheit temperature scale. From this graph you will develop a mathematical relationship between the Fahrenheit and Celsius temperature scales.

25.2	**Flow of Heat**	*How efficient is an immersion heater?*

In this Investigation you will explore how much thermal energy is supplied to water by an immersion heater. You will also make some predictions on the change in temperature if the amount of water is changed. In addition, you will calculate the efficiency of the system.

25.3	**Heat Transfer**	*How much heat is transferred through convection?*

In this Investigation you will observe both natural and forced convection. A flask of hot water with red dye will be placed in a beaker filled with cool water. The hot red water will rise into the cooler water due to natural convection. You are going to observe the process and take temperature data to analyze how much heat is transferred via convection. You will also blow through a straw to force the red dye out of the flask into the larger beaker to explore forced convection.

Learning Goals

In this chapter, you will:

- ✔ Measure temperature.
- ✔ Convert between the Celsius and Fahrenheit temperature scales.
- ✔ Understand and demonstrate physical changes due to temperature.
- ✔ Develop a mathematical relationship that describes how much the temperature of water increases when heat is added to the water.
- ✔ Discuss the relationship of heat and energy.
- ✔ Calculate the efficiency in a heating system.
- ✔ Explain three methods of heat transfer and describe applications of each.
- ✔ Analyze how energy can be transferred through convection.
- ✔ Describe the motion of liquid due to temperature differences within the system.

Vocabulary

British thermal unit (Btu)	Fahrenheit scale	latent heat	thermal energy
calorie	first law of thermodynamics	radiation	thermal equilibrium
Celsius scale	heat	specific heat	thermal insulator
conduction	heat-temperature rule	temperature	thermometer
convection	joule	thermal conductor	thermostat

25.1 Measuring Heat

If you observe a group of people waiting for a bus on a brisk winter morning, you may notice that more people have chosen to sit on a wooden bench than on a metal one. Why? Does the wooden one feel warmer? If both types of benches are found at the same bus stop, shouldn't they be the same temperature? In this chapter, you find the answer to this and other questions about temperature, the flow of heat, and thermal energy.

Figure 25.1: *On a cold day, more people will choose to sit on a wooden bench than a metal one. Can you explain why?*

Temperature

What is temperature? You have probably used a thermometer to find the **temperature** outside. Temperature is the measurement we use to quantify the sensations of hot and cold. A steaming mug of hot cocoa has a higher temperature than a frosty glass of iced tea. But what does temperature actually measure?

What does temperature measure? If we were to blow up a balloon we would fill it with billions upon billions of molecules of air. All of these molecules are constantly moving. As a result, they have *kinetic energy*—energy of motion. Some of the molecules are moving fast, some are moving slowly. They can move up, down, and sideways. Fast particles have more kinetic energy than slow particles. If we were to add up the kinetic energy of every single molecule in a balloon, and divide this sum by the total number of molecules, we would have an *average* of the kinetic energy for molecules in the balloon. This average is what temperature measures.

Temperature is a measure of the average kinetic energy of the molecules of an object.

Indirect measurement is used to find temperature Of course, it is difficult to measure the speed of individual molecules in an object, since they are much too small to see. We commonly use *indirect measurement* to find an object's temperature. An increase in the average kinetic energy of an object's molecules can cause changes in other physical properties of the object, such as its volume or electrical resistance. In the next section, you will learn how we use these physical changes to measure an object's temperature.

Figure 25.2: *As temperature increases, so does the average kinetic energy of the molecules. The size of the arrows represents the amount of kinetic energy of the molecule.*

How does a thermometer work?

Thermometers Have you ever wondered how a thermometer works? The most common thermometers contain either a red fluid, which is alcohol containing a small amount of red dye, or a silvery fluid, which is mercury. You may have also used a thermometer with a digital electronic readout. Thermometers detect a physical change in a material that results from a change in temperature. Alcohol and mercury thermometers measure the *thermal expansion* of the liquid, while digital thermometers measure *electrical resistance*.

What is thermal expansion? Most materials expand when you raise their temperature. This process is called thermal expansion. The expansion comes from the increase in molecular motion that occurs with the rise in temperature. If molecules are moving around more, they tend to bump each other around and so take up more space. That's why an inflated balloon will expand when held over a warm radiator. If you put the balloon in the refrigerator, it will shrink. Likewise, warmer liquids take up more space than cold liquids. You can easily see this in a thermometer (Figure 25.3).

How liquid-filled thermometers work Thermal expansion is the basic principle of a liquid-filled thermometer. The expansion of the liquid is directly proportional to the change in temperature. For example, for every degree the thermometer heats up, the fluid inside might expand so that it takes up one more millimeter of space in the narrow tube.

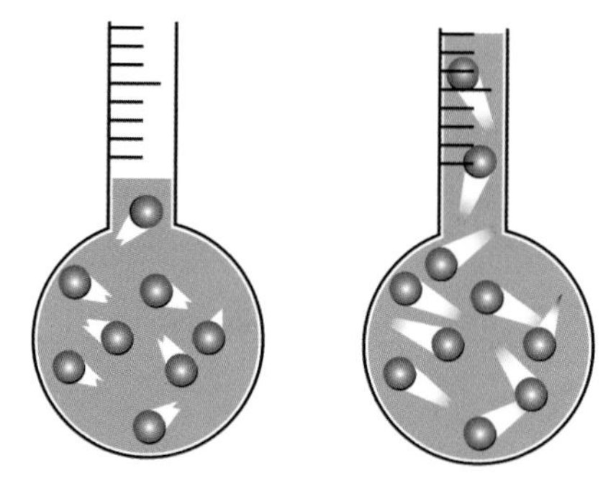

Figure 25.3: *The expansion of liquid in a thermometer is directly proportional to the increase in temperature.*

Temperature changes and bridges

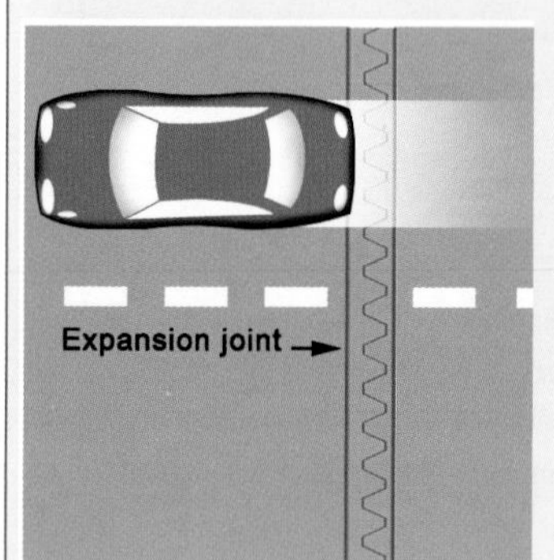

Most solids also expand in response to an increase in temperature, but the expansion is very small. For solid steel, the thermal expansion is on the order of one ten-thousandth. This means that a 1-meter steel rod will expand 0.01 millimeters for every degree Celsius of temperature increase. Although this may seem difficult to detect, temperature changes can have dramatic effects on large structures such as buildings and bridges. For instance, a 100-meter-long bridge could be up to 10 centimeters longer on a hot summer day than on a cold winter day. In order to prevent damage to the structure, civil engineers use expansion joints in bridges as shown in the figure at left.

Science in your home

Have you ever had trouble opening a jar of salsa or jelly because the lid was too tight? One method of opening the jar is to run it under warm water. As the glass jar and metal lid heat up, they both expand. However, the expansion rate of the metal is more than twice the rate of the glass. Thus the lid will loosen as you heat the jar!

A note of caution: If the water is extremely hot, the glass may break.

How digital thermometers work

Another physical property that changes with temperature is electrical resistance. The resistance of a metal wire increases with temperature. Since the metal is hotter, its atoms are shaking more. The shaking interferes with the movement of electrons, causing greater resistance. Digital thermometers measure this change in resistance. Most commonly, platinum metal is used in digital thermometers.

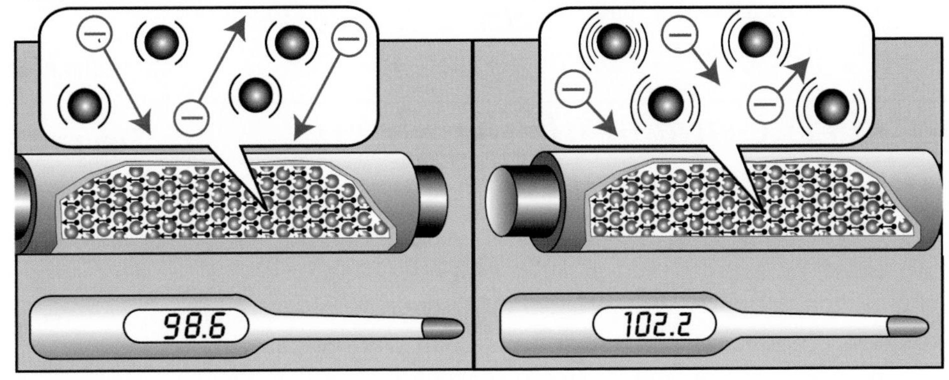

Temperature scales

The Fahrenheit scale

You are probably most familiar with the English system of measuring temperature, known as the **Fahrenheit scale**. It was developed in 1714 by Gabriel Fahrenheit (1686-1936), a German physicist who was the first person to use a mercury thermometer. He chose the lowest temperature he could create in his lab (using water, salt, and ice) to be the zero point of his scale. For the other end of the scale he used the temperature of the human body as 100 degrees. Eventually the Fahrenheit scale was standardized so that the freezing point of water is 32 degrees and the boiling point is 212 degrees.

The Celsius scale

In 1742, Anders Celsius (1701-44), a Swedish astronomer, invented a temperature scale in which there were 100 degrees between freezing and boiling. He called this scale the centigrade scale. In 1948 this official scale of the metric system was named the **Celsius scale** in honor of him. Most countries in the world use the Celsius scale (Figure 25.4).

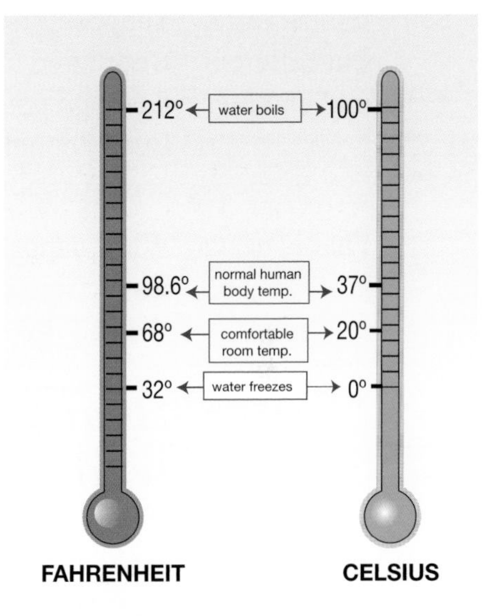

Figure 25.4: *A comparison of the Fahrenheit and Celsius temperature scales.*

Thermal energy and heat

Energy changes

As you have read, changes in temperature are directly related to changes in energy. When you heat a pot of soup with an electric hot plate, *electrical energy* is converted into *thermal energy*.

What is thermal energy?

Thermal energy and temperature are not the same. Temperature measures the *average* kinetic energy of the molecules of a material. Thermal energy is the *sum* of all the kinetic energy of the molecules of a material.

Thermal energy is the sum of all the kinetic energy of the molecules of a material.

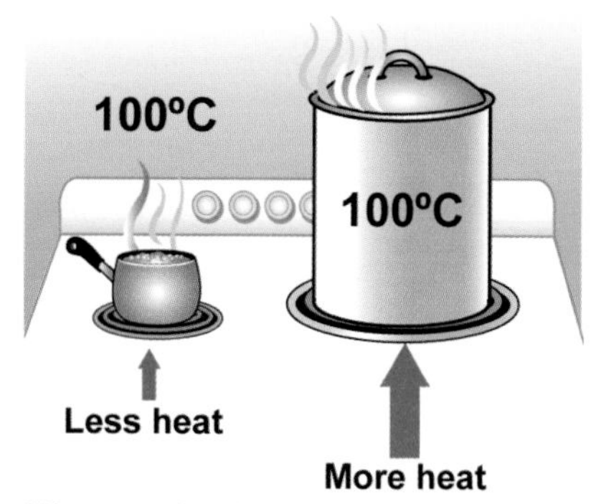

Figure 25.5: *Even though the two containers of soup are at the same temperature, the large pot contains more thermal energy because it took more energy to heat it.*

Same temperature, but different thermal energies

Suppose you are asked to heat up a single cup of soup and a huge pot of soup. Both have to reach the same temperature. Which takes more energy? Heating up the huge pot takes more energy because it is like heating up many individual cups. Even though the two containers of soup are at the same temperature, the pot contains more thermal energy because it took more energy to heat it (Figure 25.5).

What is heat?

What happens when you hold an ice cream cone on a hot day? Thermal energy flows from your hand and the surrounding air to melt the ice cream (Figure 25.6). We call this flow of thermal energy heat.

Heat is the flow of thermal energy due to a temperature difference between two objects.

Figure 25.6: *On a hot day, thermal energy flows from your hand and the surrounding air to melt the ice cream.*

When does heat flow?

In the scientific sense, heat occurs only when there is a difference in temperature. Heat flows naturally from the warmer object to the cooler one. In the case of the melting ice cream, the thermal energy lost by your hand and the surrounding air is equal to the thermal energy gained by the ice cream. The total amount of energy stays balanced.

Measuring heat

Understanding heat is important The flow of thermal energy (which we call heat) is happening around us all the time. Thermal energy from the sun, for example, warms our planet every day. At night, some of this heat flows back out to space. The flow of thermal energy is also found whenever a car (or any other large machine) is running. These machines have special systems like radiators and fins to manage heat.

The calorie Heat is an important concept in so many aspects of our lives. There are three different units of energy that relate directly to heat. The metric unit usually used in chemistry to measure heat is the calorie. The **calorie** is defined as the quantity of heat needed to increase the temperature of 1 gram of water by 1 degree Celsius. You may have noticed that most food packages list "Calories per serving." The unit used for measuring energy content of the food we eat is the kilocalorie, which equals 1,000 calories. The kilocalorie is often written as Calorie (with a capital C). If a candy bar contains 210 Calories, it contains 210,000 calories!

The joule The **joule** is the most common unit of heat used for physics and engineering. The joule is a unit used to measure all forms of energy, not just heat. The joule is smaller than the calorie. There are 4.18 joules in one calorie (Figure 25.7).

The British thermal unit Still another unit of heat you may have heard of is the **British thermal unit**, or Btu. The Btu is often used to describe heat produced by heating systems or heat removed by air-conditioning systems. A Btu is the quantity of heat it takes to increase the temperature of 1 pound of water by 1 degree Fahrenheit.

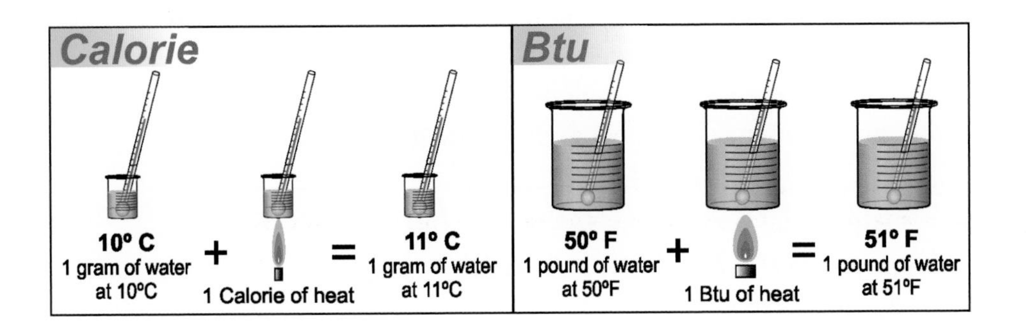

James Prescott Joule

In the 1840s, English physicist James Prescott Joule (1818-89) proved that the law of conservation of energy also applied to heat. Until then, physicists only considered the law of conservation of mechanical energy, which did not include heat. Joule showed that when he converted electrical energy and kinetic energy into thermal energy, energy was still conserved. The unit for heat and energy is named in his honor.

Unit	Equals
1 calorie	4.186 joules
1 Calorie	1000 calories
1 Btu	1055 joules
1 Btu	252 calories

Figure 25.7: *Conversion table for units of heat.*

25.2 Flow of Heat

When you take an apple pie out of the oven, why is the filling sometimes hot enough to burn your mouth while the crust is barely warm? Why does a cast-iron skillet heat up faster than an aluminum one? Why does the water in an outdoor swimming pool feel cool during the day and warm at night? The answer to each of these questions involves the concept of *specific heat*. In this section, you will define specific heat, learn to use the heat equation to solve problems involving heat transfer, and discover how the law of energy conservation applies to situations involving thermal energy.

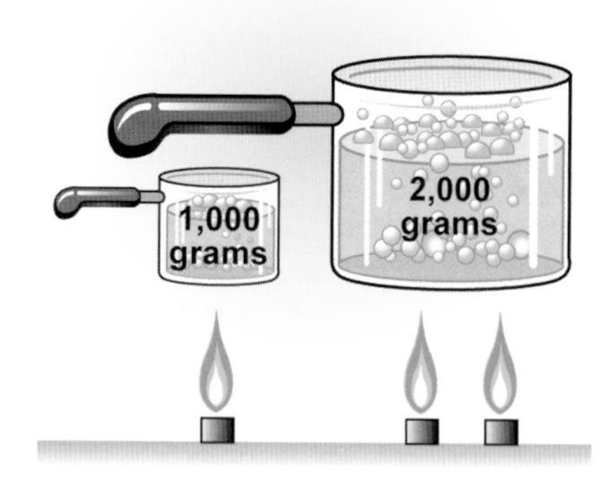

Figure 25.8: *It takes twice as much energy to heat 2,000 grams of water to boiling temperature as to heat 1,000 grams to the same temperature.*

Measuring heat

Temperature and mass If you add heat to an object, how much will its temperature increase? It depends in part on the mass of the object. If you double the mass of the object you are going to heat, you need twice as much energy to increase the temperature (Figure 25.8).

Temperature and type of material The amount of temperature increase also depends on the kind of material you are heating. It takes more energy to raise the temperature of some materials than others. Suppose you apply 100 calories of heat to a beaker containing 100 grams of water. The temperature goes up one degree. If you add the same amount of heat to 100 grams of iron, the temperature goes up 20 degrees (Figure 25.9). As water and iron illustrate, substances vary greatly in their resistance to temperature change. Knowing how materials resist temperature change is important. For example, if you know that apple pie filling is much less resistant to temperature change than pie crust, you might test the filling temperature before taking a bite!

Specific heat The **specific heat** is a property of a substance that tells us how much heat is needed to raise the temperature of one gram by one degree Celsius. A large specific heat means you have to put in a lot of energy for each degree increase in temperature. Specific heat is usually measured in calories per gram per degree Celsius $\frac{\text{calorie}}{\text{gram}^\circ\text{C}}$.

The specific heat of a substance is the amount of heat needed to raise the temperature of one gram by one degree Celsius.

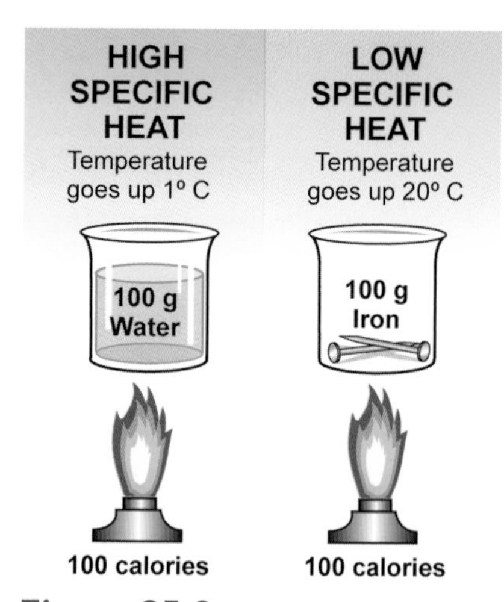

Figure 25.9: *When the same amount of heat is added to 100 grams of water and 100 grams of iron, the iron's temperature gain is 20 times the temperature gain of the water.*

Specific heat and engineering

Engineers use specific heat to design better products

Knowing the specific heat of substances helps engineers design better products. For example, playground slides used to be made of steel. When these slides absorbed thermal energy on a hot summer day, their temperature would increase so much that they would be too hot to use. Now, most playground slides are made of durable plastic, which has a much higher specific heat. A plastic slide remains at a safe and comfortable temperature, even on a hot summer day.

The graph below compares the specific heats of various materials.

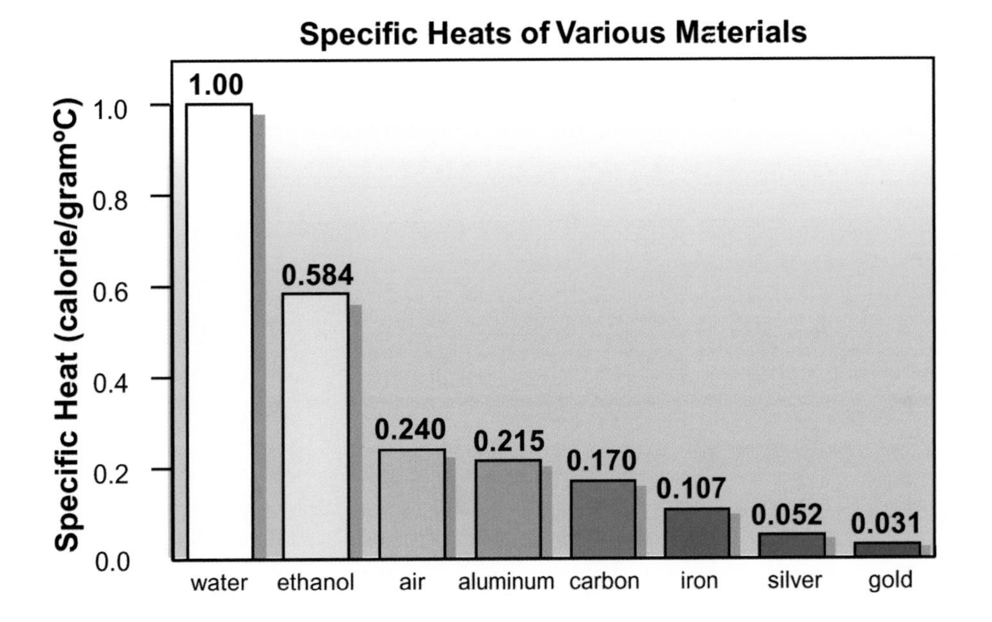

Joseph Black

Scottish chemist Joseph Black (1728-99) developed the theory of specific heat in 1760. Black also recognized the difference between heat that increases the temperature of a substance and heat that melts or boils a substance. For instance, if we add heat to water, the temperature starts to rise. Once the temperature of water reaches 100°C, it boils. Any heat added to boiling water causes water to turn to gas, but it does not raise the temperature. Black called the heat used to boil or melt substances latent heat because it could not be sensed with a thermometer. Latent means *hidden*.

The specific heat of water

Water has a high specific heat

Water has a higher specific heat than many other common materials. Its specific heat is over four times greater than that of air. When the sun shines on a body of water like a swimming pool, thermal energy flows into the water and the surrounding air. The temperature of the water does not rise as fast as the air temperature because of the difference in specific heat. That is why the water in a swimming pool feels refreshingly cool even on a hot summer day.

Water has greater resistance to temperature change than does air

Although the temperature of the pool water doesn't increase much over a hot sunny day, the water absorbs a great deal of thermal energy. At night, the water has to release a whole calorie of thermal energy per gram in order to cool one degree Celsius. By contrast, the air only has to release 0.240 calorie per gram to cool one degree. Therefore, at night, the water cools more slowly than the air. If you jumped into the pool several hours after sunset, the water would feel warmer than the surrounding air.

Photo courtesy NASA/JPL-Caltech

Figure 25.10: *About 75 percent of Earth's surface is covered by water.*

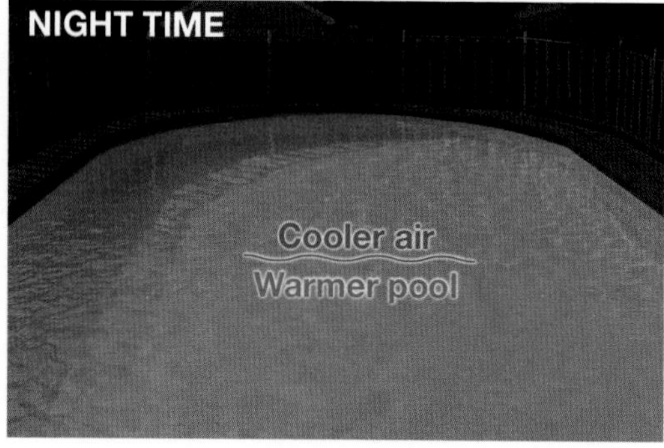

Water's high specific heat helps regulate Earth's temperature

The high specific heat of water is very important to our planet. Water covers about 75 percent of Earth's surface (Figure 25.10). One of the fundamental reasons our planet is habitable is that the huge amount of water on it helps regulate the temperature. Land, because it has a low specific heat, experiences large changes in temperature when it absorbs heat from the sun. Water tends to have smaller changes in temperature when it absorbs the same amount of heat. During the daytime, oceans help keep Earth cool, while at night, they keep Earth warm by slowing the rate at which heat is emitted back into space.

The heat equation

How could you figure out how much energy it would take to heat a swimming pool or boil a liter of water? The whole story of heat flow is told by the equation below. The equation tells you how much heat (Q) it takes to change the temperature (ΔT) of a mass (m) of a substance with specific heat (c).

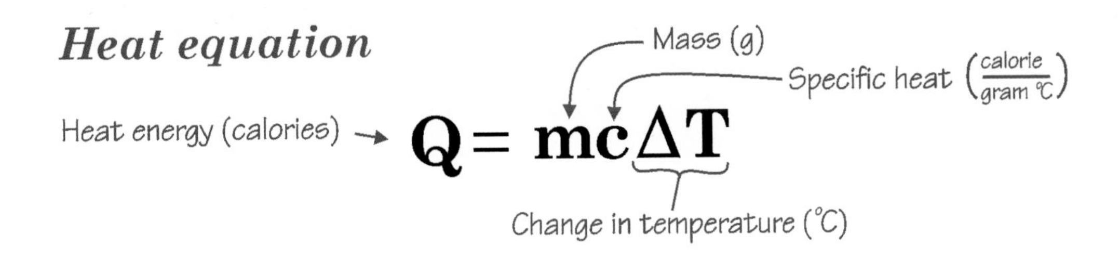

Heat flow and the origin of the word *calorie*

We now understand that the flow of heat is due to the transfer of energy. However, until the 1840s, scientists thought that heat traveled by an invisible fluid called *caloric*, which comes from the Latin word for heat. We still use the word *calorie* even though we no longer believe in a fluid called caloric.

Example:

How much heat energy is needed to raise the temperature of 1,000 grams (1 liter) of water from 20°C to 100°C?

1. Identify the variables in the equation.
   Heat equation: $Q = mc\Delta T$
   Q = trying to determine
   m = mass of water = 1,000 grams
   c = specific heat of water = 1 calorie/g °C
   $\Delta T = 100\ °C - 20\ °C = 80\ °C$
2. Plug the variables into the equation and solve.
   $Q = (1{,}000\ g) \times (1\ calorie/g\ °C) \times (80\ °C)$
   Q = 80,000 calories

Flow of heat and equilibrium

Energy can flow from one object to another

When heat flows from a warm mug of hot cocoa to your hand, there is an exchange of energy for both objects. The warm mug loses energy and cools down. Your hand gains energy and warms up. When you touch the mug, your hand is in *thermal contact* with the mug (Figure 25.11).

Figure 25.11: *When you hold a mug of hot chocolate, your hand is in thermal contact with the mug.*

What is thermal equilibrium?

Have you ever filled your kitchen sink with hot water to wash dishes? If the water was too hot, you may have added cold water to cool down the hot water. The temperature of the water in the sink eventually reaches a balance where everything is evenly warm. Whenever you have a hot object or substance in thermal contact with a cold one, heat will flow from the hot object to the cold object until they are at the same temperature, which means they are in thermal equilibrium.

Energy loss is equal to energy gain

Suppose you were able to take some objects or substances in thermal contact with each other and place them in a container that would not allow any energy to leave the system. For example, you place a cup of hot water mixed with a cup of ice into the container. Because the hot-water-and-ice mix is isolated from the outside, the energy that the hot water loses must equal the energy that the ice gains. This is an example of the law of conservation of energy. When we are talking about heat, this law is also known as the first law of thermodynamics. Both laws state that the energy in an isolated system is conserved.

The first law of thermodynamics states that in an isolated system the total amount of thermal energy remains constant.

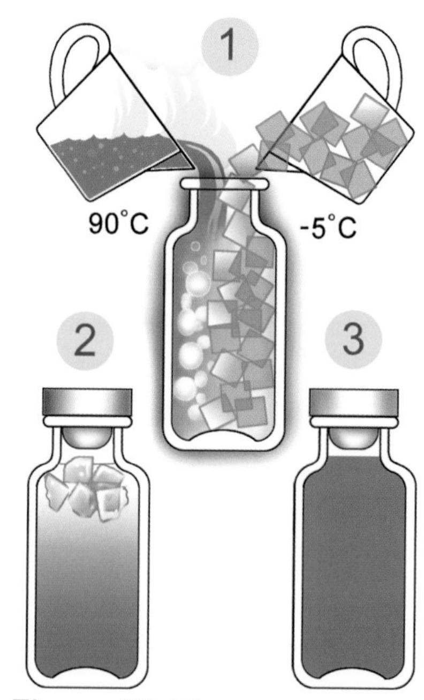

Figure 25.12: *When hot water and ice are placed in a closed system, (1) the energy lost by the hot water is equal to (2) the energy gained by the ice. Eventually, the contents reach thermal equilibrium (3).*

When do objects reach thermal equilibrium?

Objects reach thermal equilibrium when they reach the same temperature. When you submerge a thermometer in water to measure its temperature, you need to wait for a few seconds until you see that the mercury or alcohol level of the thermometer stops rising. At that point, the thermometer and the water will have reached the same temperature. Both objects transfer energy (heat) until they reach thermal equilibrium. Thus, the reading you get is the thermometer's own temperature.

25.3 Heat Transfer

Thermal energy flows from a material at a higher temperature to a material at a lower temperature. This general process is called **heat transfer**. How is heat transferred from material to material, or from place to place? It turns out there are three quite distinct mechanisms of heat transfer. In this section, you will learn about **conduction**, **convection**, and **radiation**.

What is conduction?

What is conduction? Conduction is the transfer of heat by the direct contact of particles of matter. If you have ever grabbed a mug of hot cocoa, you have experienced conduction. Conduction occurs between two materials at different temperatures when they are touching each other. Conduction can also occur *through* a material. For example, if you stir a cup of boiling water with a metal spoon, the heat will be transmitted from the water through the spoon to your hand (Figures 25.13 and 25.14).

Conduction is the transfer of heat by the direct contact of particles of matter.

How is thermal energy transferred? When your hand wraps around a mug of hot cocoa, the fast-moving molecules in the mug collide with the slower-moving molecules in the skin of your hand. The average kinetic energy of the molecules of your skin increases and, as a result, your skin temperature increases.

What happens as these collisions take place? The transfer of energy between molecules is like a bumper car ride at an amusement park. Some bumper cars start out going fast and others slow. Soon they are all hitting each other. When a fast car bounces into a slow car, the fast car slows down a bit and the slow car speeds up a bit. The cars may change direction as well. As each car changes direction it then hits other cars around it. Pretty soon all the cars in the arena are bouncing off each other at about the same average speed. When this happens, they are in equilibrium.

Figure 25.13: *A metal spoon placed in hot water quickly transmits the heat to your hand.*

Figure 25.14: *When a warmer material, like the hot water in this cup, comes in contact with a cooler material, like the spoon, there are lots of collisions between the atoms and molecules of each material.*

Collisions allow the transfer of energy needed to reach thermal equilibrium

The same thing happens at the atomic level. As collisions occur, the atoms and molecules of the warmer material slow down, and the atoms and molecules of the cooler material speed up. Some of the kinetic energy of the hotter material is transferred, one collision at a time, to the cooler material. Soon, both materials are at the same temperature. This is how two materials reach thermal equilibrium by conduction.

Conductors and insulators

Which state of matter conducts best?

Conduction can happen in solids, liquids, and gases. However, the more densely packed atoms or molecules of a solid can conduct more heat because there are many more collisions taking place. The low density of gases means that relatively fewer collisions occur, making air, for instance, a poor conductor of heat. This explains why many materials used to keep things warm, such as fiberglass insulation and down jackets, contain air pockets that slow the transfer of heat.

Figure 25.15: *A foam cup is a better thermal insulator than a glass cup. Therefore, liquid in a foam container will retain heat longer than it would in a glass container.*

What are thermal insulators and thermal conductors?

In general, materials that conduct heat easily are called thermal conductors and those that conduct heat poorly are called thermal insulators. For example, metal is a thermal conductor, and a foam cup is a thermal insulator. You may remember that the words *conductor* and *insulator* are also used to describe a material's ability to conduct electrical current. There is a reason for this common usage. In general, good electrical conductors like silver, copper, gold, and aluminum are also good heat conductors. Remember, metals are good conductors of current because there are many free electrons among the metal atoms. When a metal conducts heat, these free electrons transfer the kinetic energy through the material.

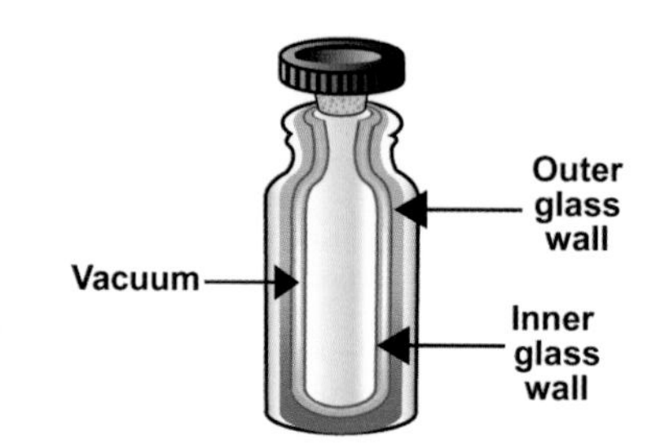

Figure 25.16: *Inside a thermos. Although the space between the two glass walls isn't a perfect vacuum, enough air molecules are removed to prevent most heat transfer by conduction and convection.*

A thermos uses a vacuum to prevent heat transfer by conduction

Conduction happens only if there are atoms and molecules available to collide with one another. In the vacuum of space, heat transfer by conduction cannot occur. One way to create an excellent thermal insulator on Earth is to mimic this vacuum. A thermos bottle (also known as a "vacuum flask") keeps liquids hot for hours using a vacuum as insulation. A thermos bottle consists of a small glass bottle surrounded by a slightly larger one (Figure 25.16). Air molecules have been removed from the space between the layers of glass. This prevents heat transfer by conduction. A small amount of heat is conducted through the cap and the glass (where the two walls meet), so eventually the contents will cool.

What is convection?

The second type of heat transfer is called convection. This type of heat transfer is involved in processes like heating our homes, increasing the speed at which water boils, and transferring energy through the atmosphere.

What is convection?

Have you ever warmed your hand by placing it over a candle? Most of the heat energy from the flame is moved from it to your hand by the movement of air. The air right above the flame heats up and expands. Because the expanded air is less dense, it rises, bringing the heat to your hand (Figure 25.17). This heat transfer process is called convection. Convection comes from a Latin word meaning *to carry together.*

Figure 25.17: *The air right above the flame heats up and expands, transferring heat to your hand.*

Convection is the transfer of heat by the actual motion of a fluid (liquid or gas) in the form of currents.

Convection can occur in all fluids, whether liquids or gases. Convection occurs because warmer fluids are less dense and rise. Cooler fluids are denser and sink. This motion of fluids causes currents.

Sea breezes are due to convection

Near coastlines, convection is responsible for *sea breezes*. During the daytime, the land is much hotter than the ocean. A sea breeze is created when hot air right above the land expands and rises. This rising air exerts pressure on the air high above the land. The air high above the land gets pushed aside, toward the sea. The air over the sea sinks as it is cooled because of the water's temperature. This air is compressed as it sinks. Because the air pressure is lower over the land, the cooling, sinking, compressing air over the sea rushes toward the land. This convection cycle creates a sea breeze (Figure 25.18).

In the evening, the ground cools rapidly but the ocean remains warm because of water's high specific heat. Now warm air rises over the water and is replaced with cooler, denser air from over land. The cycle reverses. This is known as a land breeze.

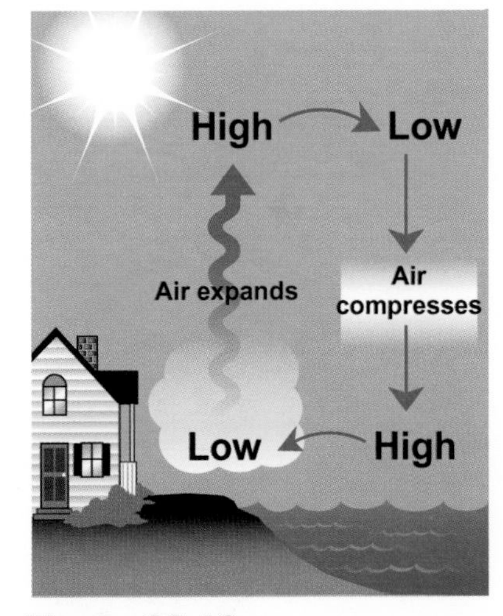

Figure 25.18: *A convection cycle creates a sea breeze.*

Convection happens all around you

Why wearing a sweater keeps you warm

Through the process of convection, the air surrounding your body warms up, rises, and carries the heat away. A wool sweater prevents this from happening by trapping air in many small pockets so that it cannot flow and carry the heat away. Similarly, in cold weather birds trap pockets of warmer air by fluffing their feathers.

Radiators heat rooms through convection

Convection enables a radiator to heat an entire room. The air surrounding the radiator warms due to conduction, and becomes less dense than the cold air on the far side of the room. The warmer air rises and cooler air from the far side of the room replaces it. Then the cooler air is warmed and rises. This air circulation transfers heat from the radiator to the far side of the room.

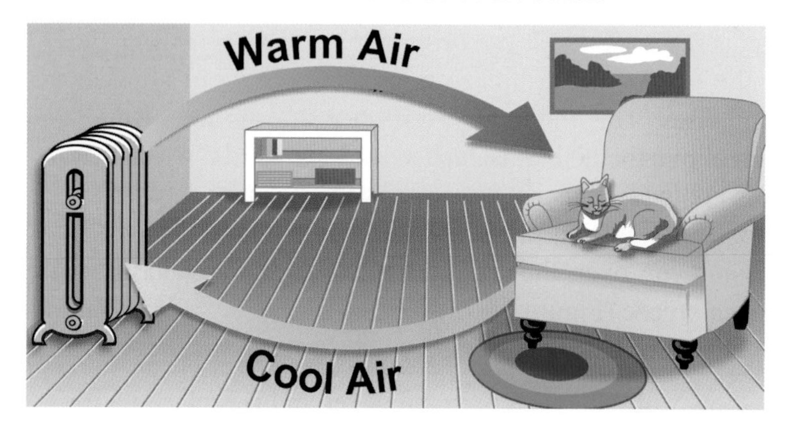

Alfonso Ortega

Does your computer ever freeze up when you are playing a game with lots of graphics? Sometimes this happens because computer processors can overheat when they have to perform a lot of complicated tasks.

Dr. Alfonso Ortega, a mechanical engineer and professor at Villanova University, is searching for better ways to help computers keep their cool.

Dr. Ortega studies how convection can be used to carry heat away from the processor. He runs cool liquid past the processor. The processor's heat is transferred to the liquid. The hot liquid is carried away, cooled down, and circulated back to the processor again.

In order to figure out how to use convection efficiently, Dr. Ortega used the human brain as a model. The brain is cooled by bringing blood in contact with it. The heat from the brain is transferred to millions of tiny blood vessels. These vessels empty into larger veins. Then the blood circulates through the body, cooling down in the process.

Source: SACNAS.org

What is radiation?

If you stand in the sun on a cold day and it is not too windy, you will feel the sun's warmth, no matter how cold it is outside. How does the warmth of the sun reach Earth? In this section, you will learn about another type of heat transfer known as **radiation** which is responsible for the way the sun warms our planet.

Radiation can occur in the vacuum of space

You know that conduction and convection require matter to transfer heat. Neither of these methods can transfer heat from the sun to Earth, because space is a vacuum. However, electromagnetic waves can transfer energy through a vacuum. This is fortunate because the Earth receives most of its heat in the form of electromagnetic radiation from the sun (Figure 25.19). Most of the sun's energy that is radiated to Earth is in the form of visible light or infrared radiation, along with a small amount of ultraviolet radiation. (These are types of electromagnetic waves.)

Radiation is the direct transfer of energy by electromagnetic waves.

Reflectors and absorbers

When electromagnetic waves from the sun strike Earth, some are absorbed and others are reflected. Black and dark colored objects tend to absorb all the light that falls on them. White objects, on the other hand, reflect light of all wavelengths. That's why you will stay cooler if you wear a white T-shirt outdoors on a hot sunny day rather than a dark colored one. The dark T-shirt would absorb more of the sun's energy, so you would feel hotter. Shiny objects also tend to reflect radiation, while a dull object made from the same material is a better absorber.

Some recipes call for you to cover the edges of a pie crust with aluminum foil while baking to prevent them from browning too quickly. Which side of the foil would you place outward, the shiny or the dull side? Why?

Emitters of radiation

Objects that are good absorbers of radiation are also good emitters of radiation. Thus, after sunset, a black road surface emits radiation and cools quickly, whereas the white sandy surface of a beach would not emit radiation efficiently and would cool slowly (Figure 25.20).

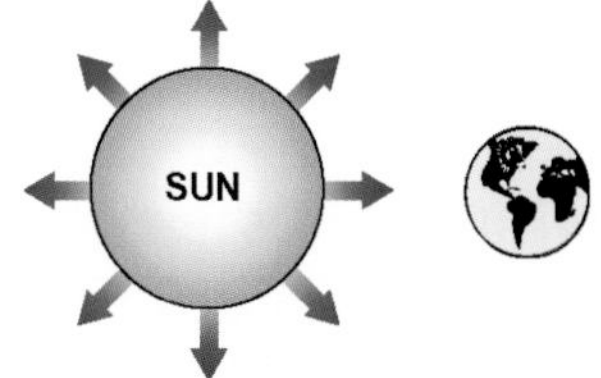

Figure 25.19: *The sun's electromagnetic radiation heats Earth.*

Figure 25.20: *A black road surface is a good absorber and good emitter of radiation. A white sand beach is a poor absorber and poor emitter of radiation.*

Chapter 25 Review

Vocabulary review

Match the following terms with the correct definition. There is one extra definition in the list that will not match any of the terms.

Set One

1. temperature
2. thermal expansion
3. thermal equilibrium
4. thermal energy
5. heat

a. A property of most materials: they expand when heated
b. The sum of all the kinetic energies of the molecules of a material
c. A measure of the average kinetic energy of the molecules of an object
d. The flow of thermal energy due to a temperature difference between two objects
e. If two objects are at the same temperature, they must contain the same amount of this
f. When two objects in thermal contact have reached the same temperature

Set Two

1. specific heat
2. first law of thermodynamics
3. conduction
4. convection
5. radiation

a. Transfer of heat by actual motion of a fluid in the form of currents
b. Transfer of heat by direct contact of particles
c. Amount of heat needed to increase the temperature of 1 gram of water 1° Celsius
d. Transfer of heat by electromagnetic waves
e. An object will remain at rest unless acted on by an unbalanced force
f. In an isolated system, the total amount of thermal energy remains constant

Concept review

1. How does a thermometer work?
2. Explain the difference between temperature and thermal energy.
3. Water is used in many machines to cool moving parts that would otherwise overheat due to friction. Why is water a good choice?
4. What happens to the individual molecules in an object when you increase the object's temperature? Why does this cause the object's size to increase?
5. Describe the flow of thermal energy that occurs when you hold a cold can of soda in your hand.
6. Due to its large mass, an iceberg has more thermal energy than a hot cup of coffee. Describe the flow of thermal energy that occurs if the cup of coffee is placed in thermal contact with an iceberg.
7. Why are some solid materials good thermal insulators while others are good conductors? Give an example of each.

8. Why is air a poor conductor of heat? How can air be used as an insulator? Give two examples.
9. Why does hot air rise?
10. Why doesn't convection occur in a solid material?
11. A blacktop road leads to a white sand beach. On a warm sunny day, which surface will heat up faster? Which will cool down faster at night? Explain why.
12. Using what you have learned about conductivity, explain why, on a cold winter day, a metal park bench feels colder than a wooden park bench, even though they are really the same temperature.

Problems

1. Convert the temperature at which paper burns, 451° Fahrenheit, to degrees Celsius.
2. A teapot contains 500 milliliters of water. Five thousand calories of heat are added to the teapot. What is the increase in the temperature of the water?
3. How much energy will it take to increase the temperature of 200 milliliters of water by 12°C?
4. One liter of water at 20°C is mixed with 3 liters of water at 80°C. What is the equilibrium temperature of the mixture?
5. In the previous problem, how many calories of heat are transferred from the hot water to the cold water?
6. A microwave oven uses microwave radiation to vibrate water molecules in food. The vibration increases the average kinetic energy of the water molecules, which increases the temperature of the food. If you place a ceramic coffee mug filled with water into the microwave oven and heat it for 90 seconds, the water will be very hot. Although the ceramic material contains no water, the cup itself gets warm. Why? Does the handle of the cup get hot too? Why or why not? Use the words radiation, conduction, and convection in your answer.
7. Two beakers each contain 1 kilogram of water at 0°C. One kilogram of gold at 100°C is placed in the first beaker. One kilogram of aluminum at 100°C is dropped into the other beaker.

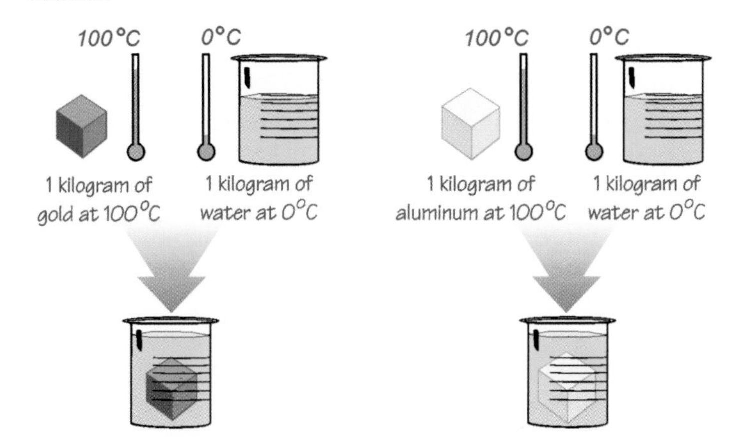

   a. Compare the amount of thermal energy contained in the aluminum and gold.
   b. After each beaker has reached thermal equilibrium, will they be at the same temperature or different temperatures? If they are different, tell which is warmer.
   c. Explain your answer to part (b). Use the concept of specific heat in your explanation.

Applying your knowledge

1. Look at or have someone show you the water level in an automobile radiator. You will notice that the radiator is filled up to the cap with water. Next to the radiator there is an overflow container. As the car runs and the water gets very hot, what happens to the water? What have engineers included in the design of the radiator system to return the water from the overflow into the radiator?

2. The first settlers in Colorado were very concerned about fruits and vegetables freezing in their root cellars overnight. They soon realized that if they put a large tub of water in the cellar, the food would not freeze. Explain why.

3. For one or more of the following write a short paper or give a presentation of your research:
   a. Scottish chemist Joseph Black (1728-1799) developed the theories of specific and latent heat. Research his life and how he made these discoveries.
   b. Lord Kelvin (1824-1907), a British Physicist, developed the idea of absolute zero, the coldest attainable temperature. Research absolute zero, the Kelvin scale, and Lord Kelvin's life.

4. A thermostat controls the switch on a furnace or air conditioner by sensing the temperature of the room. Explain, using conduction, convection, and radiation, where you would place the thermostat in your science classroom. Consider windows, outside and inside walls, and where the heating and cooling ducts are located. You can also sketch your answer—draw your classroom, showing room features and placement of the thermostat.

5. Building materials such as plywood, insulation, and windows are rated with a number called the "R value." The R value describes a material's insulating ability. Use the Internet or visit a building supply store to research the R value of at least three building materials used in the exterior walls of homes in your community. Then draw a diagram or build a three-dimensional model that shows a cross-section of a typical exterior wall. Label the R value of each material. Add the R values together to give the total R value for the wall.

6. Find out how much insulation is recommended for homes in your community. Where is the most insulation recommended—in the ceiling, walls, or floors? Using what you know about heat transfer, explain why.

7. Professional chefs often use convection ovens for baking cakes, pies, and other desserts. What is the difference between a convection oven and a conventional oven? Name some advantages of baking with a convection oven.

8. If you ask a group of third-graders what a refrigerator does, they may tell you that it "makes things cold." They might be surprised if you told them that a refrigerator is a machine that moves heat. Find out how a refrigerator works, and prepare a short presentation for an elementary-school class to share your knowledge. Create a worksheet with a simple diagram for the students to label and keep.

UNIT 9 Energy in the Earth System

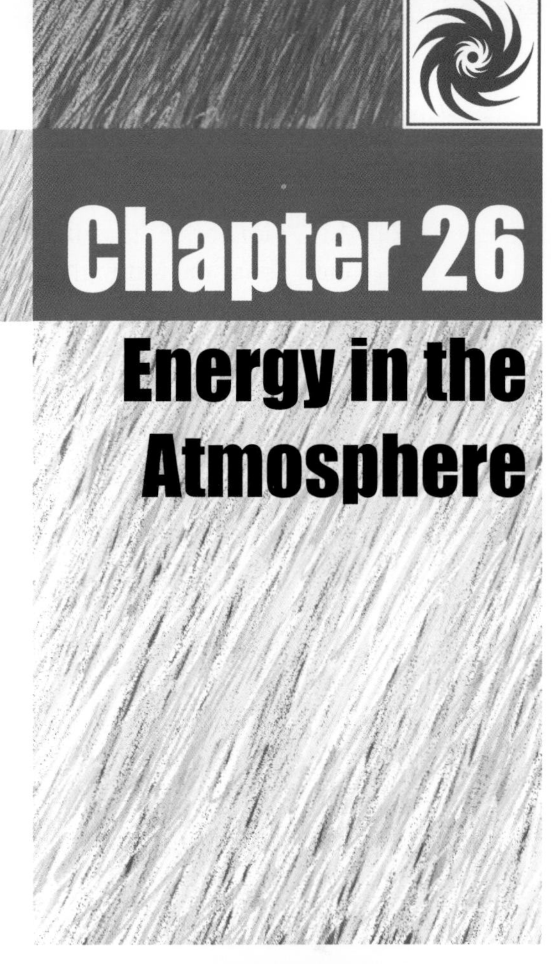

Chapter 26 Energy in the Atmosphere

In this chapter, you will learn what is in Earth's atmosphere, and why it contains more oxygen than other planets' atmospheres. You will learn how to measure atmospheric pressure and how pressure changes affect athletes. You will learn about layers of Earth's atmosphere and how ozone depletion is changing one layer. Finally, you will learn about energy in the atmosphere and the issues of greenhouse gas emission and global warming.

26.1	**The Atmosphere**	*Can you measure pressure in the atmosphere?*

In this Investigation you will build your own barometer. You will design a system to calibrate your barometer's pressure reading and to compensate for temperature changes to ensure an accurate measurement.

26.2	**Layers of the Atmosphere**	*Where do you find high concentrations of ozone?*

In this Investigation you will explore ozone concentrations in the lower atmosphere. You will test and compare ozone levels in locations around your school.

26.3	**Energy in the Atmosphere**	*Understanding factors that affect Earth's temperature*

In this three-part investigation you will first construct a model to demonstrate the effect of greenhouse gases on Earth's temperature. Next, you will graph the heat of fusion of ice and explore how this property allows ice to act as a thermal buffering system for Earth. Finally, you will compare the specific heat of water and air, and learn how water's high specific heat keeps Earth from experiencing extreme temperature changes.

Photo courtesy NASA/JPL-Caltech

Learning Goals

In this chapter, you will:

- ✔ Learn about the thermal structure and chemical composition of Earth's atmosphere.
- ✔ Compare and contrast the atmospheres of Venus, Earth, and Mars.
- ✔ Find out how life on Earth has changed Earth's atmosphere.
- ✔ Build and calibrate a barometer to measure atmospheric pressure.
- ✔ Learn how changing atmospheric pressure affects the weather.
- ✔ Describe the layers and the corresponding temperature changes in the atmosphere.
- ✔ Learn about ozone's helpful role in the stratosphere and harmful role in the troposphere.
- ✔ Measure ozone levels in your school.
- ✔ Describe energy transfer in the atmosphere.
- ✔ Discuss greenhouse gas emission reduction and other means of slowing global warming.
- ✔ Model factors affecting Earth's temperature, including greenhouse gases, thermal buffering properties of ice, and water's high specific heat.

Vocabulary

atmosphere
atmospheric pressure
barometer
chlorofluorocarbons
exosphere
global warming
greenhouse effect
ionosphere
mesosphere
ozone
stratosphere
thermosphere
troposphere

26.1 The Atmosphere

Earth's atmosphere is a layer of gases surrounding the planet, protecting and sustaining life. It insulates us so that we don't freeze at night. Its ozone layer protects us from the sun's ultraviolet rays, which cause eye and skin damage. Earth's atmosphere also contains the carbon dioxide needed by plants for photosynthesis, and the oxygen we need to breathe.

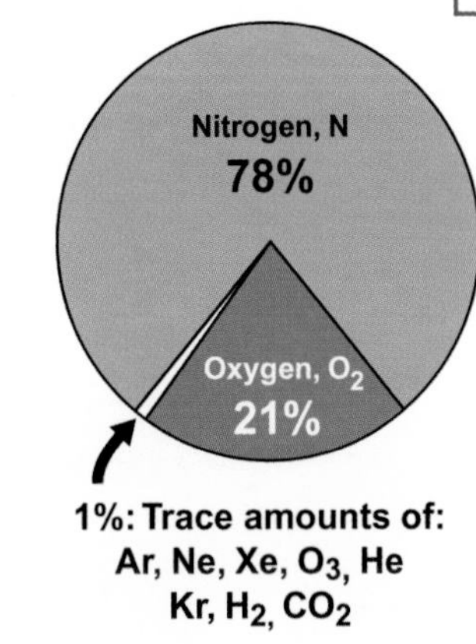

Figure 26.1: *Gases in Earth's atmosphere*

What's in Earth's atmosphere?

Earth's atmosphere is 78% nitrogen

You may be surprised to learn that the most abundant gas in Earth's atmosphere is nitrogen (N_2). Nitrogen gas makes up about 78 percent of Earth's atmosphere (Figure 26.1). Nitrogen is released into the air by volcanoes and decaying organisms. Nitrogen is a vital element for most living things. Protein, an essential substance in body tissues, contains nitrogen. However, this nitrogen is not absorbed directly from the air. Instead, the nitrogen is changed into nitrates (NO_3) by nitrogen-fixing organisms in the soil. Plants absorb nitrates from the soil and use them to make proteins. We eat plants (especially their seeds) or meat to obtain these proteins. Figure 26.2 describes Earth's nitrogen cycle.

21% oxygen

The second most abundant gas is oxygen, which makes up 21 percent of Earth's atmosphere. Atmospheric oxygen enables us to process the fuel we need for life. The remaining 1 percent of Earth's atmosphere is made up of 0.93 percent argon and 0.04 percent carbon dioxide. There are also tiny amounts of neon, helium, methane, krypton, and hydrogen, which we call trace gases.

Why Earth's atmosphere exists

This wonderful protective layer exists around Earth because our planet has just the right balance of size and distance from the sun. Scientists explain that at the time of Earth's formation, the heat from the sun drove off most of the lightweight elements such as hydrogen and helium. Earth would have remained a rocky airless world except that as it cooled, earthquakes and volcanoes spewed out heavier gases like nitrogen and carbon dioxide. Earth's mass gives it enough gravitational pull that these gases stayed around. Although the planet Mercury was formed in a similar way, its mass is too small and it is too close to the sun to have retained much of a layer of gas surrounding it. Venus, Earth, and Mars, however, retained their atmospheres.

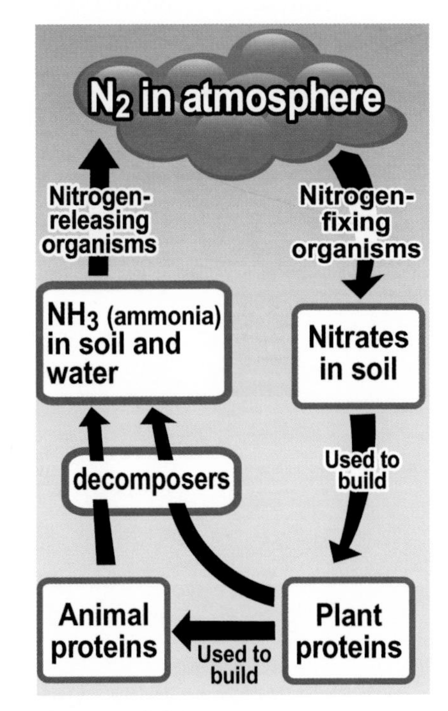

Figure 26.2: *The nitrogen cycle.*

Why does Earth's atmosphere have more oxygen than other planets?

The atmospheres of Venus, Earth, and Mars were formed in similar ways, so we might expect them to contain similar elements. Table 26.1 compares the atmospheres of these planets.

Table 26.1: *The atmospheres of Venus, Earth, and Mars*

Planet	Major gases in atmosphere			
Venus	96% CO_2	3% N_2	0.1% H_2O	
Earth	0.04% CO_2	78% N_2	21.0% O_2	0.93% Ar
Mars	95% CO_2	3% N_2	1.6% Ar	

Similarities between Venus and Mars

Venus and Mars show striking similarities in the makeup of their atmospheres. They are mostly carbon dioxide, with a small amount of nitrogen. Earth, on the other hand, is very different. Ours is the only planet with a large amount of oxygen and just a tiny amount of carbon dioxide. Why is Earth so different?

Life changed Earth's atmosphere

Through photosynthesis, life on Earth has actually changed the planet's atmosphere. Many of the earliest and simplest forms of life used (and still use) photosynthesis to obtain energy from the sun. This process breaks down carbon dioxide, uses carbon to build the organism, and releases oxygen into the air.

Where does the carbon go?

When organisms die and decompose, some of the carbon from their bodies is released as carbon dioxide back in to the air. However, if all of the carbon used by life processes returned to Earth's atmosphere, our atmosphere would still be like that of Venus and Mars. Instead, some of the carbon used to build living organisms ends up staying in the ground. Earth stores carbon in several ways.

How Earth stores carbon

Many water organisms use carbon (along with calcium) to form shells of calcium carbonate. When the organisms die, these shells sink to the bottom of the water and stay there. The carbon doesn't return to the atmosphere. Huge piles of calcium carbonate have built up over the years, creating some of our land forms. "Fossil fuels" (oil, coal, and natural gas) also store carbon from decaying plants and animals in the ground. Another process stores carbon in a type of rock called limestone.

Tiny builders

Phytoplankton such as this coccolithophore use carbon dioxide dissolved in seawater for photosynthesis. They also use the carbon to form intricate calcium carbonate shells like the one shown above. Although each organism is only 0.5 millimeters across, these and other calcium carbonate shells pile up over the centuries, creating beautiful structures like the White Cliffs of Dover in Britain.

What is atmospheric pressure?

Air pressure is the measurement of the force of air molecules pushing on the walls of a container, like inside a basketball.

Air molecules exert pressure

Did you know that the air molecules on the outside of the basketball or other container are also exerting pressure? The pressure of air molecules in the atmosphere is a result of the weight of a column of air pressing down on an area. Atmospheric pressure is a measurement of the force of air molecules in the atmosphere at a given altitude.

Atmospheric pressure is a measurement of the force of air molecules in the atmosphere at a given altitude.

How we withstand air pressure

At sea level, the weight of the column of air above a person is about 9,800 newtons (2,200 pounds)! This is equal to the weight of a small car. Why aren't we crushed by this pressure? First, there is air inside our bodies that is pushing out with the same amount of pressure, so the forces are balanced. Second, our skeletons are designed to withstand the pressure of our environment.

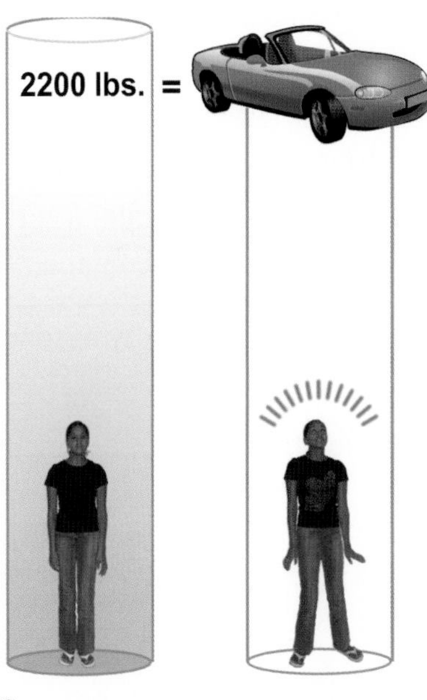

Contrast these systems with those used by deep-sea animals. Fish that live at a depth of 10,000 feet are under pressure 300 times greater than we withstand. Instead of thick, strong bones, deep-sea creatures have cell membranes that contain a material that would be liquid at Earth's surface. The intense water pressure makes the material more rigid, so that the fish's body tissues hold their shape and function properly. Each organism on Earth is uniquely adapted to thrive in the pressure of its particular environment.

Why do ears "pop"?

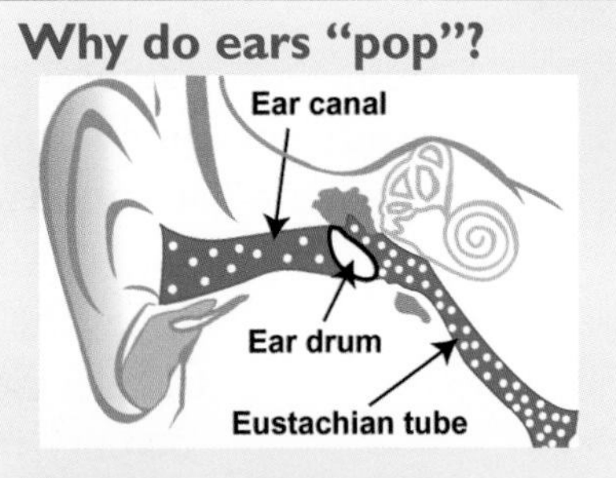

Have your ears ever "popped" on an airplane? When an airplane goes through a rapid altitude change, the air pressure around your body changes, but the air pressure inside your body remains the same. For example, when an airplane ascends, the air in the ear canal becomes less dense than the air in the eustacian tube. Then the air inside the eustacian tube pushes outward on the eardrum.

If you yawn widely, you can sometimes equalize the air pressure pushing against your eardrum from the inside with the pressure pushing from the outside. Your eardrum "pops" when the pressure suddenly becomes equal again.

How is atmospheric pressure measured?

Barometers measure air pressure

Atmospheric pressure is measured with an instrument called a barometer. The oldest type of barometer is a *mercury barometer* (Figure 26.3). It consists of a tube sealed at one end and partially filled with mercury. The open end of the tube stands in a dish of mercury. As air presses down on the mercury in the dish, it forces the liquid in the tube to rise. When the air pressure is greater, the mercury travels farther up the tube. The air pressure at sea level generally causes the mercury in a barometer to rise 29.92 inches. The table below describes ways that air pressure is measured.

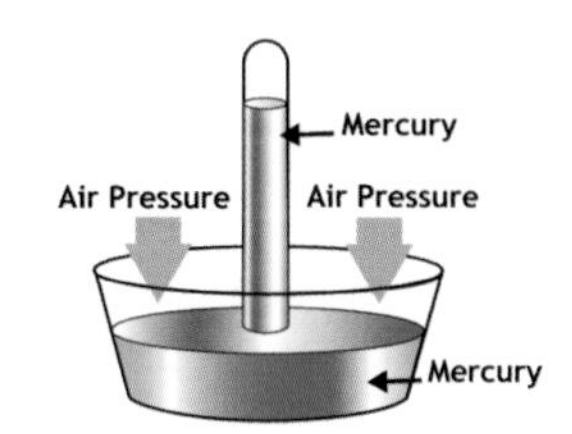

Figure 26.3: *A mercury barometer.*

Table 26.2: *Units of air pressure*

Unit	Description	Relationship
inches of mercury (in Hg)	Unit describing the height of a column of mercury in a barometer.	29.92 in Hg = 1 atm
atmospheres (atm)	One atmosphere is the standard air pressure at sea level. Used by divers to compare pressure under water with surface pressure.	1 atm = 1.013 bar
pounds per square inch (psi)	English unit commonly used to measure pressure of air in a container, like a tire or ball.	1 psi = 6,895 pa
pascals (pa)	Metric unit commonly used to measure pressure of air in a container.	1 pa = 1 N/m^2
bars	Metric unit used to measure atmospheric pressure, most often in the form of millibars.	1 bar = 10,000 pa

Figure 26.4: *An aneroid barometer.*

Aneroid barometers

Mercury barometers have a downside: Mercury is a poisonous liquid, and it evaporates rapidly at room temperature, creating unhealthy vapors. You would not want to have a mercury barometer in your living room! Most barometers in use today are *aneroid barometers*. They have an airtight cylinder made of thin metal. The walls of the cylinder are squeezed inward when the atmospheric pressure is high. At lower pressures, the walls bulge out. A dial attached to the cylinder moves as the cylinder changes shape, indicating the change in air pressure.

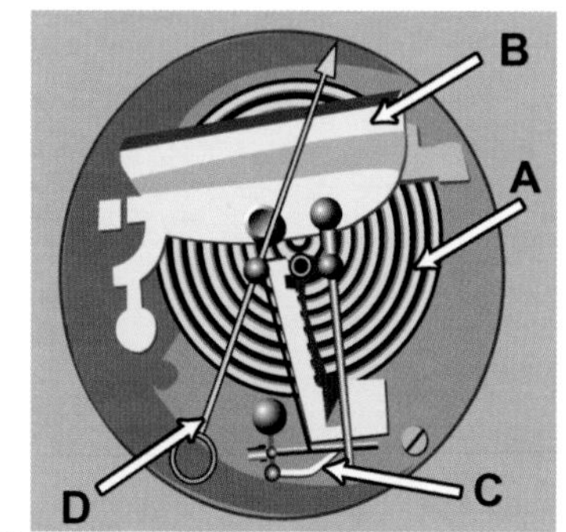

Figure 26.5: *Inside an aneroid barometer. Letter A shows the airtight cylinder, to which a spring, B, is attached. C is a series of levers that amplify the spring's movement. A small chain transfers the movement to the pointer, D.*

Atmospheric pressure changes with altitude

Figure 26.6: *Supplemental oxygen is needed by mountain climbers at high altitudes.*

Why do climbers attempting to reach the summit of Mount Everest carry oxygen tanks? Why do sports teams from coastal areas want to arrive several days before their event in Denver, Colorado? The answer to both questions is: because the pressure of the atmosphere changes as you rise above sea level. Read on to find out more.

A giant pile of cotton balls

Earth's gravity prevents the nitrogen and oxygen molecules that make up 99 percent of our atmosphere from flying off into space. You can imagine the molecules of the atmosphere to be like a giant pile of cotton balls. At the top of the pile, the cotton balls would be loosely spread out. But the cotton balls at the top press down on the ones underneath, and those cotton balls press down on the ones below them. The cotton balls at the bottom of the pile are packed together much more tightly than the ones at the top.

Greatest pressure at the bottom

Think about what it would be like to be a cotton ball at the bottom of the pile. You would feel like you were getting squashed by the pressure of all the cotton balls above you!

Air pressure is greatest at sea level

A similar thing happens in the atmosphere. The molecules at the bottom are packed together very densely, because the weight of the molecules above presses down on them. The air pressure is greatest at sea level (the bottom of the atmosphere). As you get farther and farther from sea level, the molecules get more and more spread out, so that there are fewer molecules above you pushing down. These two factors mean that air pressure decreases very rapidly as you gain altitude.

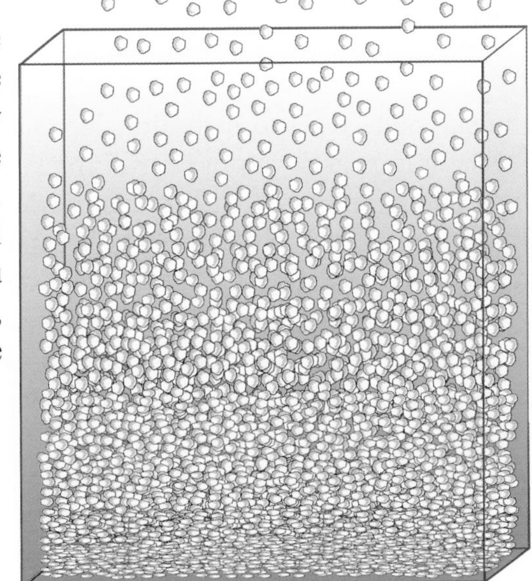

As altitude increases, atmospheric pressure decreases rapidly

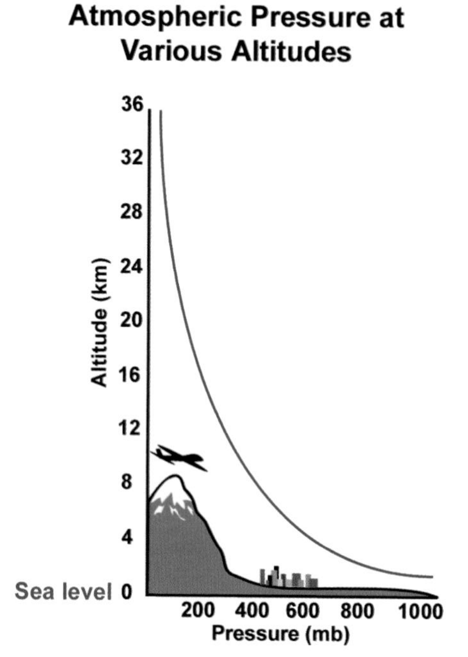

This graph shows that as altitude increases, atmospheric pressure decreases rapidly. At sea level, atmospheric pressure averages about 1,013 millibars. At the top of Mount Washington, New Hampshire (the highest point in the northeastern United States, at 1.917 kilometers), the average atmospheric pressure is 800.3 millibars. At the top of Mt. Everest, a height of 8.85 kilometers, atmospheric pressure averages only 334 millibars, only one-third of the pressure found at sea level.

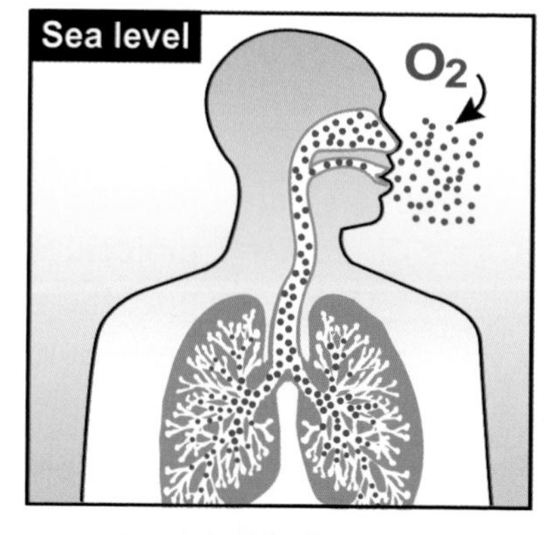

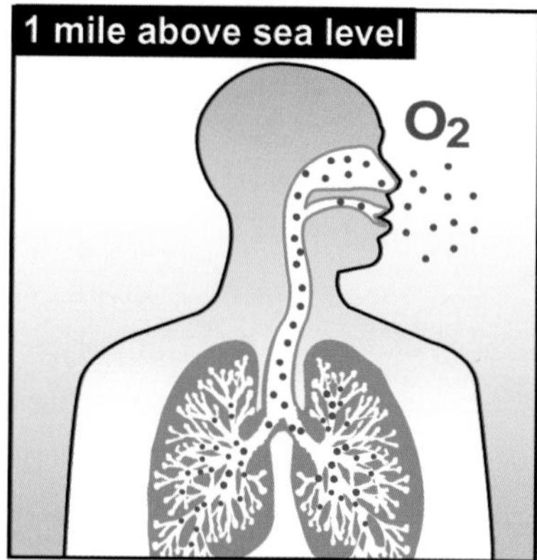

Figure 26.7: *One breath of air at sea level contains many more oxygen molecules than one breath at 1.609 kilometers (one mile above sea level).*

Adjusting to high altitudes

How does the human body react to high altitude? Our bodies have to adjust to lower oxygen levels in less dense air. In Denver (nicknamed the "mile-high city" because it is about one mile, or 1.609 kilometers, above sea level), athletes who have trained at sea level need about a week to become acclimated to their new surroundings. Within a week, their bodies undergo several changes. Breathing becomes deeper and larger portions of the lungs become involved in oxygen exchange. They produce extra red blood cells so that they can transport the available oxygen more efficiently. They also release more of an enzyme that helps the blood release oxygen to the body tissues. Without these changes, even well-conditioned athletes would feel tired and winded in so-called "thin air."

26.2 Layers of the Atmosphere

You probably know that temperature at the top of a high mountain is usually colder than at the base. But did you know that the temperature doesn't just keep decreasing as you go farther and farther up in the atmosphere? Actually, the temperature first decreases, then increases, then decreases, and then increases again. Scientists divide Earth's atmosphere into four different layers. As you will see, the divisions are based on these zigzags in temperature.

The four layers

The troposphere

We live in the **troposphere**, the layer that extends from 0 to approximately 11 kilometers (36,000 feet) above Earth's surface. About 90 percent of the atmosphere's mass is found in the troposphere. Almost all of Earth's water vapor, carbon dioxide, dust, airborne pollutants, and terrestrial life forms exist here.

Temperature decreases as you go up in the troposphere

The troposphere is heated by the infrared radiation from Earth's surface; therefore, it is warmest closest to that surface. On average, for every one kilometer you go up in the atmosphere, the temperature drops about 6.5° Celsius. At the top of the troposphere, the temperature is about -60°C. At this temperature, the water vapor has changed to ice. Without this cold region, water molecules could rise to a point where they would break down into hydrogen and oxygen. The lightweight hydrogen could then escape into space. Earth would lose the water that is so critical to life.

Weather occurs in the troposphere

The name troposphere contains the Greek root *tropo*, meaning "to turn or change." The troposphere is the region where clouds form and dissipate, and where all the weather happens. When you hear about airplanes "flying above the weather," this means that they are flying above the troposphere.

Temperature increases as you go up in the stratosphere

Above the troposphere lies the **stratosphere**, extending from about 11 kilometers to 50 kilometers above Earth's surface. In the stratosphere, the temperature actually *increases* as you go up. Why? High in the stratosphere there is a thin layer of **ozone**, the three-atom form of oxygen (O_3). The ozone absorbs the high-energy ultraviolet radiation from the sun. This process not only warms the stratosphere, it also protects us from the skin and eye damage caused by ultraviolet radiation.

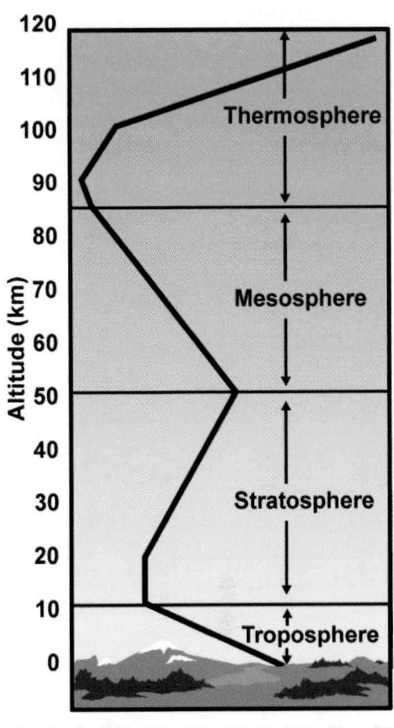

Figure 26.8: *The atmosphere is divided into layers based on temperature changes.*

In the mesosphere, the temperature falls as you go up

Above the stratosphere, the temperature begins to drop again. This marks the beginning of the **mesosphere**, which extends from 50 to 80 kilometers above Earth. The mesosphere is the coldest layer of the atmosphere, and at its outer reaches the temperature can be as low as -90°C. You may be surprised to learn that it is in this extremely cold layer that meteors burn up as they fall toward Earth. Friction created when air molecules rub against the meteor causes the meteor to burn, creating what we see as "shooting stars" in the night sky.

High temperatures in the thermosphere

The outer region of Earth's atmosphere is called the **thermosphere**. This part of the atmosphere is very thin. A cubic meter of air at Earth's surface contains 100,000 times as many molecules as a cubic meter of air in the thermosphere. The molecules in the thermosphere have a lot of kinetic energy, because the energy from the sun hits them first. Temperatures in this layer can reach 1,800°C.

Very little heat transfer

Interestingly, if you could hop out of a space shuttle into the thermosphere, you wouldn't feel hot. Temperature, as you remember, measures the average kinetic energy of the molecules of a substance. Heat, on the other hand, involves the transfer of energy from one object to another. Because the air molecules in the thermosphere are so far apart, very few of them would collide with you, so there would be very little heat transferred.

Divisions of the thermosphere

The thermosphere is further divided into two regions, the **ionosphere** and the **exosphere**. In the ionosphere (80-550 kilometers above Earth), the sun's ultraviolet light ionizes atoms and molecules. This process releases energy, which is why such high temperatures are recorded in the thermosphere. The ionosphere makes it possible for you to tune into AM radio stations that originate a hundred or more miles away. The radio signals are rebroadcast by the ions in the ionosphere back to Earth.

Satellites in the exosphere

The exosphere is the region extending from 550 kilometers above Earth. It does not have a specific outer limit. In this region, the atmosphere gets thinner and thinner. Lightweight atoms and molecules escape into space. Satellites orbit Earth in the exosphere, providing the photos used in television weather reports, transmitting long distance telephone calls, gathering intelligence information, and broadening our understanding of deep space through the use of special telescopes.

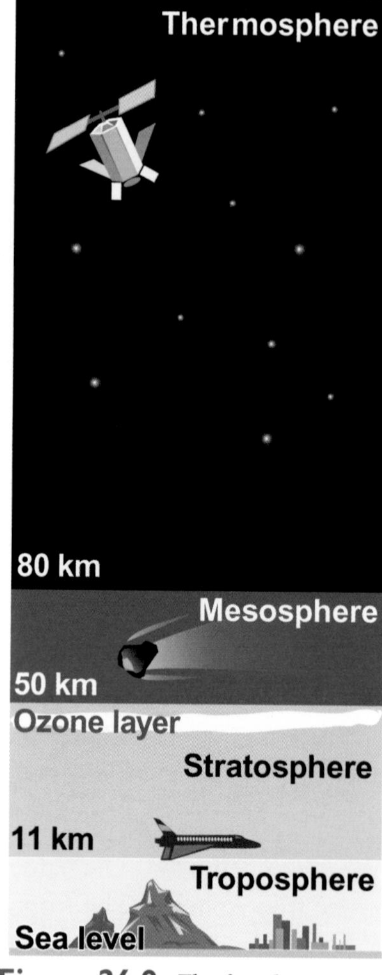

Figure 26.9: *The four layers of the atmosphere include the troposphere, where we live; the stratosphere, which contains the ozone layer; the mesosphere, where meteors burn; and the thermosphere, where satellites orbit Earth.*

Chlorofluorocarbons and ozone depletion

The thinning ozone layer

In the 1970s, scientists noticed that the ozone layer in the stratosphere above Antarctica was thinning. The detection of chlorine in the stratosphere led to the remarkable discovery that human activity is responsible for the loss of ozone. The culprit, it turns out, is a group of chemicals called chlorofluorocarbons (or CFC's). These chemicals were once commonly used in air conditioners, in aerosol spray cans, and for cleaning machine parts. While most airborne chemicals break down in the troposphere, chlorofluorocarbons stay intact until they travel up to the stratosphere (a journey taking anywhere from 6 to 26 years!), where they finally disintegrate, releasing chlorine. The chlorine reacts with ozone molecules, leaving behind ordinary diatomic oxygen, which does not block incoming ultraviolet radiation.

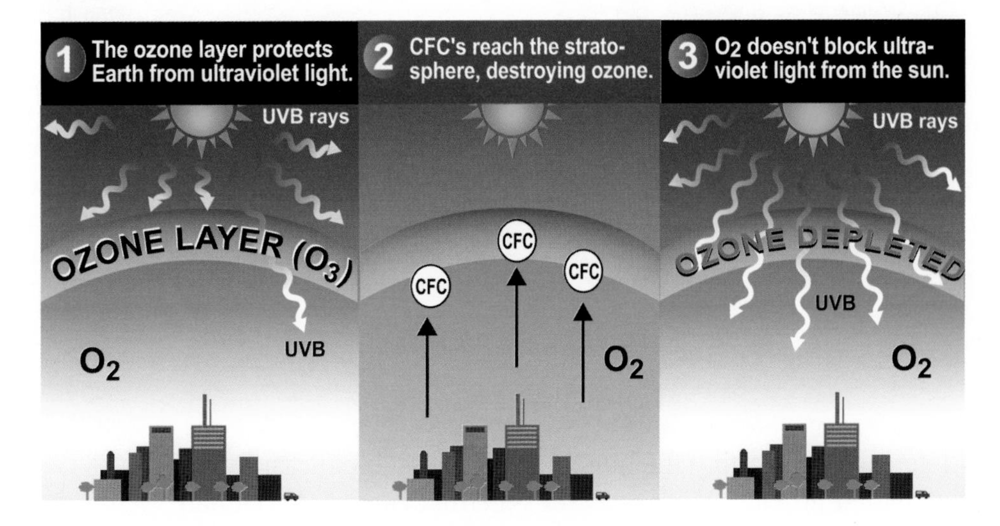

Repairing the damage

In the London Agreement of 1991, more than 90 countries banned the production and use of CFC's except for limited medical uses. This kind of international cooperation shows that we can make progress in repairing damage to our atmosphere. However, it will take several decades for the existing CFC's to break down. As a result, the problem of the "ozone hole" may get worse before it gets better.

The CFC-ozone reaction

Several processes destroy ozone in the stratosphere. Different processes operate under different atmospheric conditions. One common process starts when ultraviolet light (*hv*) hits a CFC molecule, and a chlorine atom breaks off:

$$CFCl_3 + hv \longrightarrow CFCl_2 + Cl$$

The Cl atom reacts with O_3, giving off O_2 and ClO. Two ClO molecules combine to form Cl_2O_2. When Cl_2O_2 encounters ultraviolet light, it disassociates, generating O_2 and two chlorine atoms.

$$(1)\ 2[Cl + O_3 \longrightarrow O_2 + ClO]$$
$$(2)\ 2ClO \longrightarrow Cl_2O_2$$
$$(3)\ Cl_2O_2 + hv \longrightarrow 2Cl + O_2$$
$$\text{Net: } 2O_3 + hv \longrightarrow 3O_2$$

As you can see, chlorine atoms are used in the first step but produced in the third. This means that a few chlorine atoms can repeat this sequence of reactions again and again, destroying a great many ozone molecules.

26.3 Energy in the Atmosphere

Our sun, through the process of nuclear fusion, converts 5 million tons of its own mass into energy every second. The sun broadcasts some of that energy as electromagnetic radiation. Earth receives only two-billionths of this radiation, but that is enough to sustain conditions needed for life here to exist.

What happens to solar energy once it enters Earth's atmosphere?

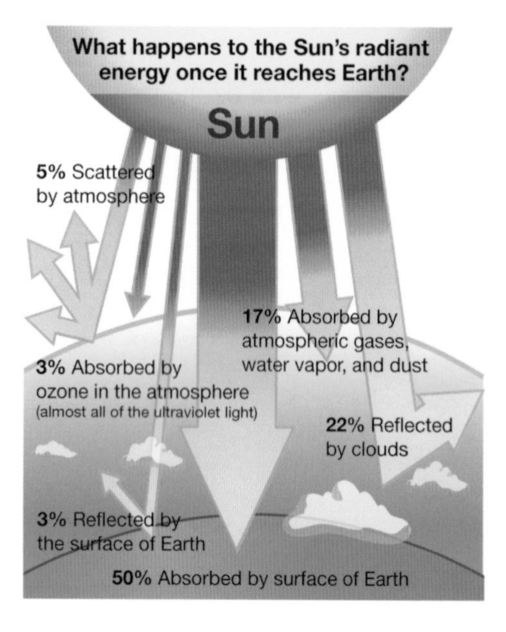

Outgoing radiation

So how does the energy that radiates from Earth get back out to space?

As Earth's surface absorbs incoming solar radiation, it gives off infrared radiation. Some of the infrared radiation is absorbed by air molecules and the energy is transferred through the atmosphere by convection, evaporation, condensation, and radiation. Eventually, the energy is transferred all the way back out to space.

Incoming radiation Even though Earth intercepts only a tiny fraction of the radiation broadcast by the sun into space, this radiation provides most of Earth's thermal energy. About half is absorbed by Earth's surface, about a quarter is absorbed or scattered by the atmosphere, and about a quarter is reflected directly back to space.

Earth's average temperature stays constant Every day, Earth absorbs more and more radiation from the sun. Why doesn't the planet just keep getting hotter? Earth's temperature remains at a relatively constant average of 27°C because the same amount of energy that is absorbed by Earth radiates out from Earth as infrared radiation. See the sidebar at right to find out more about how the energy radiating from Earth gets back to space.

The greenhouse effect and global warming

Greenhouse effect

You have probably heard of the greenhouse effect. This phrase, first used in 1937, describes the fact that molecules in the atmosphere keep Earth warmer than it would be without an atmosphere. How does this work?

Imagine an empty bucket with a hole near the bottom. If you pour water into that bucket at the same rate that the water spills out the hole, the bucket will never get full. However, if you fill the bucket partially with pebbles, it will take longer for the water to get through the bucket and out the hole. Even though the same amount of water still enters and exits the bucket, the water level in the bucket now stays at a constant *non-zero* level.

There are molecules in the atmosphere that act like the pebbles in the bucket. They make it take longer for the infrared radiation to escape back into space. Even though the same amount of energy (like the water in the bucket) is constantly coming into and leaving the planet, it takes time for the energy to pass through the atmosphere. While this energy remains in the atmosphere, it keeps Earth warm.

Greenhouse gases and global warming

Carbon dioxide (CO_2), methane (CH_4), nitrous oxide (N_2O), and water (H_2O), the so-called "greenhouse gases," are the molecules that act most like the pebbles in the bucket. Notice that all of the greenhouse gas molecules have at least three atoms joined together. They are larger than the nitrogen (N_2) and oxygen (O_2) molecules that make up most of Earth's atmosphere. Their large size makes them very good absorbers of infrared radiation. As a result, they are most responsible for increasing the time that the sun's energy remains in the atmosphere. The longer this energy remains in the atmosphere, the warmer Earth's average temperature will be. We call this process global warming.

Earth's "energy budget"

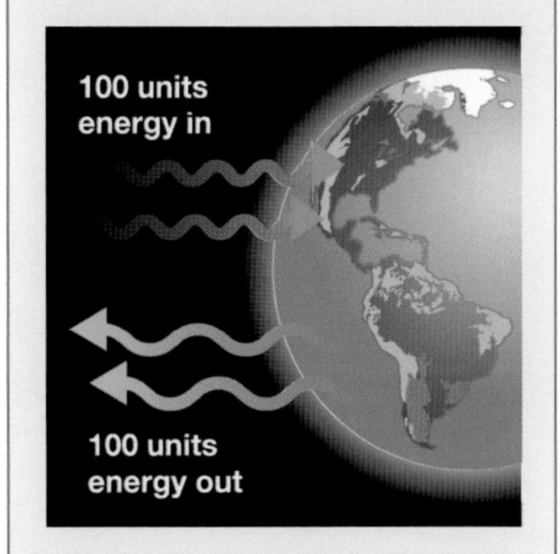

For every 100 units of radiation that enters Earth's atmosphere, 100 units exit. The incoming radiation is mostly in the form of visible and ultraviolet light. These light waves have higher frequency and shorter wavelength than the infrared waves that are emitted by Earth. They pass through the atmosphere faster than the infrared rays. The time lag between incoming and outgoing radiation means that there is energy in the atmosphere keeping Earth warm.

Some global warming occurs naturally

Some global warming due to greenhouse gases is normal on Earth. For centuries before the Industrial Revolution, the amount of carbon dioxide in the atmosphere was 0.028 percent, or 280 parts per million. This naturally produced CO_2 kept Earth at an average temperature about 30°C warmer than it would have been without any CO_2 in the atmosphere.

While some global warming occurs naturally, human activities add extra greenhouse gas molecules to the atmosphere, which may warm the planet further.

CO_2 levels increasing

The present amount of CO_2 in the atmosphere is 370 ppm. Scientists project the level will rise to 700 ppm by 2100, due mainly to the burning of fossil fuels. Higher CO_2 levels may cause climate changes. Seven hundred parts per million would probably cause an increase in average global temperature of 1.5 to 3.5°C. Although this increase may seem insignificant, it could have far-reaching effects.

Ocean flooding and erosion

Scientists have already observed that the open waters amid the floating ice on the Arctic Ocean are expanding every year because the glaciers are melting. In the past century, ocean levels have risen between 10 and 25 centimeters, according to the Intergovernmental Panel on Climate Change. Along with the flooding that may occur if this trend continues, coastal areas would be subject to stronger wave action, resulting in greater erosion and large-scale destruction of both property and natural habitat.

Altered agricultural areas

Areas such as the Great Plains in the United States might become drier and dustier because of increased evaporation resulting from higher average temperatures. This could cause much of the rich topsoil to blow away, leaving desert-like conditions behind. However, areas of Canada, Northern Europe, and Siberia that are now too cold for significant farming could become suitable for agriculture.

Figure 26.10: *Adding greenhouse gases to the atmosphere is like adding more pebbles to the bucket. It takes longer for radiation to escape from the atmosphere, so Earth's average temperature rises.*

Global warming on Venus

The planet Venus, as you may remember, has an atmosphere 90 times denser than Earth's. Most of Venus's atmosphere (96%) is made up of carbon dioxide, one of the greenhouse gases. The carbon dioxide slows the rate at which radiation escapes from the atmosphere. As a result, the average surface temperature on Venus is more than 500°C. Even though Mercury is closer to the sun, Venus is the hottest planet in the solar system, due to its thick atmosphere.

Change in ocean current paths

The increase in average global temperature could cause some shifting of big ocean currents, actually causing certain parts of the world to become cooler. For example, if the direction of the Gulf Stream current changed, the British Isles, which are at the same latitude as the northern portion of Canada's Labrador and Newfoundland province, would be much colder than they are now.

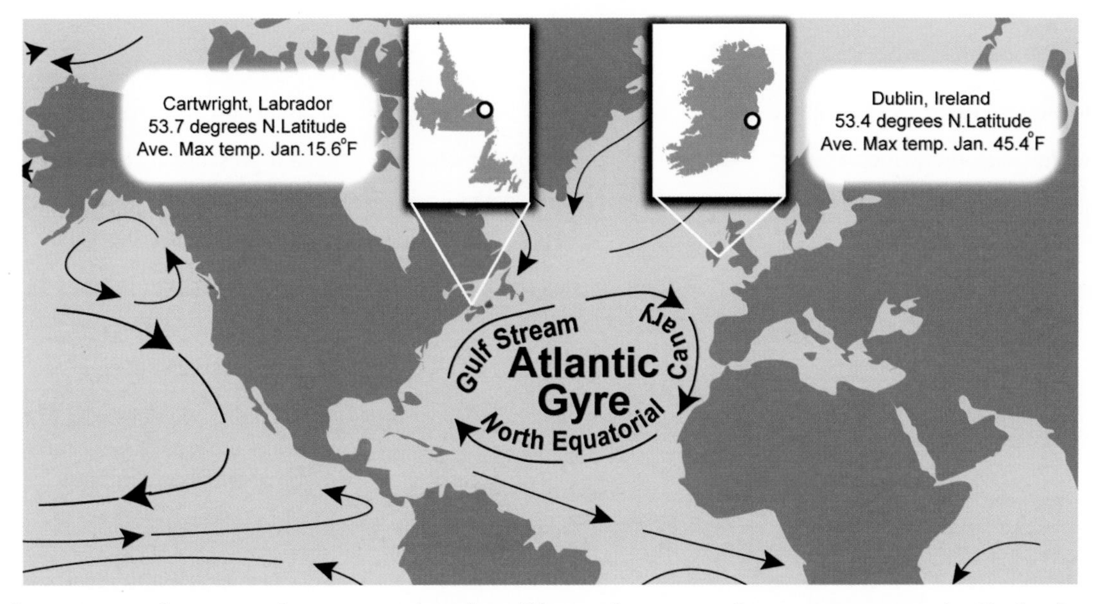

Reducing greenhouse gas emissions will require more than one solution

Lowering greenhouse gas levels will require more than one approach. Reducing power plant emissions and reducing the use of gasoline-powered cars and trucks are two important proposals. New technologies that produce fewer greenhouse gas emissions, such as the gas-electric hybrid car and hydrogen fuel cell, also play a significant role. Reviving some older methods of transport, such as using barges and trains for intercity transport of consumer goods, could also reduce greenhouse gas emissions.

For discussion:

1. Which of the changes listed above would be easiest to bring about?
2. How do you think governments should encourage and/or enforce these changes?
3. What additional steps should be taken to lower greenhouse gas levels?

Hydrogen-powered cars

Someday, you may drive a car with zero greenhouse gas emission. Hydrogen-fuel cell researchers are working with automobile manufacturers to design and test cars that run on a system of battery-like cells that convert hydrogen and oxygen to water, producing electricity and heat.

These hydrogen fuel cells are currently used by NASA to power the space shuttles' electrical systems. The only by-product of the fuel cells is water—which the astronauts use for drinking.

The biggest challenge facing researchers is finding the best source of hydrogen. Pure hydrogen is hard to store and transport. One proposal is to use methanol, which can be stored and delivered like gasoline. A device called a reformer removes hydrogen from methanol and delivers it to the fuel cell.

Chapter 26 Review

Vocabulary review

Match the following terms with the correct definition. There is one extra definition in the list that will not match any of the terms.

Set One

1. atmosphere
2. atmospheric pressure
3. oxygen
4. nitrogen
5. carbon dioxide

a. Most abundant gas in Earth's atmosphere
b. Increases rapidly as altitude increases
c. Measurement of force of air molecules in the atmosphere at a given altitude
d. Layer of gases surrounding a planet
e. Most abundant gas in atmosphere of Venus
f. 21% of Earth's atmosphere

Set Two

1. mercury barometer
2. aneroid barometer
3. 1atm
4. inches of mercury
5. ozone

a. Standard air pressure at sea level
b. Air pressure at sea level is 29.2 __________
c. Measures atmospheric pressure by the rise and fall of mercury in a tube
d. The three-atom form of oxygen
e. A molecule that is harmful to humans when found in the stratosphere
f. Airtight cylinder made of thin metal, with walls that squeeze in or bulge out depending on atmospheric pressure

Set Three

1. ionosphere
2. mesosphere
3. stratosphere
4. thermosphere
5. troposphere

a. Region of atmosphere 50 to 80 km above Earth's surface; meteoroids burn up here
b. Bottom layer of Earth's atmosphere; contains 90% of atmosphere's mass
c. Outer region of Earth's atmosphere; has very high temperatures
d. Region of the atmosphere where all of the oxygen is found
e. Region of atmosphere in which the sun's ultraviolet rays ionize atoms and molecules
f. Layer of atmosphere from 11 to 50 km above Earth, with thin layer of ozone near the top

Set Four

1. greenhouse gases
2. global warming
3. electromagnetic radiation
4. infrared radiation
5. chlorofluorocarbons

a. The energy Earth receives from the sun
b. Chemicals formerly used in air conditioners and aerosol spray cans
c. Given off by Earth and its atmosphere as heat
d. Large molecules that trap Earth's heat and are increasing the temperature of the planet
e. An increase in Earth's temperature due mainly to increased CO_2 in the atmosphere
f. The three-atom form of oxygen

Concept review

1. What is in Earth's atmosphere? How has life on Earth changed Earth's atmosphere?
2. Explain how Earth's atmosphere formed.
3. Name one type of barometer and explain how it works.
4. Describe the four layers of Earth's atmosphere. Be sure to include the thermal characteristics of each layer.
5. Describe what would happen to Earth's water cycle if the top of the troposphere were as warm as the surface of Earth.
6. What is ozone? Where in Earth's atmosphere is it found? How does ozone affect your life?
7. If Earth constantly receives energy from the sun, why doesn't it keep getting hotter and hotter?
8. What would happen to Earth if there were no "greenhouse effect?"
9. What might happen to Earth if the amount of greenhouse gases in the atmosphere doubles? Name two possible outcomes.
10. List two ways that humans have increased the amount of greenhouse gases in the atmosphere. Suggest a means of reducing each.

Problems

1. Venus has an atmosphere that is much denser than Earth's, while Mars' atmosphere is much less dense than Earth's. Use the library or Internet to research how oceans on Venus and Mars may have affected the density of their atmospheres.
2. Carbon dioxide is the most abundant gas in the atmospheres of Venus and Mars. Why is this not true of Earth? Name at least one way that carbon is stored on Earth.
3. Would you expect a barometer to have a higher reading in Alaska's Denali national park or in Florida's Everglades national park? (Hint: An atlas may help you.)
4. Earth receives most of its energy from the sun. However, some of Earth's energy is internal energy. What is the primary source of this internal energy? What percentage of Earth's total energy comes from this source?
5. Scientists use computer models to predict the effect of the increase in greenhouse gases on the planet. What are some of the benefits and limitations of computer modeling systems?
6. The "ozone hole" above Antarctica varies in size over the course of a year. What causes the natural variation in the ozone layer?
7. Mexican chemist Mario Molina first wondered about the effects of chlorofluorocarbons in the atmosphere in 1973, when he was a graduate student in California. In 1996, he and two colleagues were awarded the Nobel prize in Chemistry for their discovery and exposure of the role of CFC's in ozone depletion. Research the life and work of Mario Molina. Develop an illustrated timeline of the twenty-three years he spent working on this project.

Applying your knowledge

1. Satellites are used for many different purposes, including weather monitoring, communications, intelligence gathering, and for collecting images of the universe through special telescopes. Research one type of satellite and provide a 5 minute report to your class about how it works, the shape and speed of its orbit, and how it affects your daily life.

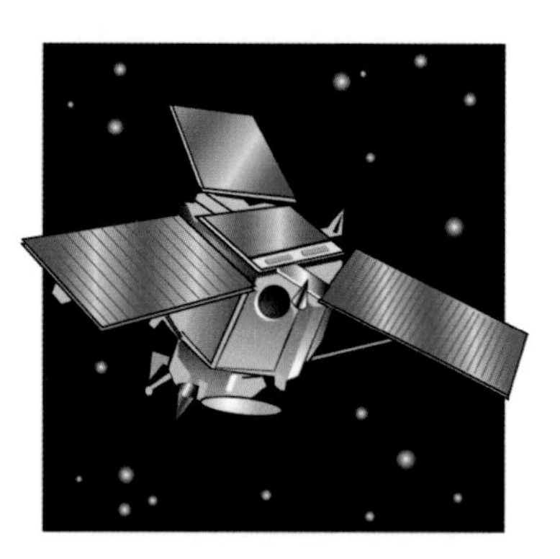

2. Visitors to high-altitude regions may suffer from Acute Mountain Sickness (AMS) if they do not allow their bodies to acclimate to the new surroundings. Research guidelines for preventing this condition. Design a brochure for travelers that describes symptoms of AMS and provides recommendations for preventing and/or treating them.

3. The Kyoto Protocol is a 1997 document that came out of a United Nations-sponsored meeting to address the issue of reducing greenhouse gas emissions. Use a library or the Internet to research the Kyoto Protocol. What are some of the means it suggests for reducing greenhouse gas emissions? What are some of the arguments for and against putting these ideas into practice?

4. If you live in or visit high-latitude regions during the winter months, you may have the opportunity to observe an aurora in the nighttime sky. An aurora looks like a curtain of colored light flickering in the sky. Use a library or the Internet to find out what causes the auroras, which layer of the atmosphere is involved, and which locations on Earth provide the best viewing sites. You may wish to search the terms "aurora borealis," as auroras are known in the northern hemisphere, "aurora australis," as they are known in the southern hemisphere, or "northern lights," the common term for this phenomenon.

UNIT 9

Energy in the Earth System

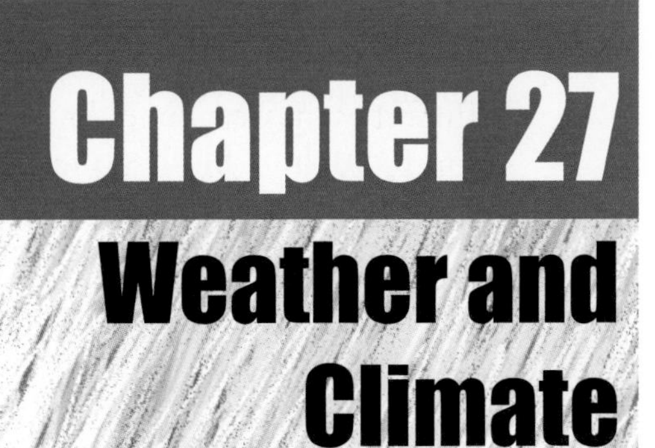

Chapter 27

Weather and Climate

Why does the temperature on Earth vary from place to place? What causes wind and ocean currents? How do you read a weather map? In this chapter you will find answers to these and other questions about weather, storms, and climate.

27.1	**Variations in Earth's Heating and Cooling**	*How can we demonstrate the seasonal changes in incoming solar radiation?*

In this Investigation you will use a globe, solar cell, and flashlight to model the seasonal changes in intensity of solar radiation due to the tilt of Earth's axis.

27.2	**Global Winds and Currents**	*How are currents, temperature, and ocean salt related?*

In this Investigation you will model how water temperature and saltiness change the density of ocean currents. These changes cause currents to float, sink, plunge to the ocean bottom and jet to the surface.

27.3	**Weather patterns**	*How is relative humidity measured?*

In this Investigation you will make and use a sling psychrometer to measure and graph water content in the atmosphere.

27.4	**Storms**	*How does Doppler radar work?*

In this Investigation you will learn how Doppler radar works and how it is used to track storms and other weather events.

27.5	**Weather and Climate**	*How do zoos model climates?*

In this Investigation you will research an animal living in a particular biome and design a suitable zoo habitat for the animal.

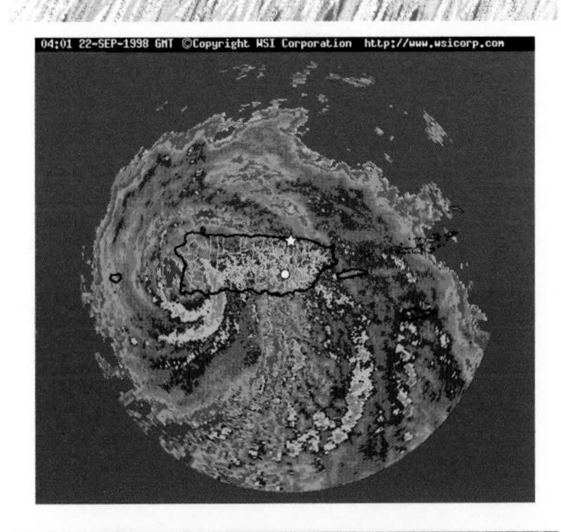

Learning Goals

In this chapter, you will:

- ✔ Learn how Earth's rotation, Earth's axial tilt, and distance from the equator cause variations in the heating and cooling of Earth.
- ✔ Learn how the heating of Earth's surface and atmosphere by the sun causes convection cycles in the atmosphere and oceans, producing winds and ocean currents.
- ✔ Learn about tools meteorologists use to predict weather, and how to read a weather map.
- ✔ Make and test your own weather instrument.
- ✔ Model a doppler radar system.
- ✔ Learn about the physical features that interact to form the climate of each of six important land biomes.

Vocabulary

air mass	El Niño-Southern Oscillation	longitude	temperate forest
biome	grassland	polar easterlies	temperature inversion
cold front	gyres	prevailing westerlies	trade winds
Coriolis effect	isobars	stratiform cloud	tropical rainforest
cumuliform cloud	jet stream	stratocumulus cloud	tundra
desert	latitude	taiga	warm front

27.1 Heating and Cooling of Earth

Why isn't Earth evenly heated by the sun? In this section you will learn how the heating and cooling of Earth is affected by several factors. These include Earth's tilt and position in space, global wind patterns, ocean currents, and the high specific heat of water. To understand this complex system, you will build on what you know about radiation, conduction, convection, and specific heat.

Identifying locations on Earth

Satellite data is used to map patterns of heating and cooling

Much of the data that scientists collect about patterns of heating and cooling on Earth comes from satellite images (Figure 27.1). The National Oceanic and Atmospheric Administration (or NOAA) uses infrared photography to map how much heat is reflected or emitted from different areas of Earth each day. Scientists who analyze this data need a way to pinpoint locations on the infrared photographs of Earth. One common system is with a man-made grid of latitude and longitude lines (Figure 27.2).

Latitude lines

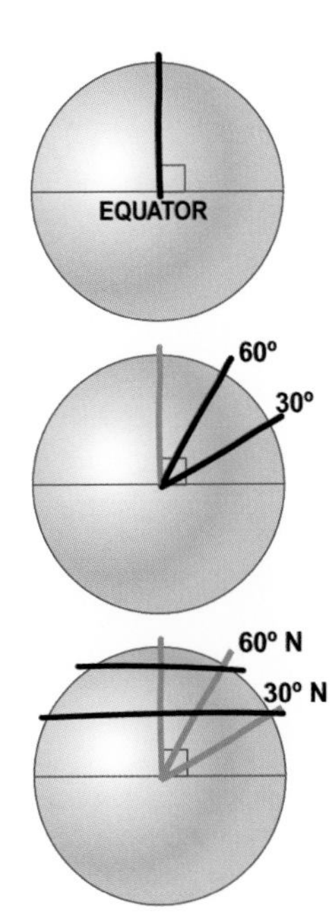

Latitude lines measure distance from the equator. These lines run parallel to the equator and are labeled in degrees north or degrees south (Figure 27.3).

To figure out how the lines were originally labeled, draw a line on a globe from the north pole straight down to the equator. This line forms a 90-degree angle with the equator.

Next, draw 30- and 60-degree angles between the equator and the north pole.

Finally, draw lines parallel to the equator along these measured angles. These are the 30-degree north and 60-degree north latitude lines.

The same process is used to measure latitude in degrees south of the equator. You can find information about the latitude of a particular location by consulting an atlas or the Internet.

Figure 27.1: *This image shows infrared radiation emitted by cloud tops, land, oceans, ice, or snow. The coldest areas (usually high clouds in the atmosphere) appear the brightest white. NOAA photo.*

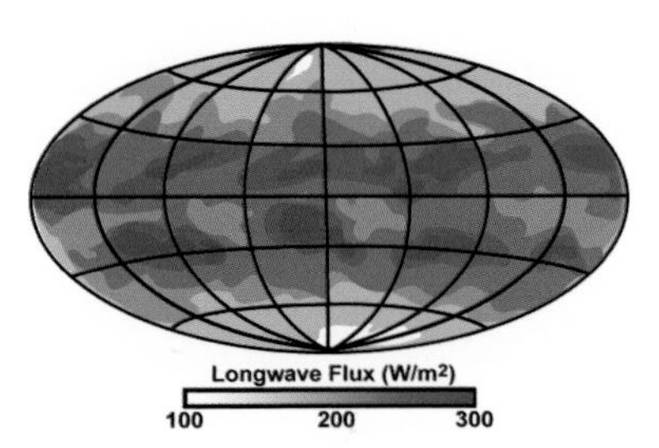

Figure 27.2: *Scientists use data from infrared photographs to map heat emitted from Earth's surface. NASA image.*

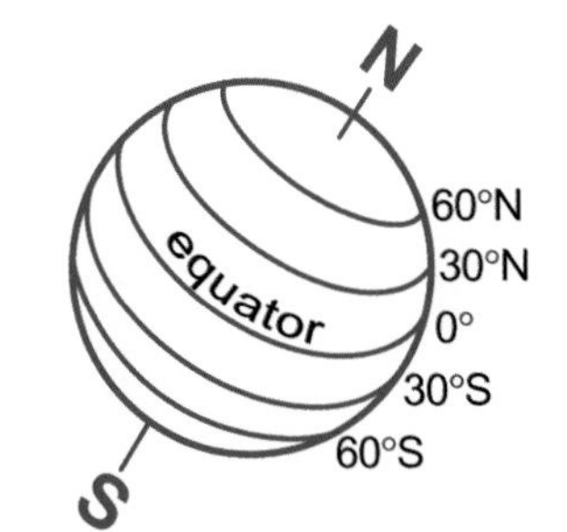

Figure 27.3: *Latitude lines.*

Longitude lines

Longitude lines run vertically from the north pole to the south pole. There are 360 equally-spaced longitude lines around the globe. The line that runs through Greenwich, England, is labeled 0 degrees longitude and is called the prime meridian. Lines *east* of the prime meridian are numbered from 1 to 179 degrees east, while lines *west* of the prime meridian are numbered from 1 to 179 degrees west. The 0- and 180-degree lines are not labeled east or west.

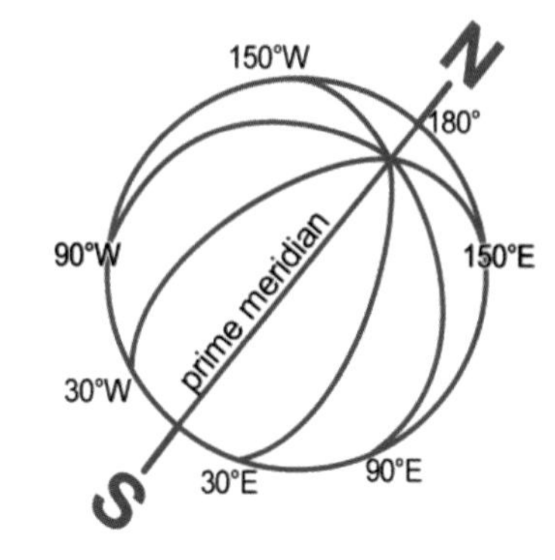

Figure 27.4: *Longitude lines.*

Latitude and longitude lines form a grid

Latitude and longitude lines form a grid that scientists use to locate various points on a satellite photo. This enables them to use the photos for climate research. For example, they can measure the spread of desert conditions across isolated parts of Africa, or compare the date each year when ice sheets melt in remote arctic locations.

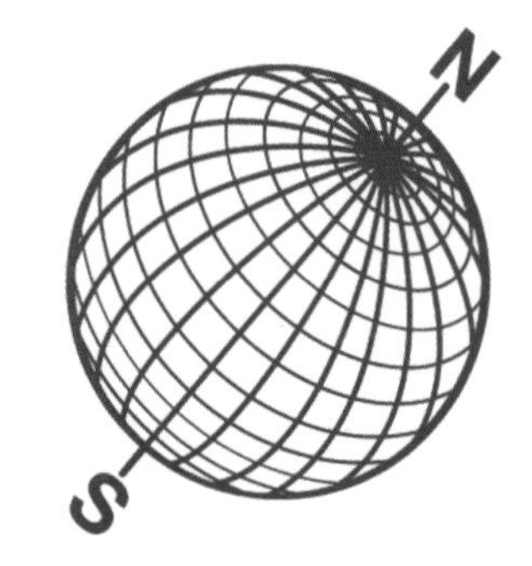

Figure 27.5: *Latitude and longitude lines form a grid.*

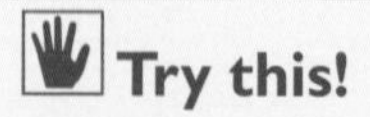

Try this!

On a clear night, you can use the North Star to estimate your own latitude.

The North Star is located at the end of the handle of the Little Dipper (the seven principal stars in the constellation Ursa Minor).

Once you locate the North Star, point to it with one outstretched arm. Extend your other arm toward the horizon.

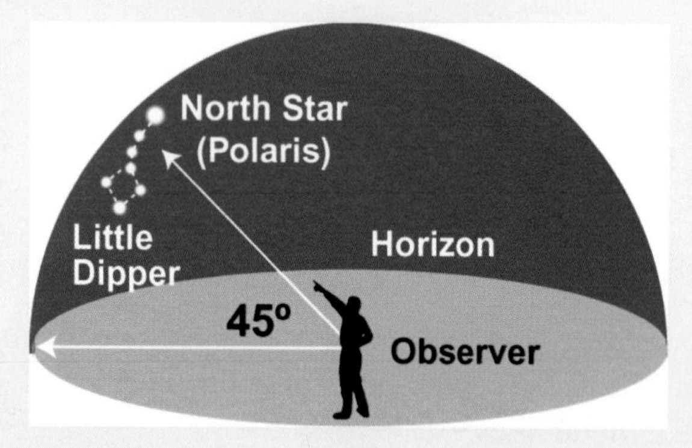

Have a friend use a protractor to estimate the angle formed by your two arms.

The measure of the angle tells you your latitude. If the angle is 45 degrees, then you are located around 45° N latitude.

Temperature and latitude

Earth's temperature varies with latitude

In the northern hemisphere, we often associate "going south" with "getting warm." Birds, for example, fly south for the winter. States in the American South and Southwest are known as the sunbelt states. But in the southern hemisphere, the opposite is true. Birds fly north for the winter. The warmest part of Australia is the northern section. Generally, as latitude (or distance from the equator) increases, the amount of incoming solar radiation decreases.

At higher latitudes, solar radiation is less intense

The hottest part of Earth is near the equator, where the sun is closest to directly overhead year round. At the north and south poles, temperatures are much colder. To understand why, imagine shining a flashlight on a sheet of paper as in Figure 27.6. It makes a very bright, small spot. However, if the piece of paper is at an angle, the light is spread out over a larger spot and is less intense. The same thing happens to the sun's energy, which reaches the north and south poles at an angle. There, sunlight is spread out and thus less intense, while at the equator, the sunlight is direct and more intense (Figure 27.7). As a result, the average yearly temperature at the equator is 27°C (80°F), while at the north pole it is -18°C (0°F).

90°

15°

Figure 27.6: *If you hold a piece of paper at a 90-degree angle to a lamp and then at a 15-degree angle, where does the light have a larger area? Where is the light brightest and hottest?*

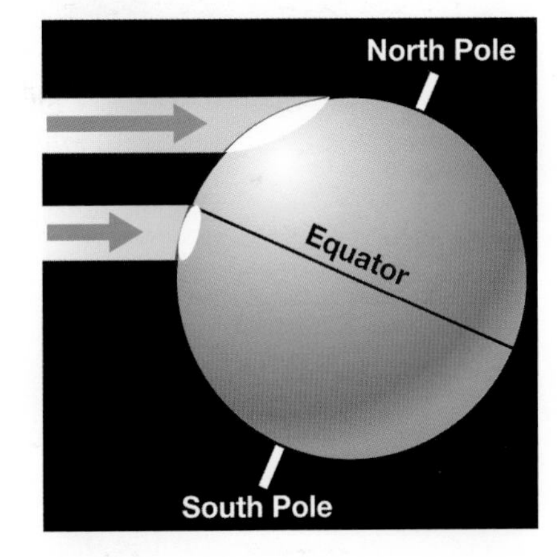

Figure 27.7: *This is how the sun's radiation reaches Earth. Sunlight is more intense at the equator.*

Temperature and Earth's rotation

Daytime heating and nighttime cooling

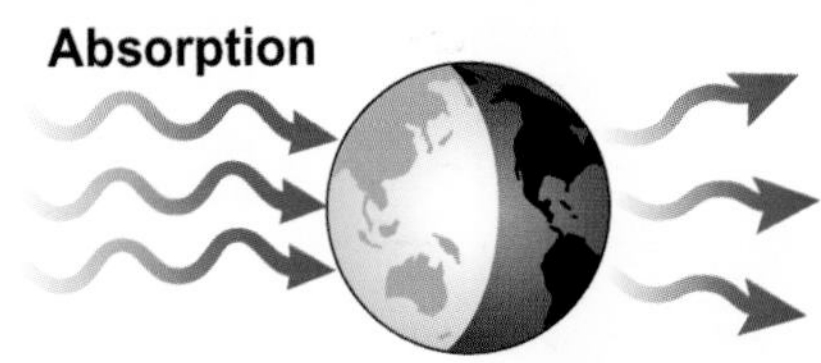

As Earth rotates, the portion of the globe facing the sun absorbs more solar radiation than it emits, and warms. Earth constantly emits some of the absorbed energy as infrared radiation. This emission of heat cools the dark side of the planet. Have you ever noticed that clear nights are often cooler than cloudy ones? That's because on a clear night, more of the emitted radiation escapes into space. Clouds absorb some of the radiation emitted by Earth's surface, keeping temperatures near the ground a little warmer.

Daytime heating in Arctic regions

You may know that in summer, the arctic regions experience daylight almost around the clock. With all that time to absorb heat, why don't they get very warm? There are two reasons. First, the sunlight is not intense, and second, snow reflects a great deal of the incoming radiation. Only a small percentage is absorbed.

Why does Earth have seasons?

A common misunderstanding

Why is it cold in the winter and hot in the summer? Many people believe the answer is that Earth is closest to the sun in summer and farthest away in winter. In reality, distance from the sun has very little to do with seasons. Earth's orbit is almost circular. The difference between Earth's maximum and minimum distance from the sun is too small to cause changes in the seasons.

Earth's tilt causes seasons

The reason we have seasons is that Earth's axis is tilted at an angle. In January, the northern hemisphere is tilted away from the sun, and the southern hemisphere is tilted toward the sun. Rays of sunlight reaching the northern hemisphere are more spread out and less intense than those reaching the southern hemisphere. As a result, it is winter in the northern hemisphere and summer in the southern hemisphere.

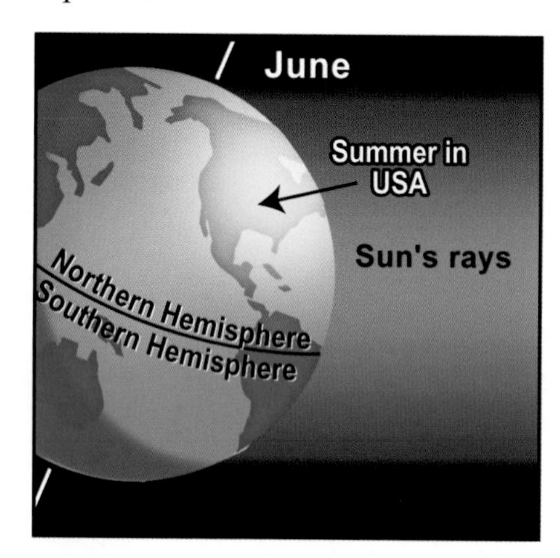

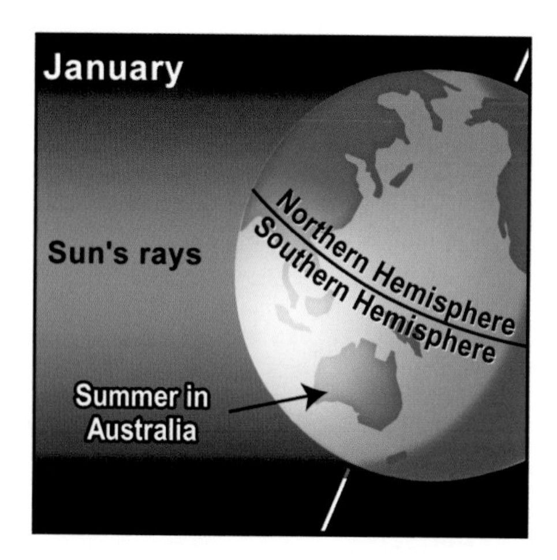

As Figure 27.8 shows, in June, Earth has traveled halfway around its orbit and is on the opposite side of the sun. Now the northern hemisphere is tilted toward the sun. It receives more direct solar energy, and experiences summer conditions. The southern hemisphere is tilted away from the sun in June, and experiences winter.

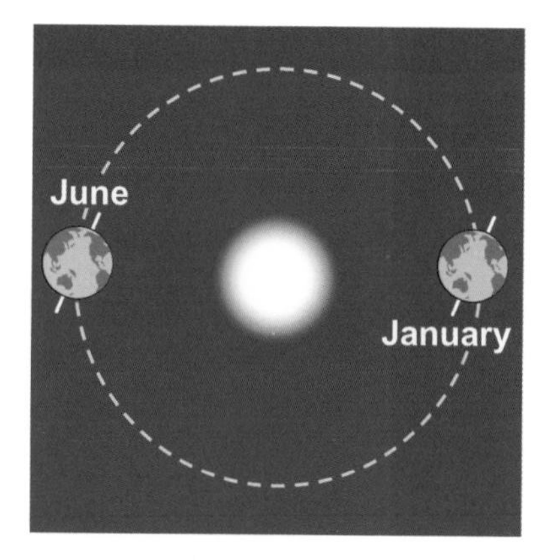

Figure 27.8: *Because of the tilt of Earth's axis, in June the northern hemisphere is tilted toward the sun. In January, the southern hemisphere is tilted toward the sun.*

27.2 Global Winds and Ocean Currents

Did you know that if Earth were heated evenly, there would be no wind? It's hard to imagine life without pleasant breezes or gigantic gales. In this section, you will learn why Earth is a windy planet, and how global winds create ocean currents.

Convection in the atmosphere

Thermals are small convection currents in the atmosphere

Have you ever seen a hawk soaring above a highway and wondered how it could fly upward without flapping its wings? The hawk is riding a *thermal*—a convection current in the atmosphere. A thermal forms when a surface like a blacktop highway absorbs solar radiation and emits energy as heat. That heat warms the air near the surface. The warmed air molecules gain kinetic energy and spread out. As a result, the heated air near the highway becomes less dense than the colder air above it. The heated air rises, forcing the colder air to move aside and sink toward the ground. Then this colder air is warmed by the heat from the blacktop, and it rises. A convection current is created. Hawks and other broad-winged birds often ride the rising warm air several hundred meters high!

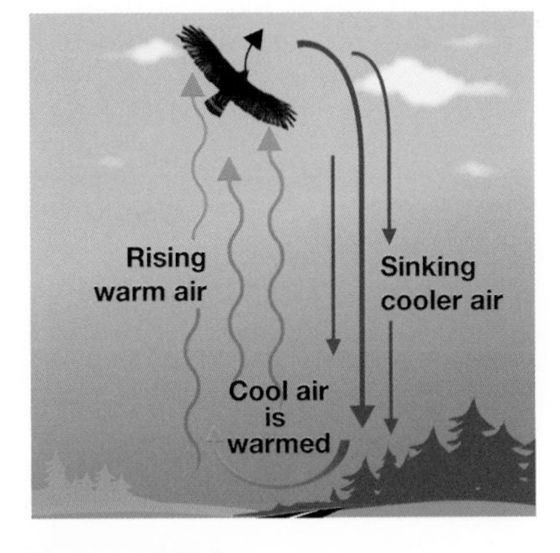

Figure 27.9: *Hawks ride convection currents called thermals.*

Giant convection currents

While thermals form on a local level, there are also giant convection currents in the atmosphere. These form as a result of the temperature difference between the equator and the poles. Warm air at the equator tends to rise and flows toward the poles. Cooler, denser air from the poles sinks and flows back toward the equator. When air flows horizontally from an area of high density and pressure into an area of low density and pressure, we call the flowing air **wind**.

Global wind cells

While it might seem logical that air would flow in giant circles from the equator to the poles and back, the reality is more complicated than that. The warm air from the equator doesn't make it all the way to the poles because of Earth's rotation. In fact, the combination of global convection and Earth's rotation sets up a series of wind patterns called *global wind cells* in each hemisphere (Figure 27.10). These cells play a large role in shaping weather patterns on Earth.

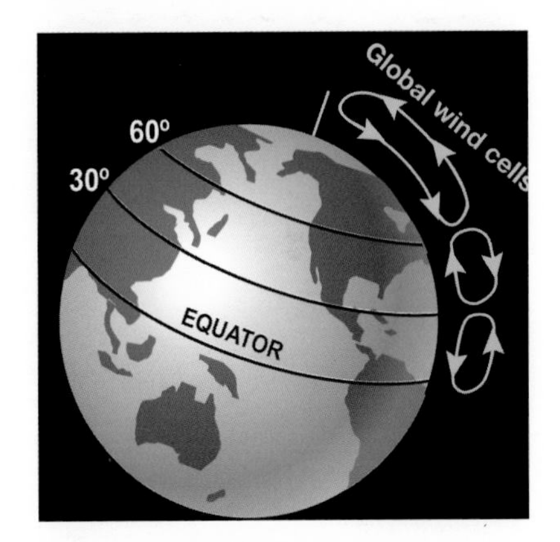

Figure 27.10: *These smaller circular wind patterns exist in both the northern and southern hemispheres. We call them global wind cells.*

The Coriolis effect

Why does Earth's rotation affect the path of air currents?

To understand why Earth's rotation affects the path of air currents, imagine the following situation: You are a pilot who wants to fly an airplane from St. Paul, Minnesota, 700 miles south to Little Rock, Arkansas. If you set your compass and try to fly straight south, you will probably end up in New Mexico! Why? As you are flying overhead, Earth is rotating counterclockwise beneath you. This makes it appear that you have bent your path westward.

How air currents bend

The same thing happens with air currents. Because of Earth's rotation, cold air from the north pole flowing south seems to bend to the west, while warm air from the equator flowing north seems to bend to the east (Figure 27.12).

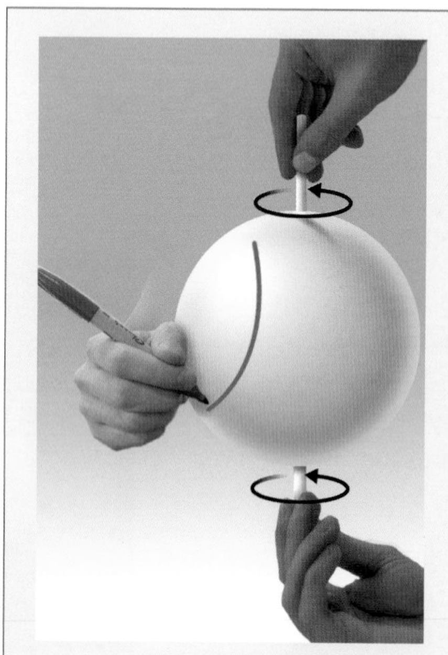

To understand why air currents seem to bend, try this demonstration:

Place a large Styrofoam ball on a skewer. Ask a partner to rotate the skewer so that the ball turns in a counterclockwise direction. Using a permanent marker, try to draw a line from the top of the ball toward an imaginary equator.

Next, start at the center and try to draw a line straight up. What happened?

Now turn the ball over and switch roles. Your partner should demonstrate the way air currents would flow in the southern hemisphere.

The Coriolis effect

This bending of currents is called the Coriolis effect, after the French engineer-mathematician Gaspard Gustave de Coriolis (1792-1843), who first described the phenomenon in 1835.

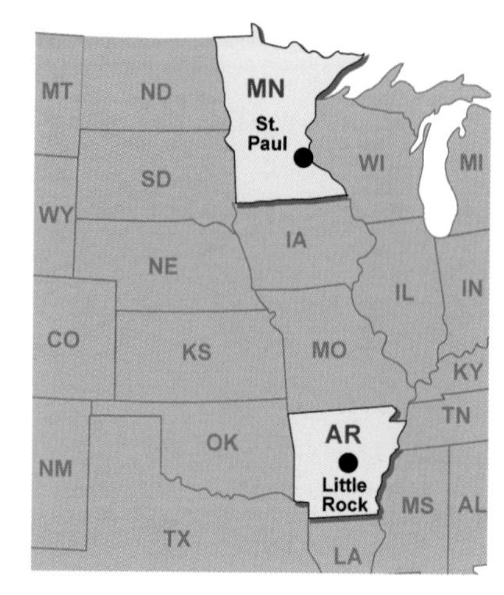

Figure 27.11: *Pilots planning to fly from St. Paul, Minnesota, to Little Rock, Arkansas, must take the Coriolis effect into account.*

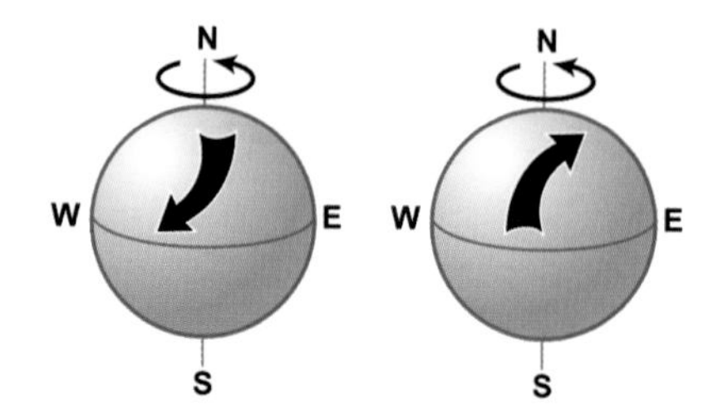

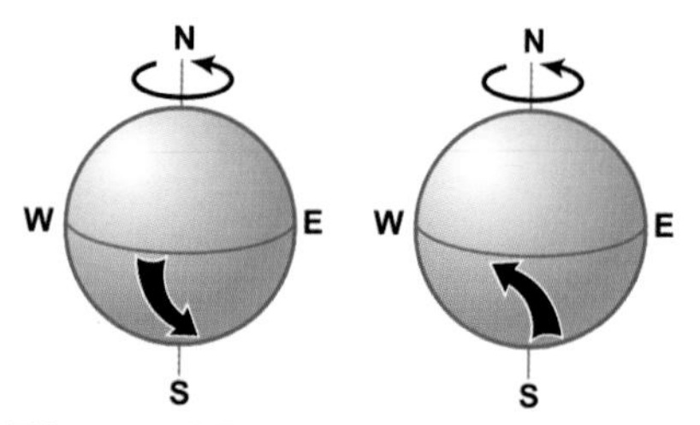

Figure 27.12: *Because of the Coriolis effect, global air currents seem to bend.*

Global wind patterns

There are three important global surface wind patterns in each hemisphere. These wind patterns have been very important to the history of civilizations, because cultures were spread across the globe by sailors following wind currents.

Describing wind Winds are described by the direction from which they originate. A west wind blows from the west toward the east. A southwest wind blows from the southwest toward the northeast. In the northern hemisphere, a southwest wind is associated with pleasant, warm breezes. Would the same be true in the southern hemisphere?

Trade winds The **trade winds** are surface wind currents that move between 30° latitude and the equator. You learned earlier that the air around the equator warms, rises, and flows toward the poles. At about 30°N and 30°S, it cools, sinks, and flows toward the equator again. The Coriolis effect bends the trade winds moving across the surface so that they flow from northeast to southwest in the northern hemisphere and from southwest to northeast in the southern hemisphere (Figure 27.13).

Polar easterlies Another major wind pattern is called the **polar easterlies**. Polar easterlies form when the air over the poles cools, sinks, and spreads along the surface to about 60° latitude. Like the other global winds, this polar wind is bent by the Coriolis effect. The air flows from northeast to southwest in the northern hemisphere, and from southeast to northwest in the southern hemisphere.

Prevailing westerlies Since the trade winds set up a high pressure area at about 30°N latitude and the rising air of the polar easterlies sets up a low at 60°N, air along the surface between 30° N and 60°N moves northward, from high to low pressure. The air bends to the right due to the Coriolis effect, creating the **prevailing westerlies**. Most of the United States is between 30°N and 60°N, so most of our weather patterns move from west to east. Using Figure 27.13 as a guide, can you describe how the prevailing westerlies move in the southern hemisphere?

The polar front At about 60 degrees latitude, the polar easterlies meet the prevailing westerlies, at a boundary called the polar front. Here the dense polar air forces the warmer westerly air upward. Some warmer air flows toward the poles, and some flows back toward the 30 degree latitude line, completing the middle global wind cell.

Sailing with the wind

The trade winds were named by sailors who crossed the North Atlantic in the 17th and 18th centuries in search of goods to bring back to Europe. The trade winds provided a helpful push on their journey west.

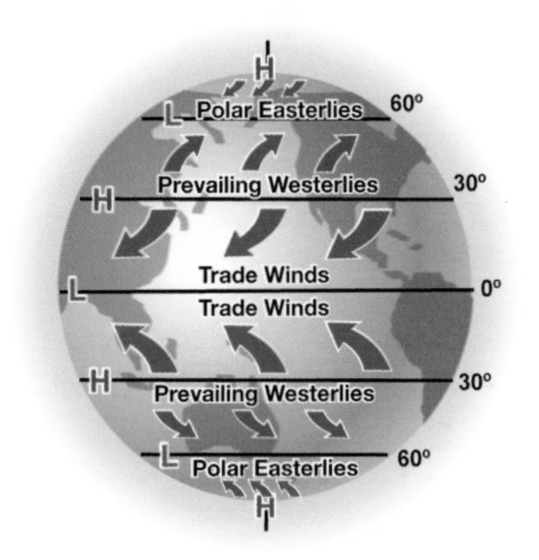

Figure 27.13: *Notice how the global surface wind patterns in the northern and southern hemispheres bend due to Earth's rotation. Can you see that the wind always flows from high pressure to low pressure?*

Surface ocean currents

What are surface ocean currents?

When a global wind moves over the surface of the ocean, it pushes the ocean water along its path. The global winds move ocean water in recognizable patterns that we call *surface ocean currents*. The Gulf Stream is one well-known example of a surface ocean current. The Gulf Stream moves northward from Mexico's Yucatan Peninsula, around the coast of Florida, and northeast to Nantucket Island, Newfoundland's Grand Banks, and then off toward the British Isles.

How surface ocean currents move

The global wind patterns and Earth's rotation cause surface ocean currents to move in large circular patterns called **gyres**. The gyres move clockwise in the northern hemisphere and counterclockwise in the southern hemisphere. The major clockwise gyres are Kuroshio gyre in the Pacific, and the Atlantic gyre, formed by the Gulf Stream, Canary, and North Equatorial currents.

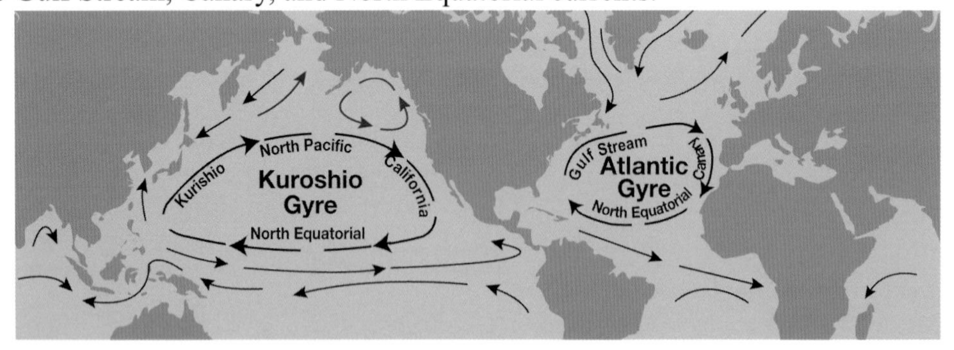

Deep ocean currents

Ocean currents can also occur deep within the ocean. These currents, called *thermohaline currents*, move slower than surface currents and are driven by temperature and density differences in the ocean. Surface and thermohaline currents work together to move huge masses of water around the globe.

Ocean currents and climate

Ocean currents play a big role in heating and cooling some parts of Earth. Did you know that you can find palm trees on the northeast coast of Scotland? This part of Scotland is on the same latitude as southern Norway and the northern tip of Newfoundland. But because the Gulf Stream surrounds Great Britain with warm water from the Caribbean, Scotland has much milder winters than other places at the same latitude.

Tracking ocean currents

Oceanographers often study ocean currents using high-tech methods like satellite infrared photographs that map ocean temperature. Since 1991, Oregon researcher Curtis Ebbesmeyer has been supple-menting this research with a low-tech but very effective method: studying cargo spilled from ships. His research has followed spills of 60,000 running shoes into the North Pacific, 29,000 bathtub toys into the waters near the International Date Line, and over 4.5 million plastic toy bricks off the coast of Britain. By mapping where these items wash ashore, researchers can make better mathematical models to predict the motion of objects in ocean currents and waves. These models can help predict the movement of oil spills and of lost ships, making cleanup or rescue easier and faster.

27.3 Weather Patterns

How do meteorologists predict the weather? What factors influence whether you will see sunshine, clouds, or precipitation on any given day? In this section, you will learn how air temperature, pressure, and water content in the atmosphere work together to produce different kinds of weather. You will explore cloud formation, precipitation, air masses, and fronts. You will learn what the symbols on a weather map mean, and how different kinds of storms develop.

What factors influence the weather?

Air temperature and pressure You have already learned about two important factors that shape the weather in a given region: temperature and pressure. Higher temperatures cause air near the equator to expand and rise, initiating the processes that produce wind and ocean currents. Pressure differences between warm and cold air masses cause air to flow from regions of high to low pressure. The greater the difference in pressure, the greater the speed of the air flow, or wind.

Water in the atmosphere A third important factor that shapes weather patterns is, of course, water. You cannot have rain, snow, sleet, or hail without water in the atmosphere. Even when the skies are totally blue, there is some water present in the atmosphere. The amount varies widely, from just 0.1 percent in the atmosphere above Antarctica to as much as 3 percent above a tropical rain forest. Why do clouds and precipitation sometimes form from this water, while at other times the skies are blue? It depends on the rate of phase changes happening in the atmosphere.

Temperature, air pressure, and water content in the atmosphere are the three most important factors that influence weather patterns.

Joanne Simpson

Joanne Simpson was born in Boston in 1923. As a child, she loved to watch clouds. She was fascinated with airplanes and earned her pilot's license at age 16. As a student pilot, Simpson had to take a meteorology course. She was fascinated by the processes that caused weather patterns. She enrolled in the University of Chicago's meteorology program.

Simpson completed a master's degree and wanted to earn her Ph.D. But the all-male faculty felt that women were unable to do the work, which included night shifts and flying planes. Simpson refused to give up. She became the first woman to receive a Ph.D in meteorology. Simpson went to Woods Hole Oceanographic Institute to study how tropical cumulus clouds called "hot towers" carry moisture, transfer heat, and release energy. She found that these hot towers release energy to the hurricane eye and act as a hurricane's engine.

Simpson is currently a NASA chief scientist at Goddard Space Flight Center, studying rainfall, satellite images, and hurricanes.

Phase changes in the atmosphere

Temperature and pressure influence phase changes

Recall from your study of properties of matter that the state of water (whether it is a solid, liquid, or gas) depends on both temperature and atmospheric pressure. As temperature increases, the random motion of the water molecules increases, and more of the bonds holding water molecules together are overcome (Figure 27.14). Therefore, as temperature increases, the rate of evaporation increases. But that's not the whole story. Pressure also affects changes of state. As atmospheric pressure decreases, it becomes easier for water molecules to escape from the liquid to the gas state (Figure 27.15). Therefore, a decrease in pressure also increases the rate of evaporation.

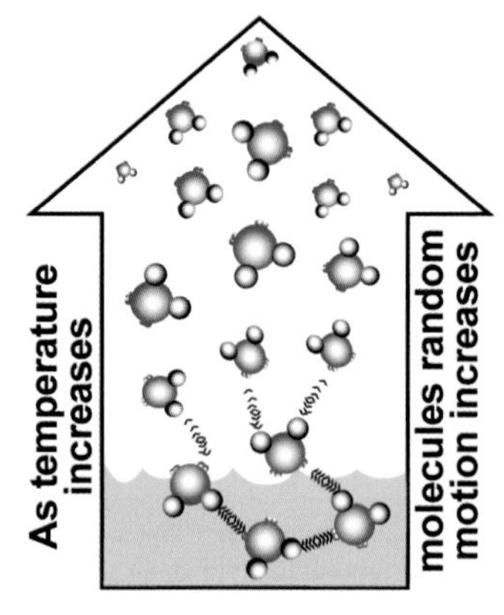

Figure 27.14: *As temperature increases, more bonds between water molecules are overcome.*

The three phases of water in the atmosphere

Water in the atmosphere exists in all three states. High in the troposphere, there are ice crystals. Tiny water droplets, much too small to see, are suspended throughout the troposphere virtually all the time. They are considered liquid water and not gas because they are made of microscopic "clumps" of water molecules. Other water molecules in the atmosphere are truly in the gas state, separate from all other molecules.

Water constantly changes phase

Because the combination of temperature and pressure in the atmosphere is constantly changing, water is constantly changing state. When the rate of evaporation in the atmosphere is greater than the rate of condensation, we see clearing skies.

Dew point

If the amount of water in the air remains constant, but the temperature decreases, the random motion of the water molecules will decrease. As a result, the rate of evaporation will decrease also. When the rate of condensation exceeds the rate of evaporation, we say that the air's dew point temperature has been reached.

When more water is condensing than evaporating, the air's dew point temperature has been reached.

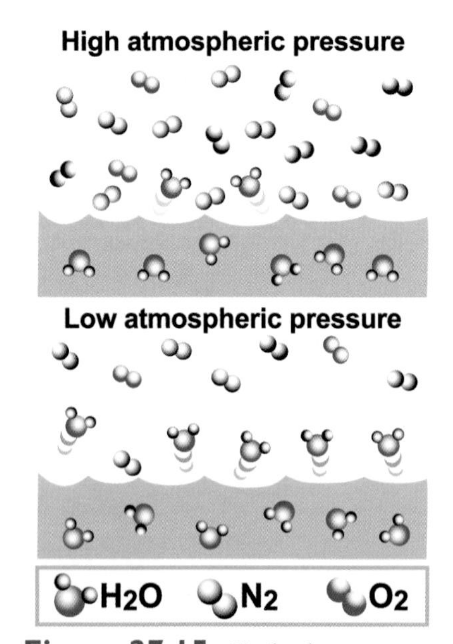

Figure 27.15: *Under low atmospheric pressure, water molecules more easily enter the gas state.*

Cloud formation

Different conditions cause different clouds

When more water in the atmosphere is condensing than evaporating, we begin to see the condensing water as clouds. Different kinds of clouds form under different conditions.

Cumuliform clouds

For example, cumuliform clouds, which look like heaps of popcorn with flat bottoms, form when pockets of air rise because of convection. These pockets of rising air usually form over land, especially an area like a blacktop road, which absorbs a great deal of heat. Why, then, don't we typically see a line of cumulus clouds right above a highway? It's because wind currents in the atmosphere blow the pockets of rising air around before they condense and form clouds.

Cumuliform clouds form when convection causes rising pockets of air in the atmosphere.

Cirrocumulus

As these air pockets cool, the water evaporation rate decreases and more condensation is evident. The flat bottom of the cloud marks the level of the atmosphere where condensation first exceeds evaporation. Small, puffy "cotton ball" type clouds high in the atmosphere (above 6,000 meters) are called *cirrocumulus*. They usually indicate fair weather.

Altocumulus

Altocumulus clouds form between 2,000 and 6,000 meters high. They usually form larger, darker puffs than cirrocumulus clouds. Sometimes they appear in rows. If the altocumulus clouds have turret-like tops, they are called "altocumulus castellatus." These clouds often appear before a storm.

Cumulus

The base of a *cumulus* cloud is usually around 1,000 meters high, but it can extend to 5,800 meters. Cumulus clouds are the tall, puffy clouds that form when air over land is strongly heated. When the sun begins to set, cumulus clouds often dissipate.

Cumulonimbus

When a cumulus cloud grows dark and stormy looking, it is given a new name: *cumulonimbus*. Later, you will learn more about how thunderstorms develop from cumulonimbus clouds.

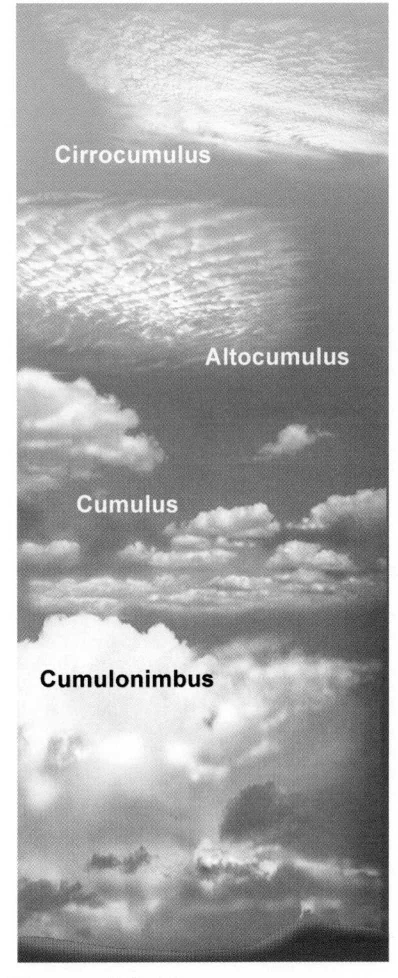

Figure 27.16: *Cumuliform clouds.*

Stratiform clouds

Stratiform clouds form when a large mass of stable air gradually ascends over a mass of colder air or a gentle incline of land. As this air ascends, it expands and cools, allowing condensation to spread evenly throughout the layer. Stratiform clouds look like smooth, flattened blankets. They can cover as much as 300,000 square miles! A sky covered with stratiform clouds will appear uniformly gray.

Stratiform clouds form when a large mass of stable air gradually rises, expands, and cools.

Cirrostratus clouds look like a translucent white coating across the sky. They are high clouds, located at least 6,000 meters above the ground. Cirrostratus clouds are made of ice crystals. As a result, the sun shining through the crystals is refracted. The refracted light looks like a "halo" around the sun.

Altostratus clouds are the most easily recognizable stratiform clouds. If the sky looks like a smooth gray sheet and no shadows form on the ground, you are seeing altostratus clouds located between 2,000 and 6,000 meters high.

Below 2,000 meters, stratiform clouds are called simply *stratus* clouds. Stratus clouds look like fog that doesn't quite reach the ground. When a stratus cloud turns dark gray, it signals the approach of a weather front and rain to go with it. These rain clouds are called *nimbostratus*.

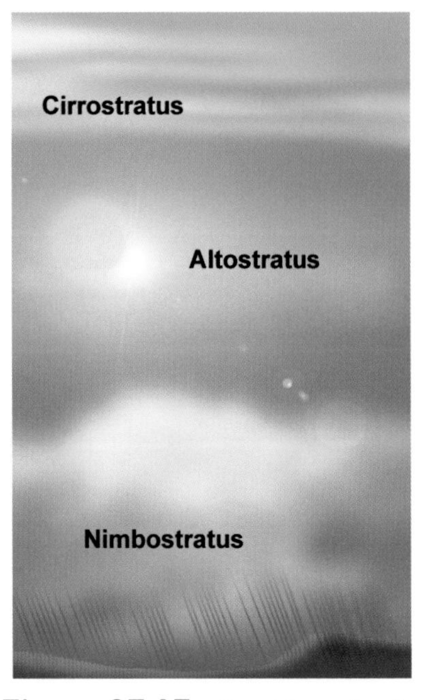

Figure 27.17: *Stratiform clouds.*

Stratocumulus clouds

Sometimes a cloud formation combines aspects of both cumuliform and stratiform clouds. We call these clouds **stratocumulus clouds**. They form when conditions in the atmosphere cause pockets of convection to occur within a stratiform cloud. As the rising air cools, the water in the pocket condenses, creating a cumuliform cloud within the stratiform cloud. This causes the formerly smooth cloud to look lumpy.

Figure 27.18: *Stratocumulus clouds.*

The last type of cloud doesn't look much like the other clouds—it is just a thin streak of white across a blue sky. **Cirrus clouds** are thin lines of ice crystals high in the sky, above 6,000 meters. If a cirrus cloud curves, it is commonly called a "mare's tail." The curving is due to a change in wind direction, and as a result may indicate that the weather is going to change.

Figure 27.19: *Cirrus clouds.*

Precipitation

How does rain form? If you cool air to a temperature lower than the dew point, and the pressure remains constant, some water vapor condenses into liquid. At first, the water molecules condense on particles of dust called *condensation nuclei*. Once a few water molecules condense, they create a site for other molecules to condense too. What starts as just a few water molecules on a speck of dust quickly grows to millions of molecules that form a water droplet with the dust in the center. If the droplets reach about 1 to 10 microns in size, they form visible clouds. So if all clouds are liquid water, why don't all clouds produce rain? It all depends on the droplets' size. Small droplets are kept aloft by wind forces and air friction. If the droplets reach about 1,000 microns (1 millimeter), they become heavy enough that the wind forces and air friction cannot keep them aloft and they fall as raindrops.

Snow and sleet Snow usually forms when both ice crystals and water droplets are present in the sky. The water droplets tend to attach to ice crystals and freeze there. When the ice crystals are large enough, they will fall to the ground as snow. However, if the air temperature near the ground is warm, the crystals will melt and the precipitation will fall as rain. Sometimes very cold air lies below warmer air, causing the water to refreeze and hit the ground as sleet.

Condensation warms the air Condensation is actually a warming process. Why? Energy was needed to break the bonds holding molecules together when the water completed the phase change from liquid to gas. This energy (called **latent heat**) is released when the water changes back into the liquid form. As a result, if it is not too windy, you can sometimes feel the air warm up a few degrees when precipitation begins to fall.

Why does dew form? Because the ground cools quickly, late at night or early in the morning the temperature of the ground is often below the dew point. Air near the ground gets cooled and some water vapor condenses in the form of dew. If the temperature is low enough, the dew freezes and we get frost.

Where does fog come from? If air within a few hundred meters of the ground is cooled below the dew point, fog will form. Fog can form under several conditions. Warm moist air could move over a cooler surface. The ground below could cool below the dew point at night. Either way, fog consists of suspended water droplets. Fog is a ground-level cloud.

Meredith Charles Gourdine

Meredith Gourdine was born in Newark, New Jersey in 1929. During high school, Meredith spent many hours helping his father, a painter and janitor, at work. Meredith paid his own expenses for most of his first two years at Cornell University. There, Gourdine discovered he had a knack for track and field. He went on to win a silver medal in the long jump at the 1952 Olympics in Helsinki, Finland.

Gourdine earned his Ph.D. in Engineering from the California Institute of Technology. He showed that if you apply a negative charge to particles in the air, they become electromagnetically attracted to the ground, and drop down. This allows fresh air to move in to the space the particles had occupied. Gourdine used this process to invent a way to clear smoke from buildings, and fog from runways. Gourdine founded a research lab and a multimillion dollar corporation that developed commercial uses for his scientific research.

Gourdine lost his sight due to diabetes, but remained an active, creative scientist and entrepreneur until his death in 1998.

Air masses and fronts

What is an air mass? An air mass is a large body of air with consistent temperature and moisture characteristics throughout. Air masses can cover areas as large as 750,000 square miles. These air masses form when air remains stationary over an area long enough to take on the characteristics of the surface below. Two common air masses affecting the United States are the continental polar air mass, which forms over the Canadian plains, and the maritime tropical air mass, which forms over the Gulf of Mexico (Figure 27.20). The continental polar air mass contains cold, dry air. In contrast, the maritime tropical air mass contains warm, moist air.

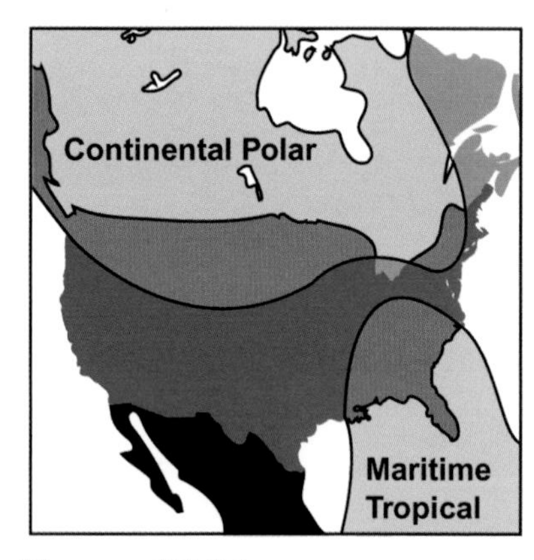

Figure 27.20: *Two major air masses that affect the weather across the United States.*

Air masses move Changing atmospheric conditions and global wind currents eventually cause these air masses to move. The continental polar air mass tends to slide south or southeast, while the maritime tropical air mass tends to slide north or northwest.

Cold fronts When two air masses collide, the result is called a *front.* Sometimes, cold air will move in and replace warm air at Earth's surface. This is known as a cold front. The warm air is forced sharply upward as the cold, denser air moves in. The cold air acts somewhat like a wedge, sliding under the warm air and pushing it up.

Cold fronts can produce rain or snowstorms As the warm air rises, it cools. This causes condensation (and often a band of rain or snow showers) to accompany the cold front. As a cold front moves through an area, the temperature and water content of the air decrease rapidly. The air sometimes cools as much as 15°F in the first hour!

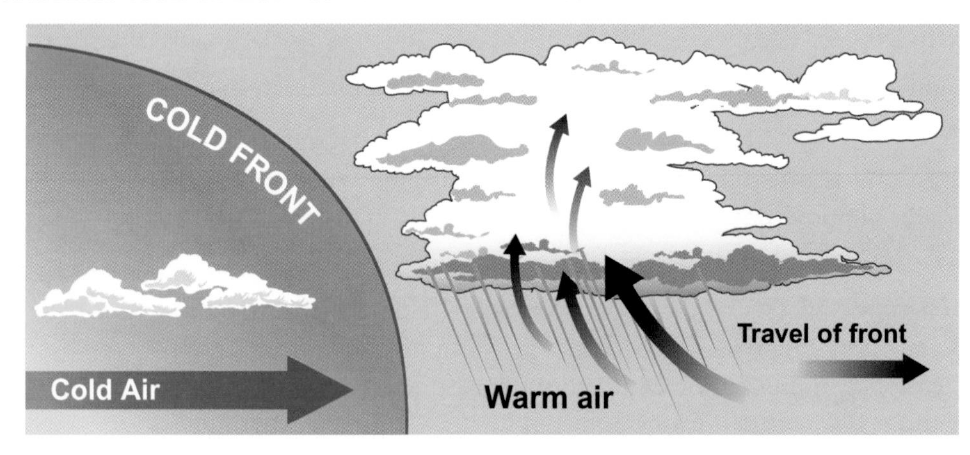

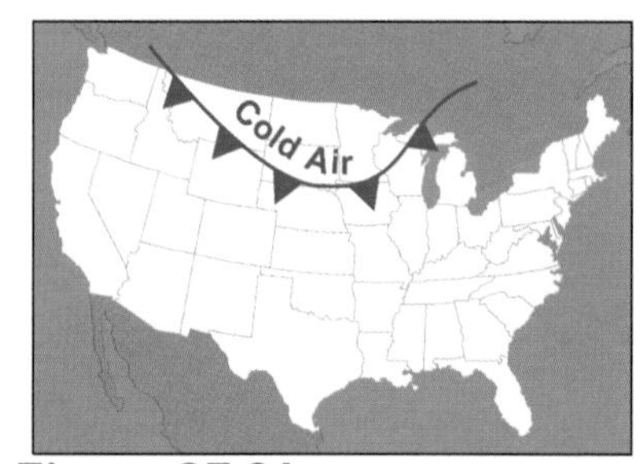

Figure 27.21: *On a weather map, a cold front is shown using a line marked with triangles. The triangles point in the direction the front is moving.*

Warm fronts At other times, warm air advances, overtaking cooler air in a region. This is known as a **warm front**. The warm air slides up over the colder air. The warm air rises and cools, but in this case the lifting is very gradual and steady. As a result, long bands of light precipitation often move ahead of the warm front. As the warm front moves through an area, there will be a noticeable increase in temperature and moisture in the air.

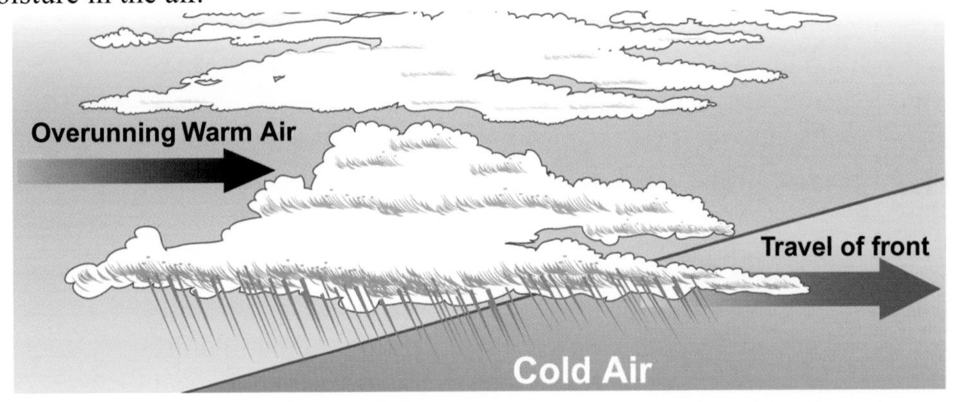

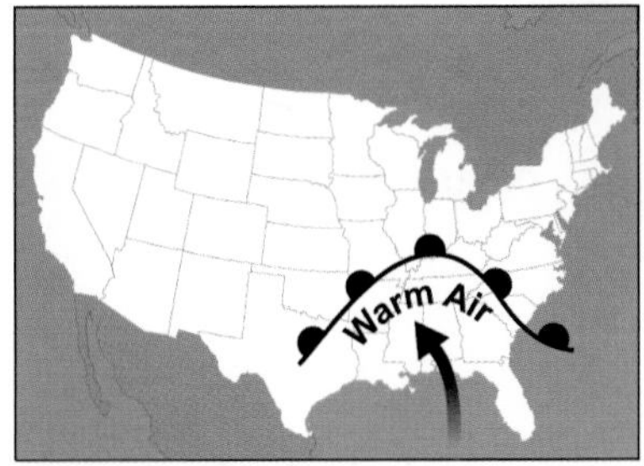

Figure 27.22: *On a weather map, a warm front is shown using a line marked with semicircles.*

Jet streams and weather fronts The movement of these large air masses is affected by high-altitude fast moving winds called the **jet streams**. There are two big jet streams in each hemisphere, formed where there are sharp boundaries between cold and warm temperatures. The jet stream winds are found near the top of the troposphere, and have speeds of at least 87 kilometers (54 miles) per hour, and sometimes as great as 320 kilometers (200 miles) per hour. The jet streams wind around the globe from west to east. In the winter, when the temperature difference between the poles and the equator is greatest, the jet streams attain their fastest speeds. The path of a jet stream can be altered by land features such as mountain ranges, or by giant cumulus clouds that act like boulders in a rushing river, changing the speed and direction of the flow. The rushing jet stream acts like a border between cold and warm air masses, so when it changes course, the air masses tend to move as well.

How were jet streams discovered? Jet streams were discovered by World War II pilots attempting to cross the Pacific Ocean for the first time. On occasion, the plane's progress would come to a halt, because the jet stream was pushing the plane backward as fast as the engines were moving it forward! Today, pilots traveling west to east often try to ride the jet stream, while pilots flying east to west try to avoid it.

Satellite photos map the jet stream's path

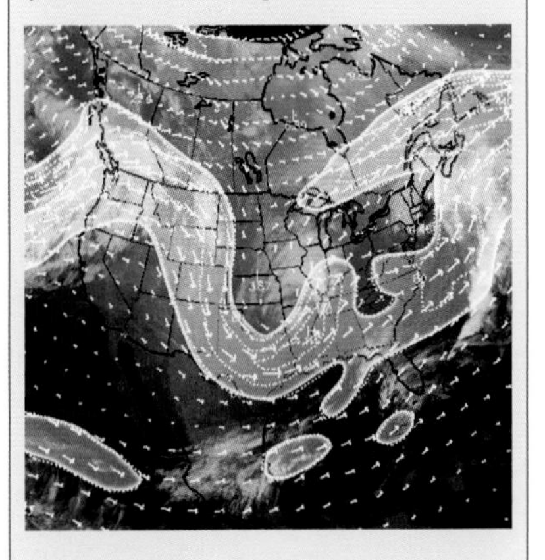

This photo was taken by the GOES-8 satellite in orbit 36,000 kilometers above Earth. It shows the path of the jet stream, which helps meteorologists predict the path of weather fronts. NOAA photo.

Low and high pressure areas

How does a low pressure area develop? When a cold front moves into a region and warm air is forced upward, an area of low pressure is created near Earth's surface at the boundary between the two air masses. Cold air rushes in to fill that low pressure region. This cold air forces more warm air to be pushed upward, and more cold air moves in. A cycle begins to develop. Due to the Coriolis effect, the air masses move in curved, rather than straight paths. As a result the moving air begins to rotate around the low pressure center. In the northern hemisphere, the moving air rotates counterclockwise around a low pressure center, while in the southern hemisphere, the air rotates clockwise. In both hemispheres, strong winds and precipitation are associated with these rotating systems.

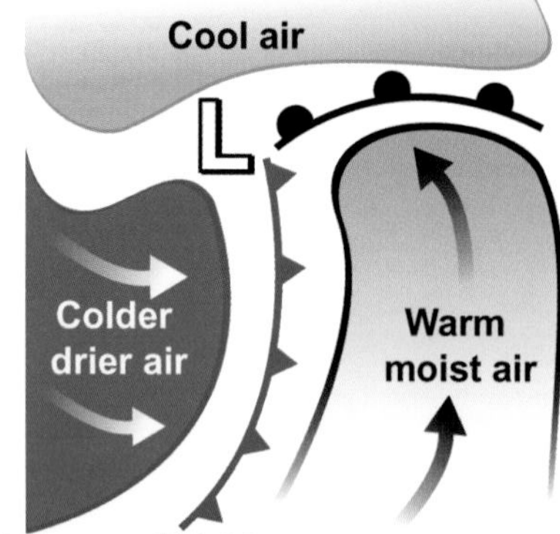

Figure 27.23: *A low pressure system as shown on a weather map.*

High pressure centers A center of high pressure tends to be found where a stable cold air mass has settled in a region. Remember that colder air is denser than warm air, and therefore creates higher atmospheric pressure. Sinking air in a high pressure region inhibits the development of the upward air movement needed to create clouds and precipitation. High pressure areas, therefore, are associated with fair weather.

What is a temperature inversion? Although high pressure is usually associated with clear skies, a condition known as a **temperature inversion** can lead to haze or smog. A temperature inversion occurs when the temperature near the ground is actually colder than the temperature higher in the troposphere. For example, if cold air settles in a valley and warm air moves in above, the warm air caps the lower atmosphere like a ceiling. As a result, the warm pollutants that rise through the relatively cool lower atmosphere stop rising when they move into the warmer upper-level air. When these trapped pollutants are exposed to sunlight, smog is formed.

Figure 27.24: *An inversion traps airborne pollutants near the ground.*

Isobars Weather maps often contain information about areas of low and high pressure. The letters H and L are used to mark centers of high and low pressure. You may also see wavy lines or circles surrounding the letters. These lines are called **isobars**. To create the isobars, meteorologists collect atmospheric pressure data from weather stations throughout the regions. Then they draw a line to connect the places that have the same atmospheric pressure. Drawing isobars helps them pinpoint the location of high and low pressure centers, and provides information about the movement of weather systems.

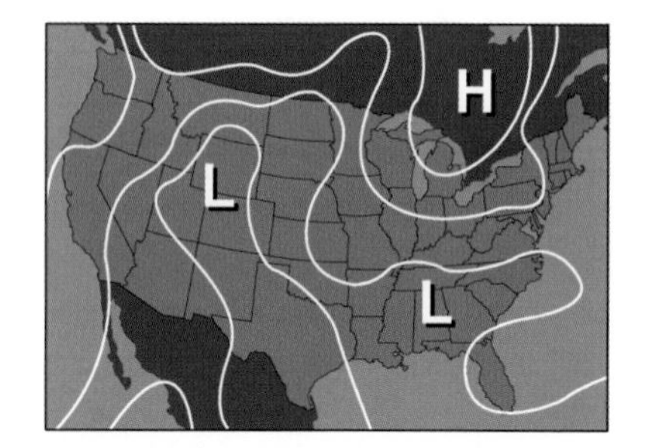

Figure 27.25: *Isobars show areas with the same atmospheric pressure.*

27.4 Storms

In the previous section, you learned that air temperature, atmospheric pressure, and water content in the atmosphere are the three ingredients that most influence the weather. In this section, you will explore how those three ingredients interact to create thunderstorms, hurricanes, and tornados.

Thunderstorms

How storm cells form

Thunderstorms arise when air near the ground is strongly warmed and rises high into the troposphere. As the air rises, it cools and condenses, forming a towering cumulonimbus cloud. Eventually some of the cloud droplets become large enough to fall as rain. Some of the colder air from high regions is dragged along with the falling rain, causing a downdraft of cooler, denser air. This downdraft, along with the updraft of rising warm air, forms a type of convection cell called a *storm cell* within the cloud.

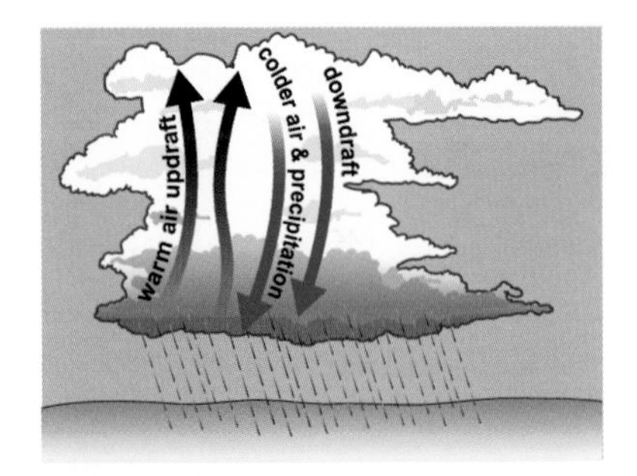

Figure 27.26: *A storm cell.*

Lightning and thunder

The process that causes lightning and thunder begins when vapor particles within the storm cell collide, and electrical charges are transferred from one particle to another. Positive charges tend to build up on smaller particles and negative charges on bigger ones. The forces of gravity and wind cause the particles to separate. Positively charged particles accumulate near the top of the cloud and negatively charged particles fall toward the bottom. The negatively charged particles at the bottom of the cloud repel negative charges in the ground, causing the ground to become positively charged. This positive charge is why people who have been struck by lightning sometimes say they first felt their hair stand on end.

The negative charges in the cloud are attracted to the positively charged ground. When enough charges have been separated by the storm, the cloud, air, and ground act like a giant circuit. All the accumulated charges flow from the cloud to the ground, heating the air along the path so that it glows like a bright streak of light. When the heated air expands, we hear thunder.

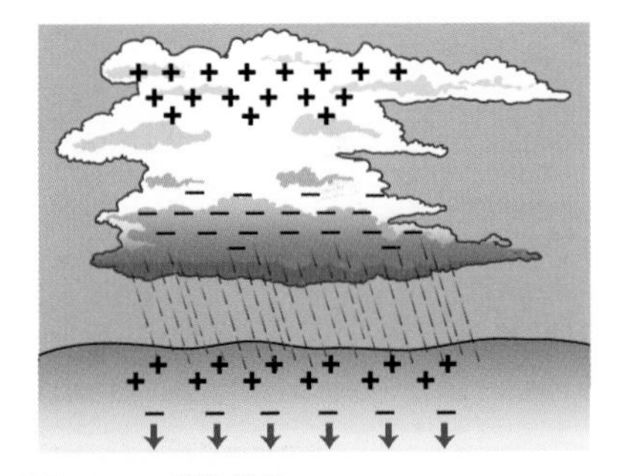

Figure 27.27: *Electrical charges build up in storm cells, causing flashes of lightning.*

A thunderstorm's end

Eventually, the downdrafts in the storm cell bring enough cool, drier air to ground level that the supply of warm, moist air is depleted. The updraft stops flowing, the rain tapers off, and the thunderstorm ends.

Hurricanes

What is a cyclone?

Hurricanes are a type of *cyclone*—a low pressure center surrounded by rotating winds. Remember that the Coriolis effect causes these winds to rotate counterclockwise in the northern hemisphere and clockwise in the southern hemisphere. The Coriolis effect is minimal along the equator, and as a result, the lack of rotating winds prevents cyclones from forming there.

How hurricanes form

Hurricanes form over ocean water that is at least 26.5°C (81°F). Warm, moist air over the tropical ocean provides the initial energy source for a hurricane. As the warm air rises, the water vapor in it condenses. Clouds and thundershowers form. The condensation releases latent heat, warming the surrounding air even more. As all of this air expands and rises, it creates an area of low pressure at the surface of the water. This pressure difference causes the surrounding air to rush toward the center. The path of this rushing air curves due to the Coriolis effect, and a rotating system forms.

What conditions are needed for a hurricane to develop?

Several conditions must be present for a rotating system to become a hurricane, which is defined as a tropical cyclone with wind speeds of at least 74 miles (119 kilometers) per hour. First, the warm ocean water must be at least 46 meters deep. Otherwise, when the storm stirs up the water, cooler water brought to the surface slows the rise of warm, moist air and the storm's strength dissipates. Second, the air must be warm and moist to a point at least 5,500 meters above sea level. As this upper-level air is pulled into the storm, it provides the water vapor that must condense and release latent heat in order to strengthen the storm even further.

The wind conditions must also be right. If preexisting winds are blowing from different directions or speeds, they can push the rising warm air in different directions and break the storm apart.

How common are hurricanes?

An average of 96 tropical cyclones form across the globe each year. More arise in the Western North Pacific and the Indian Ocean than any other area. An average of 10 tropical cyclones develop over the Atlantic, Caribbean, and Gulf of Mexico each year. Five or six of these usually reach hurricane status.

Image courtesy of the Image Science & Analysis Laboratory, NASA Johnson Space Center

Figure 27.28: *Image of a hurricane as seen by space shuttle astronauts. The blue spot in the image's center is the low pressure center, called the eye. Here, winds are calm and blue skies can be seen. However, the surrounding bands of wind and rain are fierce. NASA photo.*

Category five hurricanes

Meteorologists use the Saffir/Simpson Hurricane scale to rate hurricanes. The most severe type, a category five, has wind speeds of at least 155 mph, air pressure in the eye less than 920 mb, and a storm surge of 18 or more feet. Three category five hurricanes hit the United States in the twentieth century.

Tornadoes

Comparing hurricanes and tornadoes

A tornado, like a hurricane, is a system of rotating winds around a low pressure center. An average tornado is less than 200 meters in diameter—tiny, compared with the 640 kilometer (640,000 meter) average diameter of a hurricane! However, the wind speeds of a tornado are much greater than those of a hurricane. A tornado's wind speed can reach 400 kilometers per hour.

How tornadoes form

Both tornadoes and hurricanes form from thunderstorms. A tornado begins to form when the updrafts in a storm cell reach over 160 kilometers per hour. Winds near the top of the cloud begin rotating at a very high speed. As more air flows in, the rotation extends downward. The diameter of the rotating wind pattern narrows, causing the wind to speed up like a spinning ice skater who draws her arms and legs inward.

As the rotating wind pattern narrows and lengthens, it forms what is known as a funnel cloud. If the funnel cloud reaches the ground, it is called a tornado (Figure 27.29).

High wind speeds cause damage

The high wind speed of the tornado is the real culprit that causes damage, not the low pressure "vacuum" at the center of the funnel. The rushing wind can flatten houses to their foundation and even lift cars completely off the ground. A tornado in Broken Bow, Oklahoma, once carried a motel sign 48 kilometers and dropped it in Arkansas! Most tornadoes last around 10 to 20 minutes, although the strongest tornadoes can last an hour or more. They travel along the ground at speeds of about 40 to 60 kilometers per hour.

Figure 27.29: *When a funnel cloud reaches the ground, it is called a tornado.*

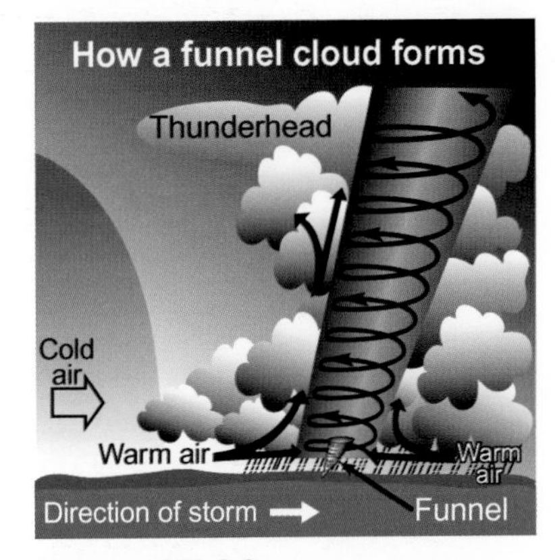

Figure 27.30: *A funnel cloud forms when updrafts in a storm cell reach high speed and begin to rotate. As the diameter of the rotation narrows and extends downward, a funnel cloud takes shape.*

The El Niño Southern Oscillation

Patterns in storm activity across the globe

Scientists studying decades of storm patterns across the globe have noticed cyclical patterns in storm activity. One such pattern is the rise and fall of thunderstorm activity in the tropical Pacific. Usually, the trade winds blow warm water from east to west across the Pacific, from Peru on the ocean's eastern edge toward Indonesia on the western side. As a result, the average water temperature off the coast of Indonesia is 6°C warmer than the average water temperature off the coast of Peru. The warm water of the western Pacific generates thunderstorms of greater frequency and intensity than what is normally seen nearer Peru.

The Southern Oscillation

For reasons not fully understood, every so often the trade winds weaken and the warm water reverses direction, flowing from the western Pacific toward South America. Along with that warm water comes greater thunderstorm activity across the Pacific. Indonesia and other western Pacific nations experience drier than normal conditions, while the eastern Pacific countries get more precipitation. This change in wind flow, air pressure, and thunderstorm activity is known as the Southern Oscillation. Nine of these events occurred between 1954 and 1994.

El Niño

Peruvian fisherman were among the first to notice the change in water temperature along their shores. They call the arrival of the warm water El Niño (or "the child," meaning the Christ child). When the warm water from the west flows back toward their shores, it cuts off a normal pattern in which cold water from the ocean depths flows up to the surface along the coast of Peru. The cold water brings many nutrients necessary for fish and other aquatic life to flourish. During an El Niño event, the warm water flowing over the cold water acts like a lid. It prevents the cold water from reaching the surface. As a result, nutrients are not available for aquatic life and the fish population declines.

Shifting jet streams

The shift in thunderstorm activity causes another El Niño Southern Oscillation (or ENSO) effect. The towering thunderstorm clouds act like big boulders in the upper atmosphere. When they move across the Pacific, they actually change the course of the fast moving upper-atmosphere winds that we know as the jet streams. As a result, entire air masses shift and the weather in places as far away as Canada and Africa are affected.

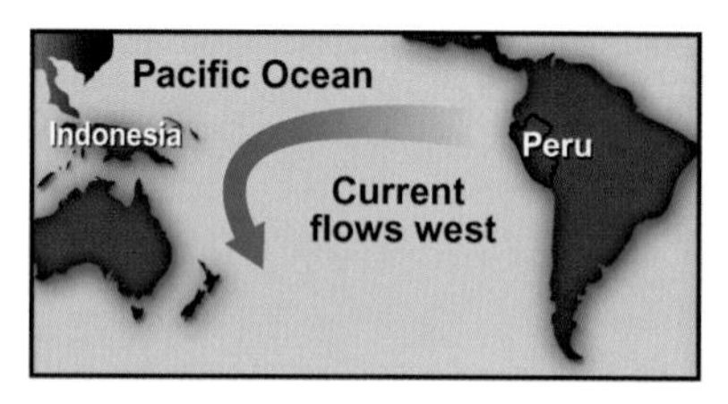

Figure 27.31: *This is the usual pattern of current flow.*

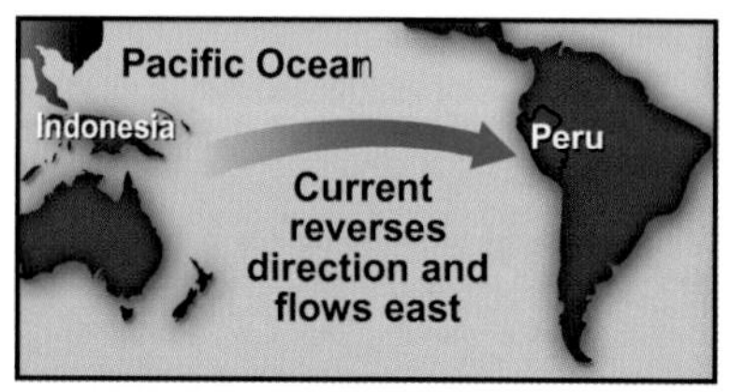

Figure 27.32: *During an El Niño Southern Oscillation event, the current reverses direction.*

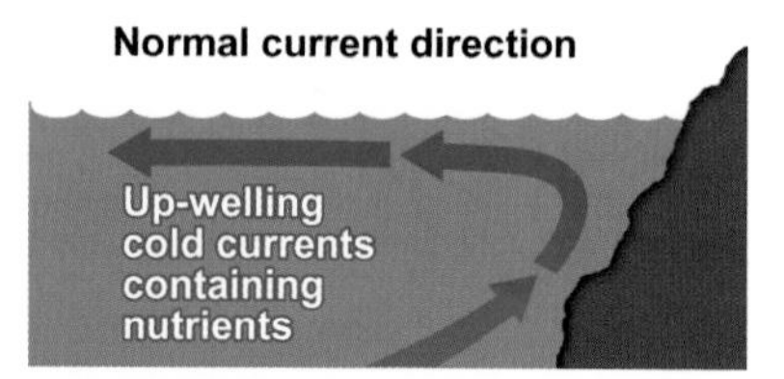

Figure 27.33: *Usually, cold water from ocean depths flows up to the surface along the coast of Peru.*

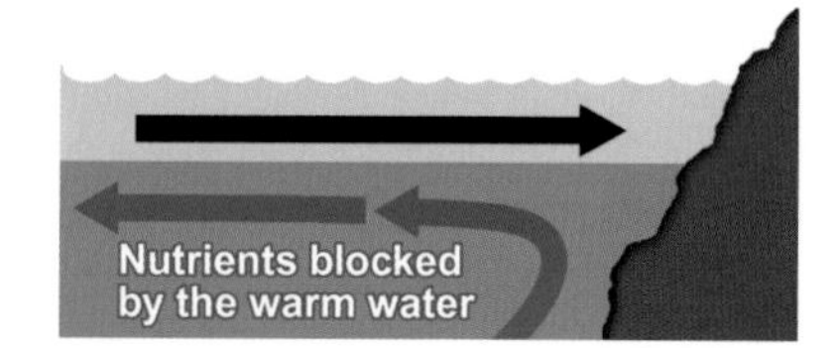

Figure 27.34: *During an El Niño event, the warm water current acts like a lid over the cold water.*

27.5 Weather and Climate

You have been studying about seasonal changes, wind and ocean currents, and weather patterns. All of these elements work together to produce different climates in different parts of the world. Climate is defined as the long-term average of a region's weather. If you wanted to know about the climate of a place you were about to visit, you might ask questions like "How hot and how cold does it usually get? What is the yearly rainfall pattern? How often is the temperature below freezing?" Climate depends on many factors, including latitude, precipitation, elevation, topography, and distance from large bodies of water. Scientists divide the planet into climate regions called biomes. Each biome has a unique set of plants and animals that thrive in its climate. Read on to find out more about six important Earth biomes.

Desert biome

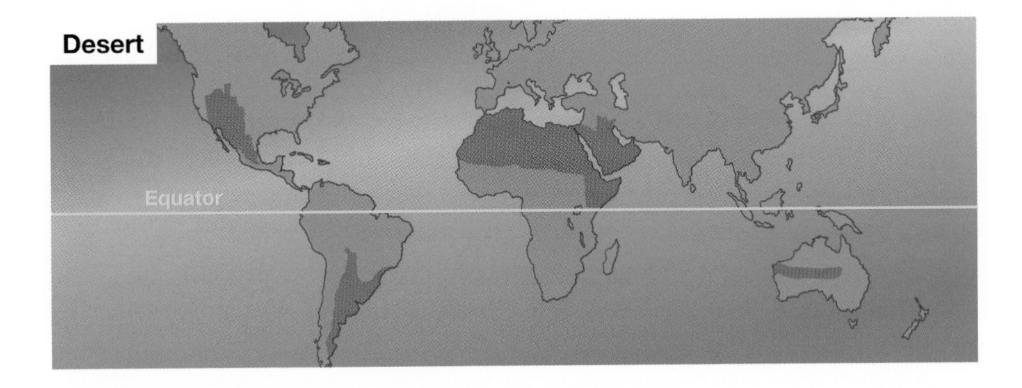

Desert regions

Deserts are regions that average less than 35 centimeters of rainfall per year. Most deserts are found between 30° N and 30° S latitude. Because of the lack of cloud cover, deserts receive more than twice as much incoming solar radiation as humid regions. They also emit almost twice as much radiation at night. As a result, deserts have large variations in daily high and low temperatures.

How do animals survive in the desert?

The desert biome is home to more species of plants and animals than any other biome except the rain forest. Desert creatures have some remark-able features that help them survive without an abundant water supply.

Desert jackrabbits have enormous ears with many blood vessels near the surface. When the rabbit is in a shady spot, the blood running through the vessels is cooled, lowering the animal's body temperature. Use a library or the Internet to learn more about desert animals' adaptations.

How deserts form You may wonder why there is so little rain in the desert. The answer depends on which desert you are talking about. The Sahara and Australian deserts are caused by regions of high atmospheric pressure found near 30° latitude lines. As you have learned, high pressure prevents air near the ground from rising and cooling. As a result, not much condensation takes place. When the condensation rate is lower than the evaporation rate, skies are usually clear and very little precipitation falls.

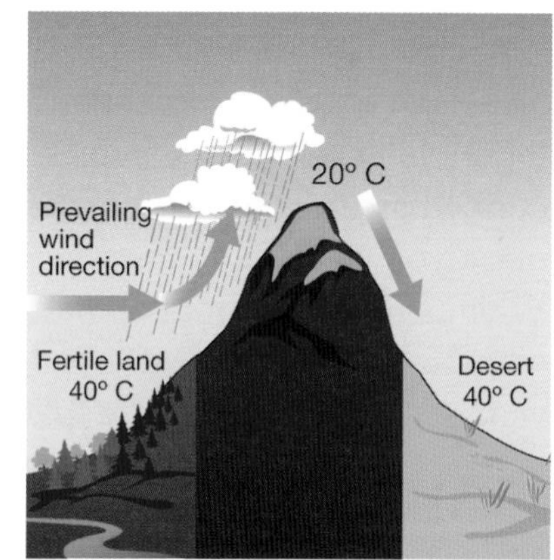

Figure 27.35: *The rainshadow effect.*

Rainshadow deserts Other deserts, such as the one found in eastern Washington state, are caused by the "rainshadow effect" (Figure 27.35). Prevailing westerly winds blow moisture-filled air from the Pacific Ocean over the Washington coast. This air rises as it travels up the western slope of the Cascade Range and cools, causing condensation and lots of rain. By the time the air blows over the mountains to the eastern side, there is very little moisture left. Olympia, Washington, on the western side of the Cascades, receives an average of 201 centimeters of rain per year. Yakima, on the eastern side, receives only 32 centimeters per year (Figure 27.36).

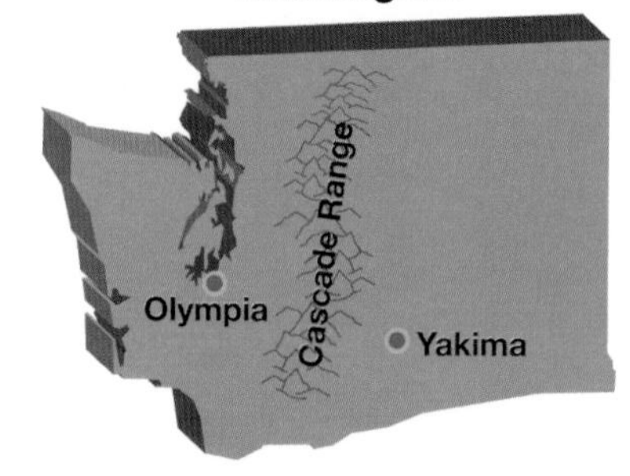

Figure 27.36: *Olympia, Washington, on the western side of the Cascade Range, receives an average of 201 centimeters of rain per year. On the eastern side, Yakima receives only 32 centimeters.*

Fog deserts A third type of desert is known as a "fog desert." Fog deserts are found on the west coasts of continents between 20° and 30° latitude. Here the prevailing winds are easterly, so moisture-filled air does not blow in from the ocean. Cold water currents run along many of these coastlines. The cold water causes air to condense as fog over the ocean. The small amount of precipitation received in these areas is from fog drifting over the land. The Baja desert of California and the Atacama desert in South America are fog deserts.

Desert life It might seem that few plants and animals could survive the harsh desert conditions, but actually many different kinds of plants and animals have adapted to desert life. In fact, only the tropical rain forest biome contains a greater number of plant and animal species.

Tropical rain forest biome

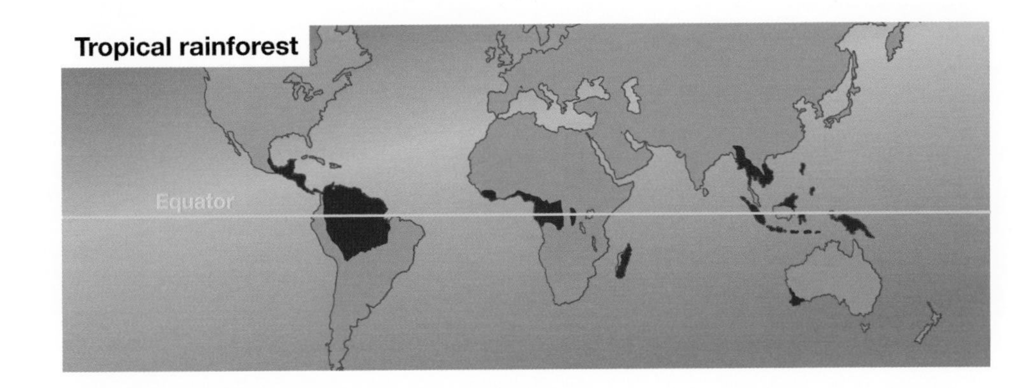

Tropical rain forests Tropical rain forests are found near the equator—between 23.5° N latitude and 23.5° S latitude. They have an average rainfall of at least 200 centimeters per year. This large amount of precipitation occurs in the area where the northern and southern hemisphere trade winds meet. The intense sun and warm ocean water cause this converging air to rise. As the air rises, it cools, condensing into clouds and rain. This cycle happens over and over, causing a period of thundershowers in the warmest part of the afternoon almost every day. Because the tropical rain forests are near the equator, the temperature varies little year round, averaging about 20° to 25° Celsius.

Rain forest life Although tropical rain forests cover less than 6 percent of Earth's land, half of all animal and plant species are found there. There can be as many as 100 different species of plants per hectare (2.47 acres). The most abundant type of plants are tall trees that form a dense canopy. Many foods we enjoy, including Brazil nuts, bananas, pineapple, cocoa, coffee, vanilla and cinnamon flavorings, and coconut originated in tropical rain forests.

Trees and global climate

According to NASA data, an area of tropical rain forest the size of North Carolina is destroyed each year. Land is cleared for crops, grazing land, lumber, or firewood. When clear cutting occurs, the thin topsoil soon washes away, exposing thick clay that is almost useless for agriculture.

This clay absorbs the sun's energy and then emits infrared radiation, which is strongly absorbed by greenhouse gases. This process warms the atmosphere.

Trees prevent some of this warming. Leaves appear green because they reflect green light. Light at this wavelength is not as readily absorbed by greenhouse gases as infrared radiation. In a forested area, more of the suns's energy is reflected directly back to space without first being absorbed by greenhouse gases. In this way, trees keep Earth cooler.

Grassland biome

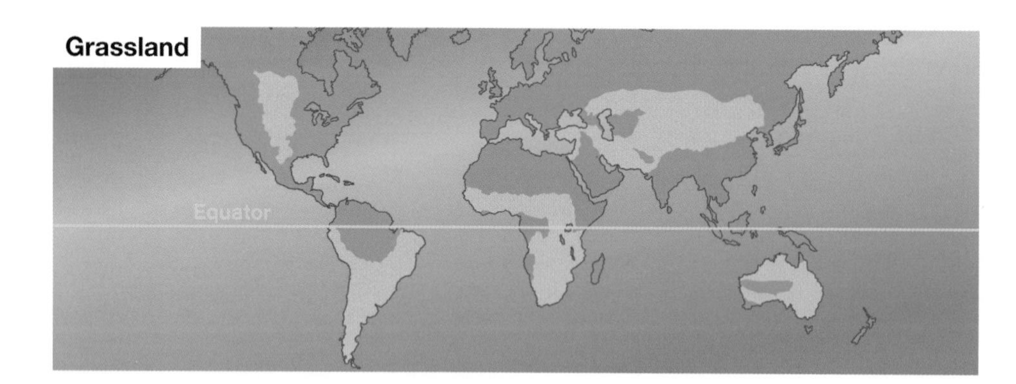

Grasslands are found on every continent except Antarctica. There are two types of grasslands: Tropical grasslands, known as savannas, and temperate grasslands.

Savannas

Savannas are found in parts of the tropics where there is not enough rainfall throughout the year to create a rain forest. Savannas are characterized by two seasons: rainy and dry. During the rainy season, which lasts for six to eight months each year, 50 to 127 centimeters of rain falls. This season is followed by a drought, which in many areas culminates with wildfires. The fires and the poor soil conditions prevent the growth of most trees. In fact, in some areas, trees grow only on termite mounds. The isolated trees found in savannas have cork-like bark or an outer coating that is able to withstand some fire damage.

Temperate grasslands

Temperate grasslands grow in the middle latitude regions and are called prairies and plains in North America, pampas in Argentina and Uruguay, veldts in South Africa, and steppes in Russia and Eastern Europe. Temperate grasslands receive most of their precipitation in late spring and early summer. Most temperate grassland is found in the interior of continents, far from large bodies of water. The average yearly rainfall is between 51 and 89 centimeters. Summer temperatures can reach over 38°C, while in the winter they can plummet below -40°C. The soil is rich in nutrients, and much of this biome has been cleared for farmland. Trees are uncommon except along river valleys.

How do savanna animals survive the periodic fires?

Many large mammals of the savanna, including the wildebeest pictured above, have long legs that enable them to outrun fires. Smaller mammals burrow under the ground and stay there until the fire has passed over them. Most birds fly away from the fire, but several species, including the Fork-tailed Drongos, actually fly *toward* the fires so that they can feast on the hoards of insects trying to escape the heat.

Temperate forest biome

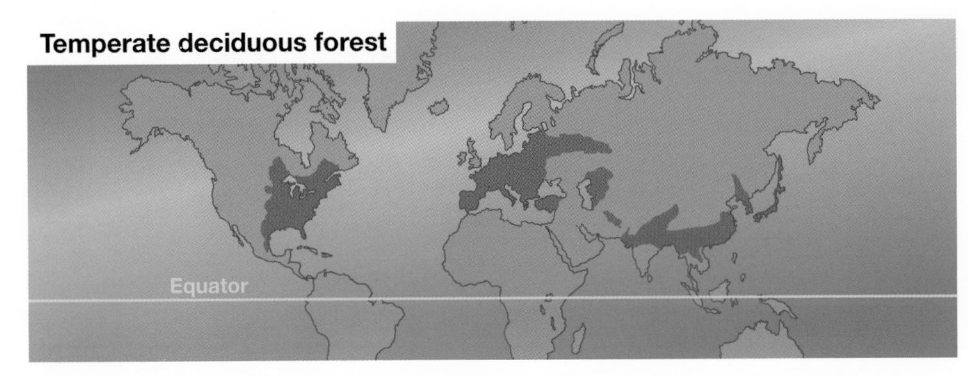

Temperate forests

Temperate forests are found in middle-latitude regions, where there are four distinct seasons. The winter temperatures in some places dip as low as -30°C, and in the summer they can be as warm as 30°C. There are between four and six frost-free months each year. Average yearly rainfall is 75 to 150 centimeters, enough to support the growth of broad-leafed trees like oak, beech, maple, basswood, cottonwood, and willow.

Why do temperatures vary more in inland regions?

Have you ever wondered why cities near the ocean don't get as hot in the summer or as cold in the winter as inland cities at the same latitude? Portland, Oregon, and Minneapolis, Minnesota, are two cities near the same latitude. Portland's average daily low and high temperature for July is 14-27°C, while in Minneapolis, it is 17-29°C. In January, Portland averages a comfortable 1-7°C, while Minneapolis averages only -16 to -6°C.

Portland's climate is milder because it is close to the ocean. Water has a high specific heat, so it warms up slowly in the spring and summer. Land has a low specific heat, so it warms up quickly. Breezes blowing off the ocean keep Portland cooler in the summer. The difference in specific heat also means that land cools off quickly, while water cools off slowly. Portland is located next to relatively warm water in the winter, so it doesn't get as cold as an inland city like Minneapolis.

Wangari Maathai

Wangari Maathai was born in Kenya in 1940. She enjoyed school and earned a scholarship to study biology in the United States. When Maathai returned to her homeland, she was shocked by what she saw. In six years, water had become scarce and forests were gone. What caused this drastic change?

Forests had been clear-cut for timber. Native plants were replaced by fast-growing cash crops that stripped nutrients from the soil. Businesses made money on these products but local people did not benefit. Villagers couldn't grow food in the spoiled soil.

Maathai founded the Green Belt Movement (GBM) in an effort to restore the land and the livelihood of native Kenyans. She taught women to plant and grow trees in the barren landscape. Fruit trees provide food and firewood and prevent erosion. GBM has has now branched out to other African nations. In 2004, Maathai won the Nobel Peace Prize for her work. She is currently the Assistant Minister for the Environment, Natural Resources, and Wildlife in Kenya's parliament.

Taiga biome

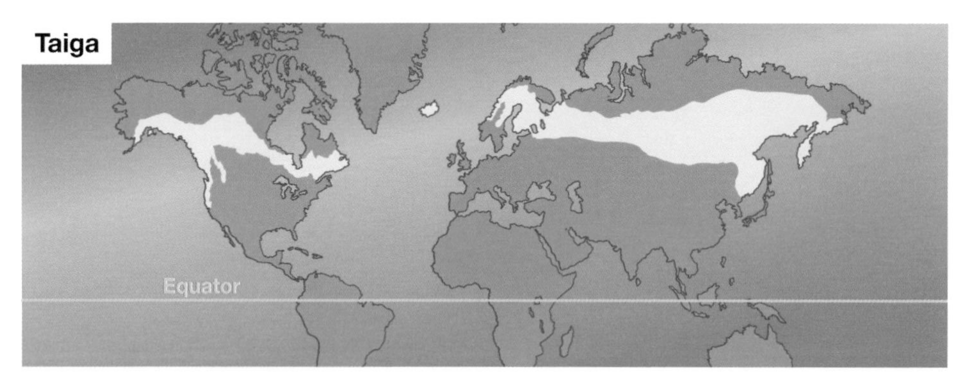

Taiga Taiga, otherwise known as boreal or coniferous forest, is the largest land biome. Taiga can be found between 50° and 70° N latitude in North America and Eurasia, including Canada and Russia. The average temperature in the taiga is below freezing for at least six months of the year. Annual precipitation averages 40 to 100 centimeters. Much of this falls during the short growing season (approximately 130 days). Summer temperatures rarely reach above 21°C.

Taiga life Evergreen trees with needle-like leaves are the most common type of vegetation found in the taiga, which is the Russian word for forest. These include pine, fir, and spruce trees. All of these trees are cone-shaped, which helps them shed snow so its weight doesn't break their branches. The needle shape of the leaves helps prevent moisture loss in the winter. This is important because trees can't take in water from frozen soil. The fact that they don't lose their needles in the fall means that they don't have to waste time in the early spring growing new ones, and can get started on photosynthesis as soon as it is warm enough. The roots of these trees are shallow and spread out wide. This makes it possible for them to take in surface water from melting snow and ice even though much of the ground underneath them is still frozen.

Snow keeps things warm!

Did you know that snow is a great insulator? In the taiga biome, a thick layer of snow (often several meters deep) falls before the coldest part of the winter. The air spaces between snow crystals prevent the ground underneath from losing more and more heat as the winter progresses.

While air temperatures may be well below zero Celsius for weeks on end, the ground temperature will remain right around freezing. Mice and other small mammals make tunnels in the snow that link their burrows and food stashes. The temperature in the burrows remains fairly constant, even when the outside air temperature plummets.

Tundra biome

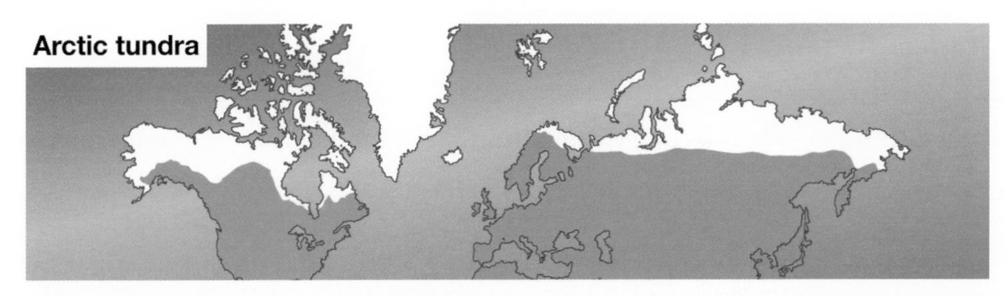

Tundra Tundra is the coldest biome on Earth. The word tundra comes from a Finnish word for treeless land. There are two types of tundra—arctic tundra, found in a band around the arctic ocean, and alpine tundra, found high in mid-latitude mountains.

Arctic tundra Arctic tundra has a growing season of only 50 to 60 days. The average winter temperature is -34°C. Summer temperatures rarely exceed 12°C. As a result of these cold temperatures, the ground is permanently frozen from 25 centimeters to about 100 centimeters below the surface. This ground is called permafrost. There is a thin layer of soil above the permafrost that does thaw in summertime, but it is not deep enough to support the growth of trees. Lichens, mosses, grasses, and a few woody shrubs are the most common plants in the arctic tundra.

Permafrost stores carbon dioxide Permafrost has a very important function on our planet: It stores carbon dioxide. Here's how the process works: Usually, when plants die, they decompose into soil. This process releases carbon dioxide into the air. However, when an arctic tundra plant dies, the cold temperatures prevent it from rapidly decaying into soil. Instead, at least part of its structure remains intact until it is frozen in the permafrost. In fact, remains of plants 1,000 years old have been found in the permafrost. Since the plant structures don't completely decay, carbon that would have been released into the atmosphere as carbon dioxide stays in the ground.

Alpine tundra Alpine tundra occurs in middle latitude regions, but at very high altitudes. Cold temperatures, windy conditions, and thin soil create an environment where only plants similar to those in the arctic regions can survive. In rocky alpine regions, lichens and mosses are the dominant plants, but in alpine meadows, grasses and small woody shrubs can be found.

What is a "carbon sink"?

Permafrost is known as a "carbon sink." A sink is an area where more carbon is stored than is released into the atmosphere. Some scientists are concerned that if Earth warms up several degrees, the permafrost will begin to melt. If this happens, the frozen plants would decompose and release carbon dioxide into the air. The permafrost would no longer serve a "sink." It would become a source of carbon dioxide (a greenhouse gas) in the atmosphere.

Chapter 27 Review

Vocabulary review

Match the following terms with the correct definition. There is one extra definition in the list that will not match any of the terms.

Set One

1. Coriolis effect
2. trade winds
3. prevailing westerlies
4. polar easterlies
5. gyres

a. Global wind pattern formed when air over the poles cools, sinks, and spreads over the surface
b. Large circular patterns of surface ocean currents
c. Global wind pattern named for the fact that sailors used these winds to travel to new lands, where they interacted with other cultures
d. Cold winds that blow in early spring
e. Global wind pattern that flows over most of the continental United States
f. The bending of wind and ocean currents due to Earth's rotation

Set Two

1. cirrus
2. cumuliform
3. stratiform
4. stratocumulus
5. dew point temperature

a. Cloud that looks like popcorn with flat base
b. Cloud type that looks like wispy white streaks high in the sky
c. Cloud type that looks like a lumpy blanket
d. Cloud type that looks like a smooth gray sheet
e. Air temperature in which more water in atmosphere is evaporating than condensing
f. Air temperature where condensation rate first exceeds evaporation rate

Set Three

1. cold front
2. warm front
3. jet stream
4. temperature inversion
5. latent heat

a. Energy stored when water changes from liquid to gas and released when water condenses
b. High altitude fast-moving wind
c. When a cold air mass moves in and replaces warm air at Earth's surface
d. When temperatures near the ground are cooler than the air temperature up high
e. Fast-moving winds near Earth's surface
f. When a warm air mass overtakes cooler air in a region

Set Four

1. El Niño
2. southern oscillation
3. climate
4. biome
5. permafrost

a. Climate region which contains plants and animal uniquely adapted to this environment
b. Distance from equator, measured in degrees
c. Area of Earth that stores more carbon than it releases into the atmosphere; found in tundra
d. Peruvian fisherman's name for the arrival of warm water currents along their shores
e. The long-term average of a region's weather
f. Description of change in wind flow, air pressure, and thunderstorm activity occurring in Pacific ocean, from Indonesia to Peru

Concept review

1. If Earth were heated evenly, every location would be at the same temperature all the time. Obviously, this is not the case! How does Earth's rotation affect its heating and cooling?
2. Explain why cooler climates are found at high latitudes and warmer climates are found near the equator.
3. What is a thermal?
4. What would you call wind that is blowing from the northeast to the southwest?
5. Name the three most important global surface wind patterns and describe where each is found.
6. What causes surface ocean currents like the Gulf Stream? How does the Gulf Stream affect the climate of Great Britain?
7. What are the three most important factors that shape a region's weather?
8. What is an air mass and how does it form?
9. Is a warm front more likely to be accompanied by fast-moving thunderstorms or long bands of light precipitation? Why?
10. How do mountains or very tall cumulus clouds shift the path of the jet stream? Why does a shift in the jet stream often cause a change in the weather?
11. If you heard a weather report that said high pressure was moving into your region, would you expect clear skies or clouds and precipitation? Why?
12. There are several important factors that shape climates. Name four of these.

Problems

1. Draw a diagram and write a paragraph to explain why the northern hemisphere experiences winter in January and summer in July.
2. Draw a diagram and write a paragraph to explain why global wind patterns are bent to the right in the northern hemisphere.
3. Describe how cumuliform, stratiform, and stratocumulus clouds form.
4. Which of these conditions is NOT necessary for rain to fall?
   a. The dew point temperature has been reached.
   b. Dust is present as a site for water condensation.
   c. Large cumulonimbus clouds develop.
   d. Water droplets grow to a size of at least 1,000 microns.
5. Describe what happens when a cold front moves through a region.
6. How does a low pressure center develop? What kind of weather do you expect from a low pressure system?
7. Describe what happens to surface ocean currents, water temperatures, and thunderstorm activity during an El Niño-Southern oscillation event.
8. Draw a diagram and write a paragraph to explain what is meant by a "rainshadow" desert.

Applying your knowledge

1. Create a three-dimensional model that you could use to teach a class of fourth graders about why Earth has seasons.
2. Polar orbiting satellites travel in the same elliptical orbit over and over again, taking photographs and collecting data about Earth. The satellite shown at right completes one orbit approximately every two hours. Below you will see a map of the satellite's "ground path," showing the locations covered by the satellite each day. Using what you have learned about the Coriolis effect, explain why the ground path of the satellite doesn't go straight north and south. How is it possible for the satellite to photograph the entire Earth in one day without changing its orbit?

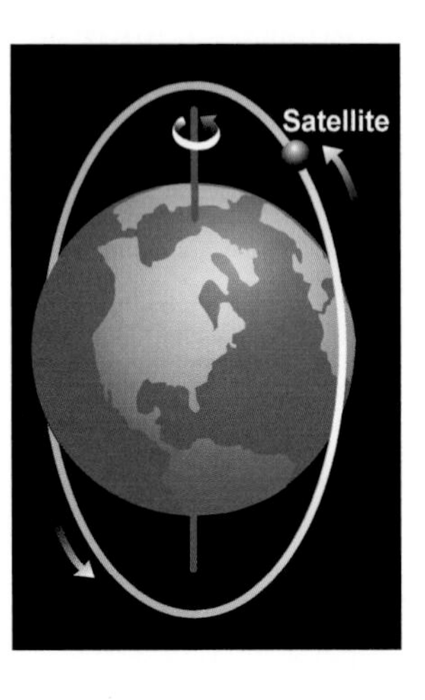

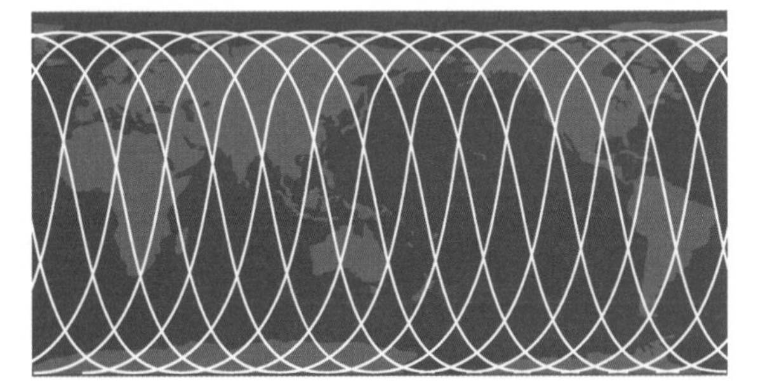

3. Hurricane Andrew was one of the strongest storms to hit the United States in the previous century. Use the Internet to research the development and path of Hurricane Andrew. What conditions caused this storm to grow so intense?
4. Use the Internet to research the National Weather Service's recommendations for staying safe during a tornado. Write an action plan for your school or home that describes the safest place to seek shelter during a tornado in your area.
5. Wilson "Snowflake" Bentley (1865-1931) was a self-educated farmer from Jericho, Vermont. He was a pioneer in the use of photomicrography—taking photographs of images seen through a microscope. Bentley took the first photomicrograph of an individual snowflake and went on to produce more than 5,000 snowflake images. By keeping detailed weather records for decades, Bentley made several important findings about the relationship between snowflake crystal structure and atmospheric conditions. Research and prepare a five minute presentation on Bentley's contributions to the field of meteorology.

6. Find out how an El Niño event affects the area where you live. Make a poster which shows what you can expect during an El Niño event, and why.
7. Permafrost is an important "carbon sink," or area that stores more carbon than it releases as carbon dioxide. Use a library or the Internet to find out what other important "carbon sinks" are found on Earth.

UNIT 10

Earth Science

Chapter 28

The Changing Earth

Powerful events cause changes on Earth's surface such that it looks different than it did 4.6 billion years ago. In this chapter, you will learn that Earth is a layered ball covered with thin pieces that move, interact, and shape Earth's surface. The theory of plate tectonics, which you will learn about in the second section, explains the dramatic movements of these pieces called tectonic plates. Friction and pressure intensify at the boundaries of the plates. When pressure is released, an earthquake occurs. While the movement of tectonic plates causes slow changes on Earth, amazing and fast changes occur when an earthquake strikes. Earthquakes are the subject of the third section.

28.1 Understanding Earth *What story is hidden here?*

Studying the Earth is like detective work—you use clues to uncover the fascinating history waiting to be told. In this Investigation, you will have the opportunity to reconstruct the underlying stories in different situations and rock formations.

28.2 Plate Tectonics *What will Earth look like in 50 million years?*

The theory of plate tectonics explains how and in what direction tectonic plates move on Earth's surface. In this Investigation, you will simulate the movement of the plates and predict how Earth will look in 50 million years.

28.3 Earthquakes *What mechanical factors affect earthquakes?*

In this Investigation, you will simulate the causes and effects of an earthquake. In the process, you will discover some of the factors that affect the timing and magnitude of an earthquake and use the results to develop a simple explanation of the cause of earthquakes.

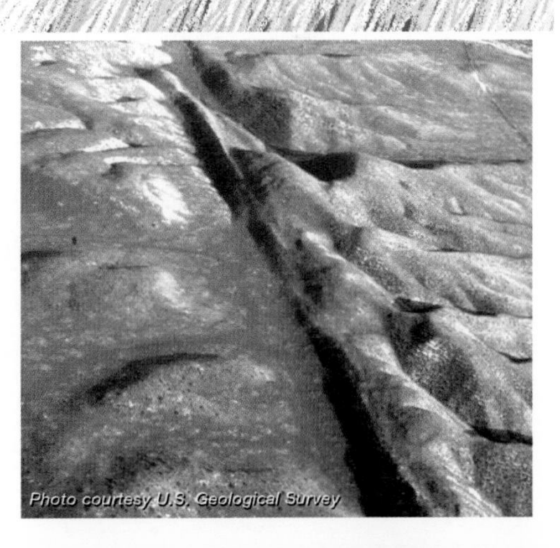
Photo courtesy U.S. Geological Survey

Learning Goals

In this chapter, you will:

- ✔ Use relative dating to sequence events recorded in a rock formation.
- ✔ Learn about Earth's interior and the role it plays in shaping Earth's surface.
- ✔ Apply basic science concepts like density, viscosity, convection, and energy transformation to Earth science.
- ✔ Learn about the theory of plate tectonics and be about to explain evidence that supports this theory.
- ✔ Learn about the three main kinds of plate boundaries: convergent, divergent, and transform.
- ✔ Learn about the causes and effects of earthquakes and where they occur.
- ✔ Learn about the role of seismic waves in understanding Earth's interior.
- ✔ Learn about the scales that are used to rate the magnitude of an earthquake.
- ✔ Calculate the location of an epicenter of an earthquake using seismic data.
- ✔ Learn how to keep safe during an earthquake.

Vocabulary

asthenosphere	focus	original horizontally	sea-floor spreading
continental drift	geology	paleontology	seismic wave
cross-cutting relationships	inclusions	Pangaea	subduction
epicenter	lateral continuity	plate tectonics	superposition
fault	lithosphere	P-wave	S-wave
faunal succession	mid-ocean ridge	relative dating	tsunami

28.1 Understanding Earth

In the 1600s, all rocks and minerals found in the ground were called fossils. Today, we define a *fossil* as the preserved remains of ancient animals, plants, or preserved evidence of life such as footprints or nests). Our understanding of fossils is based on the work of people who were fascinated by the planet Earth. The purpose of this section is to encourage your curiosity about Earth's land formations. Soon you will be able to explain mountains, earthquakes, volcanoes, and the long history of a rock. In other words, you will be able to explain some of Earth's **geology**. Geology is the study of rocks and materials that make up Earth and the processes that shape it. Below you will learn about the beginnings of geology and the methods that are used in geology today.

Figure 28.1: *This illustration is from Nicholas Steno's 1667 paper titled "The Head of a Shark Dissected."*

The beginnings of modern geology

Tonguestones and shark's teeth

In 1666, Nicholas Steno (1638-87), a Danish physician with a strong interest in science, received the head of a shark from some local fishermen. Curious about the shark's anatomy, Steno dissected the head and published his findings (Figure 28.1). While dissecting, Steno noticed that the shark's teeth resembled mysterious stones called "tonguestones" that were found in local rocks. From ancient times until the 1600s, people believed that tonguestones were mystical and had fallen from the moon. Others believed they grew inside rocks.

How did shark's teeth get into a rock?

Although scientists had noticed that tonguestones looked like sharks' teeth, they had not understood how the teeth could have gotten into a rock. In puzzling over this problem, Steno realized over time the remains of an animal will be covered by layers of sediment. After a short time, the animal's soft parts decay quickly, but harder parts like bones and teeth resist decomposing. After a very long time, the sediment surrounding a decayed animal can become a *rock formation*.

Relative dating and modern geology

Steno's explanation helped him develop ideas about how rocks and fossils form. These ideas are used in a technique called **relative dating**. Relative dating is a way to put events in the order in which they happened. This technique contributed to the development of modern geology. It is used today by **geologists** as they study rock formations and by scientists called **paleontologists** who study and identify fossils. A simple example of relative dating is presented in Figure 28.2.

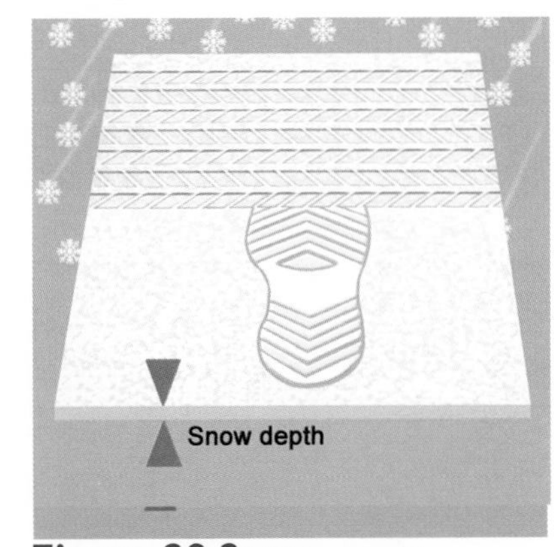

Figure 28.2: *This graphic illustrates three events: a footstep, a tire track, and snowfall. Which event happened first? Sequencing these events in the correct order is a form of relative dating.*

Steno's ideas and relative dating

What is relative dating? In Earth science, relative dating is a method used to determine the general age of a rock, rock formation, or fossil. When you use relative dating, you are not trying to determine the exact age of something. Instead, you use clues to sequence events that occurred first, then second, and so on. Steno's ideas—*superposition, original horizontality*, and *lateral continuity*—help identify the clues.

Superposition The approximate age of each layer of a rock formation can be determined by applying Steno's idea called superposition. Superposition states that the bottom layer of a rock formation is older than the layer on top because the bottom layer formed first. Stacking old newspapers in the order in which you received them illustrates superposition (Figure 28.3). The oldest newspaper tends to be on the bottom, and the newest on the top.

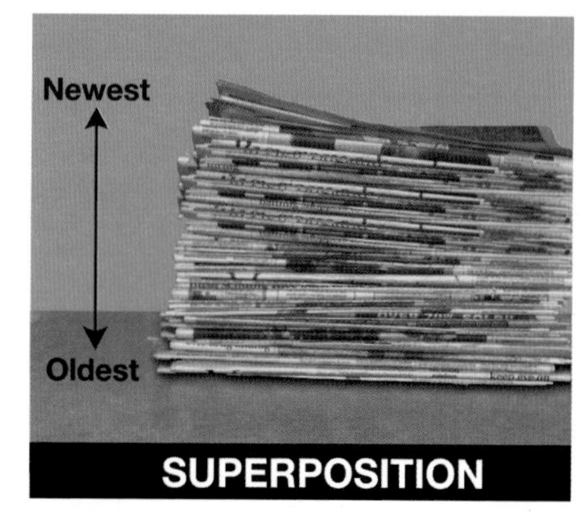

Figure 28.3: *A stack of newspapers illustrates superposition. Superposition means that the bottom layers of rock are older than the layers on the top.*

Original horizontality Original horizontality states that sediment particles fall to the bottom of a basin, such as a riverbed, in response to gravity and result in *horizontal* layers. Over time, these layers can become layers of rock. Sometimes rock layers are found in a *vertical* position. Steno realized that slow movements of Earth could move horizontal rock layers to the vertical position.

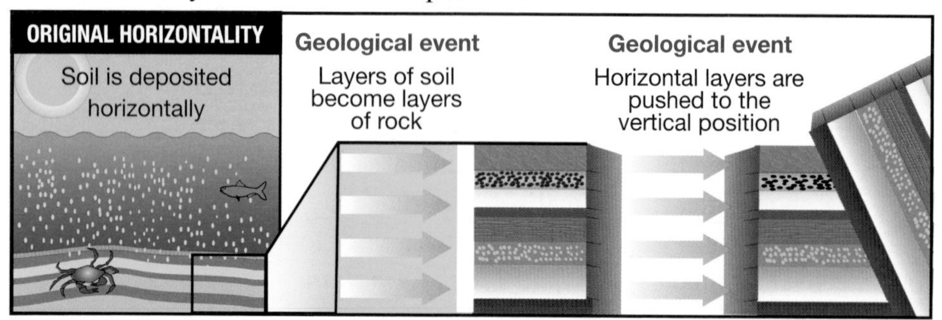

Lateral continuity Lateral continuity is the idea that layers of sediment extend in all directions when they form and before they become rock layers. For example, if you were to compare rock layers in the Grand Canyon, you would find that the layers on one side more or less match up with the layers on the other. A flowing river can interrupt these layers and an earthquake can offset them (Figure 28.4). The Colorado River formed the gap that is now the canyon of the Grand Canyon.

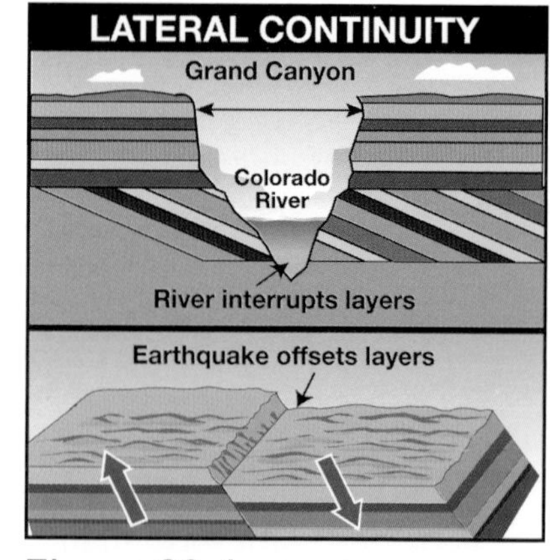

Figure 28.4: *The idea of lateral continuity states that layers of rock are continuous unless a geologic event like a river interrupts the layers or an earthquake them.*

Interpreting rocks formations

The present explains the past

Using Steno's ideas, you can begin to describe the history of a rock formation. Another important idea, developed by Scottish geologist James Hutton (1726-97), is that the *present explains the past*. In other words, if you understand the geologic processes that are happening now, you can explain what happened a long time ago. Both Hutton and Steno were important in the development of relative dating and modern geology. The following ideas are also useful in relative dating.

Cross-cutting relationships

The idea of **cross-cutting relationships** states that a vein of rock is younger than the rock that surrounds a vein. Figure 28.5 shows a rock formation with three layers and a cross-cutting vein. The layers formed first. The vein formed when melted rock oozed into the original rock, cutting across the layers. Then the melted rock solidified. The bottom layer is the oldest part of the rock formation and the vein is the youngest. The middle and top layers formed after the bottom layer and before the vein.

Inclusions

Sometimes rock pieces called **inclusions** are contained in another rock. During the formation of a rock with inclusions, sediments or melted rock surrounded the inclusion and then solidified. Therefore, the inclusions are older than the surrounding rock (Figure 28.5). A rock with inclusions is like a chocolate chip cookie. The chocolate chips are made first by a manufacturer. Then they are added to the batter before baking.

Faunal succession

Over geologic history, many animals and plants have lived and become extinct. Their remains have become fossils. The idea of **faunal succession** states that fossils can be used to identify the relative age of layers of a rock formation (Figure 28.6). For example, dinosaur fossils are found in rock that is about 65 to 200 million years old because these animals lived on Earth about 65 to 200 million years ago. We can learn what else lived with the dinosaurs by studying other kinds of fossils found in layers of rock that are this old. The fossils of modern human beings (*Homo sapiens*) are found in rock that is about 40,000 years old, but not in rock that is 65 to 200 million years old. And dinosaur fossils are *not* found in rock that is 40,000 years old. Faunal succession also assumes that evolution occurs in one direction. For example, present-day animals will not evolve into dinosaurs.

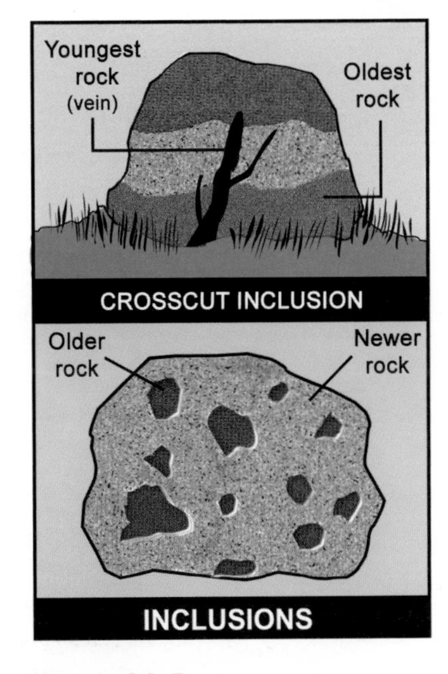

Figure 28.5: *Cross-cutting relationships versus inclusions.*

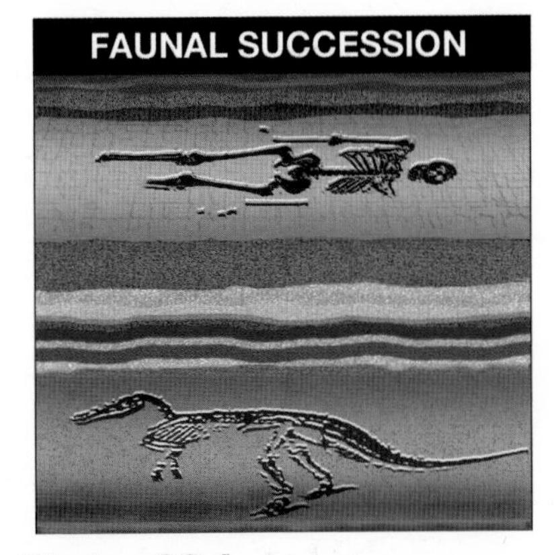

Figure 28.6: *Faunal succession. (MYA = millions of years ago.)*

Calculating Earth's age

Calculating Earth's age

William Thompson Kelvin (1824-1907), known for proposing the absolute temperature scale that came to be named after him, meticulously calculated Earth's age to be between 10 million and 100 million years. His calculations were based on his prediction of how long it would take for a hot Earth to cool.

Radioactive decay and Earth's age

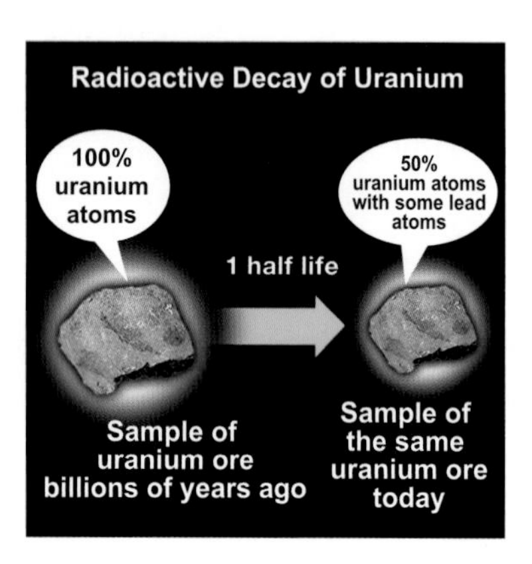

Lord Kelvin's calculation was not accurate because he did not realize that Earth has internal heat from the core and radioactive decay. Radioactivity was not understood until the early 1900s. In 1907, Earth's age was estimated by measuring the radioactive decay of uranium to lead. This estimation was performed by comparing the amount of lead to uranium in a piece of uranium ore. With improved techniques and evidence from tree rings and glaciers, the age of Earth is estimated to be about 4.6 billion years.

Comparing ages

Moon rocks, meteorites, and the solar system are estimated to be about the same age as Earth, about 4.6 billion years. This information indicates that the solar system, the moon, and Earth were formed around the same time.

The geologic time scale

The geologic time scale is a model of Earth's history. In this model, time is divided into eras and periods. Figure 28.7 includes pictures of organisms and events that characterize the periods. For example, Earth was covered with glaciers during the Ordovician period. Flowering plants evolved during the Cretaceous period. A giant meteor hit Earth at the beginning of the Tertiary period. Scientists believe this event may have ended the existence of the dinosaurs. Modern humans appeared 40,000 years ago during the Cenozoic era. Before these periods of time, the Precambrian era lasted from 4.6 billion to 570 million years ago. During this earliest time period, layers of rock at the bottom of the Grand Canyon were forming and only single-celled organisms lived on Earth.

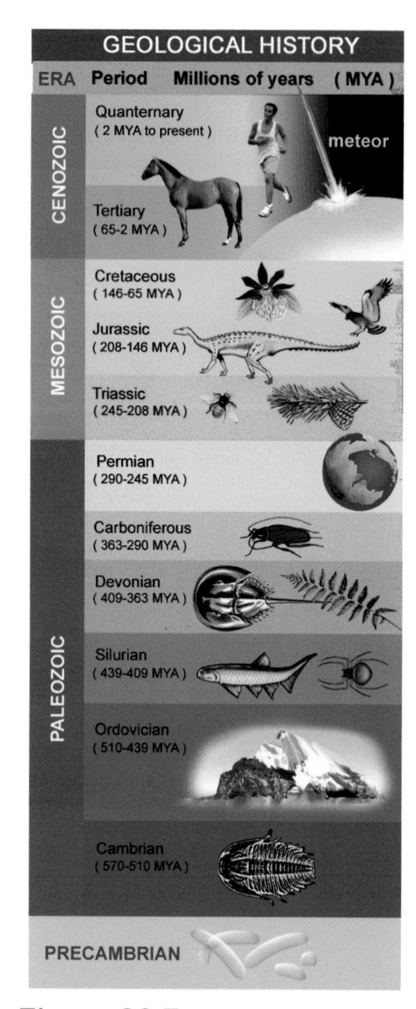

Figure 28.7: *Earth's geologic history. Some of the period names are based on the location where fossils from that time were first described. For example, fossils from the Cambrian period were first described in Cambridge, England.*

Inside Earth

Earth's beginnings and the formation of layers

Scientists believe that Earth formed when cosmic particles collected into a sphere due to the gravitational attraction between the particles. As these particles gathered, pressure inside the sphere increased. Iron particles melted and percolated to the core. The "fall" of iron to the core was accompanied by the conversion of potential energy to kinetic energy. This energy transformation generated intense heat that melted other particles in the sphere. At this point in Earth's formation, the densest materials like irb on and nickel sank to Earth's center and formed its core. Layers of less dense material formed the mantle. The least dense elements rose to the outer surface and formed our planet's crust.

The lithosphere and asthenosphere

The shallowest 100- to 150-kilometer layer of Earth is the lithosphere (*lithos* is Greek for "stone"). This layer includes the crust and upper mantle. The lithosphere is about two percent of the 12,756-kilometer diameter of Earth—like the skin of an apple compared with the whole apple. Below the lithosphere is the asthenosphere (*asthen* is Greek for "weak"), a layer of the mantle that is composed of material that flows.

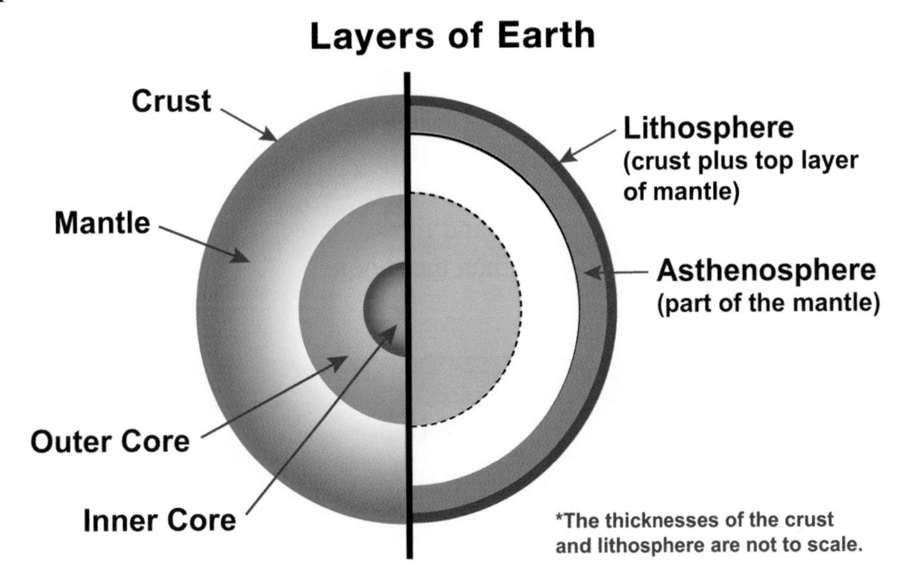

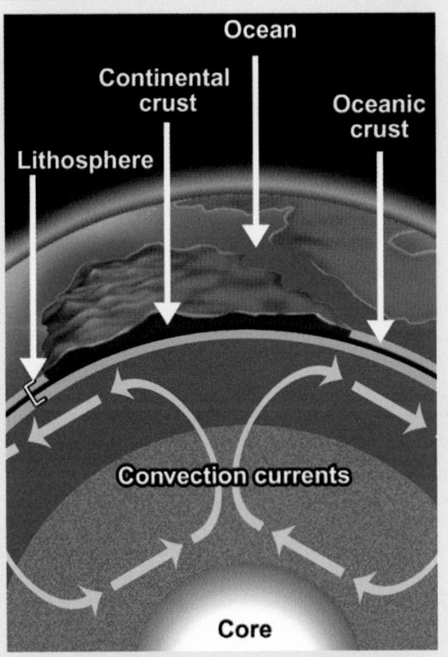

Convection inside Earth

The rocky material of the mantle moves in very slow convection currents. This movement is related to density and temperature differences in the mantle. Hot material is less dense and rises. Cold material is denser and sinks. Earth's core is a source of heat. Heat from the core warms the deep mantle and causes the material to become less dense and rise toward Earth's surface. At the surface, the hot material cools, becomes more dense, and sinks back to the core where it will be heated again.

The layers of Earth

Earth's crust Earth's surface is covered with a thin crust. There are two kinds of crust, *continental* and *oceanic* (Figure 28.8). Continental crust is older, thicker, and less dense than oceanic crust. Continental crust is composed primarily of granite, a usually light-colored rock rich in silica. Oceanic crust is made of basalt, a dark-colored rock relatively low in silica and containing iron and magnesium. Both continental and oceanic crusts are brittle and tend to crack when pushed or pulled as pieces of the crust move. A crack in the crust is called a *fault*.

The mantle The mantle of Earth is a 2,900-kilometer-thick layer of molten material between the crust and core. The density of this material is 3.3 g/cm^3. The continental and oceanic crusts float on top of the mantle because they are less dense. Blocks of foam and wood floating in water demonstrate the floating of the continental and oceanic crusts in the mantle (Figure 28.9). Being less dense, a foam block floats higher in water than wood. Likewise, continental crust floats higher in the mantle than oceanic crust. The result is that much of the water on Earth has collected on top of the oceanic crust, forming the oceans.

The core Earth has a two-layer core. The inner core is made of *solid* iron and nickel, while the outer core is made of *molten* iron, nickel, and oxygen. Both of these layers are denser than the mantle. The temperature of the core ranges from 2,000°C to 5,000°C. In comparison, the surface of the sun is estimated to be 5,500°C. The density difference between the core and the middle layer of Earth (the mantle) is twice the density difference between the atmosphere and Earth's crust. The core is about one-third of Earth's mass and a little smaller than the moon.

	Continental crust	Oceanic crust
Average thickness	10-80 km	5-10 km
Density	2.75 g/cm^3	3.0 g/cm^3
Oldest known age	3.5 billion years	200 million years
Composition	mostly granite	basalt

Figure 28.8: *The oceanic crust is made of basalt. The continental crust is made mostly of granite.*

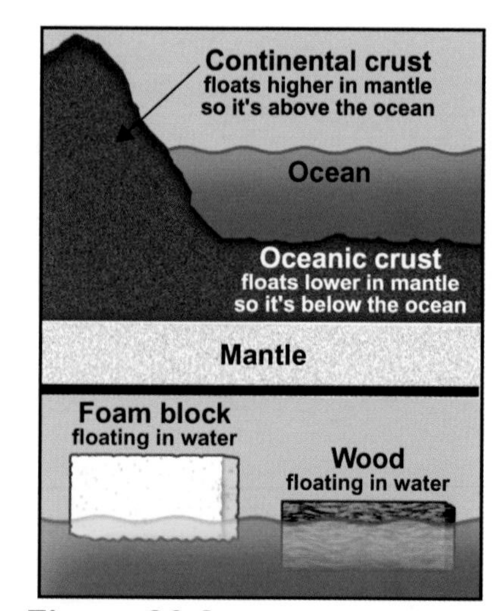

Figure 28.9: *Because oceanic crust is denser than continental crust, it floats lower in Earth's mantle. Blocks of foam and wood floating in water demonstrate this phenomenon.*

Important concepts that will help you understand Earth science

Concepts you already know

This section begins your study of the processes that shape Earth. The concepts you have learned in this section will help you understand mountains, earthquakes, volcanoes, and the formation of rocks. As you continue to read, you will see the following familiar concepts.

Concept	How the concept applies to understanding Earth
Density	The layers of Earth are separated according to **density**. For example, the core of Earth is much denser than the continental and oceanic crusts.
Viscosity	The molten material of the mantle is viscous. For example, molasses is much more viscous than water which flows very quickly. The **viscosity** of lava explains the kinds of volcanic eruptions that occur.
Convection currents	The **convection currents** in the mantle are similar to the convection currents in the atmosphere.
Potential and kinetic energy	As Earth formed, the fall of iron to the core was accompanied by the conversion of **potential energy** to **kinetic energy**. Heat was produce inside Earth as a result of this energy conversion. Also, earthquakes are caused by a conversion of **potential energy** to **kinetic energy**.
Cycles	**Cycle** is a term used to describe various processes that move matter from place to place on Earth. Water is transported on Earth via the water cycle. The energy source driving this cycle is the sun. The rock cycle is a set of processes that lead to the formation and recycling of the various kinds of rocks. Energy sources driving this cycle are climate changes (driven by the sun) and convection currents that distribute heat in Earth's mantle.

Plate tectonics

In the next section, you will learn about the theory of plate tectonics. It states that large pieces of the lithosphere called *tectonic plates* move on Earth's surface. The theory of plate tectonics explains why South America and Africa fit together like two puzzle pieces. Before reading about plate tectonics, come up with your own ideas to explain how plates move on Earth's surface and what the effects of this movement might be.

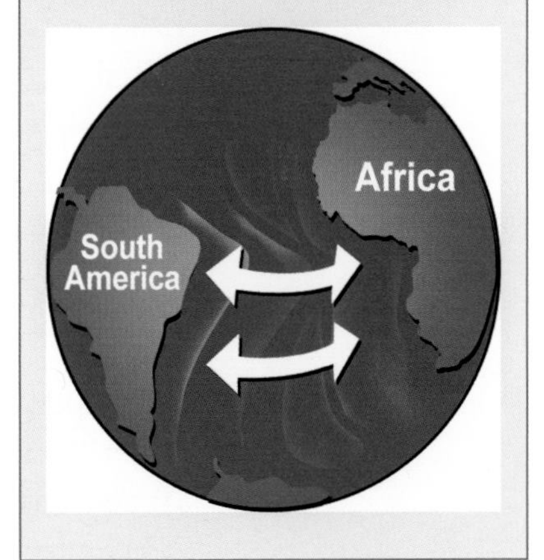

28.2 Plate Tectonics

If you look at a map of the world, it is easy to imagine the continents like puzzle pieces. In particular, South America and Africa seem to fit together. If the continents were once connected, how did they move apart? The theory of plate tectonics explains the movement of continents and other geological events like earthquakes and volcanoes. In this section, you will learn about the theory of plate tectonics.

The surface of Earth

Pangaea and continental drift In 1915, Alfred Wegener (1880-1930), a German meteorologist, wrote a book titled *The Origin of Continents and Oceans*. In this book, he proposed that millions of years ago, the land on Earth formed a single, huge landmass. He named it **Pangaea**, a Greek name that means "all lands." Wegener's theory was that pieces of Pangaea moved apart to form the seven continents (Figure 28.10). This idea was called **continental drift**. Wegener's idea was not accepted by all scientists because it did not explain what caused the continents to move.

Plate tectonics How continents moved is explained by a theory called **plate tectonics**. The term *tectonics* means construction or building. The theory of plate tectonics, stated in 1965, refers to the movement of giant pieces of solid rock on Earth's surface called **tectonic plates**. The movement of one plate causes the pulling or pushing of other plates, significantly affecting Earth's surface.

The movement of tectonic plates affects Earth's surface and causes earthquakes and volcanoes.

What is happening now? Even today, Earth's surface is changing. For example, the plates on which North America and Europe sit are continuing to separate at a rate between 1 and 10 centimeters a year. For comparison, your fingernails grow at a rate of 2.5 centimeters a year. Though this rate may seem very slow, the Atlantic Ocean is increasing in size. In contrast, the Pacific Ocean is decreasing in size. If the Atlantic continues to grow and the Pacific continues to get smaller, what might Earth look like in 50 million years?

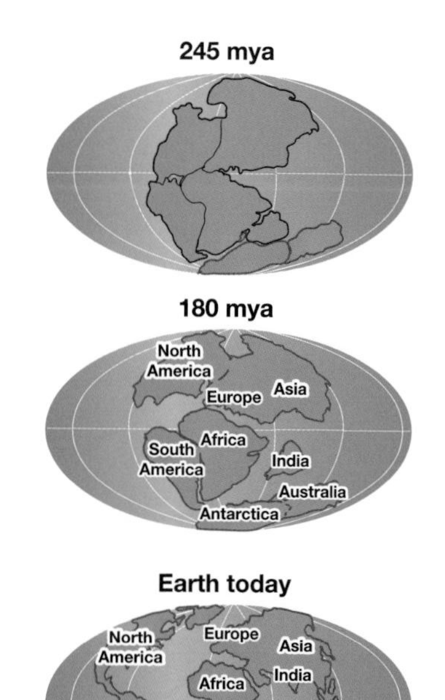

Figure 28.10: *About 225 million years ago, the land on Earth was part of one supercontinent called Pangaea. About 200 million years ago, this huge landmass began to split apart into many sections—seven of the largest sections are our continents. It is important to note that the forces that brought Pangaea together had been working for a long time. Before Pangaea, there were other earlier oceans and continents.*

Continental drift

Wegener's evidence for continental drift

For a long time, scientists could not explain why South America and Africa appeared to fit together. Wegener gathered evidence that supported his idea that *all* the continents had been connected.

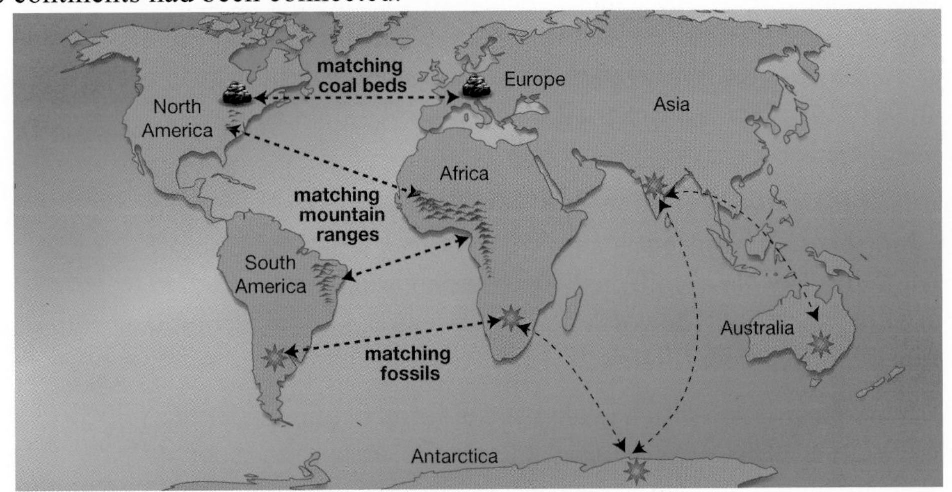

Mountains are in certain locations on Earth

Wegener's scientific colleagues thought it was foolish to propose that continents could move. Instead, they had other ideas to explain features on Earth. One idea was the "dry apple skin" model, which assumed that the Earth is shrinking and mountains are the result of the wrinkling of the crust. If this were true, mountains would be *all over* the surface of Earth. Instead, mountains tend to be in long bands. For example, there are bands of mountains on the west coast of North America and the west coast of South America (Figure 28.11).

Continental drift was not accepted until the 1960s

Wegener believed the continents had pushed through the ocean floor. However, he did not have a satisfactory explanation for how this happened. There was no known source of energy large enough to move continents through the sea floor. Also, although scientists had data about the interior of Earth from earthquakes, there were no clues in Earth's crust to show that the continents had broken through the sea floor. Given this lack of evidence to explain the mechanism of continental drift, scientists did not accept this idea. However, in the 1960s, a scientific breakthrough occurred. Evidence showed that the continents and sea floor moved *together* on Earth's surface.

Continental drift

Distribution of mountains and coal:

Mountain ranges on the east coast of South America match mountains on the west coast of Africa. The North American Appalachian Mountains match the Atlas Mountains of northwest Africa. Coal beds in North America match those in Europe.

Distribution of fossils:

Fossils of a particular plant are found on continents that are now far apart. This plant only spreads across land, not across oceans.

The past does not match the present:

Fossils of tropical plants are found on Antarctic land and glacier scratches are found on rocks near equatorial Africa.

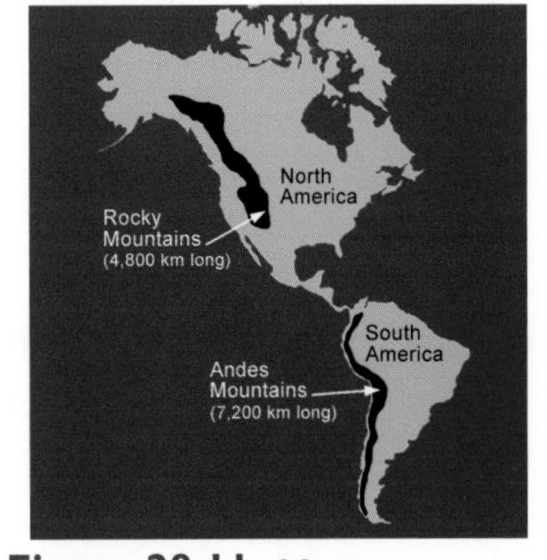

Figure 28.11: *Mountain ranges in North and South America.*

Sea-floor spreading

Mountain ranges on the sea floor

The sea floor is mostly flat. However, in the middle of the oceans (namely the Atlantic, Pacific, and Indian), there are more than 50,000 kilometers of mountain ranges called the mid-ocean ridges. The average height of the mountains at the ridges is 4,500 meters or about 2.8 miles above the sea floor. The ridges are split in the middle by either a valley or by a *rise* (see sidebar). The valleys can be as much as 800 kilometers across. However, they are usually less than 50 kilometers across for slow-spreading ocean ridges.

Echo sounding

Scientists first described the appearance of the sea floor using echo sounders. An echo sounder on a ship sends and collects sound waves. These waves bounce off objects and the sea floor. The data collected by an echo sounder is used to determine the depth of the sea floor. The combined depth readings for an area are used to make a profile of the sea floor (Figure 28.12).

Sea-floor spreading

In the early 1960s, Henry Hess (1906-69), a geologist and former commander of a Navy ship equipped with an echo sounder, used the profile of the sea floor to propose that it was spreading at the mid-ocean ridges. Around the same time, Robert Dietz (1914-95), a scientist with similar ideas, coined the term sea-floor spreading. Sea-floor spreading describes the sea floor on either side of a mid-ocean ridge as moving away from the ridge and creating a rise or valley. Hot fluid from the mantle (called *magma*) enters the rise or valley and cools, creating new sea floor (also called oceanic crust).

Proving sea floor spreading

Not every scientist accepted the idea of sea-floor spreading. If you were going to prove this idea, what would you do? What kind of evidence would you need to prove that the sea floor was spreading apart at the ridges?

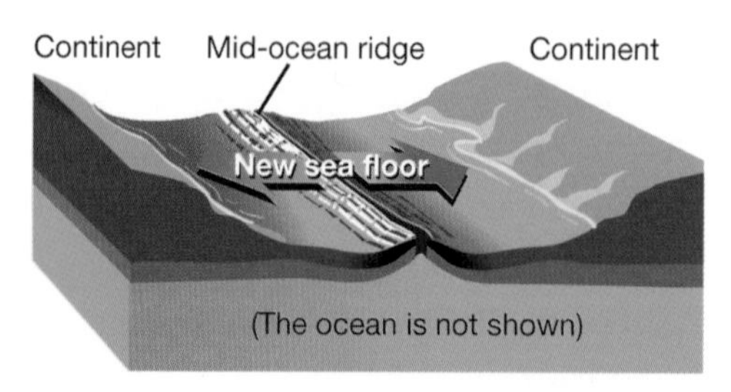

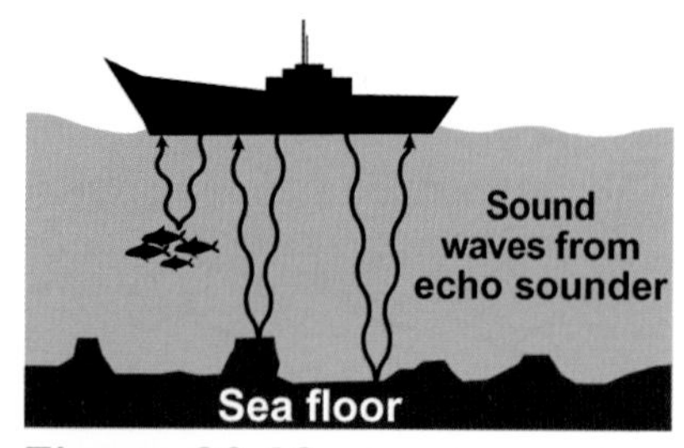

Figure 28.12: *An echo sounder is used to make a profile of the sea floor.*

Mid-ocean ridges

Mid-Atlantic Ridge

East Pacific Rise

The region near the mid-ocean ridges is elevated with respect to the rest of the sea floor because it is warm and less dense. The elevated parts form the mountainous ridges. Just what the ridges look like depends on the rate of sea-floor spreading. Wide, steep-sided valleys occur at the Mid-Atlantic Ridge because the spreading is slow. Spreading at the East Pacific Rise is faster, so a shallow valley or a *rise* occurs. A *rise* is a long mound of pushed-up crust.

Magnetic patterns on the sea floor

Earth is a giant magnet

Like a giant magnet, Earth has a magnetic north and south pole. Scientists believe Earth's magnetism is due to convection currents in the liquid outer core. These currents generate a magnetic field around Earth. Not only does this magnetic field provide us with a means of navigation, but it also blocks some of the sun's harmful electromagnetic radiation from reaching Earth's surface.

Earth's polarity has switched over time

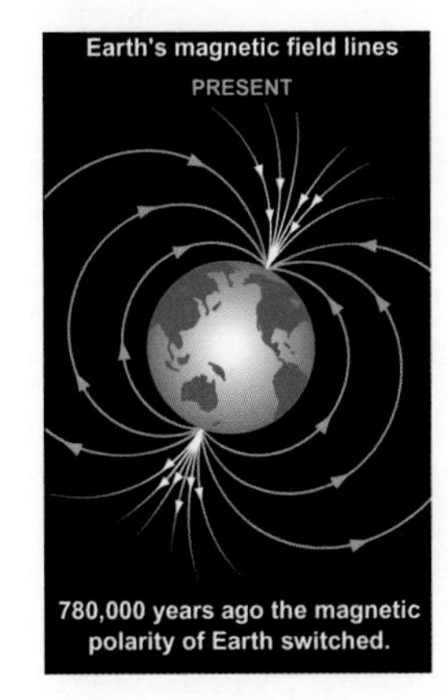

Over geologic time, the magnetic polarity of Earth has switched. Scientists believe the poles switch because of a magnetic interaction between the planet's inner and outer core. Eventually, the interaction diminishes the magnetic field to a point that encourages the poles to reverse. This reversal recharges the magnetic field. The last time Earth's polarity switched was about 780,000 years ago. Rocks on Earth act as a record of these switching events. When molten lava cools and becomes a rock, the grains in the rock are oriented with the magnetic polarity of Earth.

Magnetic patterns on the sea floor

In the 1950s and 1960s, scientists discovered that the rocks of the sea floor have a very interesting magnetic pattern. Figure 28.13 illustrates what this pattern looks like. Stripes of rock with a *north-south orientation* (normal) alternate with stripes of rock with a *south-north orientation* (reversed). Scientists also discovered that the pattern of stripes matches on either side of a mid-ocean ridge (Figure 28.13).

Evidence for sea-floor spreading

On the previous page, you were asked how you would prove that the sea floor was spreading apart at the mid-ocean ridges. Now, you have some new information. First of all, you know the polarity of Earth switches over time. Second, you know that newly formed rock records Earth's polarity. Thirdly, you know that the rocky sea floor on either side of mid-ocean ridges has a matching pattern of magnetic stripes. Together, this information provides evidence for sea-floor spreading. The matching striped pattern shows that Earth's polarity was recorded on *either side* of the ridge as lava oozed from the ridge and cooled. Since the mid-ocean ridge is a site where new sea floor is made, the newest rock is always near the ridge and the oldest rock is always far from the ridge (Figure 28.13).

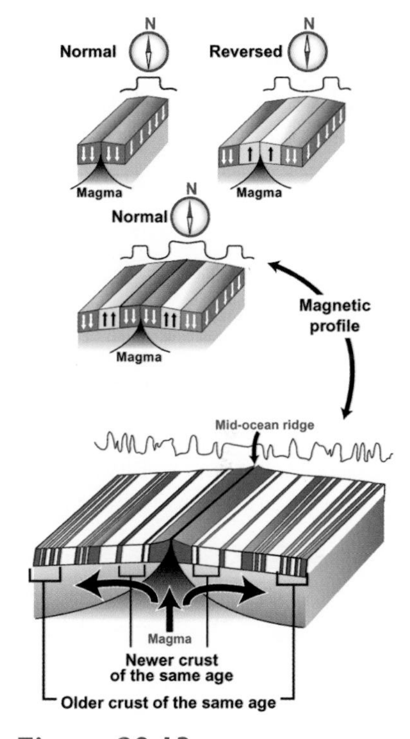

Figure 28.13: *Magnetic patterns on the sea floor show the reversal of Earth's magnetic field and provide evidence of sea-floor spreading. The blue and white stripes you see in the figure are an interpretation of a magnetic profile.*

Think about it

The sea floor is a record of geologic time. Given this, what does the thickness of each magnetic stripe mean?

The theory of plate tectonics

The theory of plate tectonics The theory of plate tectonics is consistent with the observed magnetic patterns on the sea floor, sea-floor spreading, continental drift, and the idea that the lithosphere is divided into tectonic plates. This theory also provides possible explanations for many things about Earth's geology such as mountain-building, earthquakes, and volcanoes.

Plates are pieces of the lithosphere The tectonic plates that cover Earth's surface are pieces of the lithosphere that fit together and float on the asthenosphere (a part of the mantle). There are a number of large tectonic plates on Earth's surface, and smaller plates are being identified all the time. Below is a list of the bigger plates. Find these plates on the graphic below. Then find the plate that goes with each of the seven continents. Many of the plates are made up of both continental and oceanic crust. Can you identify which of the plates are only made of oceanic crust?

The biggest tectonic plates				
Eurasian	Philippine	North American	Juan de Fuca	African
Arabian	Iranian	Antarctic	Scotia	South American
Cocos	Caribbean	Nazca	Pacific	Indo-Australian

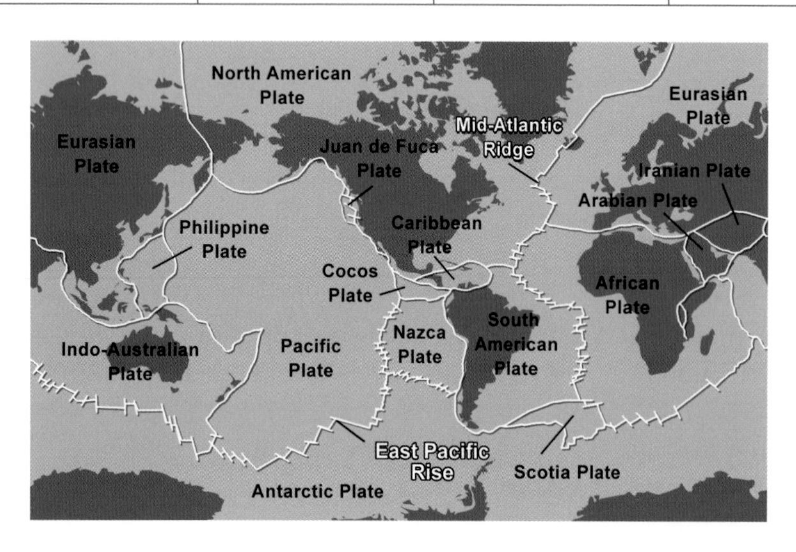

Tanya Atwater

Tanya Atwater's love for art, maps, and the outdoors led her to study geology. When she entered graduate school in 1967, many exciting discoveries were being made. The concept of sea floor spreading was emerging, leading to the current theory of plate tectonics.

Atwater's research on sea floor spreading involved twelve trips to the ocean floor in the tiny submarine Alvin. Using a mechanical arm, she and her crew collected samples on the ocean floor nearly two miles underwater! In the 1980's Atwater researched propagating rifts. Propagating rifts are created when sea floor spreading centers realign themselves in response to changes in plate motion or magma supplies. She mapped these odd rift patterns and used them to decipher ancient plate motions.

Atwater has taught at the University of California-Santa Barbara for over 25 years. She also works with media, museums, and teachers and she creates educational animations to teach people about Earth.

Describing plate boundaries

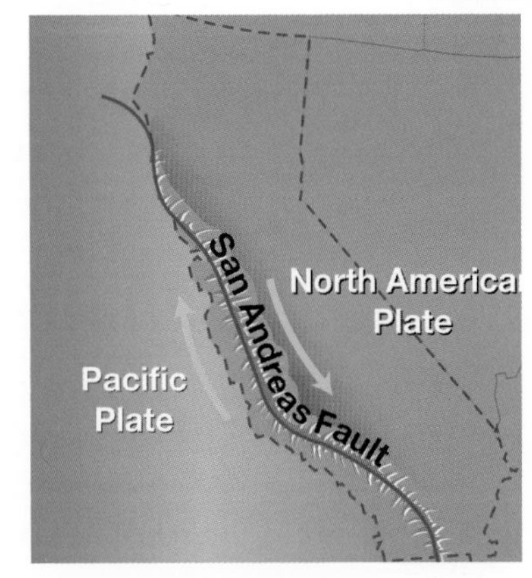

Figure 28.14: *The San Andreas fault is a transform plate boundary. The arrow shows the movement of the Pacific plate relative to the North American plate.*

Faults

Whenever one tectonic plate moves, another is affected. Most geologic activity occurs at plate boundaries. There are three main kinds of plate boundaries: divergent, convergent, and transform. These boundaries are illustrated below and described on the following pages. Each of these boundaries is associated with **faults**. Faults are breaks and cracks in Earth's crust where two pieces of the crust become offset. The build up and release of pressure at a fault causes earthquakes. Large earthquakes tend to be more frequent near convergent plate boundaries than at divergent plate boundaries. The San Andreas fault is a transform plate boundary that extends 600 mile along California's coast (Figure 28.14). Earthquakes occur frequently in regions near this kind of boundary.

Zones of activity at plate boundaries

At a plate boundary, crust can be created, consumed, or crumpled into mountains. In some cases, plates slide past each other. With all that can happen at a boundary, the effects occur over a region or *zone* rather than on a single line. The zone of activity at a plate boundary can range from tens to hundreds of kilometers wide. For example, the zone of activity for a divergent boundary spans about 30 kilometers on the sea floor and 100 to 200 kilometers on a continent.

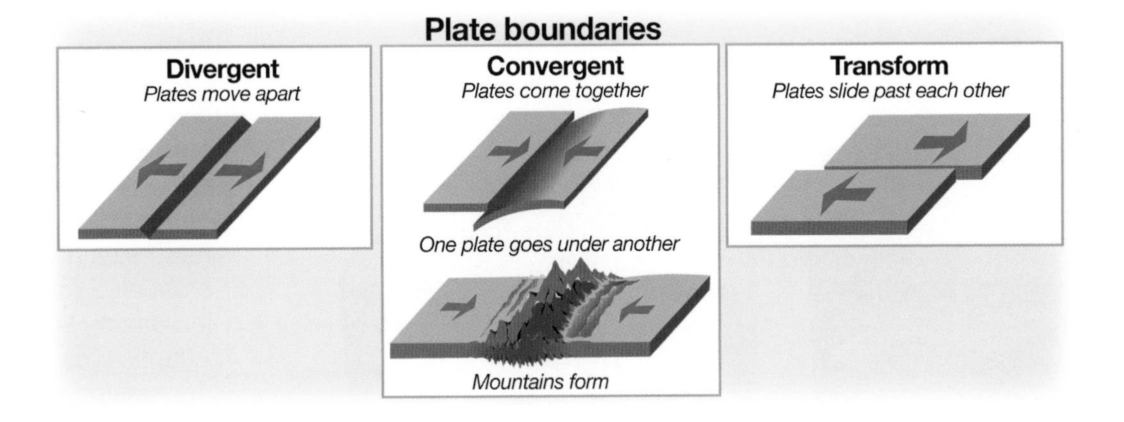

Where do earthquakes and volcanoes occur?

Earthquakes occur at all plate boundaries. Volcanoes are associated with divergent and convergent plate boundaries. Volcanoes are not associated with transform plate boundaries, where the plates are sliding past each other. However, transform boundaries are often near divergent boundaries where there is volcanic activity.

Divergent plate boundaries

Description

Divergent plate boundaries are places where plates move apart. Divergent boundaries are sites of earthquakes and volcanic activity. As molten material from the mantle reaches Earth's surface at these boundaries, new crust is created.

Diverging plates move apart. New crust forms.

Examples

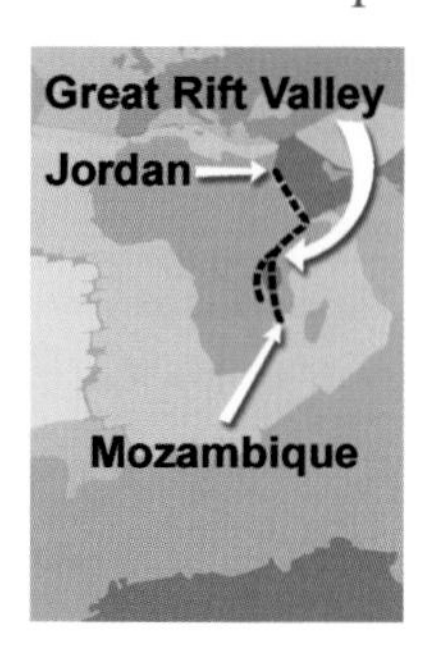

Mid-ocean ridges and associated sea-floor spreading occur at *divergent plate boundaries*. Magma from the mantle erupts along cracks created by the separation of plates along the mid-ocean ridge. In effect, a mid-ocean ridge is like a very long volcano. A continental version of a divergent plate boundary is the Great Rift Valley in East Africa. The Great Rift Valley is 6,400 kilometers long and averages 48 to 64 kilometers across. It is the largest continental rift in the world and extends from Jordan to Mozambique. As plates pull apart at the Great Rift Valley, the land sinks, forming a valley that may eventually fill with ocean water. Once underwater, the Great Rift Valley would become part of the mid-ocean ridge system. Although scientists think that eastern Africa could become a site for a new ocean, this will not happen for a very long time.

Divergent Plate Boundaries

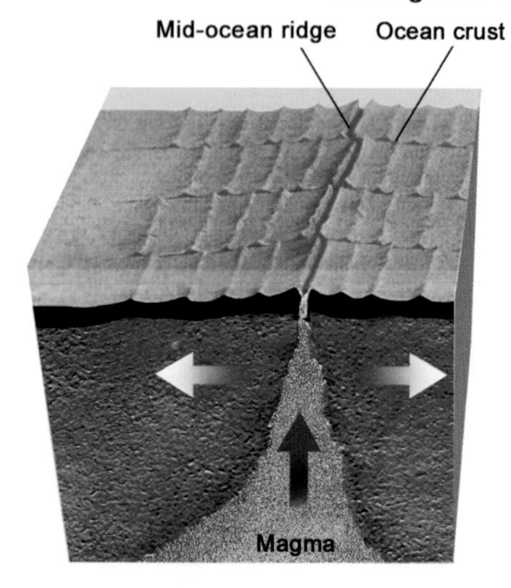

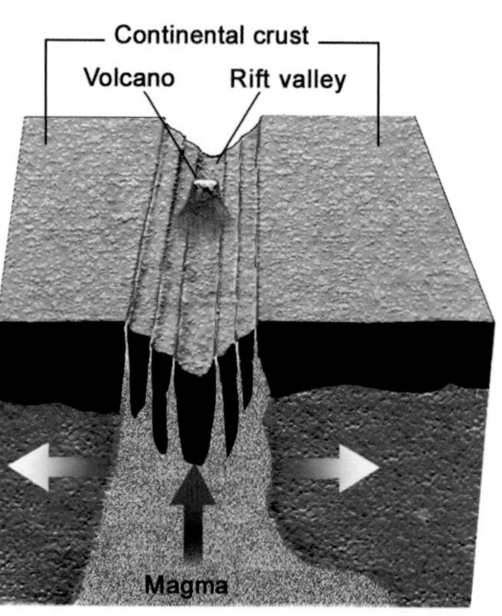

Divergent Plate Boundary	
Description	Place where plates are separating; new crust is created.
Earthquake activity?	Yes
Volcanic activity?	Yes
Examples	*Mid-Atlantic Ridge* *East Pacific Rise* *Great Rift Valley*

Why doesn't Earth get bigger and bigger?

Even though new crust is created at mid-ocean ridges, the Earth does not get bigger because crust is consumed at convergent plate boundaries (see next page). As new crust is formed at divergent plate boundaries, old, dense crust sinks and melts in the mantle. The balance between creating new crust and melting old crust also explains the increasing size of the Atlantic Ocean and the decreasing size of the Pacific Ocean.

Convergent plate boundaries

Subduction and trenches

Convergent plate boundaries occur where two plates approach each other. One result of two plates converging is **subduction**. In subduction, a denser plate slides under a less dense plate and enters the mantle, where it melts or becomes part of the mantle. Subduction can occur between an oceanic plate and a continental plate or between two oceanic plates. In either case, the subducting plate causes volcanic activity on the less dense plate. When an oceanic plate subducts under a continental plate, volcanoes occur on the continental plate such as the volcanic Cascade Mountains in the northwestern United States. When an oceanic plate subducts under another oceanic plate, an arc of volcanic islands is formed such as the Caribbean Islands. A deep oceanic *trench* marks the boundary between a subducting and an overriding plate at a convergent boundary.

Converging plates meet. Subduction occurs or mountains form.

Mountain building

The collision of two continental plates is a third kind of convergent boundary. Because both plates resist sinking in the mantle, they crumple. The crust is pushed upward forming mountain peaks and downward forming deep mountain "roots." The Himalayan Mountains are the result of colliding continental plates.

Convergent Plate Boundaries

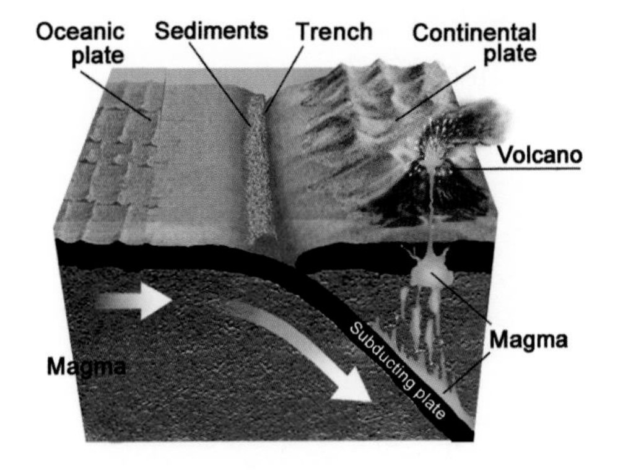

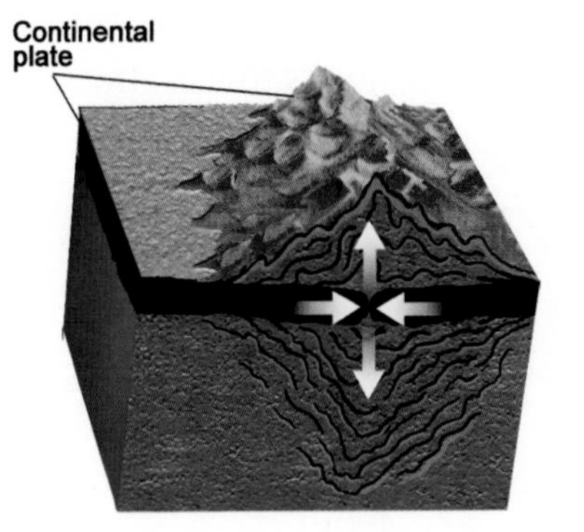

Convergent Plate Boundary	
Description	Place where plates meet; mountains form or plates are consumed by subduction.
Earthquake activity?	Yes
Volcanic activity?	Yes
Features at this boundary	*Mariana Trench* *Caribbean Islands* *Himalayan Mountains*

Deep oceanic trenches

The Mariana trench at the boundary of the Philippine and Pacific plates is the deepest trench in the world. It is 11 kilometers to the bottom. Compare this depth to the highest mountains on Earth. Mauna Loa, a volcanic mountain in Hawaii, is 10.3 kilometers from its sea floor base to its peak. Mount Everest is 8.84 kilometers high.

Transform plate boundaries

Transform plate boundaries

At transform plate boundaries, two plates slide by each other and crust is not created or consumed (Figure 28.15). The San Andreas fault in California is a well-known transform plate boundary. The build up of friction and pressure between sliding plates often results in earthquakes. Volcanic activity is not associated with transform plate boundaries; however, divergent plate boundaries which are sites of volcanic activity often occur near transform plate boundaries.

Plates slide past each other at transform plate boundaries. Crust is not created or consumed.

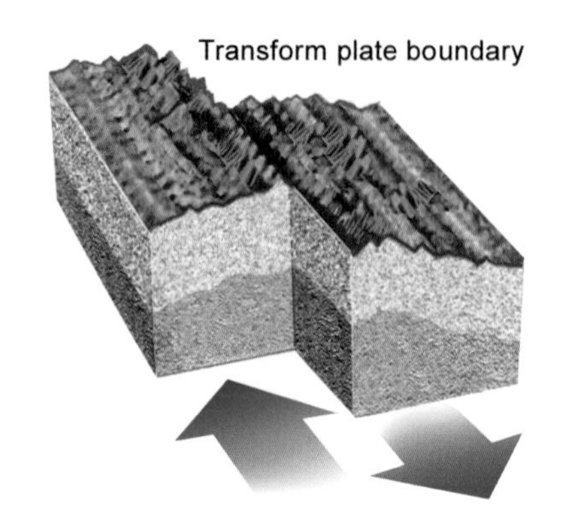

Figure 28.15: *At transform plate boundaries, plates slide past each other. Crust is not created or consumed at these boundaries.*

Transform Plate Boundary	
Description	Place where plates slide past each other; no crust is created or consumed
Earthquake activity?	Yes
Volcanic activity?	No (but divergent plate boundaries and their associated volcanoes are often near transform boundaries)
Example	*The San Andreas fault*

Movement of plates

How plates move

The movement of tectonic plates is related to the distribution of heat by convection currents in the mantle. At the mid-ocean ridges where new crust is forming, a plate is relatively hot and less dense. Away from the ridges, a plate begins to subduct because it is cooler and denser. The subduction of a plate causes the pulling apart of plates at the mid-ocean ridge. Scientists believe that this pulling effect, which depends on heat distribution, causes the interaction and movement of the plates on Earth's surface.

An analogy to explain how plates move

An air mattress floating in a pool can illustrate the motion of a plate on the mantle. If you sit on one end of the mattress, it sinks (or *subducts*) underwater. As a result, the other end of the mattress moves toward the sinking end like a divergent plate.

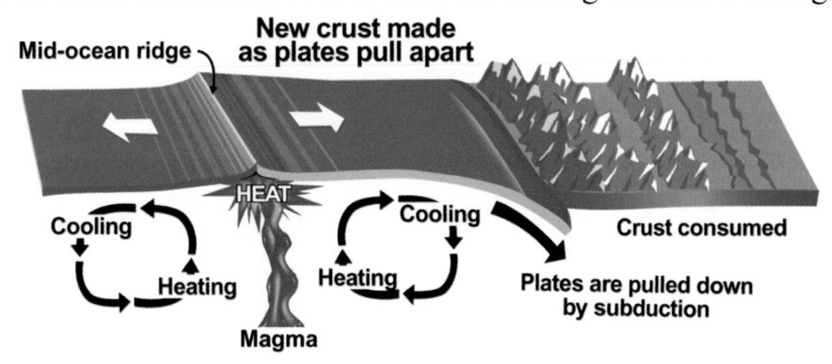

28.3 Earthquakes

The majority of earthquakes occur at the edges of tectonic plates. For example, Japan's location near convergent plate boundaries (Figure 28.16) explains why earthquakes occur regularly in that country. If you mark the locations of earthquakes on a world map, you see the outlines of Earth's tectonic plates. This section is all about earthquakes and how they are related to plate tectonics.

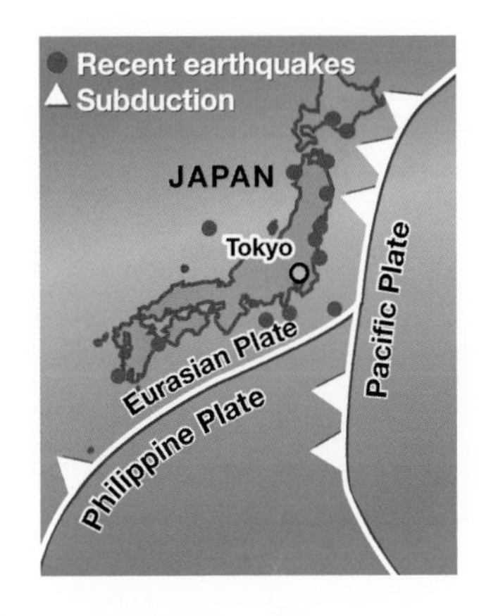

Figure 28.16: *These recent moderate earthquakes in Japan are associated with subduction occurring at plate boundaries.*

What is an earthquake?

Energy and earthquakes As tectonic plates move, friction causes the rocks at plate boundaries to stretch or compress. Like a stretched rubber band or a compressed spring, these rocks store energy. When the rocks break, change shape, or decrease in volume, the stored energy is suddenly converted to movement energy and an earthquake occurs.

Potential (stored) energy in rocks transformed to ground-shaking kinetic (movement) energy causes an earthquake.

The focus Earthquakes begin in the lithosphere at a point called a focus typically no more than 50 kilometers deep (Figure 28.17). At this depth, rock breaks easily under pressure. Earthquakes usually do not occur deeper than this because the rock is closer to the mantle, very hot, and more flexible. Deeper earthquakes (about 700 kilometers) occur at subduction zones when a subducting plate breaks.

Seismic waves The conversion of potential energy in rocks to kinetic energy results in seismic waves. Seismic waves radiate from the focus, traveling through the ground about 20 times faster than the speed of sound (about 5 kilometers per second). These waves can be slowed or bent depending on the properties of rock they encounter.

The epicenter Seismic waves reach Earth's surface at a point above the focus called the epicenter. The amount of ground-shaking is generally greatest near the epicenter, but depends on the type of rock and soil present.

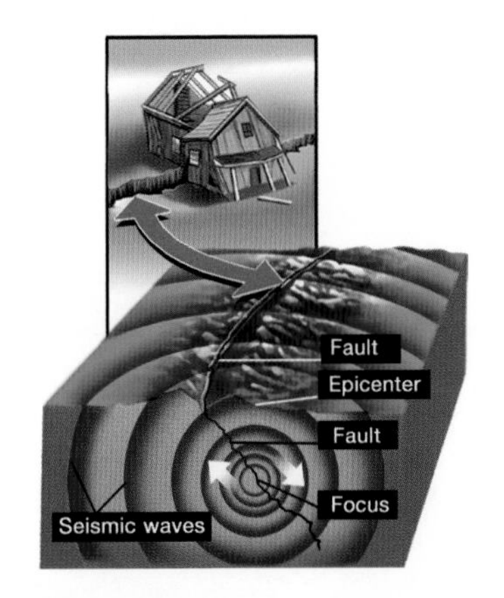

Figure 28.17: *The focus, epicenter, and seismic waves of an earthquake occurring at an active fault.*

Seismic waves

On the previous page, you learned about seismic waves. There are two main kinds of seismic waves: *body waves* and *surface waves*.

Body waves

Body waves originate from the focus of an earthquake. There are two kinds of body waves that travel through Earth (Figure 28.18). P-waves (primary waves) are compression waves that push and pull rock as they move through it. These waves travel about 5 kilometers per second. P-waves move through water and other liquids. S-waves (secondary waves) move sideways and up and down, traveling about 3 kilometers per second. S-waves do not travel through liquids.

Surface waves

Once body waves reach the epicenter of an earthquake, they become surface waves. These waves move more slowly (about 10 percent slower than S-waves), but can be very damaging. When these waves have a lot of energy, the ground rolls like the surface of the ocean. Surface waves can also move side to side and cause buildings to collapse.

What we can learn from seismic waves

People who record and interpret seismic waves are called seismologists. Seismic waves are recorded and measured by a *seismograph* (Figure 28.19). A worldwide network of seismographs at stations on land and in the oceans record earthquakes. The amplitudes of the recorded waves are related to the rating of the earthquake on the Richter scale (see next page). In addition to measuring earthquakes, seismologists use seismic waves to study Earth's internal structure. This is similar to how a doctor uses X rays to look at bone structure. P-waves and S-waves are able to travel through the Earth's interior (Figure 28.18). However, there is evidence that S-waves do not pass through the outer core. Since S-waves do not travel through liquids, this indicates to seismologists that the outer core is liquid.

What happens during an earthquake?

During the earthquake, there is a strong burst of shaking that lasts for a few minutes. The longest ever recorded earthquake occurred in 1964 in Alaska and lasted for four minutes. *Foreshocks* are small bursts of shaking called tremors that may precede a large earthquake. Foreshocks occur days to minutes before the earthquake hits. *Aftershocks* are small tremors that follow an earthquake. These may last for hours to days after the earthquake. The frequency of foreshocks and aftershocks is greatest just before and just after the earthquake.

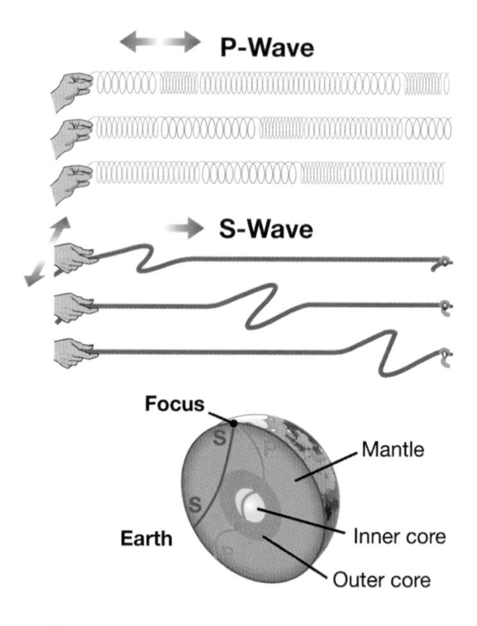

Figure 28.18: *P- and S-waves.*

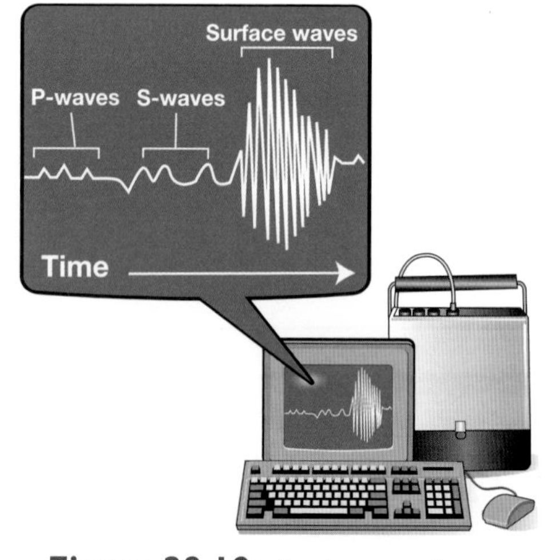

Figure 28.19: *A seismograph showing recorded seismic waves.*

Measuring the magnitude of an earthquake

The magnitude of an earthquake The magnitude or size of an earthquake is based on the energy of the seismic waves produced and the amount of ground movement and damage that results. Earthquake rating scales are described below.

The Mercalli scale The Mercalli scale has 12 descriptive categories. Each category is a rating of the damage caused to buildings, to the ground, and to people. Because earthquake damage can be different from place to place, a single earthquake may have different Mercalli numbers in each location where the quake is recorded.

The Richter scale Richter scale ratings relate to the amplitude of seismic waves recorded on a seismograph. Each level of the scale indicates a tenfold increase in earthquake magnitude measured as a tenfold increase in the amplitude of the recorded waves (Figure 28.20). Unlike the Mercalli scale, the Richter scale does not describe the amount of damage from an earthquake. The Richter scale provides accurate measurements for earthquakes that are near, but not for those that are far away.

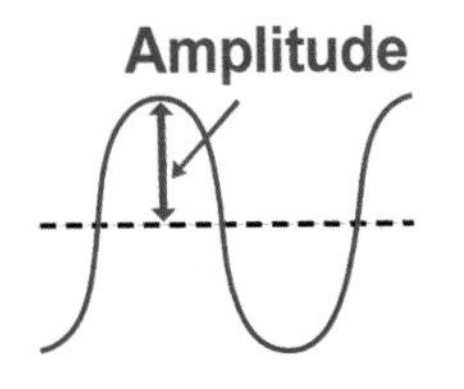

The Moment Magnitude scale The Moment Magnitude scale rates the total energy released by an earthquake. This scale can be used at locations that are close to *and* far away from an epicenter. The numbers on this scale combine energy ratings and descriptions of rock movements. Up to a rating of about 5, the Richter and Moment Magnitude scales are about the same. However, when earthquakes are larger, seismologists tend to use the more descriptive Moment Magnitude scale.

Using seismographs to understand Earth Seismographs show the kinds of waves that occur, their amplitude, and the timing of these waves. Using the network of seismographic stations and combining data from many different locations, scientists can also create a scan of Earth to distinguish hot and cool places in the planet's interior. In hot places, seismic waves travel slower. In cool places, seismic waves travel faster. This information has been used to figure out that magma from Earth's mantle is associated with mid-ocean ridges. Today, seismologists cannot reliably predict the date and exact time of an earthquake, but they can identify which areas are likely to have an earthquake in the next 10 or more years. Seismographs are also used to tell the difference between an earthquake and a nuclear explosion. Nuclear testing, which is banned world-wide, causes unique seismic waves to travel through Earth.

The Richter scale

Rating	Effects	Energy in terms of tons of TNT
< 3.5	Barely felt; recorded on seismographs.	< 73
3.5-5.4	Felt; objects toppled.	73 to 80,000
5.5-6.0	People run outside; damage to poorly built buildings.	80,000 to 1 million
6.1-6.9	Damage over a large area.	1 million to 32 million
7.0-7.9	Major earthquake; serious damage over a large area.	32 million to 1 billion
> 8.0	Great earthquake; tragic damage over an area hundreds of kilometers across.	1 billion to trillions

Figure 28.20: *The Richter scale with a description of the effects at each magnitude and the amount of energy released in terms of tons of the explosive TNT. The largest earthquake recorded occurred in Chile in 1960. It was off the Richter scale; seismologists estimated this quake to be 9.5.*

Where do earthquakes occur?

Where are earthquakes?

The majority of earthquakes occur at the boundaries of tectonic plates. The map below illustrates these boundaries and the general positions of earthquakes in the world. At the boundaries, chunks of rock below the surface are disturbed and move, causing an earthquake. Important world cities that experience earthquakes include Mexico City (Mexico), Tokyo (Japan), San Salvador (El Salvador), Santiago (Chile), and Istanbul (Turkey). Individual earthquakes also occur where there is a *fault*. A fault is a place in Earth's crust such as a crack or a *transform plate boundary.* In California, the San Andreas fault is a big fault along which lie the cities of Los Angeles and San Francisco (Figure 28.21).

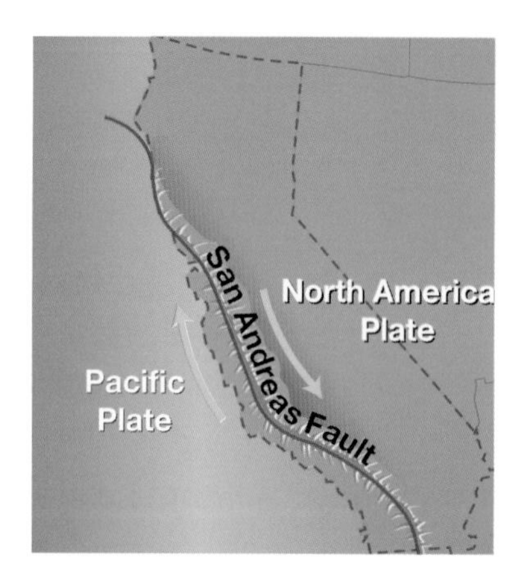

Figure 28.21: *Earthquakes occur along the San Andreas fault.*

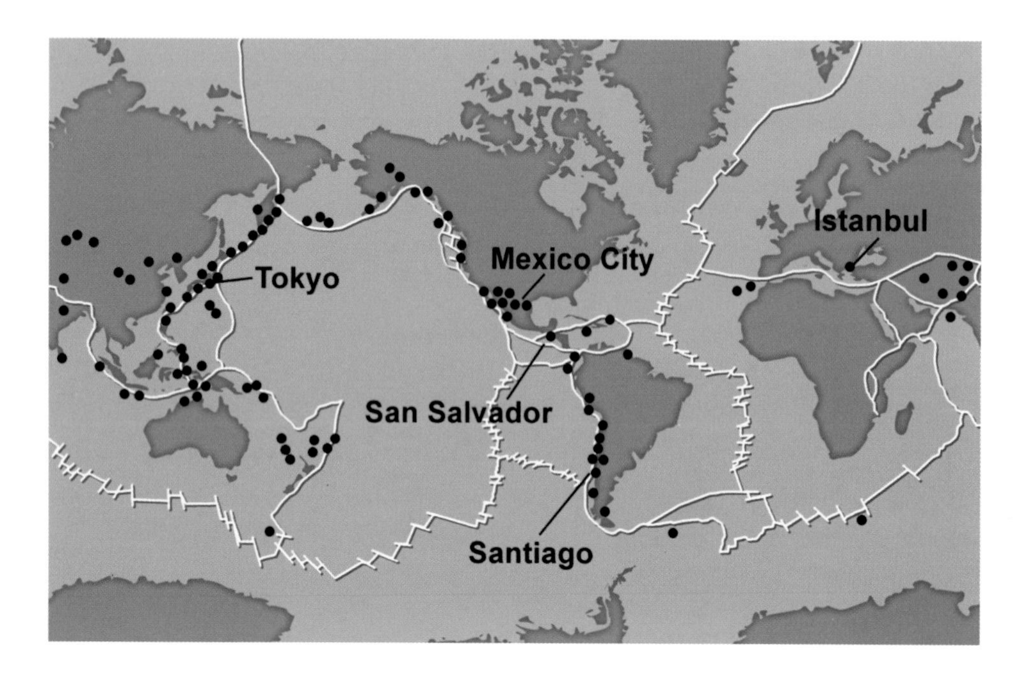

Worldwide earthquakes		
Place	**Date**	**Richter mag**
Ceram Sea, near Indonesia	1998	7.8
Vanuatu, South Pacific island	1999	7.5
New Guinea	2000	8.0
Peru, off Pacific coast	2001	8.4
Hindu Kush region, Afganistan	2002	7.4
South-central Alaska	2002	7.9

Figure 28.22: *Recent earthquakes and their Richter scale magnitude. These earthquakes are all associated with subduction zones.*

Earthquakes in the United States

Earthquakes in the United States

The west coast of the United States, including Alaska, experiences frequent earthquakes because those regions are near the San Andreas fault and a plate boundary. By comparison, the Midwest and eastern United States experience earthquakes only rarely. These regions are not near a plate boundary. The last time a major earthquake occurred in the Midwest was 1895. The last time that a strong earthquake occurred in the eastern U.S. was in 1886 when a 6.6 (Richter scale) quake hit Charleston, South Carolina.

The New Madrid fault

The New Madrid fault is a 250-mile long fault located in the Midwest. Scientists believe this fault and earthquakes in the Midwest are related to processes at plate boundaries or glaciers that once covered North America. These glaciers were so heavy that they pushed down on Earth's surface in this region. Now that these glaciers are gone, scientists believe that the surface is slowly moving back into place, with earthquakes the result.

Concern about earthquakes

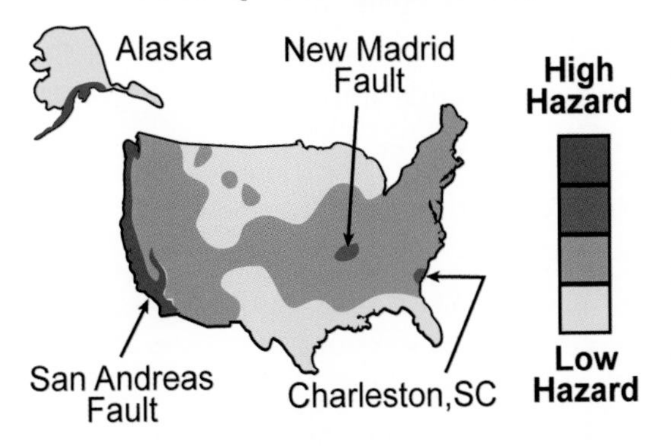

There are three main concerns if a big earthquake were to occur in the eastern or midwestern United States. First, these regions are centered on the North America Plate, where seismic waves can travel a long way without losing much energy. As a result, more earthquake damage can occur over a larger area. For example, when the Charleston quake struck in 1886, it was felt in New York City, Boston, Milwaukee, Canada, and Cuba. A second concern is that there have been no earthquakes in this region for a long time. This means that the faults may have a lot of potential energy that could release a lot of kinetic energy and cause a big earthquake. Finally, few buildings in the Midwest and East are built to withstand earthquakes, whereas buildings in the West now must be built to withstand quakes.

Frequency of Earthquakes		
Description	Richter mag	Avg. # per year
Great	> 8	1
Major	7-7.9	18
Strong	6-6.9	120
Moderate	5-5.9	800
Light	4.-4.9	~6,200
Minor	3.0-3.9	~49,000
Very minor	1 - 2.9	~9000/ day

Figure 28.23: *The frequency of earthquakes worldwide. (Information provided by US Geological Survey.)*

The importance of minor earthquakes

Minor earthquakes release stored energy in small, less destructive amounts. Rocks in areas that do not experience frequent small earthquakes may have a lot of stored energy. When this potential energy is finally converted to kinetic energy, the earthquake could be big.

What do seismologists do?

Locating an epicenter

Seismographic stations are set up around the world. These stations can measure the arrival time and speed of seismic waves but not the direction from which they are coming. For this reason, it is important to have data from three of these stations (Figure 28.24). At each station, the difference in arrival time between the P-waves (which arrive first) and the S-waves is recorded. The greater the difference in arrival time between P- and S- waves, the farther away an epicenter is from the site of recording. The next step is to use the collected data to figure out the distance to the epicenter. Once the distances are known for the three different sites, circles are drawn around each seismographic station on a map. The radius of each circle is directly related to the difference in arrival time of the P- and S-waves. The point where the three circles intersect is the estimated location of the epicenter.

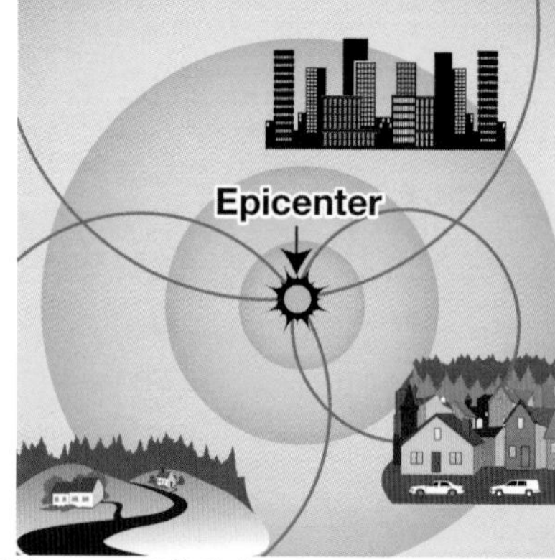

Figure 28.24: *An epicenter is identified using data collected from seismographic stations in three different locations.*

Locating epicenters with computers

For any earthquake, seismologists locate the epicenter and find out when a series of seismic waves started. Seismologists are also able to identify the focus of the earthquake. Up until the 1960s, they used graphical techniques like the one described above to locate these earthquake features. Then scientists began to take advantage of the development of high-speed computers. They wrote computer programs that could be used to detect epicenters. As these programs improved, they were also used to identify and map the boundaries of plates.

Creating artificial seismic waves

Our understanding of seismic waves has also led to creating them artificially in order to explore shallow, internal structures of our planet. Seismic vibrator trucks are designed to create artificial seismic waves by hitting the ground (Figure 28.25). As the ground is "thumped" by the truck, seismologists record the resulting seismic waves. They use this data to study underground rock structures. This information is often used by companies who are looking for oil and gas deposits. Oil and gas exploration also occurs in the oceans. Seismic waves are generated in the ocean by a gun that sends out a blast of compressed air or water from a ship. As the seismic waves bounce back to the ship, they are recorded by a hydrophone that is towed about 5 to 10 kilometers behind the ship.

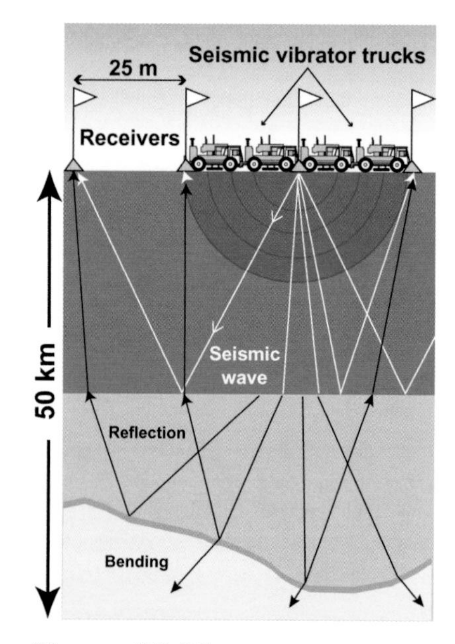

Figure 28.25: *Seismic waves created by seismic vibrator trucks.*

Problem solving: How to determine the distance to an epicenter

Data collected at three seismographic stations includes the speed of the P- and S-waves and the time between the arrival of the P- and S-waves. At each station the speed of the P-wave is 5 kilometers per second and the speed of the S-wave is 3 kilometers per second. The time between the arrival of the waves is recorded in the table at right. Given this information, what is the distance traveled by the waves from the earthquake's epicenter?

Station #	Time between arrival of P- and S- waves
1	75 seconds
2	100 seconds
3	90 seconds

Step 1: To calculate the distance to the epicenter for each station, use the equation: distance = rate x time. This equation is a rearranged version of the rate (or speed) equation: speed = distance/time.

Step 2: Use the variables listed in the bottom table at right to solve this problem.

Step 3: The distances traveled by the P- and S-waves are equal, therefore:

$d_p = d_s$

$r_p \times t_p = r_s \times t_s$

Step 4: Since the travel time for S-waves is longer than the travel time for P-waves, then:

$t_s = t_p + \text{(extra travel time)}$

Step 5: Plug this information into a equation and solve for t_p. Use the data for Station 1:

$5 \text{ km/sec} \times t_p = 3 \text{ km/sec} \times (t_p + 75 \text{ sec})$

$(5 \text{ km/sec})t_p = (3 \text{ km/sec})t_p + 225 \text{ km}$

$(2 \text{ km/sec})t_p = 225 \text{ km}$

$t_p = 112.5 \text{ seconds}$

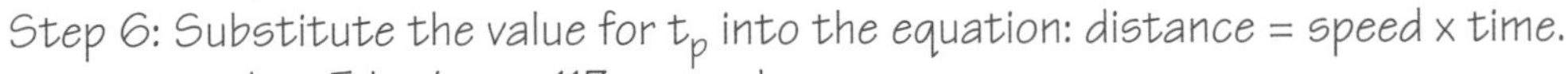

Step 6: Substitute the value for t_p into the equation: distance = speed x time.

$d_p = 5 \text{ km/sec} \times 113 \text{ seconds}$

$d_p = 565 \text{ km}$ (This is the same distance that S-waves travel.)

Step 7: Find the calculated distance for the other two stations. These distances are given in the sidebar. Then, draw a circle around each seismic station on a map that shows the locations of the stations. The radius of each circle should be proportional to the distance from the station to the epicenter. The location of the epicenter is where the circles intersect.

Variables	
d_p	distance traveled by P-waves
r_p	speed of P-waves
t_p	travel time of P-waves
d_s	distance traveled by S-waves
r_s	speed of S-waves
t_s	travel time of S-waves

Answers

Distances to the epicenter:

Station 1: 565 km

Station 2: 750 km

Station 3: 675 km

Preventing earthquake damage

Earthquake damage

The shaking ground during an earthquake is not very dangerous. If you were standing in an open space when an earthquake hit, you might fall when the ground moved, but you would be all right. What makes earthquakes dangerous is that the shaking causes buildings, bridges, and roads to collapse and crack. Additional side effects of an earthquake are fires that result from broken gas pipes, huge waves called *tsunamis*, and massive erosion events like mudslides and avalanches.

Damage prevention for buildings

How can buildings be built to survive an earthquake? First of all, the building foundation is very important. A structure built on loose soil will sustain more damage during an earthquake. Structures built on land that has a layer of rock below it (called bedrock) will better withstand earthquakes. Strong supports in building frames can keep a building together as it is shaken. Also, engineers have learned that structures can be built to move with the ground. When buildings are too rigid, they are brittle and thus are more likely to crack in an earthquake. Brittle materials are rock, concrete, brick, and glass. When a building is flexible, it can move with the ground as it shakes. Flexible buildings are better able to survive an earthquake. Flexible materials are wood, steel, and fiberglass. How would you design a building to withstand an earthquake? The graphic below compares the safety of certain locations during an earthquake.

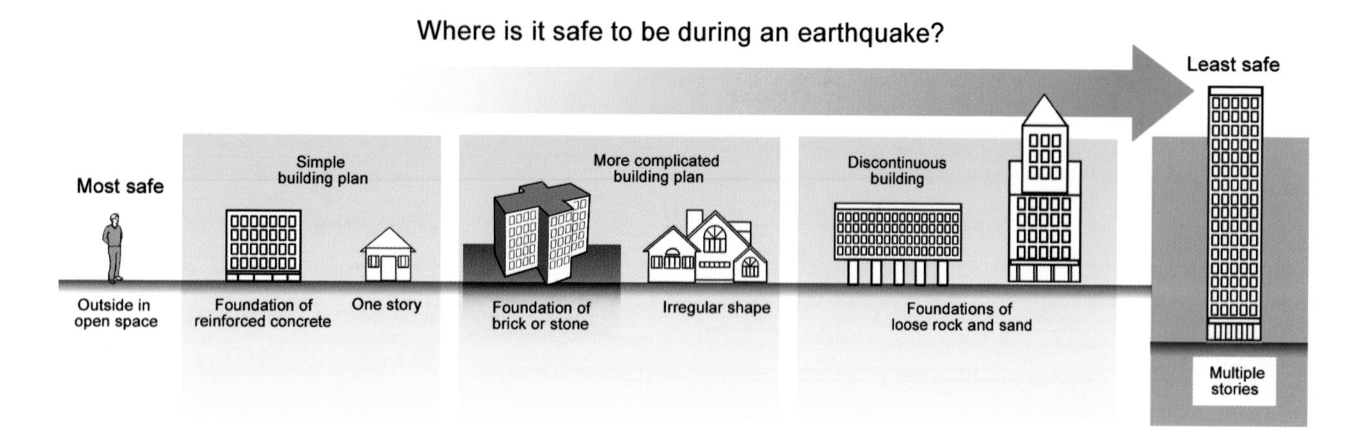

Earthquake safety tips

In 1995, a 7.2 earthquake struck Kobe, Japan. During the quake, two college students from California quickly ran to stand in a door frame to be safe. They were surprised to see each other. They had never met before. Simply knowing how to be safe during an earthquake brought them together.

Follow these safety tips in the event of a earthquake:

Getting outside is the safest thing you can do. Once you are outside:

- Get to an open area, far from buildings and objects that could fall.
- Sit down to avoid falling.

If you are inside:

- **Drop, cover, and hold:** Get under a heavy table and hold on to it to keep it from moving away from you.
- If there isn't a heavy table, stand in a door frame or near an inside wall. Protect your head and neck from falling objects.
- Stay away from windows and mirrors.

Preparing for earthquakes: tsunamis and seismic networks

What are tsunamis?

A huge wave generated by an underwater earthquake or landslide is called a **tsunami**. The speed at which this wave travels can be about 700 kilometers per hour. In the open ocean, you would not notice this wave. However, as the wave reaches a shallow area, the water piles up so that the wave may get as high as 25 meters. Tsunamis cause serious flooding and the power of their waves wrecks buildings and can cause loss of life.

Where do tsunamis occur?

Tsunamis occur in coastal areas that experience earthquakes. In particular, tsunamis occur in the Pacific Ocean and can affect countries like Japan and Indonesia. Alaska and Hawaii are also affected by tsunamis. When an earthquake happens in the area near Alaska, a tsunami may affect both the Alaskan shoreline and Hawaii (Figure 28.26).

How do scientists predict tsunamis?

Around the Pacific coastline of Alaska and the west coast of the Lower 48 states, there are ocean-bound tsunami detectors and seismographs. Scientists use information from the detectors and seismographs to forecast tsunamis. Because scientists know how fast a tsunami can travel after it has been triggered by an earthquake, they can warn people in coastal places to evacuate to higher ground. In December, 2004, in the Indian ocean, two undersea earthquakes ocurred (one at 9.0 magnitude and one at 7.3 magnitude). The tsunamis that resulted killed almost 200,000 people because of the lack of seismic networks in the Indian ocean.

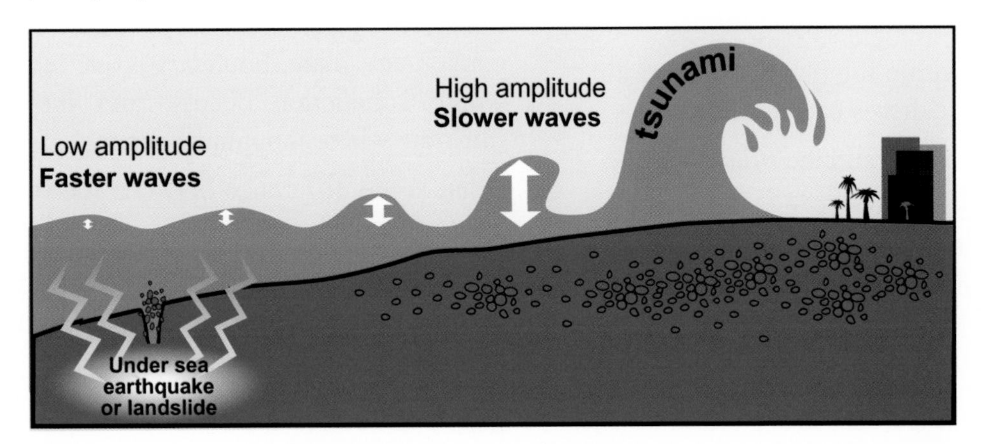

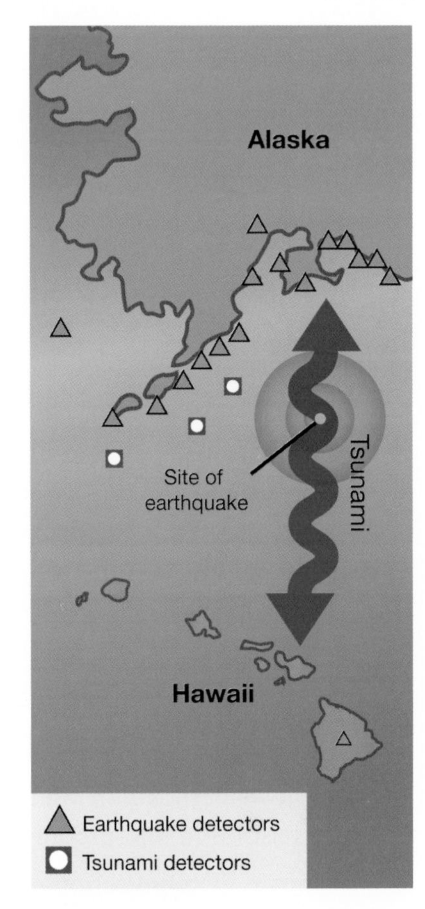

Figure 28.26: *A tsunami that occurs in the Pacific Ocean can affect shorelines in both Alaska and Hawaii.*

Chapter 28 Review

Vocabulary review

Match the following terms with the correct definition. There is one extra definition in the list that will not match any of the terms.

Set One

1. paleontologist
2. cross-cutting relationships
3. superposition
4. relative dating
5. continental drift

a. The idea that the continents were once a super-continent called Pangaea.
b. For a layered rock, the youngest layer is on top and the oldest layer is on the bottom.
c. A scientist who studies fossils.
d. A method used to determine the order in which geologic events happened.
e. The vein of rock is younger than the rock surrounding the vein.
f. A rock embedded in another rock is older.

Set Two

1. lithosphere
2. asthenosphere
3. sea-floor spreading
4. mid-ocean ridge
5. original horizontality

a. A process that occurs at diverging tectonic plates.
b. An ocean mountain range that occurs where tectonic plates diverge.
c. The layer of the mantle below the lithosphere.
d. Earth's crust plus the rigid, upper layer of the mantle.
e. Sediment forms horizontal layers under the influence of gravity.
f. A feature at converging tectonic plates.

Concept review

1. Define superposition and lateral continuity. Why are these ideas useful in interpreting how the Grand Canyon formed?
2. Compare the convection currents within the mantle to those in the atmosphere. What energy source drives each current?
3. Compare and contrast the *asthenosphere* and the *lithosphere*.
4. Which of the largest tectonic plates are mainly made of oceanic crust and do not include major continents? Use the diagram of the tectonic plates in the section entitled *Plate Tectonics* to help you answer this question.
5. Describe an example of a divergent plate boundary and a transform plate boundary. Describe two examples of a convergent plate boundary—one example should illustrate where subduction occurs, and the other example should illustrate where mountains occur.
6. What is the difference between the focus and the epicenter of an earthquake?
7. Draw a diagram that shows the difference between a P-wave and an S-wave. Describe the differences between these two kinds of earthquake waves.

Problems

1. This diagram shows a series of three lines that have been drawn on top of each other. Which line was drawn first? Which line was drawn last? Use relative dating to identify the order in which each line was drawn.

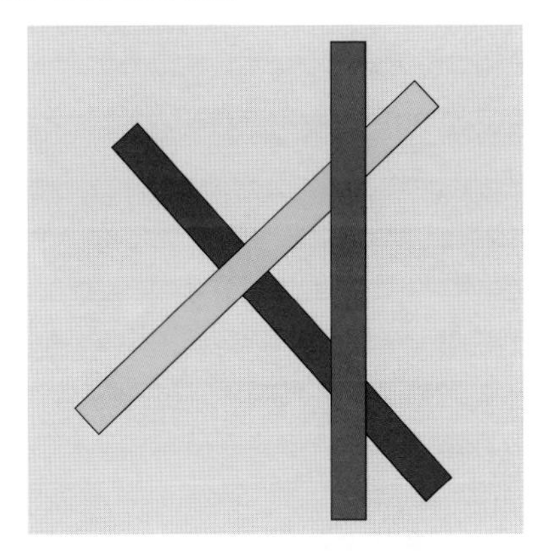

2. North America and Europe are separating at a rate of about 2.5 centimeters a year. How much farther apart will these continents be in 75 million years? Record your answer in kilometers.

3. The geologic time scale covers a very long period. To help you make sense of this length of time, compare the lengths of *each of the periods* with the lengths of something you are familiar with (e.g., a football field, a mile, or the distance from school to your house).
For example, compare history of the planet with a football field, which is 100 yards long (not including the end zones). If the age of Earth is 4.6 billion years and Homo sapiens have been on Earth for 40,000 years, where on the football field would humans have appeared?

4. Explain why the following examples support the theory of continental drift: (1) Fossils of an ancient and aquatic reptile (Lystrosaurus) have been found in rocks of the same age on the continents of Antarctica, Africa, and South America. (2) Today, you can find the same species of earthworm in southern Africa and South America.

5. The average density of Earth is 5.52 g/cm^3. You learned that the densities of the continental crust and the oceanic crust were 2.75 g/cm^3 and 3.0 g/cm^3, respectively. Come up with a hypothesis to explain why the average density of Earth is greater than the density of its crust.

6. A seismograph records the arrival of the P-waves of an earthquake and then, 3 1/2 minutes later, the arrival of the S-waves. If the P-waves were traveling at 8 kilometers per second and the S-waves were traveling at 60 percent of the speed of the P-waves, how far away is the epicenter of the earthquake?

7. Seismic waves are about 20 times faster than the speed of sound. If the speed of a seismic wave is 5 kilometers per second, would it be possible to hear an earthquake coming? Given the information provided, calculate an estimate of the speed of sound in units of meters per second.

Applying your knowledge

1. The terms *density*, *potential energy*, and *kinetic energy* were used in this unit. Each of these terms was presented in previous units. Define each term in your own words and explain why they are important for understanding earth science.
2. Review some recent popular science magazines to find out about the present day activities of geologists and paleontologists. Write a short paragraph that describes a current topic of research in the area of either geology or paleontology.
3. Another important figure in developing the field of geology is Charles Lyell (1797-1875), a Scottish geologist. Like James Hutton, Lyell was important in establishing the idea that the events in the present explain events of the past. Lyell's term for this concept was uniformitarianism. Further research the scientific contributions of both scientists on the Internet or in your local library. Explain their contributions in the form of an one-minute advertisement for television. Write the script for your advertisement and present it to your class. You may use props and other actors in your advertisement.
4. The geologic time scale shown in the section titled *Understanding Earth* illustrates some of the events that have occurred over geologic time. By doing research on the Internet or in your local library, identify when the following events occurred during Earth's geologic history: (1) the appearance of the first trees, (2) the formation of Mount Everest, and (3) the formation of the Mediterranean Sea.
5. Compare Wegener's theory of continental drift with the theory of plate tectonics. Explain why one theory became accepted while the other theory did not.
6. At the site of the Great Rift Valley in Africa, three plates are pulling apart. An eventual consequence of this is that an ocean will form between these plates. When this happens, what will this divergent plate boundary become? Hint: The Atlantic Ocean has this feature.
7. Your property and your neighbor's is separated by a newly formed fault. A year ago, an earthquake occurred at the site of this fault. A month ago, your neighbor discovered a vein of gold on her property. The location of this vein is shown on this diagram. Assuming that the vein continues on to your property, where would you start looking for it? Choose the probable location (either A, B, C, or D) and explain why you chose it. The direction of movement along the fault is shown in the diagram.

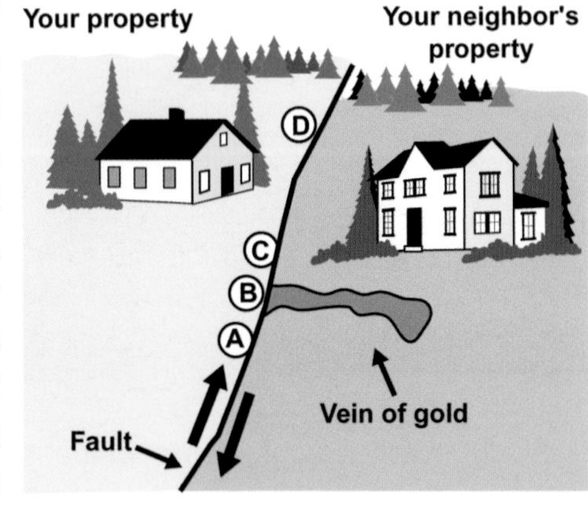

8. An earthquake in the eastern hemisphere of Earth is recorded in the western hemisphere. However, only P-waves are recorded. Review what you know about P- and S-waves and come up with an explanation for this data.
9. Define the work of a geologist, paleontologist, and seismologist, each in your own words. If you had to choose to be one of these kinds of scientists, which would you be and why?

UNIT 10 Earth Science

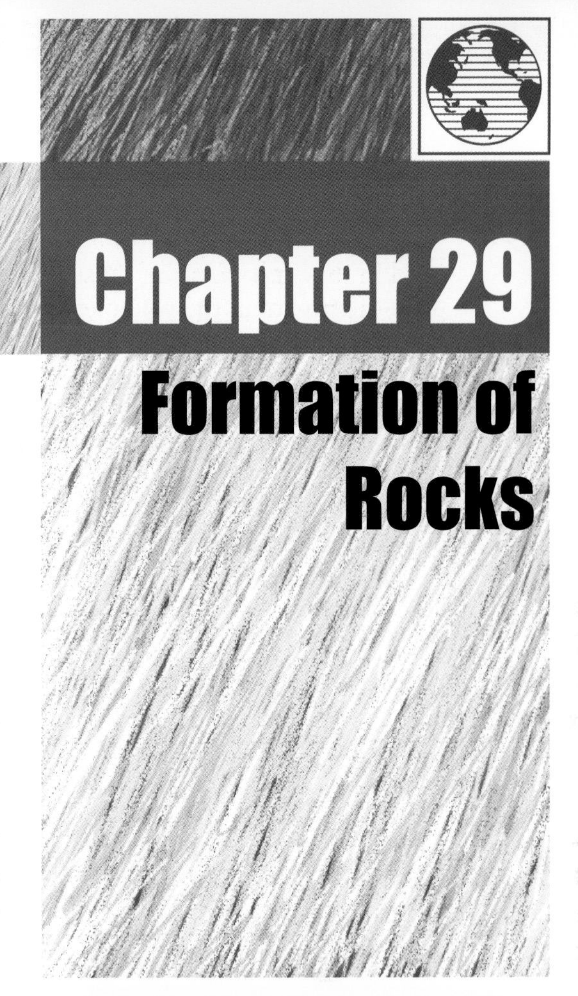

Chapter 29 Formation of Rocks

Slow, powerful processes are involved in recycling and moving rocky material from place to place on the planet. Deep within Earth, magma rises up and erupts on to the surface. When cooled, this molten rock may become a hand-sized piece of rock, part of a volcanic mountain, or part of the sea floor. Erosion of the land by water, wind, and glaciers is another way that matter moves from place to place. Erosion removes particles off rocks and minerals and moves them to another place where they may become another rock formation. The movement of tectonic plates on Earth's surface can cause rock to be pulled back into the mantle or fold into mountains. The rock cycle summarizes the history of rocks and rock formations.

29.1	Volcanoes	*Why do some volcanoes erupt explosively?*

This Investigation expands your understanding of volcanoes. You will be given information about active volcanoes and their magma composition. You will use this information to predict the geographic location of an active volcano.

29.2	The Surface of Earth	*How have meteors affected Earth's surface?*

The surface of Earth has endured a lot of erosion over it's 4.6-billion year history. By comparison, the moon's surface has remained relatively unchanged over this time. In this Investigation, you will count the number of meteor impacts for a region of the moon and extrapolate those effects for Earth.

29.3	Rocks and Minerals	*How can we interpret the stories within rocks?*

In this Investigation, you will simulate the processes that lead to the formation of the three main kinds of rocks—igneous, sedimentary, and metamorphic. You will also practice interpreting rock formations.

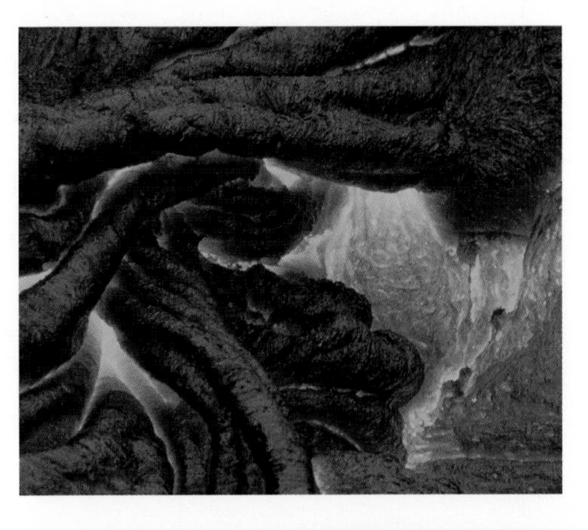

Learning Goals

In this chapter, you will:

- ✔ Learn about the role of plate tectonics in causing volcanoes and learn what causes eruptions to be gentle or highly explosive.
- ✔ Identify the main types of volcanoes: shield volcanoes, stratovolcanoes, and cinder cones.
- ✔ Learn about other forms of volcanic activity such as geysers, hot springs, hydrothermal vents, and geothermal energy.
- ✔ Learn about the constructive and destructive processes on Earth's surface like mountain-building, and erosion by wind, water, and ice.
- ✔ Learn how to interpret and use geologic hazard maps.
- ✔ Understand human impacts such as urban sprawl on Earth's surface.
- ✔ Learn how to identify the three main kinds of rocks: igneous, sedimentary, and metamorphic.
- ✔ Learn how to identify common minerals using Mohs hardness scale.
- ✔ Apply your understanding of the rock cycle to explain the properties of rocks and to interpret rock formations.

Vocabulary

caldera
cinder cone volcano
cleavage plane
crater
erosion
fault-block mountain
fold mountain
geothermal energy
glacier
hydrothermal vent
igneous rock
lava
magma
magma chamber
metamorphic rock
mineral
Mohs hardness scale
Ring of Fire
rock cycle
sedimentary rock
shield volcano
soil profile
stratovolcano
urban sprawl
vent
weathering

29.1 Volcanoes

The eruption of Mount St. Helens in 1980 reduced the height of this mountain in southwest Washington state from 2,932 meters (9,677 feet) to 2,535 meters (8,364 feet) (Figure 29.1). Before then, scientists had monitored earthquake tremors and closely watched the development of a huge bulge at the top of the mountain. Early in the morning of May 18, 1980, an earthquake triggered a landslide that caused the bulge to eject magma, water, and gases.

Mount St. Helens provided scientists with an opportunity to see what happens before, during, and after a volcanic eruption. Why do you think recording earthquakes was a good way to monitor the mountain before it erupted? What do you think caused the bulge on the top? In this section, you will learn the answers to these questions and more about volcanoes.

Figure 29.1: *Mount St. Helens before and after its eruption. Images courtesy of USGS/Cascades Volcano Observatory.*

What is a volcano?

Magma and lava

Volcanoes are sites where molten rock and other materials from Earth's mantle are released. Molten rock below Earth's surface is called magma. The magma that reaches the surface and erupts out of a volcano is called lava. Volcanoes also release gases and rock fragments into the air. Large rock fragments are called *pyroclasts*. Dust particle-sized fragments are called *ash*.

Parts of a volcano

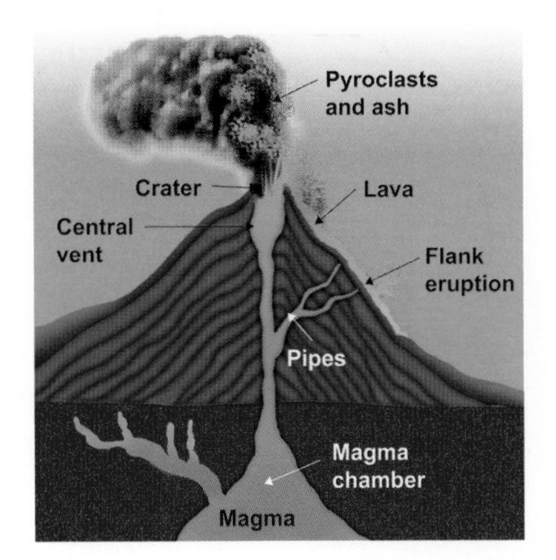

Magma is less dense than Earth's crust so it naturally rises and enters cracks in the surface. Below ground, magma pools in pockets called magma chambers. The pathways that magma takes to Earth's surface are called *pipes*. Areas where magma reaches the surface are called vents. A *flank eruption* occurs on the sides of a volcano where lava spills out of a vent. With each eruption of a volcano, layers of lava and ash build up and form a volcanic mountain. A crater is a depression at the top of a volcanic mountain that forms after an eruption.

Travel to Earth's core

In 1864, Jules Verne wrote "Journey to the Center of Earth." In this fictional tale, the characters begin and end their travels by entering and exiting a volcano. As you might imagine, a journey to the center of Earth, if it were possible, would involve enduring extremes of temperature and pressure. Earth's core is about as hot as the sun. The pressure would be very great because of the huge weight of rock layers.

How magma forms

The mantle is made of solid rock

The mantle is composed of very hot, rocky material that moves in very slow convection currents. For the most part, this rocky material is in a solid form even though it is very hot in the mantle. This solid rock melts and becomes magma under certain conditions that lower the melting point of the material (Figure 29.2).

Decreased pressure lowers the melting point

The high pressures in the mantle prevent melting. However, because of convection currents, pressure decreases occur, especially near the mid-ocean ridges. At these locations, the rocky material can rise and replace the lava that is becoming new sea floor. Sea-floor spreading creates a void that gets filled by magma from the mantle. This process affects the deeper mantle by causing a decrease in pressure. The first stage of melting is called *partial melt*. The rocky material experiences partial melt because it is composed of various minerals, each with a different melting point. When the minerals melt, the resulting magma is less dense. This is another factor that contributes to magma's ability to rise to Earth's surface.

The addition of water lowers the melting point

At subduction zones, water is the key for solid rock to melt and become magma. When subduction occurs, some water is brought in with subducted sediments. Water is also evaporated from minerals like hornblende. The water lowers the melting point of surrounding rock so that magma forms. In other words, the addition of water means that rock will melt and become magma at a lower temperature. Because of water, subduction zones are sites of volcanic activity. The Ring of Fire is the result of subduction zones surrounding much of the Pacific Ocean.

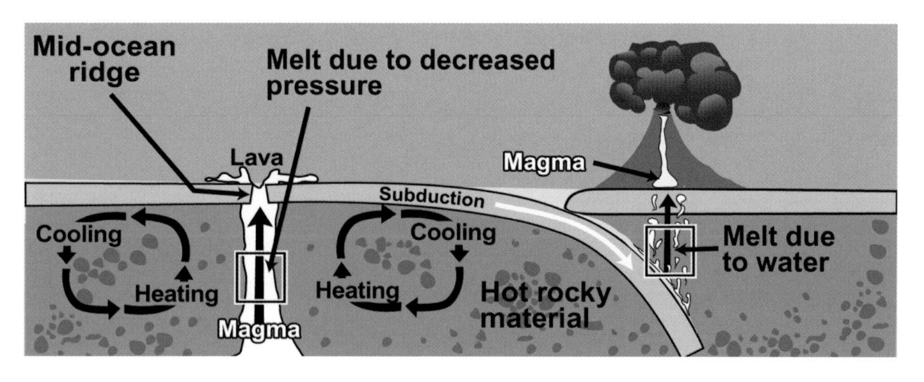

Solid rock	Melted rock (magma)
High pressure	Low pressure
No water	Water

Figure 29.2: *This table summarizes the conditions under which the rocky material in the mantle is solid or melted. Rocky material melts and becomes magma when the pressure is lowered or when water is present.*

Volcanic eruptions

Magma pools near Earth's surface in a magma chamber. Over time, pressure builds up within a chamber as the magma begins to cool and dissolved gases and water vapor are released. Any trigger that releases this pressure—like a small earthquake or a weakness in the volcano itself—results in the sudden, explosive, escape of gases, lava, pyroclasts, and ash.

Where do volcanoes occur?

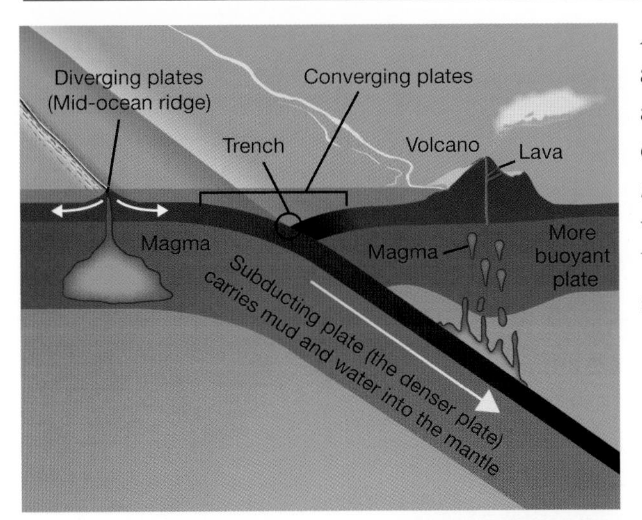

As with earthquakes, most volcanic activity is found at the edges of tectonic plates, namely at *divergent* and *convergent plate boundaries*. Unlike earthquakes, volcanic activity does not occur at *transform plate boundaries*. The mid-ocean ridges, where plates diverge, are like very long volcanoes. Volcanoes also occur at convergent plate boundaries such as where one plate subducts under another.

The Ring of Fire

About half of the active volcanoes on Earth occur along the boundary of the Pacific Ocean. This region, called the Ring of Fire, includes both volcanic activity and earthquakes. The Ring of Fire coincides with regions where the oceanic crust of the Pacific plate is subducting under other plates. The graphic at left shows how volcanoes (represented by the blue dots) are associated with plate boundaries.

Mount St. Helens is one of the volcanoes within the Ring of Fire. This volcanic mountain is part of the Cascade Mountain range. Mount St. Helens formed when the Juan de Fuca plate subducted under the North American plate.

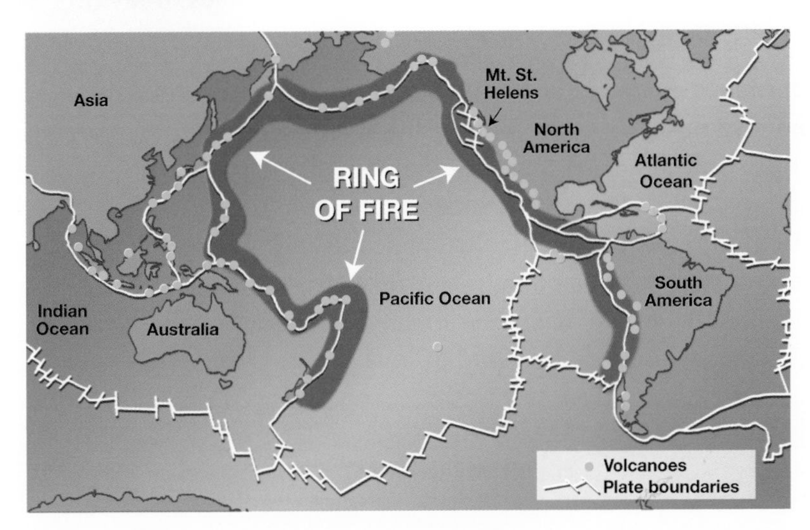

Most volcanic activity is associated with plate boundaries. About half of Earth's active volcanoes occur within the Ring of Fire.

Features of volcanoes

Viscosity of lava

The shape of a volcano depends on the material that comes out of it. Volcanoes emit lava, pyroclasts, ash, and gases. Most importantly, the shape is related to the thickness or *viscosity* of the lava. Viscosity is a measure of a fluid's flow rate. Fluids with high viscosity flow slowly. Fluids with low viscosity flow quickly. Lava's viscosity depends on how much silica it contains. The higher the silica content, the greater the viscosity of the lava.

Types and shapes of volcanoes

Low viscosity, fast-flowing lava is associated with shield volcanoes. Because this lava easily flows down hill, shield volcanoes are gently sloped and flattened. In general, these volcanoes range in height from 500 to 10,000 meters high. High viscosity lava is associated with stratovolcanoes (also called composite volcanoes). Stratovolcanoes are cone-shaped, steep-sided mountains made of layers of lava and ash. These volcanoes are around 3,000 meters high. Cinder cone volcanoes are steep stacks of loose pyroclasts (clumps and particles of lava). Cinder cones are rarely higher than 300 meters.

The explosiveness of a volcano

Lava viscosity also determines how explosive an eruption will be. Explosive eruptions occur when the lava has a lot of water and dissolved gases (carbon and sulfur dioxide and hydrogen sulfide). This happens when lava is very viscous, as in cinder cones and stratovolcanoes. These volcanoes occur on the continents so their lava contains dissolved granite-like rock (called andesite and rhyolite) that is high in silica. Gentle eruptions are associated with fast-flowing lava from oceanic crust. This lava contains basalt which has less silica, less water, and fewer dissolved gases. Shield volcanoes produce this kind of lava.

Descriptions of lava		
Silica content	**Low (45-54% silica)**	**High (54-73% silica)**
Rock composition	Melted basalt	Melted granite-like rock (andesite or rhyolite)
Viscosity	Low: flows quickly (~16 km/hour)	High: flows slowly
Kind of eruption	Gentle; less water and dissolved gas	Explosive; more water and dissolved gas
Associated volcanoes	Shield volcanoes	Stratovolcanoes and cinder cones

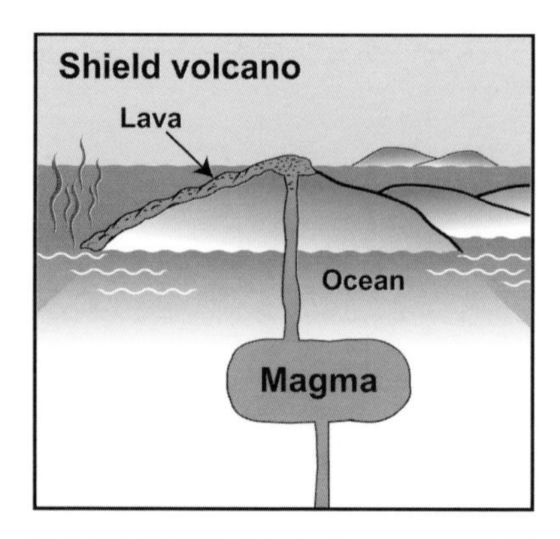

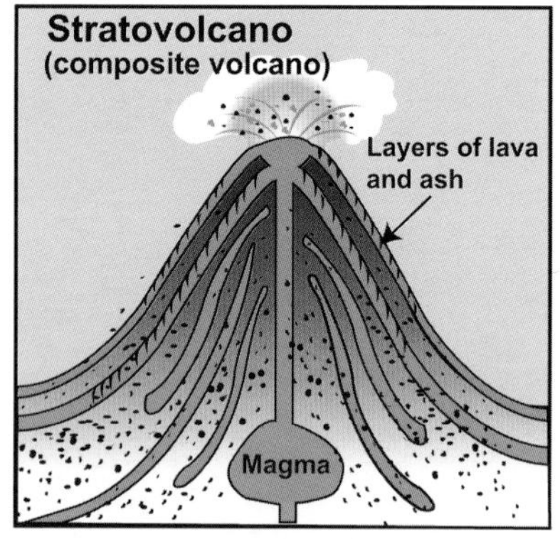

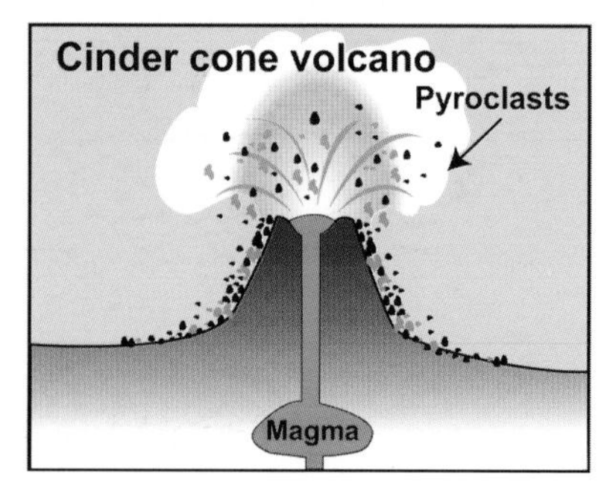

Figure 29.3: *The three main types of volcanoes.*

Shield volcanoes

More about shield volcanoes

Shield volcanoes are made of fast-flowing, basaltic lava. Although these volcanoes can become very large, their overall shape is flattened because the lava flows too quickly to accumulate on top. Most of these volcanoes form over *hotspots*. The eruptions of shield volcanoes are usually mild because the lava has low viscosity. However, if water enters the main vent, an explosive eruption may occur.

How shield volcanoes form

Scientists believe that heat from the outer core warms the lower mantle. At certain places, a blob of magma forms at the boundary between the outer core and the mantle. When the blob gets big enough, it rises toward Earth's surface as a *mantle plume* and becomes a *hotspot* (Figure 29.4). *Hotspots* originate under the lithosphere so they are nearly stationary or move at rates slower than overriding plates.

Hawaiian Islands

As an oceanic plate moves over a hotspot (over millions of years), a series of volcanoes form. The Hawaiian Islands were formed in this way. The oldest of the islands is Kaui; the biggest, Hawaii (called the Big Island), is still being formed. Hawaii alone has five shield volcanoes on it, three of them are "world record holders." Mauna Kea is the highest mountain (10.3 kilometers, measured from the seafloor; Mount Everest is 8.84 kilometers above sea level), Mauna Loa is the largest mountain by volume, and Kilauea is the most active volcano.

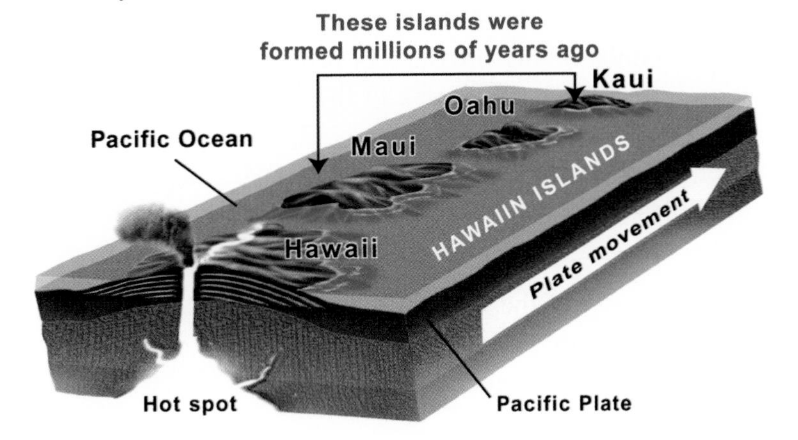

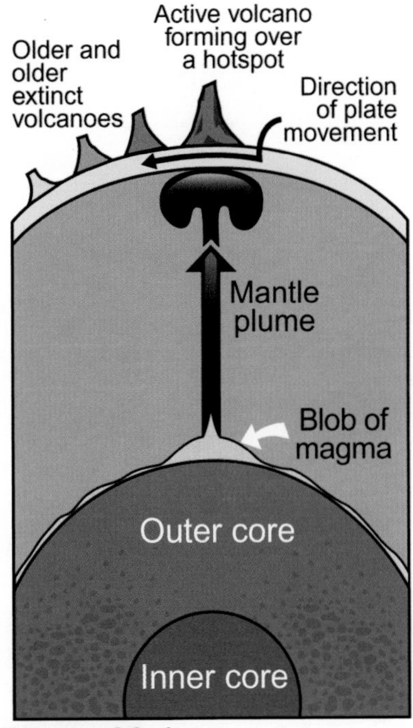

Figure 29.4: *How a hotspot forms.*

Hotspot volcanoes

The Galapagos Islands are shield volcanoes that formed over a hot spot in the Pacific Ocean. Yellowstone National Park features volcanic activity related to a continental hotspot. Iceland is an island formed by the volcanic activity of a hotspot and the Mid-Atlantic Ridge.

Stratovolcanoes (Composite volcanoes)

The Ring of Fire and subduction

The majority of the world's volcanoes are stratovolcanoes. Unfortunately, these tend to be the most explosive and destructive kind. In particular, these volcanoes are found within the Ring of Fire, which is associated with subduction zones. At some of the edges of the Pacific Ocean, thinner, denser, oceanic plates are sliding under continental plates. Stratovolcanoes are formed at these locations.

How stratovolcanoes form

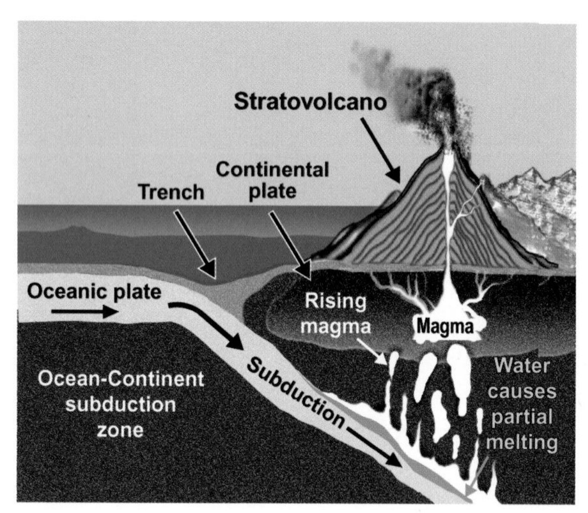

When the subducting oceanic plate encounters hot mantle, water is released. This water reduces the melting point of the surrounding rock so that it melts at a lower temperature. Because the magma is less dense than the surrounding solid rock, it rises to Earth's surface. As the magma passes through the overlying continental and oceanic crust, it dissolves continental rock which is high in silica and becomes very viscous.

Eruption of stratovolcanoes

Eventually, a significant amount of this thick magma collects in a magma chamber. As the magma rises and begins to cool, gases are released and create excess pressure in the magma chamber. This pressure is relieved when cracks occur in the overlying crust and creating passageways to the surface. If a lot of gases are present, then the result is an explosive eruption. The intensity of the eruption is amplified by the conversion of water to steam. Additionally, as magma rises to the surface, gas bubbles become larger. These expanding bubbles contribute to the intensity of the volcanic explosion.

Examples of stratovolcanoes

The Cascade Range near the west coast of the United States includes Mount St. Helens among its stratovolcanoes. They are also found in Indonesia and along the west coast of South America in the Andes Mountains of Chile.

Nuée ardentes

A *nuée ardente* is a "glowing cloud" of hot volcanic debris that is often associated with the eruption of a stratovolcano. The cloud is made of lava which floats on top of volcanic gases. After an eruption, the cloud races down the slope of the volcano at speeds greater than 60 miles per hour, smothering everything in its path.

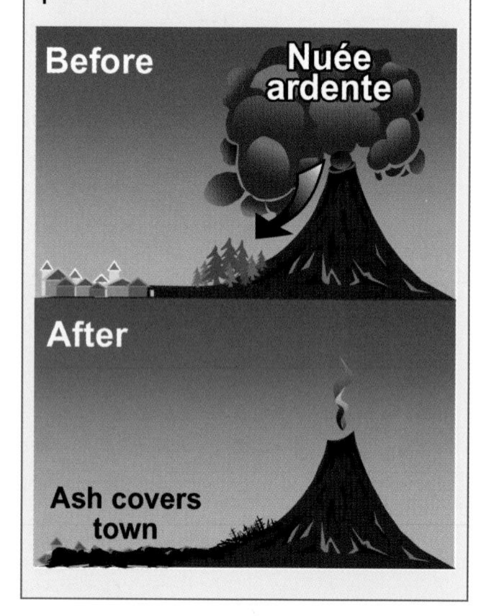

Cinder cones

More about cinder cones Cinder cones are common, relatively small volcanoes. They can form over a vent in clusters or on the side of a larger volcano. Usually, cinder cones erupt only once. The length of those eruptions, however, can range from about a month to 10 years.

How cinder cones form When water mixes with lava, it can cause an explosive volcanic eruption. The same is true if lava contains a lot of dissolved gases. When a lot of gas and water are mixed into lava, pieces of the lava are blasted out from a vent and solidify in the air. These pyroclasts, called cinders, have numerous air pockets. As the cinders settle back onto the ground, they form the cinder cone. A cinder cone is a loose, cylindrical pile of this pyroclastic material with round crater at the top. Lava from a cinder cone tends to flow out of the base rather than at the top because the cone is made of loose material.

Parícutin, Mexico cinder cone In 1943, a cinder cone volcano was born in a cornfield in Parícutin, Mexico. It began when gas-filled lava erupted from the ground. In a very short time, there was a pile of volcanic material. In the end, Mount Parícutin was a 400-meter high, steep-sided hill of ash and volcanic debris. It was active from 1943 to 1952.

Wizard Island cinder cone Another well-known example of a cinder cone is Wizard Island in Crater Lake National Park in Oregon. This cinder cone formed in a caldera called Crater Lake (see the sidebar at right). This huge depression formed when the summit of Mount Mazama collapsed following a huge explosive eruption about 7,000 years ago. Mount Mazama was a stratovolcano. Its eruption was about 40 times greater than that of Mount St. Helens. After this eruption and the formation of Wizard Island, trillions of gallons of water from melted snow and rain filled Crater Lake. This lake, at about 2000 feet, is one of the deepest lakes in the world.

Exploiting cinder cones Interestingly, cinder cone volcanoes are threatened by the fact that people like to take the materials that make up the cinder cone and use the materials for building roads and for sanding roads in the winter. Cinder cone rock is also used as decorative "lava rocks" for landscaping.

Figure 29.5: *Wizard Island in Crater Lake.*

Calderas

When a volcano erupts, the magma chamber becomes an empty pocket under the overlying rocks. Eventually, the weight of the rocks is too great and the remaining top of the volcano collapses on itself and creates a depression called a caldera.

Calderas are active volcanic sites. Magma underneath a depression continues to heat the ground and underground water. Volcanic activity associated with a caldera includes boiling mud puddles, geysers, and hot springs.

Additional sites of volcanic activity

Volcanic activity at ridges

Most volcanic activity on Earth occurs at mid-ocean ridges where plates are diverging. These regions are like long volcanoes. The Mid-Atlantic Ridge and the East African Rift Valley are slow-spreading ridges. Therefore, these ridges tend to have a valley where the plates are diverging. Volcanoes that form in these valleys are called *rift volcanoes*. An example is Mount Kilimanjaro in Tanzania, East Africa. The East Pacific Rise is a fast-spreading ridge and lacks a valley between the diverging plates. At both the Mid-Atlantic Ridge and the East Pacific Rise, lava forms new seafloor. An above sea-level version of volcanic activity is Iceland, a large island that is part of the Mid-Atlantic Ridge. Near Iceland, a volcanic eruption that started on the ocean floor formed a new island, Surtsey, in 1963 (Figure 29.6). This island experienced volcanic activity until 1967.

Figure 29.6: *The birth of a new island. Surtsey was "born" near Iceland because of a volcanic eruption from the ocean floor.*

Island arc volcanoes occur at subduction zones

You have learned that volcanic activity is associated with subduction that occurs when an oceanic plate slides under a continental plate. Volcanoes also form when an oceanic plate slides under another oceanic plate. As the denser oceanic plate is pulled downward and melted in the mantle, magma rises and enters cracks in the non-subducting oceanic plate. The result is the formation of an arc of volcanic islands along the trench at the place where the plates converge. Examples of island arcs are the Caribbean Islands and the islands of Japan.

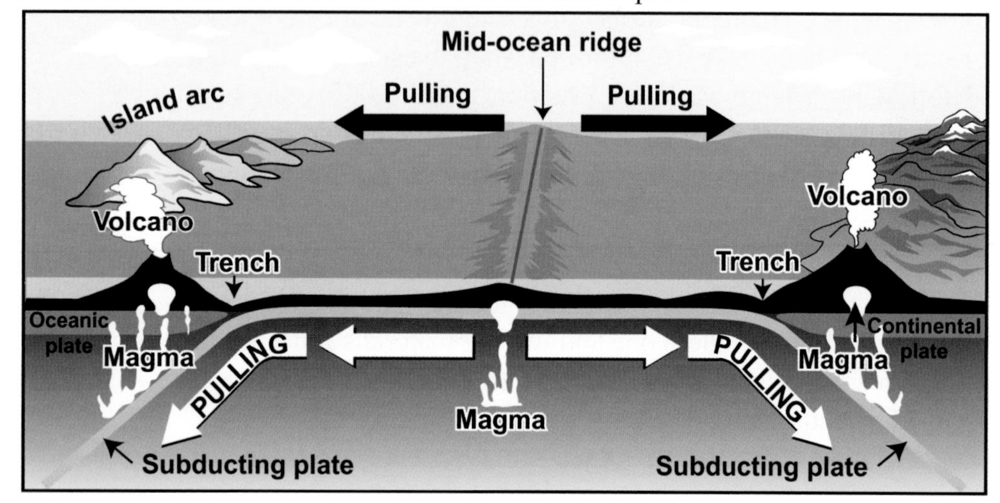

Volcanoes shape Earth

At mid-ocean ridges and active volcanoes, lava erupts on Earth's surface and cools, resulting in the formation of rocks and new land. Islands, the ocean floor, and the continents are simply solidified lava or magma. The Earth's entire surface is a product of new or ancient volcanic activity.

Hydrothermal vents

Hydrothermal vents are deep sea chimney-like structures that occur along mid-ocean ridges. Seawater that has been heated by magma to high temperatures comes out of the vents. When this hot, mineral-rich water reaches the cold water (about 0°C) at the sea floor, the dissolved materials precipitate and form the chimneys. Sulfur is an important mineral associated with these vents. Living near the vents are giant tube worms that live off bacteria that use hydrogen sulfur to make food. These bacteria use *chemosynthesis*, a process like photosynthesis, to survive. Instead of using the sun's energy to make food and oxygen from carbon dioxide and water, they get their energy from the reaction between oxygen and hydrogen sulfide (H_2S). Interestingly, the source of oxygen for chemosynthesis is oxygen from photosynthesis at Earth's surface that has dissolved in the ocean water and circulated down to the deep ocean.

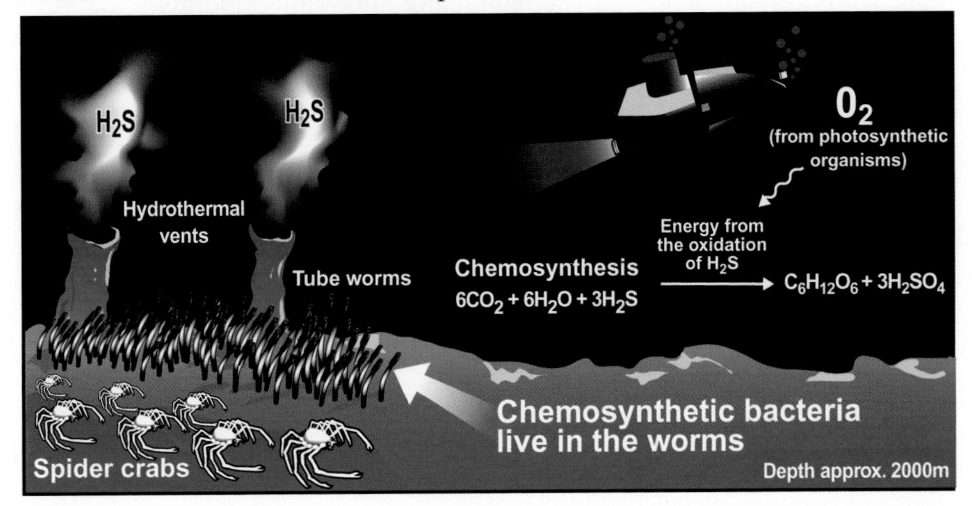

Volcanoes and the atmosphere

When volcanoes erupt, large amounts of gases and particulates are released into the atmosphere causing natural air pollution. The gases include sulfur dioxide and nitrogen oxides. The dust released by volcanoes may be responsible for temporary cooling of Earth's climate. Additionally, water vapor from volcanoes has been an important source of water for Earth's surface and atmosphere.

Special names for lava

Because of the volcanic nature of the Hawaiian Islands, some volcanic terms are Hawaiian names.

Two of these are *pahoehoe* (pah HOH ee hoh ee) and *aa* (Ah ah). These terms describe lava with relatively little silica. Pahoehoe flows quickly. When it cools and solidifies it looks like taffy and has long, curvy, wrinkles. Aa is more viscous. When it cools and solidifies it looks very crumbly, like large clumps of granola. Pahoehoe and aa are characteristic of the non-explosive, gentle eruptions on the Hawaiian Islands.

Products of volcanic activity

Geysers and hot springs

Photo courtesy of Mary Feay

Geothermal energy can heat water underground and generate steam. When this steam is released naturally, it is called a *geyser*. In Yellowstone National Park, Old Faithful is a very famous geyser that releases water and steam every 33 to 93 minutes. The geyser occurs when pressure builds up underground and forces a blast of steam and water. *Hot springs* are pools of groundwater that have been heated by pockets of magma. This heated water collects at Earth's surface. In the mountainous regions of Japan, a cold-weather monkey called the Japanese Macaque keeps warm by sitting in hot springs.

Mineral deposits and diamonds

Water heated by volcanic activity has dissolved minerals in it. As this water cools, the minerals precipitate, forming rich deposits of economically important minerals such as gold, copper, zinc, and iron. Some gemstones are also associated with volcanic activity. For example, diamonds form at high temperatures deep underground when carbon crystallizes inside rocks called *kimberlites*. Kimberlites reached the surface during violent eruptions of ancient volcanoes. Scientists believe that this magma, which was highly pressurized, moved toward Earth's surface at twice the speed of sound. At the surface, the kimberlites cooled and hardened in volcanic vents and cracks in the crust, becoming today's diamond resources. Diamonds are mined on every continent except Europe and Antarctica where they may exist but remain undiscovered. Regions that are rich in kimberlites include Australia, Russia, and, in Africa, Botswana, the Democratic Republic of Congo (formerly Zaire), and South Africa. In the United States, there are diamond mines on the Colorado-Wyoming border and in North Carolina. The latest discovery of diamonds resources has been in Canada.

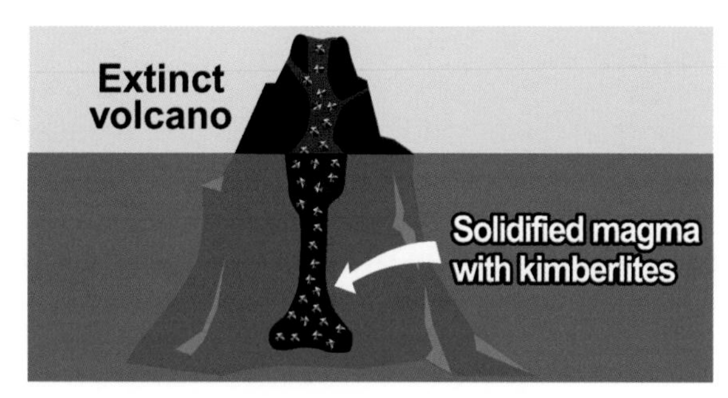

Geothermal energy

Some places on Earth do not rely on fossil fuels to have heat or heated water. This is because they are able to utilize heat and steam that is trapped in Earth's crust. This kind of energy is called *geothermal energy*. Places that use geothermal energy include Iceland, New Zealand, and Northern California.

Geothermal energy is the useful product of volcanic activity. When steam from magma collects below ground, it can be tapped just like water in a well. This steam is under pressure which makes it even more useful. In other words, the pressurized steam can be used to generate electricity. The steam is also useful for heating homes.

Describing volcanoes

Assessing the status of a volcano

The scientists who study volcanoes are called *volcanologists*. In addition to trying to predict the timing of a volcanic eruption, they determine how hazardous an eruption might be. Volcanologists spend their time observing and describing volcanic regions. An *active* volcano may soon erupt or has just erupted. Presently, there are about 500 active volcanoes on Earth, causing an average of 60 eruptions per year. A *dormant* volcano does not show signs of erupting, but it may erupt in the future. The time until the next eruption may not be for hundreds or thousands of years. Dormant volcanoes include Campi Flegrei caldera in Italy, Mount Baker and Mount Hood on the West Coast of the United States, and Nisyros, a stratovolcanic island that is part of Greece. An *extinct* volcano is one that has ceased activity. Examples of extinct volcanoes are Mount Kilimanjaro in Tanzania, East Africa; Mount Warning in Australia; 90 volcanoes in the volcanic region of France called Chaine des Puys; and Mount Elbrus in Russia, Europe's tallest mountain at over 5.4 kilometers.

Describing volcanic rock

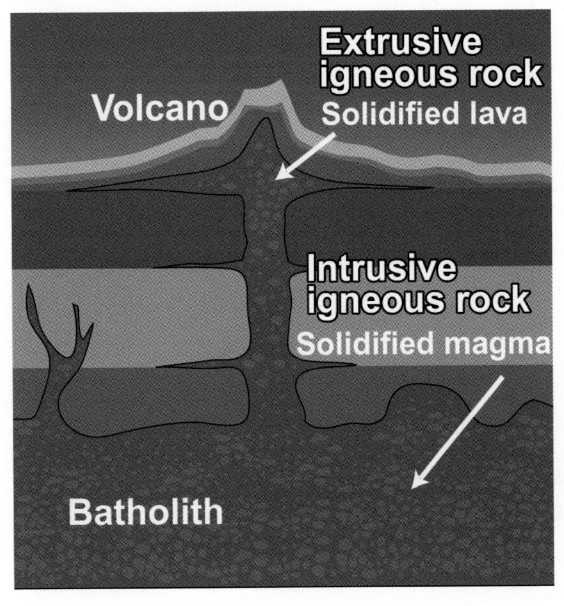

Volcanic activity results in the formation of two kinds of rocks—*extrusive* and *intrusive igneous rocks*. Rocks formed from lava, which has been erupted on the surface, are referred to as *extrusive*. These rocks cool quickly and have fine crystals as a result. Extrusive rocks are associated with volcanic eruptions. When magma cools and solidifies below Earth's surface, *intrusive igneous rocks* are formed. Because these rocks cool more slowly, they have larger crystals. A *batholith* is a large underground rock that formed when a mass of magma cooled underground.

Can volcanoes be predicted?

It is easier to predict a volcanic eruption than an earthquake because there are many more signs that a volcano might erupt. Predictors of eruptions include:

- Earthquake tremors that result from magma collecting in the ground.
- Heating of water near the volcano.
- The release of gases from the volcano.
- Changes of the volcano's surface

Which of these predictors indicated that Mount St. Helens was going to erupt in 1980?

Scientists can predict that a volcano is active and will erupt in the near future. They cannot predict the exact time it will erupt or how explosive it will be.

29.2 The Surface of Earth

A full moon in the night sky gives you a glimpse of what the moon looks like. Unlike Earth, the moon has no plate tectonic activity. Additionally, the moon is nearly free of water and lacks an atmosphere. Without plate tectonics and erosion by wind and water, the surface of the moon has stayed the same for a very long time (Figure 29.7). In comparison, Earth's surface is always changing. In this section, you will learn about forces that cause these changes.

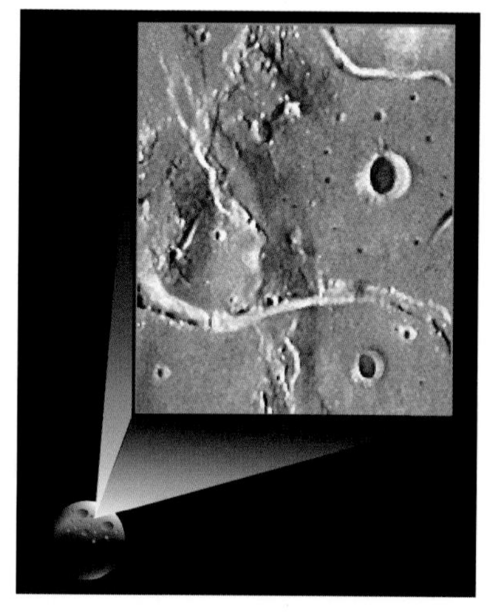

Figure 29.7: *The craters on the surface of the moon are the result of impact craters from meteorites. How does the surface of Earth compare with that of the moon?*

Earth's lithosphere

Earth's surface is constantly changing

Earth's lithosphere is very thin compared with the whole planet. Pieces of the lithosphere, called tectonic plates, move on Earth's surface. Recall that earthquakes, volcanoes, mountains, and the construction of new lithosphere are events that occur at plate boundaries. These events are changing the appearance of Earth's surface all the time. For example, the slow collision of tectonic plates continues to build mountains. Mountains that are still being built include the Rockies, Himalayas, and Alps (Figure 29.8). Somewhere on Earth, an active volcano is erupting and adding more lava to Earth's surface.

Constructive vs. destructive processes

The features we see on Earth's surface represent the dynamic balance between the *constructive processes* often associated with plate tectonics (volcanoes and mountain-building) versus the *destructive processes* of erosion associated with moving wind, water, and ice. At the same time that mountains and volcanoes are being created, wind and water are gradually wearing down these and other land formations. The eroded bits of rock are then deposited and piled up by wind or water somewhere else on Earth's surface only to become another land formation.

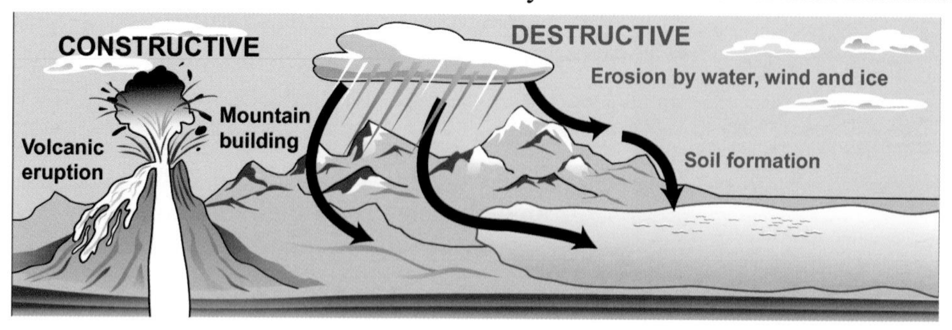

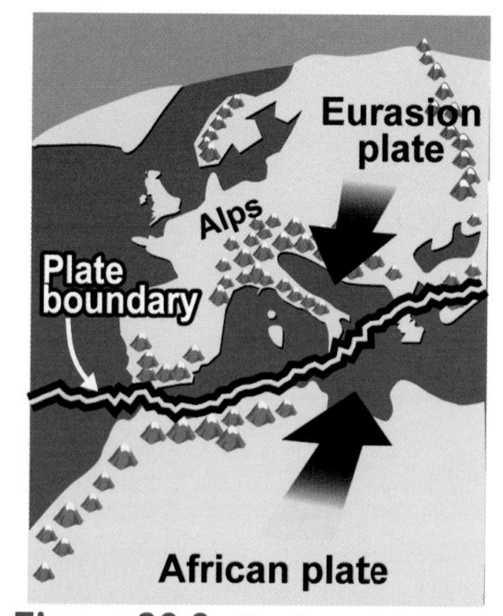

Figure 29.8: *The formation of the Alps is still occurring as the African and Eurasian plates converge.*

Mountain-building, a constructive process

How mountains form

Mountain-building is a major constructive process. Mountains form in three main ways: by folding at convergent plate boundaries; by movement of chunks of land at faults; and by volcanic activity.

Fold mountains

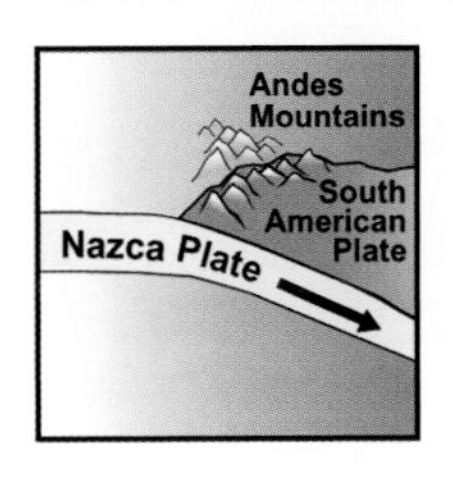

Scientists explain how fold mountains formed using the theory of plate tectonics (Figure 29.9). The Andes were formed as the Nazca plate subducted under the South American plate. At this convergent boundary between a subducting oceanic plate and a continental plate, mountains formed along the west coast of South America due to folding and faulting (breaking into chunks due to the lithosphere cracking under pressure). Mountains also form when two continental plates collide. For example, the Himalayas are fold mountains that began to form more than 40 million years ago when the Indian and Eurasian plate collided.

Fault-block mountains

Sometimes pressure at plate boundaries causes the lithosphere to crack and become a fault. A result of this cracking is a fault-block mountain (Figure 29.10). When cracks occur, pieces of the lithosphere tilt or move. Chunks of rock that slide down create a valley. The chunks that move upward or tilt form mountains. Mountains near the San Andreas fault are examples of fault-block mountains.

Mountains formed by volcanic activity

Volcanic mountains occur at subduction zones (e.g., the Ring of Fire) and at hotspots (Figure 29.11). A *volcano* is formed by the extensive layering of lava and volcanic material that builds up over millions of years with each eruption. For this reason, these mountains often stand alone; they are not part of a mountain range. A *dome mountain* is formed by a bulge of magma forcing the lithosphere upward.

Formation of the Andes Mountains

In the 1830s, Charles Darwin found seashell fossils in the Andes on the west coast of South America. Darwin's interpretation of his findings was that a powerful, slow-moving force from Earth had thrust the bottom of the sea upward and formed the Andes. The Andes are so high that even if the polar ice caps melted, there would not be enough water on Earth to completely cover these mountains. This means the Andes could not have been undersea mountains at one time.

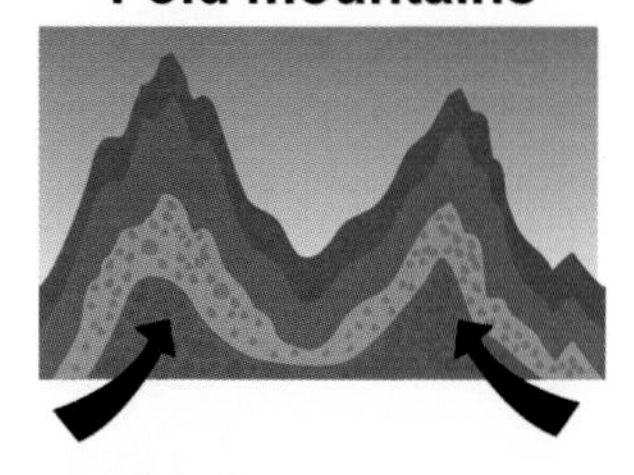

Figure 29.9: *Examples of fold mountains include the Andes and the Himalayan Mountains.*

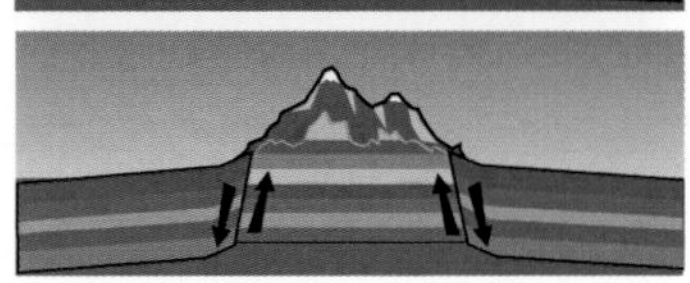

Figure 29.10: *Mountains along the San Andreas fault are examples of fault-block mountains.*

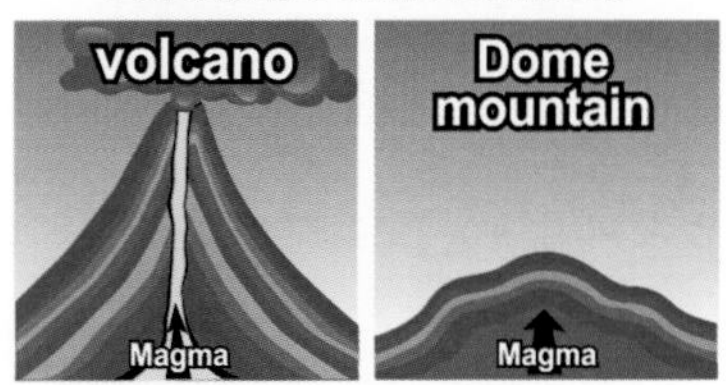

Figure 29.11: *There are numerous volcanic mountains along the Ring of Fire. An example of a dome mountain is Mount Rushmore.*

Erosion, a destructive process

What is erosion? Erosion (also known as *weathering*) is a major destructive process. This term describes the continuous physical and chemical events that cause land and rock to wear down. To understand erosion, think of a sand castle. Once you have made your sand castle, it does not take long for water, wind, and people to transform your castle back to a pile of sand. Likewise, mountains are made of rock and soil. They are eroded by wind and water in the form of rain, streams, and ice in the form of glaciers. Mountains grow or get higher when they form faster than erosion occurs. However, when the mountain forming process slows down, erosion dominates. The rate of erosion is related to the height and steepness of the mountain—the steeper the mountain is, the faster it erodes because it is easier to push material down a steep slope than a gradual slope. Mountain building is a slow geologic process taking millions of years. Mountain weathering is rapid by comparison.

Young versus old mountains You can tell if a mountain is young or old by the shape of the peaks. Sharp mountain peaks indicate a young mountain. Although the Himalayas began forming more then 40 million years ago, the sharp peaks indicate that these mountains are relatively young. Rounded mountain peaks indicate an old mountain that has worn away for a long time. The Scottish Highlands are old, rounded mountains that are about 250 million years old. The Appalachians, also old rounded mountains, are more than 200 million years old.

Landforms shaped by water Valleys are good examples of the power of water and gravity on land. Rain falls and flows down steep-sided mountains, eventually collecting in a large body of water like a lake or ocean. At the top of a mountain, water runs quickly and carves V-shaped riverbeds. Over time, the river carves out enough room to move side to side and make the valley U-shaped. Valleys can also become U-shaped when a glacier moves through a river valley like a giant ice cream scoop. Near the ocean (or any slower body of water like a lake or pond), a river may spread out and form a delta. A *delta* is a place where a river spreads into a fan shape as it slows down and deposits large amounts of sediment. The Mississippi Delta is a well-known delta in the United States. Another well-known feature that was shaped by a river is the Grand Canyon, created as the Colorado River ran through it.

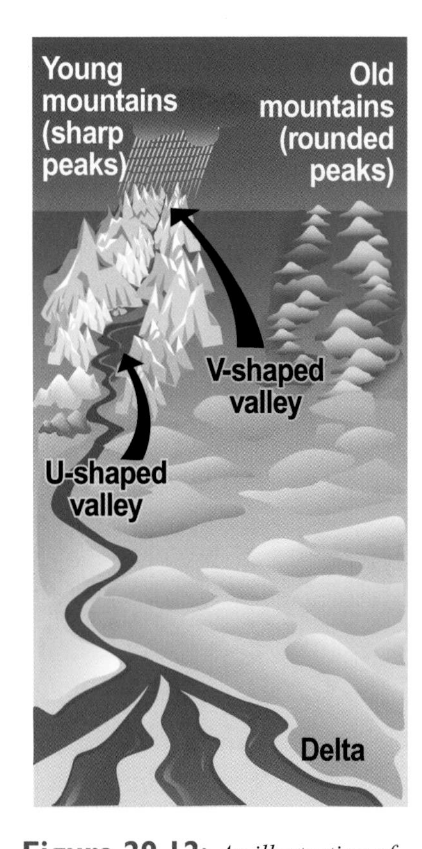

Figure 29.12: *An illustration of old versus young mountains and valleys. Older mountains have rounded peaks whereas young mountains have sharp peaks. V-shape valleys tend to be toward the tops of mountains. U-shaped valleys tend to be toward the base of mountains where rivers tend to flow in curvy pathways. A delta is a place where a river fans out as it approaches a slow-moving body of water.*

Formation of soil

What is soil? The formation of soil is the result of erosion. Soil is made of weathered rock and decayed animals and plants. For this reason, it is rich in nutrients and a suitable medium in which plants can anchor their roots and grow. Important compounds and elements would remain trapped in rocks and unavailable to plants in the soil if it was not for erosion. Ultimately, through the food chain, the nutrients are passed on to us.

The characteristics of soil The characteristics of soil depend upon the type of rock that is weathered. The main sources of soil are volcanic and mountain rocks. The characteristics of soil also depend on the type of weathering. *Chemical weathering* mostly occurs in hot, wet climates such as tropical rain forests. Examples of chemical weathering are rust formation in iron-containing minerals and erosion by rain which is always a little acidic. Some soil characteristics depend on temperature because some reactions that cause chemical weathering occur faster at warmer temperatures. *Mechanical weathering* mostly occurs in cold, dry climates such as tundras in polar regions and involves breaking up rock into smaller and smaller pieces.

A soil profile Figure 29.13 illustrates a soil profile. A soil profile is a cross-section that shows the different layers of soil in the ground. It takes a long time and a lot of weathering for soil to have all the layers you see in this figure. Young soil does not have each of these layers.

- Horizon O: A very thin layer composed of *humus*, an organic, nutrient-rich soil made from the decay and waste products of plants and animals.
- Horizon A: A dark layer called *topsoil* that is composed of more humus and small pieces of rock. It is home to many animals. For example, about 1 billion small and microscopic animals live in one cubic meter of topsoil.
- Horizon B: A layer of clay and small rocks where dissolved minerals collect. The color of this layer depends on the rock and mineral types in the layer.
- Horizon C: A layer of weathered rock pieces and minerals.
- Horizon D: Solid rock called bedrock formed in place over time. This layer is covered by the layers of soil.

Wind erosion

Like water, wind is a powerful force that causes erosion. Wind carries sediment from place to place. Wind can also increase the erosional effects of water. For example, by the time a raindrop hits the soil, it can be traveling as fast as 32 km/hour. At this speed, raindrops pound away at soil and rock. Wind further increases the speed and erosional effects of raindrops. The effects of water and wind are reduced when plants are growing in the soil. Their roots hold the soil together. Trees can also serve as a protective barrier, reducing the effects of wind.

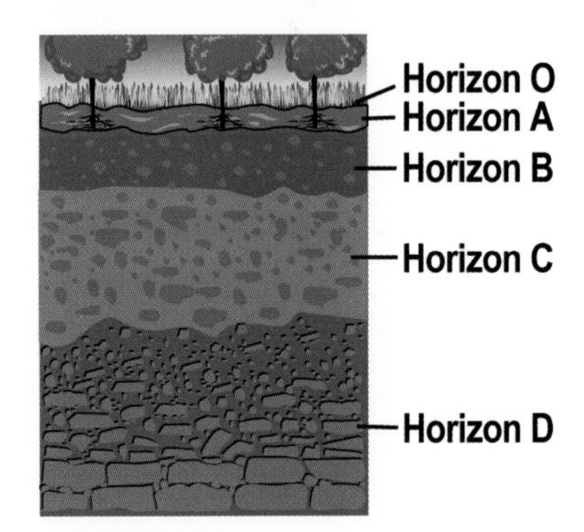

Figure 29.13: *A soil profile.*

Glaciers

What is a glacier? Glaciers at the poles are a frozen form of about 2 percent of *all* the water on Earth. Additionally, about 10 percent of Earth's surface is covered with glaciers. A **glacier** is a huge mass of ice that can be many kilometers thick and thousands of kilometers wide. Glaciers are formed from the accumulation of snow over hundreds or thousands of years. Each year more snow is piled up and does not melt during the warmer summer months. As the snow piles up and pressure increases, it changes into ice. This effect also occurs when you pack snow into a tight snowball. With the buildup of ice, a glacier becomes so thick and heavy that it flows (Figure 29.14). The force that drives this movement is gravity. Near the oceans, pieces of glaciers may break off, float away, and become icebergs.

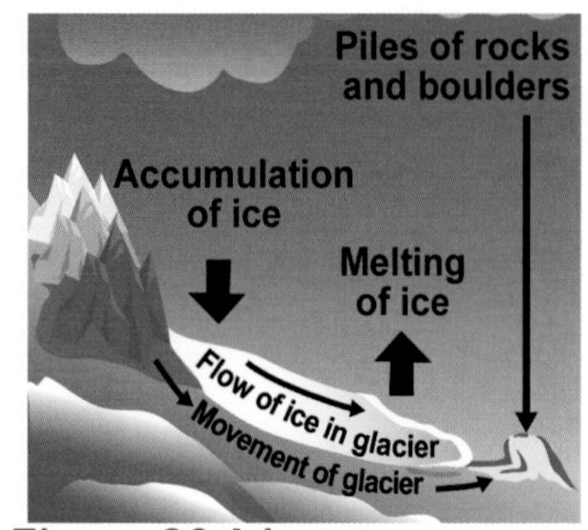

Figure 29.14: *A glacier accumulates ice faster than the ice melts. The mass of ice becomes so thick and heavy that it flows.*

Ice ages An **ice age** is a period of tens to hundreds of millions of years when the climate of Earth is very cold. During this time, much of the surface is covered with glaciers that repeatedly moved forward and backward from the poles to the equator. There have been four ice ages during Earth's history. Within each ice age, there have been shorter periods of time of thousands of years when the glacial coverage was at its maximum size. These shorter periods of time are called *glaciations*. In our present time, we are experiencing the fourth and most recent ice age that began about 1.5 million years ago. During this time, there have been several glaciations. Presently, we are in a "warm" period between glaciations. This present warm period began about 10,000 years ago.

The effect of glaciers on land About 30 percent of Earth's surface (much of North America and Europe) was covered by glaciers 10,000 years ago. As Earth's climate warmed, the glaciers melted and moved toward the poles and higher elevations, pushing around huge piles of rocks, scratching the surfaces of rocks, and eroding the mountain tops. For example, Long Island was created by a glacier bulldozing and depositing rocks during the last glaciation. The rocky soil of New England is evidence of the movement of glaciers. Scientists also believe that some earthquakes in North America are likely to be the result of the Earth slowly rebounding into place after having been pressed down by glaciers. If the glaciers on Earth continued to melt, sea level would rise about 76 meters and many big coastal cities would be flooded.

What causes ice ages?

The dominant theory to explain ice ages has to do with the tilt of Earth and its orbit around the sun. Another theory is that continental drift plays a role in cooling Earth. When Antarctica broke away from Pangaea and moved to the south pole, it became covered with ice. Like a giant reflector, ice-covered Antarctica bounces light and heat back into Earth's atmosphere. Scientists believe that this reflection may be one reason why the climate cools for long periods of time.

Geologic hazard maps

What are geologic hazard maps? Geological hazards are natural events that could result in loss of life and property damage. For this reason, it is very important for builders to consult geologic hazard maps before they begin construction of any building or home. **Geologic hazard maps** indicate the location of faults where earthquakes occur, areas where volcanoes are active, and where landslides, avalanches, floods, or other natural hazards are possible. These maps sometimes indicate the degree of likelihood that hazardous events will occur. They also indicate hazards that are associated with each other. For example, when strong earthquakes occur, water-saturated soil (usually composed of sand and silt) becomes very loose and acts like a viscous liquid. A similar action takes place when you stand in the surf on a beach and wiggle your feet. Your feet quickly sink and are buried by the water-saturated sand. During an earthquake, this effect, called *liquefaction*, results in homes, buildings, bridges, and cars sinking into the ground (Figure 29.15).

An example of a geologic hazard map Geologic hazard maps show whether or not hazards occur in a particular region. In communities where geologic hazards are common, a geologic review of the property is required before construction of a building can begin. An example of a geologic hazard map is shown below. The map shows section 25 of a geographic region that has been divided into 32 sections.

Geologic Hazard Zones

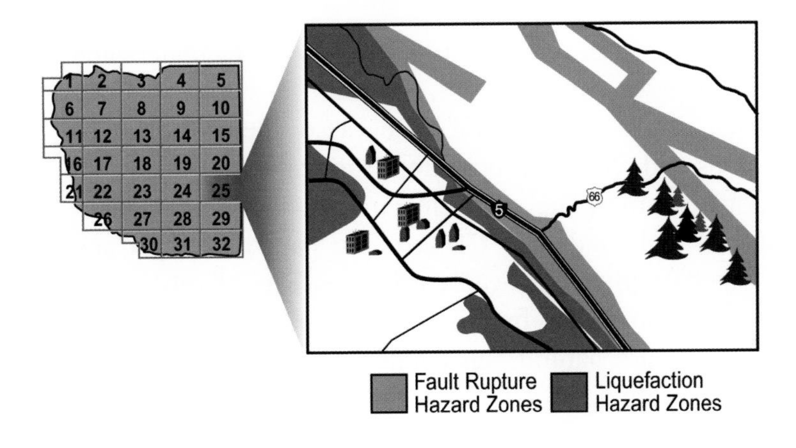

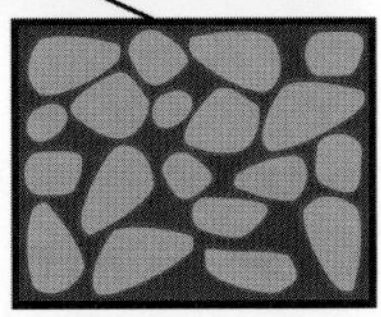

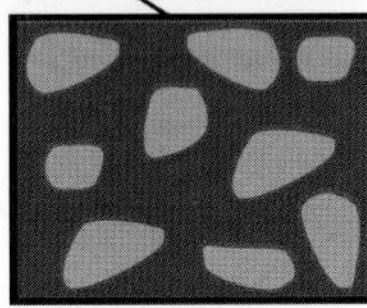

Figure 29.15: *Liquefaction occurs when soil is saturated with water. During an earthquake, increasing pressure on the soil increases the water pressure in the soil. This sometimes means that individual soil particles lose contact with each other. The result is that the soil acts like a viscous liquid.*

Topography

The term topography refers to features and formations, like bodies of water and mountains, that characterize Earth's surface. How would you describe the topography where you live?

Human impact on Earth's surface

What is urban sprawl?

As the human population grows, we take up more space. Sometimes we take up more space than we need. The term urban sprawl refers to how living areas around a city "sprawl" as they grow instead of concentrate near facilities that serve the people of the community (Figure 29.16).

The environmental impact of urban sprawl

When urban sprawl occurs, it is more difficult to serve a community using publicly-funded transportation like buses, subways, and commuter rails. As a result, more roads are built and large traffic jams make travel more difficult. Building roads changes the land. Roads and parking lots prevent water from slowly seeping into the ground to replenish the water supply in aquifers. Instead, water quickly runs off the paved surfaces causing the increased flow rate of water in nearby rivers and streams. When water flows quickly, soil and plant life on the banks are washed away and the overall health of the river and stream is reduced.

Urban sprawl changes local climate

Another effect of urban sprawl has to do with what happens when trees are cleared to make room for buildings and roads. Rooftops and road surfaces give off a lot of heat such that a region becomes an "urban heat island." When a city is hotter, there tends to be more ozone pollution which causes respiratory problems and inhibits photosynthesis in plants. Additionally, as heat rises and colder air flows into the gap left behind, an unusual number of thunder and lightning storms may occur. Although these storms can clean pollution out of the air, they also cause local flooding because there are fewer greenspaces to absorb water.

How can the effects of urban sprawl be reduced?

The first step in making a difference in reducing urban sprawl is to understand what is happening. Once you are aware of a problem, you can take steps to change some habits that create urban sprawl and the problems associated with it. To reduce the need for more roads and reduce air pollution from cars, you can walk, take public transportation, or drive more fuel-efficient cars. Another helpful habit is to maintain cars so that oil and fluids don't leak on to paved surfaces and become pollutants in our water supply. Cities can curb the effects of urban heat islands by adding heat-reflective rooftops to buildings and by planting more trees in urban areas. Trees and plants are natural "air-conditioners" that keep areas cooler through shading and by absorbing heat.

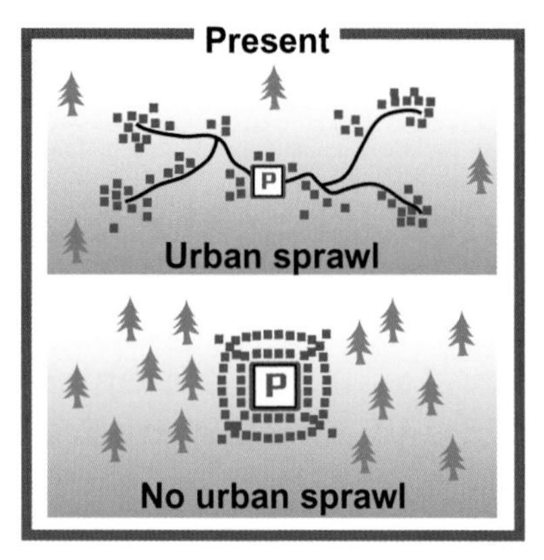

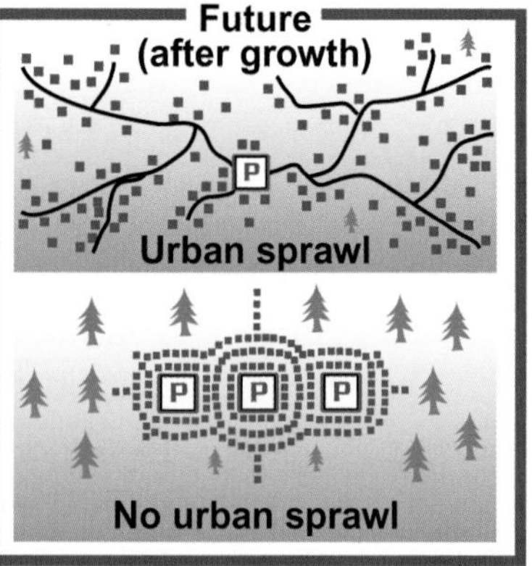

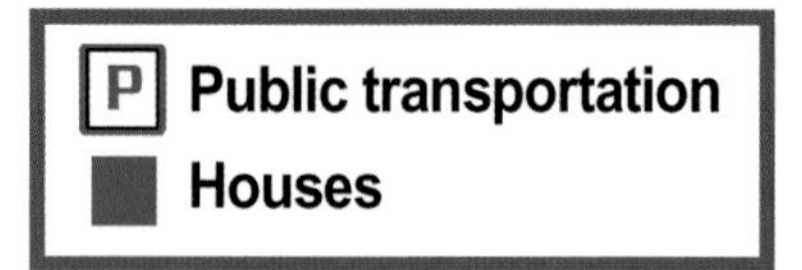

Figure 29.16: *Urban sprawl occurs when the growth of a community occurs in a way that is not organized. Growth that is not organized leads to more roads, less greenspace, increased traffic, and greater difficulty in providing public transportation.*

Extraterrestrial shaping of Earth's surface

The moon versus Earth

The surface of the moon is much different from the surface of Earth. Whereas Earth's surface has been in constant change, the surface of the moon has been preserved. In the late 1960s and early 1970s, the Apollo space missions went to the moon. By studying very small pieces of the moon rocks brought back to Earth by these missions, scientists have learned that the moon's surface is about 4 billion years old, nearly as old as the solar system. Because the moon's surface is so well-preserved, it is our best research lab for studying what was happening in the solar system 4 billion years ago.

Showers of comets and asteroids on Earth and the moon

Scientists believe that 4.1 to 3.8 billion years ago, the surfaces of the moon and Earth experienced torrential showers of comets and asteroids. The many craters on the moon's surface are evidence of these showers. By comparison, Earth has very few craters. This does not mean that Earth did not get hit by these comets and asteroids. Rather, the constant change of Earth's surface due to plate tectonics and weathering has hidden most of the evidence. There is evidence that Earth was hit in Arizona, at the famous impact crater called the Meteor Crater. This crater, whose diameter is 1.2 kilometers, was formed by an asteroid with a diameter of 24 meters.

Are there Earth rocks on the moon?

By studying the moon, scientists estimate that in a 200-million-year period, Earth would have experienced impacts from at least 17,000 asteroids. With such huge impacts, scientists believe it may be possible to find pieces of rock from Earth on the moon; these pieces would had been thrown off Earth on to the moon when an impact occurred. This idea has scientists petitioning NASA to send astronauts back to the moon to bring back more moon rocks for study.

How do you study moon rocks?

Because of the comet and asteroid showers millions of years ago, some moon rocks were blasted off the moon onto Earth. Scientists have studied these to find out more about Earth's early history.

When an impact occurred on the moon, the impact caused moon rock to melt and release argon gas. At the same time, the impact forced the rock off the moon. This moon rock landed on Earth about a million years later. As the rock traveled through space, radioactive decay in the rock released more argon gas, which became trapped in the rock.

By measuring the amount of argon in these ancient moon rocks, scientists can determine when the rock formed and when the impact occurred.

29.3 Rocks and Minerals

When you pick up a rock, you hold a lot of history in your hands. This is because any rock is the result of numerous intense processes that have created it over millions of years. Such processes include the eruption of a volcano, erosion of land by a river, and mountain-building. Each of these processes listed is important in forming one of the three categories of rocks. In this section, you will learn how rocks are classified and formed. Using this knowledge, you will be able to tell the history of a rock.

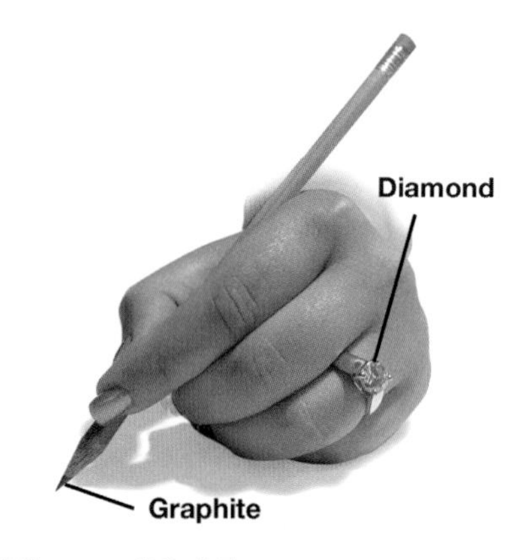

Figure 29.17: *Diamonds and graphite are made of carbon. Diamonds form within volcanic rock that explosively reaches Earth's surface. Graphite is made of organic material that has experienced high temperatures and pressures.*

Rocks are made of minerals

What is a mineral?

The history of a rock begins with minerals because they are the building blocks of a rock. A mineral is a solid, naturally-occurring object with a *defined* chemical composition. Minerals are inorganic (meaning they do not result from living things) and have a crystalline structure. Usually, a mineral is a compound of two or more elements, but it can be made of a single element. For example, metals like copper and gold are minerals that occur as pure elements. It is important to note that different minerals can have the same chemical composition but have different crystal structure. For example, graphite and diamonds are two different minerals that are made of pure carbon (Figure 29.17). A list of some common minerals and their uses is provided in the table in Figure 29.18.

About 20 minerals make up Earth's crust

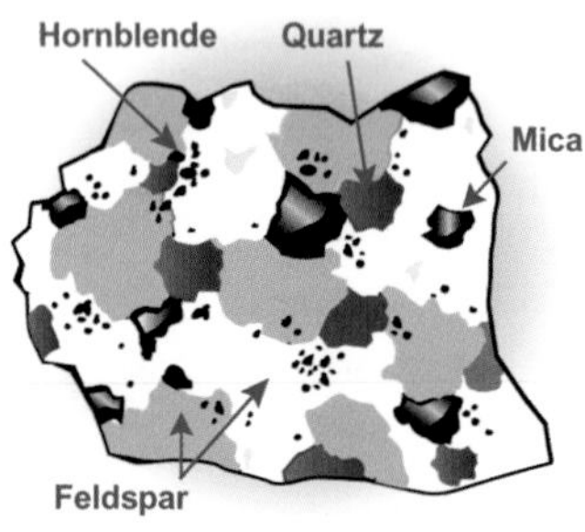

There are more than 3,000 minerals on Earth. About 20 common minerals make up about 95 percent of Earth's crust and are involved in rock formation. For example, during the underground cooling stage of the formation of a granite rock, different minerals crystallize. These distinct minerals are easy to see in a hand-sized piece of granite. Feldspar and quartz crystals make of the majority of a piece of granite. Mica and hornblende crystals are also visible. These minerals are further described on the next page.

Some common minerals	
Name (chemical formula)	Uses
silver (Ag)	jewelry, electrical wire, coins
corundum (Al_2O_3)	sandpaper, gems (e.g., rubies, sapphires)
quartz (SiO_2)	glass making, gems (e.g., onyx, amethyst)
gypsum ($CaSO_42H_2O$)	used to make Plaster of Paris

Figure 29.18: *Some common minerals and their uses.*

Common minerals

What is feldspar? The *feldspar* in granite is usually white or pink. However, feldspar can also be green or other colors. Feldspar is composed of sodium, calcium, potassium, and silica. Feldspar has cleavage planes. A cleavage plane is a region where a rock cleanly splits. The placement of a cleavage plane occurs where there are weak bonds between atoms and molecules in the mineral. Many cleavage planes in the same direction appear as parallel lines (Figure 29.19).

What is quartz? *Quartz* crystals are dark gray, white, clear or rosy, and appear to glisten as if they are wet or oily. Unlike feldspar, quartz lacks cleavage planes. When quartz breaks, it does not split along planes. Quartz is made of silicon dioxide (SiO_2) and is used in making glass. Gemstones like onyx, agate, and amethyst are made of quartz.

What is mica? *Mica* is a silicate (Si_xO_y, where *x* and *y* represent different numbers of atoms) with various ions of iron, magnesium, and sodium. A piece of mica is like a small stack of paper sheets. A stack of paper sheets and a piece of mica are described as having a single cleavage plane (Figure 29.19). The two main types of mica in granite are *white mica* (called *muscovite*) and *black mica* (called *biotite*).

What is hornblende? *Hornblende* is also found in granite. It is a dark mineral made of a mixture of elements including calcium and silicon, along with iron, magnesium, or aluminum.

More information about minerals A mineral is a material that is naturally occurring, inorganic, and crystalline. Using this definition, ice is a mineral, but liquid water is not (Figure 29.20). Do you see why? On the other hand, coal is not a mineral because it is made from living things and is not a crystal (Figure 29.20). Most minerals (except metals) also have one or more cleavage planes that also help in determining their identity.

Recognizing minerals helps identify rocks Recognizing common minerals is an important step to being able to identify a rock and understand how it formed. The majority of continents are made of granite and the most common mineral in Earth's crust is feldspar. Quartz is the second most common mineral. Since granite is a common rock, it is useful to know how to identify mica and hornblende.

There is one cleavage plane for the pages in a book.

There are three cleavage planes for a cube.

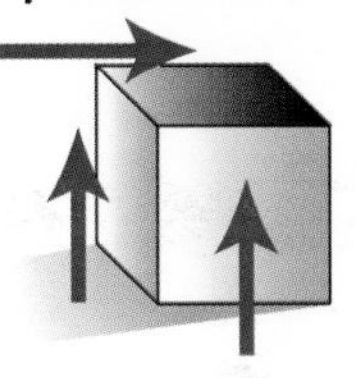

Figure 29.19: *Mica has one cleavage plane. The mineral halite has three cleavage planes and breaks into cubes. Halite is made of sodium chloride. Next time you use table salt (also sodium chloride), look at the tiny grains. Each is a miniature cube.*

mineral

Ice is inorganic and crystalline

not a mineral

Coal is derived from plants and lacks a crystal structure

Figure 29.20: *Ice is a mineral. Coal is not a mineral.*

Identifying minerals

Mohs hardness scale

Mohs hardness scale was developed in 1812 by Friedrick Mohs (an Austrian mineral expert) as a method to identify minerals (Figure 28.2). This scale uses 10 common minerals to represent variations in hardness. You can identify a mineral's place on the hardness scale by whether it can scratch another mineral. For example, gypsum (hardness = 2) scratches talc (hardness = 1). The hardest mineral, a diamond, can scratch all other minerals. Minerals of the same hardness (and without impurities) scratch each other.

Common items test the hardness of a mineral

In addition to the minerals listed in Figure 29.21, you can use common items. For example, your fingernail, a penny, and glass can be used to test the hardness of a mineral. The following scenarios illustrate how to use Mohs hardness scale.

- A fingernail scratches gypsum, but gypsum does not scratch the fingernail. The fingernail is scratched by calcite. What is the hardness of a fingernail? *Answer: 2.5*
- A penny is scratched by fluorite, but the penny cannot scratch fluorite. The penny scratches calcite and calcite scratches the penny. What is a penny's hardness? *Answer: 3*
- A piece of glass scratches and is scratched by orthoclase (a type of feldspar). The glass scratches apatite. What is the hardness of glass? *Answer: 6*

Mohs hardness scale	
Mineral	**Hardness**
talc	1
gypsum	2
calcite	3
fluorite	4
apatite	5
orthoclase	6
quartz	7
topaz	8
corundum	9
diamond	10

Figure 29.21: *The Mohs hardness scale is used to help identify minerals.*

Identifying rocks

What is a rock?

A rock is a naturally formed solid usually made of one or more minerals. Therefore, being able to recognize common minerals is very useful for identifying a rock. It is important to note that it can be difficult to identify a rock. Scientists sometimes have to rely on special microscopes to be sure about a rock's identity.

Use your powers of observation to identify a rock

Your powers of observation are your best tools for identifying a rock. Ask yourself: What does the rock look like? Where was it found? Your answers to these questions may help you determine if the rock is *igneous*, *sedimentary*, or *metamorphic*. The terms igneous, sedimentary, and metamorphic refer to how a rock was formed. You will learn about these terms on the next page.

Where to go to find out more about rocks

A rock key can help identify a rock by asking a series of questions. Keys also have diagrams or photographs to help you identify rocks. You can find a rock key at your local library. You can also learn about local rocks by contacting your state's geological survey.

What are igneous, sedimentary, and metamorphic rocks?

Igneous rocks (*ignis* means "fire")

Igneous rocks are made of magma or lava, the fiery hot material that originates in Earth's mantle. *Intrusive* igneous rocks are formed from magma that has cooled and solidified below Earth's surface. Deep underground, the temperature is very warm. Therefore, cooling and solidification of rocks takes a long time and large, visible crystals form as a result in intrusive rocks. Intrusive rocks tend to be coarse-grained. Granite is a common intrusive rock. The continents are mostly made of granite. *Extrusive* igneous rocks form from lava, molten material extruded onto Earth's surface. At Earth's surface, cooling and solidification of lava takes place relatively quickly so that very small crystals form. Extrusive rocks tend to be fine-grained. Basalt is a common extrusive rock with very small crystals. The ocean floor is made of basalt.

Sedimentary rocks (*sedimentation* means settling)

Sedimentary rocks are made of the products of weathering. Wind or water *weathers* existing rocks in a process called **erosion**. Then, wind and water deposit the eroded particles (called sediment) in layers. Mineral water flows between the particles in the layers as they *compact*. As water is forced out by temperature and pressure, the particles are *cemented*. Over millions of years, compaction and cementing turn layers of sediment into rock. The most important kinds of sedimentary rocks are *clastic*, *organic*, and *chemical*. Clastic rocks result from eroded bits of rocks being pressed together. Organic rocks, like coal, form when *layers of decaying sediments* of once living animals and plants are compacted. Over millions of years, a 20-meter layer of decaying plant material will turn into a one-meter layer of coal. Chemical rocks are formed when a *solution of dissolved minerals evaporates* leaving behind a rock with many mineral crystals. Rock salt (called halite) and gypsum are examples of chemical rocks.

Metamorphic rocks (*metamorphic* refers to a change of form)

A **metamorphic rock** is an igneous, sedimentary, or other metamorphic rock that has been transformed by pressure or frictional heat from deep burial under layers of rock or from the compression that occurs during mountain-building. Rocks that experience this intense pressure and heat are said to be *metamorphosed*. For example, numerous metamorphic rocks formed when India and Asia collided to form the Himalayan Mountains. Metamorphic rocks are often exposed at Earth's surface when layers of sediment above these rocks are eroded.

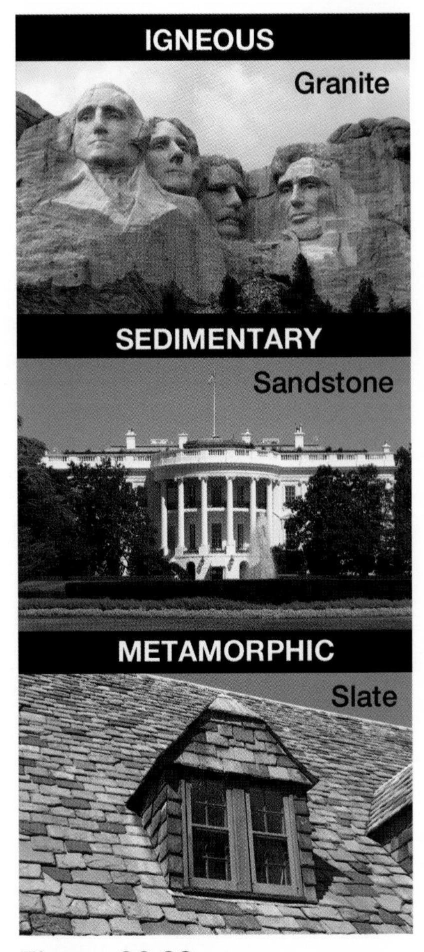

Figure 29.22: *Rocks are useful materials for creating structures that last. Mount Rushmore is a famously sculpted mountain of granite, an igneous rock. The United States' White House is made of sandstone, a sedimentary rock. Slate, a metamorphic rock, is a well-known material used in roofing.*

Identifying a rock

What does the rock look like?

When examining a rock, it is helpful to break it open to see the interior. The outside of a rock can be misleading due to color changes that occur with weathering. Next, it is important to look at the *grain* of a rock's texture. Grain refers to the fact that a single rock is made of other rock pieces or mineral crystals of various sizes and shapes and in different patterns. Rocks that are coarse-grained have large particles and the minerals that make up this kind of rock are visible. Rocks that are fine-grained have very small particles that can only be interpreted with a magnifying glass or microscope. Grains can appear as specks, crystals, or as round or angular pieces. The particles and grains in a rock can be randomly placed or organized into straight or wavy layers.

What is the composition of a rock?

Using your eyes is the first step to identifying a rock. For example, in some cases the composition of a rock can be determined by looking at its mineral crystals. With practice, you will be able to identify common minerals in rocks. To aid you in identification, you can use a magnifying glass. Often to identify crystals, geologists make thin slices of a rock for viewing under a microscope or a *microprobe*. A microprobe is used to melt a specific crystal in order to identify its chemical composition and properties. Other techniques for identifying minerals include making a streak of the mineral on a ceramic tile. The color of the streak is not always the same as the color of the mineral. For example, silvery hematite used for jewelry will leave a reddish streak. The color of the streak gives you a clue about the identity of the mineral. As you learned earlier, you can identify the relative hardness of the mineral using Mohs hardness test. Also, the smell of the rock can be helpful in identifying if a rock contains sulphur compounds. Finally, an acid test will help you identify whether or not a rock contains calcium carbonate because this substance reacts with acid. How would you determine whether or not a rock contains magnetic metals like iron or nickel? Such a rock would attract a magnet.

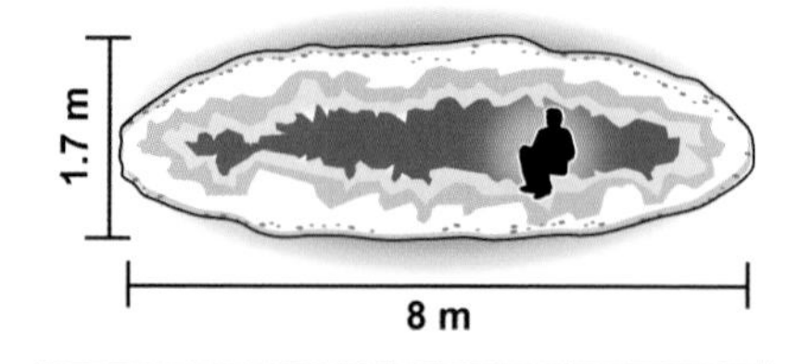

What is a geode?

A geode is a collection of minerals that forms within cavities in volcanic or sedimentary rocks. A geode is not easily classified as an igneous, sedimentary, or metamorphic rock. When you break open a geode, you find gleaming crystals. Typically, you can hold a geode in your hand. However, in May 2002, a geologist discovered a giant geode in Italy that is 8 m x 1.7 m and fits 10 people! Imagine sitting inside a geode lined with large, transparent pieces of crystalline gypsum! Scientists believe the geode may have been formed when the Mediterranean Sea evaporated 5-6 million years ago.

Identifying igneous, sedimentary, or metamorphic rocks

How do you tell if a rock is igneous?

Igneous rocks can often be identified by their texture. For example, igneous rocks have crystals that intersect at angles. However, the grain in these rocks usually does not have a pattern or a uniform orientation of crystals. The size of the grains depends on how fast the rock cooled during its formation. Some igneous rocks are glassy (very fine-grained) because they cooled quickly. Basalt is a fine-grained rock. An example of a slow-cooling igneous rock with large, easy-to-see grains, is granite. Granitic rocks are easy to find in mountainous regions where they have been exposed due to weathering. In flatter regions, this intrusive igneous rock is often buried by sediments. Mount Rushmore in South Dakota is made of granite.

How do you tell if a rock is sedimentary?

Sedimentary rocks often appear to have layers of rock pieces. Because the pieces tend to sort by size, a sedimentary rock tends to have same sized pieces or the same sized particles are organized into layers. The boundaries between pieces in a sedimentary rock are not well-defined. Sedimentary rocks are often found in areas where sediment gets deposited. Sedimentary rocks with large pieces tend to form in high-energy environments, like the bed of a fast-moving river (conglomerate rock). Sedimentary rocks with small pieces form in low energy environments like a pond, lake, or the ocean floor (shale). Sedimentary rocks are common and easily seen in the mid- and southwestern United States. For example, the Grand Canyon is a giant land formation made of layers of sedimentary rock that have been exposed by weathering.

How do you tell if a rock is metamorphic?

The grains in metamorphic rocks tend to orient themselves based on how the rock was metamorphosed. Rocks that are modified by pressure have grains oriented in lines. An example of this kind of metamorphic rock is slate formed from shale (a sedimentary rock). Rocks that are modified by pressure and heat have grains oriented in foliations (wavy patterns). These rocks appear layered or *foliated.* Examples of foliated rocks are gneiss formed from granite. Examples of nonfoliated rock include some types of marble formed from limestone. Metamorphic rocks tend to be the hardest and most weather-resistant rock of the three kinds. These rocks are often associated with mountains because the pressures that arise from mountain-building cause the formation of these rocks.

The history of a rock

Marble is a weather-resistant, crystalline rock often used by sculptors. How is marble formed?

Marble is a metamorphic rock that originates as limestone. It is thousands or millions of years old. Limestone, a sedimentary rock, was formed on the bottom of the ocean. As tiny marine creatures died, their calcium carbonate shells rained down on the ocean floor and became sediments called ooze. In ancient times, compaction and cementing hardened the ooze to limestone and preserved these tiny fossils. The limestone was raised as mountains formed. The heat and pressure created by this movement caused some rock to metamorphose into marble. The green or grey streaks in marble are the result of compounds in the limestone being forced out during metamorphosis.

The rock cycle

What is the rock cycle?

The **rock cycle** illustrates the formation and recycling of rocks by geological processes. Let's begin with a piece of granite that is part of a mountain. This granite is weathered by wind and rain. Sediments from the eroded rock are washed down the mountain where they enter a stream and then a river that empties into the ocean. These sediments are deposited on the ocean floor where they will be covered by other sediments. Eventually, these layers of sediments are compressed and cemented to form a sedimentary rock. As a sedimentary rock becomes buried deeper and deeper by more and more sediment, it experiences intense pressure and becomes a metamorphic rock. Next, this metamorphic rock is pulled down into the mantle at a subduction zone. Now the metamorphic rock melts and becomes magma. Then, the magma rises toward Earth's surface to become a intrusive igneous rock like granite or an extrusive rock like basalt. The magma could also be ejected from a volcano as lava and then cooled to become an extrusive igneous rock like pumice. Either way, the rock cycle continues as another igneous rock weathers to become a sedimentary rock, melts to again become igneous, or metamorphoses into another metamorphic rock.

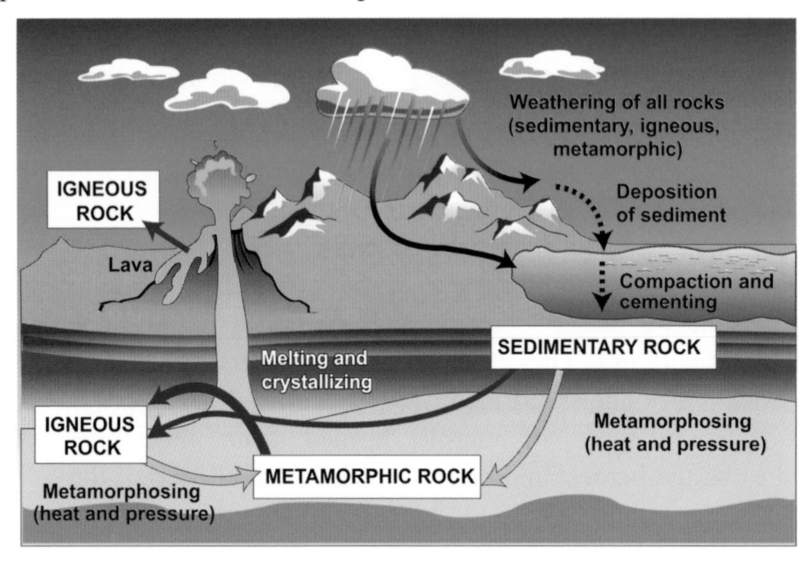

Key processes in the rock cycle

The rock cycle illustrates how matter is recycled. The processes that keep rock material moving through the rock cycle are *weathering*, *compaction* and *cementing*, *melting* and *crystallizing*, and *metamorphosing*. Additionally, the interaction of tectonic plates plays a very important role in the rock cycle. Rocks melt or metamorphose when they are subducted into the mantle. The collisions of tectonic plates create mountains. Were it not for mountain building, the weathering of rocks over time would leave the continents smooth and flattened.

Chapter 29 Review

Vocabulary review

Match the following terms with the correct definition. There is one extra definition in the list that will not match any of the terms.

Set One

1. magma
2. lava
3. Ring of Fire
4. magma chamber
5. crater

a. The pattern of volcanoes and earthquakes that occurs at the boundaries of the Pacific Ocean
b. A glowing cloud of hot volcanic material
c. A place where magma collects underground
d. A bowl-shaped depression at the top of a volcano; also, a large depression that results from an extraterrestrial object hitting land
e. Molten material from the mantle that reaches Earth's surface
f. Molten material that originates in the mantle

Set Two

1. geothermal energy
2. stratovolcano
3. shield volcano
4. hydrothermal vent
5. rift valley

a. A wide and long depression that occurs where two tectonic plates are diverging
b. An opening on the ocean floor that allows high heat and gases to escape from the mantle
c. A type of volcano that results from a hot spot
d. A violent type of volcano that is related to a buildup of pressure and viscous magma. Many of these volcanoes occur at subduction zones.
e. Energy that is generated from heat and steam in Earth's crust
f. Energy that is generated from water

Set Three

1. cleavage plane
2. urban sprawl
3. erosion
4. soil profile
5. topography

a. A reduction in greenspace and increased traffic are results of this phenomenon
b. The break down of soil, rocks, and land formations due to climate and seasonal changes
c. A cross-section of ground that shows the layers of sediment
d. A term used to describe the shape of land and the presence of bodies of water and mountains
e. A region in a mineral where it will split cleanly due to weak interactions between molecules
f. The way that crystals are arranged in an igneous rock

Set Four

1. metamorphic rocks
2. igneous rocks
3. sedimentary rocks
4. rock cycle
5. mineral

a. Rocks that are produced when magma or lava cools and solidifies
b. Rocks that are produced when layers of rock pieces are compacted to form a new rock
c. Examples include quartz and mica
d. Examples include marble, slate, and granite
e. The set of processes that lead to the formation and recycling of the various kinds of rocks
f. Rocks formed from other rocks due to intense heat and pressure

Concept review

1. Explain the difference between magma and lava.
2. Imagine you are a blob of magma coming up through the Mid-Atlantic Ridge. Describe what might happen to you on your next step in the rock cycle.
3. Write a paragraph that explains how tectonic plates are involved in causing earthquakes and volcanoes.
4. Is erosion a constructive or a destructive force that shapes the land? Explain your answer.
5. When sugar water crystallizes, rock candy is made. Would you describe large crystals of rock candy as a mineral, a rock, or neither? Justify your answer.
6. Compare and contrast the main types of rocks: sedimentary, igneous, and metamorphic. Give an example of each type.
7. List three ways the rock cycle is like the water cycle, and three ways in which these two cycles are not alike.
8. The crust of Earth is mostly which kind of rock—igneous, sedimentary, or metamorphic? Explain your answer.

Problems

1. A volcanologist finds that the silica content of the volcanic rock near an ancient volcano is 48 percent. From this information, describe the probable type of volcano and its eruption. Where might this volcano be located?
2. Glaciers covered much of North America 30,000 years ago. The average rate at which glaciers move is two meters per day. Assuming this rate is constant, how far would a glacier move in 15,000 years?
3. You are given the task of organizing a collection of minerals used to represent the variations of hardness. Seven of nine minerals have labels. You know that the collection does not contain a diamond. Use the Mohs hardness scale and the information below to identify the two unlabeled minerals.
   a. The first mineral scratches talc and gypsum. This mineral does not scratch fluorite. What is this mineral?
   b. The second mineral scratches topaz and quartz. You guess that a diamond would scratch this mineral. What is it?

Mohs hardness scale	
Mineral	**Hardness**
talc	1
gypsum	2
calcite	3
fluorite	4
apatite	5
orthoclase	6
quartz	7
topaz	8
corundum	9
diamond	10

4. In Yosemite National Park there is a large granite formation called Half Dome. The distance from the bottom of the valley to the top of Half Dome is one kilometer. The top of Half Dome is rounded instead of peaked the way most mountains look. How do you think Half Dome formed? To develop a hypothesis, answer the following questions.
   a. What kind of rock is granite? Is it intrusive or extrusive?
   b. Did Half Dome form as a result of a volcanic eruption? Did it form as a result of two continents pushing against each other?
   c. Why might Half Dome be rounded?
   d. Develop a hypothesis about Half Dome: In your opinion, how did this rock formation form?
   e. Now research the geology of Half Dome on the Internet or in your local library. How did it form? Compare your research findings with your hypothesis.

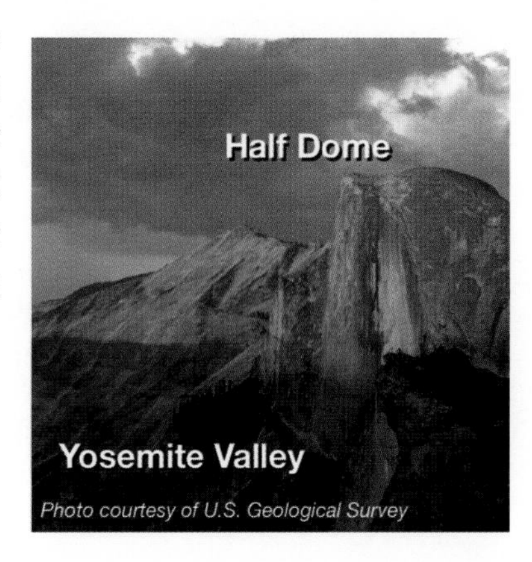

Photo courtesy of U.S. Geological Survey

Applying your knowledge

1. Use what you have learned from this chapter and the previous chapter to come up with a plan for determining the age of an extinct stratovolcano. Write down your plan as a series of steps.
2. Magma and lava have different characteristics based on their silica content. In previous units, you learned about *viscosity* and *solutions*. Review these terms and answer the following questions.
   a. Which is more viscous, magma directly from the mantle or magma that contains dissolved rock from the continental crust? Explain your answer.
   b. Are magma and lava solutions? Explain your answer.
3. Compare the effect of pressure on the change from solid rock to magma to the effect of pressure on the phase change of water from a liquid to a gas.
4. Imagine that your community has an opportunity to build a geothermal power plant and your job is to market geothermal energy to your community. What would you say to convince your community to convert from their present source of energy to geothermal energy? Use your local library or the Internet to research the benefits of using geothermal energy and find out where geothermal energy is being used in the United States. Make a brochure that explains these benefits and answers questions that people might have.
5. Many life forms depend on the ability of plants to convert solar energy to chemical energy through the process of photosynthesis. Why then is it possible for whole ecosystems to survive in the deep sea in the absence of sunlight? Explain how this is possible. Explain whether or not the sun still plays a role in the survival of such ecosystems.

6. Water and human beings each play a role in shaping Earth's surface. Which changes Earth's surface more? Justify your answer.

7. The oldest rocks that we have observed so far on Earth are 4 billion years old. You know that the Earth is 4.6 billion years old. Based on what you have learned in chapters 28 and 29, come up with a hypothesis to explain why the oldest rocks on Earth are younger than the Earth itself. Explain and justify your hypothesis in a detailed paragraph.

8. Could the rock cycle occur if Earth did not experience plate tectonics? Given your answer, explain whether or not there is a rock cycle on the moon.

9. You have learned that the polarity of Earth's magnetic field has switched over time. You also learned that the reversal of the magnetic field is recorded in rocks. If you were going to research this phenomenon, which kind of rock (igneous, sedimentary, metamorphic) would be best to study and why? In your answer, explain why the other kinds of rock would not be useful to study.

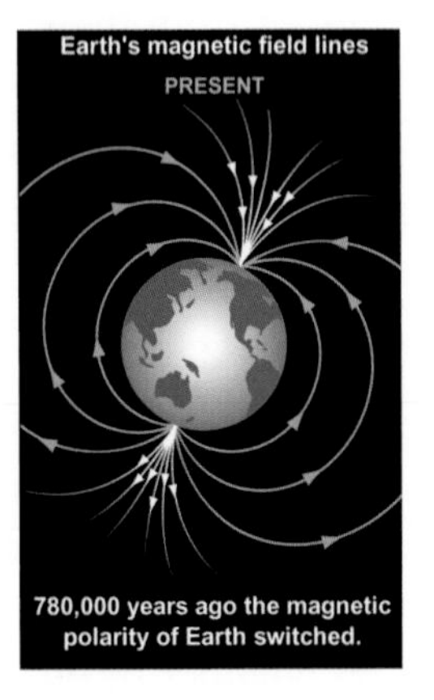

Earth's magnetic field lines
PRESENT
780,000 years ago the magnetic polarity of Earth switched.

10. A geologic hazard map shows that a number of active volcanoes follow the western coastline of South America but there are no volcanoes on the eastern coastline.
    a. Explain the pattern of volcanoes on the South American continent. Predict whether or not this pattern will change in the next 1 million years.
    b. As far as you can tell, will there ever be volcanoes on the east coast of South America? Why or why not?
    c. One of the active volcanoes is Nevado del Ruiz in Colombia. The last time this volcano erupted was 1985. What happened during this eruption? What do you predict will occur if this volcano erupts again? Answer these questions by doing research in your local library or on the Internet.

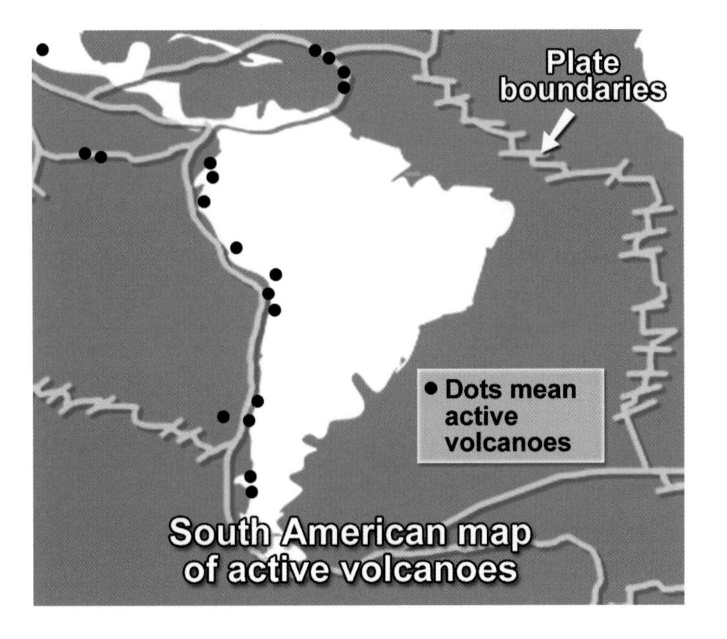

UNIT 11 Astronomy

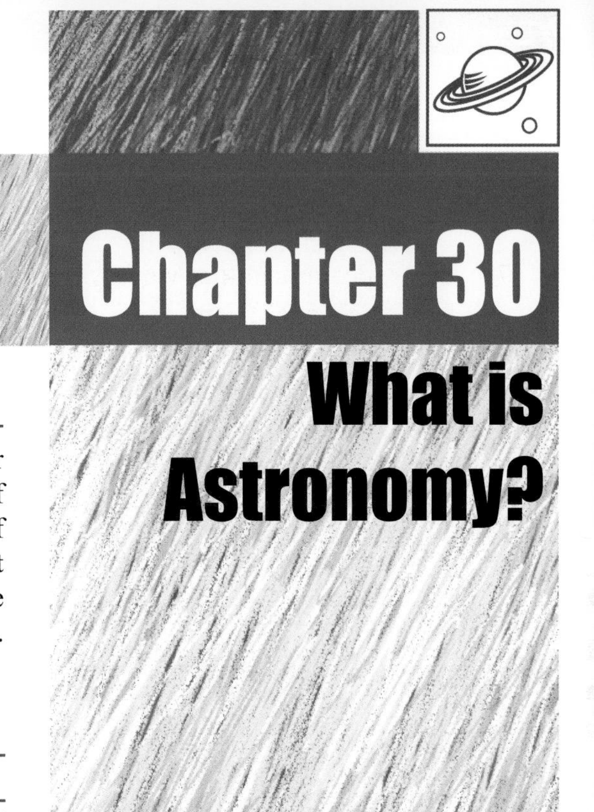

Chapter 30 What is Astronomy?

Frequently in the news we hear about discoveries that involve space. In fact, our knowledge of the solar system and beyond is expanding each year because of advancements in technology. In recent years, space probes have been sent to most of the planets in the solar system and we have seen them "up close" for the very first time. Long before the invention of the telescope, ancient civilizations made observations of the heavens that helped people keep track of time and the seasons. In this chapter, you will learn about tools and language of astronomy.

30.1 Cycles on Earth *How do we keep track of time?*

In this Investigation, you will build a solar clock and discover the variables involved with using the sun to keep track of time. You will also observe the lunar cycle over the course of a month and construct a daily calendar based on changes in the moon's appearance.

30.2 Tools of Astronomy *How does a telescope work?*

In this Investigation, you will build a simple telescope and use it to observe objects around your school. Through this exercise, you will find out how a telescope works. Next, you will use your telescope to observe the surface of the moon. Finally, you will try a more difficult task—observing the planet Jupiter and some of its moons.

Learning Goals

In this chapter, you will:

- ✔ Relate keeping track of time to astronomical cycles.
- ✔ Predict how the moon will appear based on its orbital position.
- ✔ Describe what causes the seasons.
- ✔ Describe what causes eclipses.
- ✔ Convert large numbers to scientific notation.
- ✔ Name the differences between stars, planets, galaxies, and the universe.
- ✔ Convert between kilometers and light years.
- ✔ Explain how refracting and reflecting telescopes work.
- ✔ Name some telescopes that examine other types of electromagnetic waves.
- ✔ Describe how satellites, space probes, and piloted spacecraft are used in astronomy.

Vocabulary

axis	lunar eclipse	revolution	solar eclipse
calendar	planet	rotation	star
galaxy	reflecting telescope	satellite	telescope
light year	refracting telescope	scientific notation	universe

30.1 Cycles on Earth

Did you know that two ancient cultures, the Chinese and the Mayans, independently determined that the length of a year is 365.25 days? They did this without even knowing that Earth revolves around the sun! The development of a calendar to keep track of time came from the need to be able to predict the seasons, annual floods, and other cyclical occurrences in communities' lives. In this section, you will learn where our calendar came from and why astronomical cycles on Earth occur.

 Calendars

Astronomical cycles

Do you ever wonder where our calendar comes from? Or why there is a "leap year" every four years? The answers have to do with the position of Earth in space and its relationship to the sun and moon. Today we know that Earth both spins and revolves around the sun. We also know that the moon revolves around Earth. These movements cause the *astronomical cycles* that are the basis for our calendar.

What is a calendar?

A **calendar** is a means of keeping track of all the days in a year. For thousands of years, different cultures have struggled to come up with their own calendars. Ancient civilizations developed calendars based on their observations of the sun, moon, and stars without knowing of our planet's position in space. Many such civilizations independently invented almost identical calendars. Most of these were divided into weeks and months, and included important information such as amount of daylight, position of the sun in the sky, and the phases of the moon.

Ancient calendars

Stonehenge in Great Britain is thought to be an early example (1500 BC) of a calendar. This monument, made of giant stones arranged in a pattern, marks the direction in which the sun rises and sets on the longest period of daylight of the year. This may have helped its builders to keep track of the passage of a year. Chinese astronomers in 1300 BC were the first to calculate the correct length of a year (365.25 days). The Mayans also devised a calendar with 365.25 days. This Mayan civilization (located in what is now Mexico) had no knowledge of the calendars used by other peoples. The blue box at right shows a timeline of various calendars from around the world.

Calendars through human history

20,000 years ago. Ice-age hunters in Europe scratched lines in bones to mark the passage of days.

7,000 BC. Babylonians kept a calendar with 29- and 30-day months. They needed to add an extra month every eight years.

4,000 BC. The Egyptians adopted a solar calendar with 365 days in a year. This was divided into 12 months, each with 30 days, and an extra five days at the end.

2,000 BC. Mayans of Central America calculated that there were 365.25 days in a year.

700 BC. The Roman calendar consisted of 10 months in a year of 304 days. It ignored the remaining 61 days, which fell in the middle of winter.

46 BC. Romans adopted the Julian calendar, named after Julius Caesar. It is very close to the modern calendar we use today.

The lunar cycle

Phases of the moon Have you ever noticed that the shape of the moon appears to change in a regular pattern (Figure 30.1)? This gradual change in the appearance of the moon, known as the *lunar cycle,* is one of the first discoveries that helped ancient civilizations divide the year into smaller parts. These *phases* of the moon occur because of the positions of Earth, the moon, and the sun.

Orbits The moon moves around Earth in a path called an *orbit*. The diagram below shows the positions of Earth and the sun in relation to the moon's orbit. Notice that the moon orbits in a counterclockwise direction. That is the same direction that Earth orbits the sun. How the moon appears to Earth dwellers at different positions in its orbit is shown in the diagram.

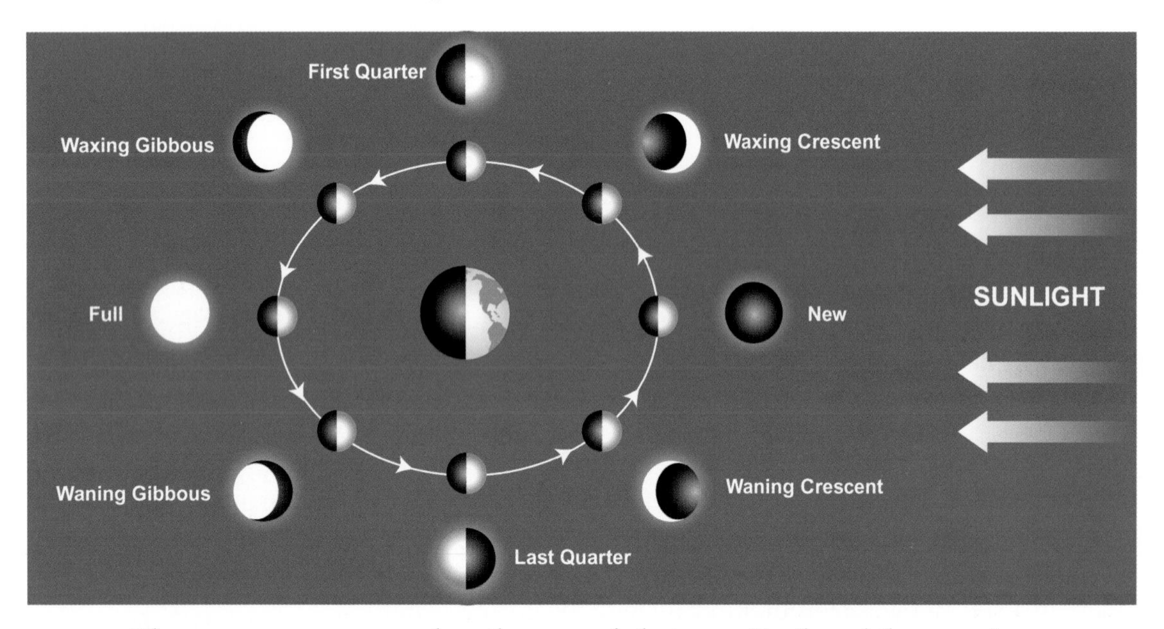

The *new moon* occurs when the moon is between Earth and the sun. A new moon is not visible in the sky because the lit side is completely facing the sun. A *full moon* occurs when the moon is on the opposite side of Earth from the sun and appears fully lit in the night sky. One complete lunar cycle, from new moon to new moon, takes 29.5 days to complete.

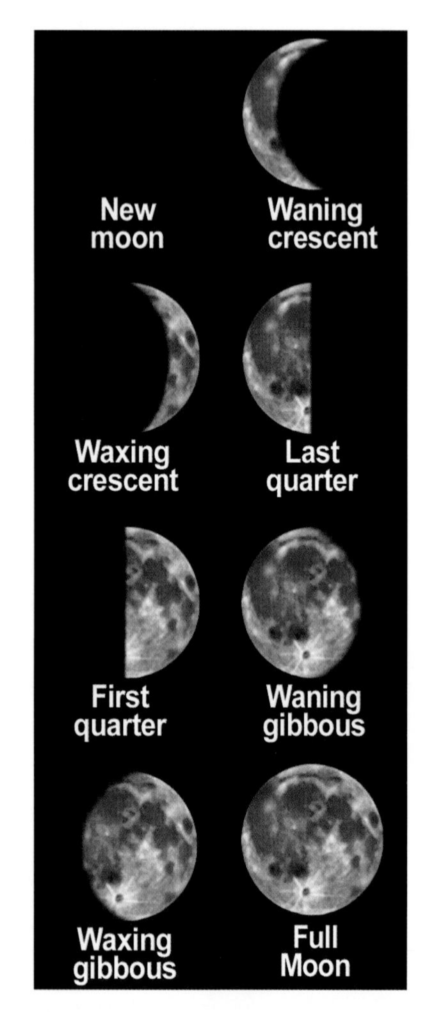

Figure 30.1: *How the moon appears from Earth in various phases.*

Dividing the year into equal parts

Days Earth's **axis** is the imaginary line that passes through its center and connects the North and South poles. Earth's spinning on its axis is called **rotation** (Figure 30.2) and it brings about day and night. If you have ever watched the sun travel during the day, you know that it appears to travel toward the west. This is because Earth rotates towards the east. It is this rotation that causes day and night. One complete rotation is called a *day*.

Years As Earth rotates on its axis, it also travels around the sun. The movement of one object around another in space is called **revolution**. Earth's path as it revolves around the sun is called its *orbit*. One *year* is the amount of time it takes Earth to complete one revolution around the sun. This is equal to 365.25 days.

Months You have read that the lunar cycle—from new moon to new moon—takes 29.5 days to complete. Early civilizations tried to use the lunar cycle as a sort of calendar. However, this did not help them predict annual events accurately because a year of lunar cycles adds up to only 354 days, not 365.25, leaving a balance of 11.25 days each year. Calendars that were based on the lunar cycle soon got ahead of astronomical cycles.

Where are the extra days? Ancient Egyptians were among the first to realize that lunar cycles were not an accurate way to divide up a year. They determined that a star called Sirius rose next to the sun every 365 days. This number of days also corresponded to the beginning of the annual flood of the Nile River. To account for the extra days in a year, they developed a calendar that had 12 months, each with 30 days, with an extra 5 days that were not part of any month.

The modern calendar That ancient Egyptian calendar added up to 365 days and eventually evolved into the calendar we use today. However, because we know that one year is approximately 365.25 days long, our calendar adjusts for this. It has eleven months with 30 or 31 days each, and one month—February—with 28 days. In a so-called leap year, February has 29 days. The extra day every four years makes up for the extra 0.25 days that occur each year.

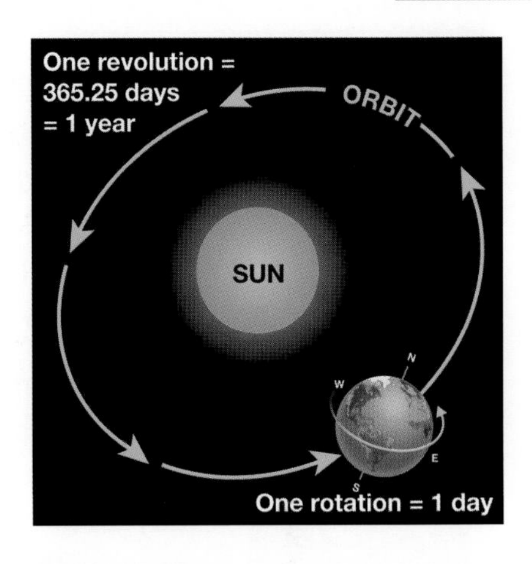

Figure 30.2: *Earth rotates on its axis.*

Counting the days in a year

Ancient cultures counted the number of days between celestial events to come up with the number of days in a year. For example, Egyptian astronomers counted the number of days between each first appearance of the star Sirius. The Mayans tracked the annual movements of the sun, moon, and planet Venus to determine the correct number of days in a year.

Dividing the day into equal parts

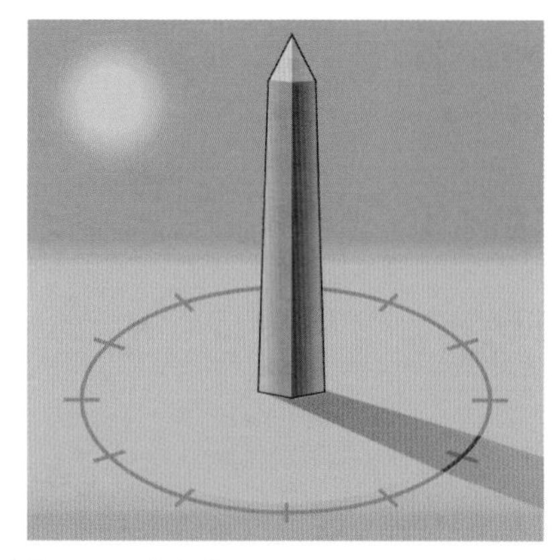

Figure 30.3: *An obelisk allowed ancient Egyptians to divide up the day into parts.*

The time of day

A *clock* tells you the exact time of day and is used to mark the division of the day into equal parts. It may be hard to imagine, but there once was a time when humans did not need to keep track of the exact time of day. The rise and fall of the sun was the only "clock" that prehistoric humans needed to regulate their daily activities. It was not until about 5,000 years ago that ancient civilizations found the need to organize their time into units smaller than day and night.

Sundials

The ancient Egyptians were among the first to divide the day into parts that were similar to hours. As early as 3500 BC, monuments called *obelisks* were built to separate the day into parts. These monuments cast a shadow that moved during the day as the sun appeared to move across the sky. Markers were placed around the base of the monument to mark the subdivisions of time during the day (Figure 30.3). Obelisks evolved into *sundials* and these became more and more accurate. By 30 BC, different styles of sundials were in use in Greece, Asia, and Italy. However, sundials could only work during the day.

Water clocks

Water clocks were among the earliest timekeepers that could be used at night. One of the oldest was found in the tomb of an Egyptian pharaoh who died in 1500 BC. Early water clocks were stone containers with sloping sides that allowed water to drip at a constant rate through a small hole in the bottom. Markings on the inside surface of the container measured the passage of "hours." Greek water clocks divided the day into 12 hours and the night into 12 hours of unequal length to adjust for the change in the amount of daylight as the seasons changed.

Modern clocks

Today we divide each rotation of Earth into 24 equal parts called *hours*. Each hour is divided up into 60 parts called *minutes* and each minute into 60 parts called *seconds*. Like the water clock, modern clocks use a constant, repetitive action or process to keep track of equal increments of time. Where the water clock uses the constant dripping of water, modern clocks use a pendulum, vibrating crystal, balance wheel, electromagnetic waves, or even atoms to mark time. Quartz clocks and watches use the properties of a quartz crystal to provide very accurate vibrations. When electric current is applied to a quartz crystal, it vibrates at a regular frequency, depending on its shape and size.

Atomic clocks

In the United States, the official time is regulated by an *atomic clock* located in Washington, D.C. Atomic clocks keep time better than the rotation of Earth or the movement of the stars. Without them, the Internet would not synchronize and the position of planets would not be known with enough accuracy for space probes to be launched and monitored. These clocks are called atomic because they use the vibrations of a cesium atom as a reference.

What causes seasons?

Seasons

As Earth revolves around the sun, we experience different seasons. Ancient civilizations realized that as the seasons changed, so did the path of the sun in the sky (or so it seemed to them). As you have learned, seasons are caused by the 23.5° tilt of Earth's axis with respect to the plane of its orbit around the sun. As Earth rotates around the sun, its axial tilt remains fixed.

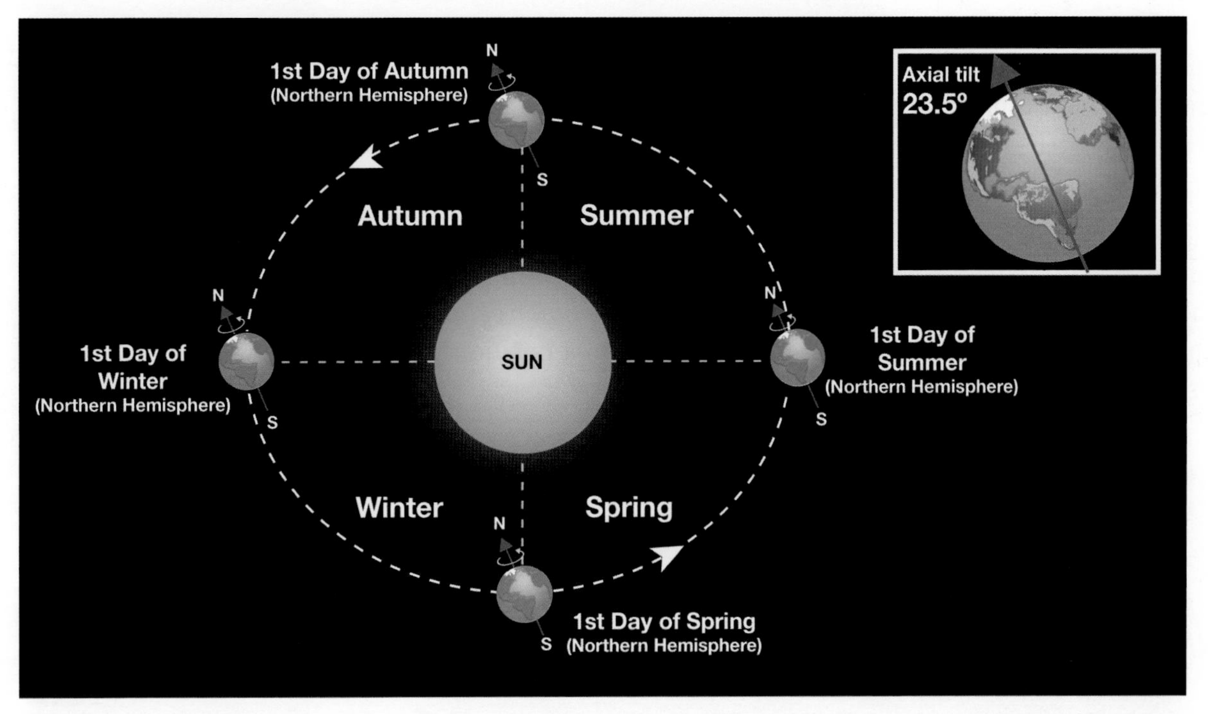

The axial tilt causes the seasons

During summer in the Northern Hemisphere, the north end of the axial tilt is facing *toward* the sun. This results in more direct sunlight and higher temperatures. Six months later, the north end of the axial tilt is facing *away* from the sun. The sunlight is spread more widely over the planet and thus is less intense, causing lower temperatures that bring winter to the Northern Hemisphere (Figure 30.4). The opposite happens in the Southern Hemisphere. The fact that Earth's axial tilt is fixed also explains why the position of the sun in the sky changes over the course of a year (Figure 30.5).

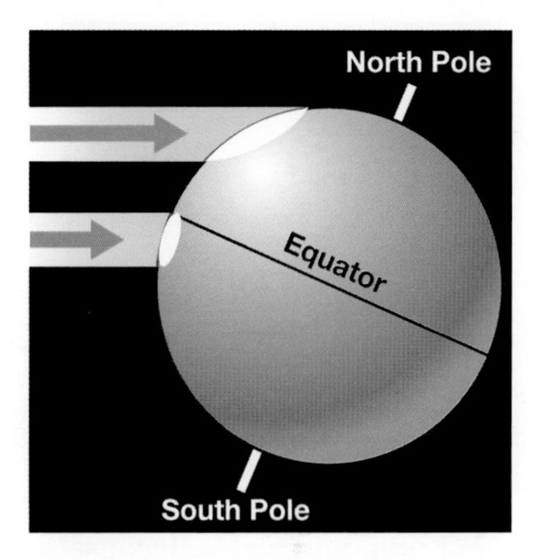

Figure 30.4: *During winter in the Northern Hemisphere, Earth's axial tilt is facing away from the sun. This means the sunlight in the Northern Hemisphere is be more spread out and less intense. Therefore, temperatures are lower in winter.*

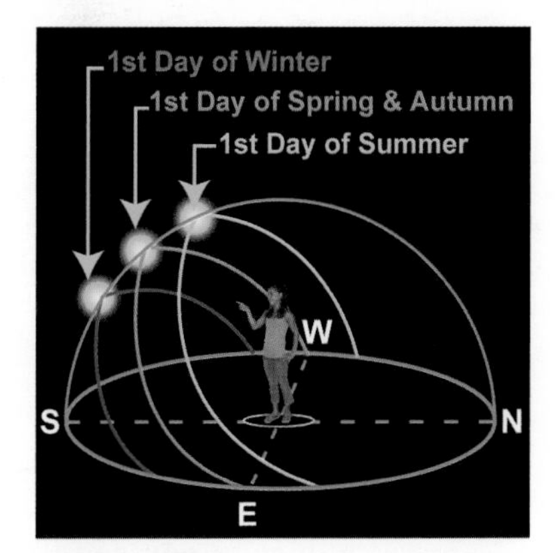

Figure 30.5: *The diagram shows the path of the sun across the sky during the year.*

What causes eclipses?

Eclipses

When the sun shines on Earth or the moon, these objects cast shadows—just like you do when you stand in the sun. When Earth or the moon cross each other's shadow, an *eclipse* occurs. A **solar eclipse** occurs when the moon's shadow falls on Earth. A **lunar eclipse** occurs when Earth's shadow falls on the moon.

The moon's orbit is tilted

If you look at the lunar cycle diagram on page 590, you may wonder why Earth's shadow doesn't cover the moon when it is between the moon and the sun. Instead, you get a full moon! The reason a lunar eclipse doesn't occur very often is that the moon's orbit is *tilted* at a 5° angle with respect to Earth's orbit around the sun as shown in Figure 30.6.

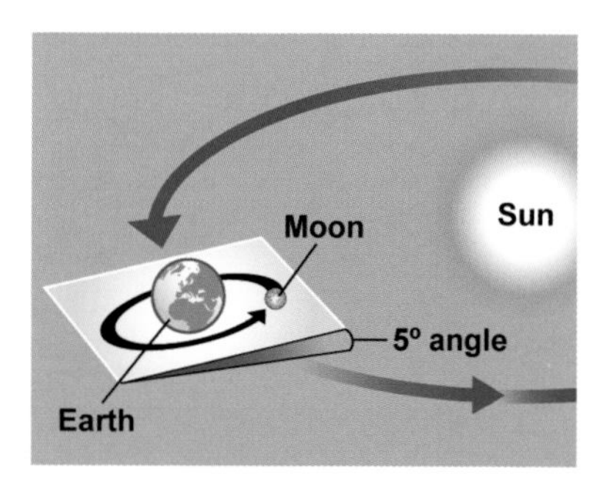

Figure 30.6: *The moon's orbit is tilted at a 5-degree angle with respect to Earth's orbit around the sun.*

Lunar eclipses

Because of this tilted orbit, in most months, Earth's shadow does not block the sunlight from hitting the moon. However, sometimes the moon is perfectly aligned with Earth during a full moon. Because of this alignment, Earth's shadow temporarily blocks the sunlight from hitting the moon, causing a *lunar eclipse*. As the moon continues to move in its orbit, it gradually moves into a position where the sunlight hits it again.

Eclipses are a coincidence

The sun is 400 times larger in diameter than the moon. It is also 400 times farther away from Earth than the moon. Because of this coincidence, the sun and moon appear to be the same size in the sky. This is why total eclipses occur.

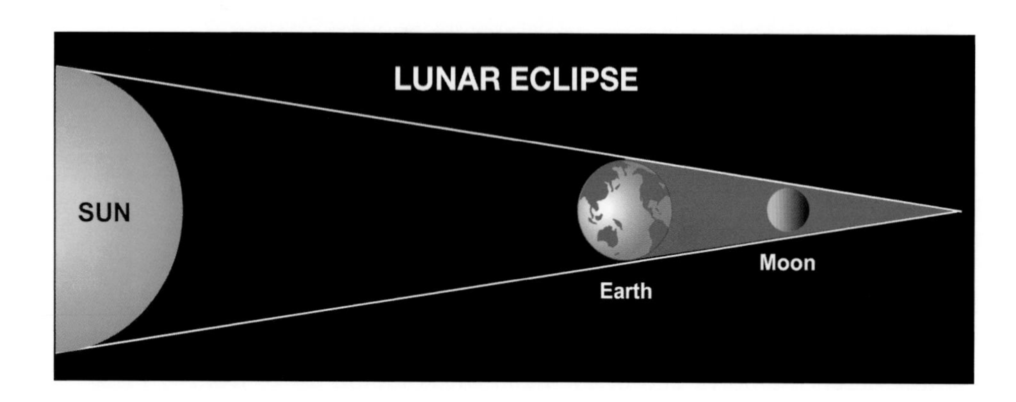

Total and partial lunar eclipses

A lunar eclipse can be total or partial and all observers on the dark side of Earth can see it at the same time. A partial eclipse occurs when only part of the moon falls in Earth's shadow. Also, during a lunar eclipse, the moon is still visible and appears reddish. Figure 30.7 shows an alignment for a partial eclipse.

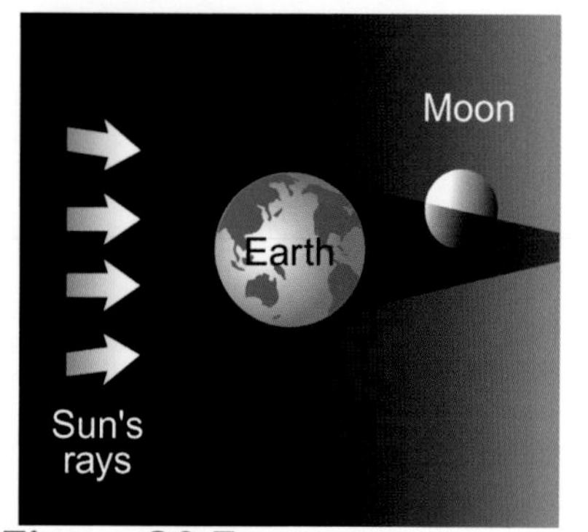

Figure 30.7: *A sun-Earth-moon alignment for a partial lunar eclipse.*

Solar eclipses During a new moon (when the side of the moon that faces Earth is not lit by the sun), the moon is almost exactly between Earth and the sun. Most of the time, however, the moon travels just above or below the sun in the sky because of the 5° tilt of its orbit. During a *solar eclipse*, the new moon is directly between Earth and the sun and the moon's shadow hits part of Earth as shown below.

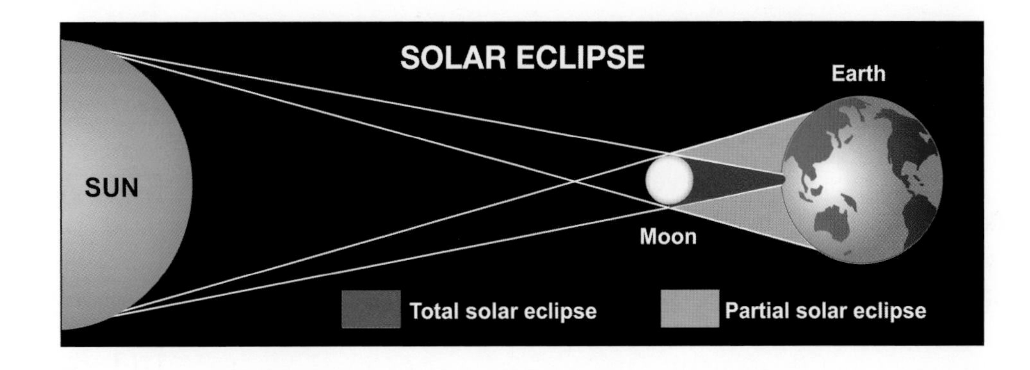

Total solar eclipse The darkest part of the moon's shadow is cone-shaped and falls on only a small part of Earth's surface. Viewers in this region experience a total eclipse of the sun because the light is completely blocked by the moon. During a total eclipse, the sun gradually disappears behind the moon and then gradually reappears. This is because the moon revolves around Earth, so it gradually moves into the path of the sunlight, and then gradually moves out again. The sun is completely blocked by the moon's shadow for about two or three minutes.

Partial solar eclipse In the diagram above, you can see that the moon casts a larger, lighter shadow on Earth's surface. Viewers in this region of the moon's shadow experience a partial eclipse. During this time, only part of the sun is blocked. You should NEVER look directly at the sun—even during a total or partial eclipse!

Benjamin Banneker

Benjamin Banneker was born in rural Maryland in 1731. His family owned a small farm. They were part of a group of about two hundred free men and women of African descent in Baltimore county.

Benjamin's grandmother taught him to read and write. He briefly attended a nearby Quaker school. Benjamin was especially fond of solving mathematical riddles and puzzles. Banneker sold produce at a nearby store owned by a man named George Ellicott. Ellicott loaned him books about mathematics and astronomy.

Banneker was soon recording detailed observations about the night sky. He performed complicated calculations to predict the position of planets and the timing of eclipses. From 1791-1797 he published his astronomical calculations along with weather and tide predictions. They were widely read across the eastern seaboard. Banneker served as an astronomer in surveying project and was appointed by President George Washington to assist in the layout of the District of Columbia.

30.2 Tools of Astronomy

You may think that astronomers spend most of their time looking at the sky through a telescope. While telescopes are an important part of the science, today's astronomers spend much of their time examining data and images on computer screens. In 1990, the Hubble Space Telescope was put into orbit around Earth. This powerful instrument constantly sends computerized images from space to Earth. Astronomers view these images on computer screens and then store the data for later use. Since the objects they observe are so far away, astronomers have developed their own units to measure them. What are the tools of astronomy? How do astronomers measure vast distances?

Figure 30.8: *The Hubble Space Telescope.*

Astronomical numbers

Scientific notation

When you look up at the night sky, do you ever think about how far away the stars are? The closest star to our sun, Alpha Centauri, is 41,000,000,000,000 kilometers away. As you can see, trying to write out such astronomical distances as 41 trillion requires a lot of zeros. Scientific notation is a mathematical abbreviation for writing very large (or very small) numbers. Using this method, numbers are written as a value between 1 and 10, multiplied times a power of 10. For example, the distance in the example above can be written as 4.1×10^{13} km. Here's a step-by-step example of how to write numbers in scientific notation. The steps are shown in Figure 30.9.

Example problem:

Earth is approximately 150,000,000 kilometers from the sun. Write this value using scientific notation:

Step 1: Move the decimal until you get a value that is between 1 and 10. Count the number of times you move the decimal.

Step 2: Write down the new number without all of the zeros.

Step 3: Write × 10 after the number.

Step 4: Write the number of times you moved the decimal as the power of 10 (the exponent). If you moved the decimal to the left, the exponent will be positive. If you moved the decimal to the right, the exponent will be negative.

Answer: Earth is approximately 1.5×10^8 km from the sun.

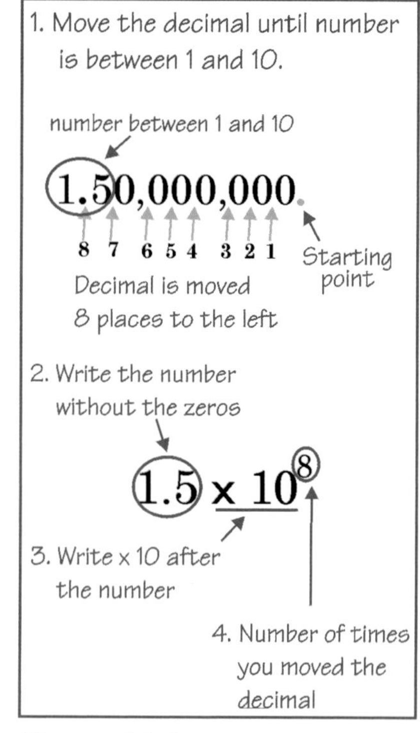

Figure 30.9: *Solving the example problem at left.*

How astronomers describe objects in space

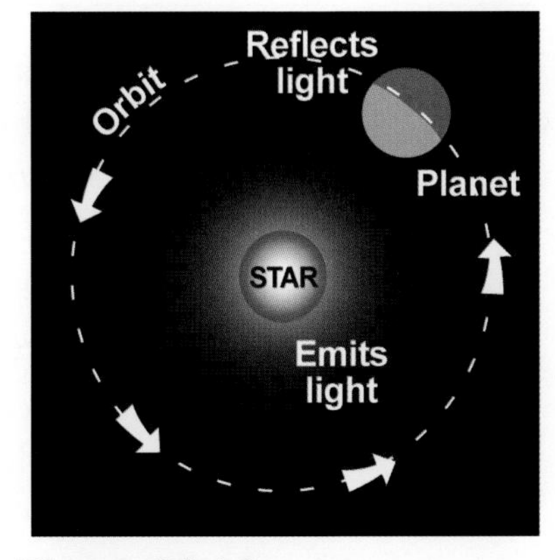

Figure 30.10: *A planet revolves around a star. Stars emit light and planets reflect light.*

What is the universe? When you look up at the sky, what are some of the objects you see? You can see the sun and the moon and, on a clear night, many stars. If you watch the sky each night over a few months, you will notice that some of those "stars" change position over time and appear to wander in the sky. These are the planets that are part of our solar system—our own small corner of the *universe*. The universe is defined as everything that exists, including all matter and energy.

Planets and stars A star is a sphere of gas that undergoes a process called *fusion*. Because this process releases so much energy, stars give off a bright light. A planet is a large, spherical piece of matter that revolves around a star. On a clear night, you can see thousands of stars, but only five planets can be seen with the unaided eye. These are Mercury, Venus, Mars, Jupiter, and Saturn. If you look through a telescope, these planets appear larger than stars. Without a telescope, they give off a steady light, whereas stars appear to "twinkle." We can see the planets because they reflect light from the sun back to Earth. Unlike stars, they do not emit their *own* light. The table below compares planets and stars.

Table 30.1: ***How to tell the difference between a planet and a star***

Feature	Planet	Star
Distance from Earth	Relatively close	Very far (except for the sun)
Appearance in the sky	Gives off a steady light	Appears to "twinkle"
Long-term movement	Slowly wanders in the sky alone	Appears to move in a group
Source of light	Reflects light from the sun	Emits its own light

Galaxies A galaxy is a huge collection of gas, dust, and billions of stars. These stars are attracted to each other by the force of gravity and are constantly in motion. If you look at the sky on a clear night, you can see what appears to be a milky-white trail across the stars. You are looking at part of the Milky Way—the galaxy to which we belong. Our galaxy contains at least 200 billion stars! Our location in the Milky Way galaxy is shown in Figure 30.11. The only way to observe other galaxies in the universe is with a very powerful telescope. Many galaxies have a spiral shape much like the Milky Way's.

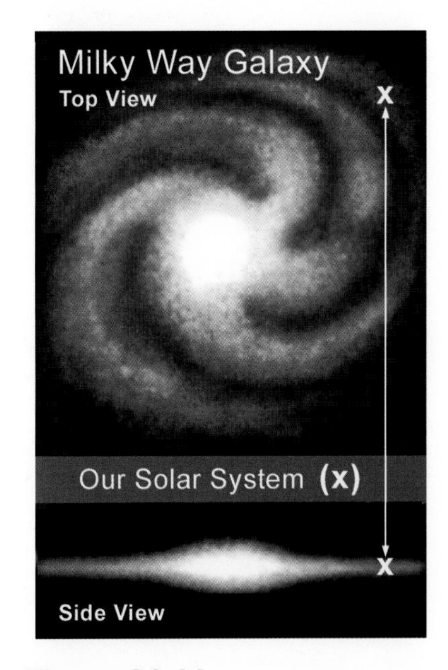

Figure 30.11: *Our location in the Milky Way galaxy.*

Units of distance in space

What is a light year?

As you have read, distances in space are huge. Because of this, scientists have developed units other than kilometers or meters to measure them. You may have heard of *light years* (ly), one of the most common astronomical terms. Even though the name may sound like it, this unit does not measure time. One light year is equal to the *distance* that light travels through space in one year.

Calculating a light year

In space, light travels at the amazing speed of 300,000 kilometers per second. How far will it travel in one year? Recall that *speed* = distance ÷ time. This means we can calculate the distance light travels in one year by multiplying the speed of light by time (by rearranging the variables). However, to get the correct value, we must also convert seconds into years since the value for the speed of light contains seconds. Here's how to solve this problem:

$$
\begin{aligned}
\text{1 light year (ly)} &= \text{speed of light} \times \text{time} \\
&= (300{,}000 \text{ km/sec}) \times \left(1 \text{ year} \times \frac{365 \text{ days}}{1 \text{ year}} \times \frac{24 \text{ hours}}{1 \text{ day}} \times \frac{3600 \text{ sec}}{1 \text{ hour}}\right) \\
&= (300{,}000 \text{ km/sec}) \times (31{,}536{,}000 \text{ sec}) \\
&= 9{,}460{,}000{,}000{,}000 \text{ km} \quad \text{or} \quad 9.46 \times 10^{12} \text{km}
\end{aligned}
$$

A light year is the distance light travels in one year through space (9.46 × 10^{12} kilometers).

Unit conversion

How many light years away is Alpha Centauri, the closest star to our sun? We already know that it is 4.1 x 10^{13} km away. We also know that one light year is equal to 9.46×10^{12} km. Using unit conversion, we get:

$$4.1 \times 10^{13} \cancel{\text{km}} \times \frac{1.0 \text{ ly}}{9.46 \times 10^{12} \cancel{\text{km}}} = 4.3 \text{ ly}$$

Can you see why light years are more useful to astronomers than kilometers?

Object	Distance from Earth (light years)
Sirius (brightest star in the sky)	8.8
Betelgeuse (appears as a red star in the sky)	700
Crab Nebula (remnant of an exploded star)	4,000
Andromeda galaxy	2.3 million

Figure 30.12: *Distance from Earth (in light years) of some well-known objects in the universe.*

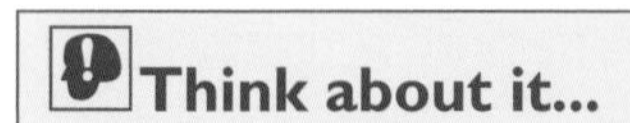

Think about it...

When you look at Alpha Centauri in the night sky, how "old" is the light you are seeing? In other words, how long did it take that light to get to Earth? The answer is easy if you use your head. Think about the definition of a light year and you'll figure out the answer! HINT: This star is 4.3 light years away.

Observing distant objects

Light years and time The blue box on the previous page points out an interesting phenomenon about observing distant objects. Since most objects in space are hundreds, even billions of light years away, the light we see is as old as the number of light years the object is from Earth. For example, the light we see from Alpha Centauri left that star 4.3 years ago. This means that when we look at the light from stars or other objects in space, we are actually looking back in time. When astronomers use a powerful telescope to view the Andromeda galaxy, they are looking back in time 2.3 million years (Figure 30.13)!

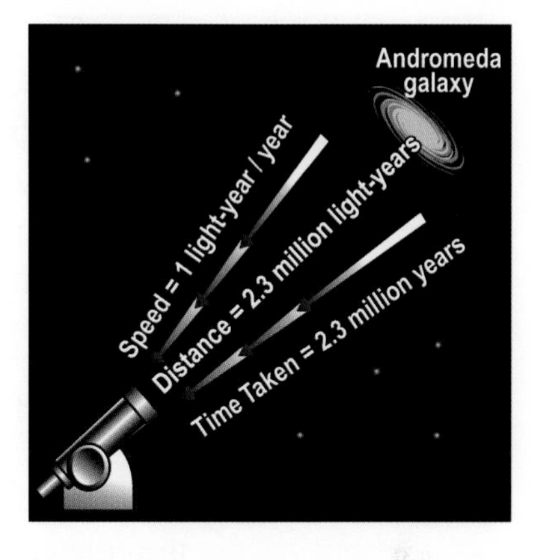

Figure 30.13: *When astronomers use a powerful telescope to look at the Andromeda galaxy, they are looking back in time 2.3 million years.*

Time as a tool of astronomy As astronomers view distant objects in space, they are actually studying ancient history. The farther away the object they are viewing, the further back in time they are looking. This fact has become an important tool that astronomers use to piece together how the universe began, and how it has changed over time. For example, by comparing stars that are relatively near with stars that are very far away, astronomers can develop theories about the life cycle of stars, including how they begin, how long they "live," and what happens when they "die."

Problem: Communication delays in space

The problem In 1969, Neil Armstrong and Buzz Aldrin were first to land a lunar module on the moon, 384,400 kilometers from Earth. You may have heard Armstrong's famous phrase, spoken when he stepped out of the module onto the moon's surface: "That's one small step for man, one giant leap for mankind." When he spoke, he was not heard immediately on Earth because of the moon's distance. How long did it take the radio waves to travel to Earth so that those words could be heard by millions of viewers? (HINT: Radio waves travel at the speed of light.)

What do you know? You know that the *distance* from the moon to Earth is 384,400 kilometers. The *speed* of light is 300,000 kilometers per second. Since speed is distance divided by *time*, you can rearrange the variables to solve for this quantity. Figure 30.14 shows the solution to the problem.

1. Equation

$$\text{speed} = \frac{\text{distance}}{\text{time}}$$

2. Rearrange variables to solve for time

$$\text{time} = \frac{\text{distance}}{\text{speed}}$$

3. Plug in the numbers and solve

$$\text{time} = \frac{384{,}400 \text{ km}}{300{,}000 \text{ km/sec}}$$

$$= 1.28 \text{ seconds}$$

Figure 30.14: *Solving the problem.*

Telescopes

History of the telescope

Before the invention of the telescope, the human eye was the primary instrument for observing the night sky. In the 1600s, Galileo was the first to use a telescope for astronomical observations. He observed craters on the moon, tiny moons around Jupiter, and the rings of Saturn (which he thought looked like "ears"). Since then, astronomers have developed increasingly powerful telescopes that continue to add to our knowledge of the universe.

What is a telescope?

A **telescope** is a device that makes objects that are far away appear closer. Telescopes come in many different shapes and sizes, from a small tube weighing less than a pound, to the Hubble Space Telescope, weighing several tons. Most of the telescopes used today are of two types; **refracting telescopes** use *lenses* and **reflecting telescopes** use *mirrors*. Both types accomplish the same thing, but in different ways.

How does a telescope work?

Have you ever tried to read the writing on a penny from 100 feet away? The reason you cannot read it with your naked eye is that the image of a penny from 100 feet away does not take up much space on your retina (the screen of your eye). Telescopes work by collecting the light from a distant object with a lens or mirror and bringing that light into a concentrated point, called the *focal point*. The bright light from the focal point is then magnified by another lens so that it takes up more space on your retina. This makes the object appear much larger and closer.

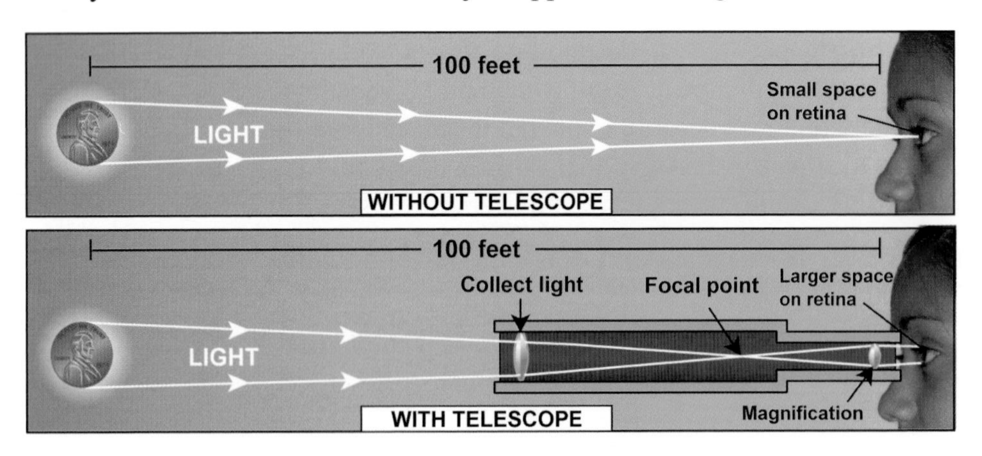

Telescope milestones

3500 BC Phoenicians discover glass while cooking on sand.

1350 Craftsmen in Venice begin making lenses for spectacles.

1608 Hans Lippershey applies for a patent for the refracting telescope.

1609 Galileo is the first to use a telescope to view craters on the moon.

1704 Newton invents the reflecting telescope.

1897 World's largest refracting telescope built and housed in Yerkes Observatory, Wisconsin.

1990 The Hubble Space Telescope is launched from the space shuttle Discovery.

Refracting telescopes

Refracting telescopes use lenses to bend, or refract light, making objects look bigger. They are made from a long *tube*, a glass *objective lens* that you point toward the sky, and an *eyepiece*—another glass lens that magnifies the object. The tube holds the two lenses the correct distance from one another. The objective lens is *convex*, that is, wider in the middle than at the edges. This lens gathers light from an object, and bends it to a focal point near the back of the tube. The eyepiece lens can be either convex or *concave* (thinner in the middle and wider at the edges). The picture below shows how light rays travel through a refracting telescope to your eye.

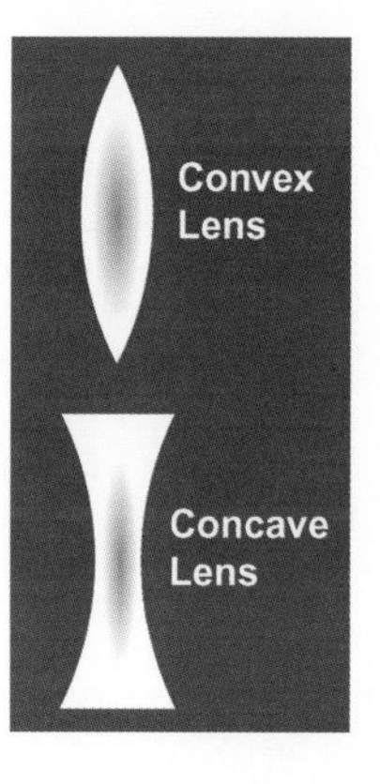

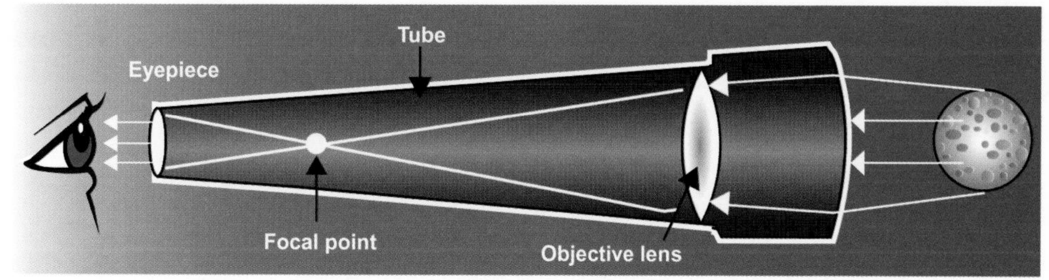

Reflecting telescopes

Reflecting telescopes use mirrors instead of lenses to gather and focus light. Isaac Newton developed this type of telescope in 1680. A mirror is made by coating the surface of a concave lens with a reflecting material. This mirror (called the primary mirror) is placed at the back of a tube. Light rays enter the tube and are reflected off the primary mirror to a focal point. Another small, flat mirror (the secondary mirror) is placed in the path of the focal point at an angle that deflects the light rays to an eyepiece, located at the side of the tube. The eyepiece performs the magnification of the image, just like in a refracting telescope. Because the secondary mirror is so small compared with the primary mirror, it only blocks a small fraction of light entering the telescope.

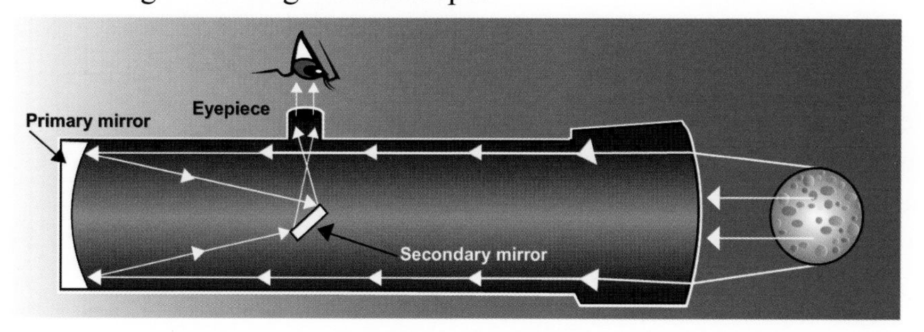

Arthur Walker

Arthur Walker was born in 1936. Arthur was an excellent student. He decided to take the entrance exam for the Bronx High School of Science. Arthur passed the exam, but when he entered the school a teacher told him that the prospects for an African-American scientist were bleak. Arthur's mother visited the school and told them her son would pursue whatever course of study he wished.

Walker went on to earn a Ph.D. in physics from the University of Illinois. He spent three years in the Air force, designing a rocket probe and satellite experiment to measure radiation that affects satellite operation. Later, Walker worked to develop the first X-ray spectrometer used aboard a satellite. It helped determine the temperature and composition of the sun's corona.

In 1974, Walker joined the faculty at Stanford University. There he used a new multilayer mirror technology to develop telescopes that were launched into space on rockets. The telescopes produced detailed pictures of the sun and its corona, bringing about significant changes in our understanding of them.

Other types of telescopes

Electromagnetic waves

So far, the telescopes you have read about collect and focus visible light. Visible light is a type of *electromagnetic wave*. Objects in the universe give off many other types of electromagnetic waves that we cannot detect with our eyes, including radio waves, infrared waves, and X rays. These waves all travel at the speed of light in space and have energies (frequencies) that increase as their wavelengths become smaller. Astronomers use different types of telescopes to view the different types of waves emitted by objects in space.

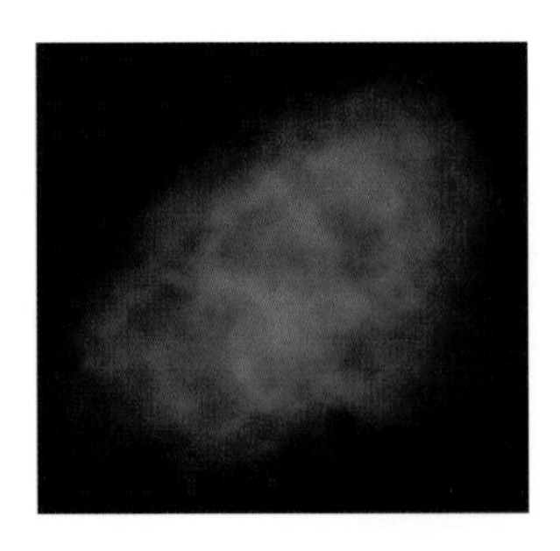

Figure 30.15: *An image of the Crab Nebula taken by a radio telescope.*

Radio telescopes

A *radio telescope* works like an extremely powerful receiver that picks up radio waves from space. Astronomers aim these telescopes toward an object such as a star and tune them until they receive waves in the correct frequency. The information is analyzed by a computer which draws an image of the source of radio waves. Astronomers use radio telescopes to produce images of stars and galaxies, analyze the chemical composition of objects, and map the surfaces of planets. Figure 30.15 shows an image of the Crab Nebula (the remnants of an exploded star) taken by a radio telescope (*Photo courtesy Very Large Array/ National Radio Astronomy Observatory).*

Figure 30.16: *An image of the Crab Nebula taken by an infrared telescope.*

Infrared telescopes

Another type of telescope looks at infrared waves. Since this type of wave is mostly absorbed by Earth's atmosphere, *infrared telescopes* are often placed on satellites that orbit above Earth. In 1983, the Infrared Astronomical Satellite (IRAS) was launched to map the entire sky at infrared wavelengths. It discovered a new comet, found evidence of another solar system, and discovered a new type of galaxy. Figure 30.16 shows an image of the Crab Nebula captured by an infrared telescope (*Photo courtesy NASA/IRAS*).

X-ray telescopes

X-ray telescopes are designed to detect high-energy radiation (X rays) from space. Since these waves cannot penetrate our atmosphere, x-ray telescopes are always placed on satellites. One of the most powerful, NASA's Chandra X-ray Observatory, was launched on the space shuttle Columbia in 1999. Its mission is to observe X rays that are emitted by high-energy objects in the universe such as stars that have exploded. Figure 30.17 shows an image of the Crab Nebula captured by an x-ray telescope (*Photo courtesy NASA/Chandra*).

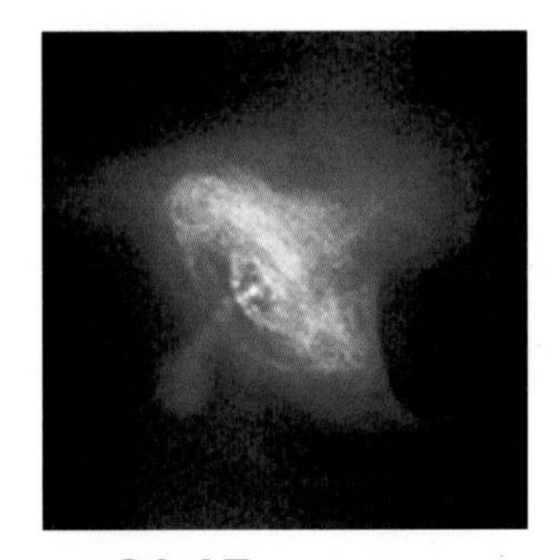

Figure 30.17: *An image of the Crab Nebula, taken by an x-ray telescope.*

Satellites and other spacecraft

Satellites A **satellite** is an object that travels in orbit around another object. The moon is a natural satellite that orbits Earth. On Oct. 4, 1957, the former Soviet Union launched Sputnik I, the first *artificial* satellite to orbit Earth. Since then, hundreds of satellites have been launched. These important tools of astronomy (and many other sciences) continuously send data back to computers on Earth for analysis.

The Hubble Space Telescope The Hubble Space Telescope (or HST) is a satellite that orbits Earth. This powerful telescope, placed out of reach of "light pollution," constantly sends images from deep space to computers back on Earth. A NASA image captured by the HST is shown below. Most of the objects in the image are not stars, which appear to have "spikes"—but galaxies, most of them *billions* of light years away! Since this image shows only a tiny fraction of the sky, what does it tell you about the number of galaxies that may be found in the universe?

Photo courtesy of NASA/HST

Remote sensing

Many satellites are designed for low Earth orbit, at altitudes between 200 and 1,000 kilometers. One of the chief functions of these satellites is remote sensing, or making observations from a distance. Images of Earth's atmosphere and surface are created from different types of electro-magnetic waves. For example, radio waves can pass through clouds so images can be made of events that may be otherwise hidden. Infrared waves can be used to monitor vegetation or temperature differences in air and water. Weather forecasters rely on satellite images of clouds in order to predict the weather and warn of approaching storms. Many of these satellites travel at speeds of 28,000 kilometers per hour and orbit Earth in about 90 minutes!

Space probes

Space probes are unmanned spacecraft that carry scientific instruments on board. Since the early 1970s, they have helped astronomers make many discoveries about our solar system. Space probes are not designed to return to Earth, but many have landed on other planets. Others have flown past planets, taking pictures as they go. Still others have remained in orbit around a planet for long periods of time to study them in great detail. Space probes have landed on—or at least flown near—every planet but Pluto. Table 30.2 lists some NASA probes and their missions.

Table 30.2: *Some NASA planetary space probes and their missions*

Planet	Probe and launch year	Primary mission and year(s)
Mercury	Mariner 10 (1973)	Mercury flyby (1974-75)
Venus	Magellan (1989)	Radar mapping of the planet surface (1990-94)
Mars	2001 Mars Odyssey (2001)	Map chemical makeup of Mars' surface (2002-04)
Jupiter	Galileo (1989)	Orbit Jupiter and some of its moons (1995-97)
Saturn	Cassini (1997)	Orbit Saturn and send a probe to its moon Titan (2004)
Uranus	Voyager 2 (1977)	Uranus flyby (1986)
Neptune	Voyager 2 (1977)	Neptune flyby (1989)
Pluto	New Horizons (future mission)	Pluto flyby (estimated 2006)

Piloted spacecraft

In April 1961, Yuri Gagarin of the former Soviet Union was the first human to travel in space, followed on May 5 by Alan Shepard of the United States. This led to the NASA Manned Lunar Program known as *Apollo* from 1963-72 in which humans successfully landed on the moon. Since Apollo, we have not sent humans back to the moon, or to any other bodies in space, mainly because of the cost of such missions. However, piloted spacecraft are still useful tools of astronomy.

Space shuttles and stations

Space shuttles are piloted spacecraft that launch from rocket "boosters" and can land back on Earth like an airplane. Developed by NASA, they are used to conduct experiments in space, to launch and repair satellites, and to transport people to and from *space stations*, such as the International Space Station (or ISS). The ISS is a joint project of six nations that orbits 450 kilometers above Earth's surface. On board, scientists conduct numerous experiments, many of which depend on constant freefall (microgravity) conditions provided by the space station.

Voyager 1 and 2

Launched in 1977, the NASA Voyager 1 and 2 probes have traveled farther from Earth than any other man-made object. Both have completed their missions and are currently headed toward the boundary where the sun's gravitational force is no longer dominant. They travel at an amazing speed of 17 kilometers per second (38,000 miles per hour)! Voyager 1 is now more than twice as far from Earth as Pluto. Both Voyagers are still sending information back to Earth via radio waves. These signals are picked up by a powerful array of radio telescopes called the Deep Space Network.

Figure 30.18: *The International Space Station (or ISS).*

How does a space shuttle work?

What is a space shuttle? The first space shuttle, *Columbia*, was launched on April 12, 1981, in Florida. After a space flight lasting more than 36 hours, it made a perfect landing in California. Before the shuttles, manned spacecraft were not reusable. Space shuttles have the ability to be launched like a rocket, orbit Earth like a satellite while performing missions, and land on a runway like an airplane.

Shuttle components A space shuttle consists of three big components: two *solid rocket boosters* (SRBs), an *external fuel tank*, and an *orbiter* (Figure 30.19). The orbiter looks similar to an airplane and contains a flight deck, living quarters, and a cargo bay for transporting objects such as satellites to and from space.

Launching a shuttle The SRBs provide most of the force required to lift the 4.5-million-pound shuttle off the launch pad. In addition, the orbiter has three main engines that burn the liquid hydrogen and oxygen fuel stored in the external fuel tank. Two minutes after launch, the SRBs separate from the orbiter and fall back to Earth on parachutes. These can be reused. After eight minutes, the external fuel tank drops away and the orbiter's main engines stop firing.

Why does a shuttle orbit? At this point, the orbiter is 250 kilometers above Earth and is moving at a speed of 28,000 kilometers per hour. Because its engines are no longer thrusting, it does not continue to travel *away* from Earth. To do this would require higher speeds. Instead, the orbiter is pulled toward Earth by the force of gravity as it moves forward at a constant speed. The combination of the pull of gravity downward and the forward motion at a constant speed, causes it to fall *around* Earth, not into it. Because there is no friction in space, the orbiter requires no fuel to maintain its orbit speed. This follows Newton's first law of motion.

Returning to Earth When the crew is ready to return to Earth, the orbiter is turned around to face the opposite direction. Small engines are fired in the rear of the orbiter to slow it down so that it begins to fall back *toward* Earth instead of around it. As the orbiter enters the atmosphere, thick tiles protect it from the heat generated by air friction. The air resistance slows the orbiter down as it glides down to Earth's surface. The orbiter uses wheels to land on a runway just like a plane. The space shuttle orbiter can be reused about 100 times before it is retired.

Figure 30.19: *Anatomy of a space shuttle.*

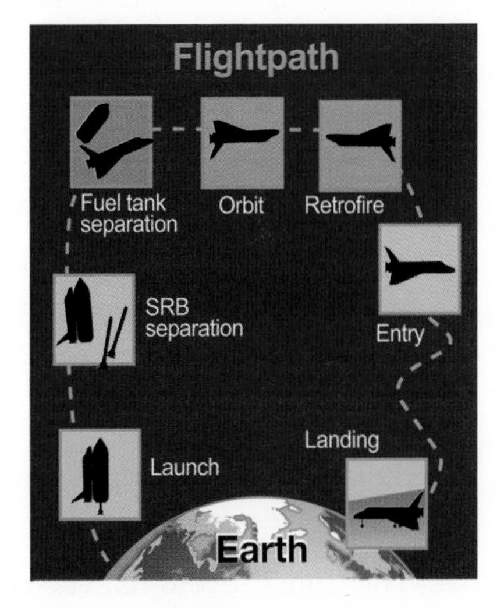

Figure 30.20: *A complete shuttle mission, from launch to landing.*

Chapter 30 Review

Vocabulary review

Match the following terms with the correct definition. There is one extra definition in the list that will not match any of the terms.

Set One

1. orbit
2. rotation
3. revolution
4. light year
5. eclipse

a. device that divides the day into equal parts
b. causes day and night to occur on Earth
c. the movement of one object around another in space
d. the path followed by an object as it revolves around another object
e. the distance light travels in one year
f. when the moon's shadow falls on Earth or Earth's shadow falls on the moon

Set Two

1. galaxy
2. refracting telescope
3. universe
4. star
5. reflecting telescope

a. a single body that emits enormous amounts of energy
b. everything that exists including all matter and energy
c. a large, spherical piece of matter that revolves around a star
d. a device that uses only lenses to focus and magnify light rays from an object
e. a huge collection of gas, dust, and billions of stars
f. a device that uses mirrors and lenses to focus and magnify light rays from an object

Concept review

1. Name two examples of astronomical cycles. For each, describe an event that is directly related to it. *Example: Moon revolves around Earth, resulting in the phases of the moon.*
2. What is a leap year? Why does a leap year occur every four years?
3. Since the moon does not produce its own light, how can you see it?
4. The lunar cycle is closely related to which part of our calendar—a year, a month, or a day?
5. Explain how you could use the shadow of a lamp post to track the time of day on a sunny day.
6. Explain the difference between solar and lunar eclipses.
7. Why is scientific notation often used in astronomy?
8. Name three differences between planets and stars.
9. Why are light years used to measure distances to stars instead of kilometers?
10. What is the difference between a refracting telescope and a reflecting telescope?
11. Explain the difference between a radio telescope and an infrared telescope.
12. What are the advantages to placing a telescope on a satellite?

Problems

1. During one revolution around the sun, how many rotations of Earth occur?
2. How long does it take Earth to revolve around the sun in *seconds*? Show all of your math.
3. The Romans used a calendar with 365 days in a year (instead of the actual 365.25 days). How many days off would their calendar be after four years? Eight years? 300 years?
4. Match the letters on the diagram with the correct terms. You may use a letter more than once

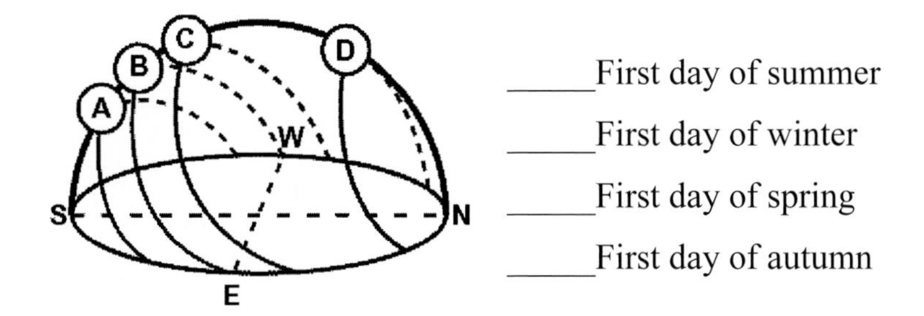

5. Match each term with its corresponding letter on the diagram below. Terms: revolution, orbit, axis, rotation.

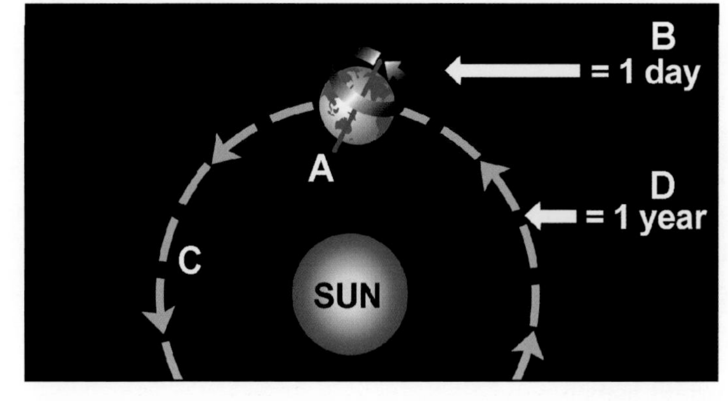

6. How would the moon appear from Earth if it were in the position shown in the diagram below?

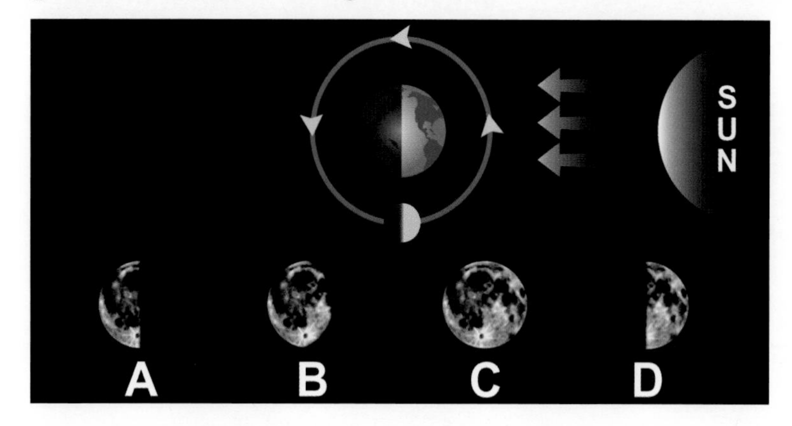

7. Write the following values using scientific notation:

   a. 156,000,000,000 kilometers

   b. 18.5 pounds

   c. 0.000000000000000000000025 centimeter

   d. 47,000,000,000,000 kilometers

   e. .0027 seconds

   f. 1.5 kilogram

   g. 93,000,000 miles

   h. 17,000 light years

8. Complete the table below by converting the distances to kilometers. You should use scientific notation in your answers:

Object	Distance from Earth (light years)	Distance from Earth (km)
Sirius (a star)	8.8	
Betelgeuse (a star)	700	
Crab Nebula (exploded star)	4,000	
Andromeda galaxy	2.3 million	

9. Suppose the sun suddenly burned out. How long would it take, in minutes, before we noticed this had occurred? (HINT: The speed of light is 300,000 km/sec and the distance of Earth from the sun is 150 million km).

10. In 1989, the space probe Voyager II reached the planet Neptune and began sending images of the planet back to Earth. Assuming these radio waves had to travel about 4.0×10^9 km, how long did it take, in minutes, before astronomers received the signals from Voyager 2? (HINT: Radio waves travel at the speed of light—300,000 km/sec.)

Applying your knowledge

1. You have read that scientists conduct experiments on board the International Space Station that depend on the constant freefall (microgravity) conditions that this environment provides. Use the Internet to find out about one of these experiments. Identify the research question, hypothesis, procedures, and results of the experiment. Develop a poster presentation about the experiment for your class. Some good Web sites include:

   www.nasa.gov

   spaceflight.nasa.gov

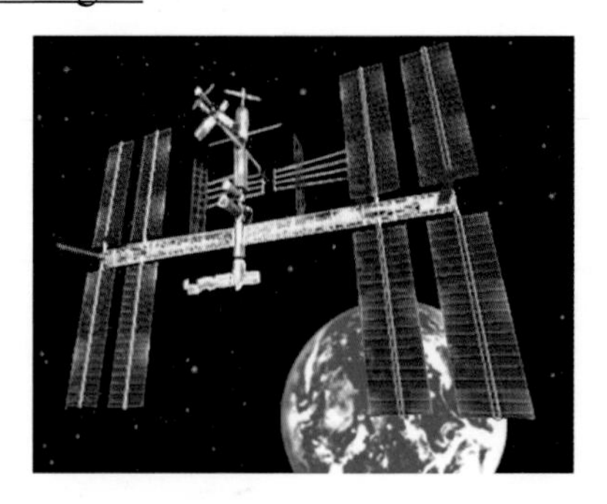

2. Our ancestors used their observations of the sky to explain many aspects of their lives including religion, philosophy, science, and architecture. For example, many different Native American tribes planned and arranged buildings to correlate directly with the alignment of Earth, the moon, and the sun. Choose an ancient culture, and prepare a short paper that describes how astronomy influenced the lives of its people. Some cultures include: Mayan, Aztec, and the Navajo tribe.

3. Search the Internet for satellite images of your community. Find an image taken by each of the following types of electromagnetic radiation: visible light, radio waves, and infrared. What kinds of information does each type of image provide? What are the scientific uses for each type of image? Some good Web sites include:

   www.ghcc.msfc.nasa.gov

   www.ssec.wisc.edu/data

   mapping.usgs.gov

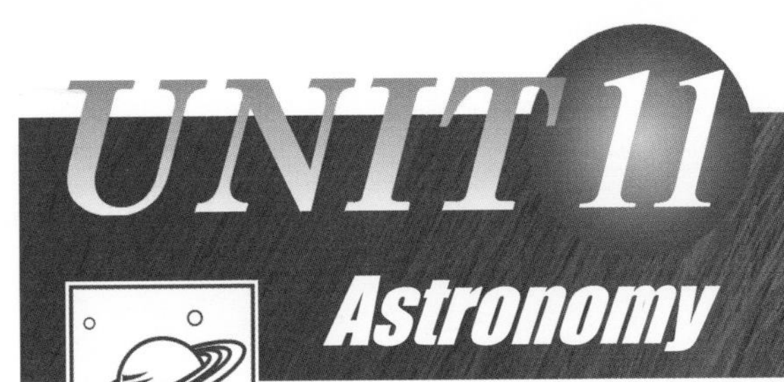

Chapter 31
The Solar System

Introduction to Chapter 31

The solar system is our own little neighborhood in the universe. It consists of the sun surrounded by the planets and numerous other objects. This chapter is about relationships between planets, their moons, and the sun. Why do planets and moons stay in orbit? How do Earth and the moon interact? What is the sun and how does it create so much energy?

31.1	Earth and Moon	*What does the length of a year have to do with Earth's distance from the sun?*

Why does the moon orbit Earth and Earth orbit the sun? In this Investigation, you will explore how objects stay in orbit. You will also discover how the orbital period of an object varies with its distance from the object it orbits, and the relationship between mass and orbital speed.

31.2	The Solar System	*How big is the solar system?*

Scale models are used to visualize large distances. For instance, the globe is a scale model of Earth, and maps are scale models of regions. To visualize distances in the solar system you will create a scale model. This model will help you visualize the true distances and sizes of objects in the solar system.

31.3	The Sun	*How can we use energy from the sun to generate electricity?*

We can harness the sun's energy in many ways. For example, a photovoltaic cell is used to convert sunlight directly into electricity. In this Investigation, you will explore how a photovoltaic cell works. You will also measure the power output of a photovoltaic cell and determine its efficiency.

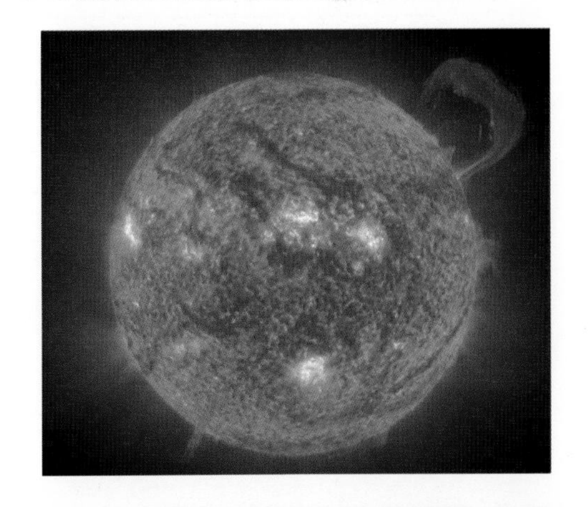

Learning Goals

In this chapter, you will:

- ✔ Describe how Earth's dimensions were determined.
- ✔ Use the equation of universal gravitation to determine mass and gravitational force.
- ✔ Explain why the moon stays in orbit around Earth.
- ✔ Describe the moon's formation.
- ✔ Define the solar system in terms of gravity.
- ✔ Characterize the planets in terms of size, distance from the sun, atmosphere, and period of orbit.
- ✔ Name and describe other objects found in the solar system.
- ✔ Describe the size and composition of the sun.
- ✔ Explain the process through which the sun produces energy.
- ✔ Identify and define the parts of the sun.
- ✔ Explain how the sun's energy can be harnessed.
- ✔ Describe how a photovoltaic cell works.

Vocabulary

asteroid	gravitational force	orbital speed	solar system
astronomical unit	law of universal gravitation	satellite	sunspots
comet	meteor	solar constant	terrestrial planets
gas planets	orbit	solar energy	tides

31.1 Earth and Moon

Earth is one of the planets that along with numerous other smaller objects revolve around the sun in our solar system. It is approximately 150 million kilometers from Earth to the sun. Revolving around Earth at a distance of 384,400 kilometers is our only moon. Since the invention of spacecraft, our knowledge of Earth and the moon has grown tremendously. In this section, you will learn important information about Earth and the moon that will help you understand the rest of the solar system.

Earth dimensions

How big is Earth?

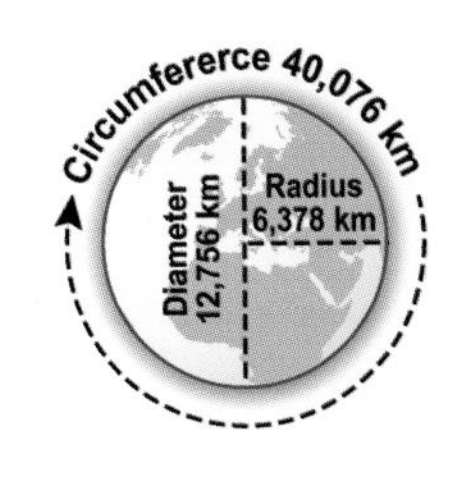

Earth's shape is almost spherical except for a slight bulge at the equator. If you were to travel exactly once around along the equator, you would travel 40,076 kilometers. This distance is the *circumference* of Earth. The *diameter*, or the distance through the center, is 12,756 kilometers and its *radius* at the equator is equal to half of this value, or 6,378 kilometers. Because of its slight bulge at the equator, if you were to measure the radius from one of the poles it would be slightly less (6,357 kilometers). Our current knowledge of Earth's dimensions comes mostly from satellite data, but how were its dimensions determined before this technology existed?

Eratosthenes and the circumference of Earth

More than 2,000 years ago, Greek astronomers knew that Earth was spherical. Eratosthenes was the first astronomer to discover a way to measure the circumference of the planet's sphere. He made a precise measurement of Earth's circumference by using *indirect measurement.* On the first day of summer in Seyene, Egypt, he could see the reflection of the sun at the bottom of a deep, narrow well. This meant the sun was *directly* overhead. Exactly one year later, he measured the angle of the sun's rays in Alexandria, which was 787 kilometers due south of Seyene. The angle he measured was 7.2 ° from the vertical. From this, he was able to compute the circumference of Earth using the following relationship:

$$\frac{7.2^\circ(^\circ\text{from Syene to Alexandria})}{360^\circ(^\circ\text{in a circle})} = \frac{787\,\text{km (distance from Syene to Alexandria)}}{x\text{ (circumference of Earth)}}$$

$$x = \frac{360^\circ \times 787\,\text{km}}{7.2^\circ} = 39{,}350\,\text{km}$$

How fast are we moving?

To make a full rotation in 24 hours, Earth must spin at a speed of 1000 miles per hour. Earth also revolves around the sun. Since it is 93 million miles away, the total distance Earth must travel through one complete trip around the sun is close to 600 million miles. Since Earth travels this distance in only 365.25 days, its average speed is 66,000 miles per hour!

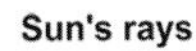

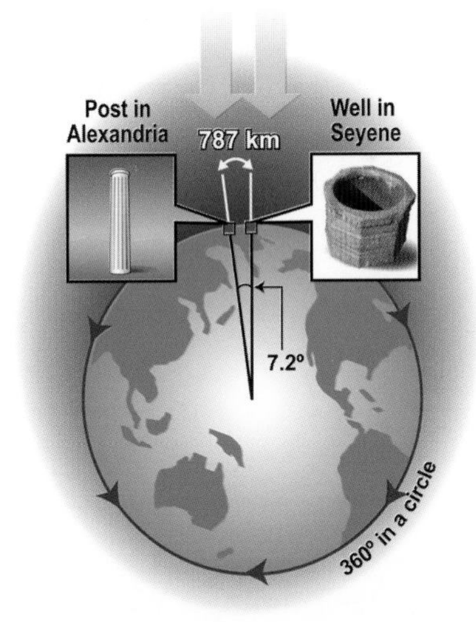

Figure 31.1: *How Eratosthenes figured out Earth's circumference.*

Mass and density of Earth

Law of universal gravitation

One of Isaac Newton's greatest discoveries helped astronomers solve other mysteries about Earth. He discovered that the force of gravity acting between two objects depends only on their masses and distance apart. This discovery, known as the law of universal gravitation, can be expressed as the following equation:

Equation of Universal Gravitation:

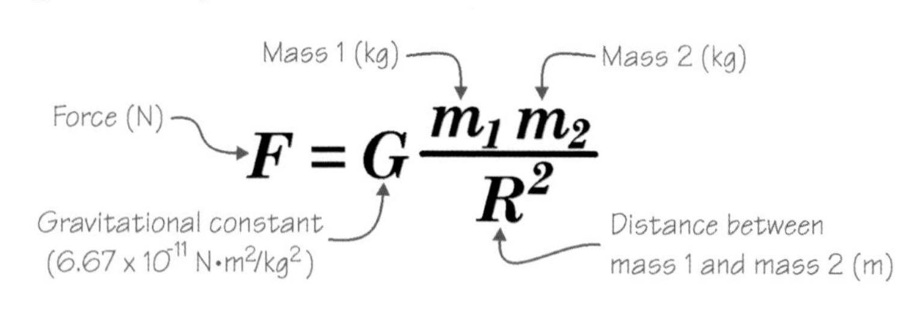

Determining Earth's mass

Newton's discovery helped scientists determine Earth's *mass*. That is because the law of universal gravitation provides all of the information needed to find this quantity (Figure 31.2). For example, Earth exerts a force (F) of 9.8 newtons on a 1-kilogram object (m_1) placed on its surface. The distance between the object and Earth (R) is equal to Earth's radius (6.4×10^6 meters). Since G (Newtonian constant of gravitation) is a constant, we can find Earth's mass (m_2):

$$9.8\,\text{N} = \left(6.67\times10^{-11}\,\frac{\text{N}\cdot\text{m}^2}{\text{kg}^2}\right)\times\frac{1\,\text{kg}\times m_2}{\left(6.4\times10^6\,\text{m}\right)^2}$$

$$m_2 = \left(\frac{9.8\,\text{N}\times\left(6.4\times10^6\,\text{m}\right)^2}{6.67\times10^{-11}\,\frac{\text{N}\cdot\text{m}^2}{\text{kg}^2}}\right) = 6.0\times10^{24}\,\text{kg}$$

Determining Earth's density

We can calculate the average *density* of Earth from its mass and volume. You have learned that density is equal to *mass* divided by *volume*. Since Earth is a sphere, we can calculate its volume using the formula $4/3\pi r^3$ where r is Earth's radius. The entire calculation (Figure 31.3) shows that Earth's average density is 5.52 g/cm³. This is about 5.5 times the density of water (1.0 g/cm³).

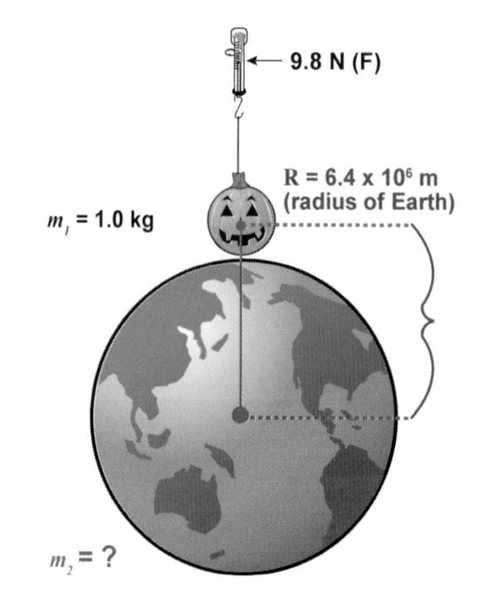

Figure 31.2: *Finding Earth's mass.*

$$\text{Volume} = \frac{4}{3}\pi r^3$$

$$V_{Earth} = \frac{4}{3}(3.14)\left(6.40\times10^8\,\text{cm}\right)^3 = 1.08\times10^{27}\,\text{cm}^3$$

$$\text{Density} = \frac{\text{mass (g)}}{\text{volume (cm}^3)}$$

$$D_{Earth} = \frac{\text{mass: } 6.00\times10^{27}\,\text{g}}{\text{volume: } 1.08\times10^{27}\,\text{cm}^3} = 5.52\,\text{g/cm}^3$$

Figure 31.3: *Calculating Earth's volume and density.*

Properties of the moon

What is the moon? Earth's only moon revolves around us at a distance of 384,400 kilometers (240,250 miles). While this may seem like a great distance, it is only a fraction of the distance of Earth from the sun—about 150 million kilometers, or 93 million miles. It is the only object beyond Earth that humans have visited.

Diameter, mass, and density If you have traveled from Boston to San Francisco, you have covered a distance that is about equal to the moon's diameter of 3,476 kilometers. the moon is about one quarter the size of Earth and its mass is 7.3×10^{22} kilograms, which is about one one-hundredth of Earth's mass. Because of the moon's small mass, its gravity does not attract an atmosphere. Its density is 3.34 g/cm^3, which is much lower than Earth's. Figure 31.4 compares Earth and the moon.

Property	Earth	Moon
Diameter	12,756 km	3,476 km
Gravitational force	9.8 N	1.6 N
Mass	6.0×10^{24} kg	7.3×10^{22} kg
Density	5.52 g/cm^3	3.34 g/cm^3
Rotation period	1 day	27.3 days

Figure 31.4: *Comparing Earth with the moon.*

Gravitational force on the moon Gravitational force is a measure of the attractive force exerted by an object (planet or moon) on a 1-kilogram object held at its surface. This quantity is measured in newtons or pounds. You just read that Earth exerts a gravitational force of 9.8 newtons on a 1-kilogram object. The moon exerts a gravitational force of only 1.6 newtons on the same object. This means that a 1-kilogram object weighs 9.8 newtons on Earth and the same object weighs only 1.6 newtons on the moon. It is easy to figure out how much something weighs in pounds on the moon if you know how much it weighs in pounds on Earth. Here is an example problem:

Example problem: An elephant weighs 2,500 pounds on Earth. How much would it weigh, in pounds, on the moon?

Solution You are asked for the elephant's weight in pounds on the moon. You know its weight in pounds on Earth. You also know how much a 1.0-kg object weighs, in newtons, in both places. To solve, you can set up a proportion:

$$\frac{\text{weight of elephant on Earth}}{\text{weight of 1.0 kg object on Earth}} = \frac{\text{weight of elephant on the moon}}{\text{weight of 1.0 kg object on the moon}}$$

Plug in the numbers you know, and solve for the unknown:

$$\frac{2{,}500 \text{ lbs}}{9.8 \text{ N}} = \frac{x}{1.6 \text{ N}} \qquad x = \frac{(2{,}500 \text{ lbs})(1.6 \text{ N})}{9.8 \text{ N}} = 408 \text{ lbs}$$

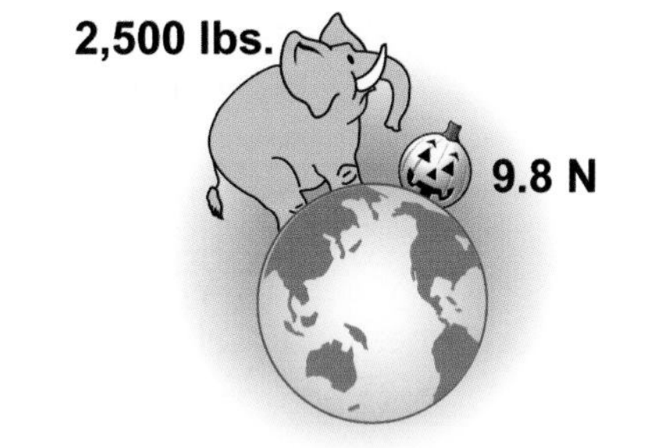

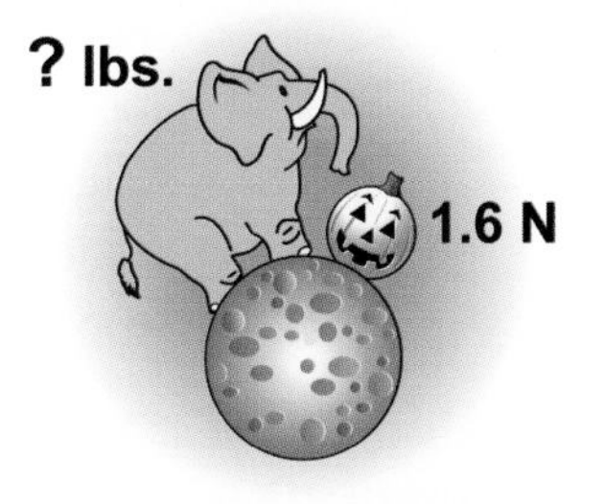

Figure 31.5: *How much does an elephant weigh on Earth and how much would it weigh on the moon?*

Why does the moon stay in orbit?

What is an orbit? An **orbit** is a regular, repeating path that an object in space follows around another object. An object in orbit is called a **satellite**. A satellite can be natural—like the moon, or artificial—like the International Space Station. Almost every object in space orbits around another object.

Gravity attracts the moon to Earth and Earth to the moon.

What keeps the moon in orbit? An orbit results from the balance between *inertia* (the forward motion of an object in space), and gravitational force. Because of the moon's inertia, it is moving in a direction *perpendicular* to the pulling force of gravity. According to Newton's first law, an object in motion will remain in motion unless something pushes or pulls on it. This means that without the pull of gravity, the moon would travel off into space in a straight line. The balance between the moon's inertia and the gravitational force between Earth and the moon results in its orbit (Figure 31.6).

At the same time, the moon is moving forward (perpendicular to the force of gravity) because of its inertia. This keeps the moon in orbit around Earth.

Figure 31.6: *Why does the moon stay in orbit? This also explains why the planets remain in orbit around the sun.*

Orbital speed **Orbital speed** is the speed required to achieve a balance between the pull of gravity on a satellite and its forward motion. The orbital speed of the moon is about 3,700 kilometers per hour. If the moon were any slower, it would fall toward Earth and eventually crash into it. If it were moving faster, it would break free of Earth's gravity and travel in a straight line into space. Because of its orbital speed, the moon falls *around* Earth instead of into it or away from it, and stays in orbit.

Orbital speed and distance The equation of universal gravitation that you used earlier shows how the gravitational force (F) between two objects is dependent on their masses and distance apart. Because the value for distance (R) squared is on the bottom of the equation, gravitational force decreases as the distance between the same two objects increases, and vice versa. A graph of this relationship is shown in Figure 31.7. If we could move the moon closer to Earth, the gravitational force would *increase*. Because orbital speed is directly related to gravitational force, the moon's orbital speed would need to increase for it to stay in orbit.

Gravity equation:

$$F = G\frac{m_1 m_2}{R^2}$$

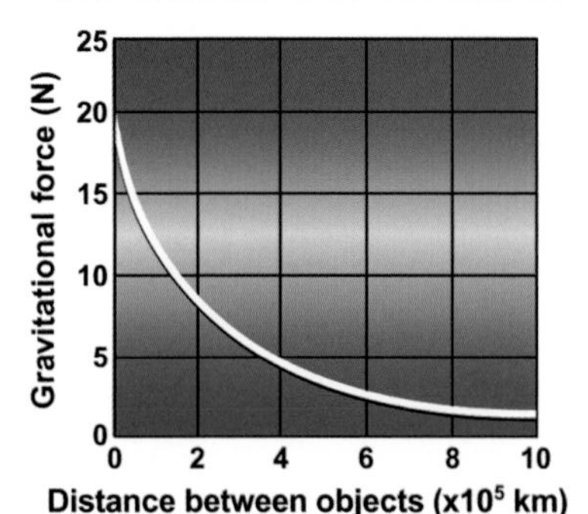

Figure 31.7: *This graph shows the mathematical relationship between gravitational force and distance (mass is constant). Why would the curve on a graph of orbital speed vs. distance look the same?*

Orbital speeds of Earth satellites Artificial satellites require high orbital speeds because they orbit close to Earth's surface. The space shuttle travels at a distance of only 250 kilometers above Earth's surface. To stay in orbit, the shuttle must travel at a speed of 28,000 kilometers per hour! To avoid air friction, all satellites travel above Earth's atmosphere (at least 200 kilometers above the surface) in the vacuum of space.

Tides

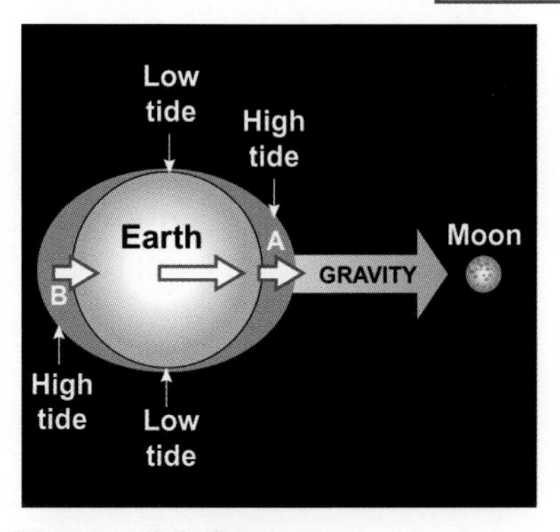

Figure 31.8: *How the moon causes tides on Earth.*

What are tides? Earth's oceans are constantly moving. Winds push on the water causing waves and currents. Ocean levels rise and fall in daily rhythms called **tides**. Tides are the result of gravitational forces exerted between Earth and the moon. In most places, ocean levels rise and fall twice each day as the moon revolves around Earth, and Earth rotates.

Gravity causes tides Earth and the moon share a common gravitational force. Because Earth is more massive than the moon, it is less affected by this force than is the moon. Tides occur because the force of gravity varies with distance. As the moon orbits, the part of Earth that is on the same side as the moon experiences greater gravitational forces than does the opposite part. Because the oceans are fluid, they are easily distorted by these gravitational forces.

High and low tides To understand tides, imagine Earth covered completely by water as shown in Figure 31.8. As the planet rotates on its axis, the water is balanced evenly on all sides by centrifugal force. The moon has a gravitational pull on this layer of water as it orbits Earth. At point A, the water is closer to the moon and is pulled toward it by gravity, causing a *high tide*. At point B, the water is farther away from the moon than is Earth. However, gravity pulls Earth toward the moon, leaving the water behind. This causes high tide on the side opposite the moon as well. *Low tides* occur between high tides. As Earth rotates under these "bulges," a given point will experience two high and two low tides for each rotation of the planet.

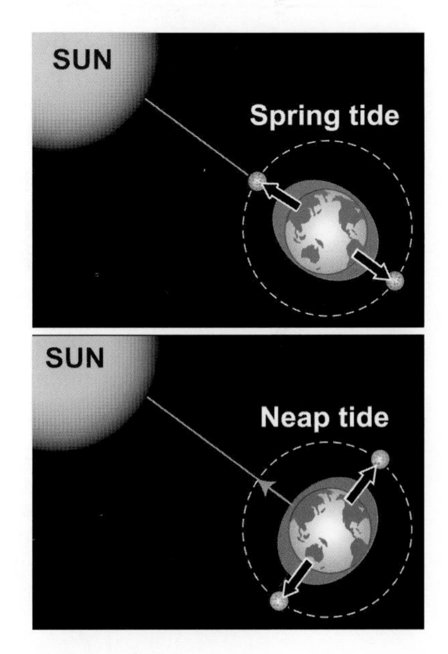

Figure 31.9: *Spring and neap tides.*

The sun's affect on tides The sun's gravitational force also pulls on Earth's water, only to a much lesser extent. Even though the sun has much greater mass than the moon, its gravitational pull on Earth's water is weaker because it is so much farther away. When Earth, the moon, and the sun are aligned (during a new or full moon), the sun's gravitational force adds to the moon's, causing very high and very low tides. These are called *spring tides* (Figure 31.9 top picture). When the gravitational pull of the moon and the sun are at right angles to each other, differences between high and low tides are at their least. These are called *neap tides* (Figure 31.9 bottom picture).

Why do we only see one side of the moon from Earth?

Gravitational locking

If you have ever observed the moon, you may have noticed that only one side of it faces Earth at all times. You may believe that because only one side faces Earth, the moon does not spin on its axis. This is not the case. In fact, one complete rotation of the moon takes 27.3 Earth days. This exactly matches the amount of time it takes the moon to complete one revolution around Earth. That is why the same side of the moon faces Earth as it spins on its axis (Figure 31.10). This same phenomenon, called *gravitational locking*, occurs between other planets and some of their moons.

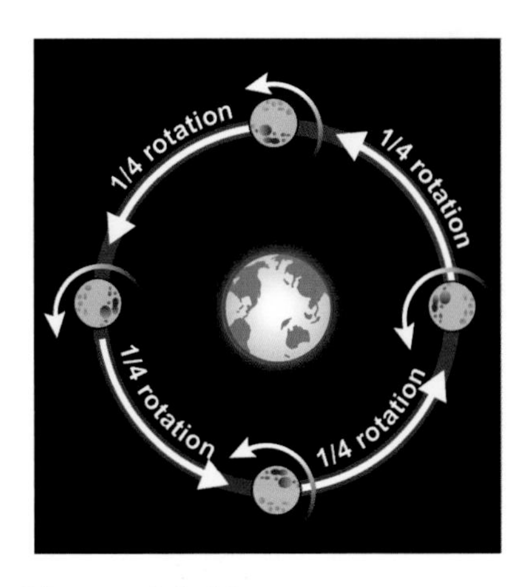

Figure 31.10: *The amount of time it takes the moon to complete a rotation is the same amount of time it takes it to revolve around Earth. Can you see why only one side of the moon faces Earth at all times?*

The moon's orbit and the lunar cycle

You have learned that it takes the moon 29.5 days to complete the lunar cycle—from new moon to new moon. Yet, you have just read that it takes the moon only 27.3 days to complete one orbit, or revolution, around Earth. There is a difference of 2.2 days between the lunar cycle and the period of the moon's revolution around Earth. Why is there a difference?

The Earth-moon system

Remember that as the moon revolves around Earth, the *Earth-moon system* revolves around the sun. This makes things more complicated. In the 27.3 days it takes the moon to revolve around Earth, the Earth-moon system has revolved about 27 degrees (out of 360 degrees in a circle) of its total orbit around the sun. The diagram below shows how the angle of the sun's rays have changed after the 27.3 days. It takes a few more days for the moon to move along its orbit to compensate for the change in angle of the sun's rays. In the meantime, Earth has moved even *farther* in its own orbit around the sun.

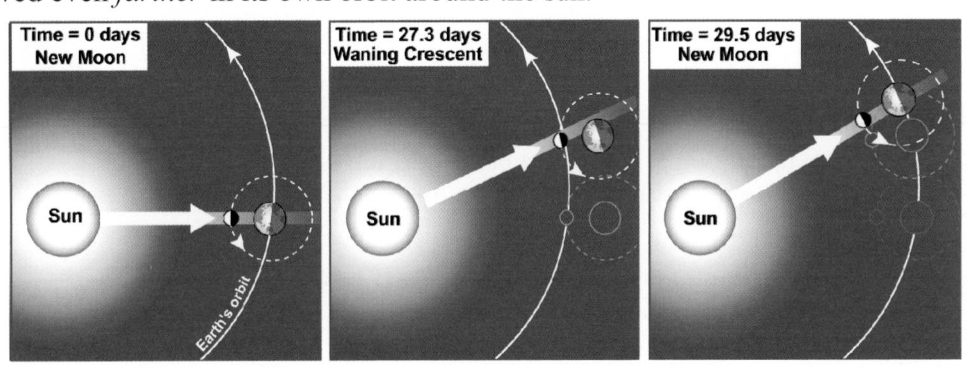

Geology of the moon

Where did the moon come from?

Throughout history, there have been many different theories about the origin of the moon. Before the Apollo landings that began in 1969, there were three main theories. Some scientists believed that the moon split off Earth during a period of very fast rotation. Others believed that the moon formed somewhere else and was "captured" by Earth's gravity. Still others proposed that the moon and Earth were formed together from a group of smaller chunks of matter when the solar system formed.

The giant impact theory

When scientists analyzed lunar rocks, they found that they were composed of much less iron and nickel than Earth. Recall that Earth's *core* is composed mostly of iron and nickel. The composition of lunar rocks closely resembled that of Earth's *mantle*. They also found that the moon's density was the same as Earth's mantle and crust combined. These discoveries gave rise to the *giant impact theory* that is widely accepted today. This theory proposes that about 4.5 billion years ago, an object about the size of Mars collided with Earth, causing material from Earth's mantle and crust to break off. This material, combined with material from the colliding object, was thrown into orbit around Earth and became the moon. Figure 31.11 shows how the moon was formed based on this theory.

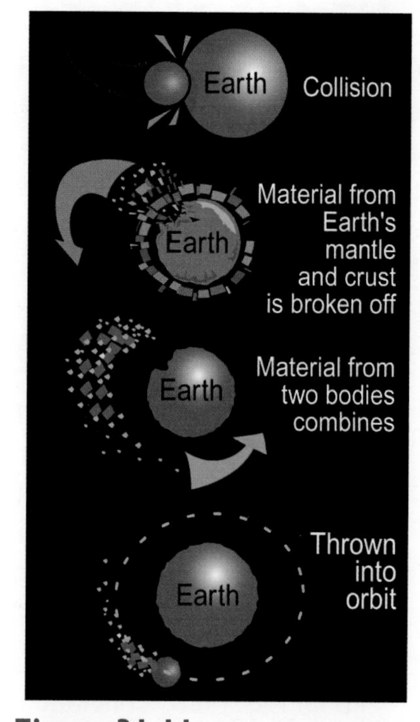

Figure 31.11: *The giant impact theory of the moon's formation.*

Craters

If you look at the moon through a telescope, you can see the three main features of its surface: craters, highlands, and maria. *Craters* are large, round pits that cover much of the moon's surface. For many years astronomers believed they were caused by volcanoes. It was only about 50 years ago that scientists concluded that the craters were caused by the impacts of meteoroids—large rocks from space. One of the moon's largest craters, named Copernicus, is hundreds of kilometers across.

Highlands and marias

When you look at the moon, some areas appear bright, while others appear dark. The brighter areas are called *highlands* because they are higher in elevation. The darker areas are called *marias* (Latin for "seas") because early observers believed they were oceans. Marias are low, dry areas that were flooded with molten lava billions of years ago when the moon was formed. Among the marias you can see through a telescope is a large one named the Sea of Rains.

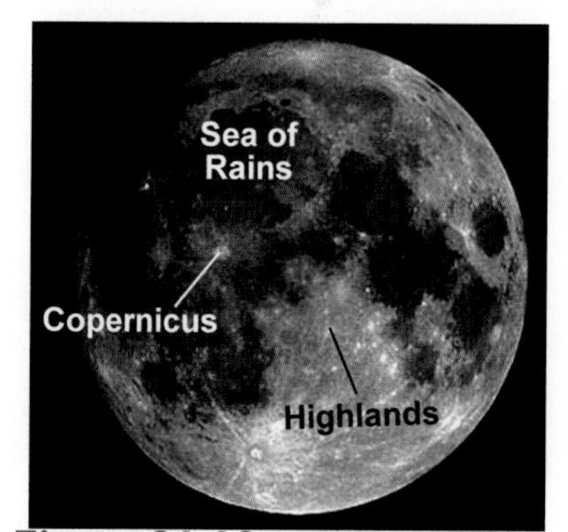

Figure 31.12: *Features of the moon are visible through a telescope or a pair of binoculars.*

31.2 The Solar System

Can you imagine what the night sky looked like thousands of years ago? With no "light pollution" from cities and street lights, ancient civilizations could make very good observations of what they saw in the sky each night. In fact, these civilizations could tell the difference between planets and stars because of the differences in the way they moved (or seemed to move) in the sky. Through these observations, early knowledge of our *solar system* began to accumulate. In this section, you will learn how that knowledge has changed over time.

How was the solar system discovered?

Early thoughts about the solar system

Through their observations of the night sky, those ancient observers noticed that five bright objects seemed to wander among the stars each night. They called these five objects *planets*, from the Greek word meaning "wandering star," and named them Mercury, Venus, Mars, Jupiter, and Saturn. In A.D. 140, the Greek astronomer Ptolemy explained that these planets, along with the moon, orbited *Earth*. For the next 1,400 years, people believed Ptolemy's ideas were correct.

Changing ideas about the solar system

In the early 1500s, the Polish astronomer Nicolaus Copernicus (1473-1543) concluded that the planets orbited the sun. More than 100 years later, his ideas were supported by the Italian astronomer Galileo Galilei (1564-1642). Using a telescope, Galileo made two discoveries that supported Copernicus. First, he saw that there were four moons orbiting Jupiter. This showed that not everything in the sky revolves around Earth. Second, he observed that Venus goes through phases like Earth's moon. He argued that the phases of Venus could not be explained if Earth were at the center of the planets (Figure 31.13).

What is an orbit?

While Galileo supported Copernicus's theory that all of the bodies in the solar system orbit the sun, other scientists were studying the nature of those orbits. In 1600, German mathematician Johannes Kepler (1571-1630) discovered that the orbits of some of the planets were not perfectly round but slightly oval or *elliptical* in shape. This explained the slight irregularities in the path of the planets across the sky. He used the detailed observations of his teacher, Danish astronomer Tycho Brahe, to arrive at his conclusions.

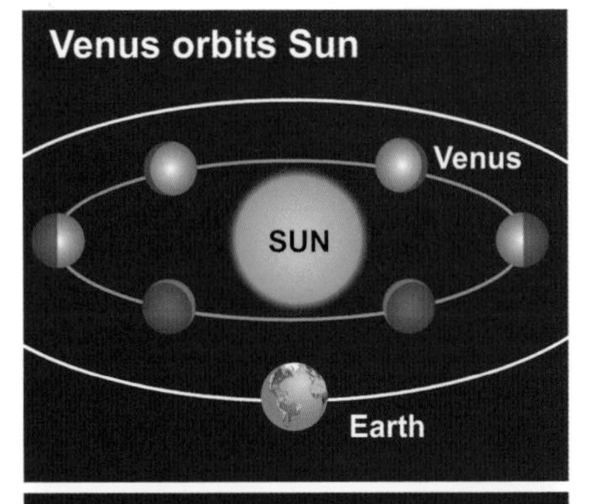

Figure 31.13: *Two of Galileo's discoveries that helped prove that Earth and the other planets orbit the sun. The top diagram shows how the phases of Venus are due to its orbit around the sun. The bottom diagram depicts moons orbiting Jupiter. This observation proved that not all objects revolve around Earth.*

What keeps the planets in orbit?

While Kepler discovered the slightly elliptical shape of their orbits, he could not explain why the planets *stay* in orbit. As you read in the last section, the work of Isaac Newton provided the answer. Newton (1642-1727) concluded that *gravity* and *inertia* keep the planets in orbit. Because of their inertia, the planets are moving in a direction *perpendicular* to the sun's attractive gravity. The reason they don't fall into the sun is because as they fall *toward* it, they are moving forward because of their *inertia*. The combination of the forward motion due to inertia, and the downward pull of gravity, keeps the planets falling *around* the sun instead of into it, as shown in Figure 31.14.

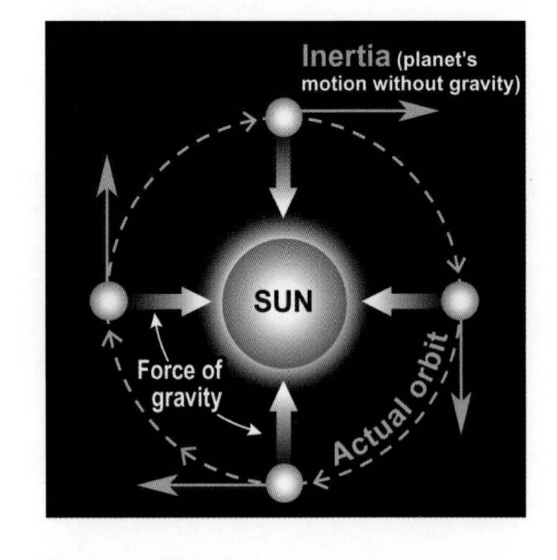

Figure 31.14: *Why do the planets stay in orbit around the sun?*

The solar system today

Today, we know that the solar system consists of the sun, the planets and their moons, and a large number of smaller objects (asteroids, comets, meteors, and dwarf planets such as Pluto). All of these objects orbit the sun.

The solar system is the region in space where the sun's gravitational force is dominant.

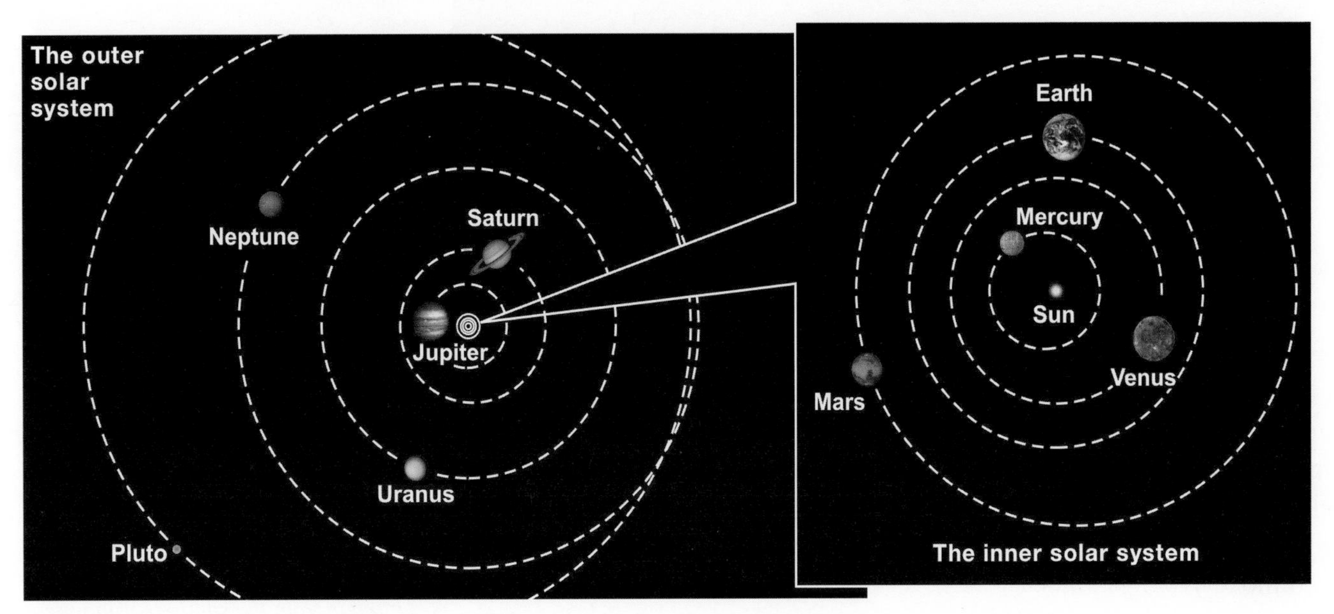

Size and distance in the solar system

Relative sizes The sun is by far the largest object in the solar system. The next largest objects are the planets Jupiter, Saturn, Uranus, and Neptune. As you can see from the scale diagram below, the planets Mercury, Venus, Earth, Mars, and Pluto, a *dwarf planet*, appear as small specks when compared with the size of the sun.

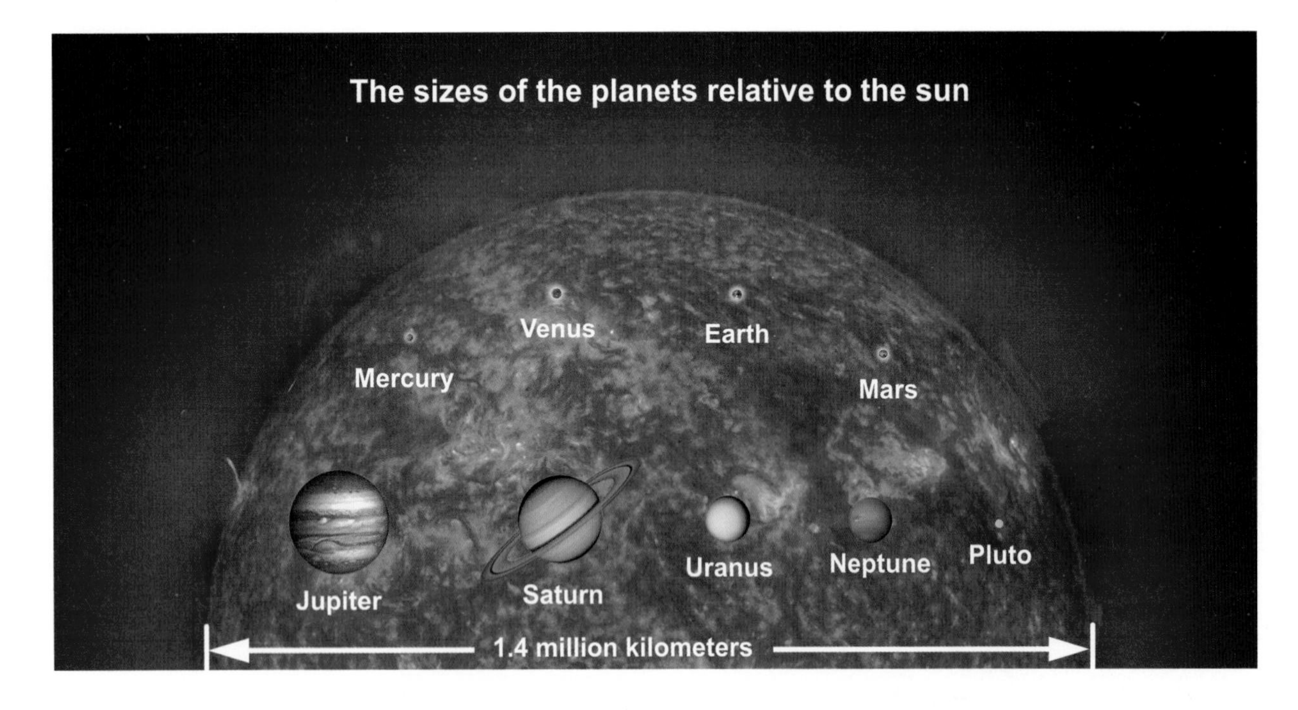

Distance Astronomers often use the distance of Earth from the sun as a measurement of distance in the solar system. One astronomical unit (AU) is equal to 150 million kilometers, or the distance from Earth to the sun. Mercury is 58 million kilometers from the sun. To convert this distance to astronomical units, divide this distance by 150 million kilometers. Mercury is therefore, 0.37 AU from the sun (Figure 31.16). Figure 31.16 lists the planets and their distance from the sun in astronomical units.

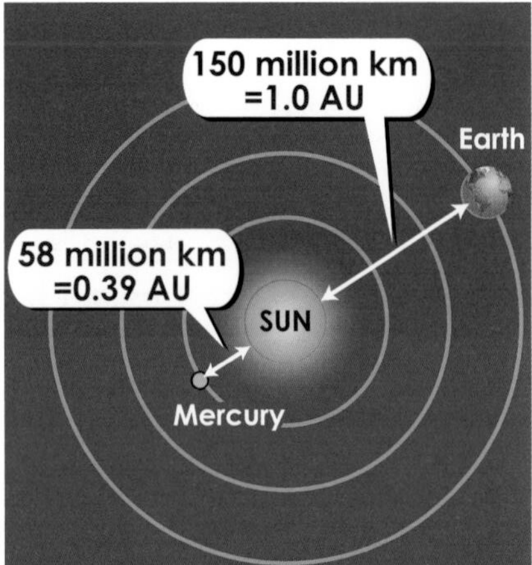

Figure 31.15: *One astronomical unit (AU) is equal to 150 million kilometers. If Earth is 1.0 AU from the sun, then Mercury, with a distance of 58 million kilometers, is 0.39 AU from the sun.*

Planet	Distance from the sun (AU)
Mercury	0.37
Venus	0.72
Earth	1.0
Mars	1.5
Jupiter	5.2
Saturn	9.5
Uranus	19.2
Neptune	30.0
Pluto (dwarf)	39.5

Figure 31.16: *Distances of the planets from the sun in astronomical units (AU).*

The planets

Classifying the planets The nine planets are commonly classified in two groups. The terrestrial planets include Mercury, Venus, Earth, and Mars. The terrestrial planets are mostly made of rock and metal. They have relatively high densities, slow rotations, solid surfaces, and few moons. The gas planets include Jupiter, Saturn, Uranus, and Neptune. These planets are made mostly of hydrogen and helium. They have relatively low densities, rapid rotations, very thick atmospheres, and many moons. Pluto is neither terrestrial nor gas, but a frozen world in a class of its own.

Mercury was named for the messenger of the Roman gods because of its quick motion in the sky.

Mercury The closest planet to the sun, Mercury appears to move quickly across the night sky because its period of revolution is the shortest of all of the planets. It is the second smallest planet (after Pluto) in both size and mass. It has almost no atmosphere (except for traces of sodium), and its surface resembles that of the moon. Mercury rotates on its axis very slowly—only one and a half times for every revolution around the sun. This makes one day on Mercury about 59 Earth days, although its year is not much longer—about 88 Earth days! The side of Mercury that faces the sun is very hot, about 400°C, while the other side is very cold, about -170°C. It has no moons.

Photo courtesy of NASA

Venus was named after the Roman goddess of love because of its beautiful, shiny appearance.

Venus Venus appears as the brightest planet and the third brightest object in the sky (after the sun and moon). It has a very thick atmosphere and an atmospheric pressure at its surface that is 90 times that at Earth's surface. Because the atmosphere on Venus is 96 percent carbon dioxide, the greenhouse effect makes it the hottest planet in the solar system with a surface temperature of more than 500°C. It is one of three planets that rotate "backward," that is, east to west. Its rotation is the slowest of all of the planets; Venus makes a little less than one rotation for each revolution around the sun. This means that a day on Venus is 243 Earth days, while a year is shorter: 225 Earth days. Like Mercury, Venus has no moons.

Photo courtesy NASA/JPL-Caltech

Earth is the only planet not named after a Roman god. Its name comes from Old English "oerthe," meaning land or country.

Earth Earth is a small, rocky planet with a thin atmosphere that is made of mostly nitrogen and oxygen. This atmosphere, along with the oceans and a moderate temperature range, are what made the formation of life possible. As far as we know, Earth is the only planet in the solar system to support life. Because of its axial tilt, this planet experiences seasons. Earth has one moon. (Earth is described in great detail in earlier chapters.)

Mars Mars appears as a reddish point of light in the night sky. It has a widely varied surface that includes deserts, huge valleys and craters, and volcanic mountains that dwarf those on Earth. The atmosphere of Mars is very thin (about 0.7 percent as thick as that of Earth) and composed mostly of carbon dioxide, with the rest nitrogen and argon. The temperatures are below freezing most of the time. Like Earth, Mars has polar ice caps, but they are composed of a combination of water and frozen carbon dioxide. Because it has an axial tilt, Mars experiences seasons like Earth. A day on Mars (24.6 hours) is similar in length to Earth, while a year (687 days) is not. Mars has two small moons named Phobos and Deimos.

Photo courtesy of ESA

Mars' red color reminded the ancients of blood so they named it after the Roman god of war.

Jupiter Jupiter is by far the largest of the planets, and the fastest rotator, spinning on its axis about once every 10 hours. A year on Jupiter is about 12 Earth years. Jupiter does not have a solid surface on which to stand. In fact, Jupiter is more liquid than gaseous or solid—more than half of its volume is an ocean of liquid hydrogen. Its atmosphere is about 88 percent hydrogen, 11 percent helium, and 1 percent methane, ammonia, and other molecules. The atmospheric pressure below Jupiter's thick clouds is more than a million times that of Earth! It has a very stormy atmosphere and one storm known as the Great Red Spot has been observed for more than 300 years. Jupiter's mass is greater than the combined masses of all of the planets, but its density is very low—about one-quarter that of Earth. With 39 moons, Jupiter is like a mini solar system. Several of its moons are as large as small planets and have interesting features.

Photo courtesy of NASA

Jupiter was king of the Roman gods. The planet's eminent brightness inspired its name.

Saturn Saturn, at almost 10 times the size of Earth, is the second largest planet. Like Jupiter, Saturn's atmosphere is made mostly of hydrogen and helium. Saturn is a fast rotator, though slightly slower than Jupiter, with a day on Saturn lasting just longer than 10 Earth hours. A year on Saturn is about 29 Earth years. The most striking feature of Saturn is its system of rings, which are visible from Earth with a telescope. While Jupiter, Uranus, and Neptune also have rings, they are faint and not visible from Earth, but detectable by other means. Saturn's rings are made up of billions of particles of rock and ice ranging from microscopic to the size of a house. Although they are hundreds of thousands of kilometers wide, the rings are less than 100 meters thick. With 30 moons, Saturn is also like a mini solar system.

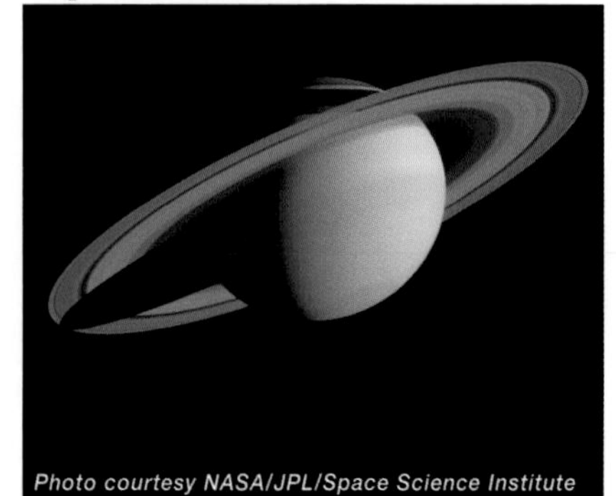

Photo courtesy NASA/JPL/Space Science Institute

Because of its slow orbit around the sun, Saturn was named after the Roman god of agriculture and time.

Uranus Because Uranus can barely be seen without a good telescope, it was not discovered until 1781. This gas planet is four times as large as Earth and has an atmosphere of mostly hydrogen and helium with small traces of other gases. Uranus has a series of faint rings that were discovered in 1977 using a very powerful telescope. This planet rotates "backward" and has an axis that is tilted 98 degrees to the plane of its orbit. A day on Uranus is only 18 Earth hours but a year takes 84 Earth years. Uranus has at least 21 moons.

Uranus is the first planet discovered in modern times and is named after the first Roman god.

Neptune Neptune is the outermost of the gas planets and, like the others, its atmosphere is mostly hydrogen and helium with small traces of other gases. It was discovered in 1846 and its discovery almost doubled the diameter of the solar system because of its great distance from the sun. Neptune's orbit is nearly a perfect circle; only Venus has a more circular orbit. Neptune has a series of faint rings but these are not visible from Earth and have only been seen in photographs taken by space probes such as *Voyager*. This planet has eight known moons, six of which were found in photographs taken by *Voyager 2* in 1989.

Photo courtesy of NASA

Because it is so far in the depths of space, Neptune was named after the Roman god of the deep sea.

Pluto Discovered in 1930, Pluto was named for the Roman god of the underworld. The first dwarf planet discovered, Pluto rotates slowly — one turn every six days — and backward. Its orbit is strongly elliptical and Pluto crosses the path of Neptune for about 20 years out of the 249 years it takes to revolve around the sun. Because their orbits are not in the same plane, Neptune and Pluto will never collide. Because it is so far away, little is known about Pluto.

Are there 8, 9, or 11+ planets? Outside the orbit of Pluto is a region called the Kuiper Belt. The Kuiper Belt stretches to 1,000 AU and is believed to contain many asteroid-size and a few Pluto-size objects. As of this writing, two Pluto-size bodies have been found, nicknamed Sedna and Xena. To avoid confusion, astronomers no longer count Pluto as a planet. Instead, Pluto is grouped along with Sedna, Xena, and similar distant bodies in the Kuiper Belt.

Table 31.1 on the next page compares the planets and some of their properties.

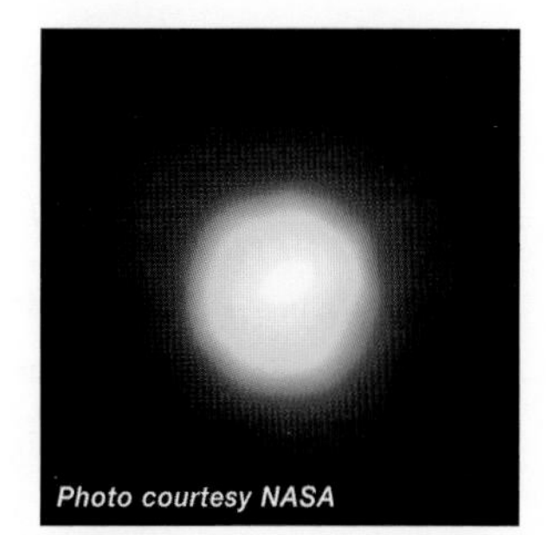

Discovered in 1930, Pluto was named for the Roman god of the underworld.

Table 31.1: *Comparing properties of the planets*

Property	Mercury	Venus	Earth	Mars	Jupiter	Saturn	Uranus	Neptune	Pluto
Diameter *(km)*	4,878	12,102	12,756	6,794	142,796	120,660	51,200	49,500	2,200
Mass *(kg)*	3.3×10^{23}	4.9×10^{24}	6.0×10^{24}	6.4×10^{23}	1.9×10^{27}	5.7×10^{26}	8.7×10^{25}	1.0×10^{26}	1.3×10^{22}
Density *(g/cm³)*	5.44	5.25	5.52	3.91	1.31	0.69	1.21	1.67	1.75
Average distance from the sun *(km)*	58 million	108 million	150 million	228 million	778 million	1.43 billion	2.87 billion	4.50 billion	5.91 billion
Moons *(number of)*	0	0	1	2	39	30	21	8	1
Gravitational force *(N)*	3.7	8.9	9.8	3.7	23.1	9.0	8.7	11.0	0.6
Surface temperature *(°C)*	-170 to +390	+450 to +480	-88 to +48	-89 to -31	-108	-139	-197	-201	-223
Rotation period *(Earth days)*	59	243	1	1.03	0.41	0.43	0.72	0.67	6.4
Revolution period *(Earth years)*	0.24	0.62	1	1.9	12	29	84	165	249
Orbital speed *(km/sec)*	47.89	35.04	29.80	24.14	13.06	9.64	6.80	5.43	4.74
Principal gases in atmosphere	Na	CO_2	N_2, O_2	CO_2	H_2, He, CH_4, NH_3	H_2, He, CH_4, NH_3	H_2, He, CH_4, NH_3	H_2, He, CH_4, NH_3	N_2, CO, CH_4

Other objects in the solar system

Asteroids Between Mars and Jupiter, at a distance of 320 million to 495 million kilometers, there is a huge gap that cuts the solar system in two. This gap is called the *asteroid belt* because it is filled with thousands of small, rocky bodies called *asteroids*. An **asteroid** is an object that orbits the sun but is too small to be considered a planet. At present, more than 10,000 asteroids have been discovered and more are found each year. The location of the asteroid belt is shown in the diagram on page 619.

The size of asteroids Most asteroids are small—less than one kilometer in diameter—but many have been found that are over 250 kilometers in diameter. The largest asteroid, named Ceres, is 933 kilometers (580 miles) across. While the majority of asteroids are found in the asteroid belt, many have highly elliptical orbits that allow them to come close to Mercury, Venus, and even Earth. Some come so close to Earth that they are known as "Earth-grazers." About 65 million years ago, a large asteroid hit Earth near Mexico, leaving a huge crater. Some scientists believe this event led to the extinction of the dinosaurs.

Comets A **comet** is an object in space that is made mostly of ice and dust. Comets are about the size of an Earth mountain. These objects revolve around the sun in highly elliptical orbits and many pass close to Earth. In 1997, the comet Hale-Bopp could be clearly seen in the night sky without the aid of a telescope. As a comet approaches the sun, some of its ice turns into gas and dust and forms an outer layer called a *coma*. The inner core of the comet is called the *nucleus* (Figure 31.18).

Evolution of a comet Because the sun releases a stream of particles called *solar wind*, as a comet gets closer to the sun, it forms a *tail*. A comet's tail can stretch for millions of kilometers into space and faces away from the sun as the comet continues its orbit (Figure 31.19). Each time a comet passes the sun, it loses more of its ice. After many revolutions, the comet may no longer have enough material to form a tail. Eventually, the comet will look more like an asteroid.

Figure 31.17: *The asteroid shown in this picture is named Ida and is about 54 kilometers wide.*

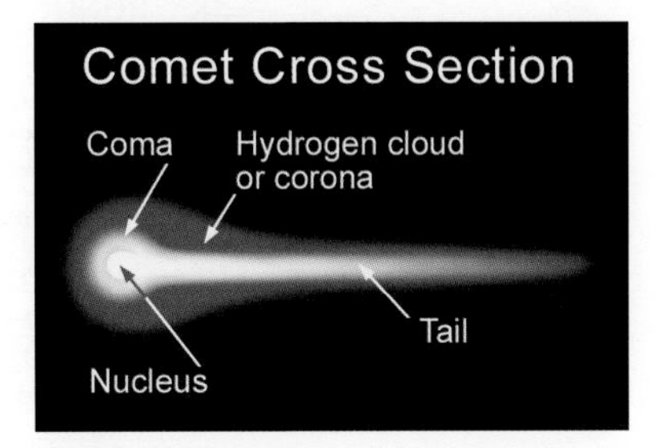

Figure 31.18: *The parts of a comet.*

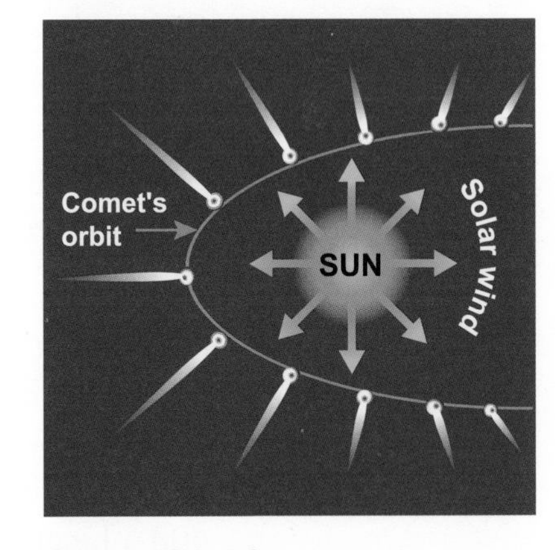

Figure 31.19: *A comet's tail faces away from the sun and can stretch for millions of kilometers in space.*

Meteors Occasionally, chunks of rock or dust break off from a comet or asteroid and form a **meteor**. Imagine a tennis ball traveling at about 30,000 miles per hour. That's about the size and speed of most meteors. These chunks of dust or rock travel through space and some of them end up hitting Earth's atmosphere. When this happens, meteors rub against air particles and create friction, heating them to more than 2,000°C. The intense heat vaporizes most meteors, creating a streak of light known as a "shooting star." Occasionally, larger meteors cause a brighter flash called a *fireball*. These sometimes cause an explosion that can be heard up to 30 miles away! If you go out into the country and look up at the sky on a clear night, chances are that you will see a meteor. In fact, a meteor can be seen in the night sky about every 10 minutes.

Name	Peak	Duration
Quadrantids	Jan. 4	2 days
Perseids	Aug. 11	4 days
Orionids	Oct. 21	4 days
Geminid	Dec. 13	varies

Figure 31.20: *Some annual meteor showers. Watch the skies for them!*

Meteor showers When a comet nears the sun, a trail of dust and other debris burns off and remains in orbit around the sun. As Earth orbits the sun, it passes through this debris, creating a *meteor shower* as the small bits of dust burn up in the atmosphere. During a meteor shower, you can see tens and even hundreds of meteors per hour. Because Earth passes the same dust clouds from comets each year, meteor showers can be predicted with accuracy (Figure 31.20).

Figure 31.21: *Meteors frequently streak across the night sky.*

Meteorites If a meteor is large enough to survive the passage through Earth's atmosphere and strike the ground, it becomes a *meteorite*. Meteorites are thought to be fragments from collisions involving asteroids. Most meteorites weigh only a few pounds or less and cause little damage when they hit. Most fall into the oceans that cover almost three-quarters of our planet's surface. In 1948, people in Nebraska saw a giant fireball that seemed brighter than the sun. The meteorite was later found in a field, buried deep in the ground. It weighed 2,360 pounds!

The Kuiper Belt The Kuiper Belt was discovered in 1992 and is named after the Dutch-American astronomer Gerard Kuiper (1905-73), who predicted its existence in 1951. It is a region beyond the planet Neptune where countless numbers of small, icy objects slowly orbit (Figure 31.22). Some astronomers believe that the Kuiper Belt is the reservoir for comets that orbit the sun in less than 200 years. So far, fewer than 400 objects have been identified, but astronomers suspect that there may be billions of them. Recently, an object half the size of Pluto was discovered in the Kuiper Belt.

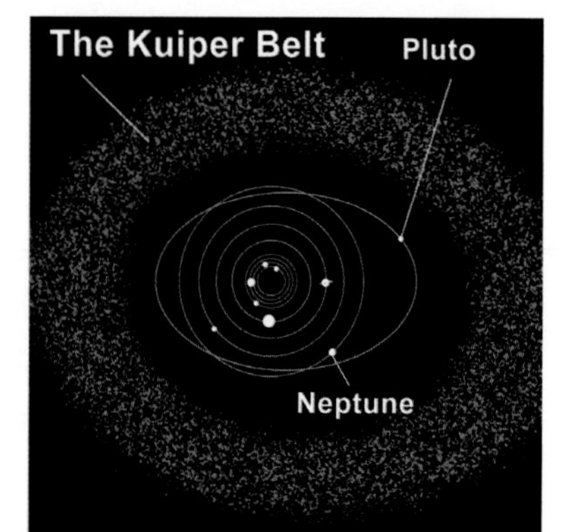

Figure 31.22: *The Kuiper Belt lies beyond Neptune.*

Science controversy: Is Pluto a planet?

Is Pluto a planet?

Recently, Pluto's status as a *planet* has been a subject of controversy. This is not the only time in history that an object's status as a planet has been questioned. According to the ancient Greeks, there were seven objects they called planets: Mercury, Venus, Mars, Jupiter, Saturn, the sun, and the moon. After the time of Copernicus and Galileo, astronomers said that there were only six planets, Mercury, Venus, Earth, Mars, Jupiter, and Saturn.

Asteroids are not planets

In 1781, William Herschel (1738-1822) discovered Uranus outside the orbit of Jupiter. The "eighth" planet, Ceres, was discovered in 1801 between the orbits of Mars and Jupiter. Soon after, three more "planets" were discovered, Pallas, Juno, and Vesta. If you were to read a science textbook from the early 1800's, it would state there were 11 planets. Then astronomers began to find dozens of smaller "planets" between Mars and Jupiter. Astronomers soon realized that Ceres, Pallas, Juno, and Vesta were not planets at all but merely asteroids.

Planet X

Later in the 1800's, astronomers realized that in addition to the sun, the orbit of Uranus was behaving as if it were influenced by another object. They theorized there must be another planet affecting its orbit. After many calculations, they discovered Neptune. However, they thought that even Neptune's orbit was being influenced by another object and began to search for what they called *Planet X*. In 1930, Clyde Tombaugh (1906-97) discovered Pluto, which was thought to be Planet X. Pluto's orbit is highly elliptical, and is not aligned in the same plane as the other planets in the solar system.

Pluto is now classified as a dwarf planet

On August 24, 2006, the International Astronomical Union (IAU) passed a new definition of a planet. The new definition excludes Pluto as a planet. According to the new definition, Pluto is classified as a "dwarf planet." Recently, astronomers have begun to find dozens of objects similar to Pluto—all small, icy, rocky, and with similar orbits.

The change in Pluto's status as a planet is a good example of the scientific method in progress. New discoveries sometimes cause scientists to revise their theories and ideas.

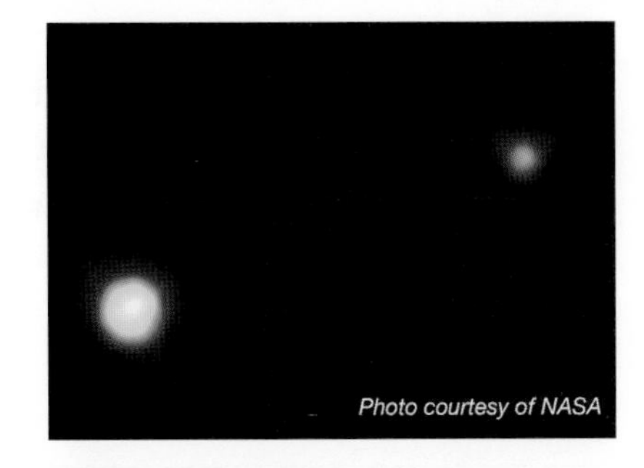

Figure 31.23: *Pluto is a very difficult planet to study. Even this NASA/HST image shows us very little about Pluto's surface.*

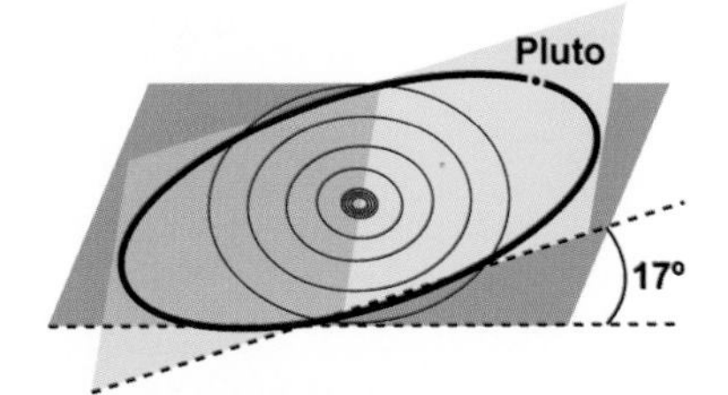

Figure 31.24: *Pluto's orbit is highly elliptical and tilts at a 17-degree angle with respect to the orbital plane of the other planets.*

Figure 31.25: *The sun would look like a bright star from the surface of Pluto.*

31.3 The Sun

Can you imagine life without the sun? In fact, life could not exist without it. The sun is the source of energy that sustains all life on Earth. It is also Earth's timekeeper, governing the seasons, the harvests, and even the sleep patterns of animals. The sun has been worshiped by civilizations throughout history. What is the sun? Why does it produce so much energy? Read on to find the answers to these questions, and many more.

Figure 31.26: *The sun is a star.*

What is the sun?

The sun is a star When you look up at the stars at night, it may be hard to believe that the sun is one of them. To the casual observer the sun looks very different from a star. The sun appears as a large golden disk in the daytime sky, while the stars twinkle as pinpoints of light in the night sky. Yet the sun is one of at least 200 billion stars in our galaxy. With the universe containing billions of galaxies, each filled with stars, you can see that our sun is only a tiny part of the universe. You will learn about the universe, galaxies, and stars in the next chapter.

A medium-sized star The sun is medium-sized compared with other stars in the universe. Its diameter is about 1.4 million kilometers, or about 109 times the diameter of Earth. Approximately 1 million planet Earths could fit inside the sun! By contrast, one of the star "supergiants" called Betelgeuse sometimes reaches a diameter that is almost 600 times that of the sun. If the sun grew to the size of Betelgeuse, it would swallow up Mercury, Venus, Earth, and Mars!

What is the sun made of? The sun is about 75 percent hydrogen, 25 percent helium, and very small traces of other elements. Unlike Earth, the sun does not have a solid surface—instead, it is made completely of gas. Because of its size, the sun contains 99.8 percent of the mass of the solar system. Because of its mass, the sun's gravitational force is strong enough to hold the entire solar system, including the nine planets, asteroids, and comets, in orbit.

Sun Facts

- The sun's diameter is 1.4 million kilometers.
- About one million Earths could fit inside of the sun.
- The core of the sun is about 15 million°C.
- The coolest parts of the sun are nearly 4,000°C.
- The outermost layer of the sun can stretch millions of kilometers into space.
- The sun is 150 million kilometers from Earth.
- The sun spins around once every 27.4 days.
- The sun is about 5 billion years old.

Where does the sun's energy come from?

Energy from the sun

Except for nuclear power, the source for almost all of our energy comes from the sun. Sunlight causes water to evaporate, which later falls as rain into rivers and streams. This flowing water can be used to generate electricity. Energy from the sun also drives the wind (created by uneven heating of Earth), which also can be used to generate electricity. Solar energy can be converted *directly* to electricity using *photovoltaic cells* like the ones found on solar-powered calculators. Even the energy we get from coal, natural gas, petroleum, and wood comes from the sun. That is because these fuels are created from *photosynthesis*. In this process, plants store energy from the sun in the form of carbon compounds. The energy in these compounds is released as heat when they are burned.

The sun's energy comes from nuclear fusion

Parts of the sun can reach 15 million°C! Where does all of this energy come from? Does the sun produce this energy from burning fuels such as oil, coal, or natural gas? Far from burning fuels, the energy output of the sun is instead produced by *nuclear fusion*. You have learned that nuclear fusion occurs when the nuclei of atoms are joined, or fused. Inside the sun, the nuclei of hydrogen atoms join together to form helium atoms. This results in the release of a tremendous amount of *energy* in the form of heat and light. Figure 31.27 shows a simple example of nuclear fusion.

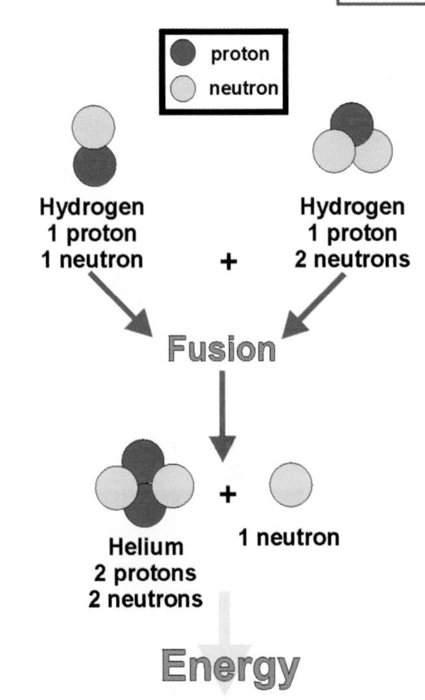

Figure 31.27: *A simple example of nuclear fusion. The fusion reactions in the sun are a lot more complicated!*

How much energy does the sun produce?

Each second, about 700 million tons of hydrogen inside the sun are converted to about 695 million tons of helium through nuclear fusion. Notice that the total mass of helium produced is slightly smaller than the total mass of hydrogen used. The "missing" mass (about 5 million tons) is converted directly into energy. This mass creates an energy output of 3.9×10^{26} watts! In 1905 Albert Einstein proposed that matter can be converted into energy. His famous equation ($E = mc^2$) shows how huge amounts of energy can be created from a smaller mass (Figure 31.28). This helps explain why such a large amount of energy is produced by fusion.

Energy
Mass

$$E = mc^2$$

Speed of light

Multiplying even a small mass by this number will result in a large amount of energy.

Figure 31.28: *Einstein's equation shows how large amounts of energy can come from a small mass.*

The solar constant

The amount of this energy that actually reaches the edge of Earth's atmosphere is known as the solar constant. While the solar constant varies slightly, the accepted value is 1,368 watts per square meter (W/m^2). To visualize this amount of energy, imagine the energy of thirteen 100-watt light bulbs spread over a square meter surface.

The sun's features and occurrences

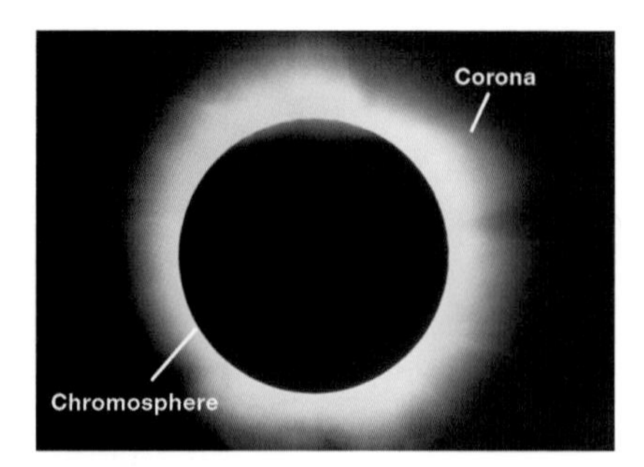

Figure 31.29: *The sun's corona and chromosphere can be seen during a total eclipse.*

The sun has three regions

Because the sun is made of gas, its surface is hard to define. The apparent surface that we can see from a distance is called the *photosphere,* which means "sphere of light." Just above it is the *chromosphere.* This is a very hot layer of plasma, a high-energy state of matter. The *corona* is the outermost layer of the sun's atmosphere, extending millions of kilometers beyond the sun. Both the corona and chromosphere can be seen during a total eclipse of the sun, as shown in Figure 31.29.

Sunspots

A safe method for viewing the sun is to use a telescope to project its image onto a white surface (You should NEVER look directly at the sun). When the sun is observed in this way, small, dark areas can be seen on its surface. These areas, called *sunspots*, may look small, but they can be as large as Earth. Sunspots are areas of gas that are cooler than the gases around them. Because they don't give off as much light as the hotter areas, they appear as dark spots on the photosphere (Figure 31.30).

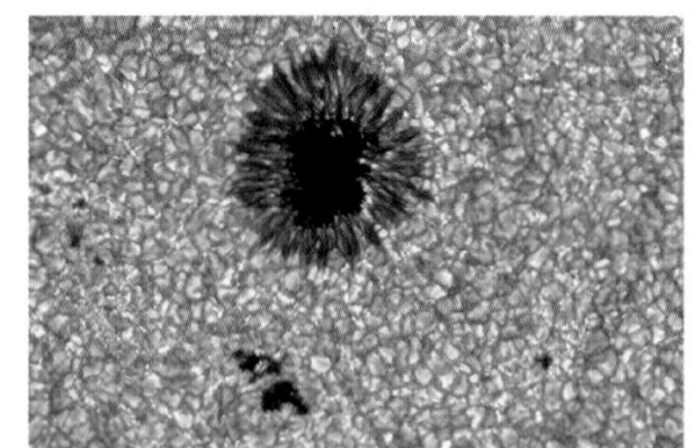

Figure 31.30: *Sunspots appear as dark spots on the photosphere.*

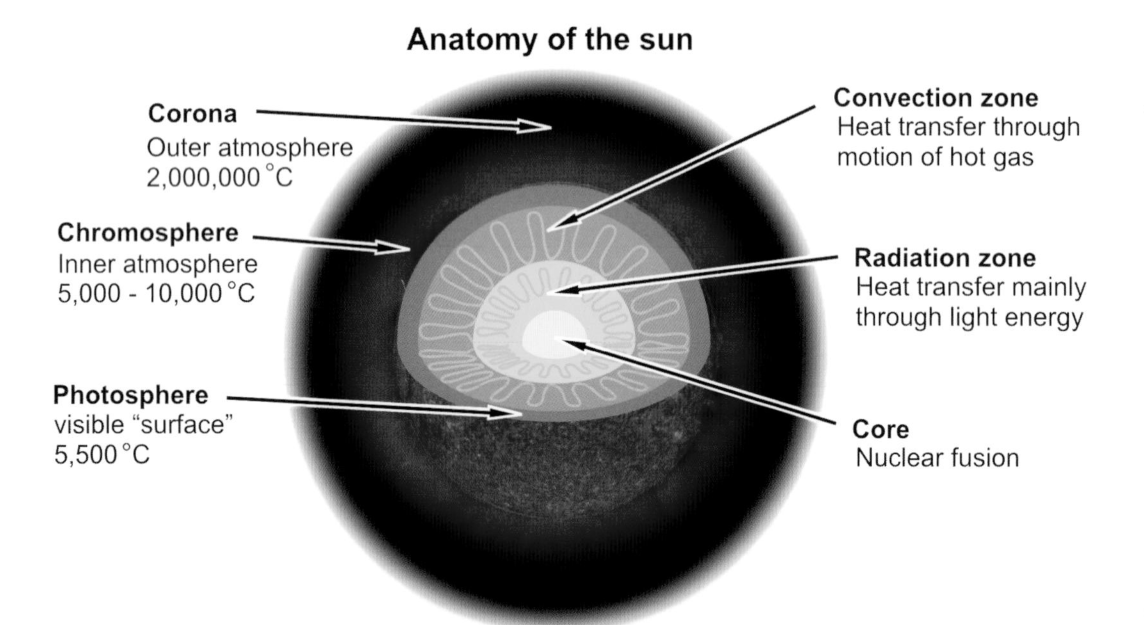

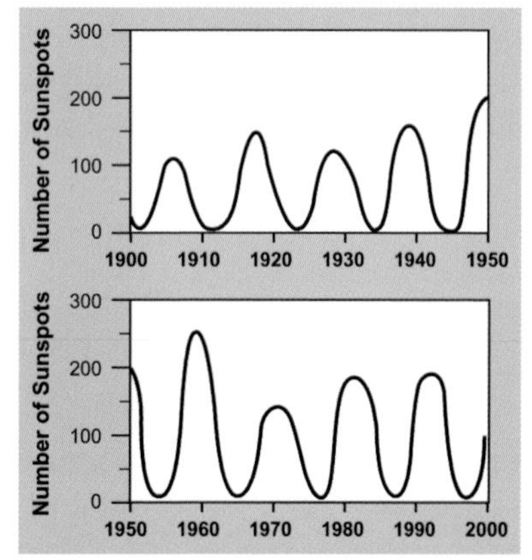

Figure 31.31: *Sunspot cycles for the years 1900 through 2000.*

Prominences and solar flares Sunspots are linked to other features of the sun. Occasionally, large "loops" of gas called *prominences* can be seen jumping up from groups of sunspots. These can be observed during eclipses and appear as loops that extend beyond the chromosphere. Sometimes prominences from different sunspot regions suddenly connect, releasing very large amounts of heat and light known as *solar flares*.

Theories about sunspots The number of sunspots seems to vary over an 11-year period known as the *sunspot cycle* (Figure 31.31 on page 630). Many scientists speculate that there is a relationship between the sunspot cycle and variations in our global climate. Two decades of satellite research have shown that at times of high sunspot number, the value of the solar constant increases slightly. While sunspots are cooler areas of the sun, as their numbers increase, so does the number of solar flares that release large amounts of heat. Does an increase in the solar constant contribute to warmer temperatures on Earth? Only through further research will scientists be able to answer this and other questions about global climate changes.

Solar wind The sun emits more than just heat and light. Another emission, called *solar wind*, is an electrically charged mixture of protons and electrons. Evidence of solar wind comes from the tails of comets. A comet's tail acts like a "wind sock" and shows that there is a continuous flow of particles coming from the sun (Figure 31.32).

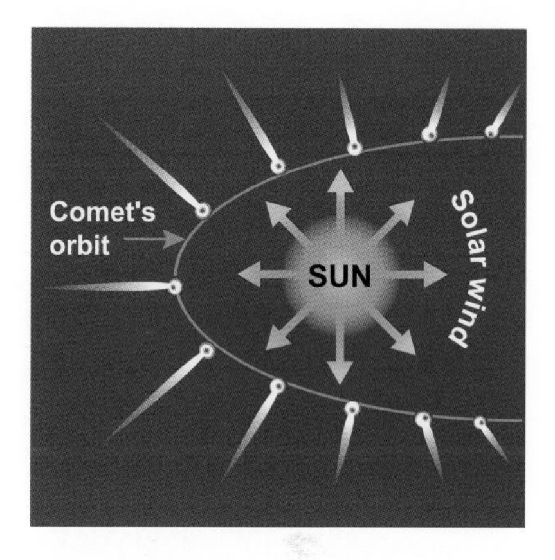

Figure 31.32: *The direction of a comet's tail provides evidence that the sun emits solar wind.*

Magnetic storms Solar flares can greatly increase the amount of solar wind emitted by the sun. These solar wind particles can affect Earth's upper atmosphere, causing *magnetic storms*. Magnetic storms can disrupt radio and television signals, interfere with telephone and cell phone signals, and even cause electrical power problems for homes and businesses.

Auroras Solar winds can also cause a mysterious phenomenon known as an *aurora* to occur. Auroras (known in the Northern hemisphere as the northern lights) occur when the protective layers of our atmosphere are energized by solar winds. This energy causes atoms and molecules in the upper atmosphere to emit light. The most common color produced is a yellow-green caused by oxygen atoms at an altitude of about 60 miles. These lights appear as curtains above the horizon (Figure 31.33).

Figure 31.33: *Auroras are a mysterious phenomenon caused by solar winds. Energy from solar winds causes atoms in the upper atmosphere to emit light.*

Harnessing the sun's energy

What is solar energy? The fusion of hydrogen into helium has been occurring on the sun for 5 billion years, and will continue for another 5 billion. As the fusion process continues, some of this energy reaches Earth in the form of *electromagnetic waves*. These waves can be classified according to their energy as shown in Figure 31.34. The only electromagnetic wave we can detect with our eyes is *visible light*. As you can see from Figure 31.34, this is only a tiny portion of the electromagnetic spectrum. When light from the sun passes through a prism, we can see that it is made up of all of the colors of the visible spectrum.

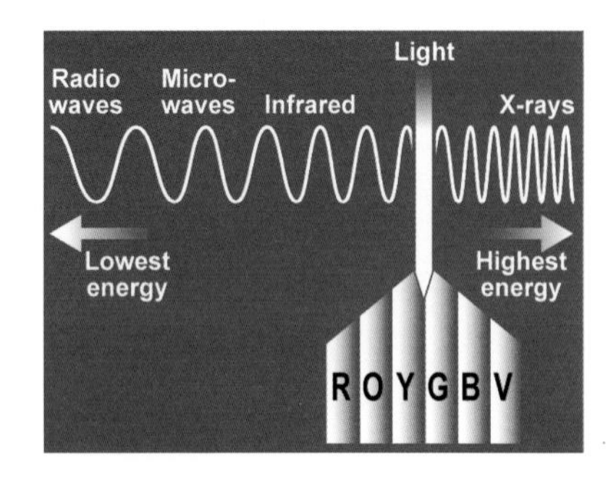

Figure 31.34: *The sun emits waves in all frequencies of the electromagnetic spectrum. The only waves we can detect with our eyes are visible light. The colors of light, from lowest to highest energy are: Red, orange, yellow, green, blue, and violet.*

How we use sunlight There are many ways to collect sunlight and use it to produce energy for our everyday needs. When we use energy from the sun it is called solar energy. Different ways of collecting solar energy are discussed below.

Passive solar heating Buildings that use passive solar heating are designed to trap the warmth of the sun. Houses can be built with large glass windows that face the direction of the sun. Sunlight passes through the windows and is trapped in the room, causing it to become warmer. Greenhouses use passive solar heating to grow plants during the winter in cold climates.

Circulated solar heating Have you ever seen a building with large glass panels covering part of its roof? Buildings with these panels use them to harness the sun's energy. Underneath the glass panels, water is circulated through tubes. The water is heated by the sun and flows into the building where it can be used for hot water or heating. The heated water can also be stored in an insulated tank for use at night.

Photovoltaic cells (PV cells) *Photovoltaic (or PV) cells*, also called *solar cells*, are devices that convert sunlight directly into electricity. You may have seen PV cells on calculators, watches, or some outdoor light fixtures. They are made out of at least two layers of a semiconductor material such as silicon. One layer has a positive charge, and the other has a negative charge. When light falls on the cell, some of it is absorbed by the semiconductor atoms, freeing electrons from the PV cells' negative layer. These electrons then flow through an external circuit and back into the positive layer. The flow of electrons produces electric current (Figure 31.35).

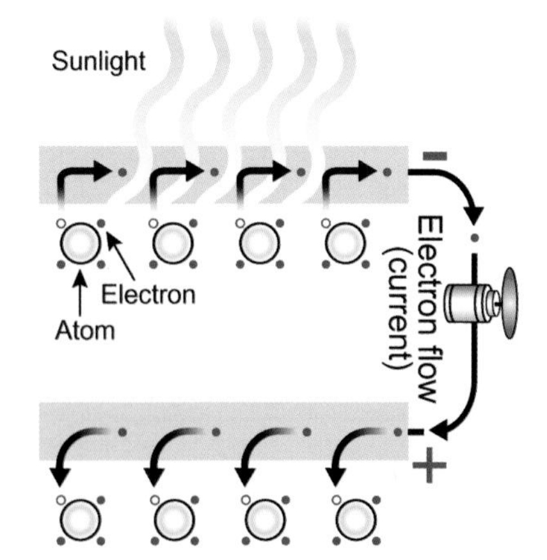

Figure 31.35: *Sunlight enters the PV cells, causing electrons to flow through a circuit to produce electric current.*

Increasing the efficiency of PV cells

The uses for PV cells In space, virtually all communications satellites are powered by PV cells. On Earth, their use is more limited. PV cells are common in remote places that do not have electrical power lines. For example, they are often used to provide power to radar stations and radio towers. However, they are not as common in places that have power lines. Since PV cells can generate electricity without producing harmful emissions, scientists are working on ways of improving them so they can be used more often.

PV cells are inefficient Low efficiency of energy conversion is the biggest obstacle to getting more electricity from PV cells. Less than 10 percent of the light energy falling on a PV cell is converted to electricity. Many research projects are underway to increase the efficiency of PV cells. One technique being tested is to make cells of multiple layers. Each layer is designed to be more efficient for a certain range of colors. For example, the top layer could be designed to be efficient with blue light. The second layer with red light, and so on.

Atmospheric conditions A second problem with generating electricity from solar energy is that clouds get in the way! Earth's atmosphere is a very active place. The top of the atmosphere receives 1,358 watts per square meter from the sun. On a sunny day, about 1,000 watts per square meter reach the ground as light. On a cloudy day less than 50 watts per square meter reach the ground.

PV cells do not work at night Because photovoltaic cells cannot make any electricity at night, they must rely on batteries to store the energy for later use. Unfortunately, the efficiency of batteries is not much greater than that of PV cells. Many scientists and engineers are doing research to improve the efficiency of batteries.

Solar power from space? Scientists are working on the possibility of collecting solar power above Earth's atmosphere. Concentrators on satellites would focus the sun's energy onto arrays of PV cells. The energy produced would then be transmitted back to Earth in the form of microwaves or laser beams and "received" by consumers much like radio and television signals. While this idea may be possible, there are many unanswered questions, including: How much will it cost? What are the health or environmental hazards of transmitting power using laser beams or microwaves?

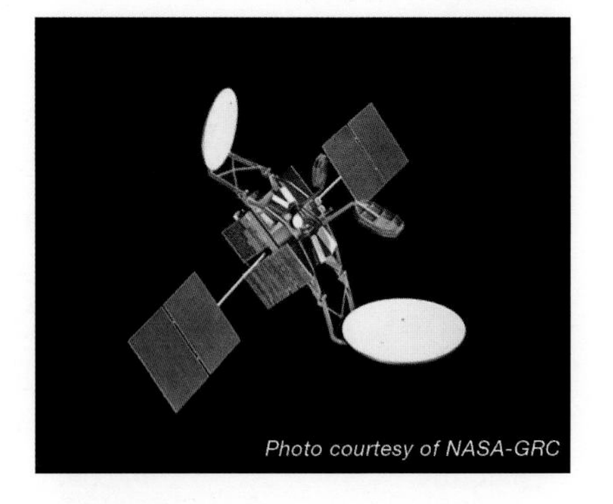

Photo courtesy of NASA-GRC

Figure 31.36: *PV cells are commonly used to power satellites. Why aren't they more common on Earth?*

Research idea: Space solar power

Conduct research on the concept of *space solar power*. Is this type of energy feasible? What are the major advantages? What are the potential hazards? Based on your research, do you think it's a good idea? Why or why not? Prepare a presentation or paper summarizing your findings. Here are some good websites:

www.space.com

spacesolarpower.nasa.gov

www.eree.energy.gov

Chapter 31 Review

Vocabulary review

Match the following terms with the correct definition. There is one extra definition in the list that will not match any of the terms.

Set One

1. gravitational force
2. satellite
3. orbit
4. orbital speed
5. tides

a. a regular, repeating path that one object in space follows around another
b. the measure of the attractive force exerted by one object on a 1.0 kg object held at its surface
c. the speed required to keep an object in orbit around another object
d. the forward motion of an object in space
e. the rising and falling of ocean levels in daily rhythms
f. an object in orbit

Set Two

1. solar constant
2. astronomical unit
3. terrestrial planet
4. gas planet
5. asteroid

a. made mostly of rock and metal and have high densities, slow rotations, and few moons
b. an object that orbits the sun but is too small to be considered a planet
c. made mostly of hydrogen and helium and has low density, fast rotations, and many moons
d. objects made mostly of ice and dust and which form a tail as they approach the sun
e. equal to the distance of Earth from the sun
f. the amount of the sun's energy that reaches one square meter at the edge of Earth's atmosphere

Concept review

1. According to Newton's law of universal gravitation, the force of gravity acting between two objects involves two variables. Name these two variables.
2. Describe how you would measure Earth's gravitational force.
3. Explain why the moon would need a faster orbital speed to stay in orbit around Earth if it were moved closer to Earth's surface.
4. Why does the sun's gravitational force have a lesser affect on tides than the moon's, even though the sun has a much greater mass than the moon?
5. Describe the *giant impact theory* of the moon's formation.
6. What is gravitational locking? How does it explain the fact that we can only see one side of the moon from Earth?
7. Describe the factors that keep a satellite in orbit.
8. What are the differences between terrestrial planets and gas planets? Which type is Pluto?
9. Why does a comet form a visible tail as it approaches the sun?
10. What is the difference between a meteor and a meteorite?
11. What are auroras and what causes them?
12. Name three ways to harness the sun's energy.

Problems

1. Use the information in the diagram below to calculate the circumference, in kilometers, of the planet.

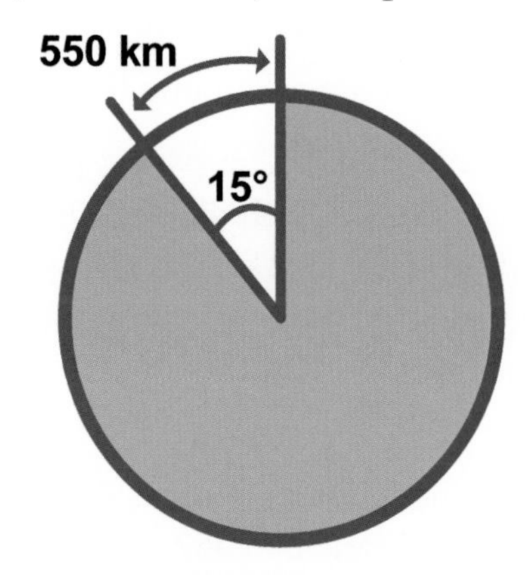

2. Jupiter exerts a gravitational force of 23.1 N on a 1.0 kg object held at its surface. Use this information and the equation of universal gravitation to calculate Jupiter's mass.
3. CHALLENGE! In the previous problem, you calculated Jupiter's mass. This value is equal to over 300 times Earth's mass, yet Jupiter's gravitational force is only about 2.5 times that of Earth's. Can you explain why Jupiter's gravitational force is not higher?
4. A large truck weighs 6,990 pounds on Earth. How much would the same truck weigh, in pounds, on Jupiter?
5. A moon rock weighs 8.5 pounds on the moon. How much would this rock weigh on Earth?
(Gravitational force on the moon = 1.6 N)
6. Venus has a mass of 4.9×10^{24} kg. Use the equation of universal gravitation to calculate Venus's gravitational force. Show all of your work.
7. Saturn has a mass of 5.7×10^{26} kg. Its radius is 60,330 km. Calculate Saturn's density in g/cm^3. Show your work. You can check your answer using Table 31.1, "Comparing properties of the planets," on page 624.
8. The sun's diameter is 1.4 million km. Its mass is 332,830 times that of Earth's. Use this information to calculate the density of the sun. Show all of your work.
9. The star Alpha Centauri is 4.13×10^{13} km from the sun. Calculate this distance in astronomical units (AU).
10. Betelgeuse appears as a twinkling red star in the night sky. It is 700 light years from Earth. Answer the following questions:
    a. How far from Earth is Betelgeuse in kilometers?
    b. How far from Earth is Betelgeuse in AU?
11. If you traveled a distance of one light year, how far did you travel in AU?
12. You have read that each second on the sun, 700 million tons of hydrogen is converted through fusion into 695 million tons of helium. There is a missing mass of 5 million tons. What happens to it? How does Einstein's equation $E = mc^2$ help explain what happens to this "missing" mass in terms of energy output from the sun?
13. You have learned that hydrogen fusion occurs inside the core of the sun. If one hydrogen atom fuses with another hydrogen atom, helium is produced. In some stars, the core becomes hot enough for the fusion of helium atoms to occur. If two helium atoms fused, what possible atoms could be formed? Support your answer with sketches of the nuclei of the atoms involved.

Applying your knowledge

1. A satellite in *geosynchronous orbit* travels at the correct orbital speed so that it takes it exactly 24 hours to orbit Earth. From Earth, a satellite in geosynchronous orbit appears to "hover" over one spot on the equator. That means a receiving dish on the Earth can point at the satellite at one spot in the sky and not have to "track" its motion.

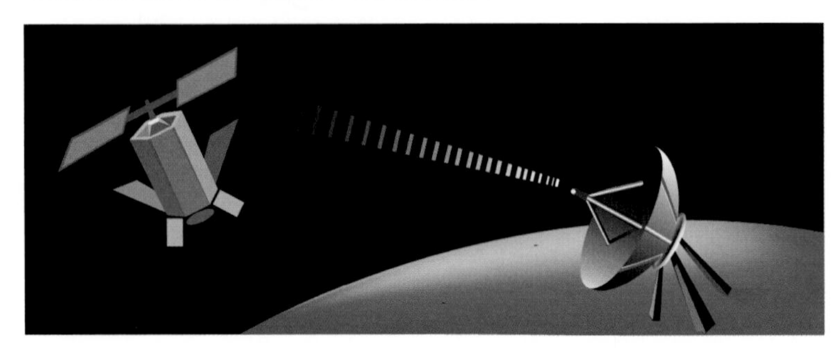

Conduct research on satellites in geosynchronous orbit. Find the following information: At what distance above Earth do these types of satellites orbit? What orbital speed is necessary for a satellite to be in geosynchronous orbit? What are these types of satellites used for? What are the advantages and disadvantages of these types of satellites?

2. Even though Mercury is closer to the sun, surface temperatures on Venus are hotter. In fact, Venus is the hottest planet in the solar system. Explain why this is so.

3. Pluto is called the ninth planet though sometimes it is actually the eight planet. Explain why.

4. Explain why the exact dates for meteor showers can be predicted with accuracy.

5. Using the density data from Table 31.1, "Comparing properties of the planets," on page 624, make a bar graph comparing the densities of the nine planets. Explain the density differences among the planets.

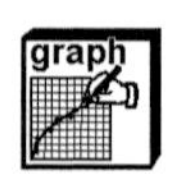

6. Use the data in Table 31.1, "Comparing properties of the planets," on page 624, graph distance from the sun on the x-axis and orbital speed on the y-axis. You may plot the distance in kilometers or astronomical units. What is the shape of the graph? How does this graph support the universal law of gravitation? Explain your answer in detail.

7. You have read that the Kuiper Belt was discovered in 1992, yet its existence was predicted in 1952. Conduct research on the Kuiper Belt to answer the following questions:

   What technology led to the discovery of the Kuiper Belt?
   What evidence was used to predict its existence?
   What is the largest Kuiper Belt Object found to date?
   How do astronomers look for objects in the Kuiper Belt?

8. Use the data in Table 31.1, "Comparing properties of the planets," on page 624 to answer the following questions:

   a. Which planet would float in a giant bathtub of water?

   b. Which planet has the most moons? What data from the table explains why?

   c. Which planets have similar atmospheres? Why do you think their atmospheres are similar?

   d. Make a graph of mass versus gravitational force. Does the graph show a strong, medium, or weak relationship? Explain the reason behind your answer.

UNIT 11

Astronomy

Chapter 32

The Universe

So far in this unit, you have learned mostly about objects that are relatively close to Earth such as other planets, their moons, and the sun. The solar system occupies a very tiny portion of the Milky Way Galaxy. This galaxy contains hundreds of billions of stars like the sun, and is one of many billions of galaxies in the universe. The universe is a term astronomers use to describe everything that exists including all matter and energy. In this chapter, you will learn about objects that are very far away including stars and galaxies. You will also read about how many scientists believe the universe began.

32.1	Stars	*What are stars made of?*

Astronomers use a spectrometer to analyze the light emitted by stars and determine the elements from which stars are composed. In this Investigation, you will use a spectrometer to analyze light and examine spectral diagrams to determine the composition and temperature of stars.

32.2	Galaxies and the Universe	*How do we use light to measure the distances to stars and galaxies?*

Distances to stars and galaxies in the universe are so vast that they are very difficult to measure. One of the tools astronomers use to measure distances in the universe is light. In this Investigation, you will discover the mathematical relationship between how bright an object appears from a distance, and how much light it actually gives off. This important relationship is used by astronomers to calculate distances in the universe.

NASA image

Learning Goals

In this chapter, you will:

- ✔ Identify the conditions necessary for fusion to occur inside a star.
- ✔ Describe the information that spectroscopy provides about stars.
- ✔ Relate the color of a star to its temperature.
- ✔ Explain the factors that determine the brightness of a star in the sky.
- ✔ Discuss the importance of the H-R diagram to astronomers.
- ✔ Explain the relationship between mass and the life cycle of a star.
- ✔ Describe the phases in the life cycle of a sun-like star.
- ✔ Discuss how the death of a massive star is responsible for the creation of elements heavier than helium on the periodic table.
- ✔ Describe how the composition and size of planets is related to their formation and proximity to the sun.
- ✔ Identify the structure of the Milky Way Galaxy and the location of our solar system within the galaxy.
- ✔ Explain how astronomers measure the distance to stars and galaxies.
- ✔ Identify the scientific evidence that supports the Big Bang theory.

Vocabulary

absolute brightness	constellation	main sequence stars	protostar
apparent brightness	Doppler shift	nebula	spectroscopy
Big Bang	H-R diagram	parallax	standard candle
Cepheid	inverse square law	planetary system	supernova

32.1 Stars

During the day, we see only one star, the sun, which is 150 million kilometers away. On a clear night, about 6,000 stars can be seen without a telescope. The closest star in the nighttime sky is Alpha Centauri—4.3 light years (41 trillion kilometers) away. Where do stars come from? How long do they last? In this section you will find the answers to these questions and more.

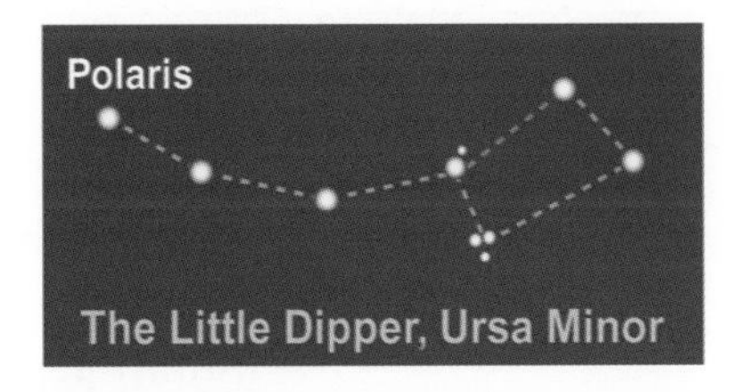

Figure 32.1: *The star at the tip of the Little Dipper's handle is called Polaris. If you look toward Polaris, you are facing the North Pole.*

Stars and fusion

What is a star? A *star* is essentially a giant, hot ball of gas. Stars generate light and heat through nuclear reactions. Specifically, they are powered by the fusion of hydrogen into helium under conditions of enormous temperature, mass, and density. When hydrogen atoms fuse, helium is created. During this process, some mass is lost and converted to energy as described in Albert Einstein's famous equation:

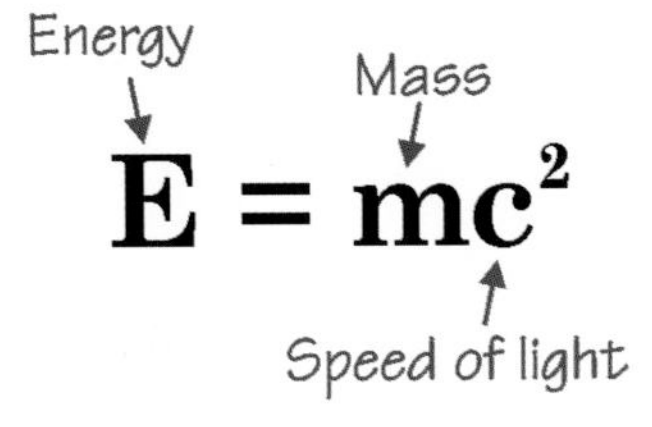

What makes fusion occur? The conditions required for the continuous fusion of hydrogen include extremely high values for temperature, density, and mass. Furthermore, hydrogen fusion does not take place throughout the star, but only deep in its core, where the temperature is hot enough. The minimum temperature required for fusion to occur is 7 million°C. The sun's core reaches a temperature of 15 million°C.

Density and mass Even though stars are made of gas, they have extremely high values for density and mass. For example, the density of the sun's core is about 158.0 g/cm^3. This is about 18 times the density of copper. The sun has a total mass that is equal to 330,000 Earths. Stars can range in mass from about 100 times that of the sun to less than one-tenth its mass. At masses lower than this, the internal temperature does not get hot enough to sustain the fusion of hydrogen.

Constellations

A constellation is a group of stars that, when seen from Earth, form a pattern. The stars in the sky are divided into 88 constellations. The largest, Centaurus, contains 101 stars. The most familiar star formation, the Big Dipper, is actually part of a larger constellation called Ursa Major (the Great Bear). The Little Dipper, part of Ursa Minor, contains Polaris, the North Star, which is located at the tip of the handle (Figure 32.1). Anybody in the Northern Hemisphere who is looking toward Polaris is facing the North Pole.

Examining light from stars

What is spectroscopy?

Stars shine because they are hot. Astronomers analyze the light emitted by stars, and other "hot" objects in space in order to determine their chemical composition and temperature. Sometimes they can even determine how fast the object is moving, its mass, and its density by analyzing the light it emits. Spectroscopy is a tool of astronomy in which the electromagnetic radiation (including visible light) produced by a star or other object (called its spectrum) is analyzed.

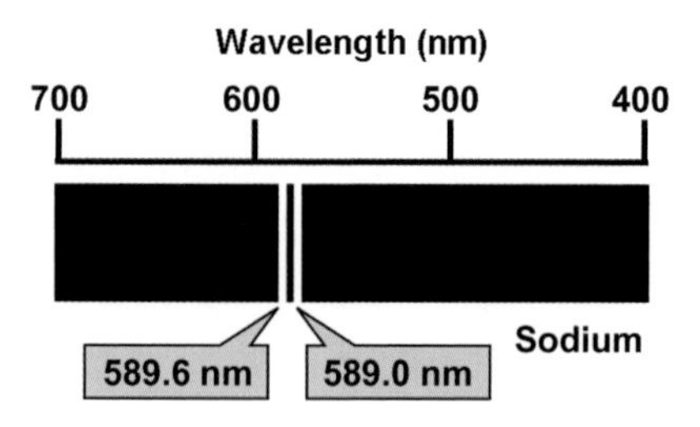

Figure 32.2: *When the element sodium is burned, two prominent yellow lines are observed at 589.0 and 589.6 nanometers on the scale of a spectrometer.*

Chemical composition of stars

During the mid-1800s, scientists used a device called a *spectrometer* to observe flames produced by burning substances. A spectrometer splits light into a spectrum of colors and displays lines of different colors along a scale. The scale measures the wavelength of each of the lines of color in nanometers (nm). The scientists discovered that each element has its own unique pattern of lines—like a fingerprint. For example, when the element sodium is burned, two prominent yellow lines at precisely 589.0 and 589.6 nanometers are observed when the light is passed through a spectrometer (Figure 32.2). *Spectroscopy* was born, and astronomers now had a tool they could use to determine the chemical composition of the stars.

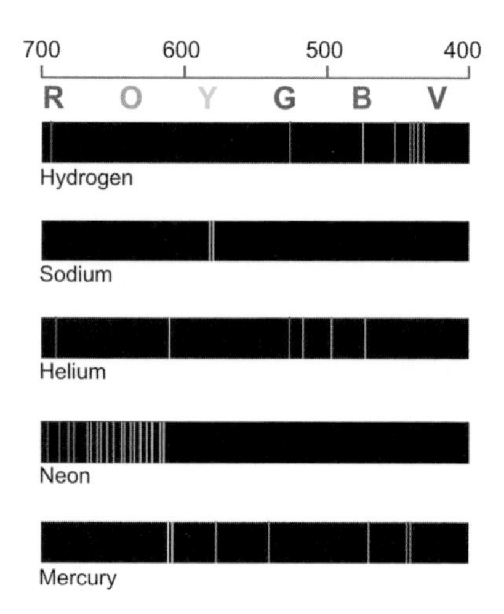

Figure 32.3: *Spectral lines for some of the other elements.*

The composition of the sun

In 1861, Sir William Huggins, an amateur astronomer in England, used spectroscopy to determine that the sun and the stars are composed mostly of hydrogen. A few years later, his countryman Sir Joseph Norman Lockyer observed a line at the precise wavelength of 587.6 nanometers. Since no known element on Earth had a line at this wavelength, he concluded that this must be an undiscovered element and named it helium, after the Greek name for the sun, *Helios*. Today, we know that hydrogen is the most abundant element in the universe, with helium second (Figure 32.3).

Color and temperature

When a bar of iron is heated, it first glows red. As its temperature increases, its color changes to orange, yellow, and finally white. The hottest objects have a bluish color. Scientists use this fact to determine the temperature of stars and other objects in space. For example, red stars have the coolest temperatures while blue stars have the hottest. Our sun is yellow, which means that its temperature is somewhere in between those of red stars and blue stars.

Classifying stars

How are stars classified?

At least 6,000 stars are visible in the night sky without the aid of a telescope. There are countless billions of stars in the universe that you cannot see. Astronomers classify stars according to their physical characteristics. The main characteristics used to classify stars are *size*, *temperature*, and *brightness*.

Sizes of stars

The sun, with a diameter of 1.4 million kilometers, is a *medium-sized* star. The closest star to the sun, Alpha Centauri, is also a medium-sized star. The largest stars, called *supergiants*, have a diameter that can exceed 1,000 times that of the sun. The largest known supergiant is 2,700 times the diameter of the sun. The next largest group of stars, simply called *giants*, are about 250 times the diameter of the sun. Stars that are smaller than the sun come in two categories, *white dwarfs* and *neutron stars*. White dwarfs are about the size of the smaller planets. Sirius B, the largest known white dwarf, has a diameter of 10,400 kilometers, making it slightly smaller than Earth. Neutron stars are even smaller—their diameter is only 20 to 30 kilometers! Figure 32.4 shows the relative sizes of each type of star.

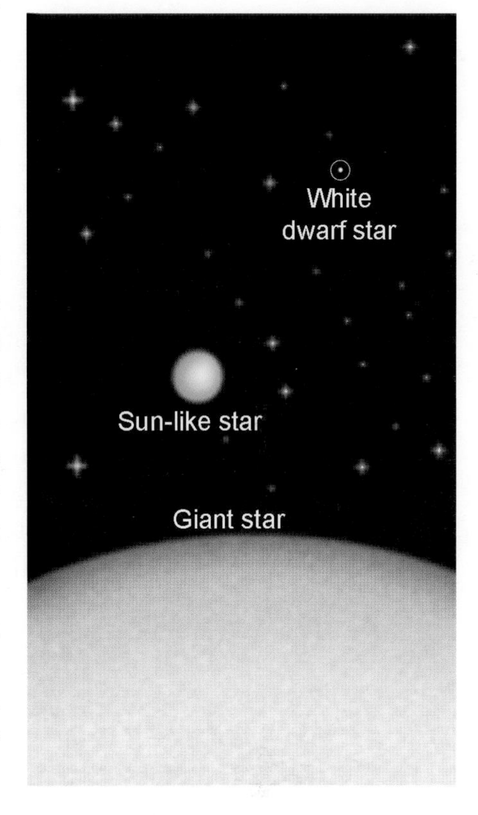

Figure 32.4: *Comparing different sizes of stars.*

Temperatures of stars

If you look closely at the stars on a clear night, you will see slight differences in their colors. This is related to the fact that their surface temperatures are different. You have already read that a red star is cooler than a white star, while blue stars are the hottest. The table below names some stars and gives their colors and their surface temperatures.

Table 32.1: *Stars, their colors, and their surface temperatures*

Star	Color	Temperature range (°C)
Betelgeuse	red	2,000 to 3,500
Arcturus	orange	3,500 to 5,000
Sun	yellow	5,000 to 6,000
Polaris	yellow-white	6,000 to 7,500
Sirius	white	7,500 to 11,000
Rigel	blue-white	11,000 to 25,000
Zeta Orionis	blue	25,000 to 50,000

Magnitudes

You will notice too that stars vary in their brightness. About 2,200 years ago, a Greek astronomer named Hipparchus classified the stars into six groups according to their brightness. He called these groups *magnitudes*. In his system, the brightest stars were called first-magnitude stars, and the faintest stars sixth-magnitude. Hipparchus' system is still in use. Because of improved tools, the magnitude scale has been extended to include fainter and brighter objects. Through a good telescope, we can see much fainter stars, almost to the 30th magnitude. This is 4 billion times fainter than the human eye can see unaided!

Apparent and absolute brightness

How bright a star appears in the sky depends on two factors: the star's distance from Earth and the amount of light (energy) it actually gives off. Astronomers define a star's brightness as observed from Earth as its **apparent brightness**. This quantity can be measured fairly easily using a *photometer* (an instrument that measures brightness). A star's **absolute brightness** is defined as the brightness the star would have if it were a standard distance from Earth. Astronomers arbitrarily set the standard distance at 10 *parsecs*. One parsec is equal to 3.26 light years. This means that 10 parsecs equals 32.6 light years.

The difference between apparent and absolute brightness

Imagine observing a candle that is two meters from you, and a campfire that is 100 meters away. From where you are, the candle appears brighter than the campfire, even though the campfire is giving off much more light. At these distances, the candle has a greater *apparent* brightness than the campfire. Suppose the candle and campfire are moved so that both are now 10 meters from you. When this happens, the campfire appears much brighter than the candle. This is because the campfire has a greater *absolute* brightness than the candle. Therefore, absolute brightness is a measure of how much light an object actually emits (Figure 32.5).

Apparent brightness decreases as distance increases

This example explains why the apparent brightness of an object depends on its absolute brightness and on how far away it is from an observer. As Figure 32.6 shows, just because one star appears brighter than another does not mean that it has a higher absolute brightness. The apparent brightness of an object decreases the farther away from it you move regardless of its absolute brightness. If you were to observe the sun from Pluto, the farthest planet, the sun would appear much dimmer. The relationship between apparent brightness, absolute brightness, and distance will be explored in Section 32.2.

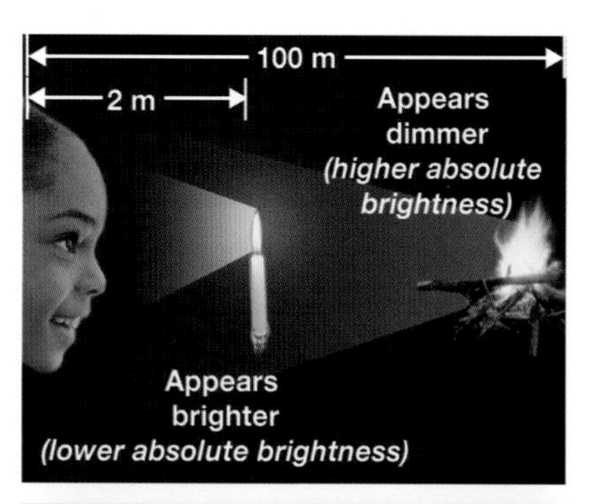

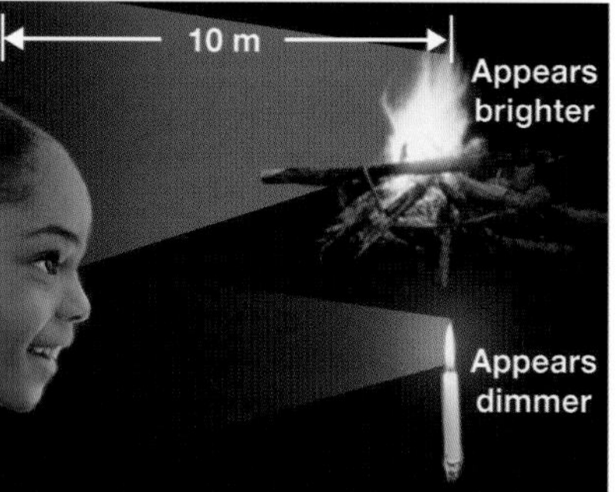

Figure 32.5: *An illustration of apparent and absolute brightness.*

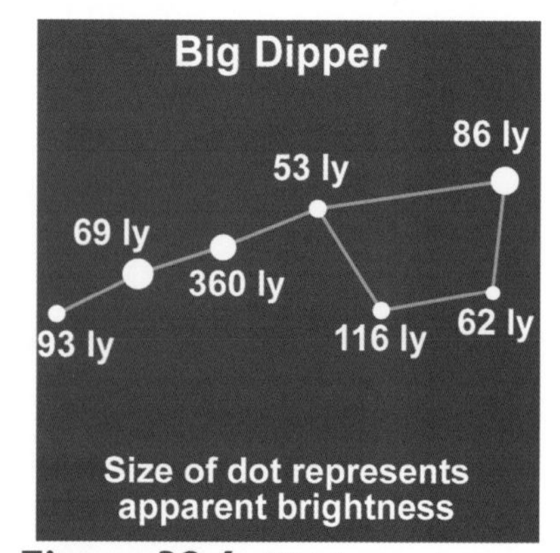

Figure 32.6: *Which star do you believe has the greatest absolute brightness? Explain your answer.*

Comparing temperature and brightness of stars

H-R diagrams In the early 1900s, the Danish astronomer Ejnar Hertzsprung and American astronomer Henry Russell developed an important tool for studying stars. They made a graph in which they plotted the temperature of the stars on the *x*-axis and the absolute brightness on the *y*-axis. The result is known as the *Hertzsprung-Russell*, or H-R diagram. In the example below, each dot on the diagram represents a star whose absolute brightness and temperature are known.

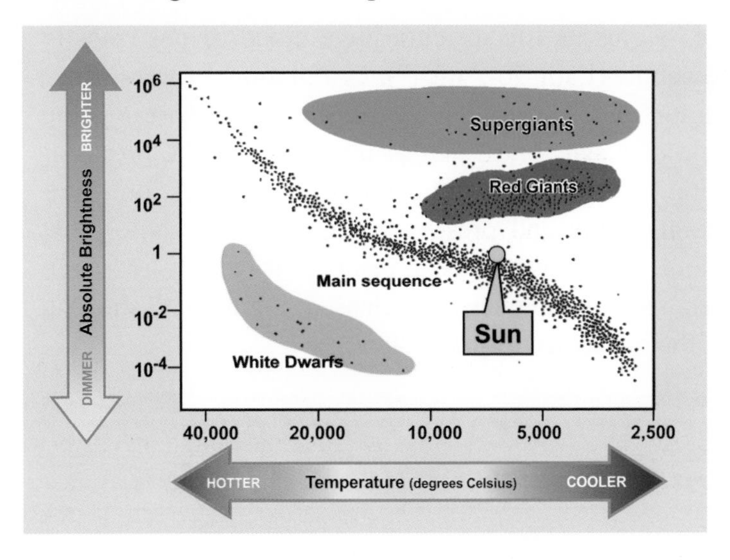

Reading H-R diagrams H-R diagrams are useful because they help astronomers categorize stars into distinct groups. Stars that fall into the band that stretches diagonally from cool, dim stars to hot, bright stars are called main sequence stars. Main sequence stars, like the sun, are in a very stable part of their life cycle (described on the next page). *White dwarfs* are in the lower left corner of the diagram. These stars are hot and dim and cannot be seen without a telescope. *Red giants* appear in the upper right side of the diagram. These stars are cool and bright and can be seen without the aid of a telescope in the night sky. *Supergiants*, both red and blue, are found in the extreme upper portion of the diagram. H-R diagrams are also useful because astronomers can use them to predict the absolute brightnesses of stars for which that value has not been determined.

Observing stars

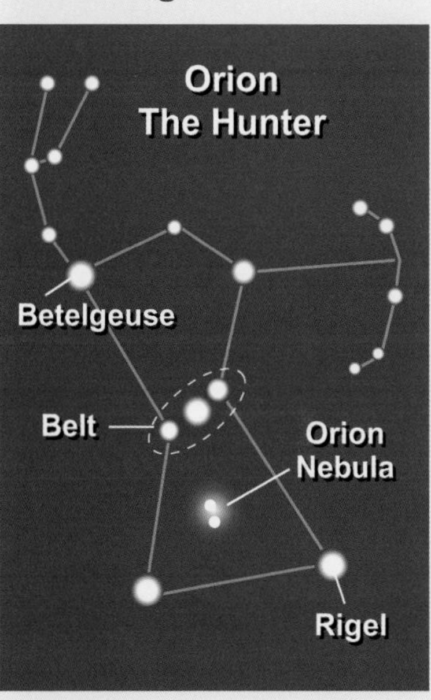

If you locate the constellation Orion in the night sky, you can see Betelgeuse, a red supergiant, and Rigel, a blue supergiant. It is easy to find this constellation because of the three stars that form its belt. Just below the belt is the Orion Nebula, which you can see with a pair of binoculars. You will learn about nebulas on the next few pages.

Life cycle of stars

Stars have a life cycle

Like living organisms, stars have a life cycle. Of course, stars are not truly "alive" but astronomers sometimes use the terms "born," "live," and "die" to represent parts of that cycle. Our sun, a medium-sized star, was born about 5 billion years ago. Because most medium-sized stars have a life span of around 10 billion years, it will live for another 5 billion years before it dies. Stars that are larger than the sun have shorter life spans.

How are stars born?

A star, regardless of its size, begins its life inside a huge cloud of gas (mostly hydrogen) and dust called a nebula (Latin for "mist"). Gravitational forces cause denser regions of the nebula to collapse, forming a *protostar*. A protostar is the earliest stage in the life cycle of a star. The gases at the center of the protostar continue to collapse, causing pressure and temperature to rise. A protostar becomes a *star* when the temperature and pressure at its center become great enough to start nuclear fusion. This is the nuclear reaction in which hydrogen atoms are converted into helium atoms and energy is released. Figure 32.7 shows a portion of the Orion Nebula, the birthplace of many stars.

A star is born when temperature and pressure become great enough to start nuclear fusion.

Main sequence stars

Once nuclear fusion begins, a star is in the *main sequence* stage of its life cycle. This is the longest and most stable part of a star's life. The length of the main sequence stage depends on a star's *mass*. You may suppose that stars with larger masses live longer than those with smaller masses because they contain more hydrogen fuel for nuclear fusion. The opposite is true. **Stars with large masses use up their hydrogen fuel more quickly than stars with small masses, so they have much shorter life spans.** Because of this, they burn brighter, and hotter than smaller stars. The main sequence stage of sun-like stars (stars with the same mass as the sun) lasts for about 10 billion years. The main sequence stage of stars over 100 times more massive than the sun lasts only a few million years. This stage for stars that are less massive than the sun can last for more than 50 billion years.

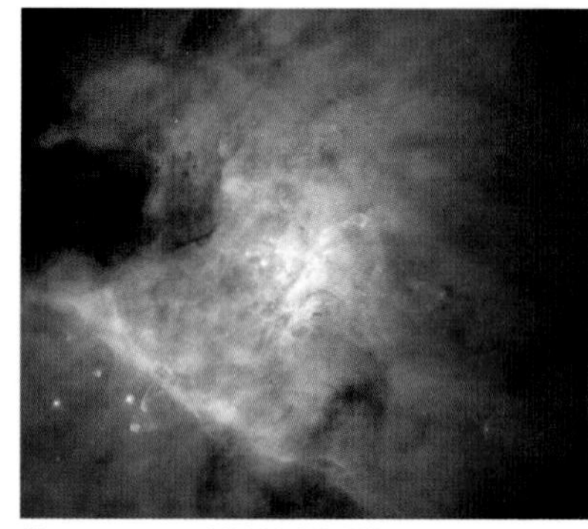

Photo courtesy of NASA-HQ-GRIN

Figure 32.7: *A NASA/HST photo of a portion of the Orion Nebula. A group of protostars is visible in the center of the nebula.*

The Orion Nebula

You can see the Orion Nebula if you look closely below the three stars that form Orion's belt. It will appear as a fuzzy spot to the naked eye on a very clear night. This nebula is over 20 light years in width. With binoculars, you can see some bright, young stars lighting up its center. With a powerful telescope, many protostars can be seen. When you look at the Orion Nebula, you are witnessing how our sun was born almost 5 billion years ago.

Old age As a star grows old, its core begins to run out of hydrogen fuel. Gravity causes the core to contract, raising its temperature and igniting the helium inside the core, along with any hydrogen in the outer layers. The star expands, and the outer layers begin to cool. At this stage in its life cycle, a small or medium-sized star becomes a *red giant*. When the sun reaches this stage in its life cycle (about 5 billion years from now), it will become so large that it will swallow up Mercury, Venus, and Earth.

Death Once the nuclear reactions in the core of small to medium-sized stars cease, there is nothing to prevent gravity from crushing the matter together as close as possible. At this stage, the core glows brightly and is called a *white dwarf*. It is about the size of Earth, and has the same mass as the sun. Because of its high density, a thimbleful of matter from a white dwarf on Earth would weigh about the same as an elephant! During the white-dwarf stage, the outer layers of the star expand and drift away from the core, forming what is called a *planetary nebula*. This is different from a nebula where stars are born.

Remnants When a white dwarf stops glowing, it is called a *black dwarf*, the final stage in the life cycle of small and medium-sized stars. The life cycle of stars is summarized in the diagram below. The death of massive stars is discussed on the following page.

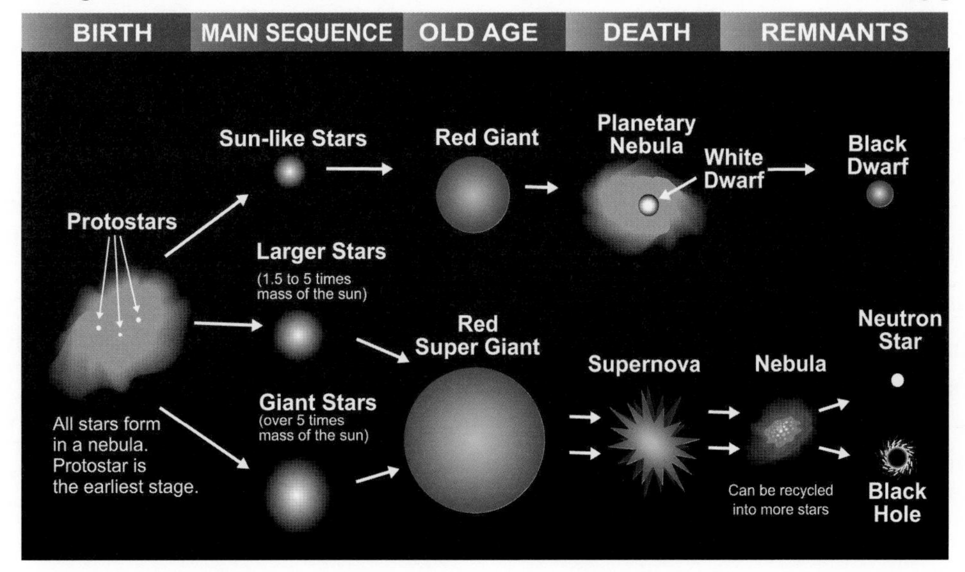

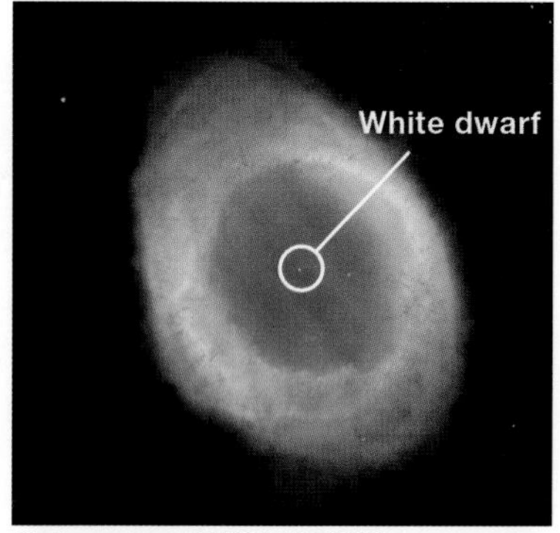

Photo courtesy of NASA-HQ-GRIN

Figure 32.8: *The famous Ring Nebula, showing the death of a sun-like star. The outer rings are called the planetary nebula. The glowing, white dwarf can be seen in the center. Photo courtesy NASA/HST.*

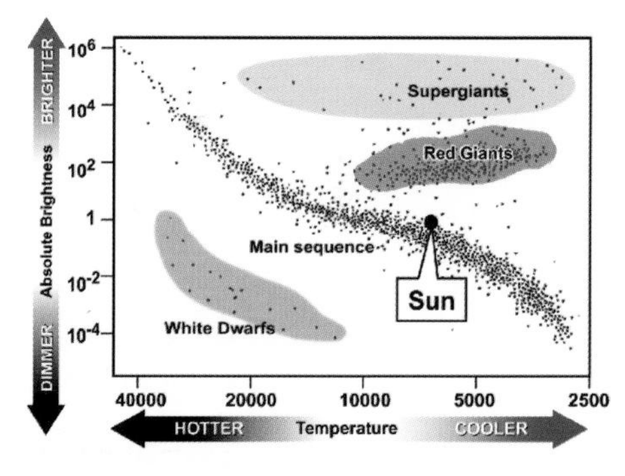

Figure 32.9: *Different stages in the star life cycle appear in clusters on the H-R diagram. Stars in the main sequence stage form the diagonal band that includes the sun. 90 percent of all stars are main sequence stars.*

The death of massive stars = the birth of elements

The creation of elements

Stars that are at least five times more massive than the sun have a different end to their life cycle. As the core begins to run out of hydrogen fuel, it yields to gravity and begins to shrink, growing hotter and denser. More heat is generated by this contraction than in a small or medium star, so the core does not become a white dwarf. Instead, the tremendous heat generated causes helium atoms to fuse into carbon and oxygen atoms. This is followed by the fusion of carbon and oxygen atoms into neon, sodium, magnesium, sulfur, and silicon. Meanwhile, the outer layers of the massive star expand and cool, making the star a *red supergiant*.

The end of fusion in the core

Once the carbon atoms in the core are depleted, it shrinks again, creating even greater pressure and temperatures. This causes the fusion of even heavier elements such as calcium, nickel, chromium, copper, iron, and others. When the core of the star contains mostly iron, the fusion stops. This is because iron's nuclear structure does not allow the fusion of heavier elements. In fact, the fusion of elements heavier than iron *requires* energy, rather than *producing* it.

Supernovas

Because a giant star has such a great mass, almost the moment fusion stops in its core, it begins to collapse from the tremendous gravity. This collapse of the entire mass of the star upon the core causes the temperature inside to rise to over 100 million °C as the iron atoms are crushed together. A huge repulsive force between the iron nuclei overcomes the force of gravity, causing a spectacular explosion to occur, called a supernova. The actual explosion takes only a few minutes (Figure 32.10). During this brief period, heavier elements such as gold and uranium are created, as atomic nuclei are smashed together. The explosion propels the matter out into space in all directions.

Neutron stars and black holes

The light and heat produced by a supernova fades over time, and the remnants become a nebula that can be recycled again to make more stars. All that remains of the original star is a core composed entirely of neutrons called a *neutron star*. This super-dense object is no more than a few kilometers in diameter! If a dying star has a core that is three or more times the mass of the sun, the force of its collapse is so strong that an explosion cannot occur. The gravitational forces are so strong that not even light can escape. All that is left is a phenomenon called a *black hole*.

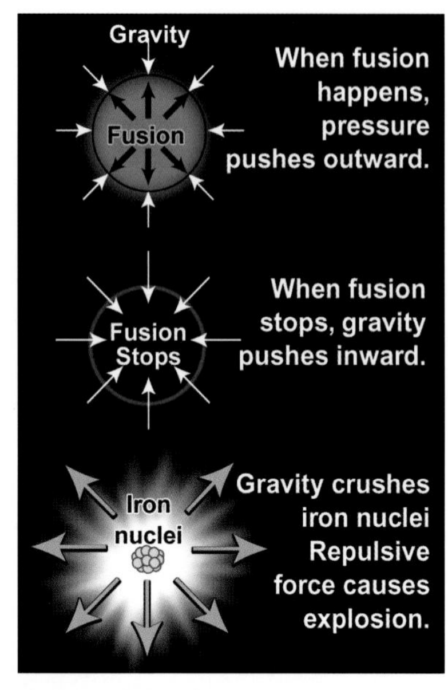

Figure 32.10: *How a supernova happens.*

Supernova sightings

In 1054 AD, a supernova was observed and recorded by Chinese astronomers. They observed a star so bright that it could be seen both night and day. The remnants make up the Crab Nebula. The only supernova to be observed in modern times occurred in 1987. Light from the explosion reached Earth on February 23, 1987, after a journey of 169,000 light years.

The formation of the solar system

Do other planetary systems exist?

In 1995, three Earth-sized planets were discovered orbiting a star much like our sun. This was among the first evidence of a star other than the sun with orbiting planets. A star with orbiting planets is called a planetary system. Since then several other planetary systems have been detected. Scientists now believe that planets are a natural by-product of the formation of stars. Therefore, planets of some type should exist around many stars in the universe.

How was our solar system formed?

The solar system was formed out of the same nebula that created the sun. As the sun was being formed 4.6 billion years ago, it was surrounded by a cloud of dust and gas. This cloud was made mostly of hydrogen and helium, but contained smaller amounts of other elements such as carbon, nickel, iron, aluminum, and silicon. As this cloud spun around, it flattened, with the help of gravity, into a disk-shape along the axis of its rotation. This explains why all of the planets formed in the same plane around the sun, and why they all orbit in the same direction.

Planet formation

At the center of the disk, temperatures became hot enough for fusion to begin, creating the sun. Farther away from the center, the heaviest molecules began to condense into solid and liquid droplets. These droplets began to collide, forming small clumps—the seeds of the planets. Through further collisions, these clumps of material grew larger and eventually formed into the planets.

The terrestrial planets

Terrestrial planets, like Earth, were formed in the warmer, inner regions of the disk. Because the heat drove off the lighter elements such as hydrogen and helium, these planets were made mostly of metals and rock. These materials made up less than one percent of the disk, so these planets could not grow very large. Because of their small masses, their gravity could not attract hydrogen and helium and their atmospheres were thin and contained little of these elements.

The gas planets

The outer regions of the disk were rich in icy materials made of lighter elements and the planets there grew comparatively large. Because of their large masses, they were able to capture hydrogen and helium through their gravitational force and so form thick atmospheres. These became *gas planets*, rich in hydrogen and helium with dense, frozen cores. The outermost planet, Pluto, is neither a gas nor a terrestrial planet, but a tiny, frozen object with a thin atmosphere.

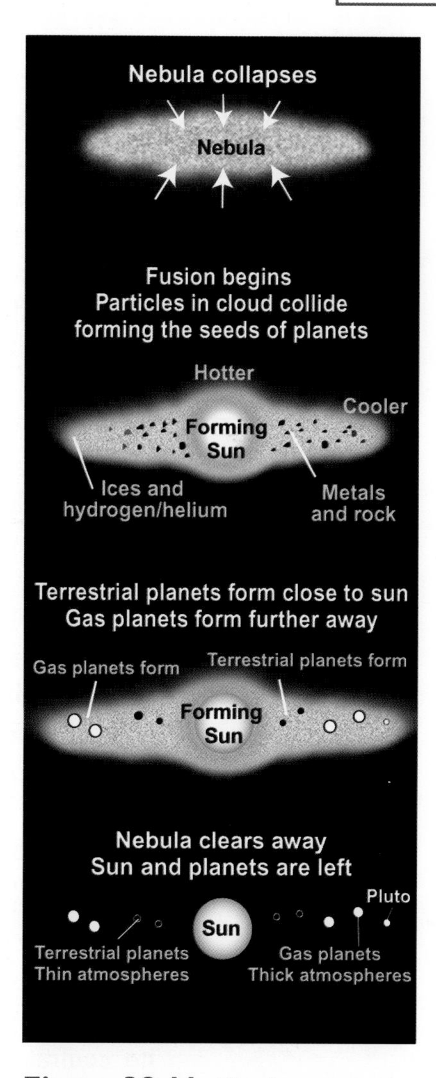

Figure 32.11: *The formation of our solar system. Scientists now believe that this is a common process in the universe.*

32.2 Galaxies and the Universe

Early civilizations believed that Earth was the center of the universe. In the 16th century, we became aware that Earth is a small planet orbiting a medium-sized star. It was only in the 20th century that we became aware that the sun is one of billions of stars in the Milky Way Galaxy, and that there are billions of other galaxies in the universe. In the past three decades, astronomers have found evidence that the universe is expanding and that it originated 10 to 20 billion years ago. In this section you will learn about galaxies and theories about how the universe began. You will also learn how astronomers measure the vast distances of galaxies and stars from Earth.

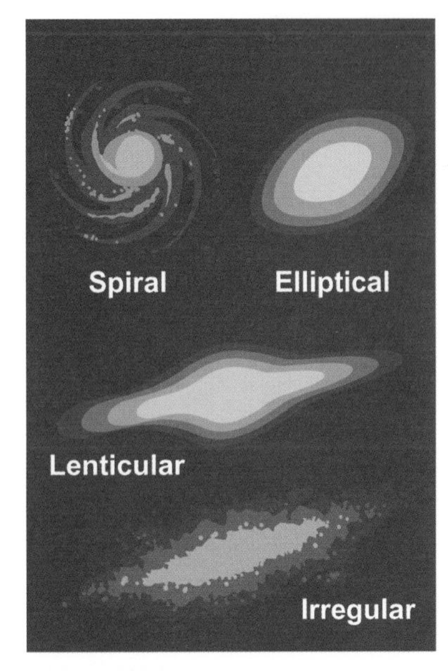

Figure 32.12: *Galaxy shapes.*

What is a galaxy?

The discovery of other galaxies A *galaxy* is a huge group of stars, dust, gas, and other objects bound together by gravitational forces. In the 1920s, American astronomer Edwin Hubble (1889-1953) discovered that there were galaxies beyond the Milky Way. He used a new, 2.5-meter reflecting telescope to establish that some of the many fuzzy patches of light long known to astronomers were indeed separate galaxies. For example, when he focused the huge telescope on an object thought to be a nebula in the constellation Andromeda, Hubble could see that the "nebula" actually consisted of faint, distant stars. He named the object the Andromeda Galaxy. Just since Hubble's time, astronomers have discovered a large number of galaxies. In fact, many new galaxies are detected each year using the telescope named after Hubble—the Hubble Space Telescope or HST.

Galaxy shapes Astronomers classify galaxies according to their shape. *Spiral galaxies* like the Milky Way consist of a central, dense area surrounded by spiraling arms. *Elliptical galaxies* look like the central portion of a spiral galaxy without the arms. *Lenticular galaxies* are lens-shaped with a smooth, even distribution of stars and no central, denser area. *Irregular galaxies* exhibit peculiar shapes and do not appear to rotate like those galaxies of other shapes. Figure 32.12 shows an example of each galaxy shape. The Cartwheel Galaxy (Figure 32.13) demonstrates what happens when two galaxies collide. This shape occurred when a large, spiral galaxy was struck by a smaller galaxy. The ring-like band of stars formed much like ripples occur when a rock is dropped into water.

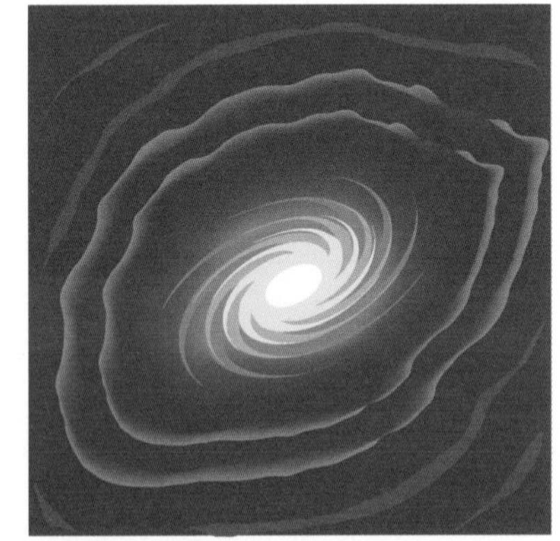

Figure 32.13: *When the Cartwheel Galaxy was struck by a smaller galaxy, a ring-like band of stars formed, much like ripples form in a pond.*

The Milky Way Galaxy

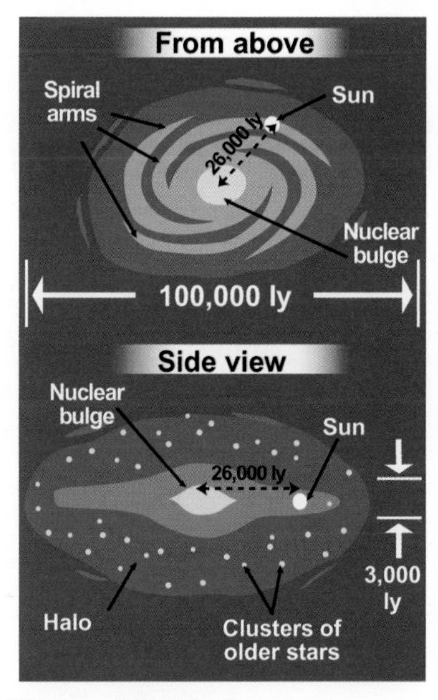

Figure 32.14: *The Milky Way is a typical spiral galaxy.*

Structure of our galaxy

The sun, along with an estimated 200 billion other stars, belongs to the Milky Way Galaxy. The Milky Way is a typical spiral galaxy. From above, it would look like a giant pinwheel, with arms radiating out from a central region. The stars are arranged in a *disk* that is more than 100,000 light years across. If you could look at it from the side, you would see that our galaxy is much flatter than it is wide. In fact, it is only about 3,000 light years thick on average. At the center of the disk is a denser region of stars called the *nuclear bulge*. Surrounding the outer regions of the galaxy is an area containing clusters of older stars known as the *halo*. Figure 32.14 shows a diagram of the Milky Way Galaxy.

The disk

The disk of the Milky Way is a flattened, rotating system that contains young to middle-aged stars, along with gas and dust. The sun sits about 26,000 light years from the center of the disk and revolves around the center of the galaxy about once every 250 million years. When you look up at the night sky, you are actually looking through the disk of the galaxy. On a very clear night, you can see a faint band of light stretching across the sky. This is the combined light of billions of stars in the disk of our galaxy, so numerous that their light merges together.

The center of the galaxy

Since we are located in the outer part of the galaxy, the *interstellar* (between the stars) dust blocks out much of the visible light coming from objects within the disk. Because of this, astronomers use infrared and radio telescopes to study our galaxy. Using these tools, they have learned that the center of the galaxy is crowded with older stars and hot dust. Recent studies have suggested that a black hole, with a mass of more than a million suns, exists at the very center of the galaxy. It is believed that this black hole has enough gravitational pull to keep in orbit all of the stars, gas, and dust in the Milky Way Galaxy.

Evidence for the black hole theory

The evidence for a huge black hole comes from measurements of the orbital speeds of stars and gas at the center of the galaxy. In one study, an infrared telescope was used to measure the orbital speeds of 20 stars over a three-year period. It was determined that these stars were orbiting at speeds of up to 1,000 kilometers per second (3 million miles per hour!). This extremely high orbital speed requires an object with a mass that is over 2 million times that of the sun.

The Local Group

The Milky Way is part of a cluster of galaxies known as the Local Group. In addition to our galaxy, the group contains other spiral galaxies such as the Andromeda Galaxy. Irregular galaxies in the Local Group include the Large and Small Magellanic Clouds. In all, there are about 40 galaxies in the Local Group. Other groups of galaxies also exist.

Determining distances to closer objects in the universe

Measuring the distance of closer stars

One of the greatest challenges facing astronomers is how to determine the vast distances of stars and galaxies from Earth. This information is key to mapping the universe. For objects that are under 1,000 light years from Earth, astronomers use a method called parallax. Parallax is the apparent change in position of an object when you look at it from different directions.

An illustration of parallax

To illustrate parallax, hold one finger about six inches from your nose. Close your left eye and look at your finger with your right eye. Next, close your right eye and look at your finger with your left eye. Because your eyes are in different positions, your finger appears to move. The same is true of stars in the sky. As Earth revolves around the sun, the stars appear to change positions in the sky over the course of one year. It is actually Earth that is changing position as it revolves around the sun, while the stars remain fixed in the background (Figure 32.15).

Parallax only works for closer stars

Parallax only works for stars that are relatively close because as distance from Earth increases, the change in angle of a star becomes less measurable. You can demonstrate this by looking at a finger held before your nose as you did before. This time, try moving your finger farther and farther away from your nose while looking at it with each eye. You will notice that the farther away it is, the smaller the movement appears to become until you can detect no movement at all.

How to measure distance using parallax

To use parallax, astronomers determine the position of a star in the sky in relation to other stars that are too far away to show movement. Next, they look at the star six months later—when Earth is on the opposite side of the sun, and measure its change in position in relation to the faraway stars. Using geometry, they can determine the distance of the star from Earth (Figure 32.16 and below).

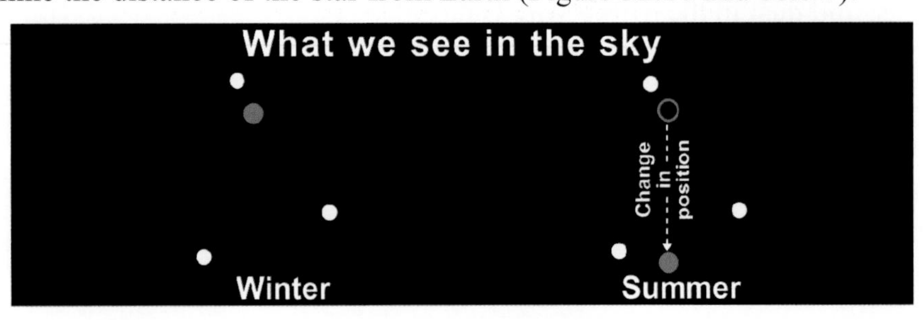

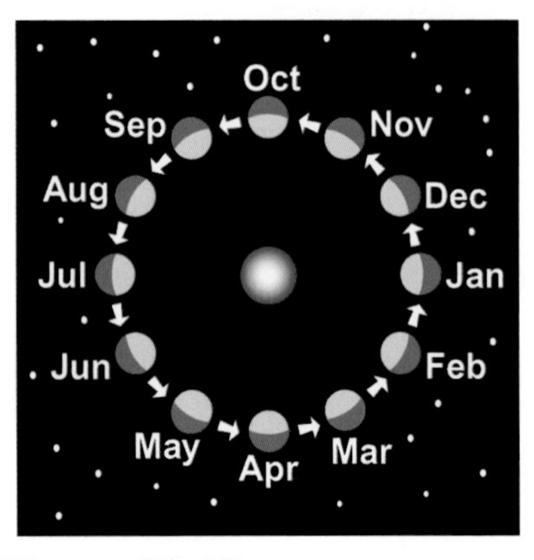

Figure 32.15: *The night side of Earth always faces away from the sun. As Earth revolves around the sun, the stars seen in the sky appear to move even though they remain fixed.*

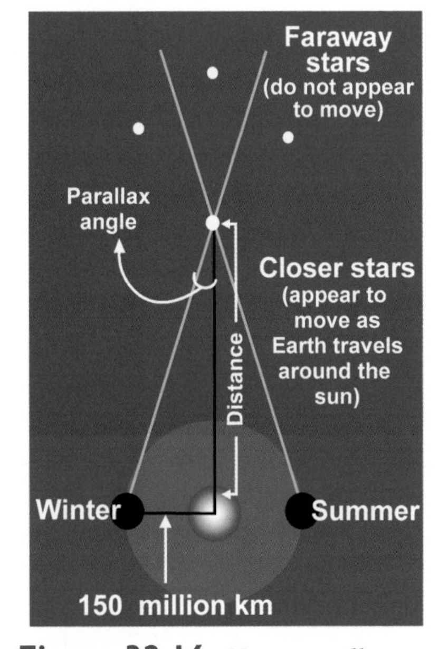

Figure 32.16: *Using parallax to measure the distance to a star.*

Measuring distances to faraway objects in the universe

The inverse square law

Light is very important to astronomers in measuring the distances to objects that are more than 1,000 light years away. Recall that the apparent brightness of an object depends on how far away it is, and how much light it actually gives off (its absolute brightness). The mathematical relationship between these variables is known as the inverse square law and is used to determine the distance to stars and galaxies.

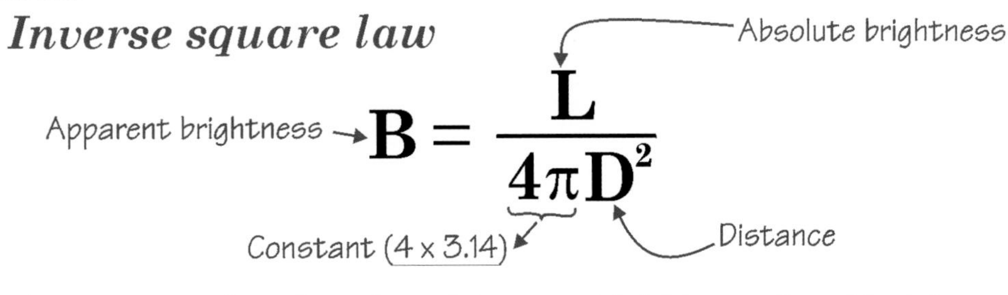

Apparent brightness vs. distance

$$B \alpha \frac{1}{D^2}$$

The inverse square law shows how the apparent brightness of an object decreases as you move away from it. The amount of decrease in apparent brightness can be quantified using the formula at left. The symbol α indicates a proportional relationship. For example, if you are looking at a candle from one meter away, and then you move two meters away, its apparent brightness will decrease by a factor of *four*. Or if you move three meters away, its apparent brightness will decrease by a factor of *nine*. By what factor will its apparent brightness decrease if you move 10 meters away? If you did an experiment where you measured the apparent brightness of a candle at various distances, starting at one meter, your graph would look similar to Figure 32.17.

Solving for distance

$$D = \sqrt{\frac{L}{4\pi B}}$$

The inverse square law is important to astronomers because if they know the apparent and absolute brightness of an object, they can determine its distance by rearranging the variables to solve for D as shown in the equation at left.

Recall that apparent brightness (B) can be easily measured using a photometer. The challenge facing astronomers is how to determine the absolute brightness (L) of faraway objects.

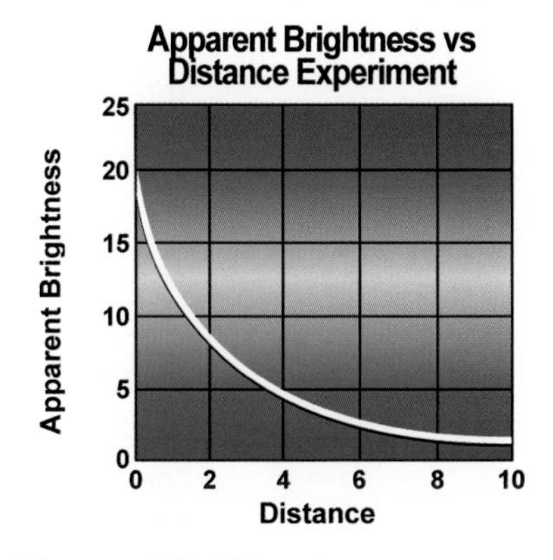

Figure 32.17: *A graph of the apparent brightness of a candle at various distances.*

Measuring brightness

Brightness is measured in units of power. In the laboratory, you can measure the brightness of a light source in *watts*. Because the brightness of objects in space is so great, astronomers developed *solar luminosity units*. One solar luminosity unit is equal to the brightness of the sun, or about 3.9×10^{26} watts. This is comparable to the combined brightness of 400 trillion trillion 100-watt light bulbs! Our galaxy emits as much light as 1.0×10^{10} suns.

Standard candles

Astronomers have found a way to *infer* values for absolute brightness (L) using a source of light called a **standard candle**. A standard candle is an object, such as a star, whose absolute brightness is known.

Measuring the distance to stars in the Milky Way

You are already familiar with one type of standard candle called *main sequence stars*. Recall that main sequence stars are found in a diagonal band on the H-R diagram. It is estimated that 90 percent of all stars are main sequence. Through observation, astronomers can determine if a star is a main sequence star by comparing it to stars on the H-R diagram. By determining the unknown star's temperature (using a spectrometer), they can infer its absolute brightness by choosing a similar main sequence star on the H-R diagram as shown in Figure 32.18. Next, they measure the unknown star's apparent brightness, and use the inverse square law to calculate its distance. Astronomers use this method to measure distances to stars in the Milky Way and nearby galaxies—out to distances of about 200,000 light years. Beyond that, astronomers cannot see main sequence stars and must rely on other types of standard candles.

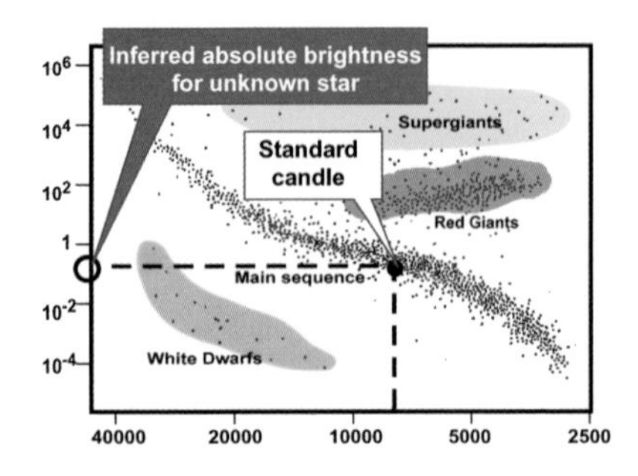

Figure 32.18: *Inferring the absolute brightness of an unknown star using the H-R diagram and main sequence stars as a standard candle.*

Measuring distances to galaxies

A second type of standard candle is called a **Cepheid** star. This type of star was discovered by Henrietta Leavitt (1868-1921), an American, in the early 1900s. Cepheid stars "pulsate" in regular periods ranging from a few days to a few weeks. Leavitt discovered that there is a relationship between the period of Cepheid star and its absolute brightness. This meant that by measuring the period of a Cepheid star, astronomers could determine its absolute brightness and then, use the inverse square law to calculate its distance. Astronomers locate Cepheids in faraway galaxies and use them to map distances between galaxies in the universe. The Hubble Space Telescope actively searches for Cepheids in faraway galaxies.

Going even farther

Beyond 100 million light years, Cepheid stars are too faint to observe—even with the Hubble. For these distances, astronomers must rely on a third type of standard candle—a certain type of supernova. By observing the rate at which light from the supernova fades after the initial explosion, astronomers can use a mathematical formula to determine its absolute brightness, and then use the inverse square law to infer the distance to the galaxy in which the supernova resides.

The North Star

The North Star is the brightest Cepheid star. Because it is only 390 light years from Earth, its distance can also be measured using parallax. This is one of the stars that helped astronomers refine the use of Cepheids to determine distances. The Cepheid star first discovered, Delta Cephei, is also relatively close to Earth at 300 light years.

The Big Bang theory

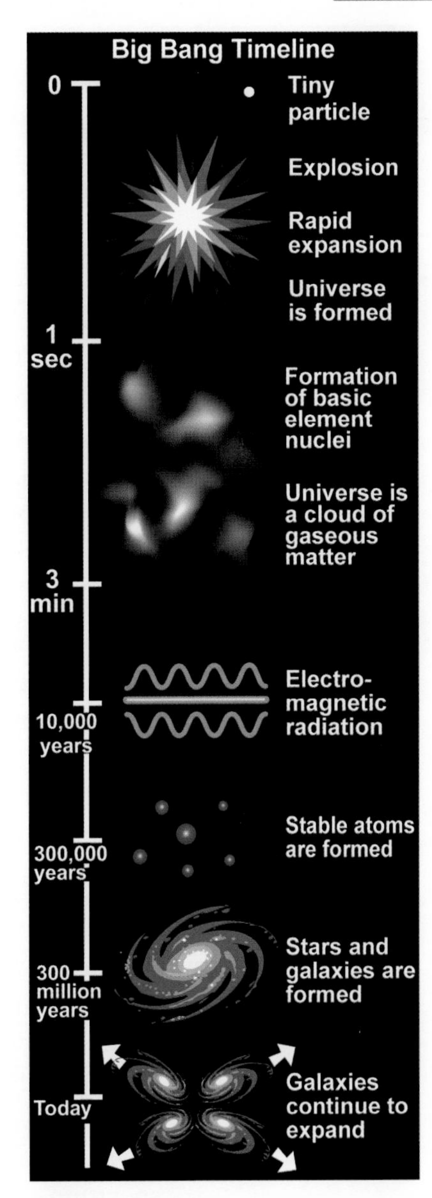

Figure 32.19: *A timeline for the Big Bang.*

What is the Big Bang theory? The *universe* is defined as everything that exists, including all matter and energy. While there are many theories about how it began, the one that has gained credibility among scientists is called the **Big Bang**. The Big Bang theory states that the universe began as a huge explosion that occurred somewhere between 10 and 20 billion years ago.

The explosion According to the Big Bang theory, all of the matter and energy in the universe started out compressed into a space no bigger than the nucleus of an atom. Suddenly, a huge explosion occurred that sent everything that makes up the universe out in all directions. For an instant, the universe was an extremely hot ball of fire that began to expand rapidly. Extreme heat from the explosion (10 billion°C) caused the formation of subatomic particles.

Formation of hydrogen and helium Immediately after the explosion, the universe began to expand and cool. Some scientists believe that it expanded from the size of an atomic nucleus, to 6×10^{30} kilometers in a fraction of a second! In less than a second, the expansion of the universe started to slow down. The universe became a cloud of matter and energy that was rapidly cooling and becoming less dense as it expanded. After a few minutes, at temperatures of around 1 billion°C, hydrogen nuclei began forming. Next, hydrogen nuclei began combining in pairs to form helium nuclei.

Radiation period Ten thousand years after the explosion, most of the energy in the universe was in the form of electromagnetic radiation of different wavelengths including X rays, radio waves, and ultraviolet radiation. As the universe continued to cool and expand, these waves were changed into a form called *cosmic microwave background radiation* which can be measured today.

The first galaxies After 300,000 years, the temperature had cooled to around 10,000°C. Lithium atoms began to form at this stage and electrons joined with the atomic nuclei to form the first stable (neutral) atoms. The universe continued as a giant cloud of gas until about 300 million years after the Big Bang. Parts of the gas cloud began to collapse and ignite to form clusters of stars—the first galaxies. The universe has continued to form galaxies since then. These galaxies continue to expand outward from the initial point of the Big Bang.

Evidence for the Big Bang

Growing evidence When it was first introduced, not everyone believed the Big Bang. In fact, the name "Big Bang" was made up by scientists to mock the theory. Unfortunately for them, the name stuck! As with any new theory, the Big Bang became more accepted as new scientific tools and discoveries established supporting evidence. In particular, scientific understanding of electromagnetic waves such as visible light, X rays, and microwaves, has provided important evidence to support the Big Bang theory.

Doppler shift In the 1800s, Christian Doppler (1803-53), an Austrian physicist, discovered that when the source of a sound wave is moving, its frequency changes. You may have noticed this effect if you have heard a car drive by with its horn blaring. As the car approaches, you hear the horn playing high "notes," and as the car passes, you hear the horn shift to lower notes as the car moves farther away. The change in sound you hear is caused by a Doppler shift (also called the Doppler effect).

How does it work? As the car is moving toward you, the sound waves are compressed relative to where you are standing. This shortens the wavelength and causes the frequency to increase (recall that wavelength and frequency are inversely related). As the car moves away, the sound waves are stretched out, causing longer wavelengths and lower frequencies (Figure 32.20). The sound of the horn changes as the car passes by because the sound waves are being compressed and then stretched. If you could measure the rate of change in the frequency, you could measure the speed of the car.

Doppler shift and electromagnetic waves Doppler shift also occurs with electromagnetic waves such as visible light, X rays, and microwaves. This phenomenon is an important tool used by astronomers to study the motion of objects in space. For example, if an object is moving toward Earth, the light waves it emits are compressed, shifting them toward the violet end (shorter wavelengths, higher frequencies) of the visible spectrum. If an object is moving away from Earth, the light waves it emits are stretched, shifting them toward the red end (longer wavelengths, lower frequencies) of the visible spectrum (Figure 32.21).

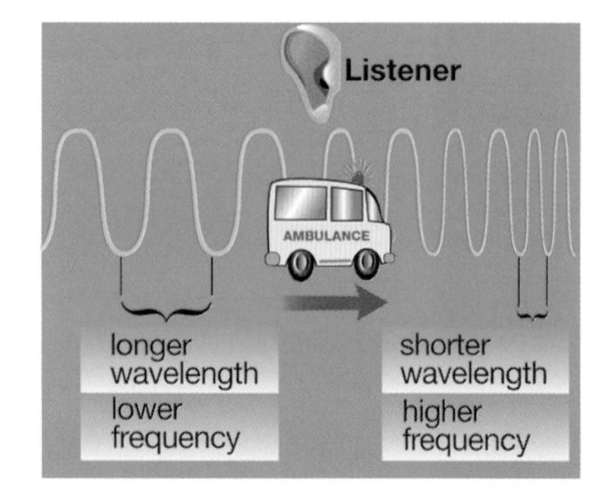

Figure 32.20: *The Doppler effect occurs when an object is moving toward or away from an observer.*

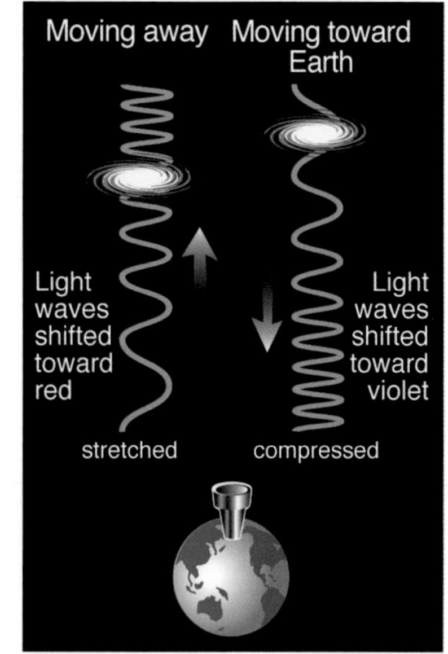

Figure 32.21: *Doppler shift is used to study the motion of objects in space.*

Sirius is moving away from Earth

In the 1890s, astronomers began to combine the use of spectroscopy and Doppler shift to study the motion of stars and other objects in space. One of the first stars they studied, Sirius, had spectral lines in the same pattern as the spectrum for hydrogen. However, these lines did not have the exact same measurements as those for hydrogen. Instead, they were shifted toward the red end of the visible spectrum. Scientists realized that this meant that Sirius was moving away from Earth. They could even determine how fast Sirius was moving away by measuring the amount that the lines had shifted toward red. The top diagram (right) shows the wavelength of hydrogen spectral lines for an object that is not moving. The bottom diagram shows the hydrogen spectral lines for a moving star. Can you see how the lines have shifted?

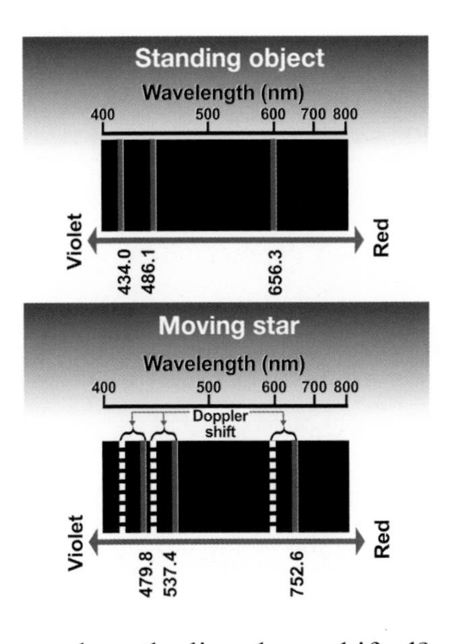

Evidence for the Big Bang

In the early 1900s, Hubble began to study the motion of galaxies. He used Cepheid stars to determine the distances of galaxies from Earth. Next, he studied the Doppler shift of each galaxy and found that the farther away a galaxy was, the faster it was moving. He was also able to determine the direction that each galaxy was moving. By the early 1930s, he had enough evidence to prove that galaxies were moving away from a single point in the universe. This supported two key parts of the Big Bang Theory: that the universe is expanding and that it originated from a single point.

Microwave background radiation

In the 1960s, Arno Penzias and Robert Wilson, two American astrophysicists, were trying to measure electromagnetic radiation emitted by the Milky Way. No matter how they refined their technique, they kept detecting a background noise that interfered with their observations. This noise seemed to be coming from all directions and had little variation in frequency. After publishing a paper describing their failed experiment, it was determined that they had discovered the cosmic microwave background radiation predicted by the Big Bang theory. Penzias and Wilson won the Nobel Prize for their discovery.

Stephen Hawking

Stephen Hawking was born on January 8, 1942, in Oxford, England. As a teenager, he invented elaborate games. As a young man, Hawking studied physics at Oxford University. In 1962, he went to Cambridge to study cosmology, the branch of astrophysics that studies the evolution and structure of the universe. At Cambridge, Stephen was diagnosed with Lou Gehrig's disease, which destroys the nerves that control muscles. Hawking was told he would become weaker, then paralyzed, and that he had only two years to live. Although devastated by this diagnosis, Hawking realized there were things he wanted to do with his time. He found he was enjoying his studies and he became engaged to Jane Wilde. Hawking said his engagement gave him something to live for, and also meant that he needed to finish his doctorate and get a job. In time, Hawking did both and became a highly-acclaimed scientist. He is known for his work on black holes, "space-time singularities," and linking Einstein's theory of relativity and quantum mechanics. He is also the author of popular books such as *A Brief History of Time* (1988) and *The Universe in a Nutshell* (2001).

Chapter 32 Review

Vocabulary review

Match the following terms with the correct definition. There is one extra definition in the list that will not match any of the terms.

Set One

1. apparent brightness	a. A cloud of gas and dust that gives rise to stars
2. absolute brightness	b. The most numerous category of stars in the universe
3. main sequence star	c. A diagram used to categorize stars
4. protostar	d. How bright an object appears from a distance
5. nebula	e. How bright an object actually is; for a star, how bright it appears from a standard distance
	f. The earliest stage in the life cycle of a star

Set Two

1. parallax	a. A star with orbiting planets
2. inverse square law	b. An object, such as a star, whose absolute brightness is known
3. standard candle	c. The universe began when a huge explosion occurred
4. Big Bang theory	d. The apparent change in position of an object when viewed from different positions
5. Doppler shift	e. The relationship between apparent brightness, absolute brightness, and distance
	f. A change in frequency of waves emitted by an object related to its movement

Concept review

1. Describe the conditions necessary to create a star.
2. Explain why spectroscopy is an important tool of astronomy.
3. What information does the color of a star provide?
4. What are the three main characteristics used to classify stars?
5. What is the difference between apparent brightness and absolute brightness?
6. What is the difference between a refracting telescope and a reflecting telescope?
7. What information about a star is required in order to plot it on the H-R diagram?
8. Why is the H-R diagram useful to astronomers?
9. Describe the life cycle of a sun-like star. Include in your description the following terms: nebula, protostar, red giant, planetary nebula, white dwarf, and black dwarf.
10. How long a star lives is related to which of the following quantities: (a) size; (b) temperature; (c) mass; or (d) color
11. How do astronomers classify galaxies?
12. What is a standard candle? How are they used to measure distances to faraway galaxies?
13. What is Doppler shift? How does Doppler shift provide evidence for the Big Bang theory?

Problems

1. A star is 15 parsecs from Earth. How far is this distance in light years? How far is it in kilometers?

2. The diagram below shows a group of stars as seen in the night sky. In the diagram, the relative size of each star indicates how bright it appears in the sky. Next to each star, its distance from Earth, in light years (ly) is shown. Use the diagram to answer the three questions below.

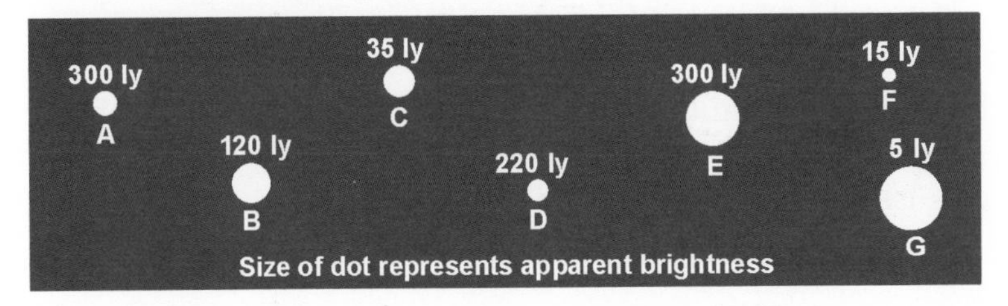

   a. Which star has the greatest apparent brightness? Explain your answer.

   b. If all of the stars in the diagram were moved to a distance of ten parsecs from Earth, which star would appear the brightest?

   c. Which star do you think has the lowest absolute brightness? Explain your answer.

3. Arrange the stars in the table below in order, from highest temperature, to lowest temperature.

Star	Color
A	white
B	orange
C	blue
D	red
E	blue-white
F	yellow

4. Use the H-R diagram below to answer the following questions.

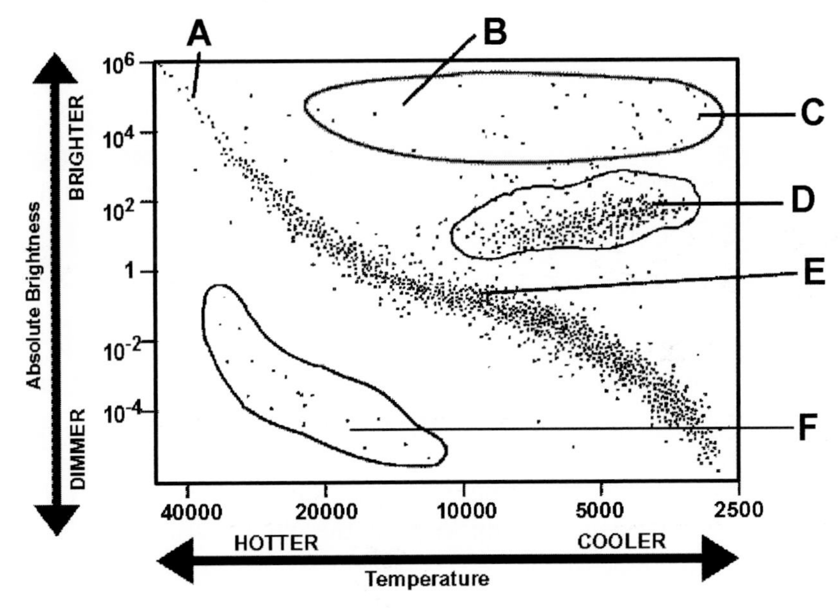

   a. Which letter corresponds to a sun-like star?

   b. Which letter corresponds to a blue supergiant?

   c. Which letter corresponds to a white dwarf?

   d. Which letter corresponds to a red supergiant?

   e. Which letter corresponds to an old star that was once a sun-like, main sequence star?

5. You are looking at a candle from 3 meters away. By what factor will its apparent brightness decrease if you move 18 meters away?

6. You are looking at a candle from 20 meters away. By what factor will its apparent brightness increase if you move 10 meters closer to the candle?

Applying your knowledge

1. The table below lists some data for six stars. Use the table, and your knowledge of stars, to answer questions **a** through **g**.

Star	Color	Solar mass (× mass of the sun)	Solar diameter (× diameter of the sun)	Prominent spectral lines (elements present)
A	white	1.0	.02	carbon, helium
B	red	6.0	400	magnesium, sodium
C	yellow-white	1.5	1.5	hydrogen
D	blue	12.0	900	hydrogen, helium
E	blue	1.5	1.5	hydrogen, helium
F	red	1.5	250	carbon, helium

   a. Which star is the final stage of a sun-like star's life cycle? Explain your answer. What is the name astronomers give to this type of star?

   b. Which star is the most like our sun? Justify your answer.

   c. Which star is a blue supergiant?

   d. Which stars could become black holes? Explain your answer.

   e. Which star will have the shortest life span? Explain why.

   f. Which stars are most likely main sequence stars? Explain your answer.

   g. Which star resembles what our sun will become in about 5 billion years? Explain your answer.

2. Everything you are made of originally came from the stars. Explain the meaning of this statement and why it is reasonable.

3. JAN FEB MAR Create a printed catalog or computer presentation about the astronomical objects you learned about in this unit (planets, stars, galaxies, etc. Follow these steps:

   a. Make a list of all of the astronomical objects you learned about in this unit (planets, stars, etc.).

   b. Write a definition and description of each type of object.

   c. Using the Internet, find images of each type of object to use for your catalog or presentation.

4. The light from two stars (A and B) is analyzed using a spectrometer. The spectral lines for these stars are shown below. Also shown are the spectral lines for hydrogen from a light source that is not moving.

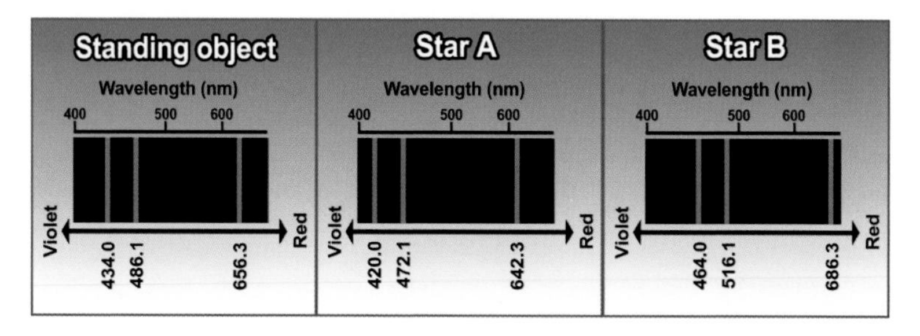

Which star is moving toward Earth? Which star is moving away from Earth? Explain your answer in both cases.

A

absolute brightness – the brightness a star would have if it were a standard distance from Earth.

accelerate – to increase speed or change direction.

acceleration – the change of speed over time.

acid – a chemical that contributes hydrogen ions, H+, to a solution.

acid precipitation – rain, snow, or fog that has a pH lower than 5.6.

acid rain – rain that has a pH lower than 5.6.

acoustics – the science and technology of sound.

addition reaction – a chemical reaction in which two or more substances combine to form a new compound.

additive primary colors – red, green, and blue.

air friction – the opposing force created by objects moving through air.

air mass – a large body of air with consistent temperature and moisture characteristics throughout.

alloys – solutions of two or more metals.

alpha decay – radioactive decay that results in an alpha particle (a helium nucleus) being emitted from the nucleus of a radioactive element.

alpha particles – a partially charged particle emitted from the nucleus of an atom during radioactive decay; also called a helium nucleus.

alternating current – an electric current that reverses its direction at repeated intervals; the abbreviation for this is AC.

amperes – the unit for measuring electrical current; the abbreviation is amp.

amplitude – the maximum distance from the average in harmonic motion; amplitude is often a distance or an angle.

anhydrous – means "without water"; describes the state of a hydrate that has lost water through evaporation.

apparent brightness – measured as a star's brightness as observed from Earth.

aquifer – an underground area of sediment and rocks where groundwater collects.

Archimedes' principle – a principle that states that the force exerted on an object in a liquid is equal to the weight of the fluid displaced by the object.

asteroid – an object that orbits the sun but is too small to be considered a planet.

asthenosphere – that portion of the upper mantle beneath the rigid lithosphere where rock flows.

astronomical unit – a measure for distance within the solar system equal to the mean distance between Earth and sun, that is, about 92,956,000 miles; the abbreviation is AU.

atmospheric pressure – a measurement of the force of air molecules in the atmosphere at a given altitude.

atom – the smallest particle of an element that can exist alone or in combination with other atoms.

atomic mass – the average mass of all the known isotopes of an element.

atomic mass unit – defined as the mass of $^{1}/_{12}$ of a carbon-12 atom (6 protons and 6 neutrons in the nucleus plus 6 electrons outside the nucleus).

atomic number – the number of protons that an atom contains.

atomic theory – a theory that states that all matter is composed of tiny particles called atoms.

average speed – how fast something moves over a certain distance.

Avogardo's number – the number of atoms in the atomic mass of an element, or the number of molecules in the formula mass of a compound when these masses are expressed in grams.

axis – the imaginary line that passes through Earth's center and connects the North and South poles.

B

balance – occurs when the number and type of atoms on the reactant's and product's sides of a chemical equation are equal.

barometer – an instrument that measures atmospheric pressure.

base – a chemical that contributes hydroxyl ion, OH-, to a solution.

battery – a device that uses chemical energy to move electrical charges.

beat – a rapid alteration between loudness and silence.

beta decay – radioactive decay that results in a beta particle (an electron) being emitted from the nucleus of a radioactive element.

beta particles – a negatively charged particle (an electron) emitted from the nucleus of an atom during radioactive decay.

Big Bang – a theory stating that the universe began as a huge explosion that occurred somewhere between 10 and 20 billion years ago.

binary compound – a covalent compound that consists of only two types of elements.

biome – a region of Earth with a unique set of plants and animals that thrive in its climate.

body wave – a seismic wave that travels through Earth; examples are P- and S-waves.

Boyle's law – pressure and volume are inversely related.

British thermal unit (Btu) – the quantity of heat it takes to increase the temperature of one pound of water by 1°F.

brittleness – a measure of a material's tendency to shatter upon impact.

buoyancy – a measure of the upward force a fluid exerts on an object.

C

caldera – a large depression at a volcano's summit that results when the remaining top of the volcano collapses following an eruption; calderas can be active volcano sites.

calendar – a system for everyday use in which time is divided into days and longer periods such as weeks, months, and years and a definite order for these periods and correspondence between them are established.

calorie – the quantity of heat required to raise the temperature of one gram of water by 1°C.

carbon dating – a technique to find out how old something is; the measure of carbon-14 in a sample that is between a few thousand and 50,000 years old.

carnivore – an organism that eats herbivores or other carnivores.

cause and effect – the relationship between an event that brings about a result and what happens due to the result.

Celsius scale – a temperature scale on which zero equals the temperature that water freezes (0°C) and 100 is the temperature that water boils (100°C).

Cepheid – a type of star whose absolute brightness is related to its period of pulsation; the North Star is the brightest Cepheid star.

Charles' law – the volume of a gas increases with increasing temperature if pressure is held constant.

chemical bond – an attraction between two or more different atoms that binds them together.

chemical change – a change in a substance that involves the breaking and reforming of chemical bonds to make a new substance or substances.

chemical equation – chemical formulas and symbols that represent a chemical reaction.

chemical formula – a representation of a compound that includes the symbols and numbers of atoms in the compound.

chemical potential energy – the energy that is stored in chemical bonds.

chemical reaction – the breaking of bonds to form new substances (called the products); atoms are rearranged in a chemical reaction.

chemical symbol – an abbreviation that represents the name of an element; used in chemical formulas.

chlorofluorocarbons – a group of chemicals that break down the stratosphere, damaging the ozone layer.

cinder cone volcano – a steep stack of loose, volcanic material called pyroclasts (clumps and particles of lava); these volcanoes are rarely higher than 300 meters

circuit – see electric circuit.

circuit diagram – the diagramatic representation of an electric circuit.

circular waves – waves that move in concentric circles.

cirrus cloud – thin lines of ice crystals about 6,000 meters high in the sky.

cleavage plane – a region where a mineral rock cleanly splits; where the bonds between molecules are weak.

climate – the long-term average of a region's weather.

closed circuit – a circuit in which the switch is turned to the "on" position, causing there to be no breaks anywhere in the wire.

cochlea – a tiny, fluid-filled bone structure in the inner ear with three tubes and a spiral.

coefficient –a number placed in front of a chemical formula to make the number of atoms on each side of a chemical equation equal.

cold front – occurs when cold air moves in and replaces warm air at Earth's surface.

colloid – a type of mixture in which the particles (atoms or molecules) are between 1.0 and 1,000 nanometers in diameter.

colloids – a type of mixture in which the particles (atoms or molecules) are between 1.0 and 1,000 nanometers in diameter.

combustion reaction – a reaction in which a substance combines with oxygen, releasing large amounts of energy in the form of heat and light.

comet – an object in space that is made mostly of ice and dust.

compounds – substances made of two or more elements that cannot be separated by physical means.

conceptual model – a written description or diagram based on ideas and observations that are used to describe how a process or object works; Sir Isaac Newton's law of universal gravitation is a conceptual model.

condensation – the process by which a substance in its gaseous state loses energy and enters its liquid state; one phase in the water cycle.

conduction – the transfer of thermal energy by the direct contact of particles of matter.

cone cells – photoreceptor cells in the retina of the eye that respond to color.

conservation of atoms – principle that states the number of each type of atom on the reactant's side must be equal to the number of each type of atom on the product's side of a chemical equation.

consonance – a combination of sounds that is harmonious or agreeable.

constructive interference – occurs when waves add up to make a larger amplitude.

continental drift – a theory stating that pieces of Pangaea moved apart to form the seven continents on Earth.

continuous – connected to itself.

controlled experiment – when one variable is changed and all the others are controlled or stay the same throughout the experiment.

controlled variables – variables in an experiment that are kept the same throughout the experiment.

convection – the transfer of thermal energy by the actual motion of a fluid in the form of currents.

converge – to bend light so that the rays come together.

convergent plate boundary – a region at which two tectonic plates come together; mountain-building, subduction, earthquakes, and volcanic activity can be characteristic of this region.

converging lens – a type of lens that bends light so that the parallel rays coming in bend toward the focal point.

Coriolis effect – the bending of air currents due to Earth's rotation.

coulomb – the unit for electrical charge.

covalent bond – a type of chemical bond formed when two atoms share electrons.

covalent compound – a compound that consists of atoms that are covalently bonded.

crater – a depression at the top of a volcanic mountain that forms after an eruption.

crest – the high point on a wave.

critical angle – the angle at which light is totally reflected back into a material.

cross-cutting relationships – an idea stating that a vein of rock that intersects layers of rock is younger than the layers.

cumuliform cloud – a cloud that looks like heaps of popcorn with a flat bottom and that forms when pockets of air rise because of convection.

current – the quantity that refers to the rate of flow of electric charges; current is measured in amps.

cyan – a greenish, light-blue that is created when red is absorbed and blue and green are reflected.

cycle – a unit of motion that repeats over and over.

D

deceleration – occurs when change in speed, or acceleration, is in the negative direction.

decomposition reaction – a chemical reaction in which a single compound is broken down to produce two or more smaller compounds.

density – a property that describes the relationship between mass and volume.

dependent variable – the variable in an experiment that changes in response to choices made by the experimenter; this variable is plotted on the *y*-axis of a graph.

destructive interference – occurs when waves add up to make a smaller amplitude.

dew point temperature – the air temperature at which the rate of condensation first exceeds the rate of evaporation.

diatomic molecules – a molecule that has only two atoms of the same element.

diffraction – the process by which waves can bend around corners or pass through openings.

direct current – electrical current flowing in one direction only; the abbreviation is DC.

dissociation – the process by which ionic compounds dissolve, that is, become separated into positive and negative ions.

dissolution reaction – a reaction that occurs when an ionic compound dissolves in water to make an ionic solution.

dissolved – the state in which solute particles are evenly distributed throughout a solvent.

dissonance – a combination of discordant or unsettling sounds.

distance – the length of space between two points.

diverge – bending light so that the rays spread apart.

divergent plate boundary – a region at which two tectonic plates move apart; the formation of new crust, earthquakes, and volcanic activity are characteristic of this region.

diverging lens – a type of lens that bends light away from the focal point.

Doppler shift – occurs when the source of sound moves, thus causing its frequency to change.

double-displacement reaction – a reaction in which ions from two compounds in a solution exchange places to produce two new compounds.

E

efficiency – the ratio of a machine's output work to input work.

elasticity – a measure of a solid's ability to stretch and then return to its original shape and size.

electric circuits – the structures that provide paths through which electricity travels.

electric motor – a device that uses electricity and magnets to turn electrical energy into rotating mechanical energy.

electrical conductivity – the ability of a material to conduct (or carry) electricity.

electrical conductor – a material that easily carries electrical current.

electrical energy – another term for electricity.

electrical force – the force that charged materials or objects exert on each other.

electrical insulator – a material that poorly conducts current.

electrical symbols – simple symbols used in circuit diagrams.

electrically charged – an object that has an excess amount of either positive or negative charges.

electrically neutral – an object that has equal amounts of positive and negative charges.

electrolytes – chemicals that form ions and conduct current when dissolved in water.

electromagnet – a strong, short-lasting magnet that can be made by inserting iron into a wire coil that is conducting an electric current.

electromagnetic force – the force that exists between electric charges; often described as electrical force or magnetic force depending on how charges interact.

electromagnetic induction – the creation of electric current when a magnet is moved inside a loop of wire; generators are devices that work using electromagnetic induction.

electromagnetic spectrum – the whole range of light (electromagnetic radiation).

electron – a subatomic particle in an atom that is negatively charged and that occupies the energy levels in an atom; electrons are involved in chemical bonds and reactions.

electroscope – an instrument that is used to detect charged objects.

elements – substances that contain only one kind of matter.

emissions – the airborne gases and particles expelled through an operating automobile's tailpipe.

endothermic reaction – a reaction in which more energy is required to break the bonds in reactants than is released from the formation of new bonds in the products.

energy – a fundamental building block of the universe; it appears in different forms (i.e., position, motion, or heat) and can travel in different ways (i.e., light, sound, or electricity).

energy level – a region around the nucleus of an atom where electrons are most likely to be found; only a certain number of electrons can be found in each energy level of an atom.

energy transformation – the conversion from one kind of energy to another kind of energy; for example, an energy transformation occurs when potential energy is converted to kinetic energy.

engineering – the application of science to solve technical problems.

engineering cycle – a process used to build devices that solve technical problems. The four steps of the engineering cycle are creating a design, building a prototype, testing the prototype, and evaluating test results.

engineers – people who design technology to solve problems.

English system – a system of measuring that uses, for example, distance units of inches, yards, and miles.

epicenter – a point on the Earth's surface that is directly above the focus of an earthquake and where the seismic waves reach first.

equilibrium – (1) in physics, occurs when the forces on an object are balanced; (2) in chemistry, the state in which the solute in a solution is dissolving and coming out of solution at the same rate.

erosion – the wearing away of the land, chiefly by rain, running water, wind, and ice.

evaporation – the process by which a substance in its liquid state gains energy and enters its gaseous state; one phase of the water cycle.

excess reactant – a reactant that is not completely used up.

exosphere – the region extending from 550 kilometers above Earth where the atmosphere gets thinner and thinner.

exothermic reaction – occurs when less energy is required to break the bonds in reactants than is released when bonds are formed to make new products.

experiment – any situation that is set up to observe and measure something happening.

experimental technique – the exact procedure that is followed each time an experiment is repeated.

experimental variable – a variable in an experiment that is changed by the experimenter; the experimental variable is plotted as an independent variable on the x-axis of a graph.

F

Fahrenheit scale – a temperature scale on which water freezes at 32 degrees Fahrenheit (or 32°F) and water boils at 212°F.

fault – a break or crack in Earth's crust where two pieces of the crust become offset.

fault-block mountain – a mountain formed by the combined processes of uplifting, faulting (breaking), and tilting of Earth's crust; also known as block mountain.

faunal succession – an idea stating that fossils can be used to identify the relative age of layers of a rock formation.

first law of thermodynamics – states that energy in a closed system is conserved.

fission – a nuclear reaction that involves the splitting of the nucleus of an atom.

fluorescent – a type of electric light bulb.

focal length – the distance from the center of a lens to the focal point.

focal point – the point at which light rays meet after having entered a converging lens parallel to the principal axis.

focus – (1) in geology, the place underground where the seismic waves of an earthquake originate; (2) the place where all the light rays that have come from an object meet to form an image after having passed through a converging lens.

fold mountain – a mountain occurring at a convergent plate boundary; a mountain formed when Earth's crust is compressed so that folds appear.

food chain – a series of steps through which energy and nutrients are transferred from organism to organism in an ecosystem.

force – a push, a pull, or any action that has the ability to change motion.

formula mass – determined by adding up the atomic mass units of all the atoms in the compound; a way to compare the masses of molecules of different compounds.

fossil fuels – hydrocarbon substances including oil, coal, and natural gas that are extracted from the Earth; fossil fuels are used as the primary source of energy in the United States.

free fall – the acceleration of a falling object under the influence of the Earth's gravitational force.

frequency – (1) in harmonics, the number of cycles an oscillator makes per second; (2) in waves, the number of wavelengths that pass a given point in one second.

friction – the force that results from relative motion between objects (like the wheel and axle of a car).

fulcrum – a fixed point on a lever.

fundamental – the name of the first harmonic.

fusion – a nuclear reaction that involves fusing nuclei from two atoms to make a different atom.

G

galaxy – a huge collection of gas, dust, and billions of stars.

gamma ray – a photon emitted spontaneously by a radioactive substance.

gas planet – a planet made mostly of hydrogen and helium and having relatively low densities, rapid rotations, very thick atmospheres, and many moons; Jupiter, Saturn, Uranus, and Neptune are gas planets.

gear – a wheel with teeth; two or more gears can be connected together to change the speed and/or direction of rotating motion.

generator – a combination of mechanical and electrical systems that converts kinetic energy into electrical energy.

geologic hazard maps – a map that indicates the locations of geologic hazards such as earthquakes, active volcanoes, landslides, avalanches, and floods.

geologist – a scientist who studies rock formations.

geology – the study of rocks and materials that make up a celestial body such as Earth and the processes that shape it.

glacier – a large mass of ice on land or a mountain top that accumulates snow and ice faster than it melts; the weight of this mass of ice causes it to flow.

global warming – an increase in the Earth's temperature due mainly to increased carbon dioxide and other heat-absorbing gases in the atmosphere.

graphical model – a model that shows the relationship between two variables on a graph so that the relationship is easily seen and understood.

grassland – a biome where the predominant form of vegetation is grasses rather than trees.

gravitational force – a measure of the attractive force between two objects that is dependent on their masses and distance apart.

gravity – the attractive force that exists between any two objects that have mass.

groundwater – water that collects underground in an aquifer; this water supplies wells and springs.

group of elements – elements that exhibit similar chemical properties; arranged in columns on the periodic table.

gyres – a large circular pattern of surface ocean currents that forms due to global surface wind patterns and Earth's rotation.

H

half-life – the length of time it takes for half an amount of radioactive substance to undergo radioactive decay.

hardness – measures a solid's resistance to scratching.

harmonic motion – motion that repeats itself.

harmonics – (1) frequencies that are multiples of fundamental notes; (2) multiples of natural frequency.

heat – a flow of thermal energy from one object to another object due to a temperature difference.

heat transfer – the transfer of energy in the form of heat that naturally flows from a material at a higher temperature to a material at a lower temperature.

herbivore – an organism that eats producers (*e.g.*, plants or algae).

hertz – a unit of one cycle per second used to measure frequency; the abbreviation is Hz.

heterogeneous mixture – a mixture in which every sample of it might have a different composition.

homogeneous mixture – a mixture in which every sample of it has the same composition.

horsepower – a unit of power; one horsepower is equal to 746 watts.

H-R diagram – a diagram showing the relationship between a star's absolute brightness and its temperature.

hydrate – a compound that has water molecules chemically bonded to its ions.

hydrochloric acid – a highly acidic substance your stomach normally produces to help you break down food.

hydrogen bond – a weak bond between the partially charged positive end of one water molecule and the partially charged negative end of another water molecule.

hydrosphere – the water layer of Earth's surface.

hydrothermal vent – a deep sea chimney-like structure that occurs along mid-ocean ridges and releases seawater that has been heated to high temperatures by magma.

hypothesis – a prediction that can be tested by experimentation.

I

ice age – a period of tens to hundreds of years when Earth's climate is very cold and much of the surface is covered with glaciers that repeatedly moved forward and backward from the poles to the equator.

igneous rock – a rock made up of magma or lava, the fiery hot material that originates in Earth's mantle.

image – a picture of an object that is formed using a mirror or lens where light rays from the object meet.

incandescence – the process of making light with heat.

incident ray – the ray that comes from an object and strikes a surface.

inclusions – rock pieces found within another rock that are older than the surrounding rock.

independent variable – the variable in an experiment that is manipulated by the experimenter and that causes changes in the dependent variable in the experiment; this variable is plotted on the x-axis of a graph.

index of refraction – a ratio that tells how much the speed of light is reduced when it passes through a material.

inertia – the reluctance of a body to change its state of motion.

input – includes everything you do to make a machine work.

input arm – when you place a lever on a fulcrum, the input arm is the side of the lever where the input force is applied.

input force – the force applied to a machine.

insoluble – a term to describe a substance that does not dissolve in water.

instantaneous speed – the speed of an object at a specific point in its journey.

inverse square law – describes the relationship between a star's apparent brightness, its absolute brightness, and its distance from an object.

investigation – one or more experiences that are all connected to answering the same basic question.

ion – an atom, which by the gain or loss of one or more electrons, has an electrical charge.

ionic bond – a type of chemical bond in which electrons are transferred between atoms, converting the atoms into ions.

ionic compound – a compound that is made up of ions.

ionosphere – a region in the thermosphere that is 80-550 kilometers above Earth and where the sun's ultraviolet light ionizes atoms and molecules.

isobars – wavy lines or circles on a weather map that connect areas with the same atmospheric pressure; they are used to locate centers of high and low pressure.

isotopes – forms of the same element that have different numbers of neutrons and different mass numbers.

J

jet stream – a high-altitude, fast-moving wind formed where there are sharp boundaries between cold and warm temperatures.

joule – a unit for measuring work; a joule is equal to one newton of force times one meter of distance; the abbreviation is J.

K

kilowatt – a measurement equal to 1,000 watts or 1,000 joules per second.

kilowatt-hour – indicates that a kilowatt of power has been used for one hour.

kinetic energy – energy that comes from motion.

Kirchhoff's current law – states the current into a branch in a circuit equals the amount of current out of the branch.

Kirchhoff's voltage law – states that over an entire circuit, the energy taken out must equal the energy supplied by the battery.

L

latent heat – the heat used to melt, boil, or evaporate a substance and released when a substance condenses or freezes.

lateral continuity – an idea stating that layers of sediment extend in all directions when they form and before they become rock layers.

latitude lines – a series of parallel lines used to measure distance from the equator.

lava – magma that reaches Earth's surface and erupts out of a volcano or volcanic site.

law of conservation of mass – states that the total mass of products of a reaction is equal to the total mass of reactants.

law of conservation of momentum – states that as long as interacting objects are not influenced by outside forces (like friction), their momentum before the interaction will equal their momentum after the interaction.

law of universal gravitation–The force of attraction between two objects is directly related to the masses of the objects and indirectly related to the distance between them.

length – a unit of measurement for distance.

lens – a shape of a transparent material, like glass, that is used to bend light rays.

lever – a stiff structure that rotates around a fixed point called the fulcrum.

Lewis dot diagram – a structural formula in which electrons are represented by dots; two dots between atoms represents a covalent bond.

light year – a measurement that is equal to the distance that light travels through space in one year.

limiting reactant – the reactant that is used up first in a chemical reaction.

lithosphere – a layer of Earth that includes the crust and upper mantle.

longitude lines – lines that run vertically from Earth's north to south pole; used with latitude lines to locate points on Earth.

longitudinal wave – a wave whose oscillations are in the same direction as the wave moves.

lunar eclipse – occurs when Earth's shadow falls on the moon.

Glossary

M

machine – a type of mechanical system.

magenta – a pink-purple color that is created when green is absorbed and red and blue are reflected.

magma – the molten rock material from which igneous rocks are formed; magma originates in Earth's mantle.

magma chamber – a pocket in which magma collects below Earth's surface.

magnetic field – an area of magnetic force that surrounds magnetic objects.

magnetic force – a force exerted on a particle or object traveling in a magnetic field.

magnetic north pole – the end of a magnetic object that points toward the geographic north pole of the Earth.

magnetic south pole – the end of a magnetic object that points away from the geographic north pole of the Earth.

main sequence star – a star that falls into the band that stretches diagonally from cool, dim stars to hot, bright stars.

malleability – a solid's ability to be pounded into thin sheets.

mantle – a layer of Earth between the crust and the core and composed of hot, rocky material; the mantle is the source of magma.

mass – a measure of the inertia of an object; the amount of matter an object has.

mass number – the total number of protons and neutrons in the nucleus of an atom.

matter – anything that has mass and takes up space.

measurement– the act or process of measuring in multiples of a specific unit.

mechanical advantage – the ratio of output force to input force.

mechanical system – a series of interrelated, moving parts that work together to accomplish a specific task.

mesosphere – the coldest layer of the atmosphere; extends from 50 to 80 kilometers above Earth.

metamorphic rock – a rock formed from preexisting solid rocks by mineral and chemical changes in response to extreme changes in temperature or pressure.

meteor – a streak of light across the night sky that is caused by a small chunk of dust or rock entering Earth's atmosphere.

metric system – a system of measuring that uses, for example, distance units of millimeters, centimeters, meters, and kilometers.

mid-ocean ridge – mountain ranges associated with convergent plate boundaries at the bottom of Earth's oceans.

mineral – a naturally-occurring, inorganic, and crystalline substance that makes up rocks.

mixture – substance that contains more than one kind of matter.

Mohs hardness scale – a tool used to identify minerals; this scale uses ten common minerals to represent variations in hardness.

mole – one set of 6.02×10^{23} atoms or molecules.

molecular formula – includes the symbols for and number of atoms of each element in a compound.

molecule – the smallest particle of a compound that retains the properties of the compound.

momentum – the mass of an object multiplied by its speed or velocity.

monoatomic ions – ions that contain only one type of atom.

musical scale – frequencies of sound that fit into a special pattern.

N

nanometer – a unit of measurement that is equal to one billionth of a meter.

natural frequency – describes how an object vibrates; for example, a guitar string strummed repeatedly has its own natural force.

natural world– the aspects of the world not created or constructed by people.

nebula – a huge cloud of gas (mostly hydrogen) and dust from which stars are formed.

negative charge – one of two types of electric charge; the other type is positive charge.

net force – the amount of force that overcomes an opposing force to cause motion; the net force can be zero if the opposing forces are equal.

neutralization – occurs when acid and base solutions are mixed in the right proportions and their characteristic properties disappear.

neutron – an uncharged particle found in the nucleus of an atom.

newton – a unit of force; the abbreviation is N.

Newton's first law of motion – states any object at rest will remain at rest unless acted on by an unbalanced force; an object in motion continues with constant speed and direction in a straight line unless acted on by an unbalanced force.

Newton's second law of motion – states that the acceleration of an object is directly proportional to the force acting on it and inversely proportional to its mass.

Newton's third law of motion – states that whenever one object exerts a force on another, the second object exerts an equal and opposite force on the first.

nonpolar molecule – a term used to describe a molecule or covalent bond that does not have partial charges; oils and fats are nonpolar molecules.

normal – a line that is perpendicular to the surface of an object.

nuclear energy – the form of energy that comes from splitting the nucleus of an atom, or fusing two nuclei of an atom.

nuclear reaction – a reaction that involves splitting the nucleus of an atom or fusing two nuclei; these reactions produce much more energy than chemical reactions.

nucleons – the protons and neutrons in the nucleus of an atom.

nucleus – the center core of an atom that contains protons and neutrons.

O

octet – an atom's eight valence electrons.

octet rule – states that atoms form bonds with other atoms by sharing or transferring them to complete their octet and become stable.

ohm – the unit of measurement for electrical resistance; the abbreviation is Ω.

Ohm's law – describes the mathematical relationship present in most circuits.

open circuit – a circuit in which there is a break in the wire so that current cannot flow; a switch turned to the "off" position is one way to cause a break in the wire.

optics – the study of how light behaves.

orbit – a regular, repeating path that an object in space follows around another object.

orbital speed – the speed required to achieve a balance between the pull of gravity on a satellite and its forward motion.

original horizontality – an idea stating that sediments settling out from bodies of water are deposited horizontally or nearly horizontally in layers that lie parallel or nearly parallel to Earth's surface.

oscillator – a system that shows harmonic motion.

output – what the machine does.

output arm – of the lever on a fulcrum, the output arm is the side where the output force is applied.

output force – the force a machine applies to accomplish a task.

oxidation number – indicates how many electrons are lost or gained (or shared) when bonding occurs.

P

paleontologist – a scientists who studies and identifies fossils.

Pangaea – a proposed former supercontinent supposedly composed of all the continental crust of Earth and later fragmented by drift into Laurasia and Gondwana; also spelled Pangea.

parallax – the apparent change in an object's position when you look at it from different directions.

parallel – lying or moving in the same direction, but always the same distance apart (i.e., never intersecting).

parallel circuit – a circuit in which the current can take more than one path.

pascal (Pa) – the SI unit of pressure. One pascal is equal to one newton of force acting on one square meter of surface.

percent yield – the actual yield of product in a chemical reaction divided by the predicted yield, and multiplied by one hundred to get a percentage.

period – the time for one cycle.

periodic motion – cycles of motion that repeat over and over again; the same as harmonic motion.

periodic table of elements – a table that visually organizes the similarities between all known elements.

permafrost – ground that is permanently frozen from 25 to about 100 centimeters below Earth's surface.

permanent magnet – a magnetic object that retains its magnetic properties without external influence.

perpendicular – forming a 90 degree angle with a given edge or surface.

pH – the exact concentrations of H+ ions and OH- ions in a solution.

pH indicator – a solution or object that changes color to identify the pH of a solution.

pH scale – a scale that runs from 0 (strongly acidic) to 14 (strongly basic, or alkaline).

phase – refers to where an oscillator is in its cycle.

photoluminescence – occurs when light energy makes something else give off light.

photoreceptors – rod and cone cells in the retina of the eye that receive light and release a chemical signal that travels down the optic nerve to the brain.

photosynthesis – a chemical reaction performed by plants in which energy from the sun is converted to chemical energy; carbon dioxide is converted to sugar in this reaction.

physical change – change in the physical properties of a substance.

physical models – models that are made of materials and that can be touched and measured; engineers construct scale physical models to test a structure before building it.

pitch – property of a sound determined by the frequency of the waves producing it.

pixel – a dot on your computer screen whose color can change depending on the three numbers your computer assigns to it.

plane waves – waves that move in straight lines.

planet – a massive, spherical collection of matter that revolves around a star.

planetary system – a star with orbiting planets.

plate tectonics – a theory stating that giant pieces of Earth's lithosphere move and interact on the surface, resulting, for example, in land formations, earthquakes, and volcanoes.

polar easterlies – a wind pattern that forms when air over the poles cools, sinks, and spreads along the surface.

polar molecule – a molecule with a positive and a negative pole.

polarization – a way of describing the direction (such as vertical or horizontal) that waves of light travel.

polarizer – a partially transparent material that lets through only one polarization of light.

polyatomic ions – ions that contain more than one type of atom.

polymer – a large molecule that is composed of repeating smaller molecules called subunits or monomers.

polymerization – the production of a very large molecule by a series of synthesis reactions.

position – a point in space of an object compared to where it started.

positive charge – one of two types of electric charge; the other type is negative charge.

potential energy – stored energy that comes from position.

potentiometer – a variable resistor.

pounds – English system unit of force.

power – the rate at which work is done.

precipitate – substance formed when one of the compounds in a double-displacement reaction is insoluble, or does not dissolve in water.

precipitation – water vapor in the atmosphere falling back to Earth in the form of rain, hail, sleet, or snow; one phase in the water cycle.

pressure – (1) a measure of the force felt by the walls of a container; (2) the force acting on a unit area of surface.

prevailing westerlies – surface wind pattern flowing from high pressure at 30° latitude to low pressure at 60° latitude; bent to the right in the northern hemisphere and left in the southern hemisphere due to Earth's rotation.

procedure – a collection of all the techniques you use to do an experiment.

producer – a plant or other organism that concentrates energy from the sun through photosynthesis.

products – substances that are produced in a chemical reaction from reactants.

proton – a subatomic particle identical with the nucleus of the hydrogen atom; found with neutrons in all atomic nuclei; carries a positive charge.

protostar – the earliest state in a star's life cycle.

prototype – a working model of a design that can be tested to see if it works.

P-wave – a primary seismic wave that pushes and pulls in the same direction that it travels through Earth; this kind of body wave is faster than an S-wave.

R

radiant energy – another term for electromagnetic energy.

radiation – (1) the process of emitting radiant energy; (2) a term to describe the particles and energy that are emitted from radioactive substances.

radioactive – a term to describe an atomic state when the nucleus is emitting radiation in the form of particles and energy until it becomes more stable.

radioactive isotope – an unstable isotope of an element that spontaneously undergoes radioactive decay.

ray diagram – a diagram which illustrates how several light rays behave as they go through an optical system.

react – describes how atoms interact when forming a chemical bond with another atom.

reactants – a substance that enters into and is altered in the course of a chemical reaction.

real image – an image formed by rays of light coming together on a surface like a screen or the retina of the eye.

recoil – backward acceleration from the reaction force.

reflected ray – the ray that bounces off an object.

reflecting telescope – a telescope that uses mirrors instead of lenses to gather and focus light.

reflection – the bounce of a wave off a surface.

refracting telescope – a telescope in which a lens gathers light and forms a real image of an object; also known as refractor telescope.

refraction – occurs when light passes from one transparent material into another and bends.

relative dating – a technique used to put events in the order that they happened.

relative mass – a quantity that allows for comparison between amounts of matter that are very small.

research question – a question that is solved through investigation.

reservoirs – protected artificial or natural lakes.

resistance – the measure of an object's ability to conduct current.

resistors – components that are used to control current in many circuits.

resonance – an occurrence whereby the natural frequency of a system is exactly in tune with a force applied to the system.

reverberation – multiple echoes of sound.

revolution – the movement of one object around another in space.

Ring of Fire – a region along the boundary of the Pacific Ocean where half of Earth's active volcanoes occur; it includes both volcanic activity and earthquakes.

rock – a naturally-formed substance made of one or more minerals; a rock can also be made of organic material.

rock cycle – the formation and recycling of rocks by geological processes.

rod cells – photoreceptor cells in the retina of the eye that respond to differences in brightness.

rolling friction – resistance created when one object rolls over another one.

rotation – Earth's spinning on its axis.

S

salinity – measures how much salt is dissolved in one kilogram of water.

satellite – an object in orbit.

saturated – the state of a mixture in which the maximum amount of solute has dissolved in a solution.

scientific evidence – any observation that can be repeated with the same results.

scientific method – a process that is used to gather evidence that leads to understanding.

scientific model – a method of representing the relationship between variables.

scientific notation – a mathematical abbreviation for writing very large or very small numbers.

sea-floor spreading – describes how the sea floor on either side of a mid-ocean ridge moves away from the ridge and creates a rise or valley.

second – a commonly used unit of time; $^1/_{60}$ of a minute.

sedimentary rock – a rock formed when eroded sediment becomes compacted and cemented.

seismic wave – a wave that results from an earthquake; there are two kinds of seismic waves: body waves (P- and S-waves) that travel through Earth and surface waves that travel along Earth's surface.

seismologist – a scientist who records and interprets seismic waves.

semiconductor – material between conductor and insulator in its ability to carry current.

series circuit – a circuit in which the current only has one path.

shield volcano – a gently sloped, flattened volcano that ranges in height from 500 to 10,000 meters high; it yields low viscosity, fast-flowing lava.

short circuit – a branch in a circuit with zero or very low resistance.

simple machine – an unpowered mechanical device, such as a lever, which has an input and an output force.

single-displacement reaction – a reaction in which one element replaces a similar element in a compound.

sliding friction – resistance created when two surfaces rub against one another.

soil profile – a cross-section of Earth that shows different layers of soil in the ground.

soil –sediment that forms as a result of erosion; it is composed of weathered rock and decayed plants and is rich in nutrients and a suitable medium in which plants can anchor their roots and grow.

solar constant – the amount of energy that reaches the edge of Earth's atmosphere.

solar eclipse – an eclipse that takes place when the new moon passes between Earth and the sun and the shadow formed reaches Earth; may be classified as total, partial, or annular.

solar energy – the energy transmitted from the sun in the form of electromagnetic radiation.

solar power – radiant energy from the sun that is harnessed for use.

solar system – the sun and the celestial bodies moving about it; the bodies are planets, satellites of the planets, comets, and meteor swarms.

solubility – refers to the amount of solute that can be dissolved in a certain volume of solvent under certain conditions.

solubility value – a number that describes a solute-solvent system; it includes the mass of solute, amount of solvent, and temperature.

solute – the substance in a solution in the smallest amount; the solute is dissolved by the solvent.

solution – a mixture of two or more substances that is homogenous at the molecular level; a solution consists of a solute and a solvent.

solvent – the component of a solution that dissolves the solute and is present in the greatest amount.

sonogram– special kind of graph that shows how loud sound is at different frequencies.

specific heat – a property of a substance that tells us how much heat is needed to raise the temperature of one gram by 1°C.

spectroscopy – a measurement of the electromagnetic radiation (including visible light) produced by a star or other object (called its spectrum).

speed – describes movement from one place to another over time; distance divided by time.

stable – (1) a term used to describe an atom that has a balance of charge; (2) a non-radioactive nucleus.

standard candle – an object such as a star whose absolute brightness is known.

standing wave – a wave trapped in one spot.

star – a sphere of gas that undergoes a process called fusion; this process releases so much energy that stars give off bright light.

static electricity – a buildup of either positive or negative charge; consists of isolated motionless charges, like those produced by friction.

stratiform cloud – a clouds that forms when a large mass of stable air gradually ascends over a mass of colder air.

stratocumulus cloud – a cloud formation that combines aspects of both cumuliform and stratiform clouds; they form when conditions in the atmosphere cause pockets of convection to occur within a stratiform cloud.

stratosphere – a layer of the Earth's atmosphere extending from about 11 to 50 kilometers above Earth's surface; the temperature rises with altitude because ozone near the top of the stratosphere absorbs the sun's ultraviolet radiation.

stratovolcano – a cone-shaped, steep-sided mountain that is made of layers of lava and ash and that is around 3,000 meters high; it yields high viscosity lava.

strong nuclear force – the force that holds protons together when they are very close together (only 10^{-15} meters apart).

subatomic particles – particles that are smaller than an atom; protons, neutrons, and electrons are subatomic particles.

subduction – a process occurring at convergent plate boundary; when a denser plate slides under a less dense plate and enters Earth's mantle.

subscript – a number in a chemical formula that show the number of a type of atom.

substance – a mixture that cannot be separated into different kinds of matter using physical means.

subtractive primary colors – magenta, yellow, and cyan.

sunspot – a dark area in the photosphere of the sun caused by a lowered temperature.

supernova – a star that suddenly bursts into very great brilliance as a result of its blowing up; it is orders of magnitude brighter than a nova.

superposition – an idea stating that the bottom layer of a rock formation is older than the layer on top because the bottom layer formed first.

supersaturated – condition of a solution when more solute has dissolved than is normally possible at a given temperature.

supersonic – motion that is faster than sound.

surface runoff – water that flows over land until it reaches lakes, rivers, or other surface water areas.

surface water – water contained in places such as lakes, ponds, rivers, streams, and reservoirs.

surface wave – a seismic wave that travels along Earth's surface.

suspensions – a type of mixture in which the particles (atoms or molecules) are larger than 1,000 nanometers in diameter.

S-wave – a secondary seismic wave that moves sideways or up and down perpendicular to the direction that it travels through Earth; this kind of body wave is slower than a P-wave.

T

taiga – the largest land biome; it is located between 50° and 70° N latitude; evergreen trees with needle-like leaves are the predominant vegetation.

tectonic plate – a giant piece of solid rock on Earth's surface; the movement of these plates affects Earth's surface and causes earthquake and volcanoes.

telescope – any device that collects radiation, which may be in the form of electromagnetic or particle radiation, from a limited direction in space.

temperate forests – a biome found in middle-latitude regions where there are four distinct seasons and enough rainfall to support broad-leafed deciduous trees.

temperature – the measurement used to quantify the sensations of hot and cold; it is related to the average kinetic energy of the object's molecules.

temperature inversion – occurs when the temperature near the ground is colder than the temperature higher in the troposphere; it can lead to haze or smog.

tensile strength – a measure of how much pulling, or tension, a material can withstand before breaking.

terahertz – a unit of measurement that is equal to 1,000,000,000 cycles per second.

terrestrial planet – one of the four small planets near the sun—Mercury, Venus, Mars, and Earth—and like Earth in its density and silicate composition.

thermal conductor – a material that easily conducts heat.

thermal energy – the sum of all the kinetic energy of a material's atoms and molecules.

thermal equilibrium – a state that results when heat flows from a hot object to a cold object until they are at the same temperature.

thermal insulator – a material that conducts heat poorly.

thermosphere – the high-temperature, outer region of the Earth's atmosphere; this part of the atmosphere is very thin.

tide – the daily rising and falling of an ocean's water levels.

time – a useful measurement of changes in motion or events; all or part of the past, present, and future.

total internal reflection – occurs when light within a material approaches the surface at greater than the critical angle and reflects back.

trade wind – a surface wind current that flows from 30° latitude to the equator; bends to the right in the northern hemisphere and left in the southern hemisphere due to Earth's rotation.

transform plate boundary – a region at which two tectonic plates slide past each other; crust is not created or consumed, and earthquakes are characteristic of this region.

transition metal – any of the elements in groups 3-12 in the periodic table of elements; they are distinguished by having valence electrons present in more than one shell.

transpiration – process in which plants open tiny pores on their leaves to gain carbon dioxide but lose water; one phase in the water cycle.

transverse wave – a wave whose oscillation is perpendicular to the direction the wave travels.

trial – each time an experiment is tried.

tropical rainforest – a biome found near the equator between 23.5° N latitude and 23.5° S latitude; characterized by heavy rainfall and a dense canopy of tall trees.

troposphere – the layer of Earth's atmosphere that extends from 0 to about 11 kilometers above Earth's surface.

trough – the low point on a wave.

tsunami – a huge wave generated by an underwater earthquake or landslide.

tundra – a biome characterized by a short growing season and very cold temperatures; the permafrost prevents the growth of trees, so lichens, mosses, grass, and a few shrubs predominate.

Tyndall effect – a way of visually distinguishing colloids from true solutions.

U

universe – everything that exists, including all matter and energy.

unsaturated – a solution in which it is possible for more solute to be dissolved.

urban sprawl – refers to how living areas around a city "sprawl" as they grow instead of concentrate near facilities that serve the people of the community.

V

valence electrons – the electrons in an atom that are involved in the formation of chemical bonds.

variables – factors that affect the results of an experiment.

velocity – describes movement from one place to another over time and in a certain direction.

vent – an area where magma reaches Earth's surface.

versorium – the earliest version of today's electroscope.

virtual image – an image formed when rays of light appear to be coming from a place other than where the actual object exists; a virtual image cannot be projected on a screen.

viscosity – a measure of a material's resistance to flow.

viscous friction – resistance created by objects moving in water or other fluids.

visible light – the light you can see in the range between 400 and 700 nanometers.

volcano – a mountain or hill generally with steep sides, formed by the accumulation of magma erupted through openings or volcanic vents; the vent itself.

volt – the measurement unit for voltage.

voltage – the amount of potential energy that each unit of electrical charge has.

W

warm front – occurs when warm air advances and overtakes cooler air in a region.

water cycle – describes how water moves around the Earth by the processes of evaporation, condensation, precipitation, and transpiration.

watershed – an area of land that catches all rain and snow and collects it in one place like a river.

watt – the metric, or SI, unit of power.

wavefronts – another term used to describe the crests of a wave.

wavelength – the distance from peak to peak, crest to crest, or trough to trough of a wave.

weight – a force created by gravity.

white noise – an equal mixture of all frequencies, like white is a mixture of all colors.

wind – air that flows horizontally from an area of high density and pressure into an area of low density and pressure.

work – the quantity of force times distance; the result of machines performing tasks.

Y

yellow – a color that is created when blue is absorbed and red and green are reflected.

A

B

C

D

E

F

G

H

I

J

K

L

M

N

O

P

S

T

U

V

W

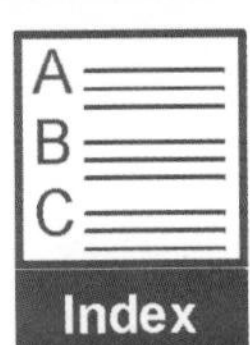

X

Y